Maps of Wiltshire: relief

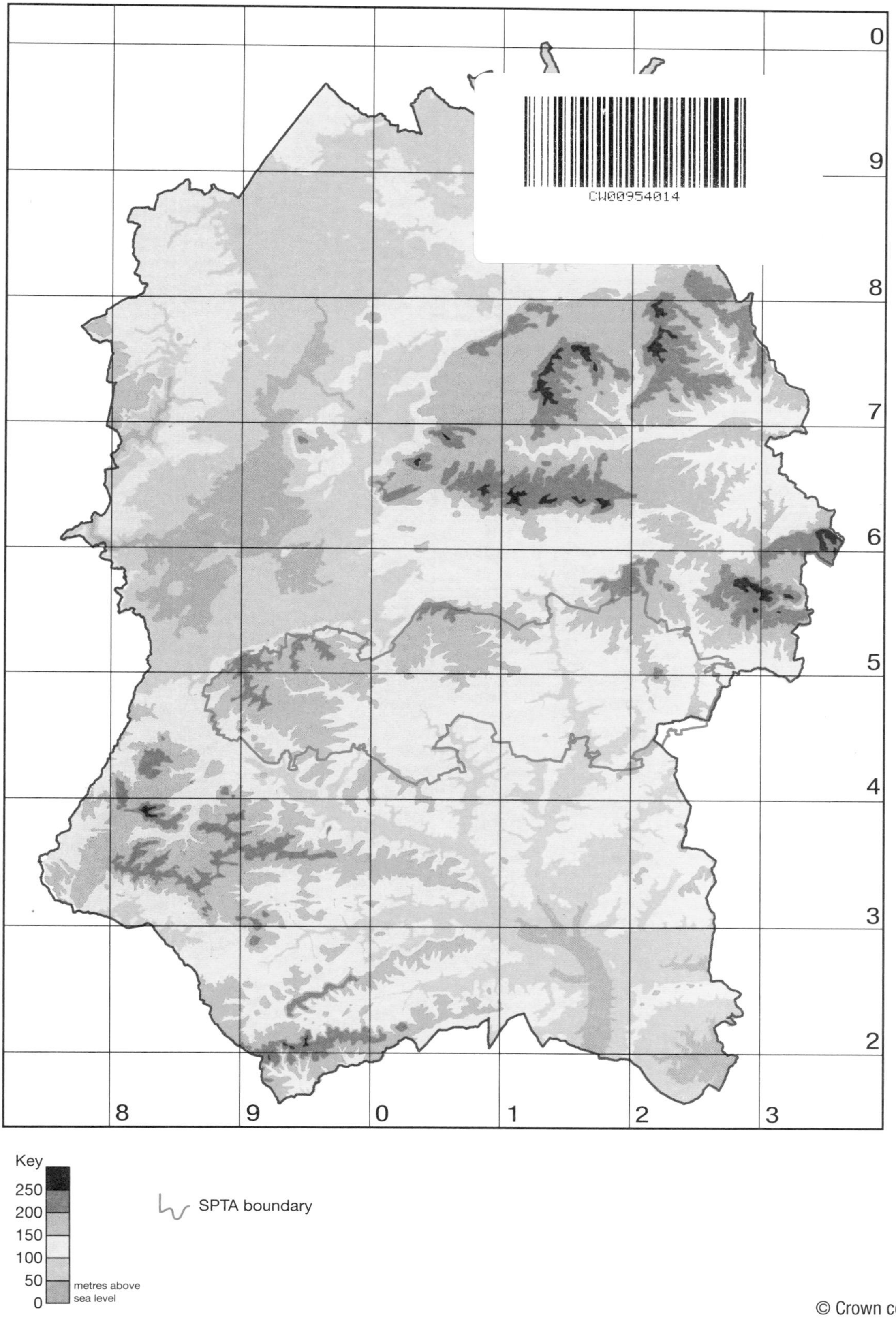

Birds of Wiltshire

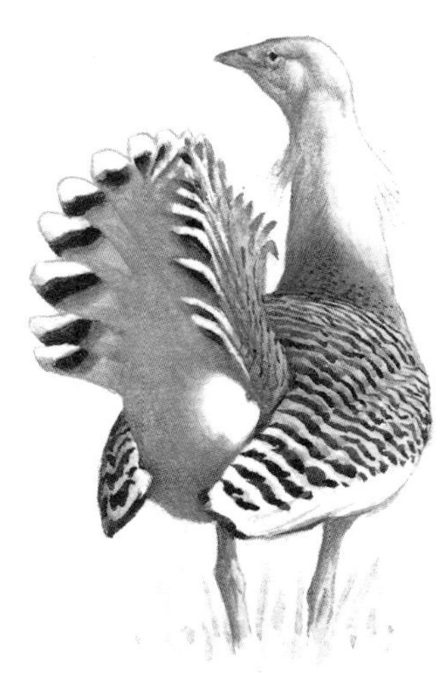

Wiltshire Ornithological Society

First published 2007 by Wiltshire Ornithological Society

www.wiltshirebirds.co.uk

ISBN 978–0–9555270–0–5

A catalogue record for this book is available from the British Library

CITATION
This book should be cited in other publications as:

Wiltshire Ornithological Society. 2007. *Birds of Wiltshire*. WOS, Devizes.

Birds of Wiltshire

Published by the Tetrad Atlas Group of the Wiltshire Ornithological Society after mapping fieldwork 1995–2000

James Ferguson-Lees Paul Castle
Peter Cranswick
Stephen Edwards Pete Combridge
Rob Turner Linda Cady

Special researchers
Mike Jackson Ian Collins

Editorial board
James Ferguson-Lees
Paul Castle
Pete Combridge
Peter Cranswick
Stephen Edwards

Other writers/editors
Nick Adams
Ian Collins
Beatrice Gillam
John Govett
John Grearson
Mike Jackson
Granville Pictor
Bill Quantrill
Phil Read
Rob Turner
Geoff Webber

Regional organisers
Mike Hamzij
Mike Jackson
Granville Pictor
John Pollard

Text/artwork manager
Linda Cady

Fundraising
John Brown

Data entry
Rob Turner
Gill Cardy
Mike Hamzij
Bill Quantrill
Rowena Quantrill
Graham Stacey

Design & production Rob Still

THE COUNTY OF WILTSHIRE

The area covered is the Ceremonial County of Wiltshire, including the Unitary Authority of Swindon that was created in 1997, and not the Watsonian vice-counties of North and South Wiltshire, which included parishes ceded to Gloucestershire and Hampshire in 1895

SPONSORS

The Wiltshire Ornithological Society gratefully acknowledges the major sponsors of *Birds of Wiltshire*:

Cobb Charitable Trust, Esmée Fairbairn Foundation, Kennet District Council, Leach Fourteenth Trust, Natural England, RJ Harris Charitable Trust, RSPB, RWE npower, Salisbury District Council, Wiltshire Natural History Forum, Wiltshire Wildlife Trust

Full lists of those who gave financial or other support appear in the Acknowledgements

Dedicated to

John Pollard (1923–2001)

and

Geoff Webber (1929–2005)

Remembered for their contributions
to Wiltshire ornithology
and not least to this project

Contents

Foreword

David W Gibbons

Head, Conservation Science, RSPB
Chairman, European Birds Census Council (EBCC), 1998–2004

Whilst I recognise that I may be preaching to the converted, a fundamental axiom of conservation is that we cannot conserve what we do not understand. It is only through the mapping of bird distributions and monitoring of their populations that we can come to an understanding of the status of each species, and thus decide which we need to worry about, and where and how we should act to restore their populations.

Although this book is very much more than simply an atlas of birds in Wiltshire, the distribution and abundance maps of the county's breeding species lie at its heart. Wildlife atlases – the mapping of species' distributions on a regular grid – are now half a century old, having been started by botanists in the late 1950s. Although it came more than a decade after the *Atlas of the British Flora* (Perring & Walters 1962), the publication of *The Atlas of Breeding Birds in Britain and Ireland* (Sharrock 1976), which was based on fieldwork in the five summers of 1968–72, was a milestone in ornithology and became one of the most quoted British sources. Following its publication, numerous bird atlases covering continental, regional, national, county and local levels have been produced around the world.

The exact number of bird atlases published worldwide is unknown, but is certainly more than 400, and probably fewer than 500. Most of these are from European countries, with France, Germany, Italy, Spain and the UK seemingly producing more than their fair share. The North Americans have not been left behind, either, as there are now two continent-wide atlases, one for wintering and one for summering birds, and many individual US and Canadian states have their own. There are also thriving atlas industries in southern Africa and some east African countries, Australia and New Zealand. Unfortunately, northern and western Africa, and most of Asia and South America have barely been covered at all.

The method developed for the first British and Irish atlas, and subsequently refined by the European Ornithological Atlas Committee, has been adopted with only subtle changes as a worldwide global standard. The group responsible for this method – chairman of which was James Ferguson-Lees, senior editor of this new *Birds of Wiltshire* – are to be congratulated for developing such a robust standard that has stood the test of time and geography. Atlas methods cannot remain static, however, and the last two decades have seen a number of developments. These have not sought to replace the existing widely loved method; rather they have built on them. In particular, more recent atlases map abundance as well as simple distribution, and have started to document geographical range change as well. Alongside these methodological changes has been a shift from atlases of breeding birds to the non-breeding season and, in some cases, year-round.

Unlike the methods to record distribution, there is no commonly agreed standard of the best way to obtain abundance information to produce a quantitative atlas; different atlases have adopted different methods. The *European Atlas* (Hagemeijer & Blair 1997) asked observers to use their local knowledge to estimate the number of pairs of each species in each 50-km square. The *Atlas of Southern African Birds* (Harrison *et al* 1997) used the proportion of field cards submitted for a given quarter-degree grid square that recorded a species as its measure of relative abundance. The *New Atlas of Breeding Birds in Britain and Ireland* (Gibbons *et al* 1993) used the proportion of tetrads in a 10-km square in which a species was recorded during a 2-hour visit as one of its measures of relative abundance. Fieldworkers for the second Swiss atlas (Schmid *et al* 1998) undertook simplified territory mapping in ten 1-km squares in each 10-km square in order to calculate relative densities per 10-km square. Observers for the *Atlas of Wintering Birds in Britain and Ireland* (Lack 1986) spent as long as they wanted in each 10-km grid square and counted all birds they came across; these counts were then adjusted to a standard six-hour recording period. Thus, there has been no real standardisation of method across these different atlases, even though there have been some common ideas.

While there are pros and cons for all these methods, whichever is used, quantification brings two main advantages: a better understanding of where the bulk of each bird species' population lives, and a more repeatable method for the future. The *Birds of Wiltshire* is among the first published county tetrad atlases to have used quantitative methods to produce abundance (as well as simple distribution) maps for both summer and winter. For this alone it is to be applauded. Others are close behind, though, and Wiltshire's birdwatchers cannot rest on their laurels as the Cumbrian atlas of breeding birds (Stott *et al* 2002) and the forthcoming Isle of Man and Surrey atlases have both also involved quantitative methods.

The maps in this book show the advantage of obtaining abundance information alongside distribution data. Look at those for the Sky Lark, for example, on page 512. The summer distribution map shows that the species is widespread in the county, occurring in all 10-km squares and nearly 90 per cent of tetrads. The summer abundance map, however, refines this information and shows that much of Wiltshire's Sky Lark population is confined to just three or four major hotspots, particularly the Marlborough Downs and Salisbury Plain. Other abundance maps, such as those for the Corn Bunting and Linnet, show similar patterns.

In addition, counts in each tetrad were restricted to a fixed period of four hours, in the form of two visits of two hours each, the first ideally in April–May and the second at least 14 days later in June–July. While this may have seemed irksome to some, it greatly increases the long-term value of the data – because when the atlas is repeated the same amount of time can be spent in each tetrad, thus allowing a more reliable estimate of change in each species' population. A small number of counties, and an increasing number of countries, have now undertaken repeat atlases, allowing them to look at the manner in which breeding ranges have changed over a period of a few decades. Unfortunately, few of the earlier atlases built in measures of fieldwork effort, so it is sometimes difficult to be certain whether an observed change in distribution is real, or simply an artefact of differing levels of time spent in the field. The *Birds of Wiltshire* has very neatly overcome this problem by insisting on timed visits.

Atlases have a wide range of uses. At their simplest, they inform and enthuse people about the natural world, a pre-requisite for taking an interest in conservation. The data have much analytical value as well. Were I to run a survey of Reed Warblers in Wiltshire, for example, I would undoubtedly use the distribution and abundance maps shown here to aid its design. At its most basic, it would be possible to ensure that the survey was conducted largely within the species' range, so that fieldworkers did not have to waste time searching inappropriate areas. Where atlas data at this scale really excel, however, is in their use for informing and guiding action on the ground. National or continental scale atlases, though valuable for other reasons, cannot really help with such decisions. This is because most conservation actions, and some types of threats to wildlife, occur at small geographical scales. For example, atlas data at the tetrad scale really could be used to investigate the impact of a major new road network in the county, whereas those at a larger geographical scale would be of little use for that. More importantly, perhaps, they allow more precise targeting of conservation action, such as species recovery projects. The Lapwing and Tree Sparrow maps, for example, could help focus the geographical locations of recovery projects for these declining farmland birds.

Such projects are real, rather than imaginary. For example, the Government funds landowners to farm in more wildlife-friendly ways through their agri-environment schemes, the most recent of which is Environmental Stewardship. The information in *Birds of Wiltshire* is already being used to ensure that taxpayers' money is spent as efficiently as possible in this county, so that the scheme may aid the recovery of a suite of farmland birds that are declining because of agricultural intensification. The data have been uploaded to the national Farmland Bird Database to identify the most important sites for the targeting of the new Environmental Stewardship scheme (Fisher *et al* 2005). It is for exactly this sort of reason that English Nature and the RSPB have both supported the book's production.

What then of the future? What might the results of a repeat atlas look like in a few decades' time? Will Nightingales and Redstarts still nest in the county? Will Little Egrets or Red Kites become relatively common breeding residents, and will the county be knee-deep in Hobbies because climate change has led to an explosion of their favoured invertebrate prey? Will Great Bustards have successfully been re-established on Salisbury Plain? I do not know the answer to these questions, but it certainly will be fascinating to see, and this atlas will enable such changes to be quantified.

Might a repeat atlas be undertaken in the future? I certainly hope so and, though it may use a revised approach, I trust that whatever new methods are adopted will still allow reliable backwards comparisons. Possibly what we might find by then is a merging of atlases and monitoring schemes. Currently these are regarded as largely separate entities, but from *Birds of Wiltshire* it is quite easy to see how one could merge into the other. For example, a random sample of tetrads could be counted in both winter and summer to allow populations to be monitored annually until the next atlas is undertaken.

A more likely change, perhaps, will not be the method itself, rather the manner in which data are collected and disseminated. Recording forms filled out in the field, submitted by post, entered onto computer over the winter, turned into maps a year or two later and published five to ten years on from the project's launch is how most atlases are currently produced. This is likely to change in the future. My vision of a repeat atlas has observations recorded in the field on hand-held digital devices, the data submitted on-line to the Wiltshire Ornithological Society's website, with instantaneously updated distribution and abundance maps for observers to view and query. There might be no actual final publication, just continually updated information. Such systems already exist, and are growing in number. Call me a Luddite, though, for I would still like to see a final publication on my bookshelf.

The production of *Birds of Wiltshire* has been a fantastic team effort. The whole project has been steered by the Wiltshire Ornithological Society's Tetrad Atlas Group, and its members deserve a special mention here: they are James Ferguson-Lees, Paul Castle, Peter Cranswick, Stephen Edwards, Rob Turner and Linda Cady. The first four of them then formed the editorial board, which co-opted Pete Combridge, tackled the considerable task of analysing and interpreting the maps and counts, and editing the final texts – as well as, with much help from Mike Jackson and Ian Collins, researching the past literature. They have not worked alone, though, and have been admirably supported by teams of regional organisers, data processors, text-drafters, artists, and designers, not to mention the 166 birdwatchers who put in a remarkable 4000 hours of fieldwork.

Birds of Wiltshire is not simply a bird atlas; it is much more than that. It is an entire county avifauna covering all 315 species recorded in the county; it provides a concise overview of Wiltshire's bird life at the turn of the millennium; and an additional chapter summarises the more significant records during 2001–05. It will become a benchmark standard for other counties to try to match. I congratulate the Wiltshire Ornithological Society for this excellent publication and commend it to you all.

Introduction

James Ferguson-Lees

The background

Though not especially large – roughly 55 km by 80 km – Wiltshire is bigger than the average of all English counties, but it is not a particularly 'fashionable' one for birdwatchers. Its rolling countryside ranges from just 25–35 m above sea level in the valleys of the Bristol and Salisbury Avons to a maximum of no more than 295 m on the rounded chalk summits of Tan Hill and Milk Hill. Roughly rectangular in shape, with the north-south axis the longer, it is bordered by Gloucestershire, Somerset, Dorset, Hampshire, Berkshire and Oxfordshire, the first four of which have a number of rich habitats, such as estuaries, saltmarshes or coasts, as well as observatories, research stations or other centres to attract visiting birders.

In contrast, Wiltshire has no coastline, no real cliffs, no estuaries, and little in the way of marshes or wetlands with muddy edges of the kinds to attract wading birds. Nor, until relatively recently, did it have many open waters to provide food and security for concentrations of wildfowl. Most of the county's dozen or more old lakes – or small series of lakes – are on country estates and the result of the artificial damming of streams in the 18th and 19th centuries; others were canal feeder reservoirs. The largest old lakes are Braydon Pond, Coate Water, Corsham Lake, Bowood Lake, those of the Longleat (including Shear Water) and Stourhead estates, and Fonthill and Clarendon Lakes. Thus, the county has no real history of drawing in birdwatchers from neighbouring areas, nor does it, at first sight, provide much refuge for the water-associated migrants or many obvious stopover points for the vagrants that, in turn, attract itinerant twitchers.

On the other hand, Wiltshire does have some good areas of old broadleaved woodland – especially in the northeast, southwest and southeast – and much open downland, while its two largest habitats of obvious and particular interest are the calcareous grasslands of Salisbury Plain, plus (part of) Porton Down, and the flooded gravel pits of the Cotswold Water Park (CWP). Salisbury Plain, over 40 km from west to east and some 16 km from north to south, has been unimproved grassland for around 6000 years and is England's largest expanse of this habitat. It is a nationally important site for breeding Stone-curlews and Quails, with high densities also of many commoner species of open grassland and scrub, and a significant wintering habitat for Hen Harriers, Merlins and Short-eared Owls, as well as the scene of the current attempt to reintroduce the Great Bustard. But it is a large area, and some 380 km^2 – long known as the Salisbury Plain Training Area (SPTA) – are owned and protected by the Ministry of Defence (MoD) with limited public access. Thus, it is perhaps not high on the itinerary of many birdwatchers, and few stop for even a short inspection when passing.

But the Cotswold Water Park – shared with Gloucestershire and Oxfordshire, and spread over a total of 100 km^2, of which about one tenth is open water – is the largest area of working and flooded gravel pits in Great Britain and now a wetland complex of considerable interest. Before the 1950s, when gravel extraction was started here, Wiltshire had remarkably few records of migrant waders (see species texts), but then the county's significance for a wide variety of wetland birds, both wintering and breeding, began rapidly to change. Many of the flooded pits are used for a variety of sports from fishing to sailing and water-skiing, but the more peaceful lakes hold many wildfowl and other waterbirds at all seasons, while winter often brings significant numbers of ducks that are scarce in southern England, such as Goosanders. Depending on water levels, a variety of passage, roosting and overwintering waders (and a few that breed) may at times be found on the muddy edges of some pits and on those that have yet to be flooded. Little Egrets can usually be seen and, in summer, this is a great area for watching Hobbies hawk dragonflies. (See Beatrice Gillam's chapter on 'Wiltshire's habitats'.)

The project

From the outset, the main purpose of this book was to set down by maps and accompanying texts the known distributions and estimated populations of all birds regularly summering in Wiltshire at the end of the second millennium. The decision additionally to include winter birds during 1998–2000 came much later. The summer maps were made possible by the efforts of more than 160 observers who spent a total of nearly 5000 hours covering the whole county and noting every bird of every species seen or heard. The units by which the fieldwork was carried out, and the data recorded, were the tetrads (2×2 km squares) of the National Grid. There are 25 tetrads in each 10-km square and, including 143 that lie partly in any one of the neighbouring counties (but with at least 20 per cent within Wiltshire), this meant a grand total of 915 tetrads (thus covering 3600 km^2, a slightly greater area than the 3485 km^2 of Wiltshire). Two 2-hour counts of all birds were made in every one of these 915 tetrads in April–July (especially May–June), during the six years of 1995–2000, to form the basis of the maps of relative abundance and our estimates of total populations. Supplementary visits in the same or other years often provided records of additional species (which could be added to the distribution maps, but not to the maps showing relative abundance). In winter, when many birds are more mobile, a single 2-hour count was made in each of a random selection of 443 tetrads during November–February in either 1998/99 or 1999/00, so that winter distribution and relative abundance could be plotted by 10-km squares.

In his Foreword, David Gibbons has outlined the history of grid-mapping of bird distributions at national levels in Britain and Ireland, in Europe and in other parts of the world since the late 1950s, when work on plant and bird atlases began. There had, however, been earlier attempts at the systematic plotting of British and Irish birds. The first were the maps compiled by WB Alexander in Fisher (1947): these used the Watsonian vice-county system – bio-geographical subdivisions of counties as units of approximately equal size – though with few exceptions (*eg* Fisher 1940), that system had never found much favour with ornithologists, who in general stuck with recording solely by counties and their greatly differing areas.

Otherwise, there had been few published attempts at mapping bird distributions anywhere in Europe before those by PAD Hollom in Peterson *et al* (1954) and, more particularly, by Voous (1960); being Europe-wide, those were inevitably based on inexact information at very small scales. In Britain and Ireland, however, the first steps at grid-mapping birds on a national basis had already been taken in 1950–52, using this essentially different and more objective technique – though the results were not published until eight years later (Norris 1960): after a pilot scheme on 100 species in the West Midlands in 1950, this plotted the British and Irish ranges of just 30 of them, selected to illustrate different types of distribution on what was almost a new standard in ornithology – the 25-km squares of the National Grid. (This was only 'almost new' because, 20 years earlier, Barn Owls had been surveyed nationally by 10–mile squares: see Blaker 1933, 1934.) Next, as 'an objective method of recording breeding distributions of common birds of prey in Britain', Prestt & Bell (1966) were the first in ornithology to use the now much more familiar 10-km squares. Soon after that, there followed the launch of the fieldwork for the first of the three national 10-km atlases, each covering the whole of Britain and Ireland, and referred to frequently in this book as the *1968–72 Atlas* (Sharrock 1976), the *1981–84 Winter Atlas* (Lack 1986) and the *1988–91 Atlas* (Gibbons *et al* 1993). Soon after the last of these came what we have termed the *EBCC Atlas* (Hagemeijer & Blair 1997), which covered the whole of Europe, though the grid used was 50-km squares.

But the plants had always been far ahead of the birds, at every stage. British botanists had long successfully used the Watsonian vice-county system, and it was they who led the way with national mapping by 10-km squares. Publication of *The Atlas of the British Flora* (Perring & Walters 1962) came six years before fieldwork for the *1968–72 Atlas* even began. Likewise, at our own local level, surveys for this *Birds of Wiltshire* did not start until two years after the publication of the tetrad atlas of *The Wiltshire Flora* (Gillam 1993).

Elsewhere in England, however, in the 1970s and early 1980s, several counties – Hertfordshire, London, Bedfordshire and Kent, in that order – published bird atlases based on the much finer grids of tetrads, or even 1-km squares. Then Hertfordshire led the way by producing a second tetrad atlas of breeding birds (Smith *et al* 1993), based on fieldwork 20 years after its first, as a means of showing and analysing the distributional changes that had taken place over those two decades. On both occasions, Hertfordshire had the advantage of housing, as a source of observer-power, the headquarters and staff of the British Trust for Ornithology at Tring. Similarly, Bedfordshire has held the RSPB headquarters and staff at Sandy since the early 1960s, while London and Kent have some of the highest densities of birdwatchers in the country. Kent, too, went on to publish its second county atlas, covering 1988–94, in the *Kent Bird Report* for 1996; and London its second in 2002 (LNHS 2002). Many other counties were initially worried that they had insufficient observers to cover their whole areas at the tetrad level, which involves surveying 25 times as many grid units as the 10-km squares of the national atlases. Indeed, coverage has always been the worry (usually unjustified) – as it was before the fieldwork for the *1968–72 Atlas* was launched nationally.

The idea of a tetrad atlas of summer bird distributions in Wiltshire was first mooted by Stephen Edwards as long ago as the early 1980s, but at that time the WOS Executive Committee decided, possibly correctly, that the county had too few birdwatchers keen and experienced enough to take on the fieldwork, let alone the huge task of analysing the results. Fieldwork had begun on the atlas of *The Wiltshire Flora* (Gillam 1993) in 1984 and, having myself carried out a comprehensive survey of the habitats and birds of the whole 37 km² of the Longleat estate that year, I met Stephen Edwards before the WOS AGM in March 1985 and we again discussed the possibility of a tetrad atlas of Wiltshire's breeding birds. He reported the earlier views of the Executive Committee, and he still believed that there were not enough observers to attempt coverage of the whole county.

Nearly nine more years were to pass before Paul Castle and I were standing on the southern edge of, perhaps appropriately, CWP68, opposite the heronry, when we again began to kick around the idea of starting a tetrad atlas of Wiltshire birds. After further discussions in the days that followed, and at the 1994 AGM, we obtained the backing of Rob Turner – whose support and views, as county recorder, were essential – and the three of us then put forward a proposal to the July 1994 meeting of the WOS Executive, seeking provisional approval.

The team

The Tetrad Atlas Group (TAG) was set up, now also including Linda Cady and Stephen Edwards, and in September 1994 the five of us went to Fleet (Hampshire) to meet John Clark and John Eyre, editors of *The Birds of Hampshire* (1993) – the acclaimed result of a similar exercise by the Hampshire Ornithological Society. They kindly gave us examples of their record cards and other recording forms, and much advice about running a tetrad atlas. Among things they regretted, however, they wished that they had taken the opportunity of making a more systematic and thorough attempt to amass field counts to support their calculations of breeding populations.

Having learnt much from our colleagues in Hampshire, we presented a detailed assessment to the Executive and the project was accepted. The first step was to divide the recording within the county into four (not exactly equal) regions, and Mike Hamzij (northwest), Mike Jackson (northeast), Granville Pictor (southeast) and John Pollard (southwest) agreed to take on the considerable task of overseeing these. Their involvement brought the number attending the meetings of TAG to nine and later, in 1998, Peter Cranswick was co-opted. In the seven years of 1994–2000, it proved necessary for TAG to hold a total of 24 meetings, in addition to the exploratory one in Hampshire. The first five were at the planning stages between mid August 1994 and 7 February 1995, followed by an extra check on organisation at the beginning of that April; there were then just two each in the winters of 1995/96 and 1996/97, but thereafter the rate increased to five between October 1997 and April 1998, three more in the summer and autumn of 1998, four scattered through 1999 and, after all the fieldwork was over, a final one on 12 April 2000. Thus, they were most frequent in the first winter (planning and organising the summer fieldwork), in the fourth winter (planning and overseeing the winter fieldwork), and in the last two complete years (ensuring that the summer coverage was complete, tying up loose ends), but were found to be necessary only a couple of times a year once the summer survey was under way (and the winter project not yet conceived).

The separate chapter on 'Atlas organisation, methods and mapping 1995–2000' sets out the procedures adopted, also reproducing the recording cards and forms used, and the detailed instructions. Nothing would, however, have been possible without the thousands of hours spent in the field by over 160 observers, who carried out the hundreds of 2-hour counts and thus produced the tens of thousands of records that were essential for the production of the maps. These observers are listed overleaf, together with the names of a few others who contributed significant casual records for particular species in which they are interested. *Birds of Wiltshire* as a whole, and the other editors in particular, are indebted above all to these people – especially to the regional organisers and 10-km stewards – without whose long hours in the field none of this would have been possible.

In the winter before each summer season of 1996–2000, an indoor meeting was held for these 'tetradders'. Always remarkably well attended by a high proportion of the participants, these meetings reviewed the previous season's results and promoted much useful discussion about future plans. Each time a number of unnamed and still inevitably incomplete maps for a selection of species were prepared by Rob Turner as a competition to see who could identify the most from their knowledge of Wiltshire's birds. Some of the maps, together with one showing the coverage to date, were then published in *Hobby*, the Society's annual publication.

The fieldwork

In 1995 alone – the first year of fieldwork – about 100 WOS members (and a few non-members, including some from outside Wiltshire) spent more than 1400 hours in 345 of the 915 tetrads. (The total number of tetrads in the county was originally thought to be 911, but a small boundary change had been overlooked and that and another reassessment increased this figure by four.) Thus, it seemed at one point that 38 per cent of the county had been covered in the first quarter of a survey that had originally been planned to last four years, but certain teething troubles became clear. In particular, a number of the cards had been inadequately completed because some observers had apparently failed to read, or not fully understood, the instructions (which, in any case, needed modification). Even so, the total of 281 cards with, at the time, fully acceptable data represented nearly 31 per cent of the county, and we still expected to complete the survey in four years. Most of the tetrads produced 30–49 species, but nine (with open country with few trees) showed fewer than 20 and, at the other end of the scale, two of eleven with 60 or more (all with rich mosaics of habitat) totalled as many as 71 and 72; an average tetrad held around 40 species. Usually about half of the species were noted as 'breeding', but in a very few cases, rather surprisingly, none at all was so reported and in others up to 90 per cent – a pattern which continued throughout the survey, except that in some tetrads the proportion with reported evidence of breeding later rose as high as 91–95 per cent.

Wiltshire atlas fieldworkers, or 'tetradders', 1995–2000

Those shown with one asterisk acted as '10-km stewards' – each responsible for arranging, or actually carrying out, the surveys in all of the 25 tetrads in one or more 10-km squares – and those with two asterisks were the regional organisers

* NP Adams
PW Adams
IR Anderson
MS Appleford
DN Ash
J Austin
RG Baatsen
MA Barrett
D Bath
V Bath
D Blackford
RF Blamey
RL Bland
* JC Booth
CA Botterell
* NJ Braine
A Bray
* B Bray
JM Brockbank
J Brown
* JHF Brown
SJW Brown
* ML Buckland
M Burstow
R Burstow
D Burton
C Buxton
RJ Buxton
LH Cady
D Camp
GC Cardy
IR Cardy
* AG Carter
P Cashman
* PE Castle
P Cleverly
W Clinch
ID Collins
P Combridge
B Corp
SJ Covey
D Cox
MT Craig
J Cumming
CA Cutforth
HA Edmunds
RJ Edwards
* SB Edwards
* HE Ennion
EJ Escott
* GC Evans
G Faulkner
IJ Ferguson-Lees
J Fishwick
PJ Foreman
PR Fox
R Fussell
SR Gardner
GN Gent
* B Gillam
CJ Gingell
AG Goddard
K Gover
JR Govett
JF Graham
CJP Gray
IJ Gray
* KJ Grearson
BG Greenough
I Grier
C Gubbins
* IE Haggett
** MJ Hamzij
DC Hanham
A Hannay
F Hardingham
EG Harris
R Hart
R Hayden
AP Hazell
C Head
GJ Head
JB Heigham
D Hempstock
MJ Hodgkins
IG Hunt
J Irvine
** MV Jackson
CM Johnson
D Jones
G Lambert
JW Lambert
J Lampard
M Lang
MJW Lee
J Leech
FE Lemon
NJ Lewis
P Lindsey
NJ Lowton
JL Marshall
J Matthews
* B Maxfield
DN McMaster
T Mills
AM Nason
* RW Nelson
BD Oram
M Oram
JP Osborne
G Pearce
MK Penn
D Pickett
** GD Pictor
RJ Pike
JAC Pitman
* NJ Pleass
** JD Pollard
WW Ponting
JA Price
MG Prior
RM Quantrill
W Quantrill
I Randall
M Randall
RJ Randall
* B Rawcliffe
* PS Read
GW Ricks
MC Robertson
EJ Rolls
JC Rolls
MJ Rolls
* AJ Rowe
JR Rowsby
MW Russell
A Rymell
SR Salkeld
JN Sears
* RT Simpson
M Smith
P Smith
GAF Stacey
GW Stone
GM Sturgess
MS Taylor
PE Truscott
* R Turner
JLA Tyler
S van de Hey
GF Waite
D Wall
C Ward
J Ward
S Ward
M Waters
* GL Webber
MG Webber
C White
* JE Wilder
AK Williams
R Williams
* NE Winter
J Wood
JK Wood
C Woods

This range of percentages was quite unexpected and it can only be supposed that a small proportion of observers had insufficient experience of the clear signs of nesting behaviour of even common birds and that, at the other end of the scale, a few may perhaps have been a little over-confident, but these extremes were few and are unlikely to have affected the overall patterns of the distribution maps.

By 1997, the third year, the number of tetrads surveyed had risen to 756, or about 83 per cent of the total. In the first two seasons, many observers had probably worked the tetrads closest to their homes, or others with which they were most familiar – and perhaps those which, on paper, seemed to be the more interesting in terms of the species likely to be found – but, although the total covered in that third year was 222 (nearly 24 per cent), it was down on each of the previous two years and it was now becoming apparent that we were unlikely to be able to complete the project within the original estimate of four years.

By the end of the summer of 1998 a further 135 tetrads (14·6 per cent) had been covered, bringing the total during 1995–98 to just over 97 per cent, but a fifth year was clearly needed to cope with the 24 tetrads that had not been touched. Moreover, with hindsight, it was realised that many of the squares surveyed in 1995 needed reworking. In that first year, observers had been asked to put counts or estimates of certain more widespread species (shown in different type on the record cards) into three categories of 'common' (more than 30), 'uncommon' (6–30) and 'rare' (fewer than six). This had been done partly because TAG had originally felt that some less experienced fieldworkers might find it too complicated to count every individual seen or heard of every species over two hours. What in fact then happened was that some observers did record every one in their notebooks, while others just estimated the numbers of those more widespread species at the end of the two hours. No satisfactory means was found of merging the estimates with the actual counts that became the standard from 1996 onwards. Therefore, TAG decided in 1998 that the only way to keep the statistics of relative abundance comparable would be to resurvey in 1999 and 2000 each of the 1995 tetrads where observers had not kept counts in their notebooks of all species.

By 1998, too, there was so much enthusiasm for the project as a whole that the idea of extending it to the winters (November–February) of 1998/99 and 1999/00 was discussed, agreed, and surprisingly rapidly organised. As it would clearly be impossible to survey all the 915 tetrads in two winters, it was decided to take a random sample of ten of the 25 tetrads in each 10-km square (two in each row of five across and down), though this became more complicated in the cases of the 15 incomplete 10-km squares at the edges of the county and a separate formula was applied to those (see chapter on 'Atlas organisation, methods and mapping 1995–2000'). In the event, a single 2-hour count was made in each of 443 (50 per cent) of 879 tetrads (different criteria were used to select peripheral 'Wiltshire' tetrads for the winter and summer surveys), which was considered representative enough for winter distribution to be plotted by 10-km squares.

The collation

In the summer surveys, observers completed record cards for each of the counts they made in each of the tetrads they were surveying and sent these via the 10-km stewards to the regional organisers – who checked them, combined the data for each tetrad on to a master card (if the observer had not already done so), and then forwarded that card to Rob Turner, who was also sent direct the casual record forms. He entered all these data on to computer, using the database system COBRA developed by Pete Fraser.

This was a huge task in itself, with which Rob Turner coped alone for the first three years, but in the later stages, especially when certain tetrads had to be resurveyed so that actual counts could be substituted for the earlier 'estimates' in 1995 of the more widespread species, some of the work was shared out to 'satellite' helpers – Gill Cardy, Mike Hamzij and Graham

Stacey. The winter data were collected by Stephen Edwards and entered on to computer by Bill and Rowena Quantrill.

The analyses of the two sets of data are fully explained in the chapter on 'Atlas organisation, methods and mapping 1995–2000'.

The book

It was originally intended that this book would simply have, for each species in summer, two maps and a facing text. In other words, it would be a straightforward atlas of the distributions of Wiltshire's breeding birds – except that it was envisaged from the outset that the second map, based on 2-hour counts in every tetrad, would show the relative abundance of each species in different parts of the county. When, however, after four seasons, it became clear that the summer fieldwork was not quite complete and that, in any case, 64 of the first year's tetrads would have to be surveyed again, it was decided to extend the project by another two years and attempt sample coverage during the final two intervening winters. Meanwhile, as already noted, the possibility of increasing the scope of the book into a full avifauna of Wiltshire, including migrants and vagrants, had been conceived, tested at one of the annual tetradders' meetings, and finally agreed.

Even then, the book might well have been finished in 2003, and published in that year or the next, had not Pete Combridge, Paul Castle and Stephen Edwards discovered, more or less independently, that old records in the *Wiltshire Archaeological & Natural History Magazine* (*WANHM*) had apparently been overlooked by both the previous two Wiltshire avifaunas, Peirson (1959) and Buxton (1981). The full extent of this treasure trove became apparent only when Paul Castle photocopied in Swindon Reference Library all the ornithological data that he could find in *WANHM*, particularly in the annual bird reports that appeared there irregularly from 1929 to 1936 (and regularly from 1946 to 1973), but also in individual notes in the magazine itself back at least to the end of the 19th century. Until that point, it had been our intention to use Buxton (1981) as the foundation on which to build. But further researches showed that earlier records in both *The Zoologist* (which was incorporated into *British Birds* in January 1917) and *The Field* (which in the late 19th and early 20th centuries was another significant and critical repository for observations on birds) had also been missed. Checking these turned up other data, including unpublished diaries – most notably those of CMR Pitman, who had been one of the editors of the pre-war Wiltshire bird reports – and it became clear that our baseline would have to be taken back to the county's first avifauna, *The Birds of Wiltshire* by AC Smith (1887).

The resulting research, analysis and writing to the stage of publication has thus taken seven years, rather than the two or three originally envisaged, and we hope that those WOS members who, at successive AGMs, understandably expressed some frustration at a project that appeared to grow and grow in duration without any tangible output will feel that the final product has justified the additional time and effort. During 2000–06 the editorial board had almost 70 evening meetings at the Crown Centre, Devizes, averaging about three hours apiece, as well as one whole day on a Saturday and two or three other meetings elsewhere: this represented well over 200 hours in each other's company, and of course we all also worked on our own for totals of hours many times that figure.

We now believe, however, that we have an accurate and as complete as possible a summary of Wiltshire's birds to the end of 2000 within the main species texts. Moreover, some aspects have been updated to 2005 in several of the additional chapters. In general, because it is impossible to apply modern-day standards of judging reports of unusual birds to those of earlier times, we have had to accept old records at their face value. In particular, some old specimens may have dubious provenance because, as elsewhere (see *eg* Nicholson & Ferguson-Lees 1962), a few people who paid good money for specimens of unusual birds to build their collections did not always check their sources. We have, however, tried to show where we think old records may be doubtful and, in some instances (*eg* Red-footed Falcon), we have been able to establish that certain unusual observations are much more satisfactory than had previously been suggested.

But the main aim of this book is to present a still picture, at the turn of the millennium, of the distribution and status of the birds that breed or regularly winter in Wiltshire, based on 5000 hours of surveying the county's 915 tetrads. The results are mapped, both by 'evidently breeding' or 'only seen' and by relative abundance. But, unusually for a county avifauna, we have estimated the summer and winter populations of all regular species, as explained in the chapter on 'Calculating population estimates of Wiltshire's birds', using the actual counts as the basis.

Moreover, we also decided to show these estimates against the backgrounds of the latest figures for the summer and winter populations of Great Britain as a whole – based on the *1988–91 Atlas* (Gibbons *et al* 1993) and the *1981–84 Winter Atlas* (Lack 1986), both updated as far as possible according to the most recent revision by the Avian Population Estimates Panel (Baker *et al* 2006) – and the breeding numbers in Europe as a whole, excluding Russia, as given in *EBCC Atlas* (Hagemeijer & Blair 1997). Some may feel that such introductions of wider backgrounds are steps too far for a county avifauna. But, in these days of ever-increasing threats to wildlife, birdwatchers and conservationists alike cannot afford to look at local areas in isolation. In many cases, the Wiltshire population may seem tiny by comparison, but in others (such as Stone-curlews and Barn Owls) this county holds significant proportions of the total British numbers.

All these data were added editorially, as often were comparisons with earlier surveys that had included Wiltshire and also appropriate references to the most recent ornithological literature. First drafts of all the species texts were produced by a team of 14 WOS members who, apart from the five of us on the editorial board – Paul Castle, Pete Combridge (co-opted in 2002), Peter Cranswick, Stephen Edwards and myself – included Nick Adams, Beatrice Gillam, John Govett, John Grearson, Mike Jackson, Granville Pictor, Bill Quantrill, Rob Turner and the late Geoff Webber, whose sudden death prevented him from approving the final versions of the texts he had drafted – so a second set of initials has been added to all of his species. But it must be emphasised that, to a greater or lesser extent, every species text and every chapter is a combination of several people's work.

Ian Collins worked into many texts the results of much research into old published data, and it is appropriate that he went back farther still to produce the chapter on 'Wiltshire's early birds', with tables listing bird-remains found in archaeological sites and place-names derived from the names of birds in Old English. Mike Jackson, in addition to producing the first draft of the chapter on 'Wiltshire's ornithological history' (which was then considerably enlarged by Ian Collins and the editors), was primarily responsible for the 'Gazetteer' and also worked with Stephen Edwards on 'Escapes and introductions'. Rob Turner produced many of the data for 'Significant additional records 2001–2005', and Mike Hamzij compiled 'Wiltshire ringing totals 1965–2005'. Apart from those mentioned elsewhere in this Introduction, the other chapters were written by the editors.

The future

The distributions of birds are essentially fluid, depending on a whole host of factors that most obviously include their habitats – so often altered or destroyed, or simply over-disturbed, by human activities – as well as the availability of their foods, any direct persecution both here and abroad, and the now accelerating changes in European weather patterns (see Phil Read's chapter on 'Weather, climate change, and their effect on Wiltshire's birds'). Small populations of species on the edges of their ranges in Great Britain are always vulnerable and several species (such as Turtle Doves and Nightingales) are at that western limit in Wiltshire, while some colonists (such as the Collared Doves which spread over the whole country in the 1950s and 1960s) are assumed to be driven by genetic or behavioural changes. Those mapped in national or county bird atlases by surveying units of the National Grid are objective representations of range and status that have, in essence, been frozen in a limited period of, usually, four to six years, but even in that time there can be marked changes. For example, the Wiltshire distributions of Wood Warblers, Redstarts and Nightjars all contracted in Wiltshire during the 1990s, while the numbers of Cuckoos clearly declined, but it would be possible to show these only by a series of maps involving annual surveys of the same areas. If six years can show obvious change, a period of 20 years can make huge differences. A tetrad or 10-km survey needs to be completed in as few years as possible, and then repeated over a comparable period after a suitable lapse of time. Every such repetition makes the whole more valuable as demonstrable measurements of populations for conservation.

The fieldwork (by 10-km squares) for the two national atlases of breeding birds – in 1968–72 and 1988–91 – was carried out with a 20-year interval. The next national bird survey is therefore planned for 2008–11 and that will also survey birds in winter from 2007/08, 26 years after the *1981–84 Winter Atlas*. Hertfordshire, under half the size of Wiltshire, was one of a handful of counties that had enough observers for the fieldwork for its first tetrad atlas to be coincided with that for the national *1968–72 Atlas* and, 20 years later, was then the first county to be able to repeat its survey at the same time as that for the national *1988–91 Atlas* – though in each case taking just a year longer (Smith *et al* 1993). The differences between some of its pairs of maps for 1967–73 and 1988–92 are striking. A number of counties will be combining their second or third atlases with the fieldwork for the next national atlas in 2008–11.

For Wiltshire, that will be too soon. WOS members will be taking part in the 10-km fieldwork, but the surviving organisers of this *Birds of Wiltshire* could not start again this year and the cost would not be justified. Moreover, Wiltshire has been one of the first to lead the way in winter tetrad surveys and, even more importantly, in assessing relative abundance by 2-hour counts and attempting to calculate total populations from these and other data. The results and techniques will need to be more widely considered and, as necessary, critically assessed before WOS organises its next one.

Because, however, we believe that this *Birds of Wiltshire* is a firm baseline on which future analyses may confidently be built, the next overview of the county's birds can, if necessary, be limited largely to map comparisons and discussion, together with an updating summary of migrants and vagrants. We hope that WOS will be able to envisage a repeat exercise along those lines, taking only four years for the fieldwork, ideally during 2017–20. A proportion of the profits from the present book will be invested to form the nucleus of the funds for such a project. The running costs of the WOS surveys and the publication of this book were funded largely by appeals to charities – written tirelessly by a former chairman of the Society, Wing-Commander John Brown, working almost entirely alone – by donations from many members, and by grants from English Nature (now Natural England), the Wiltshire Wildlife Trust, the RSPB and the Wiltshire Natural History Forum (see 'Acknowledgements'). We were originally advised that we would need a total of £30,000 and WOS reached this total before the fieldwork was completed, which gave us the freedom to extend the analysis without needing to keep to a publisher's timetable and which now means that all the money raised by the sales of the book can be used for future conservation projects – perhaps the best way for a small society to raise the money to make a real contribution to bird conservation.

It is gratifying to know that the material in this book is already being used for conservation in Wiltshire – by, for example, the RSPB in its project on farmland birds – as well as in the planning process and for Environmental Impact Assessments. We hope, too, that *Birds of Wiltshire* will continue to assist and promote the conservation of the birds of this county well into the future, not least by introducing a wider audience to the richness and diversity of the species involved.

Acknowledgements

Several hundred people have been involved in this book, in one way or another. The many who were directly concerned with the planning, organisation and fieldwork – including the 166 'tetradders' and others who contributed all the data for the maps – are recognised in the 'Introduction' to *Birds of Wiltshire*, but they were just one very important part of the whole, and the Wiltshire Ornithological Society (WOS), the Tetrad Atlas Group (TAG) and, particularly, the members of the editorial board owe much gratitude, too, in many other directions.

Grants and donations

While the compilation of *Birds of Wiltshire* would have been impossible without all those who were willing to spend hours in the field mapping the species, its publication would have been no less impossible without far more financial backing than WOS itself could possibly have provided. It was calculated at the outset that the Society would have to raise at least £30,000 to cover both the running costs and the eventual publication of what was originally conceived as no more than an atlas of breeding distribution.

During 1995–2000, exactly half of the basic costs involved in setting up the project and the organisation of the fieldwork – such as the printing of record cards, recording forms and instructions, the payment of the Ordnance Survey fees and the purchase of the COBRA software – were generously underwritten by what was then English Nature (EN, now Natural England) to a total of just over £2090. During 2001–02, to help towards publication, further grants amounting to £7000 were provided by EN (under Biodiversity Action Grant Aid), the RSPB, the Wiltshire Natural History Forum, and the Wiltshire Wildlife Trust (WWT). In all, these four organisations together contributed over £9000 – a quarter of the eventual grand total – and WOS is greatly indebted to them. As noted in the 'Introduction', the survey data collected for this book are already being used for conservation, in such projects as that of the RSPB on farmland birds, as well as in the planning process and for Environmental Impact Assessments.

At the outset, we did not know that these four bodies – two national and two within the county – would consider the project sufficiently important for them to support it in this way and, in any case, much more was needed. Therefore, a fund-raising group was formed under the auspices of the Executive Committee of WOS. This included some members of TAG and of the eventual editorial board, who are all recognised elsewhere, but several more people in particular must be mentioned here. Gill Cardy not only often hosted the fund-raising group at her house, but also represented WOS on the Wiltshire Natural History Forum. Sue Walker, of WWT, went to much trouble to draft and design an appeal leaflet. John Pollard – now greatly missed – who was the WOS treasurer for 23 years, put in good ideas on fund-raising and wisely invested the money as it came in, so that the accrued interest had increased the grand total raised in grants and donations by over £7500 by the time the balance was needed to cover publication costs. John's successor, Chris Ward, handled all the sponsorships and invested the later grants and then Roger Payne managed the finances during publication, sales and distribution.

But the one person who, above all, was responsible for eliciting a major proportion of the moneys received was Wing-Commander JHF Brown, chairman of WOS when the plans for what was originally envisaged as a straightforward atlas of Wiltshire birds were first agreed. John Brown took on the unenviable role of fund-raiser and wrote personal letters to all the most likely (and some unlikely) charities in the UK, as well as to all the local councils and utilities in Wiltshire. Some never replied, others sent kind letters of regret, but a proportion responded. Eight charities gave a total of £7825:

Esmée Fairbairn Foundation
Leach Fourteenth Trust
Cobb Charitable Trust
RJ Harris Charitable Trust
Lindeth Charitable Trust
GWR Community Trust
Verdon-Smith Family Charitable Trust
The Lalonde Trust

The largest donation, from the Esmée Fairbairn Foundation, more than revived John Brown's efforts at a time when he seemed to be receiving a lot of negative responses from charities – which, of course, have many requests for their often limited funds and, in any case, have set restrictions on the use of these.

Three bequests also came through the appeal, together totalling over £3700:

Beatrice Gillam in memory of David Blackford
The late HJ Chivers
The late AJP Sellar

No fewer than 20 local councils in Wiltshire contributed a total of £1935:

Kennet District Council
Salisbury District Council
Trowbridge Town Council
Chippenham Town Council
West Wilts District Council
Covingham Parish Council
Warminster Town Council
Marlborough Town Council
Worton Parish Council
Longbridge Deverill & Crockerton Parish Council
Fyfield & West Overton Parish Council
Little Bedwyn Parish Council
Hilperton Parish Council
North Newnton Parish Council
Codford Parish Council
Easton Royal Parish Council
Ebbesbourne Wake Parish Council
Haydon Wick Parish Council
Easterton Parish Council
Little Cheverell Parish Council

A further £1375 came from a variety of other sources:

Innogy (now RWE npower)
Center Parcs
Wessex Water
Salisbury Natural History Society
Fonthill Estate
Halcrow Group Ltd
BBC TV
Blue Circle (now Lafarge) Cement

Innogy wished their grant to sponsor a chapter and this was put towards the costs of 'Wiltshire's habitats'. Center Parcs asked that theirs be used to sponsor the texts for all the ducks. We also invited individuals to 'sponsor a species' for £25 and this raised a further £1775. Sponsors are all named at the ends of the texts concerned.

Finally, a total of just over £4000 was donated by 53 members, groups and non-members, who are listed here in alphabetical order:

NP Adams
Earl & Countess of Ancram
J Andrews
J Austin
Marquess of Bath
K Broomhall
JHF Brown
R Brownlow
Mrs P Bucknall
M Burstow
DEF Camp
Mrs G Cardy
I Cardy
D Charlwood
MT Craig
D Culverhouse
Defence Munitions Dean Hill (in memory of Mike Combridge)
Julia Drown MP
R Faulkner

IJ Ferguson-Lees
MW Fisher
G Gamage
Polly Garnett
JR Govett
C Graham
Great Bustards
(PE Castle, LH Cady, RG Baatsen)
GW Green
Green Plovers
(PW Adams, JC Booth, W Clinch, G Dicker)
GF Gubbon
P Hazell
W Johnson
Sir John Keegan
WP Lansdown
J Leech
K Lewis
Captain FD Lowe RN
Baron Margadale of Islay
ML Mortimer
AW Neish
JH Noble
G Olney
R Pattemore
NJ Pleass
JD Pollard
P Powley
EL Sawyer
South Newton Bird Count
J Stephen
Gillian Sturgess
T Sykes
R Webb
J Willcox
Wiltshire Woodlarks
(RT Simpson, B Maxfield, B Bray, A Bray)

A grand total of nearly £38,000 was raised by all these methods (including the interest on the money invested), and the excess has enabled us to make a larger and, we hope, more useful book, as well as including colour photographs of a selection of Wiltshire's habitats.

Map production

The task of creating the summer distribution and relative abundance maps in *Birds of Wiltshire* from the vast amount of fieldwork data was made much easier by the use of the COBRA software, written by Pete Fraser, which Rob Turner (assisted by Gill Cardy, Mike Hamzij and Graham Stacey in the latter stages) used to enter all the tens of thousands of summer records. Pete Fraser then helped further by modifying COBRA specifically to address mapping issues for *Birds of Wiltshire*. The winter records were compiled by Stephen Edwards, and computerised by Bill and Rowena Quantrill. All the maps were then created by Peter Cranswick using DMAP, which was developed by Alan Morton. The DMAP outlines and the background outlines of Salisbury Plain, urban areas and rivers are based on Ordnance Survey data and we are grateful for that body's permission to use these in *Birds of Wiltshire* and in publicity connected with it.

Simon Pickering and Stuart Ballard provided a map of the Cotswold Water Park (CWP), and Wendy Blyth (Defence Estates) a map of the Salisbury Plain Training Area (SPTA), which formed the bases of those reproduced on pages 840–841. We are grateful, too, to Sue Wallis and Diane Unwin of the Centre for Ecology and Hydrology (CEH) for the 2000 land cover data that accompany this book as transparent overlays.

Assistance from other organisations

Much assistance was received from other bodies, particularly the British Trust for Ornithology (BTO), and the editors have benefited greatly from data from several of its surveys, especially the Breeding Birds Survey (BBS), the former Common Birds Census (CBC) and, for instances of longevity and habitat fidelity, the ringers' Constant Effort Sites (CES), not forgetting too the long-running Heronries Census. In 1999, Sue Adams of the BTO Ringing Office supplied detailed records and summaries of 'outward' recoveries of Wiltshire-ringed birds within the United Kingdom and abroad, and 'inward' recoveries in Wiltshire of foreign-ringed birds and others marked elsewhere in the UK. Jacquie Clark later provided more ringing data and answered many questions.

Other members of the staff of the BTO willingly gave further help. Jeremy Greenwood, its director, advised on the selection of randomised tetrads for the winter survey. John Marchant, Humphrey Crick and Stephen Baillie dealt with specific queries on the Trust's long-term surveys and on *Breeding Birds in the Wider Countryside*. Stu Newson and David Noble supplied Wiltshire estimates from national BBS results, and Su Gough provided data from the 1999 Nightingale Survey. Chris Wernham also kindly sent us drafts of some texts for the *Migration Atlas* in advance of publication.

Among representatives of other organisations, Kirsty Meadows and Richard Gregory assisted with data from the RSPB surveys of the Cotswold Hills Environmentally Sensitive Area, and Dominic Ash and Nick Adams provided us with copies of the two RSPB surveys of the Salisbury Plain Training Area (SPTA). We also thank the Wildfowl & Wetlands Trust, specifically Peter Cranswick and Mark Pollitt, for access to data from the Wetland Bird Survey (WeBS). We are most grateful, too, to the Cotswold Water Park Society (CWPS), in particular to Gareth Harris, for the CWP report and for specific information on Little Ringed Plovers, Sand Martins and Reed Buntings. Edward Darling, Andrew Hoodless and Rufus Sage of the Game Conservancy Trust (GCT) answered queries about gamebirds and Woodcocks.

The editor of *British Birds* (*BB*), Roger Riddington, dealt with many other small queries, as did the then secretary of the *BB* Rarities Committee (BBRC), Mike Rogers, and the then secretary of the Rare Breeding Birds Panel (RBBP), Malcolm Ogilvie. It seems appropriate to add how invaluable we have found the annual reports of both the BBRC and the RBBP – and, not least, the annual analyses by Pete Fraser and Mike Rogers of British records of scarce migrants, also published in *BB*. In this connection, too, we are most grateful to Keith Naylor for giving us, free of charge, a list of all the Wiltshire records in his privately published *A Reference Manual of Rare Birds in Great Britain and Ireland* (1996), though our decisions on the validity of a few of the 19th and early 20th century reports have not necessarily agreed with his.

Quantel Limited allowed Linda Cady to use their photocopying facilities on behalf of TAG through the six years of the survey work. Over the course of the project, the computing system at the Wildfowl & Wetlands Trust, at Slimbridge (Gloucestershire), has been used to undertake the majority of analyses, and throughout has served as a backup of all databases and texts; in this connection, Robin Jones and Rebecca Lee provided assistance to Peter Cranswick with data analyses and storage.

We are grateful to the funding bodies, and the volunteer fieldworkers, of the various national surveys and schemes whose data we have used. The Ringing Scheme is supported by the BTO, the Joint Nature Conservation Committee (JNCC), Dúchas The Heritage Service, National Parks and Wildlife (Ireland), and by the ringers themselves. WeBS is funded by the BTO, Wildfowl & Wetlands Trust, RSPB and JNCC. JNCC acts on behalf of the Countryside Council for Wales, the Department of the Environment (Northern Ireland), Natural England, and Scottish Natural Heritage.

Individual assistance

Mike Jackson originally researched various subjects ranging from 'Wiltshire's ornithological history' to 'Escapes and introductions' and the 'Gazetteer'. Later, Ian Collins further developed the historical chapter, and also added many early references to a good proportion of the species texts, as well as attending some of the editorial meetings. We are grateful to him, too, for his archaeological summary of 'Wiltshire's early birds', as we are to Beatrice Gillam for her chapter on habitats, to Phil Read for his overview of the county's weather and to Mike Hamzij for the ringing summary. Mike Hamzij and Rob Turner were punctilious throughout the writing and editing stages in answering our endless queries on ringing recoveries and Wiltshire records respectively. We are also grateful to all the other members of the support teams listed on the title page, and to all the farmers and landowners who allowed our tetradders access.

A number of other people provided information and help over queries about individual bird species or groups of species: Nick Adams, Guy Anderson, Mike Austin, Gordon Avery, Mark Avery, Richard Baatsen, Philip Burton, David A Christie, Roger Clarke, J Clements, Martin Collinson, Mike Combridge, Jon Cox, Paul Darby, Dick Forsman, Tim Frayling, Andy Gosler, John Graham, Gareth Harris, Ben Hatchwell, Robert Hayden, F Hustings, Simon Lane, Nigel Lewis, John Marchant, Killian Mullarney, A Ovaa, Julian Parfitt, Matt Prior, Robert Prŷs-Jones, Robin Prytherch, Peter Rock, Mike Rogers, Bob Scott, Colin Shawyer, Ian Sinclair, Andrew Stanbury, David Stroud, Lars Svensson, Don Taylor, Phil Toye, Didier Vangeluwe, Glenn Vermeersch, Steve Votier, David Waters, Estlin Waters, Tony Wells, Sophie Wilcox, Andy Wilson, Neil Winter, and Eddie Wiseman. We apologise to any others who, over 12 long years of fieldwork and analysis, we may have overlooked.

Joy Newton gave much advice on the list of scientific names of the plants, which was checked later by Purgle Linham and Hanna Price of the Wiltshire & Swindon Biological Records Centre (WSBRC), and then independently by Beatrice Gillam. There was some difference of opinion in a few cases, and the final list is the editors' responsibility. Beatrice Gillam and Purgle Linham are also thanked, along with Michael Darby and Vicki Brown (WSBRC), for permission to use, and for digitising and updating, the geology map from *The Wiltshire Flora* (Gillam 1993). Dr RJ Mynott kindly translated the references to the swannery at Clarendon Palace (see 'Wiltshire's ornithological history'), which were written in medieval Latin.

Mike Fuller is thanked for the loan of Roy Pitman's diaries and for providing copies of Wiltshire bird notes from *The Zoologist*. David Ballance and Mavis Still generously read through the whole of the Bibliography and made many corrections and useful suggestions.

Beatrice Gillam wished particularly to thank the following for information or help in connection with her chapter on 'Wiltshire's habitats': Bill Ayres, Clive Bealey, Linda Birch, Bob Budden, David Burton, Paul Castle, Paul Darby, Stephen Davis, Stephen Edwards, Bill Elliott, James Ferguson-Lees, John Grearson, Gilbert Green, Gweneth Helliar, P Jordan, Barbara Last, Nigel Lewis, Roger Marris, Bruce Maxfield, Eunice Overend, Christopher Perraton, John Pollard, Brian Rawcliffe, John Rayner, Julian Rolls, Michael Smith, Anthony Tyers, and Nick Wynn.

In connection with his chapter on 'Wiltshire's early birds', Ian Collins asked us to express particular thanks to Michael Allen (Trust for Wessex Archaeology Ltd), Linda Birch (Alexander Library, University of Oxford Zoological Department), Dale Serjeantson (University of Southampton, Department of Archaeology), and Naomi Sykes (University of Nottingham, Department of Archaeology), all for help or advice and library facilities; Sheila Hamilton-Dyer for data on archaeological sites in Wiltshire; and Michael Marshman (Wiltshire Library Service) for help with Wiltshire place-names. Derek Yalden (University of Manchester, School of Biological Sciences) and his students provided free access to their work on place-names and also 'much inspiration'.

For help with their chapter on 'Wiltshire's ornithological history', Ian Collins and Mike Jackson would like to thank Angus Clarke (*The Times*), Humphrey Dobinson (past Dorcan School literature), Gina Douglas (Librarian/archivist, Linnaean Society of London), Beatrice Gillam, Alison Harding (Rothschild Library, Tring), Lorna Haycock (Librarian, Devizes Museum), Dr TE Rogers (Marlborough College) and Tim Sparks

(CEH, Monks Wood). They wish, too, to thank the library staff of the Royal College of Surgeons, London; of Dauntsey's School, West Lavington; of the Bodleian Library and Radford Science Libraries, Oxford; of the Museum of English Rural Life, University of Reading; of the General Library, Natural History Museum, South Kensington; of Devizes, Marlborough, Salisbury and Trowbridge Libraries, Wiltshire; of the City of Birmingham Library; and of the University of Southampton Library.

Lastly in this section, on WOS's behalf, we must again express our gratitude to John Clark and John Eyre, who not only gave us much advice from their experience of county tetrad fieldwork and analysis – which led to their *Birds of Hampshire* (1993) – but also came to the AGM of WOS in Devizes in March 1995 and gave a most stimulating talk which certainly helped to enthuse many of our members into becoming 'tetradders'.

Artists and photographers

After consulting Robert Gillmor, and also Keith Betton who at the time was working on the second London tetrad atlas (LNHS 2002) – both were most helpful – we wrote to a number of local and national bird-artists and no fewer than 35 agreed to draw, between them, the 309 line-drawings that in this book illustrate every species recorded in Wiltshire to the end of 2000. For many of these birds, particularly the scarce breeders and the vagrants, we had particularly to specify the plumage and the background required. In the cases of certain vagrants, for example, the only Wiltshire records have been in winter or immature plumages and so it would be unsuitable to show an adult male in summer plumage; likewise, the marsh or coastal sites that are the more usual habitats of, for example, various waterbirds or, indeed, Ravens are hardly typical of those that nest or have nested in this county. The 35 artists are:

Richard Allen
Richard Andrews
Norman Arlott
Kim Atkinson
Richard Baatsen
Ken Beint
Nik Borrow
George Brown
John Busby
Chris Button
Dan Cole
Peter Cranswick
Martin Elliot
John Gale
Robert Gillmor
John Govett
John Holloway
Rodney Ingram
Ernest Leahy
Ian Lewington
Jim Lyes
Steve Message
Chris Orgill
Simon Patient
Dan Powell
Darren Rees
Dafila Scott
Anthony Smith
Philip Snow
Rob Still
David Thelwell
Stephanie Thorpe
Gordon Trunkfield
Ian Wallace
Michael Webb

The individual vignettes can mostly be identified against this list by the initials in the corner, but two have used 'JG': of these, John Gale drew the ten raptors, and John Govett the larks, hirundines and five of the buntings. Note also that Richard Allen has used the initials 'RWA' and Richard Andrews 'RMA', while 'DIMW' are the initials of Ian Wallace. Both WOS and the editors are most grateful to all of them for giving of their time and expertise in this way.

For the jacket of the book, the incomparable Ian Lewington also kindly painted the beautiful illustrations of two Wiltshire birds whose breeding populations are nationally significant: the Stone-curlew on the front cover and the Corn Bunting on the back. He also painted the Great Bustard used on the spine and title page. These all speak for themselves and we are greatly indebted to him in particular.

At a late stage in the book, we found that advances in colour printing and the consequent decreasing costs of reproduction in recent years made it possible to include 31 photographs to illustrate the chapter on 'Wiltshire's habitats'. Thanks to the generosity of Stephen Davis, and of the WWT in memory of Steve Day, with much assistance from Patrick Cashman, Margaret Feneley, Tim Frayling, Jenny Wheeldon and Robert Wolstenholme (Natural England), Sharon Charity and Emma Day (WWT), Rachel Crees and Jodie Harris (Defence Estates), Stuart Corbett (Defence Science and Technology Laboratory Conservation Officer for Porton Down), RH Bewley and Gareth Harris (CWPS) and David Kjaer, Linda Cady and Peter Cranswick, we have been able to put together photographs of a fairly representative selection of Wiltshire habitats.

Book design and publication

We must now express our special gratitude to Rob Still, of Quetzal Communications (Old Basing, Hampshire), for all the work he has put into the design and publication of *Birds of Wiltshire* for a less than generous fee. When he had paged up the first half of the species texts, he readily agreed to switch these from the old 'Voous' order to the new recommendations of the Taxonomic Sub-Committee of the British Ornithologists' Union Records Committe (BOURC-TSC) in October 2002, which changed the sequence of several families near the beginning of the list, and uncomplainingly rearranged some 160 pages. Later decisions of the BOURC-TSC in 2004 and 2005 then caused further small rearrangements. Rob also attended about a quarter of the 70-odd three-hour evening meetings of the editorial board during 2000–06 – on each occasion driving from Old Basing (Hampshire) to Devizes and back – answering all our questions and putting in many ideas. He dealt with, at times, endless streams of queries by phone or email. And, as a consequence of the greatly extended timetable for the book (see 'Introduction'), Rob has had to transfer (more than once) the whole of the texts laid out at that stage into new versions of desktop publishing software. Apart from drawing the vignettes for six species himself, he also dealt directly with some of the other artists on our behalf. And, at the eleventh hour, he created the montage of Great Bustards at the lek, watched by a perched Whinchat and a flying Hobby, to fill the gap on pages 122 to 123.

The book has been a much bigger enterprise than we had originally envisaged, but it would have been far more difficult without Rob Still, who greatly exceeded the normal duties of a publisher. Also to be thanked are the following WOS members who also served at various times on the publication group, formed under the auspices of the Executive Committee of WOS to plan publication, sales and distribution: John Austin, Ian Collins, Roger Payne, Rowena Quantrill and Chris Ward.

And finally

Lastly, we should like to express our gratitude to our wives, partners, families and close friends for support and encouragement – and, not least, much patience – over a period of seemingly ever-extended deadlines, during which many family and social occasions often came second.

Wiltshire's habitats

Beatrice Gillam

Wiltshire is landlocked, and its geographical position in England is probably best described as central-southern. At its maximum 84 km from north to south and 59 km from west to east, it includes 33 complete, or nearly complete, 10-km squares of the National Grid – the 'core squares' throughout this *Birds of Wiltshire* – and 15 others that mostly have less than half of their area within the county.

Travellers passing from east to west across Wiltshire, whether by train through Salisbury or Swindon, or by road along the M4 in the north or the A303 or A30 in the south, will encounter very different landscapes, though all will give the impression of a county with few steep hills and little water. The topography of a landscape is dependent on geological history, subsequent colonisation by natural vegetation, and human influence. From the time when our ancestors began to clear the land of trees until the 20th century's rapidly changing farming practices, the environment has experienced many changes. Aspects of the flora have altered and the fauna, including the birds, has developed in response.

In general, climate is dictated by latitude and geographical position in relation to the nearest oceans. The effects on the land of rainfall, humidity and temperature all influence the flora that can be supported by each type of soil. In a county such as Wiltshire, the variables are not very great, but there are differences in the microclimates of different land formations. For example, the river valleys and low-lying clay vales are warmer than the open chalk downland on the higher ground, but also more prone to frost. The western side of the county receives slightly higher rainfall than the east as a result of, in part, the effect of conditions in the nearby Bristol Channel. The effects of global warming on birds is already being shown in the earlier arrival of some migrants and earlier nesting of some residents (see 'Weather, climate and their effects on Wiltshire's birds').

Geology

Of the three elements already referred to – geology, climate and humans – the first is the one that has most fundamentally fashioned Great Britain. The forms of agriculture have been influenced by the types of soil. Human building materials have been dictated by the rocks, and the siting of towns and villages chosen largely in relation to the supply of permanent water. Yet, compared with that of many other English counties, the geology of Wiltshire is 'quite straightforward' (Barron 1976). In this chapter, only brief geological details are given (see Geddes 2000 for in-depth discussion), the emphasis being on the way that geology has helped to create habitats, which in turn have influenced today's avifauna.

Chalk dominates southern and most of eastern Wiltshire (see endmap 2). This chalk mass is penetrated along the east-west lines of the Vales of Pewsey and Wardour, where the chalk cover has been arched up and subsequently removed by erosion, thus exposing the underlying strata. The Vale of Pewsey, which crosses the centre of the county and divides the Marlborough Downs in the north from Salisbury Plain in the south, exposes the Upper Greensand. The Vale of Wardour in the southwest, which lies between the West Wiltshire Downs and Cranborne Chase, exposes a variety of Jurassic strata, notably Kimmeridge Clay and sandy Portland limestones. Parts of the chalk plateau, contradictorily called 'downland', have deposits of a varied mixture of clays, sands and flints, known as Clay-with-flints. This produces an acidic soil, on which non-alkaline plants grow. Of these, gorse is of great importance for birds. Much of the chalk, especially near the surface, has numerous small joints which allow for immediate percolation of rainwater. Deeper down, the joints are closed, slowing down the water's progress through the chalk so that there is a time-lag of about three months between the period of greatest rainfall and the maximum height of the water-table. It is then that the chalk springs begin to flow and the streams and rivers are replenished until the water-table falls once more as water loss from evaporation exceeds rainfall.

Along the northwest county boundary lies the Cotswold stone belt, formed by the Great and Inferior Oolite of thick, alternating layers of limestones and clays. Steep-sided combes, eroded from an upland plateau, are typical of this area and result in fast-flowing streams found nowhere else in Wiltshire. The harder limestone band slows down the flow of the water before it tumbles over its edge on to the softer clay below in the form of waterfalls and rapids, the former once used to power woollen mills along the By Brook. The valley sides were always too steep to be cultivated and have retained their woodland covering.

Between this stone belt and the chalk lies the clay vale that runs from around Frome in Somerset north-northeastwards to Oxfordshire. Oxford Clay to the north and west covers about three-quarters of this vale and is divided from a narrower band of Kimmeridge Clay to the east and south by irregular outcrops of the Corallian. On the relatively high ground between Chippenham and Malmesbury, where Oxford Clay overlies Cornbrash, the clay vale is partly floored by the present-day floodplain of the Bristol Avon. At a slightly higher level it is flanked by extensive areas of gravel, in some places up to a kilometre wide, which represent older floodplain deposits of the river. Some of these have been exploited and are now areas of open water. Once almost completely covered by trees and then partly cleared, the impervious clays were too wet to be ploughed and were kept as pasture for feeding dairy cattle. Later, many were drained and silage took the place of hay. Now, the claylands are a patchwork of woodland – the remains of Braydon Forest – and improved pastures and unimproved meadows, many of the last owned by the Wiltshire Wildlife Trust (WWT). In the extreme north, on the county's border with Gloucestershire, the Thames floodplain, as with that of the Avon, is bordered by older gravel deposits which have been extensively exploited since the middle of the 20th century. After excavation is completed, the pits gradually fill with high quality, alkaline water forming marl lakes which have developed into the most important areas for waterbirds in Wiltshire.

The geology of the county south of Salisbury Plain can be described in two sections lying respectively west and east of the Salisbury Avon. To the west are two chalk ridges, having Clay-with-flints cappings, between which the Ebble flows east to join the Avon at Bodenham near Salisbury. To the east, there is a continuation of the chalk, its main feature being the Dean Hill upfold with Tertiary deposits of sands and clays to the north and south. On these deposits are situated the ancient oak forests of Buckholt and Melchet, remnants of which are now found at Blackmoor Copse and Bentley Wood to the north and at Langley and Franchises Woods and Whiteparish Common to the south.

The shape of the Wiltshire landscape at any given time is the result, in geological time, of the folding of the rocks and continuing erosion by running water. The county's rainfall gathers into streams and enters the sea via one of four watercourses: the Bristol Avon into the Bristol Channel, the Salisbury Avon into Christchurch harbour, the Blackwater into Southampton Water and along the Kennet-Thames valley into the Thames estuary. Most of the streams feeding the Bristol Avon flow across the gentle slopes of the clay vale at a comparatively slow rate between steep banks of alluvial silt. The one exception is the water from the stone belt as it descends through the steep-sided By Brook valley. Streams flowing over greensand or chalk feed the Salisbury Avon, where the water and the banks are shallow. As already explained, some of the feeder streams flow only when the water-table rises to the ground level. The Bourne and the Till are 'winterbournes' and, although the three main tributaries – the Wylye, the Nadder and the Ebble – are all fed upstream by winterbournes, they flow all year round at varying depths that depend on rainfall and the amount of water abstracted from boreholes.

Habitat groups

Of the six broad groups of habitats defined in the 1970s by the BTO in its Register of Ornithological Sites, the southern inland county of Wiltshire has only three: woodlands (broadleaved and coniferous); lowland grasslands (calcareous grasslands and scrub, or downland) and open waters (both natural and artificial lakes, and rivers). The large country estates and farmland which predominate in the county, increasing the diversity of the total landscape, should be added to these three broad habitats.

The above is a simplified description of the pattern of varied habitats, but a new approach was made to describe them in the late 1990s, partly in response to the Convention on Biological Diversity at Rio de Janeiro in June 1992. As the government's statutory adviser on nature conservation in England, English Nature (EN) had a key role to play in stimulating action and its development of the Natural Areas concept was an important part of that role. A Natural Area was defined as being 'not a designation, but an area of the countryside identified by its unique combination of physical attributes, wildlife, land use and culture'.

Of the 92 Natural Areas, parts of eight lie within Wiltshire. The most extensive of these is the South Wessex Downs Area, half of which is included in the county and encompasses Salisbury Plain, the West Wiltshire Downs and Cranborne Chase (endmap 2). The Thames and Avon Vales and the Berkshire and Marlborough Downs Areas are each about half the size of the South Wessex Downs Area. The Wessex Vales and Greater Cotswold Areas are small parts of nationally large areas, while the edges of the New Forest, the Hampshire Chalk and the Midvale Ridge Areas are represented in even smaller parts of the county.

From the wildlife point of view, these areas are based largely on their botanical uniqueness, mention of their ornithological content being mainly restricted to Biodiversity Action Plan (BAP) species. The profile of each Natural Area was prepared in consultation with other organisations that had experience of, and interest in, the conservation of the wildlife. Priority objectives to sustain and improve the main interests of each were set out in detail. The future of some of the rarer birds will now be overseen partly through the influence of EN (now Natural England) and, although many common species have not been mentioned specifically, the recommendations for land-use should be beneficial to them too. Until the purchase by the WWT of the site now known as Langford Lakes in 2002, none of the nature reserves in Wiltshire – the National Nature Reserves (NNRs), the WWT's nature reserves, or woodlands owned by the Woodland Trust (WT) – was managed specifically for their bird species. Some woodlands, particularly Ravensroost in the north and Blackmoor Copse (both WWT) in the south, have been improved as habitats for birds in recent years by the restoration of coppice cycles and the widening of rides. At Langley Wood NNR, schemes to diversify the habitat with birds in mind have included phased clearance of rhododendron, the retention of veteran trees, and the creation of open spaces.

The fieldwork for *Birds of Wiltshire* was not based on Natural Areas but on areas confined within tetrad squares (2 × 2 km). To a certain extent, however, the data obtained can be used to illustrate some of the differences between the Natural Areas. Since each breeding species is dependent on more than one habitat within a given area, the more varied the area the greater the number of species (see the maps in the section on species diversity within the chapter 'The status of birds in Wiltshire'). Requirements, in order of importance, are the availability of food in both summer and winter, of suitable nest-sites in summer, and of safe day and night roosts at all seasons. Descriptions and locations of some of Wiltshire's best bird habitats follow, using the BTO Sites Register category headings with brief references to Natural Areas.

Roundway Down and Covert SSSI: chalk downland with mixture of species-rich grassland, scrub and woodland (*Stephen Davis*)

Woodland

The characteristic habitats and the key issues and objectives for woodland listed by EN for each Natural Area in Wiltshire do not include any specific requirements for the avifauna because they are not of importance for BAP species. About 5000 BC, small-leaved lime was a major component of Wiltshire's natural wildwoods (*ie* primaeval forests), but today few of these ancient woodlands with limes survive, the best examples being in the Braydon and Melchet Forests on clays and in Gopher and Bidcombe Woods on the Marlborough and West Wiltshire Downs respectively (Rackham 1986, Gillam 1993). The wildwoods also contained ash, hazel, oak, wych elm and other species – all broadleaved trees and shrubs, apart from yew on the chalk. The beech, now widely planted especially on the chalk, was probably indigenous in only a few places in this county (Grose 1957).

The National Vegetation Classification (NVC) identifies two main types of indigenous woodland in Wiltshire: woods of ash, field maple and dog's mercury on calcareous soils, where hazel is characteristic, small-leaved lime and wych elm can also occur, and pedunculate oak is often common; and woods of pedunculate oak, bracken and bramble on base-poor brown earths, where silver birch can be abundant, especially in younger stands (Hall *et al* 2004). Scarcer types of woodland are: beech and dog's mercury woods on steep chalk escarpments, where ash, whitebeam and yew are often present; beech and bramble woods on base-poor Clay-with-flints on chalk, where pedunculate oak is a common associate; and woods on wet flood-plains dominated by alder and willows, but also containing ash and oak. Many of these woods have, at some time, been partly cleared and planted with conifers to bring a quicker financial return. Botanical interest is reduced in conifer woodland but, provided that the replanted proportion of the wood is not too great, the mixture creates new habitats for colonisation by a wider range of bird species.

The feeding preferences of woodland birds can be divided into three categories, according to the vertical zones of the wood's structure and to the individual species' morphology, particularly the structure of its bill. For example, Blue Tits feed mainly in the tree canopy, Marsh Tits in the lower canopy and shrub layer, and Great Tits on the ground. Therefore, woodlands without all three layers hold the fewest species. The dense shade of pure beech and mature conifer stands lack these layers and so – except for some that were planted on ancient woodland sites, as in the parkland at Longleat, which have a good lower storey – generally hold the smallest numbers and are the least important for birds.

The forests that survived to the Roman occupation were later to become the Royal Hunting Forests of the Saxon and Norman monarchs and correlate closely with the present-day distribution of ancient woodland in Wiltshire (Gillam 1993). These forests were not necessarily a continuous expanse of woodland; rather the term described the form of tenure applied to the territories and the laws that were enforced. Many present-day woods in Wiltshire are remnants of the former forests of Braydon, Chippenham or Pewsham and Melksham, Selwood, Savernake, Chute, Clarendon or Buckholt and Melchet, Grovely, and Cranborne Chase, and extensive parts of two, Savernake and Grovely, still exist.

A national survey of woodland carried out by the Forestry Commission (FC) from 1994 to 2000 found the total area of woodland exceeding 0·1 ha in Wiltshire to be 27,325 ha, representing 7·9 per cent of the land area (Smith & Gilbert 2002). Broadleaved was the dominant forest type with 55·5 per cent of all woodland; confererous represented 13·6 per cent, mixed woodland 17·1 per cent and open spaces within woodland 11·8 per cent; the remaining two per cent was coppice, coppice-with-standards and felled woodland. Oak was the main broadleaved species, and larch the main conifer. Woodland land cover increased by over 2300 ha from 7·1 to 7·9 per cent of the land area between 1980 and 1996, with the relative proportion of broadleaved to coniferous increasing from 65 to 75 per cent. Excluding blocks under 2 ha, a total of nearly 13,000 ha, or about 52 per cent, was estimated as being

West Woods: beech plantation and bluebells on former ancient woodland site clear-felled after the 1939–45 War (*Linda Cady*)

ancient woodland, and 45 per cent of that was in a semi-natural state, the remainder having been replanted (Bowsher 1987). The other 48 per cent comprised secondary woodland, either planted or naturally regenerated, or ancient woodland blocks less than 2 ha in area.

Some of the sites owned or managed by the FC are large and, having had continuous management as working woodlands, contain trees of mixed ages and species that provide a wide variety of habitats. Hens Wood, near Marlborough, is a good example. It has a large stand of mature larch with a hazel understorey, a stand of mature Douglas fir with a closed crown and no understorey, 20 ha of young Norway spruce invaded by silver birch seedlings, 6 ha of closely-planted Norway spruce for harvesting as Christmas trees, a mixed stand of Japanese larch, oak and hazel with bramble and raspberry, a long strip of middle-aged beech, and a stand of younger beech. The rides are wide and some have grassy verges with an interesting flora and insect fauna. Tree Pipits, Firecrests, Willow Tits, Siskins, Lesser Redpolls and Crossbills, all scarce elsewhere, are regularly found here.

South of Hens Wood, and also managed by the FC, is Savernake Forest SSSI, one of the largest woods in Wiltshire. Lying on chalk overlain by Clay-with-flints, it contains relicts of ancient wood pasture represented by distinctive open-crowned specimens of sessile and pedunculate oaks scattered across the forest. Plantations of beech and oak 200 hundred years old have now assumed a semi-natural structure, but the forest consists mainly of 20th century plantings of beech and oak supplemented by naturally regenerated ash, silver and downy birches, rowan and willows, with hawthorn and blackthorn scrub in open spaces. It also contains conifer plantations and larger open areas, some the result of earlier management as pasture woodland and some in frost pockets in valley bottoms that are unsuitable for the successful establishment of young trees. The ancient beech and oak trees are of particular importance to wildlife, especially insects, fungi and hole-nesting birds, including Nuthatches, Common Redstarts and the three woodpeckers. Hawfinches are regularly recorded here and an evening visit may be rewarded with a roding Woodcock or a churring Nightjar. Savernake was notified as an SSSI for its woodland and scrub bird assemblage. To the east of the forest are the smaller woods of Cobham Frith, Bedwyn Common and Chisbury Wood, all managed by the FC, and Bedwyn Brail, Wilton Brail and Foxbury Wood, all privately owned and managed. The close proximity of these woods, to each other and to Savernake, creates a wide choice of suitable feeding habitats which supply beech mast, leaf litter invertebrates and conifer seeds for wintering birds.

A similar situation is to be found in the Braydon Forest area of north Wiltshire – formerly a much more extensive Royal Forest – where Somerford Common and Webb's Wood, both also owned by the FC, are the largest of many small woods, predominantly of oak and ash, all within easy reach of each other. These two larger woods, which include stands of Norway spruce, Corsican pine and Scots pine, are managed with wildlife in mind. Many of the owners of the smaller, undermanaged woods, such as Brockhurst Wood SSSI, have been encouraged to apply for grant aid for woodland improvement under the Woodland Grant Scheme, advice being given to them through the Braydon Forest Project organised by the WWT. Since the 38·4 ha of Ravensroost Wood SSSI were purchased by the WWT in 1987, work to return this to an oak/hazel coppice rotation has begun. Breeding birds are being monitored, using the Common Birds Census (CBC) methodology, and there are indications that the numbers of passerines, particularly warblers, are increasing there.

Groups of woodlands in west Wiltshire, on different types of soil, are mere remnants of the much bigger expanse of Selwood Forest that once stretched from Stourhead north to the Cotswolds. The largest remaining areas lie within the Longleat and Stourhead estates, a high percentage of which are planted with conifers. Although the Longleat estate is now best known as a safari park and for Center Parcs, much of its 3707 ha has remained unchanged since a detailed survey of its avifauna was carried out in the mid 1980s (Ferguson-Lees 1984). The total number of species known to have been recorded at that

ABOVE Blackmoor Copse SSSI/WWT reserve, one of the richest floras in any Wiltshire wood on Tertiary strata: standards of oak and ash, and an understorey of, predominantly, coppiced hazel (*Steve Day/WWT*)

BELOW Savernake Forest SSSI: ancient trees, such as this beech, are important to wildlife, especially insects, fungi and hole-nesting Nuthatches, Common Redstarts and woodpeckers (*Patrick Cashman/Natural England*)

time was 161, approximately 80 of them breeding. Since then, the figure has fluctuated with the loss of at least seven nesting species, mostly woodland birds, and a significant decline in the number of another seven; the species affected have included Nightjar, Common Redstart and Marsh Tit. On the other hand, ten further species that had begun breeding by the end of the 20th century included Mandarin, Ruddy Duck, Firecrest and Siskin, and the gradual return of a colony of Grey Herons. In 1984, nearly 50 species were nesting in the 1690 ha of woodland and a total of 17 in the 300 ha of parkland, while the lakes, especially Shear Water and Half Mile, are visited by many waterbirds, some of which stay to breed. Another valuable habitat on the eastern edge of the estate close by Longbridge Deverill is, or at least was, a section of the Wylye running through a poplar plantation with rank ground cover; several pairs of Little Grebes nested in this area, and both Sedge and Reed Warblers, but the poplars were clear-felled in 2003 and the present status of these species there is unclear. The high number of species on the Longleat estate is demonstrated in figure 10 (see page 137) by the densities shown for three adjacent tetrads in the 10-km square ST84.

Farther north, woods on the Oxford Clay between Westbury and Trowbridge are either privately owned or belong to conservation organisations. Biss Wood is privately owned, Green Lane Wood belongs to the WWT, and Picket and Clanger Woods to the Woodland Trust. All are being managed according to conservation plans and their birds monitored either by CBC methods or as part of the BTO's Constant Effort Sites (CES) scheme. None possesses trees older than 120 years – thus limiting their availability for the larger hole-nesting species – but all have good populations of breeding woodland passerines, tits in particular being assisted by the provision of nestboxes. Until the year 2000, Picket and Clanger Woods SSSI, both notified for their woodland bird assemblages, were among the county's few strongholds for Nightingales and, with easy access, were handy for anyone wishing to become familiar with different bird songs.

West of Bradford-on-Avon are woodlands of ash and wych elm on the Oolitic Limestone, the Midford Valley Woods SSSI, notified for its woodland bird assemblage, and the Inwood, Warleigh SSSI. Bowood and Spye Parks, near Calne, part of the former Royal Forests of Pewsham and Melksham, form a significant area of woodland and parkland on Oxford Clay, Corallian Beds and Lower Greensand. Bird numbers have been logged for many years at Bowood where most of the features described above are present, including a large lake. In recent years, income has increasingly been derived from an 18-hole golf course and from the public to whom the house and garden is open for part of the year. The total number of breeding species recorded during the summer tetrad survey of 1995–2000 was 70, and a further 29 non-breeding species were seen then or in subsequent years. These are figures that are not achieved in any single habitat. Spye Park SSSI is an extensive mosaic of large expanses of some of the finest undisturbed alder woods in the county, along with oak woods, parkland and an area of dry acidic grassland containing several locally uncommon plants. This SSSI was notified as an important site for breeding woodland birds.

In the northwest a linear group of woodlands clothe the steep sides of the By Brook, which runs on the southern Cotswold Oolitic Limestone between Castle Combe and Box. Of these, Colerne Park SSSI (WT) is an ancient woodland of ash and, before the arrival of Dutch elm disease, wych elm. The proximity of these woods to water adds Kingfisher, Dipper and Grey Wagtail to the list of bird species here.

Chute Forest is the only large area of woodland to the east of Salisbury Plain. The FC-owned Collingbourne and Coldridge Woods, formerly ancient oak woodland, were felled after the 1939–45 War and planted with stands of conifers and beech. At the beginning of the 21st century, the conifers had matured and were gradually being clear-felled. Most ornithological interest is currently found around the edge of these woods but, as replanting takes place, there should be a period when the open spaces are gradually colonised by vegetation between young trees, thus creating new habitats attractive to birds.

ABOVE LEFT Savernake Forest SSSI: grazed wood-pasture among ancient trees is a key feature that is being re-created, using White Park Cattle (*Robert Wolstenholme/Natural England*) ABOVE RIGHT Savernake Forest SSSI: ancient broadleaved woodland with both sessile and pedunculate oaks (*Stephen Davis*) BELOW Center Parcs, Longleat: mixed broadleaved and coniferous woodland favoured by Firecrests and Siskins (*David Kjaer*)

The greater part of central Wiltshire lies on the chalk and is devoid of any significant areas of woodland. Lying between the valleys of the Wylye and the Nadder, south of Salisbury Plain, is a ridge of chalk overlain with Clay-with-flints. In the 1086 Domesday Survey this was recorded as a hunting forest and, therefore, was not necessarily as wooded as was Selwood Forest. Today, Grovely and Great Ridge Woods are the remnants of the ancient Grovely Forest and retain a straight Roman road throughout their lengths. Grovely Wood extends for 8 km from west to east, its irregularly shaped boundary roughly following the 150 m contour. Part of the Wilton estate, the western half of the wood is managed by the FC and the eastern half by its owner. This is another woodland that was partly cleared of broadleaved trees after the 1939–45 War to make way for commercial crops. Here, stands of beech and conifers were planted. A few of the old beech and oak survive and they, together with the extensive edge habitat, are important contributors to the diversity of bird species. Within the wood, the sequential removal and replanting of conifers results in temporary open areas which, as young trees develop, gradually pass through stages of growth of ground flora that create a series of habitats, each attractive to a succession of species: Grasshopper Warblers and Nightjars in the early stages to Tree Pipits and Blackcaps and, later, tits and birds of prey. Great Ridge Wood, one of the largest unfragmented blocks of woodland in south Wiltshire, is part of the Fonthill estate. It too is partly planted with conifers, but a few of the veteran oaks have been allowed to survive. The removal of rhododendron may eventually benefit the wood's ecology.

The Vale of Wardour is well wooded, as illustrated by the Nuthatch distribution map (page 640), whilst the Cranborne Chase SSSI, which straddles the Dorset/Wiltshire border, comprises one of the largest tracts of semi-natural woodland in the two counties. Derived from an ancient hunting forest, it has a diverse woodland bird fauna, no doubt encouraged by one of the largest areas in Great Britain where hazel coppicing is still carried out.

To the east of Salisbury lies a group of woods on London Clay, and Reading and Bagshot Beds, which extend over an area of 60 km^2 and were part of the Royal Buckholt Forest. They include from west to east Clarendon Park, Hound Wood, Blackmoor Copse SSSI (WWT) and Bentley Wood SSSI (owned by the Bentley Wood Charitable Trust). Originally ancient oak woodland with hazel coppice, most were replanted after the 1939–45 War with a mixture of conifers and indigenous hardwoods. The Blackmoor Copse, 37 ha in extent, is one exception and its avifauna is typical of this type of wet woodland habitat, having an average of 40 breeding species each year, including Woodcock and all three woodpeckers, and a total of 20 others visiting either on passage or in winter.

The extensive woodland in the extreme southeast corner of Wiltshire, part of the ancient Melchet Forest, has no doubt survived because of the seasonal waterlogging that results from the presence of London Clay. It is now part of the New Forest Natural Area and National Park. The largest, and most significant, section is the 214-ha NNR at Langley Wood which has been modified by humans to a lesser degree than most woodland in lowland England. Much of the area is unbroken oak high forest, but there is a very large range of stand-types in this exceptionally rich and varied woodland. The most notable species are small-leaved lime, wild service and hornbeam. These, together with the relative scarcity of beech, suggest that this is the best example of ancient woodland surviving in Wiltshire and the closest to the natural wildwood in both structure and species richness. The ornithological interest of this SSSI is enhanced by its wide rides, open spaces, small ponds and the Blackwater river. It was made an NNR in 1998, notified for its woodland bird assemblage which has probably been recorded more thoroughly than those of most Wiltshire's woods. Significant here are Lesser Spotted Woodpecker, Wood Warbler and Hawfinch. Other important woods in Melchet Forest that share the same range of species are Loosehanger Copse SSSI, Franchises Wood (part of the New Forest SSSI) and Whiteparish Common SSSI.

Looking to the long-term future of Wiltshire's woodland habitats, the new planting which is encouraged by the Farming and Wildlife Advisory Group, the WWT and, around Swindon, the Swindon Borough Council's Great Western Community Forest should improve conditions for the commoner bird species. But they will not replace the ancient woodland habitats for very many generations, if ever.

Heathland

In the past, heaths were closely associated with many of the woodlands on greensands and Tertiary sands but, unfortunately, this important bird habitat is now all but lost to Wiltshire. Only tiny fragments survive, as at Landford Heath SSSI and Landford Bog SSSI (WWT) in the New Forest fringe, these being remnants of once extensive heaths that stretched from Pound Bottom to Hamptworth and Landford Commons. Much of it was destroyed as recently as the 1960s and, before that, this habitat was home to breeding Montagu's Harriers, Curlews, Dartford Warblers and Red-backed Shrikes. Some heathland still survives at Spye Park SSSI, but elsewhere the heaths that have temporarily colonised

Landford Bog SSSI/WWT reserve: remnant lowland bog and wet heath, grading through scrub into birch woodland (*Steve Day/WWT*)

clear-felled woodland – in, for example, Savernake Forest, Longleat and Clarendon Park over the past 30 years – are soon shaded out by fast-growing conifers. Yet these serve to show that the potential for recreating such valuable habitats still exists. The future of Nightjars and Wood Larks in Wiltshire depends on the creation of some protected and managed heaths.

Lowland grasslands (calcareous grassland and scrub, or downland)

Wiltshire holds extensive and nationally important areas of both calcareous and neutral grasslands. The WWT gives priority to acquiring and managing these two habitats in order to conserve their unique flora and insect fauna. The wet hay meadows of north and west Wiltshire are not ornithologically rich, but many are bordered by thick, old hedgerows with spaced oak trees, which are good breeding habitats for Hobbies and Lesser Whitethroats. In the days when the grass was grown for hay and the aftermath grazed by dairy cattle, Curlews had a large choice of suitable nest-sites. These were reduced when this type of management was superseded by growing grass for silage, which involved the application of artificial fertilisers and the development of new types of grass. Now Curlews are limited to those meadows which have not been agriculturally improved. Here, the sward consists of a mosaic of habitats with a variety of heights and densities, which provide cover for the incubating Curlews and soft ground for their bills to probe for invertebrates. Although the number of pairs has decreased since the 1970s, the population has probably now stabilised and may be expected to remain constant if there is no further loss of unimproved meadows. The Blakehill reserve, near Cricklade, has enabled the WWT to increase the area of unimproved meadows, which benefits not only nesting Curlews but also breeding Sky Larks and wintering Short-eared Owls.

Calcareous grassland occurs both on the Oolitic Limestone in the Cotswold Natural Area and on the chalk in the Natural Areas of the Marlborough Downs and South Wessex Downs. Most of Wiltshire's reserves and SSSIs (pages 742–747) are on the chalk. The limestone grassland offers no habitats of particular importance for birds – in contrast to the chalk grasslands of the Salisbury Plain Training Area (SPTA) and Porton Down, which include the two largest SSSIs in the county. Although both have habitats that are unique in Wiltshire within their boundaries, it is their large size that makes them internationally important, not only for birds but for their flora and many other faunal groups that have an influence on the avifauna. The smaller nature reserves are managed mainly for their flora and associated insect fauna, birds receiving minimal mention in their management plans, and the main tools of management are grazing at specified times of year. (The large areas of the SPTA and Porton that are used for military training and experimental work are out of bounds and therefore are not subject to management.) The habitat is stable, however, changing only with the passing seasons – a rare situation for wildlife in Wiltshire.

Of the 38,000 ha (380 km²) of Salisbury Plain (see page 840) owned by the Ministry of Defence (MoD), 19,690 ha were notified as an SSSI in 1993, the qualifying criteria emphasising the presence of nine types of grassland communities. Much of the SSSI is species-rich grassland dominated by upright brome, but areas of false-oat grass are also widespread, indicating past cultivation. Salisbury Plain supports the largest known expanse of unimproved chalk downland in northwest Europe, its 12,933 ha representing 41 per cent of the British total of this rich wildlife habitat. The area is of national and international importance for breeding and wintering birds, the SSSI notification listing Stone-curlew, Quail and Hobby as breeding in nationally significant numbers and stating that the 'overall breeding assemblage is exceptionally diverse for a British dry grassland site'. Also notable are wintering Merlins, Short-eared Owls and Hen Harriers; the last of these occur annually in nationally significant numbers and SPTA is an important winter roost-site for this species. Birds of prey dependent on small mammals for their survival – for example,

ABOVE Clattinger Farm SSSI/WWT reserve, the only lowland British farm known never to have received agricultural chemicals: uninterrupted traditional management – cutting for hay and aftermath grazing – has favoured an exceptional range of meadow plants (*Steve Day/WWT*) BELOW Distillery Meadows SSSI/WWT reserve: herb-rich hay meadows and mature hedges are characteristic of the Braydon Forest, with breeding Curlews and Lesser Whitethroats (*Steve Day/WWT*)

Barn Owls and Kestrels – hunt over the large expanses of grassland, particularly in the long ungrazed MoD Danger Areas, where their prey is most abundant. The majority of SPTA has also been designated as a Special Protection Area, primarily because it holds around 10 per cent of the British population of breeding Stone-curlews, but also because of the Quails, Hobbies and wintering Hen Harriers. In addition, breeding bird surveys of SPTA (Stanbury *et al* 2000, 2005) have found Sky Larks, Whinchats, Stonechats, Grasshopper Warblers and Corn Buntings in nationally significant numbers.

Valley bottoms, where the ground is frequently disturbed by heavy MoD vehicles, are soon colonised by tall herbs, notably wild parsnip, the tops of which are used by Stonechats and Whinchats as look-outs and song-posts. Areas where vegetation is sparse because soil has been scraped off – either to build banks for military training or specifically to provide bare ground – are used by breeding Stone-curlews and passage Wheatears. Grassland with a mixed flora of grasses and broadleaved herbs supports a large community of invertebrates, including insects, spiders and snails. This type of habitat is widespread throughout the SSSI, particularly on the Centre ranges where it provides the variety of vegetable and animal food needed by gamebirds including Quails. When they are not being used for military training, areas of grassland near the perimeter of the SSSI are grazed by sheep and cattle. The grazing provides shorter grass and dung, which has its own fauna and is exploited by flocks of Common Starlings, Fieldfares, corvids and, in some locations, Golden Plovers and Lapwings.

Decisions on which areas are to be grazed and which are to be cleared of scrub are now directed by conservation staff at the SPTA headquarters in implementation of an Integrated Land Management Plan. These radical operations, combined with a planned increase in the number of tracked vehicles using the Plain in the future, will change habitats in many parts of the SPTA and will undoubtedly affect the avifauna. The most predictable change is already evident in the reduction of tussocky grass in areas hunted by Barn Owls for short-tailed field voles, their main food.

Different assemblages of species are generally found to use distinct habitats, topography and areas of SPTA (Stanbury *et al* 2000). Grasshopper Warblers, Whinchats and Stonechats are usually found within the unimproved grassland – in particular, the artillery ranges – while birds associated with farmed environments, notably Corn Buntings, are found around the perimeter. Ridges are favoured by Sky Larks, while Whinchats are concentrated in the valleys. Sky Larks prefer open grasslands, especially where livestock are present, and the reintroduction of grazing to large areas on the Centre and West ranges has favoured this species. Whinchats, Stonechats and Grasshopper Warblers are particularly associated with rank tall grasses and scattered hawthorn bushes.

The MoD also owns approximately 25,000 ha of land surrounding the SSSI, which acts as a buffer to protect villages and public roads from dangerous military activity. Most of this land is let to tenant farmers who use it for growing arable and hay crops. The arable/grassland edge includes stoned and unmade tracks with wide, rough grass verges and fences, an ideal habitat for breeding Corn Buntings and Stonechats. The verge vegetation contains a mixture of tall plants, including thistles and mugwort; these produce a large number of seeds, to which flocks of Goldfinches and Linnets are attracted in autumn. SPTA remains a stronghold for Corn Buntings and Grey Partridges, especially the East ranges.

Scattered among its huge areas of grassland habitats, SPTA has woodland, scrub and a winterbourne which flows through the East ranges to join the Salisbury Avon at Bulford. A pond on the West ranges, dug in the 1980s to prevent flooding, lies at the headwater of another winterbourne that flows through the village and the Berril valley to join the Wylye at Codford. A dewpond on the edge of the Centre ranges seldom dries out and, after heavy rain, water floods some of the valley bottoms. This is, however, essentially a dry habitat with few wetland birds featuring in the breeding maps for the area.

The timbered areas of SPTA vary from overmature trees of assorted species around the sites of old farm buildings to beech woods of varying ages and other woods planted since the 1970s, mainly of conifers in the early years. These trees now have a closed canopy and are habitats for nesting Sparrowhawks and Wood Pigeons and are probably partly responsible, together with the scrub, for the ever-increasing numbers of Magpies seen on the Plain. Carrion Crows have also increased, some pairs now nesting in large hawthorn bushes. Long-eared Owls often use old Crow and Magpie nests. On the West and Centre ranges, lone trees and others near the edges of almost every wood or group of standards now contain purpose-built nestboxes for Barn Owls and Kestrels; these have a high rate of occupancy for both these birds and for Jackdaws, Stock Doves and grey squirrels. The recent introduction of nestboxes specifically designed for the Little Owl should help to increase the population of that species. From the late 1980s, new plantations have mixed broadleaved trees with chalk-loving shrubs around the edges. These will add another valuable habitat for woodland birds in the future.

The extensive areas of scrub on SPTA nearly all lie on Clay-with-flints and are dominated by hawthorn, gorse and bramble. Significant breeding birds here are Turtle Dove, Long-eared Owl, Tree Pipit, Nightingale, Common Whitethroat, Willow Warbler, Linnet, Yellowhammer and Reed Bunting. A solitary Great Grey Shrike may be an occasional winter visitor.

The MoD estate includes 52 farms with their associated buildings and yards; many of the working farms have a pair of Pied Wagtails, but House Sparrows are rare. Other man-made structures, nearly all originally built for training purposes, are scattered across the ranges. These include disused bunkers with access above ground level, look-outs, two-storey buildings once inhabited but now standing empty with open windows and doors, and discarded tanks placed in the Danger Areas as targets. Many of these structures are used by breeding Swallows, the tall buildings by House Martins, the derelict army tanks by Stock Doves and roosting Barn Owls. Barn Owl and Kestrel boxes installed in redundant observation posts and bunkers, and in other out-of-maintenance buildings, are used as both roost and nesting sites. With the tree-sited boxes, SPTA held about 2 per cent of the British Barn Owl population in 2005 (Lewis *et al* 2006).

Porton Down, the second largest lowland grassland SSSI in the South Wessex Downs Natural Area, covers 1562 ha and is also part of a larger MoD estate. As is the case with SPTA, the land used for experimental training is surrounded by a buffer zone let to farmers. Mainly in Wiltshire but partly in Hampshire, Porton was notified for its grassland, scrub and woodland bird assemblages, including some 74 breeding species. Two of the four main types of grassland identified are of particular value for birds in contrasting ways. One has tussocky swards of upright brome and red fescue with downy oat-grass, providing habitats for small mammals – prey for owls and raptors – and nest-sites for Grey Partridges. The second type, otherwise found only in the East Anglian Brecks, is short grassland dominated by sheep's fescue with wild thyme, other small herbs and, in some places, up to 80 per cent coverage by lichens. About 12 per cent of the British population of Stone-curlews breeds on Porton, for which it was designated a Special Protection Area, though some also nest on other types of grassland there and on arable land outside the SSSI. Most of the grassland is not grazed by domestic stock, but a large, if fluctuating, population of rabbits has a major influence on the height and species composition of the sward. Porton, with large areas of short rabbit-grazed turf, remains the last site in Wiltshire where Wheatears nest with any regularity.

Much of the grassland also has chalk-loving scrub, including guelder rose, purging buckthorn, wild privet, dogwood, spindle and other berry-bearing species that provide autumn and winter food for birds. The number of juniper bushes there has been estimated at 18,000 – the largest concentration of these indigenous conifers in southern

LEFT Knook, Salisbury Plain SPA: arable reversion to grassland (*Stephen Davis*) ABOVE Imber Ranges, Salisbury Plain SPA: an army tank target and wildflowers (*Stephen Davis*) BELOW Westdown Artillery Range, Salisbury Plain SPA: the largest expanse of unimproved chalk downland in northwest Europe, important for breeding Quails, Skylarks, Grasshopper Warblers, Whinchats and Stonechats, and wintering Hen Harriers, Merlins and Short-eared Owls (*Stephen Davis*)

ABOVE Little Langford Down, WWT reserve in Grovely Wood: species-rich chalk grassland with hundreds of ancient anthills (*Steve Day/WWT*) BELOW Simms Valley, Porton Down SPA: species-rich chalk grassland with juniper scrub, an important stronghold for breeding Stone-curlews (*Stephen Davis*) RIGHT The Wansdyke at Morgan's Hill SSSI/WWT reserve: botanically rich chalk grassland on a northwest-facing scarp (*Steve Day/WWT*)

England – which have been found to host as many as 123 species of invertebrates, notably spiders, a ready source of food for passerines. They are also used as song posts in open country by Whinchats, Stonechats and Corn Buntings, and, occasionally, as nest-sites for Long-tailed Tits and Linnets. The number of bird species breeding on Porton is increased by the presence of broadleaved, mixed and coniferous plantations and by semi-natural oak and ash woodland.

Beacon Hill, Salisbury Plain SPA: chalk grassland with mature juniper scrub, rich in invertebrates (*Rachel Crees/Defence Estates*)

Unlike the unimproved calcareous grassland of SPTA and Porton Down, which is on fairly flat ground, most of that elsewhere in Wiltshire is on slopes too steep to plough. There are a few exceptions, notably Parsonage Down NNR – 276ha in area, of which 147ha are unimproved grassland – where the gentle slopes are lightly grazed year round by both sheep and cattle and the Clay-with-flints capping has a couple of hectares of hawthorn and gorse scrub. The addition of dung as a natural fertiliser throughout the year ensures a permanent supply of earthworms and other soil invertebrates. This reserve holds parties of Mistle Thrushes in early summer and large numbers of Fieldfares remain late into the spring. Flocks of Golden Plovers, corvids, Common Starlings and Black-headed Gulls feed on the downs and the back-up grassland. Wheatears and Whinchats move through in spring and, at the end of the breeding season, groups of Yellow Wagtails feed around the feet of grazing cattle. In the last two decades of the 20th century, 23 species were proved to breed in the scrub, 11 of them annually (B Gillam). The results of a 17-year CBC on 2·5ha of downland scrub at Kingston Deverill were comparable, 20 being the average number of species nesting and a further 23 having been recorded visiting during the breeding season (JD Pollard). Downland without scrub, especially on steep terrain, may not have many breeding birds, but Kestrels can often be seen hanging on the updraughts in competition with human hang-gliders and para-gliders along the highest scarps of the Pewsey Downs NNR.

Open water

Open water is scarce in Wiltshire, especially in the south. All types of this habitat are the result, deliberate or coincidental, of human activities. They range in size from very broad expanses, formed by mineral extraction, to small or medium reservoirs, ornamental lakes in the grounds of country estates, fishing lakes, canal feeder-lakes, the linear stretches of canals themselves and, of less importance to birds, small farm and garden ponds. Apart from the last, some of which are artificially lined, all are situated where the land is underlain by an impervious geological stratum.

Until the mid 20th century, open-water birdwatching in the county was restricted to a small number of reservoirs, estate lakes, and water-filled pits. When, however, gravel extraction began in the upper Thames floodplain on the boundary with Gloucestershire in the 1950s, Wiltshire's significance as an area for wetland birds, both wintering and breeding, started rapidly to change.

By 2005, the whole of what has now long been known as the Cotswold Water Park (CWP) covered a total of 10,000ha (100km²), and the area of standing open water had been expanded from 570ha in 1977 to 1000ha – approximately 30 per cent of it in Wiltshire

ABOVE Porton Down SPA, Wiltshire's second largest SSSI: important for its grassland, scrub and woodland bird assemblages (*Dstl*) BELOW Pewsey Downs NNR: this chalk grassland SSSI includes the highest ridge in Wiltshire, favoured by Wheatears and Ring Ouzels on passage, and raptors and Ravens especially in winter (*Stephen Davis*)

– comprising about 145 separate lakes in three sections. CWP West, which straddles the Wiltshire-Gloucestershire border, supports nationally important numbers of breeding Great Crested Grebes and Little Ringed Plovers, and is also nationally important for wintering Gadwalls, Common Pochards, Smews, Great Crested Grebes, Coots and Lesser Black-backed Gulls. In total, CWP West supports an average of about 11,000 waterbirds in winter (based on the WeBS 5-year mean count, excluding gulls, at the end of 2003/04).

While CWP East lies entirely in Gloucestershire and Oxfordshire, the area of the whole was expanded by 2000 to include the parishes of Down Ampney (Gloucestershire) and Marston Meysey between CWP West and East. In 2005, gravel extraction was started in this central section, which lies mostly in Wiltshire, and it is hoped that, in due course, the filled lakes will be developed for nature conservation in partnership with the RSPB as part of the Futurescapes Project.

CWP lies on the northern edge of the Thames and Avon Vales Natural Area, a river valley landscape of flood plains and small fields, many bounded by hedges containing crack willows. CWP includes several grassland SSSIs and some individual lakes designated as SSSIs because they have developed into nationally scarce marl lakes with distinctive aquatic plant communities. The water is lime-rich, because contact with the surrounding gravels often results in a deposit of calcium carbonate, or marl, on the lake bed. CWP now supports the most extensive marl lake system in Great Britain.

The development of a gravel pit into a stable water habitat passes through a series of stages which create different habitats over a varying number of years. From the original farmland, with small to medium-sized fields bounded by mature hedges and scattered trees, the pit eventually becomes a large expanse of open water. First, the topsoil and subsoil are scraped off to depths of 0·35 m to 1 m and piled at the edge of the area to be dug – later to be used in the restoration of the site – and all hedges and trees are removed. As digging reaches below the water-table and the pit begins to flood, the water is pumped out into adjacent water bodies, whence it either seeps back into the water-table or flows directly into the river. This enables the gravel to be excavated in as dry a condition as possible. As work progresses, sand and gravel faces are exposed around the edge of the pit and the scraped gravel surfaces are left uneven and interspersed with shallow pools.

During this stage, before the pit fills with water, these new habitats are exploited by Little Ringed Plovers for nesting and by other waders on passage. These 'dry' pits also occasionally hold breeding Ringed Plovers and Redshanks, and perhaps a roosting flock of Curlews. The bare gravel faces are often colonised by Sand Martins. After digging has been completed and the space created has slowly filled with water, some of the pits are left as lakes that are later used for all types of freshwater leisure activities, including fishing and water sports. Since 1997, however, when a CWP Biodiversity Action Plan was drawn up, site restoration to provide environmentally sympathetic treatment to lake shapes and surroundings – shallow margins, islands, and landscaping – has been encouraged.

These lakes have become part of the largest area of open water in the county and, because many birds migrate on broad fronts and others along river valleys, they attract a great variety of species. Common Terns first bred in 1979 and Black-headed Gulls in 1993; now a number of pairs of each regularly nest on artificial rafts, constructed and floated by WOS members, where they are safe from ground predators.

The excavated gravel is put through a washing process, which removes fine sand particles that have no commercial value. The sand is stacked in large piles and the washings are channelled into settlement lagoons where they result in sandy, beach-like areas with strips of shallow water. These are the most attractive areas for migrating and wintering waders, and for gulls and terns which feed, loaf and roost there, as well as for Common Shelducks which have bred occasionally. If left to develop naturally, these silt lagoons are quickly colonised by willow carr, common reeds and other marginal plants, which provide roost-sites for wagtails,

North Meadow NNR: this SSSI flood-meadow, important for snake's-head fritillaries, is periodically inundated by the River Thames and at such times is favoured by waders such as Golden Plovers, Lapwings and occasionally Dunlins and Ruffs (*Stephen Davis*)

ABOVE CWP lakes 68c and 68d in 2005: former silt lagoons now colonised by willows, reeds and bulrushes, favoured by wintering and breeding waterbirds and wetland warblers (*RH Bewley*) BELOW CWP lake 68c in 2006 (*G Harris/CWPS*)

ABOVE CWP lakes 68a, 68b, 74 and 95 in 2005: the wet lakes are important for wintering waterfowl, and also breeding Black-headed Gulls and Common Terns on the WOS rafts (*RH Bewley*) BELOW CWP lake 95 in 2006: a dry gravel pit favoured by breeding and passage waders (*G Harris/CWPS*)

ABOVE Shear Water, Longleat: the lake sometimes holds Goosanders in winter, and the surrounding mixed woodland, especially the conifers, attracts Firecrests, Lesser Redpolls, Siskins and Crossbills (*David Kjaer*)
BELOW Coate Water LNR/SSSI, looking towards Liddington Hill: important for breeding Tufted Ducks, Grey Herons and Reed Warblers, also for woodland bird assemblages (*Peter Cranswick*)

hirundines, Common Starlings and even an occasional Hen Harrier, and nest-sites for Reed Buntings and both Cetti's and Reed Warblers.

The variety of food provided by this wetland habitat includes the plants and animals of emergent and submergent vegetation, thus attracting birds that have varied methods of feeding and require mixed features in their environment. They include diving and surface-feeding ducks, grebes and Moorhens, occasionally even a migrant Osprey or Marsh Harrier. Aerial feeders such as Common Swifts are attracted by the abundance of insects which have spent the early stages of their lives in the water. In spring, up to 25 Hobbies gather over and around the lakes to catch hatching mayflies and later, in summer and autumn, smaller numbers remain to feed on dragonflies and damselflies, as well as on the insectivorous hirundines which are themselves hunting there. Important populations of Nightingales, Tree Sparrows and Reed Buntings also breed at CWP.

During 1995–2000, about 170 species of birds were seen at CWP and, over the last quarter of the 20th century, the total was nearly 200. This is undoubtedly Wiltshire's best aquatic habitat for both birds and birdwatchers. The footpaths, car parks and some other

Langford Lakes, WWT reserve of wet gravel pits in the Wylye valley: important for breeding Gadwalls, Tufted Ducks and Pochards, and wintering waterbirds (*Emma Day/WWT*)

areas accessible to the public are administered by the Cotswold Water Park Society, which publishes a wildlife booklet containing maps showing the numbers of the individual pits, the parking places and some of the best points for viewing wildlife (see page 841).

Other smaller lakes formed after mineral extraction have a more limited avifauna but, nevertheless, are of considerable importance in a landlocked county. Pits resulting from gravel extraction and now filled with water can be found along the valley of the Bristol Avon at Great Somerford and Lacock, and adjacent to the Wylye at WWT's Langford Lakes reserve near Steeple Langford. Gault clay was extracted for brick-making in two areas near Devizes; one to the north of the town is now a lake regularly used by wildfowl. Lastly in this category, two lakes were created in the late 19th century by the extraction of Westbury Ironstone near Westbury railway station; their steep banks prevent colonisation by short emergent vegetation around the edges and so there is little waterside cover, but Great Crested Grebes successfully breed there, and Tufted Ducks, Common Pochards and Wigeons overwinter, while Shovelers and Cormorants visit occasionally.

Three canal-feeder reservoirs – Coate Water (part of which is a designated SSSI, notified for both its open water and its woodland bird assemblages) together with its extension (dug in 1975 and now a Local Nature Reserve, or LNR), Tockenham Reservoir near Lyneham and Wilton Water near Great Bedwyn – are all large enough to be important for wintering wildfowl. In spite of boating and fishing on Coate Water, Gadwalls and Tufted Ducks occasionally breed there, Kingfishers do so regularly, and Reed and Sedge Warblers find sanctuary in the reedbeds. A raft placed in the LNR attracted its first pair of nesting Common Terns in 1999, and Cormorants have found it convenient for loafing. There is also a thriving colony of Grey Herons in an alder copse.

The canals for which these reservoirs were made now have little to offer birds. The Wiltshire and Berkshire Canal, once fed from Coate Water and Tockenham, exists as open water in only a few short stretches that were reopened by voluntary organisations in the 1990s. The Kennet & Avon Canal, which was fully restored to be used for pleasure boating in 1990, is fed from Wilton Water but has lost the importance it had, especially for Little Grebes, during its years of gradual dereliction from 1947 onwards when it was no longer used as a navigable waterway. Nevertheless, 15 pounds supply the locks with water to lift the canal 45 m up the hill to Devizes and each of these is wide enough not to be unduly disturbed in winter by walkers and cyclists. With the gradual development of submerged and emergent bankside vegetation, they have become useful refuges for loafing Black-headed Gulls, wintering wildfowl, particularly Mallards and Tufted Ducks, and for breeding Mute Swans. Coots and Moorhens nest on many of the pounds, out of sight of the next pound and their competing neighbours, thus reducing friction between these naturally aggressive species. A solitary Smew has occasionally been recorded here in winter.

Most of the remaining larger areas of open water in the county are on private land, where a river or stream has been dammed, usually by the construction of a weir. There are lakes on the estates at Braydon Pond, Bowood, Corsham, Ramsbury, Chilton Foliat, East Town Lake at West Ashton, Erlestoke, Longleat, Stourhead, Fonthill, Compton Chamberlayne, Clarendon and Wardour. Colonies of Grey Herons are now established in trees adjacent to as many as ten Wiltshire lakes, some near the smaller areas of open water.

Although not strictly an open water habitat, the lagoon area of Swindon Sewage Treatment Works has standing water up to one metre deep in winter and this evaporates slowly during the summer. The lagoons are drying beds for disused sludge and, therefore, rich in invertebrates throughout the year. Since 1993, the Thames Water Conservation Team has undertaken a variety of schemes to increase their potential for birds. Trees have been planted, a shallow-sided lagoon with four islands developed, five small lagoons transformed into a large wetland with shallow banks, two islands created (one of gravel and one of mud), and small areas of reedbeds allowed to colonise. These schemes quickly encouraged increasing numbers of wintering and migrating wildfowl, waders and gulls, and over 100 species of birds have visited this urban site since 1953. Further work is proposed to attract breeding waders such as Little Ringed Plover.

Rivers

The linear habitats of lowland river systems are of importance to a small number of specialist birds. The essential factor that influences these riparian species is the gradient of the river bed and the consequent speed of the water flow which, in turn, affects the amounts of bank erosion and the sediment deposited. In Wiltshire, the two Avons illustrate the difference between the flow of water over impervious clays and that over highly absorbent chalk.

The clay vale, which lies within the Thames and Avon Vales Natural Area, is drained by streams that flow slowly through steep banks of alluvial silt into the Semington Brook, the Marden and the Biss before the water reaches the Bristol Avon. The banks are suitable for Kingfishers to excavate their nesting tunnels, but are too steep along many stretches of water for Mute Swans to access potential breeding sites. Mallards and Moorhens are the commonest species regularly using this river system and the main river is occasionally visited in winter by Cormorants. Grey Herons also fish regularly in some areas where the shoreline is shallow. At Blackland, near the headwater of the Marden, and along the By Brook with its weirs and waterfalls, there are also bridges with ledges and crevices which provide nest-sites for Grey Wagtails.

The Wylye at Stoford: chalk river within Salisbury Avon SAC, designated for variety of fish and invertebrates; breeding birds include Little Grebes and Grey Wagtails (*Stephen Davis*)

These habitats on the By Brook are the main areas for breeding Dippers in the county and have the most ornithological interest within the small part of the Greater Cotswold Natural Area that lies in Wiltshire. The land on the adjacent Bristol Avon floodplain was formerly used for dairy farming, but much of it was drained in the last quarter of the 20th century and then either reseeded with grass for silage or used for growing other crops, neither of which produce habitats of much interest to birds. There are, however, old pollarded willows along the river banks which are favoured as nest-sites by Little Owls.

In contrast, the chalkland has few streams because the porous rock absorbs the falling rain until it reaches saturation point. Therefore, when the rainfall in autumn and early winter has been 'normal', the headwaters of the smaller streams and rivers are dry for about nine months of the year. The winterbournes then begin to flow in mid January but, if winter rainfall has been exceptionally heavy, as in 1999/00 and 2000/01, the flow may begin in November and continue into June. The Till, which must have risen regularly at Tilshead when the water-table was permanently much higher than it is today, now rises near that village only in such wet years. When floodwater on the Bourne at Leckford Crossroads remains for many weeks after abnormal rainfall, it attracts wildfowl, Coots, Moorhens and waders. Ponds created near the streams when water flows over their shallow banks are occasionally visited by Mute Swans, which may then attempt to breed.

From Upavon to Salisbury, the fast-flowing Hampshire (or Salisbury) Avon meanders through the narrow valley between the chalklands of the Plain and passes through areas of grassland, wet woodland, swamp and reedbeds. This mixture of habitats adjacent to a rich source of insect food that originates in the river is important for many breeding passerines. In addition, there are numerous villages along the banks whose buildings provide nest-sites, particularly for hirundines. From Salisbury to Downton, where this Avon enters Hampshire, the floodplain is wider. Here, and in the Wylye valley, the main course of the rivers was diverted in the 17th century and the flow controlled through systems of hatches, weirs and channels, so that the meadows could be flooded in winter. This created the right conditions to advance the growing season and provide the ewes with fresh grass before lambing, and also increased the size of the following hay crop. It was probably also suitable for wintering waterbirds (Shrubb 2003), but, by the late 19th century, the system went into decline, the abandoned water-meadows then being colonised by breeding Lapwings, Common Snipe and Redshanks.

Towards the end of the 20th century much of the land was drained and reseeded with commercial grasses and either grazed by sheep and cattle or cut for silage, resulting in the breeding waders being lost. Today, although there are still damp areas and water still flows into channels making suitable breeding habitats for Mallards and Little Grebes, the uniform grass does not produce the variety of invertebrates and grass seeds of the years of abandonment. Mute Swans, however, are to be seen on the grass throughout the year, most notably near Steeple Langford on the Wylye where a flock, sometimes numbering 100, is resident in winter.

To the east of Britford, between Salisbury and Bodenham, the system of parallel channels extends for 70 metres across the valley to the west of the river and adjacent to a group of disused gravel pits. Here, a habitat unique in south Wiltshire has developed. The Petersfinger pits are fringed with willows, low scrub and tall vegetation that includes stands of reeds. This area has a high number of breeding species, including Cetti's and Reed Warblers, the latter host to the parasitic Cuckoo. Grey Herons breed in the nearby heronry, one of the largest in Great Britain. Green Sandpipers are present for all but a few weeks in early summer and Gadwalls are regular. Winter brings Common Teals, Wigeons, Goosanders and Common Snipe. Little Egrets have become regular visitors at Britford, their number reaching double figures by the close of the 20th century.

The Bourne upstream of Hurdcott village: chalk river within Salisbury Avon SAC, including adjacent swamp and wet woodland (*Jenny Wheeldon/Natural England*).

The Salisbury Avon – designated a Special Area of Conservation because of its variety of fish and invertebrates – is at its widest in Wiltshire between Bodenham and the Hampshire boundary, and is still bordered by dozens of channels dating back to the 17th century. Breeding birds include Great Crested Grebes and Cetti's Warblers; Cormorants are regular visitors throughout the year; and wintering wildfowl are joined by Water Rails and Stonechats. Farther north, the Jones's Mill reserve owned by WWT is an area of fen vegetation, scrub and woodland along the headwaters of the Salisbury Avon near Pewsey, the best known example of a calcareous valley mire in Wiltshire. It was notified as an SSSI for its open water and woodland bird assemblages, including nesting Sedge Warblers and Reed Buntings, and wintering Common Snipe.

The Marlborough Downs lie between Swindon and Marlborough to form another chalk catchment area. Rain falling here flows into the Kennet from springs that rise in Yatesbury, Broad Hinton and Ogbourne St George. As, however, these are all winterbournes, the flow of water in the Kennet is much reduced in summer and autumn, when the river bed is usually dry above Fyfield. From there the Kennet flows through the centre of Marlborough, then through a valley about 1 km wide between chalk downlands and close to a string of villages, leaving the county near Chilton Foliat. The flat land in the valley bottom was formerly worked as flooded water-meadows, but not on the same scale as in the valley of the Salisbury Avon. The river is largely undisturbed, as much of the land through which it flows, including Ramsbury Manor Park and Littlecote Park, is privately owned. The shallow current is fast and the banks are low, with the result that flooding occurs when the springs are in full flow. The river has been widened at Ramsbury to form a lake. Willows are scattered along the banks and there are strips of woodland and areas of scrub on the valley sides.

The most important parts of this area of mixed habitats are the wet meadows between Ramsbury and Chilton Foliat, in particular Chilton Foliat Meadows SSSI, designated for its bird assemblage and once one of the most important areas in Wiltshire for breeding waders. Sadly, Common Snipe and Redshanks no longer nest there, but Little Grebe, Woodcock, Kingfisher, Nightingale, Grey Wagtail and Reed, Sedge, Grasshopper and Cetti's Warblers are among the wide range of today's breeding species. This area, in the southwest corner of the 10-km square SU37, has one of the highest numbers of breeding species in east Wiltshire (see figure 10 on page 137). Insectivorous birds, such as hirundines and warblers, move through on spring passage and migrant Ospreys have been seen in both spring and autumn. Winter visitors include Common Teals, Jack and Common Snipes, Green Sandpipers and, rarely, a Common Bittern.

Farmland

Agricultural land is arguably one of the most important bird habitats in the county. Wiltshire stands on the divide between the pastoral west of England and the arable east. Shrubb (2003) mapped the distribution of tillage by 50 km squares and found that 66 per cent or more of farmland in the western third of Wiltshire was under grass, that 66 per cent or more of the northeastern third was devoted to tillage crops, and that the southeastern third was more mixed – no doubt a result of the influence of Salisbury Plain. Mixed farmland with winter- and spring-sown crops and grassland is a valuable habitat for birds. Intensively farmed arable land is a good habitat in which to see flocks of gulls and corvids when ploughs are in action, and Lapwings and Golden Plovers on stubble or fallow land in winter. The common weed seeds of arable provide food for larks, finches and buntings in winter, and some of these in turn are prey for Hen Harriers and other raptors. There are extensive areas under arable cultivation on the chalk in both north and south Wiltshire that are some of the most important breeding habitats in southwest

ABOVE Arable fields at Rushall, Salisbury Plain: profusion of poppies encouraged by organic farming (*Stephen Davis*) BELOW Arable field margin with corn marigolds at Lydeway on the edge of Salisbury Plain: breeding birds include Yellow Wagtails and Corn Buntings (*Stephen Davis*)

England for Grey Partridge, Quail, Stone-curlew, Lapwing, Sky Lark, Yellow Wagtail, Tree Sparrow, Linnet, Yellowhammer and Corn Bunting. Turtle Dove and Barn Owl may be added to this list if the scrub and grassland of the chalk downs be included.

Other useful habitats associated with arable farms are silage clamps, especially of maize, and stubble with arable weeds. Sites where grain is regularly spilt attract Collared Doves, finches and sparrows, but nowadays are uncommon. Pasture spread with farmyard manure or grazed by sheep and cattle, and the bare ground created by feeding pigs, attract flocks of birds in winter, notably Fieldfares, Redwings, Common Starlings and also large numbers of Rooks, especially if their roost is nearby.

In the clay vales in the north, in parts of west Wiltshire from Potterne to Warminster and in the Vale of Wardour, thick hedges surrounding large blocks of small fields are important breeding areas for both summer visitors, particularly Lesser Whitethroats, and the resident Song Thrushes, finches and buntings. The Curlew is also a summer visitor, breeding in hay meadows in the clay vales of north and west Wiltshire. As Shrubb (2003) stated, 'modern pastoral farming emerges… as an increasingly barren environment for many breeding birds' because of 'high stocking rates' and a reduction in 'food supplies, particularly of invertebrates'. The maps for farmland birds published in the *Birds of Wiltshire* show marked reductions in both distribution and density in the pastoral west of Wiltshire. A wide variety of grants is now available to farmers and other landowners through many nationwide schemes including the Environmentally Sensitive Areas Scheme, Biodiversity Action Grants, and The Farm Woodland Premium Scheme. In Wiltshire, too, there are county and district grants for wildlife conservation. The aim of all these is to improve the environment for wildlife in general so that, in the future, more farmland will include habitats of value to birds. The response of wildlife to these schemes will need to be monitored to establish their validity – a daunting undertaking begun by the BTO in the late 1990s, and for which, at least locally, the maps in *Birds of Wiltshire* will act as an important baseline.

Human settlements

Agricultural land lost to construction for industrial or domestic use means, at first, the loss of suitable habitats for birds. As gardens are developed, however, and trees mature, many species that originated in woodland gradually find niches for feeding and nesting. The general public's increasing enjoyment of watching birds from the comfort of home has resulted in a year-round wish to provide food for them. This must help to offset the shortages of food available in the countryside for various species. Birds that have learnt to feed from suspended feeders include Goldfinches and Chaffinches, Robins and even Long-tailed Tits, while Dunnocks and Pied Wagtails forage for crumbs dropped on the ground below. Sparrowhawks soon home in on the regular source of prey provided by these feeding stations. Nestboxes are popular and usually successful additions to gardens.

Old buildings of all kinds that have access to roof spaces are occupied by Swifts. Modern dwelling houses, particularly those recently built in villages where House Martins are already established, are quickly adopted by additional colonies of these white-rumped summer visitors. Less welcome are increased nesting by Lesser Black-backed and Herring Gulls on flat-roofed factories in industrial sites and by permanently resident Feral Pigeons in most towns. Sparrowhawks now regularly breed in urban and suburban areas, over which Hobbies hunt Swifts and House Martins. Even Peregrine Falcons are becoming more frequent near and in urban areas, roosting on church spires and hunting for Feral Pigeons and Common Starlings.

Weather, climate change, and their effects on Wiltshire's birds

Phil Read

Lying in the relatively warm waters of the North Atlantic Drift – the northern part of the Gulf Stream – and in largely southwestern airstreams, Britain and Ireland enjoy a mild and equable climate. Wiltshire, although an inland county, has predominantly maritime weather, without the large day-night temperature variations of the Continent.

The most significant factors affecting local weather conditions are the terrain and its exposure to prevailing winds. Wiltshire averages around 720 mm of rain a year, compared with 600 mm in London and 980 mm in coastal Plymouth (Devon). The higher ground of Cranborne Chase and the Marlborough Downs are the county's wettest parts, and the sheltered areas in the lee of those hills are driest. In the southern half of the county, most rainfall comes with southerly to southwesterly airstreams; in the northern half, westerlies are filtered up the Bristol Channel. In showery northwesterlies, Wiltshire benefits greatly from the shelter of the Welsh hills and, being inland, is rather less affected by strong winds than its coastal neighbours to the south and southwest. Long-term figures show that, on average, the county has only one true gale a year (mean wind speed of 34 knots or more), compared with Plymouth's 15.

Bright sunshine is vital for the growth of vegetation and the well-being of many young birds. Wiltshire's yearly average of 1500 to 1600 hours of sun is very similar to London's and, although about 100 hours less than Plymouth's, is around 200 hours more than that of Midland England. In Wiltshire, local temperatures vary greatly with the topography of this undulating county. Hot spots are south-facing slopes of high ground; and frost hollows occur in east-to-west valleys to the north of high ground. These factors influence local distributions of plants and insects, and doubtless of birds too.

There is no question that human activities, particularly over the last 100 years, are affecting the atmosphere. What is uncertain is exactly how these will change the British weather and consequently the distributions of our birds. It is important to consider the likely effects of global warming. If emissions of greenhouse gas continue at current levels, average global temperatures are expected to rise by 2·5°C by the end of the 21st century. This may seem a small increase, but represents a rapid warming by comparison with natural climatic changes in the past. Plants and animals will have to adapt quickly if they are to survive and many will not be able to do so quickly enough. Sea levels are also expected to rise by an average of 50 cm over the next century.

A popular misconception is that global warming means that the climate in Britain will become warmer and sunnier. It is a basic law of physics that the warmer a parcel of air is, the more moisture it can contain. Moisture in the atmosphere is generally held as water vapour or cloud droplets. The general view of the experts is that the British weather will become more unsettled with an increase in extreme events, particularly storms and floods. In summers cloudier conditions will reflect solar radiation and give us cooler weather, but in winters they will prevent the escape of radiation from the earth's surface. Indeed, these were the patterns of weather we experienced in Wiltshire in the 1990s.

It is a major problem to differentiate between changes caused by global warming and those resulting from natural climate change, but the fact remains that the last two decades of the 20th century were the warmest since records began. The effects of natural climate change were dramatically illustrated by the Ice Ages, the most recent of which ended

15,000 years ago, but even during the last millennium Europe experienced contrasting episodes of colder and warmer weather. Precise temperature records have been kept only during the last 100 years and, while some of the most detailed and accurate observations in Wiltshire are taken at military sites around the county, most of those go back just to the 1939–45 War.

It is important not to take short-term extremes out of context. The long hot summer of 1975 was followed by the drought of 1976. In Wiltshire, in both years, rainfall was significantly less than the average of around 720 mm. On the other hand, of the years on either side, 1974 was much wetter (over 200 mm above the average) and 1977 was almost as wet. So those two dry summers were not necessarily part of any long-term climatic change and would have had only temporary effects on bird populations. From the mid 1980s to 1991, however, six of the seven years had less than average rainfall and, for example, it is possible that the scarcity of snails during this relatively dry spell contributed to the significant fall in the population of Song Thrushes at that time. The county's climate then became milder and wetter during the 1990s – as shown by the data from a south Wiltshire site (table 1) – and Song Thrush numbers showed signs of recovery.

In the 1990s, Wiltshire experienced a number of weather extremes that tie in with the patterns predicted as global temperatures rise. Around 100 mm of rain fell in Wiltshire in April 1998, approximately twice the long-term average for the month, but that was eclipsed by more than 150 mm in many places in the county in April 2000, which exceeded all previous records by a remarkable 50 per cent. (Wiltshire's wettest recorded April before those had been in 1966, when 100 mm of rain also fell.) These high April rainfalls applied over England and Wales as a whole, 1998 being the wettest since 1818, and 2000 the wettest since 1756. The trend of increased rainfall is also apparent in summer: June 1997 was the wettest June in England and Wales since 1879 (80 mm that month was some 30 mm above the average), but it was followed in June 1998 by a total of over 100 mm, double the county's long-term average.

Warmer, wetter winters are another predicted phenomenon that Wiltshire experienced in the 1990s. January and February 1995 were both very wet and – with over 150 mm in some parts of the county – that January was one of the wettest in the 20th century. Three years later, January and February 1998 were both unusually warm in Wiltshire: many places had their highest recorded January temperature of 14°C on the 9th; February was warmer still and not only was there an unprecedented 16°C throughout on the 14th, but also a mean maximum of around 11°C that, again, was the highest on record. Yet we can still have days or periods of exceptionally cold weather. On 23 November 1993, the maximum daytime temperature in parts of Wiltshire failed to rise above −3°C, three degrees lower than the previous coldest November day since 1930.

If extreme weather events are repeated at frequent intervals and patterns emerge, it may be safe to attribute these to global warming. One of the most noticeable changes in Wiltshire was the decrease in snowfall and, more importantly, snow cover in the 1990s. Snow – which during the 70 years of 1930–99 reached a peak in the 1960s and 1970s (table 2) – influences the distributions of wintering birds: for example, Stonechats and Dartford Warblers can survive cold but cannot feed if the ground or bushes are covered with snow or ice. Associated with snowfall are air frosts, which similarly reached a peak in the 1960s and decreased markedly during the 1990s (table 3). Persistent air frosts reduce the food supply for insectivorous birds, and ice-bound wetlands may have a serious effect on waterbird distribution in particular.

Though the exact figures are not important, as they vary around the county, the mean temperatures for February and March at one site in south Wiltshire, grouped by decades, also demonstrate increased warming during the 1990s (table 4). An analysis of 20 species of British breeding birds over a 25-year period showed a long-term trend towards earlier egg-laying (Crick & Sparks 1999). Long-term studies by the British Trust for Ornithology (BTO) have also demonstrated that, as spring temperatures have been increasing, summer visitors have been returning earlier, with a clear and statistically significant correlation between February and March temperatures and arrival dates of migrants (Sparks *et al* 1999). There is, of course, no advantage in earlier arrival if appropriate food is not available earlier as well. As most of our summer migrants are insectivorous, the earlier emergence of invertebrates is essential if they are to be able to breed earlier successfully. Problems also arise if a mild early spring is followed by a lot of wet weather in late spring and summer, so that food becomes hard to find when young birds are at their most vulnerable.

The trend towards earlier arrival dates for many summer migrants appears to hold true for several common species in Wiltshire also – though this can be based only on the first recorded dates each year. While too small a sample to be statistically significant, the first dates of six common summer migrants during 1970–2004 (figure 1), taken from WOS casual records, correlate well with the national picture. (The Garden Warbler also shows this trend more strongly than most, but has been omitted here because the song of first arrivals is not infrequently confused with that of the Blackcap, a species that now often overwinters.) It is, of course, much more difficult to pinpoint dates of the main arrivals of summer visitors, which may occur over several days and not necessarily be immediately obvious. Other summer migrants that show clear trends towards earlier arrival in Wiltshire are the Cuckoo, Swift, Barn Swallow, Tree Pipit, Yellow Wagtail, Common Redstart, Wheatear and Grasshopper Warbler. The Reed Warbler illustrates only a slightly earlier trend, whilst both the Whinchat and the Spotted Flycatcher appear to be arriving later, although this may be a result of their relative scarcity in recent years.

The fortunes of the Dartford Warbler, which is resident in Great Britain, have improved dramatically as a result of the recent absence of hard winters. Down to only 11 known pairs after the exceptionally harsh winter of 1962/63, the population had grown, despite periodic fluctuations, to well over 1900 occupied territories in ten counties from Devon

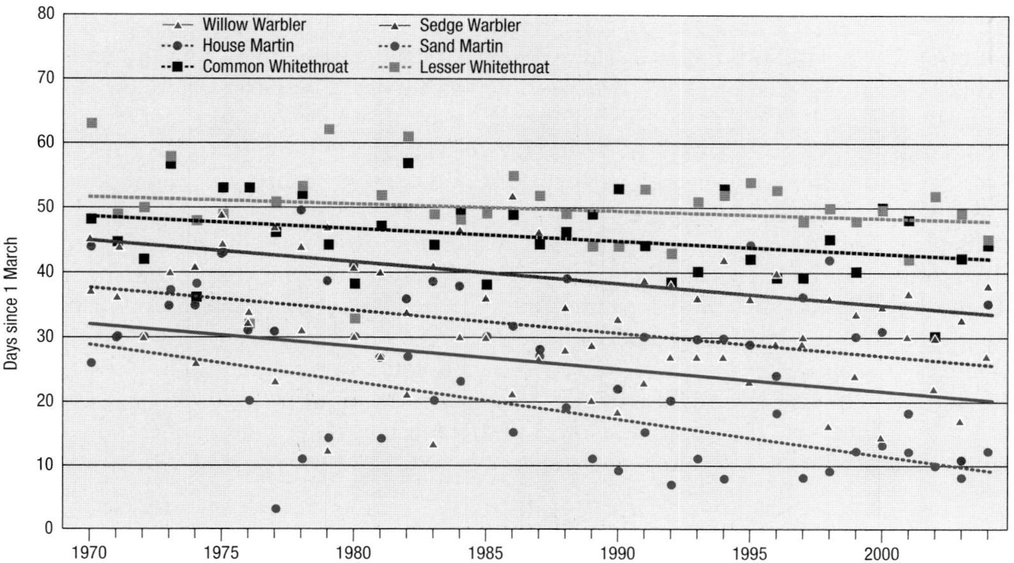

Figure 1. Dates of earliest records of six summer migrants in Wiltshire 1970–2004, showing trends towards earlier arrivals

to Norfolk by the year 2000 (Ogilvie *et al* 2002) – though the species remains rare and erratic in Wiltshire. As almost 1000 pairs in total now breed in neighbouring Hampshire, Dorset and Somerset, an increase in the county's population might be expected, should year-round temperatures rise, but suitable habitat is limited and any increase is unlikely to be dramatic.

To establish which species may be the first to benefit, it is necessary to look south to Hampshire and Dorset, and across the Channel to France, for evidence of range expansion. Two obvious recent examples are Little Egrets and Cetti's Warblers. Given a continuation of mild winters, we can expect both these to go on increasing in Wiltshire; Little Egrets already occur widely and there is abundant suitable but as yet unoccupied habitat for Cetti's Warblers in the county's river valleys.

Having spread gradually northwards in western France since the 1920s – halted by periodic reductions and withdrawals in severe winters – Cetti's Warblers reached the Channel coast in 1961, in which year Hampshire also produced the first acceptable British record. This inconspicuous warbler, usually located by its loud and explosive song, was first found in Wiltshire in 1980 and, although only 15 singing males were recorded in the county in 2000, all in the valleys of the Salisbury Avon and the Kennet, the national total that year was nearly 700 (Ogilvie *et al* 2002).

Little Egrets, extremely rare in Great Britain until the 1960s, subsequently became regular visitors in increasing numbers, although there was no Wiltshire record until as recently as January 1992. Since the first breeding by this species in Dorset in 1996, numbers in southern England had increased to 68–77 pairs by 2000 (Ogilvie *et al* 2002) and there were late summer roosts of over 100 in a number of places on the south coast (Musgrove 2002). Unlike its cousin, the Common Bittern, which suffers so much in frozen conditions, the Little Egret is an adaptable feeder and its willingness to forage on both coastal marshes and fast-flowing chalk streams should help it to survive short-term winter freezes.

Although the numbers of Little Egrets and Cetti's Warblers have increased significantly in the last 20 years, it is likely that other factors, in addition to climatic warming, are affecting their movements. Otherwise, more birds on the northwestern edges of their range in continental Europe might have been expected to follow suit. The Serin, which has nested in England but failed, as yet, to establish itself convincingly, and the Fan-tailed Warbler (or Zitting Cisticola) are two possible candidates. The latter extended its range eruptively to and beyond the northern French coast in the 1970s and first bred in the Netherlands in 1974. After that, however, severe winters are thought to have resulted in its retreat, and nesting had ceased in northwest and central France, the Netherlands and Switzerland by the late 1980s.

Whatever climatic changes we experience in the next 100 years, there is no doubt that some species will benefit and others suffer. There is also no doubt that human activities over the next century have the potential to alter the landscape considerably. Changes in agriculture, forestry, and water and wetland management may have positive or negative influences, depending on the degree to which such practices are influenced by conservation thinking, though it is currently difficult to conceive that climate change will have anything but a negative impact. The combined effect of these influences – and the effect to which it changes the birdlife of Wiltshire – remains to be seen. The future is in our hands.

Table 1. Ten-year means of rainfall and temperature at a south Wiltshire site over seven decades 1930–1999
Absolute maximum temperatures can be expected to fall if summers become cloudier

		Temperature			
Decade	Rainfall (mm)	Mean min (°C)	Mean max (°C)	Absolute min (°C)	Absolute max (°C)
1930–39	740	5·7	13·4	−7·7	29·2
1940–49	711	5·8	13·7	−8·0	30·4
1950–59	757	6·0	13·4	−7·3	28·2
1960–69	693	5·6	13·1	−9·0	27·4
1970–79	721	5·8	13·4	−7·2	28·1
1980–89	701	6·1	13·6	−7·3	29·5
1990–99	751	6·3	14·0	−6·7	29·3

Table 2. Numbers of days with falling and lying snow at a south Wiltshire site over seven decades 1930–1999

Decade	Snow falling	Snow lying
1930–39	132	63
1940–49	168	120
1950–59	192	86
1960–69	241	138
1970–79	230	60
1980–89	159	92
1990–99	73	20

Table 3. Numbers of days with air frosts at a south Wiltshire site over seven decades 1930–1999

Decade	−5°C or less	−10°C or less
1930–39	61	2
1940–49	68	6
1950–59	66	3
1960–69	562	4
1970–79	46	3
1980–89	57	3
1990–99	31	0

Table 4. Mean February and March temperatures at a south Wiltshire site over seven decades 1930–1999

Decade	February mean (°C)	March mean (°C)
1930–39	4·2	5·9
1940–49	4·0	6·1
1950–59	3·5	6·0
1960–69	3·6	5·5
1970–79	4·5	5·6
1980–89	3·7	6·1
1990–99	4·8	7·0

Wiltshire's early birds

Ian Collins

'The history of birds in Britain is revealed both by the place-names that invoke them and the archaeological evidence' (Yalden 2002), but traditionally few, if any, county avifaunas have dealt with these aspects. Fisher (1966) gave an excellent overview of the early British avifauna, but that failed to engender any lasting interest amongst ornithologists in general.

Most early archaeological excavations recorded avian skeletal remains simply as 'bird', largely because there was insufficient comparative material for identification. More recently, this previously neglected area has received considerable attention, with study collections amassed and a number of private researches carried out. It is now possible for the majority of bird finds to be identified to species level, thus adding to knowledge of avifaunas in periods for which standard specimen and sight records are of course unavailable. Yet zoo-archaeologists still fail to circulate their findings much beyond their specialist field; the bulk of this information goes largely unnoticed and unappreciated by ornithologists, who lamentably fail to incorporate such evidence as there is into their understanding of bird distributions (Tomiałoj 2000).

To date there have been no discoveries of fossil remains of birds in Wiltshire, but the county has long been recognised as having a rich and plentiful supply of archaeological sites of interest. Many papers relating to this area have been published over a long time, but it is only comparatively recently that any bird remains have been accurately identified. Table 5 details species records extracted from papers found to contain references to identified avifaunal remains. The list may prove not to be exhaustive, but the information is widely scattered and much has not yet been published.

With one or two possible exceptions – such as the Black Grouse, Red Kites and White-tailed Fish-eagles, and the frequency of Ravens in the list – this does not add a great deal to our knowledge of species distribution within the county. But it does raise one particularly interesting point. Why has a large bird with such food potential as the Great Bustard not featured at any site yet excavated? It is known that the species was present in Wiltshire in some numbers in the 16th, 17th and 18th centuries (*eg* Muffett 1655, Aubrey 1656–91, Pennant 1768, Mullens 1921) and that it bred in Great Britain during the medieval period (Yalden 2000). So does this indicate that it was a fairly recent addition to the county's avifauna, or do unidentified remains of this large and potentially important source of protein for our ancestors still languish in museums or collections? Most place-names in England are of Anglo-Saxon or Norse origin, dating largely between about 500 and 1000 AD, and typically consist of two elements – noun and adjective, or two nouns (Yalden 2002). Whilst Rackham (1986) complained of 'the tradition among place-name scholars of not admitting ignorance, clutching at straws, and reading into place-names more than they say', biogeographers and others have given the subject more attention, and Gelling (1987) took Rackham's criticism to task. That many names are associated with birds is well established, but systematic interpretation has as yet been undertaken for relatively few species. The names of a number of locations in Wiltshire can be associated with birds (table 6), the interpretations being those given by Gover *et al* (1939), with the implication that the species concerned were found, and presumably regular or common, at those places.

There can be little or no controversy over the identity of Crane, (Red) Kite, (Common) Buzzard or Raven in table 6, but 'hawk', 'mousehawk' and 'eagle' require further consideration. The word 'hawk' has been – and in rural areas often still is – applied to any small or medium-sized raptor. (The term 'hawking' has also been used to include falconry,

Table 5. Birds recorded from archaeological sites in Wiltshire

'Poss intrusion into Bronze Age' is short for possible later intrusions into Bronze Age deposits

Species	Date	Location	Reference
Mute Swan	Medieval or late medieval	Salisbury	Hamilton-Dyer (2000)
Greylag Goose	Late Bronze Age	Potterne	Coy (1983)
Greylag Goose	10th century	Trowbridge	Bourdillon (1993)
Greylag Goose	Medieval	Box	Fisher (1987)
Greylag or domestic goose	Early Iron Age	Budbury	Bramwell (1970)
Greylag or domestic goose	Late 8th to early 9th century	Ramsbury	Coy (1980)
Greylag or domestic goose	11th to 12th century	Yatesbury	Sykes (1996)
Goose, possibly Greylag and Bean	Romano-British	Great Bedwyn	Allison (1997)
Goose sp	Iron Age	Blunsdon St Andrew	Coy (1982b)
Goose sp	Medieval or late medieval	Salisbury	Hamilton-Dyer (2000)
Teal	Late Bronze Age	Potterne	Coy (1983b)
Teal	Romano-British	Great Bedwyn	Allison (1997)
Teal	10th century	Trowbridge	Bourdillon (1993)
Teal	Medieval	Salisbury	Coy (1986)
Mallard	Neolithic	Durrington	Harcourt (1971)
Mallard (probable)	Medieval	Salisbury	Coy (1986)
Mallard	Bronze Age	Burderop Down	Maltby (1992)
Mallard	Late Bronze Age	Potterne	Coy (1983b)
Mallard	Romano-British	Great Bedwyn	Allison (1997)
Mallard	10th century	Trowbridge	Bourdillon (1993)
Mallard	12th century	Trowbridge	Bourdillon (1993)
Mallard or domestic duck	Early 9th century	Ramsbury	Coy (1980)
Common Scoter ?	Early Iron Age	Budbury	Bramwell (1970)
Duck sp	11th to 12th century	Yatesbury	Sykes (1996)
Black Grouse	Undated Saxo-Norman	Trowbridge	Bourdillon (1993)
Grey Partridge	13th century	Trowbridge	Bourdillon (1993)
Grey Partridge	Poss intrusion into Bronze Age	Burderop Down	Maltby (1992)
Pheasant	18th century	Salisbury	Coy (1986)
Cormorant	Neolithic	Durrington	Harcourt (1971)
Grey Heron	Medieval or late medieval	Salisbury	Hamilton-Dyer (2000)
Red Kite	Neolithic	Durrington	Harcourt 1971
Red Kite	Late 8th to early 9th century	Ramsbury	Coy (1980)
Red Kite	11th to 12th century	Yatesbury	Sykes (1996)
Red Kite	Medieval or late medieval	Salisbury	Hamilton-Dyer (2000)
White-tailed Fish-eagle	Neolithic	Coneybury Henge	Maltby (1990)
White-tailed Fish-eagle	Late Bronze Age	Potterne	Coy (1983b)
Goshawk	Romano-British	Great Bedwyn	Allison (1997)
Common Buzzard	Late Bronze Age	Potterne	Coy (1983b)
Common Buzzard	Iron Age	Blunsdon St Andrew	Coy (1982b)
Common Buzzard	12th century	Trowbridge	Bourdillon (1993)
Kestrel	Poss intrusion into Bronze Age	Burderop Down	Maltby (1992)
Peregrine Falcon	12th century	Ramsbury	Coy (1980)
Corncrake	Undated (Neolithic?)	West Kennet Long Barrow	Pigott (1962)
Crane	Late Bronze Age	Potterne	Coy (1983b)
Crane	Iron Age	Blunsdon St Andrew	Coy (1982b)
Golden Plover	Bronze Age	Rockley Down	Maltby (1992)
Golden Plover	Romano-British	Great Bedwyn	Allison (1997)
Lapwing	Neolithic	Coneybury Henge	Maltby (1990)
Wader, smaller than Snipe	13th to 16th century	Trowbridge	Bourdillon (1993)

Species	Date	Location	Reference
Common Snipe	Romano-British	Great Bedwyn	Allison (1997)
Common Snipe	Late 8th to early 9th century	Ramsbury	Coy (1980)
Common Snipe	10th century	Trowbridge	Bourdillon (1993)
Common Snipe	Medieval	Salisbury	Coy (1986)
Woodcock	Neolithic	Durrington	Harcourt (1971)
Woodcock	Late Bronze Age	Potterne	Coy (1983b)
Woodcock	Romano-British	Great Bedwyn	Allison (1997)
Woodcock	7th to 11th century	Trowbridge	Bourdillon (1993)
Woodcock	Undated Saxo-Norman	Trowbridge	Bourdillon (1993)
Woodcock	Medieval	Salisbury	Coy (1986)
Woodcock	Medieval or late medieval	Salisbury	Hamilton-Dyer (2000)
Guillemot	Late Bronze Age	Potterne	Coy (1983b)
Stock Dove	Early Iron Age	Budbury	Bramwell (1970)
Pigeon *Columba* sp	Romano-British	Great Bedwyn	Allison (1997)
Pigeon *Columba* sp	10th century	Trowbridge	Bourdillon (1993)
Pigeon *Columba* sp	Medieval	Salisbury	Coy (1986)
Pigeon *Columba* sp	Poss intrusion into Bronze Age	Burderop Down	Maltby (1992)
Barn Owl	Romano-British	Great Bedwyn	Allison (1997)
Sky Lark or Wood Lark	Bronze Age	Wilsford	Yalden & Yalden (1989)
Sand Martin	Bronze Age	Wilsford	Yalden & Yalden (1989)
Barn Swallow	Bronze Age	Wilsford	Yalden & Yalden (1989)
Wren	Romano-British	Avebury	Iles (1996)
Blackbird	Neolithic	West Kennet Long Barrow	Pigott (1962)
Blackbird	Late Bronze Age	Potterne	Coy (1983b)
Blackbird	Romano-British	Great Bedwyn	Allison (1997)
Thrush *Turdus* sp	Bronze Age	Bishop's Canning Down	Maltby (1992)
Thrush *Turdus* sp	Romano-British	Great Bedwyn	Allison (1997)
Thrush *Turdus* sp	Medieval	Salisbury	Coy (1986)
Thrush *Turdus* sp	Poss intrusion into Bronze Age	Burderop Down	Maltby (1992)
Jay	Early Iron Age	Budbury	Bramwell (1970)
Jay	Romano-British	Great Bedwyn	Allison (1997)
Jackdaw	Neolithic	West Kennet Long Barrow	Pigott (1962)
Jackdaw	Romano-British	Great Bedwyn	Allison (1997)
Rook	Early Iron Age	Budbury	Bramwell (1970)
Rook or Crow	Bronze Age	Bishop's Canning Down	Maltby (1992)
Rook or Crow	Romano-British	Great Bedwyn	Allison (1997)
Rook or Crow	Undated Saxo-Norman	Trowbridge	Bourdillon (1993)
Crow	Late Bronze Age	Potterne	Coy (1983b)
Crow	16th to 17th century	Yatesbury	Sykes (1996)
Raven	3300 BC	Stonehenge	Serjeantson (1995)
Raven	Neolithic	Durrington	Harcourt (1971)
Raven	Late Bronze Age	Potterne	Coy (1983b)
Raven	Early Iron Age	Budbury	Bramwell (1970)
Raven	Iron Age	Blunsdon St Andrew	Coy (1982b)
Raven	Iron Age	Longbridge Deverill	Harcourt (1965)
Raven	10th century	Trowbridge	Bourdillon (1993)
Raven	Medieval	Salisbury	Coy (1986)
Common Starling	Romano-British	Great Bedwyn	Allison (1997)
Common Starling	Medieval	Salisbury	Coy(1986)
House Sparrow	Romano-British	Great Bedwyn	Allison (1997)
Unidentified sparrow	Late Bronze Age	Potterne	Coy (1983b)
Greenfinch ?	Medieval or late medieval	Salisbury	Hamilton-Dyer (2000)
Unidentified small passerine	Neolithic	Coneybury Henge	Maltby (1990)

although the differences between hawks and falcons were well understood even in medieval Britain.) Here 'hawk' probably refers to Sparrowhawk, but Kestrel, and even Goshawk, cannot be ruled out; 'mousehawk' was a frequent term for Kestrel in earlier times. As for the 'eagle', Reid-Henry & Harrison (1988) opined that the White-tailed Fish-eagle, rather than the Golden Eagle, was the Raven's companion as scavenger on the battlefields of Norse and Anglo-Saxon times; and this view was reinforced by Baxter (1993) who stated that, in Anglo-Saxon poems, the White-tailed Fish-eagle was called the *earn*, a word closely related to the Gaelic *erne*, by which name this species was known in old ornithological works, such as those of Newton (1893–96) and Dresser (1871–81).

More recently, Hough (1998) suggested that the initial element of two Wiltshire place-names, Bemerhills and Bemerton, as well as the lost 'Bemerehill', is the Old English (Anglian) *bēmere*. This is considered to mean 'trumpeter', thus giving rise to the 'hill of the trumpeters' or 'farm of the trumpeters'. As there is little or no evidence of trumpets in Anglo-Saxon Britain, Hough argued that it was more plausible to take it as referring to a bird with a trumpet-like voice. Hough made a case for this to be the Common Bittern,

Table 6. Wiltshire place-names derived from Old English bird-names

Place	Map reference	Derivation	Meaning	Reference
Cranefurlong		'cran, furlong'	Furlong where crane	Boisseau & Yalden (1998)
Cranemede		'cran, maed'	Crane's meadow	Boisseau & Yalden (1998)
Cranhill	ST8755	'cran, hyll'	Crane's hill	Boisseau & Yalden (1998)
Cranley Farm	SU0278	'cran, leah'	Crane's wooded clearing	Boisseau & Yalden (1998)
Cranmore	SU1663	'cran, mor'	Crane's marsh	Boisseau & Yalden (1998)
Crannell	SU0259	'cran, hyll'	Crane's hill	Boisseau & Yalden (1998)
Glydecumbe		'gleoda, cumb'	Kite's coombe	Boisseau (1995)
Hafoc hlinc		'hafoc, hlinc'	Hawk ridge	Boisseau (1995)
Hawkeddge	ST8653	'hafoc, hrycg'	Hawk ridge	Boisseau (1995)
Hawkham	ST9056	'hafoc, cumb'	Hawk's coombe	Boisseau (1995)
Hawkley	ST8175	'hafoc, leah'	Hawk's clearing	Boisseau (1995)
Hawks Grove	SU2328			Boisseau (1995)
Hawkshord	ST8261			Boisseau (1995)
Kite Close	SU0993	'cyta'		Boisseau (1995)
Kite Hill	ST9944	'cyta, hyll'		Boisseau (1995)
Kite's Nest		'cyta, nest'		Boisseau (1995)
Kite's Stile	ST9064	'cyta'		Boisseau (1995)
Petty Ridge	ST8141	'puttoc, hrycg'	Kite ridge	Boisseau (1995)
Pickledean	SU1367	'poel, dael'	Mousehawk valley	Boisseau (1995)
Pitton	SU2131	'putoc, tun'	Kite's enclosure	Boisseau (1995)
Pit Furlong	ST9332	'puttoc, Furlang'	Furlong where kite	Boisseau (1995)
Puthall Farm	SU2368	'putoc, healh'	Kite's nook	Boisseau (1995)
Puttelestyche		'pyttel, sticce'	Ridge where mousehawk	Boisseau (1995)
Rainscombe House	SU1663	'hraefn, cumb'	Raven's coombe	Moore (2002)
Rams Cliff	SU0152	'hremn, clif'	Raven's cliff	Moore (2002)
Ramsbury	SU2771	'hraefn, burh'	Fort where raven	Moore (2002)
Ramshill Copse	SU2332	'hraefn, hyll'	Raven's hill	Moore (2002)
Ramshill Farm	ST8926	'hraefn, hyll'	Raven's hill	Moore (2002)
Ranscomb	SU1257	'hraefn,cumb'	Raven's coombe	Moore (2002)
Ravenshurst	SU0993	'hraefn, hyrst'	Raven's wood	Moore (2002)
(N & S) Wraxall	ST8175	'wrocc, heath'	Buzzard's nook	Boisseau (1995)
Wrokcumb		'wrocc, cumb'	Buzzard's coombe	Boisseau (1995)
Yarnbury Castle	SU0340	'earn, burh'	Eagle castle Castle	Yalden (*in litt*) 2003
Yarnfield	ST7637	'earn, feld'	Eagle field	Yalden (*in litt*) 2003

but, whilst the location of Bemerton, in the Nadder valley, might be a reasonable location for that species at that time, it is highly unlikely that Bemerhills meant 'Bittern Hill'. In personal discussion, Derek Yalden has postulated that the Crane might be a more reasonable choice. Gelling (1987) made a plea for historians of the countryside and its inhabitants to take seriously references to creatures in place-names. It is important that studies such as those forming the data for this piece are continued. And it is to be hoped that, at some point in the not far distant future, the will and the funds can be found to unearth all those remains (particularly any of Wiltshire origin) that are lying in museums and other collections, simply labelled 'bird', and subject them to modern accurate identification processes.

Wiltshire's ornithological history

Ian Collins & Mike Jackson

14th to 17th centuries

Apart from the archaeological evidence (see 'Wiltshire's early birds'), the earliest known references to birds in Wiltshire come from the ORolls Patent [an official proclamation from the King] of Edward III, as recorded by Colt Hoare (1822–40). Two are of particular interest, as they appear to be the only references that relate to the swannery at Clarendon Palace. Written in medieval Latin and translated here as accurately as possible, the first of these – dated 20 August 1331 and entitled '*Oconcerning* an investigation into the swans from the Forest and Manor of Clarendon' – was addressed to the king's '*Obeloved* and faithful servants *Hildebrand* of London and John of Mise'. It relates that the king had come to understand that his swans, which belonged in the Forest and Manor of *Clarendon*, had become scattered along the banks of the river Avon, in the counties of Hampshire and Wiltshire, despite his keeper, who was from *Beauchamp*. He was giving the two named characters the commission of investigating the whereabouts of the swans and restoring them. The second reference – dated 2 May 1345 and entitled *Oconcerning* the enquiry about the royal swans that have been stolen from the Manor and Forest of *Clarendon* – was addressed to *Egidius of Beauchamp*, the keeper of the Manor and Forest of *Clarendon*, Richard of *Lustehall* and *Thomas Beauver*. The king was complaining again that the swans, which belonged to the estates and which were worth £100, were scattered along the banks of the Avon, 'abducted by force of arms by certain *malefactore* in contempt of his rule and against his peace'. He was instructing them and two justices to identify the guilty and bring them to justice 'in accordance with the law and custom of the land'.

The next record of any kind also concerns swans, when Taylor (1623) wrote of very large numbers on the Avon below Salisbury (see Mute Swan). Also known as 'the water poet', John Taylor was a Thames wherryman who wrote quite eloquently about his lengthy voyages in a small craft around the coasts and waterways of Britain, as well as composing and publishing poetry.

We now come to the first reference to Great Bustards on Salisbury Plain (Muffet 1655). Dr Thomas Muffet or Moffett [1553–1604] was an eminent physician of his time. His original work is generally ascribed to 1595, but was not published until over 50 years after his death, when it was edited, corrected and added to by Christopher Bennet [1617–55], another physician of note (Mullens & Swann, 1917). Quite how much Bennet added is not known, but the chapters dealing with the description and observations of wild birds were almost certainly Muffet's own work.

John Aubrey [1626–97], the son of a landed gentleman, was born at Easton Percy, or Pierse (now Piercy). He was educated at Malmesbury Grammar School and in 1642 entered Trinity College, Oxford, where his studies were interrupted by the Civil War and, though he became a student of the Middle Temple, he was never called to the Bar. He is widely and best known as an antiquarian and was the first person to draw attention, in 1649, to the previously ignored megaliths at Avebury. On the death of his father in 1652, he inherited large estates, some of which were encumbered by complicated debts. He used his newly found wealth to entertain and cultivate the friendship of contemporary celebrities – which was fortunate, in view of what was to come. 'The earliest efforts to establish a Society for the study of the history of Wiltshire, of which we have any record, were made by John Aubrey at a meeting of gentlemen in Devizes in 1659. At this meeting it was decided to divide the county into areas with an accredited local representative in each. This excellent idea, however, fell through' (Cunnington 1930). In 1663 he was elected a member of the Royal Society, but became embroiled in ill-advised and costly lawsuits until, in 1670, he was finally forced to sell Easton Percy. In 1671, he received a patent allowing him to make antiquarian surveys under the Crown and formed large topographical collections of Wiltshire and Surrey. Apart from his 'Miscellanies' (1696), none of his work was published in his lifetime. In 1847, the Wiltshire Topographical Society published some of his collection of notes, written between 1656 and 1691, as the 'Natural History of Wiltshire'. These were edited by John Britton, who gave 'the apathy which prevailed in his time amongst Wiltshire men towards such topics' as the reason why they had not been published earlier. Eminent though Aubrey may have been in some ways, his chapter on birds is disjointed and rambling. It comprises just one-and-a-half pages and tells us very little about the 15 species or groups of species mentioned. These were 'Larkes ... buntings ... Linnets ... Woodpeckers severall sorts ... wheat-eares ... bustards ... gray crowes as at Royston ... rookes ... feasants ... Bittern ... Herons ... sparrow-hawkes ... hobbies ... Sea-mewes [gulls]'; the fifteenth was domestic goose. Despite this, it is still an important document, for the details it does give are the only insight we have on the avifauna of Wiltshire at that time.

18th century

In 1780 a small, 45-page octavo booklet was published, costing one shilling, with a disproportionately long title: 'A DISCOURSE on the Emigration of British Birds; or, This Question at last Solv'd: Whence come the STORK and the TURTLE, the CRANE and the SWALLOW, when they know and observe the appointed Time of their Coming? Containing a curious particular and circumstantial ACCOUNT of the respective Retreats of all those BIRDS OF PASSAGE, Which visit our Island at the Commencement of SPRING and depart at the approach of WINTER; as, the CUCKOW, TURTLE, STORK, CRANE, QUAIL, GOAT-SUCKER, THE SWALLOW TRIBE, NIGHTINGALE, BLACK-CAP, WHEAT-EAR, STONE-CHAT, WHIN-CHAT, WILLOW-WREN, WHITE-THROAT, ETOTOLI*, FLY-CATCHER &c &c. ALSO a copious, entertaining, and satisfactory Relation of WINTER BIRDS OF PASSAGE: Among which are the WOODCOCK, SNIPE, FIELDFARE, RED-WING, ROYSTON CROW, DOTTEREL, &c, &c. SHEWING the different Countries to which they retire, the Places where they breed, and how they perform their ANNUAL EMIGRATIONS, &c. with a short Account of those BIRDS that migrate occasionally, or only shift their Quarters at certain Seasons of the Year'.

These were further described as 'REFLECTIONS on that truly admirable and wonderful Instinct, the ANNUAL MIGRATION OF BIRDS! By a Naturalist'. Despite the detail of the title, the name of the 'naturalist' was not given. At the end of the Introduction appeared an address 'Market Lavington, Wiltshire' (Bircham 1993). It must have sold well for it finally went into four editions, by which time it had increased to 64 pages. The fourth edition, published in 1814, carried the name of George Edwards, a then well-known ornithologist, instead of the modest pseudonym of 'a Naturalist'. Swainson (1840), listing the work under the heading 'Edwards', said that he had not seen it and did not know if it was 'by the George Edwards mentioned above' – so there were still doubts about the original authorship some 60 years after the original publication. Professor Alfred Newton, being interested in the history of ornithology, as evidenced by the introduction to his seminal *Dictionary of Birds* (Newton 1893–96), obtained a copy and was intrigued by the anonymity of the author. Noting that the writer's address was in Wiltshire, he wrote to the Reverend AC Smith, with whom he was well acquainted, asking if he could find any

* It is apparently impossible to determine what species was the 'Etotoli' (Gladstone 1928).

evidence to its author. Smith's investigations led him to the conclusion that it was John Legg (Smith 1894).

John Legg [1755–1802] was an advanced but almost completely neglected ornithologist. He was born in Market Lavington (Mullens & Swann 1917). His *Discourse on the Emigration of British Birds*, published when he was only 25, broke new ground in the field of migration and was far in advance of general belief at the time. He refuted the theories that birds spend the winter hibernating in a torpid state in holes in trees and buildings, or at the bottoms of lakes or ponds. He supported the arguments for migration and probably made the first systematic observation of migrants in Wiltshire. By marking the bill and claws of a flycatcher (almost certainly, a Spotted Flycatcher), he proved that it was the same individual that returned the following year, to the same nest-site near his house. He made penetrating observations on the Common Swift, Sand Martin, Barn Swallow and House Martin. How widely his treatise was accepted is not known, but, because of the number of reprints, it must have attracted some considerable notice. He appears to have borrowed part of his title, and the description of the Woodcock, from an anonymous essay published in 1703 and entitled '*An Essay towards the probable solution of the Question whence come the Stork and the Turtle*... By a Person of Learning and Piety'. This was later revealed (in the Tonkins 1811 edition of Carew's *Survey of Cornwall*) to be by the Honourable Francis Roberts (Mullens & Swann 1917). Legg died young, a bachelor, when only 47; at the time of his death he was apparently engaged in the preparation of a large work to be entitled *A New and Complete Natural History of British Birds*, but the manuscript was never discovered (Smith 1894). Legg explained, on page 21 of his *Discourse*, that 'It is a work which has lain by me finished some years but has not yet been published... It will be comprised in two large volumes octavo, and will speedily appear. The publication of this performance has been purposely delayed, in order that it may be rendered as perfect and complete as possible'. Smith attempted to trace the manuscript but failed (Bircham 1993), and Gladstone (1928) also confirmed that it had not been found – a sad epitaph to a talented ornithologist.

Late 18th and early 19th centuries

George Montagu [1753–1815], soldier turned naturalist, has been widely bestowed with the title 'Founder of British Ornithology'. He was born, one of thirteen children, at the family home, Lackham House, which was later destroyed by fire. (There has been some dispute about his year of birth – given variously between 1751 and 1754 – but the parish register at Kingsbridge, Devon, notes the date of his burial as 24 June 1815 and his age as 62: see Mearns & Mearns 1988.) Before he was 17, he entered the army and, at the age of 18, married Anne Courtenay, probably by elopement as the union was not blessed by either set of parents. Not long after, his regiment was posted to America, where he started his collection of bird skins. Rising to the rank of Captain, he served for a short period in the American War of Independence, but became very disillusioned with its brutality. He retired from the army in 1777 and, returning home, subsequently joined the Wiltshire militia, in which he rose to the rank of Lieutenant-Colonel. He and his family, which by now included his reconciled mother-in-law, lived in various manor houses in Wiltshire, settling for a while at Easton Grey, but his marriage was beginning to fail. In 1797, he inherited the family estates, but failed to secure them because he left his wife and moved to Devon. There he set up home at Knowle House, near Kingsbridge, with Mrs Eliza Dorville, who was herself still married. By the standards of the time, this was a remarkably flagrant act by a man of Montagu's position, and in 1799 he was court-martialled at Plymouth. In 1800 he fell into a protracted series of litigation with his eldest son, which cost him dear and, with this son's extravagances, resulted in the loss of most of the family estates.

Montagu contributed significantly to early knowledge of British birds. In 1802, most of his work was published in his two-volume *Ornithological Dictionary, or Alphabetical Synopsis of British Birds*, illustrated by Eliza Dorville. This was followed by a supplement in 1813, in which many observations by Robert Anstice are recorded and gifts of bird specimens from him mentioned; their correspondence has since been published (Dance 2003). Amongst his most notable achievements, Montagu showed that the 'Greenwich Sandpiper' was the Ruff in winter plumage and that the 'Ash-coloured Sandpiper' was the Knot. He was also the first person to describe the Roseate Tern, and is usually credited with naming the American Bittern as well – the latter in 1813 from a vagrant killed at Piddletown (now Puddletown) (Dorset) – but another description, by Thomas Rackett, of the same specimen was published a month earlier (see Macdonald & Grant 1951). It is also of local interest that Montagu's description of the Grey Phalarope in his *Ornithological Dictionary* was taken from one killed on a pond at Alderton, in northwest Wiltshire. He clarified the long-standing confusion between the two British harriers that have grey males and brown females – the females of both were at one time regarded as another species, the 'Ringtail Harrier' (see page 274) – though he used the name 'Ash-coloured Falcon' for a male Montagu's Harrier shot in Wiltshire. (Somewhat oddly, the name *'Busard Montagu'* was first used in France before becoming universally accepted.) He is also credited with the first British records of Cirl Bunting, as well as of Cattle Egret, Little Gull and Gull-billed Tern. The Reverend AC Smith called him 'one of the most acute observers and one of the most reliable authors of his age'.

In addition to his ornithological studies, he wrote the *Testacea Britannica, a History of British Marine, Land and Freshwater Shells*, a monumental work also illustrated by Eliza Dorville and published in 1803 at a time when few other naturalists were interested in that area of study. He extended his interest to mammals and, in a cavern near Torquay, amongst a colony of greater horseshoe bats, he discovered and subsequently described the lesser horseshoe bat for the first time. In 1815, too, he described, as new to science, the bottle-nosed dolphin from an individual specimen that was stranded in the mouth of the Dart (Devon). Soon afterwards, he stepped on a rusty nail, and after four days succumbed to tetanus. He was buried at Kingsbridge Parish Church and was succeeded by his wife, his estranged and disinherited elder son and the children borne him by Eliza Dorville, all of whom he acknowledged.

Montagu, an early fellow of the Linnaean Society, had frequent correspondence with Gilbert White [1720–1793] of Selborne (Hampshire) but, despite his considerable contribution to early natural history, he failed to achieve the latter's renown. It has been said that his writing lacked style and often contained grammatical errors (Mearns & Mearns 1988). This, along with his scandalous reputation, almost certainly contributed to this regrettable oversight on the part of his peers. That all his outstanding achievements were accomplished without any formal training is all the more remarkable. A most apt epitaph for this remarkable man, came from Charles Kingsley (1855): 'Certainly, the best naturalist, as far as logical acumen, as well as earnest research, is concerned, whom England has ever seen, was the Devonshire squire, Colonel George Montagu, of whom the late E. Forbes well says, that "had he been educated a physiologist" (and not, as he was, a soldier and a sportsman), "and made the study of Nature his aim and not his amusement, his would have been one of the greatest names in the whole range of British science." I question, nevertheless, whether he would not have lost more than he would have gained by a different training. It might have made him a more learned systematizer; but would it have quickened in him that "seeing" eye of the true soldier and sportsman, which makes Montagu's descriptions indelible word-pictures, instinct with life and truth? "There is no question," says E. Forbes, after bewailing the vagueness of most naturalists, "about the identity of any animal Montagu described ... He was a forward-looking philosopher; he spoke of every creature as if one exceedingly like it, yet different from it, would be washed up by the waves next tide. Consequently his descriptions are permanent".'

The beginnings of a more orderly approach to the study of birds, and indeed of all aspects of natural history, were already to be found in the 18th century work of Linnaeus. Nearer to Wiltshire, Gilbert White's *Natural History of Selborne*, published in 1789, gave inspiration to many (and still does). In the Victorian era the study of natural history was thought to be a pathway to a greater knowledge of God (Barber 1980). This gave amateur naturalists an excuse, if they needed one, for widespread 'collection' of specimens. That was the era of the great collectors, many of whom were clergymen, who saw no apparent conflict between the worship of God and the killing of large numbers of birds for preservation as stuffed specimens. The widespread belief at the time that all living creatures, plant and animal, were put on earth for man's delectation did not make killing a moral problem. Improvements in firearms also made collecting easier.

In Wiltshire, before the turn of the 19th century, William Maton [1774–1835] wrote a small book, *The Natural History of a Part of the County of Wiltshire, comprehended within the distance of ten miles round the city of Salisbury*. This was not published until 1843, eight years after his death, yet he started his collection of specimens for this work as early as 1792. It contained just four pages on birds, in which he mentioned only 23 species; according to Smith (1887), 'anything more meagre and more absolutely misleading, on account of its wholesale omissions, than the wretched account he gives of Wiltshire birds, it is impossible to conceive'. This was probably undeserved, for Maton was an accomplished naturalist and, although ornithology was not his foremost interest, he would almost certainly not have offered for publication such an abbreviated account were it not for his very busy life and premature death.

Maton was the eldest of the four children born of a highly regarded Salisbury wine merchant. His father had served the city in the highest office and was usually referred to as 'Mr Chamberlain Maton'. William Maton himself was educated at the Free Grammar School in Salisbury, where his passion for scientific pursuits interfered considerably with the progress of his legitimate studies. During his early years his interests were noticed and encouraged by several eminent gentlemen of scientific leanings. He entered Queen's College, Oxford, in 1790 and soon became a zealous assistant to Dr John Sibthorp in his preparation of the *Flora Oxoniensis* and *Flora Græca*. It is believed that, but for this association, conchology might have prevailed. Maton was elected a Fellow of the Linnaean Society in 1794, when only 21, and in that year read his first paper to that august body, describing a new species of bivalve mollusc, which he named *Tellina rivalis*, from the Avon near Salisbury. That same summer he was invited by his friends and mentors, the Reverend Thomas Rackett and Charles Hatchett, to accompany them on a tour of Cornwall, which included portions of Dorset, Devon and Somerset, and Maton filled his journal with everything he could observe connected with the mineralogy, geology, antiquities and natural history of those counties. This resulted in his publication, in 1797, of his *Observations relative chiefly to the Natural History, Picturesque Scenery, and Antiquities of the Western Counties of England, made in the years 1794 and 1796*. That same year, having gained his MA from Oxford, he entered himself as a pupil at the Westminster Hospital and in 1800, now a Bachelor of Medicine, began to practice as a physician, achieving his doctorate the following year and eventually elected a Fellow of the Royal College of Physicians. He was considered a physician of some eminence and even gained Royal patronage, while his other work resulted in his being regularly re-elected vice-president of the Linnaean Society. His later life was encumbered by the necessity to pay off considerable debts left on the death of his father, in 1816, and the need to provide for his dependants – these purported to have cost him a sum exceeding £20,000. The selfless manner in which he accomplished this did not go unnoticed and for that and the use of his talents he was awarded the Freedom of Salisbury in 1827. He had always relished the thought of retirement and having the time to enjoy his various interests. In 1834, with this in mind, he purchased Redlynch House, near Downton. Sadly, however, scarcely six months elapsed before he succumbed to an unexpected and painful death at the old family home in Spring Gardens.

The Reverend George Marsh [1812–62] spent his childhood in Winterslow and was appointed vicar of Sutton Benger in 1836. He was a thoroughly practical ornithologist and, as was the developing custom in the Victorian era, he built up a substantial collection of stuffed birds. He noted 157 species as having occurred in the county – including such rarities as a White-tailed Fish-eagle, a Honey-buzzard and a Rough-legged Buzzard, the last two of which were shot by Marsh himself. When a Golden-winged Woodpecker (now known as the Northern Flicker) was shot at Amesbury Park in 1836 and the bird came into his possession, he took pains to verify its authenticity. Alfred Newton, however, maintained that he knew of another specimen that had been sent from Greenland and therefore refused to admit the species to the British List, a view echoed by Hony (1915a). At that time, of course, it was not thought possible that North American landbirds were capable of crossing the Atlantic in favourable meteorological conditions – even if they may sometimes rest on ships for parts (even large parts) of their journeys. Another Northern Flicker was obtained in Dorset within a few days and, whilst it is difficult to be sure of the veracity of old specimens, the possibility of their having occurred naturally should perhaps not be dismissed out of hand (see page 737); this species is not currently included on the British List, though it has been recorded in Ireland. Marsh conversed regularly with a large number of gamekeepers and country workers, and also maintained a wide circle of correspondents, including the Reverend AC Smith, so was kept well informed about the local avifauna. He made many notes on birds commoner then than they are today, including Grey Partridges, Woodcocks, Wrynecks, Hooded Crows, Ravens, Common Starlings and Tree Sparrows, as well as Dotterels on spring and autumn passage. He also experimented on the palatability as food of many other species, including Whinchat, Stonechat, Wheatear, Blackbird, Fieldfare, Redwing, and Yellowhammer, as well as the more usual Black Grouse, Capercaillie (not in Wiltshire), Red-legged and Grey Partridges, Quail, Golden Plover and Curlew. Marsh made notes of his observations, at both Winterslow and Sutton Benger, in his interleaved copy of Yarrell's *History of British Birds*, dated 5 August 1842. (That copy is now in the ornithological library of the Natural History Museum at Tring, Hertfordshire.) Smith (1887) made use of notes from Marsh, but did not refer specifically to his annotated copy of Yarrell. Marsh's standard in recording information makes one wish that he had been more productive in literary matters.

Founding of the Wiltshire Archaeological & Natural History Society

'In 1839 John Britton established the first Wiltshire Topographical Society. He induced a few friends to form a committee, and was fortunate enough to obtain the interest of the then Marquis of Lansdowne, who became the Patron of that Society as he subsequently was of our own Society' (Cunnington 1930), but 'Diminishing both in numbers and finances the Society dragged out a feeble existence until 1850, when it was decided to suspend further operations until a more favourable period should arrive'. They did not have to wait long, as in 1853 the Wiltshire Archaeological & Natural History Society (WANHS) was formed, the first major society in the county to include the study of natural history in its aims. The inaugural meeting was held in the Town Hall, Devizes, on 12 October that year, with the aforementioned Marquis of Lansdowne in the chair. The proposed aims were

'To promote the study of both Antiquities and Natural History'. The first annual report was published in 1854 under the title of the *Wiltshire Archaeological Magazine* (later to become the *Wiltshire Archaeological & Natural History Magazine*, *WANHM*) 'and continued ever since, teems with articles concerning the archaeology, history, topography, geology, folk lore, ornithology, botany, and in fact almost every conceivable subject connected with Wiltshire' (Cunnington 1930).

The Marlborough district and the second half of the 19th century

The honour of writing the first account of the birds of the Marlborough district went to Reginald Bosworth Smith [1839–1908], who compiled the bird notes added to the Reverend TA Preston's *Flora of Marlborough* (1863). He was born at West Stafford Rectory (Dorset), where his father was the incumbent, and educated at Milton Abbas School, Blandford, before going to Marlborough College in August 1855. He went up to Oxford, graduated with a BA in 1862, was appointed a Fellow of Trinity College the following year, and was awarded his MA in 1865. In 1864 he had begun his life's work as a Classics master at Harrow School, where he remained until retirement in 1901 took him to Bingham's Melcombe (Dorset). A series of six articles of his, published in the *Nineteenth Century* between November 1902 and February 1904, formed the basis for his only other ornithological work, *Bird Life and Bird Lore* (1909). He died at his home on 18 October 1908.

The Marlborough College Natural History Society (MCNHS), founded on 9 April 1864 by a small number of members of the school was, for just over a century, one of Wiltshire's chief ornithological groups. The Reverend TA Preston was elected its first president. For many years, the students were allowed to cycle into the countryside within a ten-mile radius of the college to collect ornithological data and, 18 months after the society's inauguration, the first of the MCNHS's annual reports was published.

Everard Ferdinand im Thurn [1852–1932] was educated at Marlborough College and then at Exeter College, Oxford. While still at Marlborough, he wrote a small book, *Birds of Marlborough*. The area covered was within a radius of eight miles around the town. In 1876, he wrote an appendix to the book, which appeared in the *Report of the MCNHS* for that year. It gave a brief account of the occurrence and habits of each of 127 species and included local names, the dates when the first eggs were found and, for summer visitors, the dates when they were first seen in the Marlborough area. In his preface, im Thurn admitted that his book was not quite the first on the ornithology of Marlborough (see Bosworth Smith 1863), but it is quite remarkable that he was still only 16½ years old when he left Marlborough College. He went on to achieve high office in colonial administration. His first appointment, in 1882, was as magistrate for the Pomeroon District of British Guiana [Guyana], where he spent eight years. It was during this period that he and Harry Perkins, a Crown Surveyor, undertook an expedition to climb the 2772 m of Mt Roraima, which took them seven weeks just to reach the base of the cliff. Their route ascended from the southeast, which is still known today as the 'im Thurn route', and gained the summit on 18 December 1884. When he returned to England, he undertook to present lectures on this expedition, one of which was attended by Sir Arthur Conan Doyle. So impressed was Conan Doyle by this expedition that he used it as the inspiration for his 1912 novel, *The Lost World*. Later, im Thurn went on to a highly successful career in the Colonial Service, being successively appointed as Lieutenant-Governor of Ceylon [Sri Lanka], Governor of Fiji and High Commissioner for the Western Pacific. Amongst other honours, he was knighted (KCMG) in 1905. During his career he produced many scientific papers, but these were concerned chiefly with anthropology. His little Marlborough book, and its subsequent appendix, appear to be his only ornithological publications.

The Reverend Alfred Charles Smith [1822–98], born in Devizes, the son of another clergyman, was appointed rector of All Saints, Yatesbury. He became a local secretary of WANHS on its foundation in 1853 and then one of its general secretaries from 1857 to 1890; he also began to edit its *Wiltshire Archaeological and Natural History Magazine* (*WANHM*) in 1864 'and the work was most ably carried on by him until his resignation in 1882' (Cunnington 1930). Smith claimed to have knowledge of only the birds of western and northern Europe until, because of ill-health, he had 'been obliged to spend many winters and springs in warmer climates' and thus obtained a wide experience of those of southern Europe, Egypt and Nubia. His important work on *The Birds of Wiltshire*, published in 1887, the same year as his father's death, was to a large extent a collation based on a series of papers on the ornithology of the county that he wrote for *WANHM* during 1857–70. It was the first comprehensive avifauna of Wiltshire, and the varied and widespread nature of the records in it resulted from his correspondence with a broad circle of ornithologists and bird-collectors, both in the county and elsewhere. His poor health forcing him to leave the management of his living to his curates meant that, when not travelling abroad, he lived at the family home – Old Park, Devizes – and claimed that that gave him the time to compile the book. Despite its rambling and verbose style, it is full of interest and he himself stated that it 'has no pretensions of a scientific character, nor does it aspire to be other than a plain account of the Birds of Wiltshire, written by a Wiltshire man, and for Wiltshire people'. He also contributed reports and letters to the *Zoologist* on a regular basis.

Another clergyman, the Reverend Arthur Philip Morres [1816–85] was a contemporary of Smith, and for most of his life the vicar of Britford. His first published work is said to have been 'Rare Birds of Wiltshire', which appeared in the *Zoologist* in 1877. When Smith ended his articles in *WANHM,* Morres contributed a series from 1878 to 1885 on 'The Occurrence of some of the Rarer Species of Birds in the Neighbourhood of Salisbury'. A collation of those articles was subsequently published privately under the same title. Many of these notes, especially on seabirds and waterbirds, were from the lower Avon and the Christchurch area (Dorset), and only a few of them appear to be his own observations, but Smith acknowledged Morres's assistance in his own work and referred to him as an 'able ornithologist'.

Two renowned writers on wildlife with strong Wiltshire connections

Richard Jefferies [1848–87], well known for his sensitive writing on the natural history, rural life and agriculture of late Victorian England, was born in north Wiltshire, at Coate, near Swindon, where his family farmed a smallholding of about 16 ha. As a youth, Jefferies spent much of his time walking through the countryside around Coate and along the wide chalk expanses of the Marlborough Downs. He regularly visited Burderop Wood and Liddington Hill and, on longer trips, explored Savernake Forest and the stretch of the downs to the east; but Liddington Hill was his favourite haunt, crowned with its ancient fort commanding superb views of the north Wiltshire plain and downs. Jefferies befriended the gamekeeper of the local estate and became skilled at shooting game – though, after a while, the sense of wonder he experienced in observing the wildlife often prevented him from pulling the trigger. In 1866, at the age of 17, he obtained a reporter's job on the *North Wiltshire Herald*, based in Swindon, and two years later, joined the *Wiltshire and Gloucestershire Standard*. He also started to write articles and pamphlets on agricultural issues and local history topics, but achieved little success as a freelance until, drawing on his experience of gamekeeping and knowledge of natural history, he wrote a series of articles for the *Pall Mall Gazette*, which were reprinted as *The Gamekeeper at Home* (1878); it sold well, as did a second collection of articles from the same source, *Wildlife in a Southern County* (1879a). These two books contain many fine and vivid sketches of the countryside around his former home at Coate, and show Jefferies's keen eye for observing living creatures and the subtle workings of nature. Further books of collected articles soon followed: *The Amateur Poacher* (1879b), and *Hodge and His Masters* and *Round About a Great Estate* (1880a, b). Jefferies remains unsurpassed as a descriptive writer on the landscapes and natural history of the south of England and as a chronicler of its rural life (Keith 1965, Looker & Porteous 1966).

William Henry Hudson [1841–1922], in contrast, was born in Argentina, but travelled to England in 1869 and became a British subject in 1900. His early writings concerned the natural history of South America, but he is best known for the account of his rambles in the New Forest in *Hampshire Days* (1903), his romantic novel *Green Mansions* (1904), and his autobiographical *Far Away and Long Ago* (1918). For 18 years he lived in London in great poverty, until a book on the wildlife of Argentina's La Plata made his name (Hudson 1892). Thereafter he was acclaimed as the finest nature writer of his time. Whenever possible he travelled to other parts of the country, including Wiltshire, and began to develop an expert knowledge of British birds and the English countryside. In 1894 he was elected Chairman of the RSPB Committee (now Council). His work *A Shepherd's Life: Impressions of the South Wiltshire Downs* (1910) is the story of Caleb Bawcombe, describes life in south Wiltshire before the turn of the 20th century, and includes a chapter on the *Bird Life on the Downs*.

When Hudson died, he was buried in Broadwater Cemetery, Goring-by-Sea (West Sussex), coincidentally the final resting-place of Richard Jefferies too.

The 20th century through to the end of the 1939–45 War

By the beginning of the 20th century, bird recording was well established in Wiltshire – thanks to the efforts of several individuals, some of whom have already been mentioned. Interest was fostered by the formation of societies, wider education, and a much more available ornithological literature.

George Bathurst Hony [1894–1970] published 'Notes on the Birds of Wiltshire' in the journal *British Birds* in March 1914. This was reprinted, with minor amendments, in *WANHM* in June 1915 and formed an addendum to Smith's *The Birds of Wiltshire*. Hony listed those of Smith's records that he considered to be unsatisfactory (including the Golden-winged Woodpecker), but otherwise summarised records of additional breeding species and rare visitors. At the time he was only 21, but he wrote with authority and had already been elected a member of the British Ornithologists' Union. In 1917, in *WANHM*, he published 'A Bibliography of Wiltshire Zoology' that included a section on birds, but ornithology appears to have played no further part in his life after the 1914–18 War. He published other papers on different branches of natural history in *WANHM*, but subsequently his interests appear to have lain in farming. He was, however, also credited with valuable work in labelling and reorganising the bird collection of the WANHS.

The 'Report on the Birds of Wiltshire for 1929' was the first annual systematic list of birds published in *WANHM*. In addition to the records for that year, the current status of each species in the county was given, the first such complete review since Smith (1887). During the 19th and early 20th centuries, apart from the articles by Smith (1857–70), Morres (1878–85) and Hony (1915a), the occasional bird notes published in *WANHM* had been mostly of unusual records, particularly of scarce visitors. In contrast, the annual bird reports published for 1929 to 1934 and for 1936 (though not, unfortunately, for 1935, or 1937 onwards) were the result of a concerted effort by local ornithologists to raise the standard of recording in Wiltshire. In July 1930, Canon EH

Goddard said in his presidential address to WANHS that 'The Birds of Wiltshire have been fully dealt with in the past, and in the recently issued *Magazine* is contained the first of what it is hoped may be a series of annual reports on birds which may bring our knowledge up to the present time' and he continued by encouraging everybody to report 'anything interesting or unusual that they observe in the bird world'.

The Reverend MW Willson, editor of the 1929–32 reports, wrote in the first editorial, 'The number of contributors and the volume and general interest of the local reports are all satisfactory features of the first year of the scheme, but there are still several districts not covered by any observer'. The aim was to achieve good coverage across Wiltshire and, no doubt encouraged by the quality of the first report, the number of contributors increased from 29 in 1929 to 37 in 1934.

Meanwhile, CMR (Roy) Pitman – a 'great all-round naturalist' (Fuller 1995) – had succeeded Willson as editor of the 1933–34 and 1936 reports. Referred to as 'the county ornithologist' in the *Salisbury Times* in February 1939, he lived at Whaddon, near Salisbury, and his main study areas were the Avon valley, the woodlands from Clarendon Park to Bentley Wood, the New Forest borders, and the southern edge of Salisbury Plain. His surviving ornithological diaries, covering 39 of the 58 years from 1928 to 1986, have been of considerable value in the writing of some of the species texts in this *Birds of Wiltshire*.

Those who contributed to the inter-war bird reports included many clergy, military officers and even a viscount. (The clergy had, of course, been the driving force behind Wiltshire ornithology during the 19th century.) Two of the inaugural 1929 report's younger contributors – destined to play major roles in the development of British ornithology – were EM (Max) Nicholson and PAD (Phil) Hollom; the latter was only 17 at that time, but was later to publish several significant books on birds, not least as one of the three authors of the first European field guide (Peterson *et al* 1954 *et seq*), and was also for many years an editor of *British Birds* and of *Birds of the Western Palearctic* (*BWP*). Max Nicholson was still up at Oxford in 1929 and the previous year had organised the first National Census of Heronries – now the longest-running bird census anywhere in the world – went on in 1932 to found the British Trust for Ornithology (BTO), becoming its first honorary secretary and later chairman; after the 1939–45 War he was appointed director-general of what was then the Nature Conservancy as well as, among many other things, being a co-founder of the World Wildlife Fund (now Worldwide Fund for Nature), senior editor of *British Birds* and the first chief editor of *BWP*.

Other notable contributors to those early birds reports in *WANHM* included CW (Con) Benson (during 1931–32), later renowned in the field of tropical ornithology in, especially, Africa and the islands of the Indian Ocean; Captain (later Major-General) CB Wainwright (during 1931–36), who after the 1939–45 War became closely associated with Abberton Reservoir (Essex), where he and GA Pyman found breeding Gull-billed Terns in 1950 (*BB* 45: 337–339) and where, as a keen ringer, he concentrated especially on decoy-trapping ducks; and Ralph Whitlock (during 1934–67), a well-known writer and broadcaster on country matters at that time. It was also in 1932 that Cyril Rice began submitting records to *WANHM* and, eventually, *Hobby* – the beginning of a 45-year association, during which time he also produced particular papers on Common Redstarts, Corn Buntings and wintering Blackcaps in Wiltshire.

The threatening clouds of the late 1930s and the 1939–45 War itself temporarily suspended many ornithological activities; the 1936 bird report was the last of that first series to be published, in December 1937. The editor, Roy Pitman, was called up for wartime duties in 1939, as doubtless were many of the other contributors, and there was a gap in the published ornithological record from 1937 to 1942.

In December 1943, however, the first of two highly condensed wartime summaries of bird notes was published in *WANHM* and together these briefly covered 1943 to 1945; they were almost entirely the work of the MCNHS, and were written by Guy Peirson, who had been another of the contributors to the earliest bird reports from 1929.

Lewis Guy Peirson [1897–1957], born in Cornwall, was to have a lifetime's interest in documenting the birds of Wiltshire, and could well be described as the giant of this county's ornithology through the first half of the 20th century. He taught at Marlborough College from 1919 to 1954, was president of the Natural History Society there for 26 years and, in 1919, wrote *A Handlist of the Birds of the District [of] Marlborough and ten miles round*, which he updated in 1930 and 1939. (Subsequent *Handlists* of the Marlborough district were published by Halliday & Randolph 1955 and by Kennedy 1966.) The first chairman of the new Natural History Section of the WANHS, formed in 1946, Peirson was one of the recorders of the 'Wiltshire Bird Notes' until 1956 and, after his retirement to Devon, compiled the *Handlist of Wiltshire Birds*, which was published after his death in 1957. The lengthy obituary in the *Report of the MCNHS* amply reflected the affectionate respect given to this quiet, gentle man by his contemporaries and former students.

Another well-known Wiltshire school, Dauntsey's, at West Lavington, formed a bird club, known as the Bird Trust, in 1936. Brief annual reports appeared in *The Dauntseian* magazine until 1959, when the Bird Trust amalgamated with the school Natural History Society. During its early years, the Bird Trust participated in ornithological survey work in the West Lavington area, in the Wildfowl Trust's National Wildfowl Counts in 1955–56, and in the BTO Nightjar Survey in 1958; there was also a small ringing group, which, in 1937, ringed 201 birds of eight species (see 'Wiltshire ringing totals 1965–2005'). Since 1959, however, records appear to have become sparse.

Post-war developments

Until the end of the 1939–45 War, although bird and other natural history notes were published more or less regularly by the WANHS, the emphasis was mainly on the archaeological side of the Society's remit. In June 1947 it was reported in *WANHM* that 'During the summer of 1946 a few people, who had felt the need of a more active Natural History organisation in Wiltshire and who had already grouped themselves unofficially into a Field Club, approached the President of the Society asking if room could be made for them within the Society, as they were unwilling to form any rival organisation'. This scheme to form a separate Natural History Section (NHS) was drawn up by Ruth Barnes.

A committee was formed and Mrs Barnes, assisted by Guy Peirson, was authorised by the main committee of the WANHS to implement her ideas. By the time of its first AGM in 1947, the NHS had 110 members, over one third of whom were also full members of the WANHS. That year the annual bird reports were started in June, with the publication of the one for 1946, and thereafter were produced annually in *WANHM* until 1973 (after which WOS and *Hobby* took over the task: see below).

The county recorder in 1946 was Ruth Barnes herself; she was joined as co-recorders by Guy Peirson during 1947–56, by Geoffrey Boyle during 1955–68, by RL Vernon during 1958–61, and by Eric Ennion and Charles Bridgman during 1962–68. There were 24 contributors to the first post-war bird report for 1946 – a total that had increased to 53 by 1950 and 68 by 1960. Amongst the early contributors were 'C. J. Henty, R.A.F.' (in 1953), more usually known as Cliff Henty, then doing his National Service; Squadron-Leader Norman Orr (during 1954–56), widely travelled and a contributor to many books and journals, later a member of the Councils of the RSPB and the Society for the Promotion of Nature Reserves (now the Royal Society for Nature Conservation) and of the Council for Nature; Jack Mavrogordato (during 1957–58), a well-known falconer; and Major WM Congreve (during 1946–64), an equally well-known oologist, who provided eggs from his own collection for the photographs in PAD Hollom's *The Popular Handbook of British Birds* (1952).

Ruth Gwladys Barnes [1901–81] was born in North Wales, but it was not until the family moved to Tring (Hertfordshire), where she had access to the reservoirs and the Rothschild Museum, that her interest in matters ornithological first took root, under the guidance of Charles Oldham. Nevertheless, she was an ornithologist of repute before moving to Wiltshire. She joined the BTO in 1933, shortly after its foundation, and in the 1950s became the Trust's first regional representative for Wiltshire, a position she held for 26 years; in 1963 she was awarded the Bernard Tucker Medal in recognition of her outstanding service to BTO field investigations in the county. She was elected the first president of the Wiltshire Ornithological Society (WOS) on its formation. In his obituary of her in *Hobby* for 1981, John Buxton wrote that 'Her success was due both to her accurate knowledge of birds and to the persuasive charm which won over many others to assist in the work of recording birds in the county, where she organized censuses of Grey Herons and Mute Swans, and surveys for the Atlas of Breeding Birds [Sharrock 1976]'. It was also she who had earlier edited Guy Peirson's *Wiltshire Birds* (1959), which was published in 1959 after his death.

Eric Arnold Roberts Ennion [1900–81] was an almost exact contemporary of Ruth Barnes, and a well-known figure in British ornithology and bird art long before he retired to Wiltshire in 1961. In an introduction to *The Living Birds of Eric Ennion* (1982), John Busby described him as 'very much part of the post-war revival of interest in nature, and a much loved figure. He put into practice the concept of Field Study Centres, where people from all walks of life could come together to study nature, and he was one of the pioneers of bird observatory work. As a naturalist, he wrote books and articles for a wide public and broadcast regularly on the BBC's nature programmes. Above all, his illustrations and paintings introduced a new spirit into the portrayal of birds'. A doctor in the family practice in Cambridgeshire for 20 years, Ennion gave up medicine after the 1939–45 War to become the first warden of Flatford Mill Field Study Centre, in the heart of Constable country on the Suffolk Stour, running courses on biology and painting. Five years later, he and his wife moved to open Monks' House Field Centre near Seahouses (Northumberland) where, as director, he concentrated on birds and, in particular, migration for the next ten years.

The Ennions retired to Wiltshire in 1961, to take over the old watercress farm at Shalbourne, where, while son Hugh rebuilt the watercress beds, Eric was able to devote himself to painting and to running drawing courses and summer schools at various zoos and colleges, as well as at the Ennion home. As already noted, he was quickly enlisted by Ruth Barnes to join her and Charles Bridgman as co-recorders of the bird reports in *WANHM* from 1962 to 1968; and the illustration of a Hobby on the front cover of Buxton (1981) was reproduced from his picture entitled 'Some Wiltshire birds'. While he was still at Monks' House, he and Robert Gillmor had arranged an exhibition of contemporary bird art in Reading and that led, in 1964, to the formation of the Society of Wildlife Artists, with Eric as its first chairman. In 1979 and 1980 he was also one of the judges of the 'Bird Illustrator of the Year' competition organised by *British Birds*. He published a number of books and served on the Councils of the BTO, the RSPB and the British Ornithologists' Union, but it is for his thousands of character-catching field sketches of birds, his hundreds of highly distinctive watercolours and, to those who knew him, his enthusiasm, humour and generosity that he will long be remembered. Active to the last, he was sketching in Savernake Forest shortly before he died in February 1981.

Geoffrey Boyle was a contributor to *WANHM* and *Hobby* from 1947 right through to 1999, his output including papers on Nightingales and Grey Herons in Wiltshire, and he was the BTO Heronries Census coordinator for the county from 1981 to 1993. Charles Bridgman, another contributor to *WANHM* from 1958, was a member of the WOS Executive Committee during 1975–78 and 1979–85, and editor of *Hobby* during 1981–86, as well as writing papers for it on House Martins, Stonechats, and birds' use of operational airfields; earlier he had published an unusual paper in *British Birds* about Common Starlings and other birds nesting in aircraft (Bridgman 1962). Dr Stephanie Tyler – later widely known for her conservation work in Wales, her whole family's capture and prolonged confinement by rebels in Ethiopia and, not least, her studies of birds of mountain rivers in four continents, most notably of dippers and wagtails – also contributed to *WANHM* during 1968–72, including papers on wildfowl and one of her first on Grey Wagtails.

The surge of other new local societies in the 1950s to 1970s

The Salisbury and District Field Club, formed in 1952, had its name changed to the Salisbury and District Natural History Society in 1961. Its remit was to record the natural history within a ten-mile radius of the city. An introduction to the Field Club's first report, in 1953, was written by Ralph Whitlock. That, and subsequent annual reports, contained detailed notes on bird observations. One of the Field Club's more unusual surveys was of birds roosting on Salisbury's street lamps (1960 Report). The newly named Society continued to produce annual bird notes, now as systematic lists and including information on status. The 1961 report included a summary of 276 birds ringed by its members. Among its more unusual records were the first pair of Black Redstarts found breeding in the county, at Bulford in 1975, and the identification of a Nutcracker at Wilton in 1985, but the latter has never been submitted to the Wiltshire Records Panel or the *British Birds* Rarities Committee. In 1980, it reported that Cirl Buntings were seen regularly at two sites at Winterslow, these presumably being the January and February records mentioned on page 714.

In 1964, Julian Rolls, Richard Lee and Rod Faulkner formed 'The Bustards', the North Wiltshire Ornithological Group; it survived for two years, did a considerable amount of ringing and produced two annual bulletins that contained much of interest on rare and unusual visitors, seasonal movements and migration in the north of the county. Two records that aroused particular interest at the time were a long-staying Common Bittern at Corsham Lake – seen for 15 weeks to 8 April 1964 – and the breeding of a pair of Curlews at Yatton Keynell in the same year.

During the 1960s and 1970s, several other natural history societies were formed in the county. Those at Box, Tisbury and Sedgehill did not issue newsletters or bulletins, but the Westbury Naturalists' Society still circulates an annual report to its members, including lists of the birds recorded in the Westbury area. RSPB groups in Salisbury and Swindon also produced reports of bird observations made at their field meetings throughout the year.

The Dorcan School Ornithological Society at Swindon was formed in 1972 under the inspired leadership of Humphrey Dobinson, earlier a founder of the Cape Clear Observatory (Co Cork). It published seven cyclostyled reports packed with observations on birds of the area, surveys, censuses, nestboxes, ringing and migration. Perhaps the single most noteworthy record was Wiltshire's last known nesting of Red-backed Shrikes: three eggs were laid near the school in 1977, but later the eggs disappeared. After 1980 little was heard of the Society, but the schoolboys inspired by Dobinson in that period had included Nigel Pleass (later a member of the executive committee of WOS), David Paynter (now warden of the Wildfowl & Wetland Trust's Slimbridge reserve) and David Walker (now warden of Dungeness Bird Observatory).

Bird reports continued to be published in *WANHM* until 1974, when 'discussions took place amongst a few Wiltshire ornithologists about the feasibility of forming an ornithological society to cover the whole county' (Govett 1994). The Wiltshire Ornithological Society (WOS) was founded on 30 November 1974, and an inaugural public meeting held at Lackham College of Agriculture, under the chairmanship of Peter Walters, on 18 January 1975. Ruth Barnes was elected president; Geoff Webber became county recorder and Rob Turner a co-opted member of the committee. The membership had grown to about 130 by February 1975 and to some 230 by May. By the end of the year the first quarterly newsletter, *WOS News*, produced by John Govett, and the first edition of the annual report, *Hobby*, edited by Beatrice Gillam, were sent to members. In 1975 Geoff Webber received nearly 20 per cent more records than in 1974, largely as a result of the formation of WOS and its rapidly increasing membership.

Table 7 lists the honorary officers and bird report editors of WOS. Especially noteworthy for their long service to the society are Anna Grayson (secretary 1978–97), John Pollard (treasurer 1977–2000), and Rob Turner (co-opted to the executive committee in 1975, a full member of that committee since 1977, and county recorder since 1983).

Two remarkable Wiltshire stalwarts in the second half of the 20th century

Geoffrey Lawrence (Geoff) Webber [1929–2005] started work at the age of 14 with the Great Western Railway, became an apprentice and, after National Service in the RAF, returned there to remain associated with GWR and its successors for the rest of his working life, until he took early retirement in 1988. Geoff was a founder member of WOS and its first county recorder, as well as being active in WANHS for many years before that. His first contributions to Wiltshire ornithology, published in the 'Wiltshire Bird Notes for 1953' in *WANHM*, included a report of a pair of Red-backed Shrikes nesting near Swindon and the county's first record of Lapland Buntings at Swindon STW.

This last site played a big part in Geoff's history, for it was here, with Dennis Felstead who trained him as a ringer, that Geoff caught Wiltshire's first Aquatic Warbler in 1958 and followed that with discovering the county's first Broad-billed Sandpiper (1962), Solitary Sandpiper (1965), Temminck's Stint (1970) and Long-billed Dowitcher (1974), the last found with his son Max, by then also a keen birder. Coate Water was another regular haunt where Geoff's diligence and field skills resulted in two more 'firsts' for the county – Barred Warbler (1980) and Purple Heron (1981). His final addition to the Wiltshire list was a Whiskered Tern that he and Ken Beint discovered at CWP in 2002. The Solitary Sandpiper and a Savi's Warbler at Coate Water in 1965 were also noteworthy in that Geoff added both – the former with the aid of Rod Faulkner and Julian Rolls – to the list of birds ringed in Britain. He remained an enthusiastic ringer – later joined by Max – until failing eyesight forced him to stop.

Geoff's contribution to the written record was considerable. In 1960 his first paper published in *WANHM* reported on an enquiry into the status of Red-backed Shrikes in the county. In 1965 he wrote the first 'Wiltshire Ringing Report', in 1968 was one of the editors of the 'Wiltshire Bird Notes' in *WANHM* and from 1969 became the sole county recorder. He updated Peirson (1959) with a *Supplement to "Wiltshire Birds"* (1968) and later wrote the systematic list for Buxton's *Birds of Wiltshire* (1981). The latter was really the first major account of the county's avifauna to be published since AC Smith's *The Birds of Wiltshire* (1887) almost a century earlier. In 1983 Geoff handed over the reins of the county recordership to Rob Turner, who thereafter compiled the bird reports quarterly for *WOS News* and annually for *Hobby*.

Edward John Mawby Buxton [1912–89] was born at Bramhall, Cheshire, and educated at Malvern and New College, Oxford, where he took Greats, wrote poetry and developed

Table 7. Honorary officers of the Wiltshire Ornithological Society and editors of *Hobby* 1975–2006

Year	President	Chairman	Secretary	Treasurer	Recorder	*Hobby* editor
1975	RG Barnes	P Walters	JR Govett	GW Stone	GL Webber	B Gillam
1976	RG Barnes	P Walters	JR Govett	GW Stone	GL Webber	B Gillam
1977	RG Barnes	GW Stone	JR Govett	JD Pollard	GL Webber	B Gillam
1978	RG Barnes	GW Stone	AJ Grayson	JD Pollard	GL Webber	B Gillam
1979	RG Barnes	EL Sawyer	AJ Grayson	JD Pollard	GL Webber	B Gillam
1980	RG Barnes	EL Sawyer	AJ Grayson	JD Pollard	GL Webber	B Gillam
1981	–	EL Sawyer	AJ Grayson	JD Pollard	GL Webber	CJ Bridgman
1982	EJM Buxton	GNS Robertson	AJ Grayson	JD Pollard	GL Webber	CJ Bridgman
1983	EJM Buxton	GNS Robertson	AJ Grayson	JD Pollard	R Turner	CJ Bridgman
1984	EJM Buxton	GNS Robertson	AJ Grayson	JD Pollard	R Turner	CJ Bridgman
1985	EJM Buxton	JR Govett	AJ Grayson	JD Pollard	R Turner	CJ Bridgman
1986	EJM Buxton	JR Govett	AJ Grayson	JD Pollard	R Turner	GW Stone
1987	–	JR Govett	AJ Grayson	JD Pollard	R Turner	GW Stone
1988	–	GNS Robertson	AJ Grayson	JD Pollard	R Turner	GW Stone
1989	–	JHF Brown	AJ Grayson	JD Pollard	R Turner	SM Palmer
1990	–	JHF Brown	AJ Grayson	JD Pollard	R Turner	SM Palmer
1991	–	JHF Brown	AJ Grayson	JD Pollard	R Turner	SM Palmer
1992	–	GW Stone	AJ Grayson	JD Pollard	R Turner	PE Castle
1993	–	JHF Brown	AJ Grayson	JD Pollard	R Turner	PE Castle
1994	–	JHF Brown	AJ Grayson	JD Pollard	R Turner	PE Castle
1995	–	JHF Brown	AJ Grayson	JD Pollard	R Turner	PE Castle
1996	–	PE Castle	AJ Grayson	JD Pollard	R Turner	PE Castle
1997	–	PE Castle	LH Cady	JD Pollard	R Turner	PA Cranswick
1998	–	PE Castle	LH Cady	JD Pollard	R Turner	PA Cranswick
1999	–	J Austin	LH Cady	JD Pollard	R Turner	PA Cranswick
2000	–	J Austin	LH Cady	CJ Ward	R Turner	PA Cranswick
2001	–	J Austin	M Nuttall	CJ Ward	R Turner	PA Cranswick
2002	–	PE Castle	M Nuttall	CJ Ward	R Turner	PA Cranswick
2003	–	PE Castle	PA Deacon	R Payne	R Turner	RM Quantrill
2004	–	PE Castle	PA Deacon	R Payne	R Turner	RM Quantrill
2005	–	RM Quantrill	PA Deacon	R Payne	R Turner	RM Quantrill
2006	IJ Ferguson-Lees	RM Quantrill	PA Deacon	R Payne	R Turner	PE Castle

an interest in archaeology. He had begun an intense interest in birds while at Malvern and started to watch nests from hides, keeping detailed notes of his observations. In 1939 he married Marjorie Lockley, the sister of Ronald Lockley who had founded the first British bird observatory, on the island of Skokholm (Pembrokeshire), in 1933 (Lockley 1935). That was the beginning of his involvement with bird observatories and serious ornithology. Shortly after the outbreak of the 1939–45 War, he joined the army, where his knowledge of Norwegian, gained from his love of the Norse sagas, saw him attached to what was to become No 1 Commando. This unit was engaged in the desperate but unsuccessful defence of Norway, and capture resigned him to German prison camps for the remainder of hostilities. During this long and difficult incarceration he began to make detailed observations of the birds he saw, encouraging fellow prisoners to do likewise.

By what now seems to be an incredible coincidence, several keen ornithologists – including John Barrett, Peter Conder and George Waterston, all later to become distinguished national figures, especially in the conservation field – found themselves together with Buxton at various times in different camps. All made detailed studies – in particular in the camp at Eichstätt, in the narrow Altmühl valley of Bavaria – which, after the war, resulted in a number of significant publications, not least Buxton's beautifully written monograph, *The Redstart* (1950), which was based largely on the data he had amassed there. It is still, arguably, among the most enjoyable of species monographs. Buxton was also involved in one of the war's most bizarre examples of scientific co-operation; whilst incarcerated, he managed to contact Professor Dr Erwin Stresemann, long one of Germany's leading ornithologists and editor of *Journal für Ornithologie*, at the Berlin Museum. Stresemann sent him rings and useful literature, including a copy of the scarce first volume of Niethammer's *Handbuch der Deutschen Vogelkunde*, which now resides in the Alexander Library at the Edward Grey Institute in Oxford. But Buxton's wartime writings were not confined to matters ornithological. A series of poems, written in the camps, came to the attention of Macmillan's chief literary advisor. His opinion, that they constituted 'the best volume of verse yet written under the pressure of war', persuaded Macmillan to publish them as *Such Liberty* (1944).

On returning to England after the war, Buxton was recruited to succeed Lord David Cecil as lecturer in English Literature at New College, Oxford, in 1946, and was appointed Emeritus Fellow in 1949. In 1946 he was a driving force in the establishment of the Bird Observatories Committee and served on the BTO's Ringing Committee. He co-wrote *Island of Skomer* with his brother-in-law (Buxton & Lockley 1950), which led to the fuller development of Skokholm as an observatory. He was also the man who, in 1954, introduced the mist-net to Great Britain, revolutionising the ringing movement (see 'A brief history of ringing in Wiltshire' below).

His professional literary output continued with several scholarly publications, but he never again published any poetry, his wartime experiences seemingly having killed that part of his imaginative creativity. When he left Oxford in 1955, Buxton and his wife made their home at Cole Park, Malmesbury, and he was involved in the formation of the Wiltshire Trust for Nature Conservation. In 1977, shortly after the death of his wife, he left the lovely house at Malmesbury and settled in East Tytherton. He retired from his readership at Oxford in 1979, but continued the association with his college. In 1980 he edited *The Birds of Wiltshire* (1981) and was voted president of WOS the following year. He continued to contribute occasional pieces for ornithological journals, the last to *Ibis* on House Martins in 1986. He died on 11 December 1989, five days before his 77th birthday. Perhaps this remarkable man should always be remembered as a 'poet, scholar and ornithologist', as he was described in his obituary in *The Times*. A memorial service in his honour was held at St Cross, Oxford, on 3 March 1990.

Survey work by WOS members through to the early 1990s

The first survey initiated by WOS in 1974 lasted for two breeding seasons; the subject was the distribution and the numbers of nests of House Martins in Wiltshire, the results being published in *Hobby* for 1977. Subsequently, in addition to the long-standing annual Heronries Census, WOS members took part in a number of other surveys, several of them national ones organised by the BTO, and local results of these were published in *Hobby*: National Rook Survey (1975), National Nightingale Survey (1976), Mute Swan Survey (1978), Wiltshire Barn Owl Survey (1977–79), Nightingale Survey in Wiltshire (1980), Roding Woodcock Survey (1984) and Tree Sparrow Survey (1993). Many WOS members worked 10-km squares for both the *1981–84 Winter Atlas* and the *1988–91* Atlas, and in ongoing national surveys of Lapwings, Waterways, Garden Birds, Sky Larks, and Birds and Organic Farming. In addition to these countywide and national surveys, a number of individual Common Birds Censuses and comparable local studies have been published in *Hobby*, including those by Gillam (1984, 1996), Palmer (1987, 1992), Griffiths (1988), Crease (1989), Winter (1991), Green (2000), Austin (2002) and Rock (2004, 2005). In 1991, *Wiltshire Birds*, edited by Stephen Palmer, was issued as an update of Buxton's *The Birds of Wiltshire* (1981). What it is hoped is a complete list of all publications concerned primarily or solely with Wiltshire's birds up to 2005 has been built into the Bibliography on pages 808–839, where all such items are asterisked.

All of this brings the recent history up to the early 1990s, and much of what has happened subsequently will be found in this book.

Salisbury Plain and SPTA

Land on Salisbury Plain for military training was first purchased in 1897, and within five years a total of 17,600 ha was in the hands of the then War Office. This included live firing areas, public access to which was prohibited. Subsequent purchases up to and after the 1939–45 War brought the total to over 38,000 ha which – together with airfields, including Boscombe Down – make up about one third of the whole Plain. Some of this land is farmed under agricultural tenancy agreements, and the 16,200 ha now reserved exclusively for military use are grazed under special licence.

For many years, bird records from the military areas of the Plain were sparse or non-existent. In the 1970s, three MoD Conservation Groups were formed – Imber (West), Larkhill & Westdown (Centre) and Bulford (East) – the members of which include both military and civilian, among them several WOS members. The latter provide ornithological expertise and continuity of observation not possible for the military because of the transitory nature of many postings. With the formation of these groups came the issuing of access permits for approved civilians to enter many of the previously proscribed areas. This brought a considerable increase in records of such species as Quail, Hen Harrier, Merlin, Stone-curlew, Short-eared Owl, Whinchat and Stonechat. Checklists of the birds of Imber and Larkhill ranges have been produced, the former in 1977 and 1980 by the Imber Conservation Group, and the latter in 1971 by Colonel EDV Prendergast. These lists briefly describe the status at the time of all the species that have been found on those two ranges. Since 1977 the MoD Conservation Groups have monitored Hen Harrier winter roosts, and since 1983 these have formed part of the Hawk & Owl Trust's national survey (Turner 1978, Howells 1986a, b, Castle 1993, Castle & Clarke 1995). John Pollard was one of the stalwarts of the monitoring of the Hen Harrier roost, regularly watching in all weather conditions from 1978 to 2000. The MoD publishes an annual conservation magazine, *Sanctuary*, which includes articles on the birds of its Wiltshire Estates. In 2000 and 2005 the Defence Estates and the RSPB carried out breeding bird surveys of SPTA (Stanbury *et al* 2000, 2005). Porton Down, purchased by the then War Office in 1916, has a chalk grassland SSSI covering over 1500 ha and a conservation group with an active bird subgroup, whose members have carried out MoD bird counts since 1993, a CBC since 1994, and annual censuses of selected species; a newsletter is produced annually.

A brief history of ringing in Wiltshire

In 1767 'a piece of copper' bearing a man's initials and the year was attached to the leg of a 'Crane' (which may or may not have been a Grey Heron) that had been downed by a trained hawk in the Salisbury area; the bird was then shot by the same man 16 years later. This was possibly the first instance of 'ringing' in Great Britain, but human curiosity subsequently led to various attempts at marking birds to determine their movements, though it was not until the last years of the 19th century, in Denmark, that modern bird-ringing – attaching a lightweight aluminium ring stamped with a unique number and a return address to a bird's leg – was pioneered. Two British ringing schemes were set up almost simultaneously in 1909: in London by HF Witherby and in Aberdeen by Dr (later Sir) A Landsborough Thomson. Although ringing at Aberdeen was terminated – along with much else – by the 1914–18 War, the London scheme continued unbroken under Witherby's guidance until June 1937, when responsibility was passed to the newly formed BTO. (For recent reviews of the development of ringing in Great Britain, see Clark & Wernham 2002, Wallace 2004.)

Few data on ringing before 1965 are now easily accessible. In the early years, however, of what Witherby called 'the "British Birds" Marking Scheme', ringers were sufficiently few in number for those who had marked 20 or more in any one year to be named in his annual report in *BB* and for most recoveries to be listed individually. Those lists showed that Mr A Bankes, of Salisbury, was the sole ringer active enough in Wiltshire then to be generating recoveries. Indeed, he seems likely to have been the one and only ringer in the county at that time. During 1909–14 he marked an annual average of 141 birds: his totals built up from 34 in the very first year of the scheme to a peak of 320 in 1912, which put him at 10th in the table of British ringers that year, just missing out on a personal mention in the accompanying text. Seven recoveries of his during 1910–17 were published: four of them – a Dunnock, a Robin, a Blue Tit and a Common Starling – were found at the place of ringing (the first two retrapped and released again by Bankes) within four to eight months. The other three recoveries all involved Lapwings ringed as 'nestlings' in different years: the first was found (presumably dead) near Salisbury by F Martin 19 months later and the other two, ringed in May 1912 and June 1913, were recovered at Lympstone (Devon) in January 1917 and near Crozen (France) in January 1914 respectively. (In view of the low numbers of birds being ringed in those days, it was remarkable to have had as many as three Lapwing returns, including a foreign one, because the recovery rate for this species over the 95 years to 2004 has been only 1·5 per cent.) Bankes's name did not appear in the ringing lists after the 1914–18 War, so perhaps he was a casualty of that terrible conflict.

The next published mention of ringing in Wiltshire was in 1937, when Dauntsey's School ringed 201 birds of eight species (see above), and the next after that not until 1949, when a brood of Montagu's Harriers was found to have been ringed by a now unknown person (*WANHM*). It is very possible that others were ringing birds in Wiltshire under Witherby's scheme long before either of those years, and between them, but old records before computerisation are very difficult and expensive to access now. In 1955 John Buxton, then a member of the BTO Ringing Committee and a prime mover in this field of recording, moved to Wiltshire and, confining his ringing activities to his garden, reached the milestone of 5000 on 14 August 1975 when he trapped 'a "new" species, my fifty-ninth, a male Sparrow Hawk' (Buxton 1976). His total did not include any Collared Doves, which 'did not arrive [in Wiltshire] till 1967', but did include what is still the only Hawfinch to have been ringed in the county. It was Buxton, indeed, who first introduced Japanese mist-nets to Great Britain; he had been shown them by Dr A Schifferli, of the ornithological station at Sempach (Switzerland), ordered a gross and, with the assistance of Anthony le Sueur of

Jersey, demonstrated their use by throwing his handkerchief several times into a (fairly small) mist-net at the Bird Observatories Conference in Oxford in January 1956.

In such a brief outline as this, it is impossible to name everyone who has made a contribution to ringing in Wiltshire, but – with apologies to those not mentioned – a few examples are chosen to illustrate the activities of the county's ringers. Dennis Felstead (active during 1957–59) was another local pioneer. Geoff Webber, trained by Felstead in 1959 and still actively ringing until 1983, added to the list of species ringed in Great Britain when he netted a Savi's Warbler at Coate Water in May 1965 and, with Julian Rolls (active 1964 to date), a Solitary Sandpiper at Swindon STW in September 1966. Rolls, who like Webber has made a sustained contribution to local ornithology, wrote a useful account of ringing in the inaugural edition of *Hobby* (Rolls 1975a).

Reg Kersley was another notable personality, in whose obituary (*Hobby* 21: 3) Rob Turner wrote, 'His efforts to encourage participation by others in his love and interest in birdlife led him to organise not only ringing sessions in Wiltshire and at Chew Lake but also with his wife Val, the much enjoyed birding weekends at Portland. He was also instrumental [in 1988] in setting up the West Wilts Ringing Group [WWRG]'. Another of Kersley's initiatives was to organise a two-year ringing-based study of Greenfinches at Chippenham (Kersley & Marsh 1983). The other founders of the WWRG were Rob Turner, Tony Rowe, Richard Pike and Ian Grier; the group now also includes Mike Hamzij (currently the county's ringing recorder), Graham Deacon and Matt Prior, the last two of whom are making important contributions, by colour-ringing, to the study of two species that are of particular conservation concern, Tree Sparrow and Willow Tit. WWRG members have also added three rare buntings to the Wiltshire list: an Ortolan in 1986, a Little in 1989 and a Rustic in 2004. The Bulford Ornithological Group and, in particular, Rob Hayden have been ringing Kestrels and owls in nestboxes they have actively provided on the eastern section of SPTA since 1992, and Tony Crease was ringing in that area during 1987–89.

Although individual ringers, such as Andrew Carter, have also ploughed lone but productive furrows on their local patches, the total number active in the county at any one time remained roughly the same over the last 40 years of the 20th century: 12 in the early 1960s (GL Webber) and 14 in both 1975 (Rolls 1975a) and 2000. In the last of those years, however, the RSPB – by then making a considerable contribution to the monitoring and protection of Stone-curlews in Wiltshire and elsewhere in southern England – was an additional force. Finally, Major Nigel Lewis must be applauded for his sterling work since the mid 1980s in providing hundreds of nestboxes for owls and raptors on Salisbury Plain, and elsewhere in southern Wiltshire, most notably for Kestrels and Barn Owls (see pages 288 and 466), though his boxes also attract a number of pairs of Tawny and Little Owls; by the end of the millennium, too, he was putting up a few experimental nest-baskets for Hobbies (which most often lay in empty Carrion Crow nests).

From 1965 (the first year for which records are currently available from the BTO), over 164,000 birds of 133 species had been ringed in the county by the end of the millennium and more than 226,000 of 146 species by the end of 2005, a notable achievement of which Wiltshire's ringers can feel justifiably proud (see 'Wiltshire ringing totals 1965–2005').

Changes in Wiltshire's birdlife

Paul Castle

Although *Birds of Wiltshire* provides the most comprehensive picture of the county's birds to date, it can only be a snapshot of the situation as it appeared at the end of the second millennium. Yet anyone who has watched birds for a few years knows that neither the distribution nor the abundance of any species is constant. This chapter aims to highlight some of the more significant changes that have taken place in Wiltshire's birdlife, particularly over the last two centuries. No fewer than 38 species have been found nesting for the first time since 1800, but some of those must be considered unusual or unlikely to be repeated with any regularity. By contrast, eight breeding species became extinct during the 19th century and, although five of those have nested again in the 20th century, a further six have been lost since the 1939–45 War. Currently, 116 species breed regularly in Wiltshire and a further 30 have done so in the past or are irregular nesters.

Apart from a few early writings (see 'Wiltshire's ornithological history'), our knowledge of the county's birds before the 19th century is limited largely to archaeological remains and interpretation of place-names (see 'Wiltshire's early birds'), but these may be sufficient to identify the historical avifauna, as has been done for some other counties. For example, the archaeological record of the neighbouring Somerset Levels is particularly rich, indicating the presence of breeding Cormorants in the Bronze Age and Dalmatian Pelicans in the Iron Age (Stewart 2004). Whilst wetlands in Wiltshire would have been far less extensive, archaeological and place-name records of White-tailed Fish-eagles and Cranes suggest that these were probably regular visitors in past millennia, if not breeding species along with Greylag Geese in the natural wildwoods and swamps of the valleys of the Bristol and Salisbury Avons and the Thames. Human factors – specifically, hunting, woodland clearance and wetland drainage – are likely to have brought about the demise of these and other species before recorded history. The chalk downlands were largely cleared of trees between 4500 and 1500 BC as humans first created grasslands and then agricultural land (Rackham 1986), and the original woodland avifauna would gradually have been replaced by birds of steppe country, such as gamebirds, harriers, larks and pipits.

From the late 18th century, written ornithological accounts help us to piece together a more comprehensive account of these changes (summarised in the time-line on page 97). As firearms became more accurate and more widely available from the 18th century onwards, the indigenous gamebirds started to decline. The most impressive denizens of the downs were the Great Bustards and hunting pressure hastened their extinction as breeders early in the 19th century (the last recorded nest was in 1801). Black Grouse – gamebirds of heaths and forest edges – suffered a similar fate about 1820, except in the extreme southeast where some continued to be shot for another 30 years or so. In contrast, Grey Partridges were increasing as a result of changing farming practices, and they and introduced gamebirds benefited from the game preservation ethos of the 19th century, which was accompanied by the persecution of many species of supposed 'vermin'. This persecution eventually saw the demise of all larger raptors in Wiltshire. Hen Harriers became extinct as breeders early in the 19th century, Red Kites followed suit by 1840, and Common Buzzards by about 1850, and Montagu's Harriers had declined from being regular to only occasional breeders by the 1880s (Smith 1887); it is even possible that Honey-buzzards also fell into this category. Peregrines apparently ceased to breed earlier in the 19th century – although they were probably always scarce and there are upwards of ten records of their laying eggs and sometimes raising young on Salisbury Cathedral between the 1860s and early 1950s. Ravens, although not raptors of course, were similarly persecuted by gamekeepers and the last recorded nesting was also in the 1880s.

But there were other human pressures too. River-keepers persecuted Grey Herons and Kingfishers. Increasing drainage of wetlands for cultivation probably resulted in the loss of breeding Spotted Crakes and Water Rails in the late 19th and early 20th centuries respectively (*1875–1900 Atlas*). Many small passerines were commonly trapped for food and the cage-bird trade, or destroyed as 'pests'. At this same time, too, the late Victorian and Edwardian mania for collecting eggs and stuffed birds seriously affected some rarer and decreasing populations. Despite this background of decline, two species did colonise Wiltshire in the late 19th century: Curlews were first recorded nesting in 1876, and Dippers in 1897. Non-native birds were also introduced, usually for sport or embellishment: Red-legged Partridges were released from around 1830 (Pheasants had been imported since at least medieval times) and Little Owls, first successfully introduced into Great Britain in Northamptonshire in 1889 and in Kent in 1896, colonised Wiltshire in 1915.

Probably, however, the greatest human impact in recent times has been in the broad-scale changes to habitats through agriculture. Shrubb (2003) wrote, 'Major periods of recession in agriculture occurred between 1815 and about 1840 and between the late 1870s and about 1900. There was some recovery during the first decades of the twentieth century, particularly under the stimulus of the 1914–18 War, but it was insufficient to reverse the trends set after about 1875, and there was a major slump from 1921 to 1939. It is important to realise that these periods of recession primarily affected the arable regions of the south and east'. Such habitat change will undoubtedly have affected the abundance, if not distribution, of many of the more widespread and common species of open landscapes.

With the enclosure of the commons, the 19th century saw a major loss of semi-natural grassland. Then followed a decrease in tillage and an expansion of grassland, mainly in arable districts, such as much of Wiltshire, during the periods of agricultural recession. After 1945, farming spread, thanks to extensive government support, grants being available for land drainage and for ploughing old grassland, while mixed farming declined and both arable and livestock farming became more intensive. Habitat changes, especially the loss of old grasslands, have been implicated in the extinction of four species in the 20th century. Wrynecks, already scarce in 19th century Wiltshire, were last recorded nesting in 1950, and Corncrakes soon afterwards in 1952. Two and a half decades later, in 1977 and 1978 respectively, came the last known reports of breeding Red-backed Shrikes and Cirl Buntings. These four species, once much more widespread in at least southern England, have now all but disappeared from Great Britain, apart from Corncrakes in the Hebrides and Cirl Buntings in Devon. Whilst Corncrakes declined because meadows were 'improved', which resulted in earlier hay crops and the loss of marsh vegetation, such as clumps of yellow iris, the other three all depended on abundant insects that were greatly reduced in numbers by more intensive agriculture and the use of pesticides (*eg* Peakall 1962, Evans 1997).

There were some 6000 to 8000 ha of water meadows in Wiltshire at the end of the 18th century (Davis 1794); these were an intensively managed grass monoculture and therefore probably not significant for breeding waterbirds, but their use had started to decline from about 1840 (Sheail 1971) and during the 20th century became important habitats for nesting birds as the old drainage channels silted and 'weeds', such as rushes, were allowed to invade the grassland. The suitability of old water meadows for nesting birds was short-lived, however, as drainage and excessive water abstraction led to their drying out. Three species that favour open riparian wetlands increased during the 20th century only to decrease again. Common Redshanks began to colonise old water meadows in 1907 and spread until the 1970s, but thereafter declined almost to extinction in the 1990s. Similarly, Common Snipes rarely bred in Wiltshire in the 19th century, but from a single nest in

1909 had become 'A fairly common resident' by 1929 (*WANHM*), only to decrease again from 1949; their numbers fell even more rapidly during the 1980s and 1990s. Likewise favouring the old water meadows frequented by those two waders, Common Teals were occasional nesters in the 19th century and from 1936 to 1969, but their breeding too was last proved in 1976. Another and very different bird associated with rivers, especially in osier beds with nettles or meadowsweet, the Marsh Warbler – very much on the edge of its range in Great Britain – also nested sporadically in small numbers from 1900 until 1983, though only singletons have been recorded a mere five times since then and with no indication of any taking up residence.

As the 20th century progressed, however, more species were gained than lost. The creation of estate lakes and canal-feeder reservoirs in the 18th and 19th centuries, and in Wiltshire especially the gravel pits in the 20th, provided new opportunities for colonisation. Assorted aquatic habitats – from the bare gravel of new pits to mature flooded lakes and silt-beds colonised by reeds – encouraged a range of waterbirds to breed. In Great Britain as a whole, Great Crested Grebes were originally hunted almost to extinction for their skins and plumes, but protection afforded by legislation introduced in the 1870s allowed these handsome birds to recover and exploit the new habitats, colonising Wiltshire in about 1912. Tufted Ducks first bred in the county in 1926 and subsequently extended to still waters and flowing rivers alike, their national increase being fuelled by the spread of freshwater mussels.

The newly available wetland habitats at CWP and elsewhere – including the provision by WOS of floating rafts for nesting terns and gulls – are particularly important for many of the other species that have colonised Wiltshire in recent decades; the CWP lakes also act as magnets for migrant waterbirds on passage, in particular waders such as Greenshanks that are now regularly recorded only because of the extensive wetlands there. Natural increases in ranges accounted for the county's colonisation by Common Pochard in 1962, Little Ringed Plover in 1970, Common Tern in 1979, Water Rail in 1982, Ringed Plover in 1989, Common Shelduck in 1990, and Black-headed Gull in 1994. Shovelers have been proved to nest just twice, in 1946 and 1994, and Common Sandpipers and Cormorants once only, in 1980 and 1994 respectively; roosting Cormorants had increased steadily after being afforded protection nationally in 1981. Oystercatchers bred for the first time in 2002, though it remains to be seen whether they become regular breeders; and Garganeys for the first time in 2003, on a farm pond.

The colonisation of the county by several other wildfowl emanated from deliberate releases and escapes from collections. Introductions and reintroductions nationally were responsible for the spread of both Canada and Greylag Geese, which started nesting in Wiltshire in 1968 and 1976 respectively, and also Red-crested Pochards from 1976, Ruddy Ducks from 1977, and Mandarins from 1986, while the spread of Gadwalls, first recorded breeding in the county in 1984, was a combination of both a natural increase and introductions.

Although habitats have a great influence on bird populations, some of the most exciting changes in the past 20 years have resulted from reduced persecution. A succession of wild bird protection acts, a decline in gamekeeping during the 1914–18 and 1939–45 Wars, the withdrawal of pesticides (most notably DDT in 1984), and a reduction in the use of poison baits have resulted in Wiltshire skies once again being graced with the presence of a wider variety of raptors: Honey-buzzards were regular from at least the early 1960s, albeit in very small numbers; a few pairs of Montagu's Harriers re-established themselves from the 1930s to early 1950s and then again from the 1980s after an intervening decline; and Hobbies, perhaps benefiting from the increased availability of dragonflies and damselflies around gravel pits (Prince & Clarke 1993) spread from the 1970s. First re-established in the 1930s, Common Buzzards extended their Wiltshire range dramatically during the 1980s and 1990s. Ravens (although not raptors) and Peregrines then followed their eastwards spread, and became firmly re-established from 1994 and 1995 respectively (although, as already noted, the latter had bred intermittently on Salisbury Cathedral). Escapes or illegal releases resulted in Goshawks breeding in 1979 and then annually from 1999, while a reintroduction programme in the Chilterns saw the re-establishment of Red Kites in Wiltshire from 2000. Hen Harriers nested in 2003 – against a background of increasing winter numbers that reached a highest-ever total of 23 during 2005/06.

Several species of gulls have also shown marked increases in the county. The availability of human waste, especially at landfill sites, has been a key factor encouraging Lesser Black-backed and Herring Gulls to colonise, from 1984 and 1995 respectively. Nesting on urban rooftops of large factories, part of a growing trend nationally, these gulls spread eastwards into Wiltshire from the Severn Estuary. Lesser Black-backed Gulls, in particular, have also increased nationally as wintering birds, and large flocks now roost at CWP. Mediterranean Gulls, extreme rarities in Wiltshire until 1992, became annual passage migrants in small numbers from the 1990s.

Several species have colonised the county as a result of the natural expansion of continental populations during the 20th century. Collared Doves spread dramatically northwards across Europe from the southern Balkans during the early 20th century, arrived in eastern England in the 1950s, first nested in Wiltshire in 1962 and increased quickly everywhere. Black Redstarts have been known to breed in the county on only five occasions – the first record in 1975 – having colonised parts of England in the 1920s (and particularly London bomb sites in the 1939–45 War) after spreading north on the Continent. Firecrests, which seem to favour open mixed woodland with exotic conifers, were first found breeding in Hampshire in the 1960s, spread to other counties in the 1970s, and established themselves in Wiltshire from 1983. After expanding north from the Mediterranean, Cetti's Warblers began to appear in southern England in the early 1960s, were first proved to breed in England in 1972 and colonised Wiltshire from 1987; this species, which is very vulnerable to cold weather, has probably benefited from the succession of milder winters since the 1980s, perhaps a consequence of global warming. More regular in the past, Dartford Warblers – the only other resident warblers – and Wood Larks have both bred sporadically, but as overspills from buoyant populations in Hampshire.

Global warming may also be implicated in the rapid spread of Little Egrets which, after becoming increasingly frequent wanderers to southern England in the 1980s, first bred in Dorset in 1996 and subsequently in several other counties, colonising Wiltshire in 2003. It has been suggested that their spread may simply be the reoccupation of an historic range, made possible by reduced persecution (Bourne 2003) (but see page 251); they were certainly widely killed for their plumes in former times.

Taking advantage of the new habitat created by conifer plantations, Crossbills and Siskins were first noted breeding in Wiltshire in 1932 and 1987 respectively, though both species have bred only sporadically since; the former is well known for widespread breeding in the UK after eruptions from Fenno-Scandia. Colonists from western oakwoods, Pied Flycatchers bred in 1931 and in various subsequent years, particularly in the 1990s, but they too remain irregular. More characteristic of upland moors, Short-eared Owls nested in 1964, 1999, 2000 and 2005, and, after inadequately supported claims in the early 1970s (page 294), Merlins were proved breeding in 2005.

Against these increases, populations of farmland birds have been in free-fall since the 1970s, with significant decreases in, for example, numbers of Grey Partridges, Lapwings, Turtle Doves and Sky Larks. Changes in agricultural operations, especially the switch to autumn-sown cereals and the increased use of chemicals, as well as the loss of weedy marginal areas, are largely to blame. Despite this, Wiltshire still holds important populations of many farmland birds, in part because the county lies on the interface between pastoral southwest England and the predominantly agricultural land to the east –

providing a mix of habitats essential to these species' well-being – and conservation action is now stabilising or even increasing numbers of Stone-curlews and Tree Sparrows.

The 1990s also witnessed significant decreases for certain woodland birds: Lesser Redpolls were last proved to breed in Wiltshire in 1990, and Lesser Spotted Woodpeckers, Common Redstarts, Wood Warblers and Willow Tits are all greatly reduced in both numbers and range within the county. Overgrazing of woodland by burgeoning deer populations may be a contributory factor, as well as a reduction in the availability of dead timber (which is valuable for essential insect foods and, in the case of the Willow Tit, small rotten boughs or stumps are important as sites for excavating nest-holes). Much woodland is no longer managed – especially by coppicing – and this has resulted in dense stands of trees rather than the open structure favoured by such species as Common Redstarts or the young coppices frequented by Nightingales.

Widespread in southern England during the 19th century, Wheatears now nest only very occasionally in the county, most recently in 1991, 2000 and 2005; like Wood Larks, they used to breed on chalk downland heavily grazed by rabbits, a habitat nowadays rare away from Porton Down. Most was lost under the plough to arable farmland, and the surviving fragments are less heavily grazed.

What the future may hold for Wiltshire birdlife can only be speculation. Will there be a continuing upsurge in raptor populations as they regain lost ground, and will Red Kites become as widespread as Common Buzzards in ten or 20 years' time? Perhaps Marsh Harriers and even Ospreys, along with Common Bitterns and Bearded Tits, will colonise some of the new wetland habitats planned for CWP over the next 30 years. Salisbury Plain may be returned to a treeless grazed landscape stretching to the horizon with displaying Great Bustards, Wood Larks and Wheatears. Much new woodland, planted in the Great Western Community Forest in the northeast of the county in particular, will mature, and it is to be hoped that a more environmentally sympathetic agricultural policy and associated incentives for farmers will enhance the wider countryside, helping species of woodland and farmland to recover. One day we may even see those icons of our ancestors, White-tailed Fish-Eagles and Common Cranes, return as regular visitors, especially if current visions of rebuilding biodiversity on a landscape scale are turned into reality.

Figure 2. Time-line showing last years of recorded breeding and first years of colonisation or recolonisation by various bird species in Wiltshire against political, agricultural and ecological changes 1800–2005

Major events that have affected bird numbers and distribution in Wiltshire are given in the left-hand side of the time-line, alongside the years of their occurrence or introduction. Those events that had a generally positive effect on birds are in green text, and those that had an overall negative influence are in black. (It should be noted that although the wars were felt to have been generally beneficial, there were also negative consequences, for example, through the loss of downland as part of the 'dig for victory' campaign.) Most of these events operated at a much larger scale than just Wiltshire, or Great Britain, and will have affected some birds' fortunes nationally or internationally. In the right-hand side of the time-line, birds ranged left and right were, respectively, lost and gained as breeding species in Wiltshire in the years indicated. Species that were lost but later recolonised appear in both columns and are identified by an asterisk (*); species that colonised but were then lost are also listed in both columns, but with a dagger (†). Species that (re)colonised as a result of introduction are in italics. Isolated breeding occurrences that did not herald the start of regular or wide-scale breeding are indicated by the species' name being in upper and lower case letters; where breeding was felt to constitute the start of genuine colonisation of the county, the name is given in capitals. This assessment is, however, subjective, particularly for species that are scarce, breed only sporadically, or nest at few localities in the county. Further, breeding may have gone unnoticed without dedicated searching by skilled observers, so that gains and losses may have occurred before or after the years listed, and some apparent colonisations and extinctions may reflect changes in observer effort rather than genuine changes in status. (Short-eared Owl, Black Redstart and Pied Flycatcher have all bred on a number of occasions but, as sporadic breeders, are not classed as colonists; only the first year of breeding is noted.) There is inevitably a degree of subjectivity in assessing whether first breeding since 2000 represented the start of colonisation for some of the species listed.

Events	Year	LOSSES	GAINS
	1800	1801 or later Great Bustard	
Game preservation increases	1810		
Enclosure of open countryside, increase in arable use through protection of farm incomes	1820	c1820 Black Grouse	
	1830	c1830 Hen Harrier*	*RED-LEGGED PARTRIDGE* 1830
	1840	c1840 Red Kite*	
	1850	c1850 Common Buzzard*	
	1860		
1869 ~ Preservation of Sea Birds Act Agricultural depression begins, resulting in less drainage and less fertilisers	1870		CURLEW 1876
1880 ~ Wild Birds Protection Act	1880	1880 Raven* 1881 Spotted Crake 1885 Water Rail*	
	1890		DIPPER 1897
	1900		†MARSH WARBLER 1900 COMMON REDSHANK 1907
1914–18 War reduces persecution	1910		GREAT CRESTED GREBE 1913 *LITTLE OWL* 1915
	1920		TUFTED DUCK 1926
Felling of ancient woodlands, replanted with conifers 1939–45 War reduces persecution	1930		COMMON BUZZARD 1930 Common Bittern 1930–33 Pied Flycatcher 1931 CROSSBILL 1932 Hen Harrier 1936
Modernisation of agriculture begins with increased use of pesticides (DDT/Dieldrin, organochlorides), drainage of wetlands, and switch from hay to silage	1940		
Rabbits hit by myxomatosis 1954 ~ Wild Birds Protection Act	1950	1950 Wryneck 1952 Corncrake 1953 Montagu's Harrier* 1955 Peregrine*	
Sahel drought 1968–69 impacts summer migrants	1960	1962 Wood Lark*	HONEY-BUZZARD 1961 COMMON POCHARD 1962 COLLARED DOVE 1962 Short-eared Owl 1964 *CANADA GOOSE* 1968
Development of gravel pits Loss of heathlands, meadows and downland	1970	1976 Common Teal 1977 Red-backed Shrike 1978 Cirl Bunting	LITTLE RINGED PLOVER 1970 Black Redstart 1975 *GREYLAG GOOSE* 1976 *Red-crested Pochard* 1976 *RUDDY DUCK* 1977 *Goshawk* 1979 COMMON TERN 1979
1981 ~ Wildlife & Countryside Act affords protection for many birds, including Curlew and Cormorant Switch to autumn-sown crops, decline of mixed farming, drying of old water meadows	1980	1983 Marsh Warbler	Common Sandpiper 1980 WATER RAIL 1982 MONTAGU'S HARRIER 1982 FIRECREST 1983 GADWALL 1984 LESSER BLACK-BACKED GULL 1984 *MANDARIN* 1986 CETTI'S WARBLER 1987 SISKIN 1987 Ringed Plover 1989
Re-introduction scheme for Red Kites in Chilterns	1990	1995 Common Snipe	Common Shelduck 1990 Cormorant 1994 BLACK-HEADED GULL 1994 RAVEN 1994 PEREGRINE 1994 HERRING GULL 1995 WOOD LARK 1998 GOSHAWK 1999
Re-introduction scheme for Great Bustards on Salisbury Plain	2000		*RED KITE* 2000 *RED-CRESTED POCHARD* 2000 WATER RAIL 2001 Oystercatcher 2002 Garganey 2003 LITTLE EGRET 2003 Hen Harrier 2003

Atlas organisation, methods and mapping 1995–2000

Peter Cranswick, James Ferguson-Lees, Stephen Edwards & Paul Castle

At the heart of *Birds of Wiltshire* are the maps showing distribution and breeding in the county. Indeed, this book was conceived purely as a breeding atlas, only later evolving into a complete avifauna covering both the contemporary winter situation and the full historical picture (see 'Introduction'). From the outset, however, the atlas aspect alone was ambitious in its intent, aiming to show not only the distribution of presence and breeding, but also relative abundance, one of the first county atlases to do so.

In keeping with almost all county atlases since the 1970s, the breeding season maps use tetrads (2 × 2 km squares) as the basic recording unit – a considerably finer level of detail than the 10-km squares of the national atlases. This scale enables bird distributions to be matched to many habitat and other landscape features, and highlights differences between species that would otherwise not be apparent. Such detail requires a concomitant level of survey effort, and the requirement to conduct fieldwork in 915 tetrads was therefore spread over a six-year period for the summer survey. (It was originally intended to be four years, but, owing to slight changes in methods needed to iron out certain teething problems encountered during the first season, some tetrads had to be re-surveyed; and a very small number of tetrads – for example, where special access had to be arranged for MoD land – were in fact surveyed during a sixth summer: see 'Introduction'.) Only after several years of summer fieldwork had been undertaken was a winter atlas mooted, and only at that stage was it apparent that there was both the interest and enthusiasm from observers. Of necessity, winter fieldwork could not be as thorough in its coverage – a four-year winter survey begun near the end of the summer fieldwork programme would have delayed the book still further, and the shorter winter days restricted most people's opportunities to the weekends. Consequently, the winter atlas had to be based on a sample survey over two winters: fieldwork was undertaken in 10 of the 25 tetrads in each 10-km square, with the intention of mapping distribution and relative abundance at the 10-km square level.

The Wiltshire atlas began at a time when major changes were being introduced for broad-scale breeding surveys in the UK, with the switch from the Common Birds Census (CBC) to the Breeding Bird Survey (BBS). Such timing meant that the Wiltshire atlas did not benefit from the accompanying scientific advances in survey design. But it is perhaps unlikely that these methods would have been adopted, even had they been in more widespread use at that time. More than anything else, the Wiltshire atlas required a simple and easily implemented approach if it were to cover every tetrad in a large county that has both a relatively small human population, let alone number of birdwatchers, and large areas that are considered – at least compared with many other parts of Great Britain – to be of relatively little interest for birds.

The success of any atlas relies, nevertheless, on a standardised approach to surveying in order that the resulting maps are robust, meaningful and comparable. Survey methods for Wiltshire were based broadly on the previous national atlases, and benefited especially from the advice of the organisers (Clark & Eyre 1993) of the Hampshire tetrad fieldwork (see 'Introduction') and, later, in connection with the winter sampling, of the BTO. The value of both standardisation and complete coverage of all tetrads in the county is amply demonstrated by the resulting maps. Compare, for example, the summer distribution maps for Chiffchaff and Willow Warbler, which show that the former avoids higher ground, and that the latter breeds more patchily throughout; and examine their relative abundance maps, which demonstrate the Chiffchaff's liking for the clay vales in the northwest and the woods and valleys of the southern half, while the Willow Warbler appears to exploit both heavily wooded areas but also the scrub found on the high ground of the Marlborough Downs and Salisbury Plain, while occurring only at low densities in the northeast. Conventional 10-km square mapping would simply have shown both species as breeding in every 10-km square.

We believe the maps in *Birds of Wiltshire* to be some of the most detailed and informative of contemporary county atlases in the UK. An overview of the organisation of the project and of the methods used for the surveys, and explanations of how the maps were produced – at the same time drawing attention to some potential limitations of the systems used – are provided below to enable a fuller understanding and proper interpretation of the results, and also to allow appropriate comparison of any future atlas against this baseline.

SUMMER ATLAS

Organisation

To oversee the atlas survey, WOS set up a Tetrad Atlas Group (TAG), comprising Linda Cady, Paul Castle, Stephen Edwards, James Ferguson-Lees, Rob Turner and, later, Peter Cranswick, which was responsible for overall organisation, survey design and co-ordination. Working with the group were four regional organisers – Mike Hamzij, Mike Jackson, Granville Pictor and John Pollard – backed by a network of 10-km square stewards, each of whom was responsible for arranging surveys of the 25 tetrads within one or more 10-km squares (figure 3). (More detail on the roles of TAG, the regional organisers and the 10-km stewards are given in the 'Introduction', together with a list of all the individual 'tetradders'.)

Figure 3. 10-km square stewards for the Wiltshire summer atlas fieldwork 1995–2000

AGC	AG Carter	KJG	KJ Grearson
AJR	AJ Rowe	MJH	MJ Hamzij
BB	B Bray	MLB	ML Buckland
BG	B Gillam	MVJ	MV Jackson
BM	B Maxfield	NJB	NJ Braine
BR	B Rawcliffe	NJP	NJ Pleass
GCE	GC Evans	NPA	NP Adams
GDP	GD Pictor	NW	N Winter
GLW	GL Webber	PEC	PE Castle
HE	H Ennion	PR	P Read
IH	I Haggart	RN	R Nelson
JCB	JC Booth	RT	R Turner
JDP	JD Pollard	RTS	RT Simpson
JEW	JE Wilder	SBE	SB Edwards
JHFB	JHF Brown		

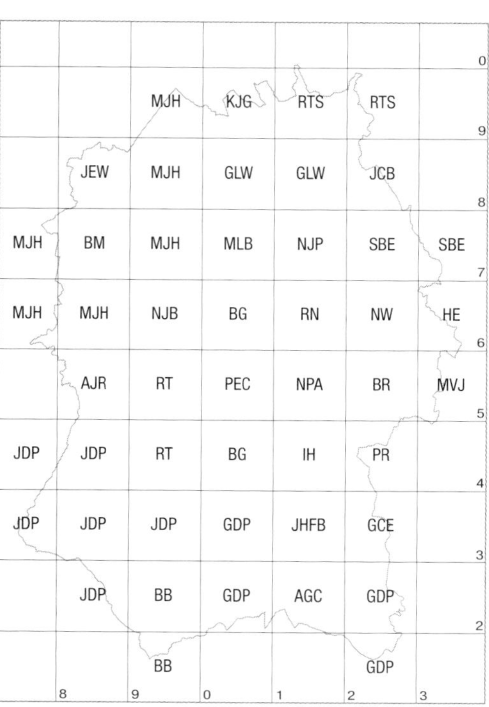

WILTSHIRE ORNITHOLOGICAL SOCIETY

TETRAD ATLAS BREEDING BIRD SURVEY

RECORD CARD (REVISED 1996)

Counts for <u>all</u> species now required for timed visits.

Date	Timed Visit	Untimed Visit
1998	☑ (✓)	☐ (✓)

Largest Feature in Tetrad	10-km Sq	Tetrad	Total Time Spent in Tetrad
WEST HILL	ST94	H	

Name J. D. POLLARD

Address

Postcode Tel No.

		S	B	Count			S	B	Count
0007	Little Grebe				0529	Woodcock			
0009	Great Crested Grebe				0541	Curlew			
0072	Cormorant				0546	Redshank			
0122	Grey Heron				0582	Black-headed Gull			
0152	Mute Swan				0591	Lesser Black-backed Gull			
0161	Greylag Goose				0615	Common Tern			
0166	Canada Goose				0665	Feral Pigeon			
0167	Barnacle Goose				0668	Stock Dove	S		3
0173	Shelduck				0670	Wood Pigeon		B	29
0178	Mandarin				0684	Collared Dove		B	2
0182	Gadwall				0687	Turtle Dove			
0184	Teal				0724	Cuckoo			
0186	Mallard				0735	Barn Owl			
0194	Shoveler				0757	Little Owl		B	2
0196	Red-crested Pochard				0761	Tawny Owl			
0198	Pochard				0767	Long-eared Owl			
0203	Tufted Duck				0778	Nightjar			
0225	Ruddy Duck				0795	Swift	S		1
0269	Sparrowhawk				0831	Kingfisher			
0287	Buzzard	S		1	0856	Green Woodpecker	S		1
0304	Kestrel	S		1	0876	Great Sp Woodpecker		B	4
0310	Hobby				0887	Lesser Sp Woodpecker			
0358	Red-legged Partridge				0974	Woodlark			
0367	Grey Partridge				0976	Skylark		B	20
0370	Quail				0981	Sand Martin			
0394	Pheasant	S		4	0992	Swallow		B	11
0407	Water Rail				1001	House Martin		B	8
0424	Moorhen				1009	Tree Pipit			
0429	Coot				1011	Meadow Pipit		B	8
0459	Stone Curlew				1017	Yellow Wagtail			
0469	Little Ringed Plover				1019	Grey Wagtail			
0470	Ringed Plover				1020	Pied Wagtail			
0493	Lapwing				1050	Dipper			
0519	Snipe				1066	Wren		B	12

		S	B	Count			S	B	Count
1084	Dunnock				1486	Treecreeper			
1099	Robin		B	6	1539	Jay			
1104	Nightingale				1549	Magpie	S		5
1121	Black Redstart				1560	Jackdaw		B	68
1122	Redstart				1563	Rook		B	70
1137	Whinchat		B	6	1567	Carrion Crow	S		9
1139	Stonechat				1572	Raven			
1146	Wheatear				1582	Starling		B	105
1187	Blackbird		B	10	1591	House Sparrow	S		1
1200	Song Thrush				1598	Tree Sparrow			
1202	Mistle Thrush				1636	Chaffinch		B	9
1220	Cetti's Warbler				1649	Greenfinch			
1236	Grasshopper Warbler				1653	Goldfinch	S		1
1243	Sedge Warbler				1654	Siskin			
1251	Reed Warbler				1660	Linnet	S		1
1262	Dartford Warbler				1663	Redpoll			
1274	Lesser Whitethroat				1666	Crossbill			
1275	Whitethroat		B	4	1710	Bullfinch			
1276	Garden Warbler				1717	Hawfinch			
1277	Blackcap	S		2	1857	Yellowhammer		B	4
1308	Wood Warbler				1877	Reed Bunting			
1311	Chiffchaff				1882	Corn Bunting	S		1
1312	Willow Warbler	S		2					
1314	Goldcrest								
1315	Firecrest								
1335	Spotted Flycatcher								
1349	Pied Flycatcher								
1437	Long-tailed Tit								
1440	Marsh Tit								
1442	Willow Tit								
1461	Coal Tit								
1462	Blue Tit	S		2					
1464	Great Tit		B	3					
1479	Nuthatch								

Signifies that evidence of breeding was noted for that species in the tetrad

The count of individuals recorded during the timed 2-hour visit

Indicates that the species was only seen in the tetrad (with no evidence of breeding)

Figure 4. Front of completed record card for the Wiltshire summer atlas fieldwork 1995–2000

Both sides of a blank record card are reproduced in appendix 1, together with the summer casual record form and the summer instructions as revised for 1996–2000

Announcements and guidance for the surveys were published in the Society's quarterly bulletin, *WOS News*, and an initial workshop for observers was held to explain the methods and to provide an opportunity for questions. A review of data and feedback after the first season's fieldwork identified a number of necessary revisions to the methods and improvements to the guidelines. Consequently, a revised record card (figure 4) and instructions (appendix 1) were issued, and further workshops held in advance of the second and subsequent seasons fieldwork. Regular feedback from the survey was provided through articles in *WOS News* and annual progress reports in *Hobby* (Ferguson-Lees & Castle 1995, Ferguson-Lees & Turner 1996, Castle & Turner 1997, Pictor & Turner 1998, Edwards *et al* 1999, Cranswick *et al* 2000).

Survey methods

Fieldwork for the summer maps used whole tetrads as the basic recording unit. An inclusive approach was taken to those tetrads that straddle the county boundary, so that any with at least 20 per cent of their area within Wiltshire were surveyed in their entirety. Including the 143 'marginals' that this involved, a total of 915 tetrads was surveyed for the summer atlas.

All introduced or otherwise established species were included, such as Red-crested Pochard, Pheasant, Feral Pigeon/Rock Dove and, of course, Little Owl. Lingering passage migrants were excluded as far as possible, but any species seen using a tetrad in the breeding season was noted. Although the original survey instructions asked observers to exclude birds simply flying over, this was revised after the first season and birds in flight were then included, to ensure Common Swifts and hirundines in particular but also, for example, Common Buzzards and Lesser Black-backed Gulls were not under-recorded.

The summer mapping in essence comprised two distinct projects that ran simultaneously: one to determine distribution and evidence of breeding by tetrad, the other to assess relative abundance. Timed visits to each tetrad ensured a standardised approach and thus comparable abundance data across the county. Although these provided the majority of all data for the summer atlas, supplementary 'casual' visits were also made to ensure as comprehensive as possible a picture of distribution and breeding. For example, evening visits provided data on nocturnal species, and observations in February and March (before the start of the survey period for timed visits) were required for early breeders.

Timed visits

Timed visits were undertaken between 1 April and 31 July, a period that covers the breeding seasons of most species in southern England. A total of four hours' timed survey was undertaken in each tetrad, divided into two equal 2-hour visits. Observers were encouraged to carry out timed visits within the ten weeks from the last week of April: the first in late April or May and, at least 14 days afterwards, the second in June or early July. Thus, where possible, the first three weeks of April were avoided, as most summer visitors have not arrived, as were the last three of July, when counts may be confused by the presence of juveniles and when many species, particularly woodland passerines, become hard to locate. Both visits to an individual tetrad were made in the same year (table 8, figure 5).

When making a timed visit in a tetrad, observers were instructed to use a route covering as many different habitats as possible, including, for example, parts of wetlands, woods, agricultural land and human settlement. Reference to an Ordnance Survey map in advance was recommended, to help the location of habitats that might otherwise be overlooked, such as a pond or even a corner of a wood that fell mainly in the next tetrad. The need was emphasised for the visit to include the odd hamlet or farm in any extensively wooded or rural tetrad so that species such as Collared Dove, Pied Wagtail and House Sparrow would

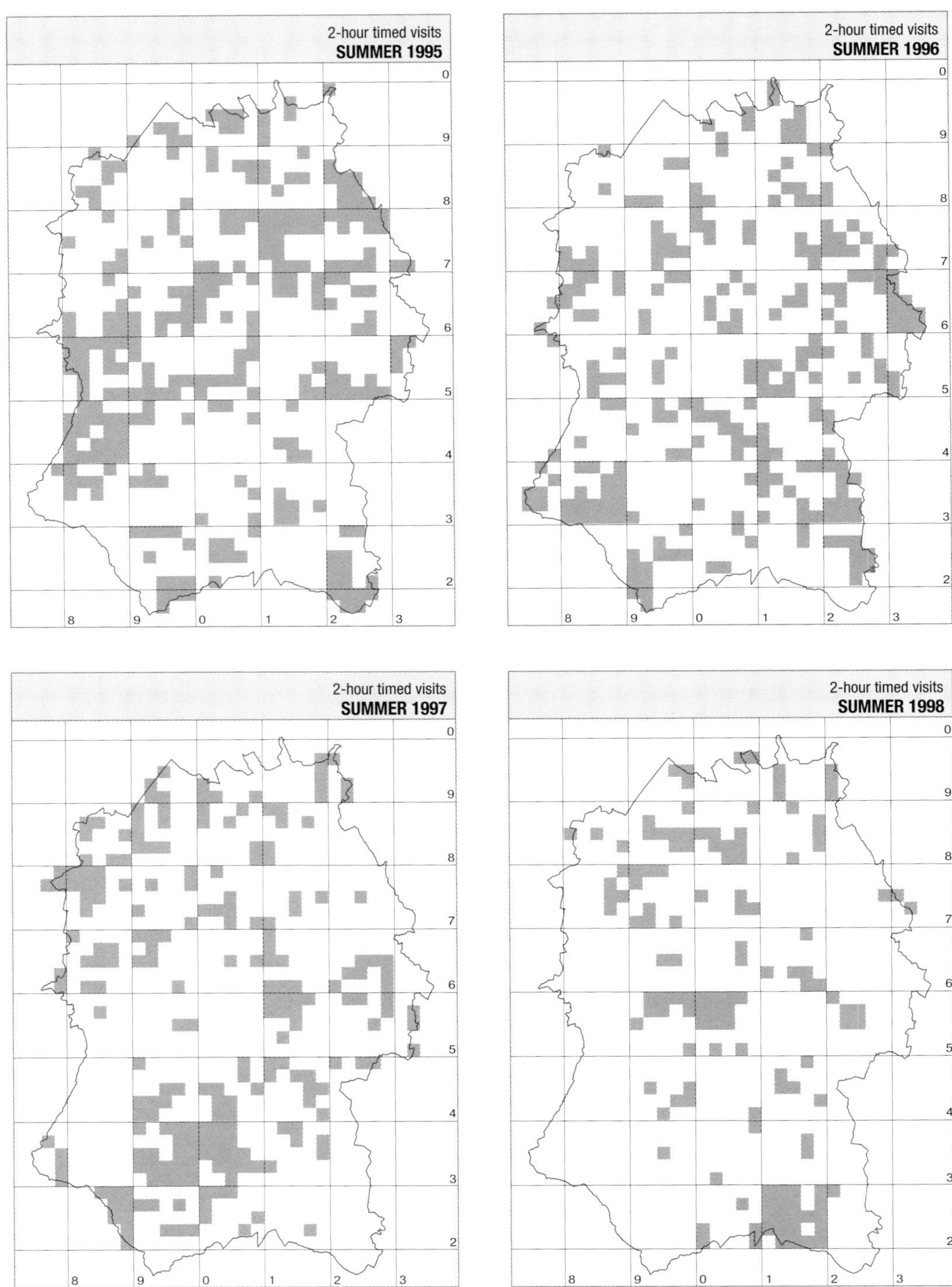

Figure 5. Tetrads in which two 2-hour timed visits were first made for the Wiltshire summer atlas fieldwork 1995–2000

Tetrads surveyed for the first time in 2000 are included in the map for 1999 (See also caption to table 8.)

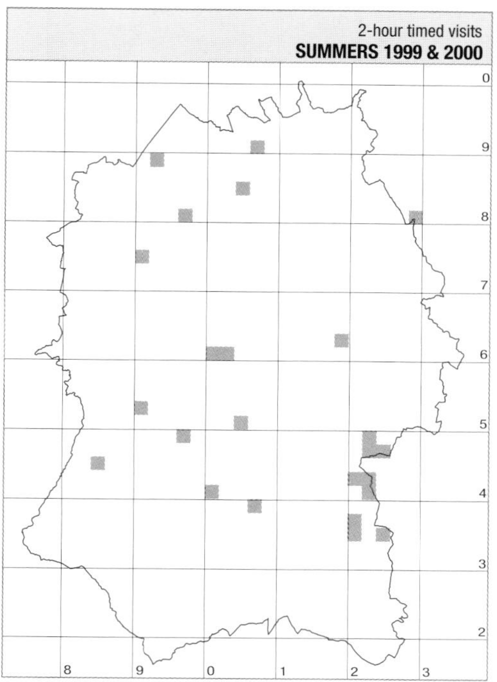

Figure 5 (continued)

be less likely to be overlooked. If such habitats were widely separated within the tetrad, counts could be suspended while moving between these areas – so that parts of the 2-hour survey could be made in a variety of habitats. Observers were advised that the second of the 2-hour visits could follow the same route as the first, or be partly or completely different.

Numbers of all species encountered (seen or heard) were recorded during timed visits. Originally, the instruction was to record more numerous species simply in one of three categories, namely 'common' (more than 30), 'uncommon' (6–30) or 'rare' (fewer than six), but this proved unsatisfactory for many reasons – and from 1996 onwards 2-hour counts of all species were requested. (A key factor in extending to the fifth and sixth years of summer fieldwork was the need to rework any tetrads where the observers concerned had not kept records of their actual counts of common species in 1995 – in which case they were asked simply to make just one 2-hour count of all species during May–June, not April or July, in 1999 or 2000.) For colonial breeding species – in Wiltshire, only Grey Heron, Sand Martin and Rook – observers were requested to record only the number of nests (flagging this as a breeding total in the relevant column of the record card); if a colonial species was seen without there being any evidence of nesting in a tetrad, they were asked to note the number of individuals counted (entering this simply as 'seen' on the card). Observers were also asked to exclude juveniles from the count totals, although it is likely that small numbers – particularly of species that nest early and of others counted during visits later in the survey period – will have been included in error.

Table 8. Numbers of tetrads in which two 2-hour timed visits were made in each of the survey summers in Wiltshire 1995–2000

Tetrad totals relate to the year in which they were first covered. (As explained in the 'Introduction', the commoner species in a proportion of the 1995 tetrads had to be surveyed again in 1999 and 2000 because of a change in methodology, but here, and similarly in figure 5, these tetrads are treated as counted in 1995.) The percentage values are the cumulative proportions of the total to be surveyed in each region. The few tetrads surveyed for the first time in 2000 are included in the 1999 figures

	Totals	1995		1996		1997		1998		1999 & 2000	
		Tetrads	Per cent	Tetrads	Per cent	Tetrads	Per cent	Tetrads	Per cent	Tetrads	Per cent
Northeast	304	103	33·9%	90	63·5%	67	85·5%	40	98·7%	4	100·0%
Northwest	212	69	32·5%	50	56·1%	57	83·0%	31	97·6%	5	100·0%
Southeast	172	37	21·5%	48	49·4%	41	73·3%	36	94·2%	10	100·0%
Southwest	227	72	31·7%	65	60·4%	57	85·5%	28	97·8%	5	100·0%
Totals	915	281	30·7%	253	58·4%	222	82·6%	135	97·4%	24	100·0%

Casual visits

To ensure as comprehensive a picture as possible of distribution and breeding, timed visits were supplemented by casual visits. The constraints applied to timed visits to ensure comparable data – the set amount of time, the time of day and the time of year – were removed in order that accurate pictures of distribution and breeding could be provided for all species. For example, casual visits were encouraged in February–March for early nesters, and evening visits for owls and other crepuscular or nocturnal species. (See section on 'Seasons for recording: considerations for future surveys' at the end of this chapter.) Further, casual visits were made to try to find additional species not recorded during 2-hour visits – inevitably, a number would be missed in many tetrads in such a limited time – and to try to establish 'breeding' by any that had otherwise only been 'seen'.

Casual visits were not restricted to the same breeding season as the two timed visits, and could be made in any of the atlas years.

Evidence of breeding

A species was recorded as breeding when one or more of the following activities was observed: song, if heard in the same location 14 or more days apart between 1 April and 31 July, as evidence of, at least, established territory-holding; courtship behaviour; adult visiting probable nest-site; nest building, including excavating a nest-hole; occupied or recently used nest; brood patch on trapped bird; distraction display or other behaviour indicating presence of eggs or young; adult carrying nest material, faecal sac, or food; or hatched eggshells, downy chicks, or recently fledged young.

A record of 'breeding' in the distribution maps in *Birds of Wiltshire* thus covers both of the categories of 'confirmed' and 'probable' traditionally used in national and county atlases, while 'seen' equates to the category 'possible'.

Map production

For each tetrad, a summary data card was completed, identifying those species for which breeding evidence had been recorded, and the peak count from the two timed visits. Data were input by a small team, co-ordinated by the county recorder, Rob Turner, and were held in the database COBRA. For each record, the following information was entered: Euring code, species name, date, status ('breeding' or 'seen'), count, 10-km square, tetrad identification letter (see figure 7 on page 107). Data were checked visually for obvious errors by the regional organisers and by the county recorder and others inputting the information. Species maps were also provided to the 10-km square stewards to check for obvious errors.

Distribution maps

The summer distribution maps were compiled primarily from the information provided on WOS atlas record cards, from both timed and casual visits. For a small number of species, where it was felt that the result significantly understated the true extent of distribution, additional records were used. In most cases, these extra data were drawn from the normal records submitted by WOS members to the county recorder and used to compile the annual county report in *Hobby*. The distribution maps for Red Kite, Hobby, Curlew, Little Owl, Dipper and Hawfinch were all significantly enhanced, as were those of around a further dozen species to a much lesser extent, by adding such records for 1995–2000. Maps for Barn and Tawny Owls were improved considerably by data from various nestbox schemes, as well as from the WOS files. The records of Stone-curlews were provided by the RSPB Wessex Stone-curlew Team, which each year uses both tape-recording by night and intensive fieldwork by day to locate pairs in Wiltshire and adjoining counties.

For a number of sensitive species, principally rare breeders in Wiltshire, records have been mapped centrally within the relevant 10-km squares – primarily to reduce the risk of revealing locations to egg-collectors and others who might cause disturbance. The 10-km squares with centralised records have all been shaded green to highlight the difference in mapping treatment.

It should be noted that, as surveys were made over a six-year period, the maps reflect an 'average' picture of distribution in Wiltshire over that time; any changes or fluctuations during 1995–2000 will not be discernable from a single map. Sharp declines in some species, such as Wood Warbler, may have led to maps showing an apparently patchy distribution if some tetrads within core breeding areas were surveyed at the start of the period and others at the end, by when the species may have disappeared. It is conceivable that some species were over-represented by the use of casual records over a six-year period: if, for example, a single pair of Mute Swans moved within its territory in different years, it could have been recorded breeding in two adjacent tetrads. Such cases are, however, certainly few and far between and it is likely that a far greater number of individuals went undetected than were double-counted in this way.

Relative abundance maps

Abundance maps have been generated using only data collected during timed visits. These depict relative – rather than absolute – abundance, making no allowance for those individuals missed in any tetrad by the observers (see the chapter 'Calculating population estimates of Wiltshire's Birds' for further discussion). The highest count from the two 2-hour visits to each tetrad was used to map abundance.

Up to six abundance categories were used for each species, distinguished by different intensities of shading. To illustrate variations in abundance across the county most clearly, the aim was to have equal numbers of tetrads in each category; this was achieved, where possible, by choosing certain count values as the lower and upper limits for each. Often, however, this was not possible: for example, if only three different count values were recorded across the county (for example, where the maximum count was only three, and the only counts were of one, two or three birds), a maximum of just three abundance categories could be used; in such cases, the numbers of tetrads in each abundance category were constrained by the counts, and could not be adjusted to provide equal numbers in each. In general, the category of highest abundance often contained fewest records, but also spanned a greater range of values than other categories.

Inevitably, the abundance maps under-represent the full distribution of these species: two 2-hour visits will have missed certain species found only locally or at low densities in some tetrads, although the instruction to visit as many different habitats as possible during each survey will have mitigated this to some extent. The largest potential problem is undoubtedly the risk of inclusion of fledged juveniles in counts made later in the season. This is, however, unlikely to have been significant for all but a small number of species whose juveniles are similar in appearance to females or to both adults, although it may have led to higher abundance values, compared with other species, for early breeders which form post-breeding family groups or flocks (*eg* Long-tailed Tits). Nevertheless, the patterns of relative abundance within the county depicted by the maps do accurately match features of geography and landscape in many cases – which gives confidence that they are representative for the majority of species.

Additional information is presented in the abundance maps for colonial species. For Grey Herons and Sand Martins – which both have relatively few breeding sites in Wiltshire – the positions and sizes of colonies are shown on top of the standard abundance map by circles of varying diameter. (WOS records were used to identify the peak count at each colony during the survey period.) For Rooks, however – whose colonies are numerous and widespread throughout the county – only counts of nests are mapped. (Counts of Rooks away from their colonies were made in many tetrads, including those that appear blank on the relative abundance map, but, for simplicity, these data have not been mapped.) Only after the completion of the atlas fieldwork was it recognised that colonies of Lesser Black-backed and Herring Gulls were both more numerous and larger than previously thought. A specific survey to assess these gull colonies was subsequently undertaken but, coming three and four years after the atlas fieldwork was completed, the results are not shown on the atlas abundance maps but presented as separate figures within those species accounts.

Wiltshire Winter Bird Mapping Survey G.L. WEBBER

10-km Square: SU18

M	M	Y	Y
0	1	9	9

EURING	SPECIES	A	B	C	D	E	F	G	H	I	J	K	L	M	N	P	Q	R	S	T	U	V	W	X	Y	Z	MAX COUNT	Office Use
	Time Spent in Tetrad		2h		2h		2h					2hr																
0007	Little Grebe											2															2	
0009	Gt Cr Grebe																											
0072	Cormorant																											
0122	Grey Heron		1		1																						1	
0152	Mute Swan				6																						6	
0166	Canada Goose																											
0179	Wigeon																											
0182	Gadwall											2															2	
0184	Teal																											
0186	Mallard		3		13		4					19															19	
0194	Shoveler																											
0198	Pochard																											
0203	Tufted Duck																											
0218	Goldeneye																											
0223	Goosander																											
0225	Ruddy Duck																											
0269	Sparrowhawk		1				1					2															2	
0287	Buzzard						2					1															2	
0304	Kestrel						1																				1	
0358	Red-lg Partridge																											
0367	Grey Partridge																											
0394	Pheasant						1																				1	
0407	Water Rail				1																						1	
0424	Moorhen		2		12		2					7															12	
0429	Coot				3							20															20	
0485	Golden Plover																											
0493	Lapwing		14				41																				41	
0519	Common Snipe																											
0529	Woodcock																											

Figure 6. Top of first side of completed recording form for the Wiltshire winter atlas fieldwork 1998/99–1999/00

Organisation

The existing network of regional organisers and 10-km square stewards set up for the summer atlas was used to organise fieldwork for the winter atlas. A recording form and instructions were issued to all observers (figure 6).

A blank recording form is reproduced in appendix 1, together with the winter instructions

E	J	P	U	Z
D	I	N	T	Y
C	H	M	S	X
B	G	L	R	W
A	F	K	Q	V

Figure 7. Letter designations of tetrads in a 10-km square, and priority tranches used to select tetrads for survey in the Wiltshire winter atlas fieldwork 1998/99–1999/00
The first tranche of priority tetrads is shaded dark green, the second light green

Survey methods

The winter fieldwork was designed to map, by timed counts, both the distribution and the relative abundance of birds in Wiltshire at that season. As the idea was conceived several years after the start of the summer fieldwork, it was decided to attempt this survey in only two winters – 1998/99 and 1999/2000.

As in summer, tetrads were surveyed in their entirety, even if they cross the county border. For the winter survey, however, tetrads were included only if their centres fall inside the Wiltshire boundary. Moreover, it was impracticable to try to survey every tetrad in just two winters, and so a sampling system was designed. In each 10-km square, just ten of the 25 tetrads were earmarked for survey, these having been selected at random using the 'Latin squares' approach to minimise bias. Thus, the tetrads B, D, F, H, K, P, T, U, W and X – two in each row and in each column of five in every complete 10-km square (see figure 7) – were identified as priorities for the survey. Where time permitted, observers were asked to visit as many of the other tetrads as possible, to provide a more representative picture.

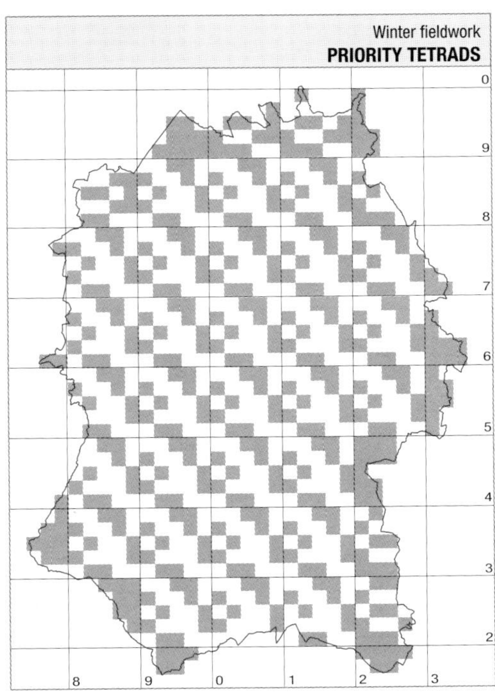

Figure 8. Priority tetrads for survey during the Wiltshire winter atlas fieldwork 1998/99–1999/00

For 10-km squares that straddle the border, so that not all their tetrads fall within Wiltshire, the potential for bias increases if priority tetrads lie outside the county and so are not surveyed. Consequently, further priority tetrads were added to the list to minimise this effect. These were identified according to the proportion of Wiltshire tetrads in the 10-km square concerned: if the 10-km square contains 20 or more of the 25, only as many

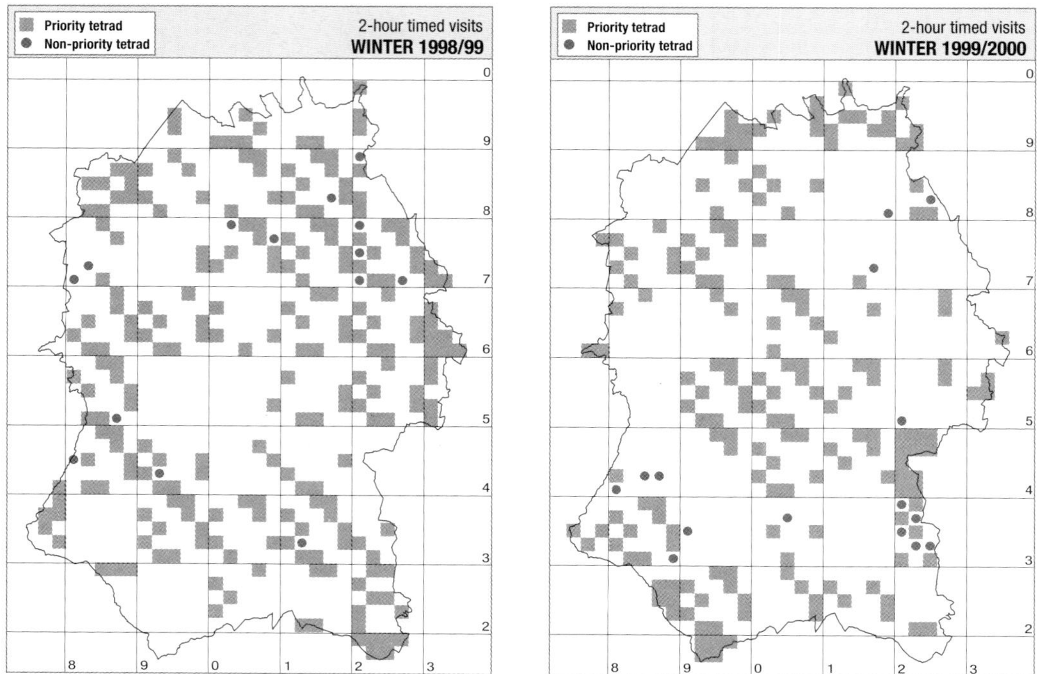

Figure 9. Tetrads in which timed visits were made for the Wiltshire winter atlas fieldwork 1998/99–1999/00

of the first tranche of ten priority tetrads that fall inside the county were surveyed; in a square with between ten and 19 tetrads inside, any of an additional five – A, J, M, R and Y – were also surveyed; and, if the 10-km square contains fewer than 10 tetrads in Wiltshire, all were surveyed (see figure 7). On this basis, 879 tetrads were regarded as within the county, and 414 of those were identified as priority for the winter survey (figure 8). Observers could also cover additional tetrads, once those identified as priority had been surveyed, to increase the level of coverage: some 29 further tetrads were visited, chosen by the observers, so that analyses for winter were based on data from 443 tetrads in total (figure 9).

Observers were asked to undertake a single 2-hour timed visit to each tetrad and count the numbers of all species seen or heard. In the first winter, they were requested to make visits between the beginning of November and the end of February; in the second, this period was extended slightly to encompass the nearest weekends, from 30 October to 5 March. In contrast to the summer, no casual visits were made to supplement timed counts, and no data from other sources were used for the winter maps.

As in summer, observers were asked to take a route that covered as many different habitats within the tetrad as possible, and were again permitted to suspend their counts while moving between different parts of the tetrad. If bad weather significantly hampered the fieldwork, they could stop the survey and return on another date to complete their counts, but in such cases the resumed survey had to be made in the same winter and, if possible, in the same month.

As in summer, too, all species were surveyed, but observers were asked to exclude birds overhead – such as gulls flying to roost – unless they were considered to be actively using the tetrad – for example, hunting raptors. It was again suggested that surveys be done in the morning, although this timing was less critical than it was for the summer fieldwork.

Map production

Data were input into Excel spreadsheets and a series of simple checks performed (*eg* validating species codes, reviewing the total count for each species, maximum counts per tetrad, and dates of observations).

Relative abundance, expressed as the number of birds counted in each tetrad, was then calculated for each 10-km square as the mean of the counts in all tetrads surveyed in that square. This value was then applied to all tetrads in the square or, in the case of partial 10-km squares, to all tetrads falling within Wiltshire.

To provide figures comparable between summer and winter (see 'Calculating population estimates of Wiltshire's birds'), the number of individuals counted during the winter survey was converted into an 'extrapolated total' by applying the mean count from the surveyed tetrads to all tetrads in each 10-km square. This number then represented the number of birds that could have been expected to be recorded had all tetrads been covered for the winter survey.

As in summer, up to six abundance categories were used for the winter maps. Because, in general, a greater range of numbers was recorded in winter, these categories were designed to give a more even spread of abundance values. (Summer categories, in contrast, were chosen to provide roughly equal numbers of tetrads in each category.) In many cases, the category of lowest abundance contains the greatest proportion of records – that is, the most 10-km squares fall into this category – and this applies particularly to species with patchy distributions, or occurring at low densities in many areas.

The patterns of abundance and distribution shown by the winter maps for most species appear to accord reasonably well with major geographical features, although the much coarser level of precision in the winter mapping precludes comparison with many fine-scale landscapes in the county. Because of the lower survey effort in winter than in summer – just one 2-hour visit to fewer than half of all tetrads, and no supplementary visits to confirm presence – there is a greater likelihood that species will have been missed. Coverage of just a proportion, rather than all tetrads, within a 10-km square will have produced the same effect. Although pooling data for all tetrads will have overcome this problem to a certain extent, some maps appear to show absences from areas known or expected to support particular species. Comment on particularly notable instances is made in the relevant species accounts.

It should also be noted that the fieldwork in winter involved a longer survey period than was generally practicable in summer, fully spanning four months. There will have been much variation in abundance during the course of that time, for example, because of the different arrival and departure dates of different species. Winter weather – both within but particularly outside Wiltshire and, indeed, outside Great Britain – will also have played a significant role in determining numbers in the county. Temperatures in Wiltshire during winter 1998/99 were around normal throughout, though January was rather mild and there was a cold spell in mid February; they were also around average in the first half of 1999/2000, but both January and February were particularly mild. These conditions were reflected across Britain as a whole and, indeed, across much of Europe, although there was a noticeably cold spell in northern and eastern Europe in November 1998. Thus, the winter survey is likely to have included periods of passage or significant movements of several species – such as Lapwings, Golden Plovers, Sky Larks and winter thrushes – that doubtless contributed to considerable variations in the totals recorded. Winter numbers of many birds will have changed in response to the prevailing conditions, and also as a result of the breeding success in the preceding summer, and there are thus likely to have been much greater differences between the two winters of the survey in the numbers of particular species than there were of most breeding birds over the six years of the summer survey. Consequently, in pooling the data from tetrads to produce a figure for each 10-km square, the maps represent an average of both within- and between-winter variations in numbers.

Other maps

Some species occur in only small numbers in Wiltshire, and often at a limited suite of sites, but do so with sufficient regularity for there to be a pattern to the records. Few or no observations were made of these birds during the atlas fieldwork, and so a further style of maps has been used for certain species – such as Mediterranean Gull and Great Grey Shrike – to show the pattern of their occurrence and distribution in the county.

Maps of 11 scarce species that are regular in Wiltshire have been devised to show 'bird-years' for each site at which they were found during 1995–2000*. Because these mostly occur either as winter visitors or as passage migrants, the 12–month period from July to June was used to define a bird-year (and therefore here termed 'bird-winters'; an individual present from December into January would otherwise register as two bird-years if calendar years were the definition). Differing sizes of circles are used to indicate the number of bird-years at each site. Sites are defined as generally accepted areas used by the relevant species: thus, CWP is treated as a single site for Smews and Goosanders (rather than a number of circles being used to identify each lake at which they were seen), and broad sections of Salisbury Plain have been treated as a single site where it is believed that records of Great Grey Shrikes have involved the same individual roaming over an extended winter territory. (For Peregrine, however, all records during winters 1998/99 and 1999/2000 have been summed by tetrad.)

Seasons for counting birds in summer and winter: considerations for future surveys

The experience gained in this exercise, and not least the early mistakes, should also make the next Wiltshire bird atlas a rather simpler task. The initial instructions must be absolutely clear with no possibility of misinterpretation, and all birds of all species must be counted in each 2-hour tetrad survey from the beginning in both the summer and winter periods. Winter should probably again be based on November–February, but so far as possible the summer counts should be concentrated in May and June. Counts before the beginning of May are likely to be too early for the main arrivals of the majority of summer visitors and, as June advances, distinguishing between adults and juveniles can become an increasing problem for quite a few species. A number of exceptions have, however, to be borne in mind both for future surveys and for interpreting the maps presented in this *Birds of Wiltshire*:

1. Crossbills nest mostly in January–February and their young fledge by March–April. (Any noted in May and June are as likely to be immigrants.) They are the earliest of our early nesters, but Grey Herons and Ravens start in February and, although the young Ravens will tend to stay with their parents in the same general area after fledging, some young Grey Herons may leave the nest and the area of the colony by the end of April (while the young of late pairs can still be in the nest in August).

---

* 'Bird-years' are calculated as the number of individuals of a species at a single site during the course of a year, summed for the relevant period of years. Thus, a site that recorded one individual at the same site in each of five years, such as a single returning Great Grey Shrike, would constitute five bird-years; and a flock of five Goosanders at Coate Water in just one year would also constitute five bird-years. Note that single birds recorded on separate occasions but believed or known to be different individuals – for example, a male in one week, and a female in the following week – would be treated as two bird-years.

2. Nests of Grey Herons and, importantly, Rooks need to be counted in the second and third weeks of April, before the leaves come out. Both these species and Sand Martins are all best counted at colonies. Even though occupancy of nests and nest-holes is unlikely to be full – particularly in the case of Rooks – single Grey Herons, mixed flocks of adult and juvenile Rooks, and foraging Sand Martins are all far more difficult to assess away from the colonies.

3. Evidence of breeding by ducks is best obtained by seeing ducklings swimming with the females. In Wiltshire, most ducks lay eggs in late April or May and have ducklings visible by early June at the latest, but Tufted Ducks almost never lay before mid May, and frequently not until June or even early July, so that their broods are seldom seen before mid June and often not until July and August. Mallards, on the other hand, may nest at any time from February to August, and ducklings may be seen from mid March to September, even December. (Precocious female Mallards may also sometimes lay eggs in their first autumn.)

4. Proof of breeding by Great Crested Grebes is easy enough in view of their long nesting season that frequently results in the stripy youngsters being conspicuous from March through to October or even December, but Little Grebes – despite nearly as long a season and two or three broods – are much shyer and sometimes the only evidence of their presence is in their trilling calls from inside emergent vegetation. Moorhens and Coots have long breeding seasons, and two or three usually obvious broods, during March through to August, while the more secretive Water Rails utter their curious mixtures of grunts, squeals and screams from February through to August. (Night visits to tetrads with suitable habitat just might turn up the whiplash call of a Spotted Crake.)

5. Another family with long breeding seasons is that of the four resident pigeons – Rock Dove/Feral Pigeon, Stock Dove, Wood Pigeon and Collared Dove – all of which may have two, three or even four broods and be proved nesting in almost any month, though particularly from February to October or November, while the migrant Turtle Doves nest from mid May to, when they have two broods, mid September.

6. Barn Owls may occupy their nests almost year-round: although their main breeding season is from April to October, they can have eggs from the end of February and, if they have two broods, young at any time to mid December; their distinctively shiny black pellets on the ground below the sites are, when fresh, a good indication of occupancy. The generally single-brooded Tawny and Long-eared Owls have eggs and, later, young from the end of February through to June. The main problem with all these three species is their essentially nocturnal behaviour – though Barn Owls occasionally hunt in daylight, Tawny sometimes call by day (or one roosting in a tree may be accidentally flushed or have attention drawn to it by the mobbing of smaller birds), and Long-eareds at a winter roost will at times warm themselves in early morning sunlight. The Tawny Owl, in particular, is greatly under-recorded in *Birds of Wiltshire* because too few night visits were made to many tetrads. Owls often have to be located by sound, and the widespread Tawny is most vociferous from January to May when establishing its territories (less so in June–July and October–December), while the much scarcer Long-eared is noisiest in the first quarter of the year. Thus, night drives through a number of tetrads, with periodical stops to listen, may be just as profitable for these in the latter half of the winter. When vole populations are high, Short-eared Owls may rear two broods and have young through to late July.

7. Several other nocturnal birds are also best located by late evening or night visits. Quails may be heard calling in April or May, but the bulk arrives from late June onwards. Nightjars are mainly in late May, June and July, but Woodcocks continue their distinctive 'roding' display-flights from March through July, followed by some recurrence in autumn.

8. Most raptors have occupied nests in April to July, and are noisiest when they have older young, but adults are often most obvious during their pre-breeding display flights on fine days in February and March. Two of three summer-visitors, however – Honey-buzzard and Montagu's Harrier – do not start breeding before late May or June, while most Hobbies arrive in mid May, lay their eggs in mid June, hatch in mid July, and rear their young in mid August, the adults being noisiest from the time when these are half-grown.

9. The need to concentrate the summer counts in May and, ideally, the first half of June is primarily for the migrant passerines. Many of the resident songbirds have two broods and most are singing, or easily seen collecting food for their nestlings, from March or April to July. But quite a few of the summer visitors from Africa do not arrive in any numbers before the beginning of May and some (*eg* Reed Warbler, Spotted Flycatcher) often do not nest until the end of that month or (especially Marsh Warbler) even early June. In contrast, Long-tailed Tits frequently start nesting in March and the young can fledge before the end of April.

10. The use of song in the same place, presumably by the same individual, on two (or more) occasions at least 14 days apart for passerines, pigeons and (drumming) woodpeckers – one of the criteria used in the summer fieldwork – is not firm proof of breeding, but in general it is good evidence of a male holding territory and at least awaiting the arrival of a female with which to pair. (It has less relevance for Cuckoos, whose females hold the territory while the males wander.) Some summer-visitors have very short song-periods (Nightingale barely extending into June, Marsh Warbler hardly starting before June) and, while some species and individuals sing throughout the season, others do so very irregularly once paired.

11. Timed counts attempted in July are fraught with problems. In estimating populations, it is important to count only adults and, while many juveniles are distinctive enough, others are not easily distinguished on brief views and numbers of, for example, Collared Doves (juveniles collarless) and House Sparrows (juveniles very like females once the yellow sides of the gape are lost) can easily be overestimated. Many birds also start moulting in July, and then become silent and secretive; by the end of that month most summer visitors and many residents have ceased singing. (This is even more marked in August when, however, Yellowhammers seem to come into their own: the males have been singing since March, but in August's comparative silence their songs often stand out.)

12. Winter counts need to be staggered through the four months, so that adjacent tetrads are not all surveyed in, say, November or February. There are two reasons for this. First, the earlier half of the winter is usually warmer and drier than the later and, if there is severe weather – which greatly affects both numbers and movements – it is much more likely to be in January and February. Second, for a species to maintain a population at a particular level, the equivalent of the previous year's breeding production must die or move elsewhere; the rates of mortality are likely to increase in colder weather and the same applies to any dispersal that has not taken place the previous autumn. Thus, midwinter counts might be ideal, but, at least theoretically, the equivalent of these can be achieved by evenly spreading the counts of the tetrads in a particular 10-km square across the four winter months.

13. Finally, we recommend that winter surveys be attempted throughout the full period of any atlas. The popularity of the winter fieldwork for *Birds of Wiltshire* bears out that opportunities for this are widely welcomed, at least in southern parts of Great Britain. If, for any reason, coverage of all tetrads is impracticable at that season, it would be better to aim for a sample survey design that allowed mapping at no larger scale than 5 × 5 km, because the 10-km maps in *Birds of Wiltshire* are, by comparison, much less useful than the summer tetrad ones.

Calculating population estimates of Wiltshire's birds

Peter Cranswick

Estimates of bird numbers are both inherently interesting and an essential conservation tool. The limited funds available for conservation need to be directed at the most deserving species and sites, and population size is one of the criteria used to identify priorities: small populations often indicate those in trouble or, at least, at greater risk. For species that are not monitored annually, periodic reviews of population size may also serve to assess trends in numbers.

Producing estimates is rarely straightforward. Species whose distribution is restricted to relatively few sites, and which are reasonably easy to observe and count, lend themselves most readily to this exercise. The national annual surveys of wildfowl have thus enabled estimates of wintering numbers to be calculated on a regular basis. Colonial birds – Grey Herons, Rooks, Sand Martins – are also fairly uncomplicated to assess, both because their nests are comparatively easy to count and because their populations are concentrated at relatively few locations that are usually well-known, or at least easily found. Rare species, if only because their very rarity affords them a greater level of attention from birdwatchers, are often in effect monitored through casual observations, and *ad hoc* records may be sufficient to estimate numbers. But this assumes that observers have identified all key sites over a period of years; often, particularly for birds that are difficult to find or easily overlooked, those sites at which the species can readily be seen are visited frequently, while other, potentially suitable, sites are neglected. For many common species, however, the task is considerably more complicated, and extensive and scientifically robust surveys are necessary to estimate numbers with any degree of confidence.

Even where suitable data are available, producing estimates of bird populations is beset by a number of problems. The abundance of several species is rapidly changing – for example, the marked increase and spread of Common Buzzards in recent decades – while many animal populations fluctuate naturally for a variety of reasons. Estimates based on a survey in a single year, even if produced from targeted surveys especially designed for that particular species, may thus not be representative. Even in Wiltshire, large changes in abundance were obvious for some species during the years of the atlas fieldwork – for example, marked declines in Cuckoos and Wood Warblers – and it is likely that targeted surveys would have produced quite different results in each of those years.

The WOS atlas fieldwork sought to provide patterns of relative abundance for common species within Wiltshire. Providing county estimates was not one of the original intentions of *Birds of Wiltshire*, but as the scope of the book grew into a comprehensive avifauna, it was a natural extension to address this aspect also. But producing estimates as, in effect, an afterthought creates a series of additional and fundamental problems. County totals have been calculated or compiled from a variety of sources and methods, in many cases involving a degree of guesswork and intuition. We recognise these limitations, and accept that such figures would probably not stand up to the scientific review required for national or regional estimates.

Nevertheless, it is also true that few appropriate data exist with which to produce local estimates, and it is apparent that there are problems with some results from surveys that purport to achieve this. For example, the Breeding Bird Survey (BBS) – a national scheme to assess trends in widespread and common species – has been used to produce national population totals by summing estimates calculated for individual counties. The number of 1-km squares surveyed for the BBS in Wiltshire in the late 1990s was relatively small, and just 38 were covered in 2000 as the county's contribution to the national analysis (S Newson). Although this widely respected and scientifically sophisticated scheme provides apparently good estimates for many species in Wiltshire, it is no surprise that, covering only 1 per cent of the county's landscape, the 38 1-km squares are not representative of all habitats or all species. Consequently, its estimates for a number of species are clearly not plausible: some fall below the number counted during WOS timed surveys (which themselves will represent only a small proportion of the true total), while certain other widespread species were not recorded at all by the BBS in Wiltshire.

This is not, of course, intended to discredit the BBS, nor does it argue that the WOS counts provide appropriate data for population assessment. But it does highlight the role and value of local surveys and expertise, and justifies exploring other data sources and approaches for producing county estimates. Despite its obvious limitations, we have sought to combine the results of the Wiltshire tetrad fieldwork with more robust data sources – and an element of expert local judgement also. Whilst therefore lacking scientific validity, we offer these estimates for Wiltshire in the hope that they will serve to refine and improve the methods used to produce both national and local figures, and that they provide a baseline at the end of the last millennium against which to measure future estimates for the county.

Estimates of breeding and wintering numbers in Wiltshire are provided in 'The status of birds in Wiltshire'. An overview of the methods used to derive these is given below. Further details (and many of the data) appear in appendix 4, and explanations for individual estimates can also be found in the relevant species accounts.

BREEDING ESTIMATES

Common and widespread species

Producing accurate estimates of abundance for common and widespread bird species has long been a problematic area that has challenged both researchers and statisticians. Data from a number of long-running surveys in the UK and from national atlases have been used for this purpose, but, whilst they have produced the best estimates to date at regional and national scales, those surveys were aimed primarily at serving different objectives: for example, the Common Birds Census (CBC) was designed to assess long-term changes in populations, and the *1988–91 Atlas* aimed to map both distribution and relative abundance.

Recent advances in survey design have sought to overcome some of the inherent limitations of existing schemes in producing population estimates. The BBS has enabled accurate and robust estimates to be calculated by using a relatively simple technique and for relatively little survey effort (Gregory *et al* 1996). It was introduced nationally in the mid 1990s, and for this and a number of other reasons was not adopted for the fieldwork in Wiltshire – partly because there was no intention originally to produce county estimates, and partly because the surveying of over 3600 1-km squares (as against 915 tetrads) would probably have proved impossible. Nevertheless, the results of a number of local surveys that adopted BBS methods have been used to assess population sizes for many species in Wiltshire.

Breeding Bird Survey

The BBS produces estimates of species density within 1-km squares. Two 1-km transects are walked by the observer in a 1-km square (ideally, two straight parallel transects 500 m apart, though inevitably the routes deviate to some extent because of physical barriers or issues of access). As well as recording the numbers of birds, the observer assesses the distance from the transect to the birds by placing them in one of three distance bands (0–25 m, 25–100 m, and >100 m), running parallel to the transect. The number of birds recorded decreases with their distance from the transect, simply because distant birds are harder to detect, but 'distance' analysis uses the numbers of birds in each band to calculate how many were missed by the observer. Because the 1-km squares are selected at random within the survey area – though, by prior analysis of habitat data, they are representative of the types and extents of the different habitats there – and because the transects are, in effect, placed at random within the 1-km squares, the densities of species obtained by distance analysis can be applied to the whole survey area in order to produce estimates of the total numbers of each species.

The BBS is a nationwide survey, aiming to assess trends and numbers at a national scale. The selection of survey squares is made, however, at a county level, reflecting the organisation of the scheme through BTO regional representatives. Consequently, data from the national BBS squares in Wiltshire enable a population estimate to be calculated for the county, and estimates are presented here from a national analysis by the BTO (S Newson). As this is a national scheme, with the intention that the same squares continue to be covered each year, a relatively small number of these is surveyed in any one county and, as already noted, BBS estimates for Wiltshire were calculated by using data from just 38 1-km squares (a little over one per cent). Although this provided reasonable estimates for many birds, it was apparent through comparison with other sources that estimates for some species were not representative.

A number of surveys have been undertaken in recent years to provide estimates at local or regional scales in the UK, most notably the RSPB surveys of a number of Environmentally Sensitive Areas (ESAs). Such surveys are more intensive than the national BBS, covering a large number of 1-km squares within the survey area in order to provide accurate estimates. Surveys undertaken in southern or western England, and in habitats broadly similar to those found in Wiltshire, might then be used to provide estimates for the county, by applying the calculated species densities to the area of Wiltshire. Those most relevant to Wiltshire are the RSPB surveys of the Cotswold Hills ESA (an area covering much of the eastern third of Gloucestershire) in 1997 and 2002, and of the Chilterns Area of Outstanding Natural Beauty (covering parts of Oxfordshire, Buckinghamshire, Hertfordshire and Bedfordshire) in 2002 (Mustoe *et al* 1998, Shurmer 2002, Dodd & Meadows 2003). The mean densities from the two Cotswold surveys and those from the Chilterns survey have been applied to Wiltshire to produce estimates for species found commonly in either of these areas (appendix 4).

Within Wiltshire itself, the Salisbury Plain Training Area (SPTA) has been the subject of intensive surveys by BBS methods in both 2000 and 2005 (Stanbury *et al* 2000, 2005). Although those provided accurate estimates for this important area (see chapter on 'Wiltshire's habitats'), they focused on the open grassland, and so the results cannot directly be more widely applied. Nevertheless, the data have been used here to calculate Wiltshire populations for several species characteristic of calcareous grassland: the SPTA estimates obtained by using BBS methods have been extrapolated to the county as a whole, by applying the ratio of birds counted during the WOS timed surveys in those tetrads that fall within SPTA to the total counted by WOS timed surveys throughout the county (appendix 4). The Wiltshire populations of such species as Sky Lark and Meadow Pipit calculated by this approach are arguably among the most accurate of the county's estimates for common birds.

A particular advantage of this last method was that it made use of the WOS tetrad counts. These being the most comprehensive and representative dataset for the county, further ways of using them in calculating estimates were explored. The RSPB surveys, like the WOS timed surveys, involved the counting of all birds seen or heard. Comparing the species densities calculated by 'distance' methods with the RSPB survey figures produces a ratio of 'real' to counted numbers; which might then be applied to the WOS tetrad data to produce estimates for Wiltshire. Thus, if 250 Blackbirds were counted in 50 selected 1-km squares by BBS methods (an average of five per 1-km square), and 'distance' analysis produced a density of 15 per 1-km square, the ratio of 'real' to 'counted' is 3:1. In other words, for every Blackbird that was detected, another two were missed. Ratios calculated in this way, using the RSPB surveys of the Cotswolds and the Chilterns, have been applied to the numbers counted during WOS timed surveys (appendix 4).

It should be stated immediately that any self-respecting statistician or analyst would frown upon such abuse of 'distance' analysis results. Further problems arise in applying the resulting ratios to WOS tetrad data, not least because the BBS counts involved walking for 2 km within a 1-km square, while WOS observers walked for two hours within a tetrad of four 1-km squares. Consequently, some assumptions have to be made about the unknown and varying distances walked by WOS observers, to make the amount of effort comparable for both surveys before applying the extrapolation (see appendix 4 for further details). Still, despite the obvious potential for criticism, this approach has been adopted as one of the ways of deriving a series of estimates which, in combination and in the absence of any single definitive method for producing Wiltshire estimates, might be used to provide some confidence in those figures chosen as the official range.

Pairs

The common currency for breeding estimates is the number of pairs or territories. Converting the figures obtained by the various methods outlined above to pairs is, however, not simply a case of dividing the total by two, since the sexes of any species are not equally detected during breeding surveys – for example, males are often more easily located (even if not necessarily seen) because they sing. Further, depending on the date of the survey, one bird of a pair may be on the nest and therefore 'unavailable' to be detected. Consequently, a 'pair factor' was derived for each species to convert the number of individuals calculated into numbers of pairs, varying from 1·0 (*eg* for Grasshopper Warbler, where it was considered that only males would be detected, and therefore each individual equated to a breeding pair) to 0·5 (where it was considered that both of a pair were equally likely to have been detected, so that the total was divided by two to produce the estimate of pairs).

Three factors were used by the RSPB surveys that employed BBS methods to convert numbers of individuals to pairs, namely 0·5, 0·75 and 1·0. (The median 0·75 was used for those territorial species where it was felt that, in general, three out of four individuals recorded were males on territory: see Stanbury *et al* 2000). Since the selection of the particular pair factor has an especially large influence on the final estimate – using a pair factor of 0·5 rather than 0·75 will reduce the total by a third – two further factors were also adopted for the Wiltshire estimates, mid way between the first and the second, and mid way between the second and third, namely 0·63 and 0·83. Lastly, since the allocation of one of these five pair factors to a particular species is largely a subjective matter, four experienced field surveyors were asked to select one of these five factors for each species and the mean of these values was used as the final pair factor (see appendix 4).

The use of pairs or territories as units of population estimates is a convenient simplification for many species, given the variety of mating systems used by birds (many are polygynous, polyandrous or polygynandrous). The units used for Wiltshire estimates follow those in the most recent revision of national estimates by the Avian Population Estimates Panel (Baker *et al* 2006).

Inconspicuous species

Distance analysis relies on the assumption of complete detection on the transect line – in the case of the BBS, that all individuals within the 0–25 m band are recorded. In reality, this is unlikely to be the case. Some individuals, particularly of less conspicuous or more skulking species, are likely to be overlooked, especially in woodland or scrub habitat, or if the survey does not coincide with their periods of singing or calling. Thus, the time of day, time of year and even prevailing weather are all likely to influence detection, and an individual bird may simply have sat quietly when the observer passed.

To allow for individuals likely to have been overlooked in the closest distance band – over and above those missed because of differing detectability of the sexes, accounted for by the pair factor – a 'detection factor' was also applied to the estimates. In some cases, for particularly skulking species, a factor as low as 0·5 was applied (50 per cent of individuals likely to have been overlooked), but for most species where it was felt that individuals would have been overlooked, detection factors ranged from 0·8 (20 per cent missed) to 0·95 (5 per cent); for many species, however, this factor was 1·0 (all individuals likely to have been detected).

Because, as with the pair factor, such assessments are highly subjective, the detection factor applied to the estimates was the mean of figures chosen by four experienced field surveyors (see appendix 4). It should be added that such a factor forms no part of formal 'distance' analysis. Although it has not been reviewed by any scientific authority, we hope it further develops and enhances the estimates provided in *Birds of Wiltshire*.

Non-BBS species

Other relatively common species are not covered by the BBS, or were not sufficiently common in any of the squares surveyed by the BBS in Wiltshire, the Cotswolds or the Chilterns, to be included in the above analyses. In some cases, an estimate is available from only one data source that is known or is thought to be inaccurate. For example, the 38 BBS squares in Wiltshire surveyed as part of the national scheme – in theory, the most accurate of the approaches – has greatly underestimated numbers of certain species, presumably because of the small sample size. Thus, the BBS estimate of 2988 Barn Swallows in Wiltshire is far smaller than the 8675 counted during the WOS timed surveys.

For these species, estimates have mostly been calculated by a combination of the estimates for other species and informed guesswork. For instance, where estimates believed to be accurate are available for related species, the ratio of the WOS timed counts to the final estimate has been applied to any congeneric for which no reliable estimate is available. Less precise figures – both for the ratio and for the estimate – are then given, reflecting the greater uncertainty involved. Details of the approach used are described in the relevant species account in these cases.

Targeted surveys

A number of species are subject to special or targeted surveys, particularly those that occur in particular habitats and those that breed in colonies. In many cases, such surveys are undertaken nationally. For example, there have been annual counts of Grey Heron nests in the UK ever since 1928, and periodic censuses of Mute Swans have been made at roughly 10-year intervals since the mid 1950s, as have surveys of introduced geese, whereas the three national surveys of Nightingales have been less regular – in 1976, 1980 and 1999. The methods, frequency and intensity of surveys differ (some attempting complete coverage, others only sample coverage from which a total estimate is then extrapolated), but many such schemes, even though national, also enable estimates for Wiltshire to be derived, often with a high degree of confidence.

In addition to national schemes, some surveys have been undertaken solely at the county level, often organised by or through WOS or its predecessors, to deduce numbers of a species of local interest within Wiltshire. Many of these were made in the middle of the 20th century – for instance, Common Redstarts in 1949–51 (Rice 1952) and Grey Wagtails in 1971 (Tyler & Tyler 1972) – but any carried out in the early 1990s, such as that of Curlews in 1994 (McGrath 1995), have been drawn upon to produce contemporary county estimates. (No censuses of this kind were undertaken in the late 1990s, as all possible effort was then focused on the tetrad fieldwork.) Surveys did not necessarily attempt complete coverage, but often concentrated on strongholds known or believed to support the vast majority of the Wiltshire population: thus, the 1994 Curlew survey covered just the Braydon Forest area.

Wiltshire rookeries were counted locally in the late 1940s (Cawkell 1948–50, Cross 1949–50), throughout the county as part of a national survey in 1975 (Gillam 1976), and sampled in 1980 (Gillam 1981). For the 1995–2000 tetrad survey, the counting of Rooks' nests was initially left to observers as part of the April–July surveys, but this meant that some rookeries were overlooked (or, at best, their nests could not be counted) once the tree foliage had emerged in late April; therefore, an additional survey of Rooks, attempting a complete census of all colonies, was specifically encouraged in the last year of fieldwork. (It must be added that, while its concentration in rookeries makes this species relatively easy to census, it is now well understood that by no means all nests are necessarily occupied.) Although no co-ordinated effort was made to survey Sand Martins, casual counts of nest-holes at the county's few colonies during the period of the summer survey fieldwork enabled a relatively accurate estimate of this species also (though, again, not all holes may be occupied).

The conservation importance of the Stone-curlew – not least in Wiltshire, which holds a significant proportion of the British population – meant that data from ongoing surveys by RSPB of this species' breeding strongholds were available for an accurate county total. Several nestbox schemes to improve and monitor the breeding fortunes of other scarce birds in Wiltshire – notably Barn Owls and, latterly, Tree Sparrows – effectively served as censuses since these schemes support the vast majority of the county's populations.

Further detail on the use of targeted surveys to produce estimates of breeding numbers in the county is given within the individual texts, while the results are shown in table 9 on pages 124–135 in 'The status of birds in Wiltshire'.

Uncommon and rare species

For many of the scarcer birds in Wiltshire, the estimates of breeding numbers have, in effect, been produced by expert assessment, usually based on 'casual' observations over a period of years. Species that are rare, whether nationally or locally, often generate sufficient interest for individual observers to seek them out, specifically to confirm breeding, at known or traditional sites. For example, estimates of the county totals of Firecrests, Hawfinches and Crossbills have been derived in this way. In some cases, numbers from well-known sites have been used as the minimum for the estimated range of figures, and the upper limit has then been calculated by allowing for the likelihood of the species being overlooked in areas of similar habitat known to be little visited.

In many instances, such estimates can be corroborated by totalling the tetrads in which the species was recorded as breeding during the fieldwork, or by making simple estimates of the numbers of pairs likely to occur in each occupied tetrad. This applies particularly to those wildfowl, restricted to certain habitats, whose numbers on individual lakes or other wetlands are often reasonably well known from casual visits during the 1990s.

Accuracy and precision of estimates

For many commoner birds, data are available to calculate total numbers by two or more of the above methods. Because it is often impossible to say which of these is likely to be the most accurate, the estimate is then given as a range, using the minimum and maximum figures calculated. For some species, however, it is clear that one or more estimates are unlikely to be representative – for example, where the estimate is exceeded by the number simply counted during the WOS timed surveys, or where one or two estimates differ markedly from three or four others – and such outliers have been excluded from the range derived.

Selecting which values should be treated as outliers is a largely subjective process. In some cases, the different estimates cover a broad range of values, all relatively evenly spaced. A number of factors have been considered when selecting which figures to use, notably estimates for related species and a general impression of relative abundance (numbers recorded by WOS timed surveys are normally assumed to give a reasonable indication in such cases as, for example, whether Marsh or Willow Tits are the more numerous). In some instances, where only two (obviously different) figures are available or, indeed, where only one figure is given but that method has been shown to provide inaccurate estimates for some related species, there is perhaps no clear basis on which to judge their accuracy. Where relevant, comment is provided within the individual species texts if it is felt that the true estimate is likely to be nearer one or other end of the range, or it is difficult to provide clear guidance on which may be the more accurate.

For rarer species, where it seems reasonable, we have sought to provide a range by using the minimum and maximum numbers of breeding pairs recorded during recent years, or by allowing for any we believe to have been missed through incomplete coverage.

As with other estimates used in this book, those for Wiltshire have been rounded up or down to three significant figures.

WINTER ESTIMATES

Common and widespread birds

BBS species

As in the summer fieldwork, the counted totals of bird numbers during winter do not equate to county estimates, because observers covered only parts of the tetrads and because, even along the transect routes, the survey methods used do not enable calculation of the numbers missed because of their distance from the observer.

Winter estimates have, however, been produced here for many common and widespread species by using the ratio of counts at that season to those recorded in the summer surveys. Thus, if twice as many individuals were recorded as in summer, a winter estimate is derived by doubling the summer estimate calculated from the various BBS data, as described above. It should be noted, however, that winter fieldwork covered only a sample 443 of the tetrads in Wiltshire, and the ratio uses the 'extrapolated' winter total, which allows for those tetrads not visited (see 'Atlas organisation, methods and mapping 1995–2000').

Such an approach makes a number of assumptions, in particular that the ability to detect a species is the same in summer as in winter. This is not necessarily the case. In summer, many males were not seen, but their presence noted only by song; in winter, however, many species flock together, again making them more obvious to the observer. It is not possible to quantify the effect of these factors on the resulting estimates for Wiltshire. Nevertheless, in the absence of any existing widespread surveys or methods of estimating winter abundance of common species, particularly passerines, it is hoped that this approach offers a reasonable first attempt at producing estimates for many of these species at a county level.

Ratios of summer to (extrapolated) winter counts as a way of producing winter estimates are available for 62 species (appendix 4). Where the summer estimate was a range, the ratio was applied to both minimum and maximum values, thus giving a range for the winter figures also. The summer estimates used to calculate winter figures were the number of individuals, before the pair and detection factors were applied (see above).

Species that are only winter visitors have no summer estimates, or counts, with which to calculate winter figures. In these cases, the ratio of winter estimates to winter counts for similar species was used to convert counts into estimates. Thus, for Fieldfares and Redwings, the ratios of winter counts to estimates for the three resident thrushes were calculated. These suggested that the ratios of minimum and maximum estimates to counts were, roughly, 2·5 and 7·5. Thus, extrapolated counts of the two winter visitors were multiplied by these figures to give the ranges of their winter estimates. The equivalent values for Bramblings, Siskins and Lesser Redpolls, based on the ratios for the resident finch species, were six and 11 (see appendix 4).

For 21 resident species, the ratio of (extrapolated) winter to summer counts was considerably below 1·0, because far fewer individuals were recorded in winter. For those regarded as essentially resident, this is believed to be largely a consequence of their being more easily overlooked then, for example, because they sing less. Treecreepers, Nuthatches and Marsh and Willow Tits are often inconspicuous in winter, neither forming obvious flocks (other than joining mixed foraging parties of the commoner tits) nor being particularly vocal. Where the ratio of timed winter to summer counts was 0·9 or less, and where it was considered that the species' habits in winter were largely responsible for the apparently smaller numbers – rather than any genuine drop in abundance – winter calculations were based on summer figures. In most cases, it was assumed that winter estimates would have broadly matched the number of breeding pairs multiplied by two, plus a small component for young of the year. The species concerned are made clear in the relevant texts. It should be noted, however, that the numbers of most resident small passerines – particularly of inexperienced juveniles – will decline through the winter from a post-breeding high, and that the rate of decline will increase in severe weather.

The numbers of several species, notably gamebirds and Mallards, are increased substantially in autumn as a result of releases for shooting. In the light of this and the apparently low numbers of Red-legged Partridges, Grey Partridges and Pheasants recorded during timed surveys, it was felt that Wiltshire estimates for these could not be calculated with any degree of confidence.

Non-BBS species

For several species for which no BBS data are available, winter numbers have been estimated by approximations from the breeding figures and some knowledge of autumn movements. Thus, the winter estimates for certain more or less sedentary species are based on the summer figures, with an allowance for surviving young, and revised up or down according to whether or not significant movements into or out of the county in winter are believed to occur. This approach is required where few or no data exist for the species concerned, as is the case for the commoner raptors. Although the counts from the WOS tetrad fieldwork allow some sort of assessment of the estimates for such species – and published data from national or other surveys may also provide average densities for comparison – it is inevitable that figures reached by this approach are likely to be the least accurate of those produced for *Birds of Wiltshire*.

Targeted surveys

A number of species are the subject of dedicated winter surveys. Most notably, monthly counts of wildfowl at many large waterbodies are organised for the Wetland Bird Survey (WeBS), and numerous others are also regularly submitted to the WOS county recorder as casual records. Estimates of the numbers of many swans, geese and ducks in Wiltshire can be produced simply by summing the counts from the different sites. (Only data from the second half of the 1990s have been used.) Adjustments have been made for certain widespread species, such as the Mallard, because a large component of the population is likely to occur on smaller ponds and rivers that are not covered by WeBS.

Although not part of any regular surveys, some other birds that occur in large numbers at traditional sites – such as Lapwings, Golden Plovers and gulls – elicit sufficient interest for observers to make regular counts. In these cases, to arrive at winter estimates for Wiltshire as a whole, counts reported in *Hobby* can be used in the same way as WeBS data for wildfowl. Estimates have also been possible for a few species that, although less common, occur at just one or two sites and are counted regularly: Dunlins at CWP are a good example. Some estimates have been based on other local or national samples. Research by the Game Conservancy Trust into habitat use by wintering Woodcocks, for instance, has enabled average densities to be calculated, which have then been applied to the area of the county. Such cases are highlighted in the texts.

Rare species

As for summer estimates, some species rare in Wiltshire during winter attract sufficient interest for them to be sought out and regularly reported by particular observers; numbers can then be estimated on the basis of record cards submitted to the Wiltshire county recorder. These include conspicuous birds, such as Bewick's Swans, which are unlikely to go unnoticed, and a number of others that, occupying particular habitats or certain sites, are regularly watched. The roosts of Hen Harriers on Salisbury Plain and, to some extent, of Long-eared Owls in several parts of the county are two examples, though the numbers using any unknown temporary or even regular roosts cannot be quantified; thus, estimates for these species should be treated as minima. Numbers of other 'popular' birds, particularly those that are readily seen, such as Peregrine Falcons and Red Kites, can be estimated simply on the basis of submitted records, probably with a reasonable degree of confidence. The data sources used, and any allowances made for the particular habits of the species concerned and the amount of human effort in recording it, are explained in the individual texts.

Accuracy and precision of estimates

With the exception of some derived from WeBS data, estimates for most species in winter are likely to be less accurate than for those in summer. Indeed, as many are based on the summer estimates, any errors in those are likely to have been compounded in the winter figures.

Ranges are given on the same basis as for summer estimates. In some cases, the range simply reflects the degree of uncertainty over the estimate. For others, ranges reflect the varying numbers between winters, which for many species fluctuate to a much greater degree than in summer, according to productivity, weather and other factors operating outside Wiltshire and even the UK.

For some species, particularly the commoner wildfowl, just a single figure is given. This does not necessarily imply a greater confidence in these estimates – and in the same way as winter visitors, they are likely to vary between years – but in the absence of a clear basis on which to revise figures up or down, or to know what sort of margins should be given around the single number, no range is given.

The status of birds in Wiltshire

Peter Cranswick

The Wiltshire List

At the end of 2005, the total number of bird species that had been recorded in a wild state in Wiltshire was 315. The status and distribution of all but six of these – which were noted in the county for the first time after the end of 2000 (see 'Significant additional records 2001–2005') – are described in detail in the individual accounts that make up the major part of *Birds of Wiltshire*. The up-to-date assessment of status provided here for species that occur commonly in the county is based on the decade of the 1990s – or, where there was a marked change over that period, during 1995–2000 – to match the period of intensive fieldwork that provided the basis for the distribution and relative abundance maps in this book. For most other birds, the general assessment ends at 2000, but it also takes note of subsequent records of species new to the list since 2000, or of breeding for the first time.

The 315 species on the Wiltshire List (table 9) are those found in categories A, B or C of the British List, the criteria for which are either having been recorded in an apparently wild state in Great Britain or, although introduced, having established self-sustaining populations in this country. This may be compared with the British total of 572 species – ten of which are in Category B (not recorded in a wild state since 31 December 1949) and ten only in Category C (introduced) – at the end of April 2006 (*BOURC*). We have, however, chosen to consider the Caspian Gull *Larus* (*argentatus*) *cachinnans* as a distinct species – rather than follow the British Ornithologists' Union Records Committee's current treatment of it as a subspecies of the Herring Gull – in view of the widely held belief that it will be raised to species level in the near future.

Of the Wiltshire total, 147 species (47 per cent) have nested on at least one occasion and three more (Ring Ouzel, Redwing and Golden Oriole) may also have done so, but without there being clear evidence. Three of the 147 – Black Grouse, Great Bustard and Cirl Bunting – are former breeders now extinct in the county, while Corncrake, Wryneck, Marsh Warbler and Red-backed Shrike are former breeders that still occur as vagrants. Both Wood Lark and Dartford Warbler, formerly more frequent, are nowadays only irregular breeders. At the end of the 20th century, 116 (37 per cent) continue to breed on a regular basis, even

though some do so only in very small numbers. This figure does not include the Little Egret – one of four species to have nested in the county for the first time since 2000 – although all indications are that it is only a matter of a few years before it will be regarded as such; and an increase in the regularity of breeding by Red Kite and Goshawk since 2000 suggests that their status will soon change similarly. As many as 125 species (40 per cent) winter regularly in Wiltshire, albeit some again only in small numbers, and 88 of these (28 per cent) are also regular as breeders. The Hooded Crow was once an annual winter visitor, but there have been no recent records. A further 33 species (10 per cent) can be regarded as mainly passage migrants through the county, neither breeding nor wintering regularly, although three in this category – Mediterranean and Yellow-legged Gulls, and Crossbill – occur widely outside what are regarded as the normal passage periods for migrants in Great Britain.

Another 125 species are so infrequently recorded in Wiltshire that they can be regarded as no more than vagrants. Indeed, five of these must be considered former vagrants, having not been found in the county since the 19th century. Five of the 125 were, however, once regular breeders in the county, their demise in all cases reflecting national declines. One species – Great Bustard – occurs in both categories, having formerly bred and then been reduced to vagrant status, though it is hoped that the current reintroduction programme on Salisbury Plain may yet see this species returned to being part of Wiltshire's regular breeding avifauna.

As many as 13 (4 per cent) of the species on the Wiltshire List are here as introductions or escapes. Three of these – Greylag and Barnacle Geese, and Rock Dove (Feral Pigeon) – are found naturally elsewhere in Great Britain, but those that occur in Wiltshire are believed to have derived from introduced stock. Nine breed regularly in the county and a tenth, Red-crested Pochard, does so at least occasionally, while the remaining three have occurred as vagrants from established populations elsewhere in Great Britain. The Ruddy Shelduck is included in this last group, although the origins of past records, and the case for genuine vagrancy, remain a much-discussed issue. It should also be noted that the Red Kites that breed in Wiltshire also derive from introduced stock but, as part of a deliberate reintroduction programme for conservation purposes, they are not included among these 13. (Some Red Kites in Wiltshire have been wanderers from the native Welsh population.) A large number of other bird species have also been recorded in the county but, as obvious or likely escapes (many are simply escaped cagebirds) that are not considered to have come from self-sustaining populations, these are not included as part of the Wiltshire List. A summary of the records of these species is given in the chapter 'Escapes and introductions'.

Table 9. Status and population size of all bird species recorded in Wiltshire 1800–2005

Notes to table 9

This table includes all species recorded in Wiltshire by the end of 2005. For each, a brief summary of status in the county is given. For the commoner birds, statements about breeding, wintering or passage describe their status during 1990–2000 or, if there was a marked change over that time, during the latter half of that period.

The principal status of each is listed first. Thus, a common winter visitor that also nests rarely is described as 'Winter migrant, rare breeder'. If abundance in summer and winter are roughly equal, breeding status is given first. Species are identified as migrants if the majority of those in Wiltshire come from another country or, at least, occur as a result of an obvious north-south or east-west change in distribution within Great Britain; any whose occurrence in the county is seasonal, but which are likely to have derived from nearby counties (including a number of largely coastal species that are also found inland in small numbers at certain times of year) – rather than having undertaken what is commonly regarded as long- or even short-distance migration – are described as 'visitors'. Others still, whose movements are less predictable, are noted as 'wanderers'. Inevitably, the distinction between these terms is vague or debatable in some cases – and it must also be remembered that a component of the population of many species that are regarded primarily as residents will have migrated to or from the county to breed or to overwinter – and the terms used are intended simply as a general guide to status in the county.

Breeding status is further qualified if the species or its frequency of breeding is rare or irregular. The term 'rare breeder' is used for those which nest regularly (or at least in most years) but normally number fewer than 10 'pairs'; 'occasional' denotes those which breed irregularly (much less than annually); 'has bred' identifies any which have nested, in general, on fewer than five occasions in all; and 'former breeder' refers to those which used to do so, at least occasionally, but which have not been found nesting for a considerable period. Note that many rare or occasional breeders have been classified as 'migrant' if thought to come from outside the county – although, given the small number of individuals involved, it is often difficult or impossible to know whether such birds are migrants, visitors or wanderers. Any that were first recorded nesting during 2001–05 are specifically noted as such. Birds that occur in the county as BOU Category C species are termed 'naturalised'.

No qualification of abundance is given for wintering status: a species is described as wintering if it occurs regularly in the county at that season, even though its numbers may be small. Many species that are summer or winter migrants also occur commonly on passage, but these are generally noted as passage migrants only if their abundance in spring or autumn is markedly greater than might have been expected from breeding or wintering numbers. As with wintering birds, no qualification of passage status is given. The term 'scarce visitor' is, however, used for Mediterranean and Yellow-legged Gulls, because neither of these readily conforms to any of the above categories.

Estimates are given only for species that occur regularly in the county. Breeding estimates are the numbers of 'pairs' (or 'territories': see *APEP* for the generally accepted breeding units that apply to each species), while winter estimates are the totals of individuals. No estimates are given for passage numbers.

The derivations of estimates are as follows:

- Atlas – an approximation derived from WOS fieldwork during 1995–2000 (*eg* based on the number of tetrads in which the species was recorded as breeding)
- BBS – derived from a combination of WOS and BBS fieldwork in Wiltshire and adjacent counties
- Survey – derived from a specific or targeted survey (usually of a single species)
- WeBS – derived from the Wetland Bird Survey and/or other counts of wintering waterbirds
- WOS – derived from casual records submitted to WOS (not through tetrad fieldwork)
- Best est (Best estimate) – an expert guess where none of the above methods provided adequate data

Although only one source is given for each species in the table, it should be noted that, in many cases, individual estimates were derived from a combination of the above approaches (see 'Calculating population estimates of Wiltshire's birds' for full details of the methods).

For vagrants, the total number of records in Wiltshire to the end of 2000 is given (see 'Significant additional records 2001–2005' for more noteworthy occurrences since then). Those species recorded in the county for the first time since 2000 are specifically noted as such.

BoCC gives the conservation status from Birds of Conservation Concern (Gregory *et al* 2002): 'R' denotes Red-list and 'A' Amber-list species; * signifies species which are Amber-listed in the UK, but where individuals in Wiltshire are from naturalised populations (see also pages 139–140).

No	BoCC	English name	Scientific name	Status	Summer Pairs	Summer Source	Winter Individuals	Winter Source
1	A	Mute Swan	*Cygnus olor*	Resident breeder	125–150	Atlas	1200	WeBS
2	A	Bewick's Swan	*Cygnus columbianus*	Winter migrant			0–20	WOS
3	A	Whooper Swan	*Cygnus cygnus*	Vagrant (23 records)				
4	A	Bean Goose	*Anser fabalis*	Vagrant (3–4 records)				
5	A	Pink-footed Goose	*Anser brachyrhynchus*	Vagrant (15 records)				
6	A	White-fronted Goose	*Anser albifrons*	Winter migrant			0–10	WOS
7	*	Greylag Goose	*Anser anser*	Re-introduced rare resident breeder	5–10	Atlas	20–30	WOS
8		Canada Goose	*Branta canadensis*	Naturalised resident breeder	500–600	Atlas	2000	Atlas
9	*	Barnacle Goose	*Branta leucopsis*	Naturalised rare resident breeder	1–3	Atlas	5–20	WOS
10	A	Brent Goose	*Branta bernicla*	Vagrant (26 records)				
11		Egyptian Goose	*Alopochen aegyptiaca*	Naturalised wanderer			1–5	WOS
12		Ruddy Shelduck	*Tadorna ferruginea*	Former possible vagrant or escape				
13	A	Common Shelduck	*Tadorna tadorna*	Passage and winter visitor, occasional migrant breeder	0–1	WOS	10–20	WOS
14		Mandarin	*Aix galericulata*	Naturalised resident breeder	30+	Best est	100+	Best est
15	A	Wigeon	*Anas penelope*	Winter migrant			500–2000	WeBS
16	A	Gadwall	*Anas strepera*	Winter migrant, resident breeder	10–20	WOS	200	WeBS
17	A	Common Teal	*Anas crecca*	Winter migrant, rare migrant breeder	0–5	WOS	1500–2000	WeBS
18		Green-winged Teal	*Anas carolinensis*	Vagrant (2 records)				
19		Mallard	*Anas platyrhynchos*	Resident breeder, winter migrant	1500	Atlas	6000	Atlas
20	A	Pintail	*Anas acuta*	Winter migrant			10–30	WOS
21	A	Garganey	*Anas querquedula*	Passage migrant, has bred (since 2000)				
22		Blue-winged Teal	*Anas discors*	Vagrant (since 2000)				
23	A	Shoveler	*Anas clypeata*	Winter migrant, occasional migrant breeder			100–150	WeBS
24		Red-crested Pochard	*Netta rufina*	Naturalised occasional resident breeder			30–40	WOS
25	A	Common Pochard	*Aythya ferina*	Winter migrant, rare migrant breeder	0–3	WOS	500	WeBS
26		Ring-necked Duck	*Aythya collaris*	Vagrant (6 records)				
27		Ferruginous Duck	*Aythya nyroca*	Vagrant (6 records)				
28		Tufted Duck	*Aythya fuligula*	Resident breeder, winter migrant	150–300	Atlas	1000	Atlas
29	A	Scaup	*Aythya marila*	Winter migrant			0–5	WOS
30	A	Eider	*Somateria mollissima*	Vagrant (2 records)				

No	BoCC	English name	Scientific name	Status	Summer Pairs	Summer Source	Winter Individuals	Winter Source
31	A	Long-tailed Duck	*Clangula hyemalis*	Vagrant (10 records)				
32	R	Common Scoter	*Melanitta nigra*	Passage migrant				
33	A	Velvet Scoter	*Melanitta fusca*	Vagrant (4 records)				
34	A	Goldeneye	*Bucephala clangula*	Winter migrant			40–70	WeBS
35		Smew	*Mergellus albellus*	Winter migrant			5–15	WOS
36		Red-breasted Merganser	*Mergus serrator*	Winter migrant			1–2	WOS
37		Goosander	*Mergus merganser*	Winter migrant			100–175	WeBS
38		Ruddy Duck	*Oxyura jamaicensis*	Naturalised winter migrant and breeder	5–6	WOS	40–60	WeBS
39	A	Red Grouse	*Lagopus lagopus*	Former vagrant (5 records)				
40	R	Black Grouse	*Tetrao tetrix*	Former breeder				
41		Red-legged Partridge	*Alectoris rufa*	Naturalised resident breeder	n/a		n/a	
42	R	Grey Partridge	*Perdix perdix*	Resident breeder	2500	Best est	n/a	
43	R	Quail	*Coturnix coturnix*	Migrant breeder	40–80	WOS		
44		Pheasant	*Phasianus colchicus*	Naturalised resident breeder	n/a		n/a	
45	A	Red-throated Diver	*Gavia stellata*	Vagrant (26 records)				
46	A	Black-throated Diver	*Gavia arctica*	Vagrant (11 records)				
47	A	Great Northern Diver	*Gavia immer*	Vagrant (21 records)				
48		Pied-billed Grebe	*Podilymbus podiceps*	Vagrant (1 record)				
49		Little Grebe	*Tachybaptus ruficollis*	Resident breeder	200	Atlas	250–500	Atlas
50		Great Crested Grebe	*Podiceps cristatus*	Resident breeder, winter migrant	50–60	Atlas	250	WeBS
51	A	Red-necked Grebe	*Podiceps grisegena*	Vagrant (26 records)				
52	A	Slavonian Grebe	*Podiceps auritus*	Vagrant (21 records)				
53	A	Black-necked Grebe	*Podiceps nigricollis*	Vagrant (28 records)				
54	A	Fulmar	*Fulmarus glacialis*	Vagrant (7 records)				
55		Cory's Shearwater	*Calonectris diomedea*	Vagrant (1 record)				
56	A	Manx Shearwater	*Puffinus puffinus*	Vagrant (32 records)				
57		Wilson's Storm-petrel	*Oceanites oceanicus*	Vagrant (1 record)				
58	A	European Storm-petrel	*Hydrobates pelagicus*	Vagrant (12 records)				
59	A	Leach's Storm-petrel	*Oceanodroma leucorhoa*	Vagrant (22 records)				
60	A	Gannet	*Morus bassanus*	Vagrant (24 records)				

No	BoCC	English name	Scientific name	Status	Summer Pairs	Summer Source	Winter Individuals	Winter Source
61	A	Cormorant	*Phalacrocorax carbo*	Resident, winter migrant, has bred			200	Atlas
62	A	Shag	*Phalacrocorax aristotelis*	Vagrant (26 records)				
63	R	Common Bittern	*Botaurus stellaris*	Winter migrant, has bred			0–5	WOS
64		Little Bittern	*Ixobrychus minutus*	Vagrant (6 records)				
65		Night Heron	*Nycticorax nycticorax*	Vagrant (11 records)				
66		Squacco Heron	*Ardeola ralloides*	Vagrant (3 records)				
67		Cattle Egret	*Bubulcus ibis*	Vagrant (since 2000)				
68	A	Little Egret	*Egretta garzetta*	Passage migrant, has bred (since 2000)			30+	WOS
69		Great White Egret	*Ardea alba*	Vagrant (1 record)				
70		Grey Heron	*Ardea cinerea*	Resident breeder, winter migrant	225–275	Survey	600–750	Atlas
71		Purple Heron	*Ardea purpurea*	Vagrant (6 records)				
72		Black Stork	*Ciconia nigra*	Vagrant (3 records)				
73		White Stork	*Ciconia ciconia*	Vagrant (12 records)				
74		Glossy Ibis	*Plegadis falcinellus*	Vagrant (2 records)				
75	A	Spoonbill	*Platalea leucorodia*	Vagrant (11 records)				
76	A	Honey-buzzard	*Pernis apivorus*	Passage migrant, rare migrant breeder	1–2	Best est		
77		Black Kite	*Milvus migrans*	Vagrant (8 records)				
78	A	Red Kite	*Milvus milvus*	Winter wanderer, re-introduced rare breeder			10–20	WOS
79	R	White-tailed Fish-eagle	*Haliaeetus albicilla*	Former vagrant				
80	A	Marsh Harrier	*Circus aeruginosus*	Passage migrant				
81	R	Hen Harrier	*Circus cyaneus*	Winter migrant, has bred			15–30	WOS
82	A	Montagu's Harrier	*Circus pygargus*	Rare migrant breeder	0–3	WOS		
83		Goshawk	*Accipiter gentilis*	Occasional resident breeder and wanderer				
84		Sparrowhawk	*Accipiter nisus*	Resident breeder	200–500	Atlas	750–1500	Best est
85		Common Buzzard	*Buteo buteo*	Resident breeder	400	Atlas	1300–1500	Best est
86		Rough-legged Buzzard	*Buteo lagopus*	Winter migrant			0–3	WOS
87	A	Osprey	*Pandion haliaetus*	Passage migrant				
88	A	Kestrel	*Falco tinnunculus*	Resident breeder	500–700	Atlas	1500–2000	Best est
89		Red-footed Falcon	*Falco vespertinus*	Vagrant (10 records)				
90	A	Merlin	*Falco columbarius*	Winter migrant, has bred (since 2000)			25–40	Atlas

No	BoCC	English name	Scientific name	Status	Summer		Winter	
					Pairs	Source	Individuals	Source
91		Hobby	*Falco subbuteo*	Migrant breeder	70–80	Atlas		
92		Gyr Falcon	*Falco rusticolus*	Vagrant (2 records)				
93	A	Peregrine	*Falco peregrinus*	Winter migrant, rare resident breeder	1–2	WOS	30–50	WOS
94	A	Water Rail	*Rallus aquaticus*	Winter migrant, occasional resident breeder			100+	Best est
95	A	Spotted Crake	*Porzana porzana*	Vagrant (25 records), has bred				
96	R	Corncrake	*Crex crex*	Passage vagrant, former breeder				
97		Moorhen	*Gallinula chloropus*	Resident breeder, winter migrant	2500–5000	Best est	5000–15,000	Best est
98		Coot	*Fulica atra*	Resident breeder, winter migrant	400–600	Atlas	3200	Atlas
99	A	Crane	*Grus grus*	Vagrant (4 records)				
100		Little Bustard	*Tetrax tetrax*	Vagrant (7–8 records)				
101		Great Bustard	*Otis tarda*	Former breeder, then vagrant; reintroduction scheme begun				
102	A	Oystercatcher	*Haematopus ostralegus*	Passage wanderer, has bred (since 2000)				
103		Black-winged Stilt	*Himantopus himantopus*	Vagrant (2 records)				
104	A	Avocet	*Recurvirostra avosetta*	Vagrant (4 records)				
105	R	Stone-curlew	*Burhinus oedicnemus*	Migrant breeder	40–60	Survey		
106		Cream-coloured Courser	*Cursorius cursor*	Vagrant (2 records)				
107		Collared Pratincole	*Glareola pratincola*	Vagrant (2 records)				
108		Little Ringed Plover	*Charadrius dubius*	Migrant breeder, passge migrant	1–5	WOS		
109	A	Ringed Plover	*Charadrius hiaticula*	Passage migrant, occasional migrant breeder				
110		Kentish Plover	*Charadrius alexandrinus*	Vagrant (4 records)				
111	A	Dotterel	*Charadrius morinellus*	Passage migrant				
112		Golden Plover	*Pluvialis apricaria*	Winter migrant, passage migrant			8000–12,000	Best est
113	A	Grey Plover	*Pluvialis squatarola*	Passage migrant				
114	A	Lapwing	*Vanellus vanellus*	Winter migrant, passage migrant, resident breeder	750–1000	Atlas	12,000–20,000	Atlas
115	A	Knot	*Calidris canutus*	Passage migrant				
116		Sanderling	*Calidris alba*	Passage migrant				
117		Little Stint	*Calidris minuta*	Passage migrant				
118	A	Temminck's Stint	*Calidris temminckii*	Vagrant (11 records)				

No	BoCC	English name	Scientific name	Status	Summer Pairs	Summer Source	Winter Individuals	Winter Source
119		White-rumped Sandpiper	*Calidris fuscicollis*	Vagrant (2 records)				
120		Pectoral Sandpiper	*Calidris melanotos*	Vagrant (6 records)				
121		Curlew Sandpiper	*Calidris ferruginea*	Passage migrant				
122	A	Purple Sandpiper	*Calidris maritima*	Vagrant (1 record)				
123	A	Dunlin	*Calidris alpina*	Passage and winter migrant			10–100	WOS
124		Broad-billed Sandpiper	*Limicola falcinellus*	Vagrant (2 records)				
125		Buff-breasted Sandpiper	*Tryngites subruficollis*	Vagrant (1 record)				
126	A	Ruff	*Philomachus pugnax*	Passage and winter migrant				
127		Jack Snipe	*Lymnocryptes minimus*	Winter migrant			30–50+	Best est
128	A	Common Snipe	*Gallinago gallinago*	Winter migrant, occasional migrant breeder			1000+	Best est
129		Great Snipe	*Gallinago media*	Vagrant (8+ records)				
130		Long-billed Dowitcher	*Limnodromus scolopaceus*	Vagrant (1 record)				
131	A	Woodcock	*Scolopax rusticola*	Resident breeder, winter migrant	300–350	Survey	18,500	Survey
132	R	Black-tailed Godwit	*Limosa limosa*	Passage and winter migrant				
133	A	Bar-tailed Godwit	*Limosa lapponica*	Passage migrant				
134	A	Whimbrel	*Numenius phaeopus*	Passage migrant				
135	A	Curlew	*Numenius arquata*	Migrant breeder, passage and winter visitor	25–40	Atlas	25–40	Atlas
136	A	Spotted Redshank	*Tringa erythropus*	Passage migrant				
137	A	Common Redshank	*Tringa totanus*	Passage and winter visitor, rare migrant breeder	0–5	WOS	0–10	WOS
138		Greenshank	*Tringa nebularia*	Passage migrant				
139		Lesser Yellowlegs	*Tringa flavipes*	Vagrant (1 record)				
140		Solitary Sandpiper	*Tringa solitaria*	Vagrant (1 record)				
141	A	Green Sandpiper	*Tringa ochropus*	Winter and passage migrant			40–60	Best est
142	A	Wood Sandpiper	*Tringa glareola*	Passage migrant				
143		Common Sandpiper	*Actitis hypoleucos*	Passage migrant, has bred				
144	A	Turnstone	*Arenaria interpres*	Passage migrant				
145	R	Red-necked Phalarope	*Phalaropus lobatus*	Vagrant (2 records)				
146		Grey Phalarope	*Phalaropus fulicarius*	Vagrant (50+ records)				
147		Pomarine Skua	*Stercorarius pomarinus*	Vagrant (1–2 records)				
148		Arctic Skua	*Stercorarius parasiticus*	Vagrant (10 records)				

No	BoCC	English name	Scientific name	Status	Summer Pairs	Summer Source	Winter Individuals	Winter Source
149		Long-tailed Skua	*Stercorarius longicaudus*	Vagrant (2 records)				
150	A	Great Skua	*Stercorarius skua*	Vagrant (13 records)				
151	A	Mediterranean Gull	*Larus melanocephalus*	Scarce visitor				
152		Laughing Gull	*Larus atricilla*	Vagrant (1 record)				
153		Little Gull	*Larus minutus*	Passage migrant				
154		Sabine's Gull	*Larus sabini*	Vagrant (2 records)				
155	A	Black-headed Gull	*Larus ridibundus*	Passage and winter migrant, resident breeder	20–40	WOS	15,000–20,000	Best est
156		Ring-billed Gull	*Larus delawarensis*	Vagrant (5 records)				
157	A	Common Gull	*Larus canus*	Winter and passage migrant			4000	Atlas
158	A	Lesser Black-backed Gull	*Larus fuscus*	Passage and winter migrant, resident breeder	100–200	Best est	5900	Atlas
159		Caspian Gull	*Larus cachinnans*	Vagrant (3 records)				
160		Yellow-legged Gull	*Larus michahellis*	Scarce visitor				
161	A	Herring Gull	*Larus argentatus*	Passage and winter migrant, resident breeder	25–50	Best est	500–750	Best est
162		Iceland Gull	*Larus glaucoides*	Vagrant (2 records)				
163		Glaucous Gull	*Larus hyperboreus*	Vagrant (5 records)				
164		Great Black-backed Gull	*Larus marinus*	Winter and passage migrant			10–25	WOS
165	A	Kittiwake	*Rissa tridactyla*	Passage migrant				
166		Ivory Gull	*Pagophila eburnea*	Vagrant (1 record)				
167	A	Little Tern	*Sternula albifrons*	Passage migrant				
168		Gull-billed Tern	*Gelochelidon nilotica*	Vagrant (1 record)				
169		Caspian Tern	*Hydroprogne caspia*	Vagrant (2 records)				
170		Whiskered Tern	*Chlidonias hybrida*	Vagrant (since 2000)				
171		Black Tern	*Chlidonias niger*	Passage migrant				
172		White-winged Black Tern	*Chlidonias leucopterus*	Vagrant (3 records)				
173	A	Sandwich Tern	*Sterna sandvicensis*	Passage migrant				
174		Common Tern	*Sterna hirundo*	Passage migrant, rare migrant breeder	1–10	WOS		
175	R	Roseate Tern	*Sterna dougallii*	Vagrant (2 records)				
176	A	Arctic Tern	*Sterna paradisaea*	Passage migrant				

No	BoCC	English name	Scientific name	Status	Summer Pairs	Summer Source	Winter Individuals	Winter Source
177	A	Guillemot	*Uria aalge*	Vagrant (3 records)				
178	A	Razorbill	*Alca torda*	Vagrant (5 records)				
179		Little Auk	*Alle alle*	Vagrant (25 records)				
180	A	Puffin	*Fratercula arctica*	Vagrant (16 records)				
181		Pallas's Sandgrouse	*Syrrhaptes paradoxus*	Former vagrant (2–3 records)				
182		Feral Pigeon/Rock Dove	*Columba livia*	Naturalised resident breeder	2000–3000	Atlas		
183	A	Stock Dove	*Columba oenas*	Resident breeder	3050–6720	BBS	5530–12200	BBS
184		Wood Pigeon	*Columba palumbus*	Resident breeder	95,300–250,000	BBS	481,000–1,260,000	BBS
185		Collared Dove	*Streptopelia decaocto*	Resident breeder	11,900–19,800	BBS	20,000–33,000	BBS
186	R	Turtle Dove	*Streptopelia turtur*	Migrant breeder	100–150	Atlas		
187		Ring-necked Parakeet	*Psittacula krameri*	Naturalised vagrant				
188	A	Cuckoo	*Cuculus canorus*	Migrant breeder	300–400	Best est		
189	A	Barn Owl	*Tyto alba*	Resident breeder	275–300	Atlas	1000	Best est
190		Scops Owl	*Otus scops*	Vagrant (5 records)				
191		Snowy Owl	*Bubo scandiaca*	Vagrant (1 record)				
192		Hawk Owl	*Surnia ulula*	Vagrant (1 record)				
193		Little Owl	*Athene noctua*	Naturalised resident breeder	300–400	Atlas	600–1000	Best est
194		Tawny Owl	*Strix aluco*	Resident breeder	800–1200	Best est		
195		Long-eared Owl	*Asio otus*	Resident breeder, winter visitor	10–25	Best est	25+	Best est
196	A	Short-eared Owl	*Asio flammeus*	Winter migrant, occasional migrant breeder			10–40	WOS
197	R	Nightjar	*Caprimulgus europaeus*	Migrant breeder	15–20	WOS		
198		Common Swift	*Apus apus*	Migrant breeder	4500–6000	Atlas		
199		Alpine Swift	*Apus melba*	Vagrant (3 records)				
200	A	Kingfisher	*Alcedo atthis*	Resident breeder	100–150	Atlas	200–400	Best est
201		Bee-eater	*Merops apiaster*	Vagrant (5 records)				
202		Roller	*Coracias garrulus*	Vagrant (2 records)				
203		Hoopoe	*Upupa epops*	Passage migrant, has bred				
204	R	Wryneck	*Jynx torquilla*	Passage migrant, former breeder				
205	A	Green Woodpecker	*Picus viridis*	Resident breeder	2100–2820	BBS	5000–7500	Best est
206		Great Spotted Woodpecker	*Dendrocopos major*	Resident breeder	3140–4590	BBS	7500–12,500	Best est

No	BoCC	English name	Scientific name	Status	Summer Pairs	Summer Source	Winter Individuals	Winter Source
207	R	Lesser Spotted Woodpecker	*Dendrocopos minor*	Resident breeder	75–100	Best est	200–300	Best est
208	R	Wood Lark	*Lullula arborea*	Winter visitor, rare resident breeder	0–5	WOS	30–60	WOS
209	R	Sky Lark	*Alauda arvensis*	Resident breeder, passage and winter migrant	43,800–56,100	BBS	20,500–60,800	BBS
210		Shore Lark	*Eremophila alpestris*	Vagrant (since 2000)				
211	A	Sand Martin	*Riparia riparia*	Migrant breeder	750–1000	WOS		
212	A	Barn Swallow	*Hirundo rustica*	Migrant breeder	7500–10,000	Atlas		
213	A	House Martin	*Delichon urbicum*	Migrant breeder	7500–10,000	Atlas		
214		Red-rumped Swallow	*Cecropis daurica*	Vagrant (since 2000)				
215		Richard's Pipit	*Anthus richardi*	Vagrant (1 record)				
216		Tawny Pipit	*Anthus campestris*	Vagrant (1 record)				
217	A	Tree Pipit	*Anthus trivialis*	Migrant breeder	500–700	BBS		
218	A	Meadow Pipit	*Anthus pratensis*	Passage and winter migrant, resident breeder	20,400–23,100	BBS	60,800–68,800	BBS
219		Rock Pipit	*Anthus petrosus*	Vagrant (13 records)				
220		Water Pipit	*Anthus spinoletta*	Winter and passage migrant				
221	A	Yellow Wagtail	*Motacilla flava*	Migrant breeder	300–500	Atlas		
222	A	Grey Wagtail	*Motacilla cinerea*	Resident breeder, winter migrant	300–500	Atlas	500–750	Atlas
223		Pied Wagtail	*Motacilla alba*	Resident breeder, passage and winter migrant	5050–7580	BBS	13,100–19,600	BBS
224		Waxwing	*Bombycilla garrulus*	Vagrant				
225		Dipper	*Cinclus cinclus*	Resident breeder	15–20	Atlas	30–60	Best est
226		Wren	*Troglodytes troglodytes*	Resident breeder	56,500–94,000	BBS	75,000–150,000	BBS
227	A	Dunnock	*Prunella modularis*	Resident breeder	23,500–49,300	BBS	28,600–60,100	BBS
228		Robin	*Erithacus rubecula*	Resident breeder, winter migrant	55,400–116,000	BBS	65,800–138,000	BBS
229	A	Nightingale	*Luscinia megarhynchos*	Migrant breeder	50–75	Best est		
230	A	Bluethroat	*Luscinia svecica*	Vagrant (4 records)				
231	A	Black Redstart	*Phoenicurus ochruros*	Passage and winter migrant, has bred			1–10	WOS
232	A	Common Redstart	*Phoenicurus phoenicurus*	Migrant breeder	20–60	Atlas		
233		Whinchat	*Saxicola rubetra*	Migrant breeder	750–1120	BBS		
234	A	Stonechat	*Saxicola torquata*	Resident breeder, passage and winter migrant	353–498	BBS	650–1000	BBS

No	BoCC	English name	Scientific name	Status	Summer Pairs	Summer Source	Winter Individuals	Winter Source
235		Wheatear	*Oenanthe oenanthe*	Passage migrant, occasional migrant breeder				
236	R	Ring Ouzel	*Turdus torquatus*	Passage migrant, may have bred				
237		Blackbird	*Turdus merula*	Resident breeder, winter migrant	65,100–112,000	BBS	101,000–174,000	BBS
238	A	Fieldfare	*Turdus pilaris*	Winter migrant			125,000–175,000	BBS
239	R	Song Thrush	*Turdus philomelos*	Resident breeder, winter migrant	10,100–21,200	BBS	25,000–50,000	BBS
240	A	Redwing	*Turdus iliacus*	Winter migrant, may have bred			60,400–181,000	BBS
241	A	Mistle Thrush	*Turdus viscivorus*	Resident breeder	2980–6770	BBS	7500–15,000	BBS
242		Cetti's Warbler	*Cettia cetti*	Resident breeder	15–20	WOS	30–60	WOS
243	R	Grasshopper Warbler	*Locustella naevia*	Migrant breeder	150–275	Atlas		
244	R	Savi's Warbler	*Locustella luscinioides*	Vagrant (1 record)				
245	R	Aquatic Warbler	*Acrocephalus paludicola*	Vagrant (3 records)				
246		Sedge Warbler	*Acrocephalus schoenobaenus*	Migrant breeder	2340–4680	BBS		
247	R	Marsh Warbler	*Acrocephalus palustris*	Vagrant, former breeder				
248		Reed Warbler	*Acrocephalus scirpaceus*	Migrant breeder	1100–2200	BBS		
249		Icterine Warbler	*Hippolais icterina*	Vagrant (1 record)				
250		Melodious Warbler	*Hippolais polyglotta*	Vagrant (1 record)				
251		Blackcap	*Sylvia atricapilla*	Migrant breeder, winter migrant	16,100–37,800	BBS	114–269	BBS
252		Garden Warbler	*Sylvia borin*	Migrant breeder	3320–4850	BBS		
253		Barred Warbler	*Sylvia nisoria*	Vagrant (1 record)				
254		Lesser Whitethroat	*Sylvia curruca*	Migrant breeder	2990	BBS		
255		Common Whitethroat	*Sylvia communis*	Migrant breeder	23,300–38,600	BBS		
256	A	Dartford Warbler	*Sylvia undata*	Irregular visitor, occasional breeder				
257		Yellow-browed Warbler	*Phylloscopus inornatus*	Vagrant (7 records)				
258	A	Wood Warbler	*Phylloscopus sibilatrix*	Migrant breeder	20–30	Atlas		
259		Chiffchaff	*Phylloscopus collybita*	Migrant breeder, winter migrant	12,200–28,000	BBS	202–464	BBS
260	A	Willow Warbler	*Phylloscopus trochilus*	Migrant breeder	6520–23,200	BBS		
261	A	Goldcrest	*Regulus regulus*	Resident breeder, winter migrant	15,500–22,200	BBS	15,900–22,600	BBS
262	A	Firecrest	*Regulus ignicapilla*	Migrant breeder, passage and winter migrant	10–20	WOS		
263	R	Spotted Flycatcher	*Muscicapa striata*	Migrant breeder	1500–3000	BBS		
264		Red-breasted Flycatcher	*Ficedula parva*	Vagrant (1 record)				

No	BoCC	English name	Scientific name	Status	Summer Pairs	Summer Source	Winter Individuals	Winter Source
265		Pied Flycatcher	*Ficedula hypoleuca*	Passage migrant, occasional breeder				
266	A	Bearded Tit	*Panurus biarmicus*	Vagrant (12 records)				
267		Long-tailed Tit	*Aegithalos caudatus*	Resident breeder	10,900–19,700	BBS	37,200–67,000	BBS
268		Blue Tit	*Cyanistes caeruleus*	Resident breeder	39,300–106,000	BBS	81,900–220,000	BBS
269		Great Tit	*Parus major*	Resident breeder	26,600–50,500	BBS	61,400–117,000	BBS
270		Coal Tit	*Periparus ater*	Resident breeder	6050–9730	BBS	12,000–20,000	Best est
271	R	Willow Tit	*Poecile montanus*	Resident breeder	250–750	Best est	500–1500	Best est
272	R	Marsh Tit	*Poecile palustris*	Resident breeder	2640–4860	BBS	5000–8000	Best est
273		Nuthatch	*Sitta europaea*	Resident breeder	2300–3030	BBS	5000–8000	Best est
274		Treecreeper	*Certhia familiaris*	Resident breeder	1000–4000	Best est	3000–10,000	Best est
275	A	Golden Oriole	*Oriolus oriolus*	Vagrant (28+ records), may have nested				
276	R	Red-backed Shrike	*Lanius collurio*	Passage vagrant, former breeder				
277		Lesser Grey Shrike	*Lanius minor*	Vagrant (1 record)				
278		Great Grey Shrike	*Lanius excubitor*	Winter migrant			1–5	WOS
279		Southern Grey Shrike	*Lanius meridionalis*	Vagrant (1 record)				
280		Woodchat Shrike	*Lanius senator*	Vagrant (7 records)				
281		Jay	*Garrulus glandarius*	Resident breeder	2500–3000	BBS	5000–7500	BBS
282		Magpie	*Pica pica*	Resident breeder	9200–17,100	BBS	17,400–32,400	BBS
283		Nutcracker	*Nucifraga caryocatactes*	Vagrant (3 records)				
284	A	Chough	*Pyrrhocorax pyrrhocorax*	Former vagrant (5 records)				
285		Jackdaw	*Corvus monedula*	Resident breeder	20,600–49,400	BBS	76,900–185,000	BBS
286		Rook	*Corvus frugilegus*	Resident breeder	36,553	Survey	41,800–81,700	
287		Carrion Crow	*Corvus corone*	Resident breeder	11,300–25,100	BBS	27,600–61,500	BBS
288		Hooded Crow	*Corvus cornix*	Former winter visitor				
289		Raven	*Corvus corax*	Resident breeder	8–12	WOS	30–75	WOS
290	R	Common Starling	*Sturnus vulgaris*	Resident breeder, winter migrant	18,300–52,400	BBS	140,000–402,000	BBS
291		Rose-coloured Starling	*Sturnus roseus*	Vagrant (7 records)				
292	R	House Sparrow	*Passer domesticus*	Resident breeder	17,900–49,500	BBS	23,900–66,200	BBS
293	R	Tree Sparrow	*Passer montanus*	Resident breeder	60–75	Survey	400	Survey
294		Chaffinch	*Fringilla coelebs*	Resident breeder, winter migrant	78,100–160,000	BBS	182,000–374,000	BBS

No	BoCC	English name	Scientific name	Status	Summer		Winter	
					Pairs	Source	Individuals	Source
295		Brambling	*Fringilla montifringilla*	Winter migrant			200–5000	Best est
296	A	Serin	*Serinus serinus*	Vagrant (1 record)				
297		Greenfinch	*Carduelis chloris*	Resident breeder, winter visitor	24,600–50,500	BBS	37,500–77,100	BBS
298		Goldfinch	*Carduelis carduelis*	Resident breeder	18,100–27,100	BBS	30,000–44,900	BBS
299		Siskin	*Carduelis spinus*	Winter migrant, resident breeder	20–50	Best est	3170–5820	BBS
300	R	Linnet	*Carduelis cannabina*	Resident breeder, passage and winter migrant	27,100–37,200	BBS	64,700–88,800	BBS
301	R	Twite	*Carduelis flavirostris*	Vagrant (11 records)				
302		Common Redpoll	*Carduelis flammea*	Vagrant (4 records)				
303	A	Lesser Redpoll	*Carduelis cabaret*	Winter migrant, occasional migrant breeder			1100–2100	BBS
304		Crossbill	*Loxia curvirostra*	Irruptive visitor, occasional breeder	0–50	Best est	0–1000	Best est
305	R	Bullfinch	*Pyrrhula pyrrhula*	Resident breeder	6500–10,400	BBS	10,400–16,600	BBS
306	A	Hawfinch	*Coccothraustes coccothraustes*	Resident breeder	40–100	Best est	100–250	Best est
307		Lapland Bunting	*Calcarius lapponicus*	Vagrant (2 records)				
308	A	Snow Bunting	*Plectrophenax nivalis*	Vagrant (25 records)				
309	R	Yellowhammer	*Emberiza citrinella*	Resident breeder	18,500–57,500	BBS	28,200–87,600	BBS
310	R	Cirl Bunting	*Emberiza cirlus*	Former breeder				
311		Ortolan Bunting	*Emberiza hortulana*	Vagrant (1 record)				
312		Rustic Bunting	*Emberiza rustica*	Vagrant (since 2000)				
313		Little Bunting	*Emberiza pusilla*	Vagrant (2 records)				
314	R	Reed Bunting	*Emberiza schoeniclus*	Resident breeder, winter migrant	1530–2220	BBS	1850–2700	BBS
315	R	Corn Bunting	*Emberiza calandra*	Resident breeder	4510–6050	BBS	6320–8480	BBS

Species diversity

Summer

In addition to the mapping of the distributions and the relative abundance of species, the WOS fieldwork has enabled an assessment of ornithological diversity across Wiltshire as a whole. That for summer is probably the most comprehensive and detailed yet published for any county in the UK. This assessment is, as highlighted elsewhere (see 'Calculating population estimates of Wiltshire's birds'), subject to a number of biases, not least the differing conspicuousness of species and the differing abilities of observers. Nevertheless, the data show a high degree of consistency and the general patterns revealed by the analysis show a pleasing correspondence with our expectations.

Summer fieldwork, and additional information used for mapping distributions at that season, recorded a total of 124 species in Wiltshire during the summers 1995–2000. (Some rare or sensitive breeding species, and vagrants, have been excluded.) At least 20 were found in every tetrad during the summer surveys and almost two-thirds of tetrads held between 40 and 60 (figure 10). There was no obvious large-scale pattern to species diversity in the county. Nevertheless, most species-rich tetrads in Wiltshire are generally associated with water, notably the Cotswold Water Park (CWP), southeast Swindon, the Kennet east of Marlborough, the Avon valley north of Salisbury, and the upper reaches of both the Wylye and the Nadder. (There are also a number of small wooded lakes in the area around the upper Nadder.) Not surprisingly, the regions with the fewest species were the western parts of the Salisbury Plain Training Area (SPTA) and, less obviously, the area immediately east and north of Chippenham, as well as the upper Bourne valley. (In contrast, lower down the Bourne, as it crosses back into Wiltshire, was an area of high bird diversity.) The tetrad with the highest count of species (87) was SU18V, at the southeast corner of Swindon, where the most obvious feature is perhaps junction 15 of the M4, but a mix of habitats includes part of Coate Water, a small river valley, several villages and farms, some patches of woodland, a chalk escarpment and the route of a now dismantled railway. The pattern of numbers of species breeding in each tetrad, as might be expected, closely matches that of summer species diversity (figure 10). One exception is the area of the Cotswolds north of Malmesbury, where there was an obvious high density of breeding species in an area of relatively low overall diversity. This may, however, be a result of observers' differing interpretation of the breeding criteria.

Four species were found in 900 or more of the 915 tetrads that lie wholly or partly (at least 20 per cent) within Wiltshire for the purposes of the summer fieldwork, and the ten most widespread were all recorded in at least 93 per cent of the tetrads (table 10). The proportion in which any species was found breeding was, naturally, rather lower: just two species were recorded as breeding in 90 per cent or more of tetrads; and the tenth most widespread breeding species was noted as such in only a little over two-thirds of the total (table 11). As many as 43 species were found in at least 50 per cent of the tetrads in summer, but only 26 were found breeding in the same proportion.

Despite the differences between proportions 'seen' and 'breeding', the most widespread species were, in general, also those recorded as breeding in the most tetrads: eight of the top ten in the first category were also the among the top ten in the second. A number of species, however, showed marked differences between their overall occurrence and the number of tetrads in which they were recorded breeding. For several, such differences were to be expected: Common Swifts, Kestrels, Common Buzzards and Cuckoos were found in, very roughly, 500 more tetrads than those in which they were recorded as breeding. But others are more difficult to explain: Pheasants, Stock Doves and Goldfinches were recorded as breeding in, respectively, 477, 384 and 361 fewer tetrads than they were simply seen in. (A complete list of the number of tetrads in which each species was found and recorded as

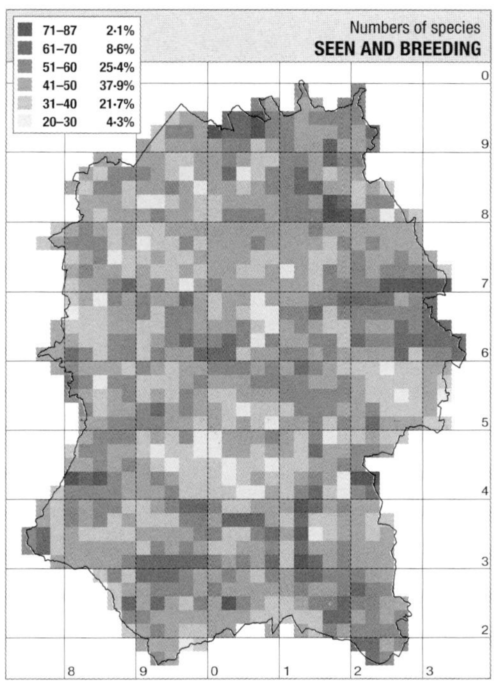

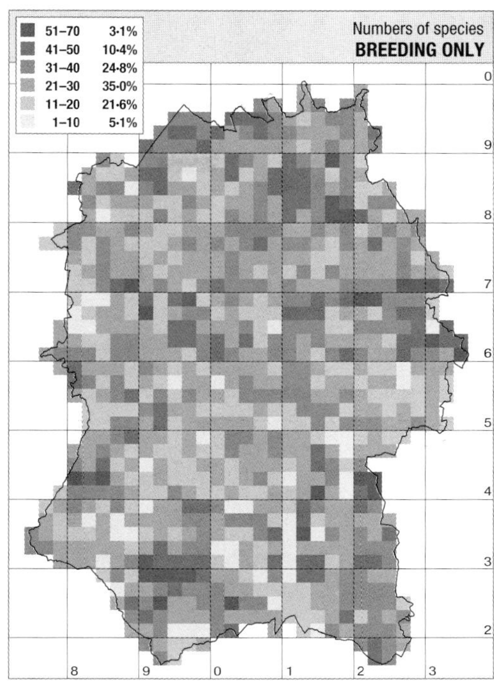

Figure 10. Numbers of species recorded in Wiltshire during the summer tetrad surveys 1995–2000

breeding during the summer tetrad surveys is given in appendix 2.)

Timed visits to assess summer abundance revealed a pattern partly similar to that of species diversity (figure 11). The areas supporting most individual birds were an extended region stretching from northern Swindon to encompass Savernake Forest and Avebury; and the southwest of the county, particularly Longleat–Shear Water and the mid and upper reaches of the tributaries of the Salisbury Avon. A number of tetrads with large numbers of birds were, however, seemingly isolated within areas of low numbers.

Over 313,000 individual birds were counted during the timed summer surveys (based on the higher of the two 2-hour visits to each tetrad: see 'Atlas organisation, methods and mapping 1995–2000'). Between 200 and 400 were counted in just over half the tetrads, but fewer than 100 in 21 of them. The tetrad with the highest recorded number (SU09H) is in the heart of CWP. (The total of individuals counted in

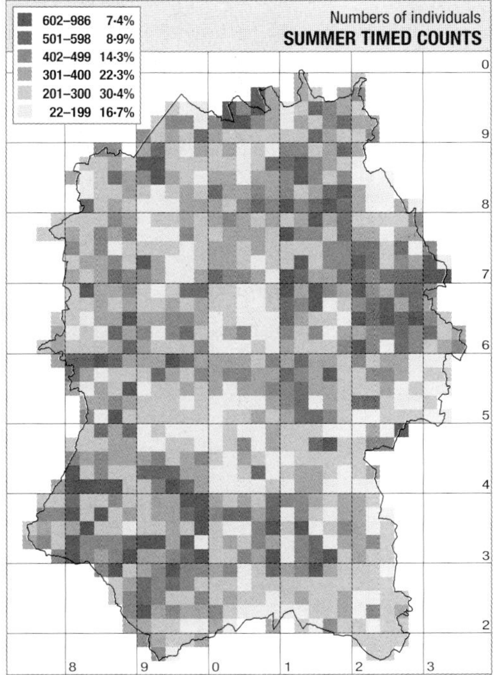

Figure 11. Numbers of individual birds counted in Wiltshire during the summer tetrad surveys 1995–2000

Table 10. The ten most widespread species in Wiltshire as recorded by the summer tetrad surveys 1995–2000

Species	Tetrads	Per cent
Wood Pigeon *Columba palumbus*	912	99·7%
Chaffinch *Fringilla coelebs*	910	99·5%
Blackbird *Turdus merula*	909	99·3%
Wren *Troglodytes troglodytes*	906	99·0%
Carrion Crow *Corvus corone*	889	97·2%
Great Tit *Parus major*	887	96·9%
Robin *Erithacus rubecula*	885	96·7%
Blue Tit *Cyanistes caeruleus*	885	96·7%
Barn Swallow *Hirundo rustica*	859	93·9%
Jackdaw *Corvus monedula*	855	93·4%

Table 11. The ten species breeding most widely in Wiltshire as recorded by the summer tetrad surveys 1995–2000

Species	Tetrads	Per cent
Blackbird *Turdus merula*	847	92·6%
Chaffinch *Fringilla coelebs*	833	91·0%
Wren *Troglodytes troglodytes*	791	86·4%
Wood Pigeon *Columba palumbus*	772	84·4%
Blue Tit *Cyanistes caeruleus*	760	83·1%
Robin *Erithacus rubecula*	759	83·0%
Great Tit *Parus major*	717	78·4%
Common Starling *Sturnus vulgaris*	669	73·1%
House Sparrow *Passer domesticus*	644	70·4%
Jackdaw *Corvus monedula*	621	67·9%

Table 12. The ten most numerous species in Wiltshire as recorded by by 2-hour timed counts during the summer tetrad surveys 1995–2000

Species	Count
Rook *Corvus frugilegus*	36,553
Wood Pigeon *Columba palumbus*	30,854
Common Starling *Sturnus vulgaris*	22,187
Jackdaw *Corvus monedula*	17,201
Chaffinch *Fringilla coelebs*	15,217
House Sparrow *Passer domesticus*	13,825
Blackbird *Turdus merula*	12,695
Wren *Troglodytes troglodytes*	9635
House Martin *Delichon urbicum*	8720
Barn Swallow *Hirundo rustica*	8675

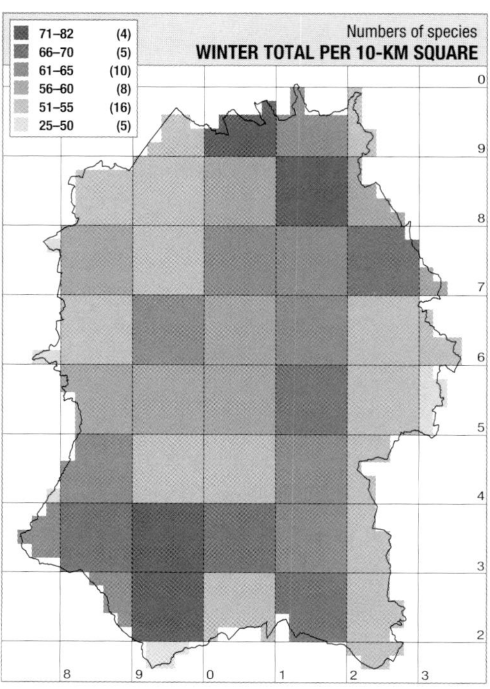

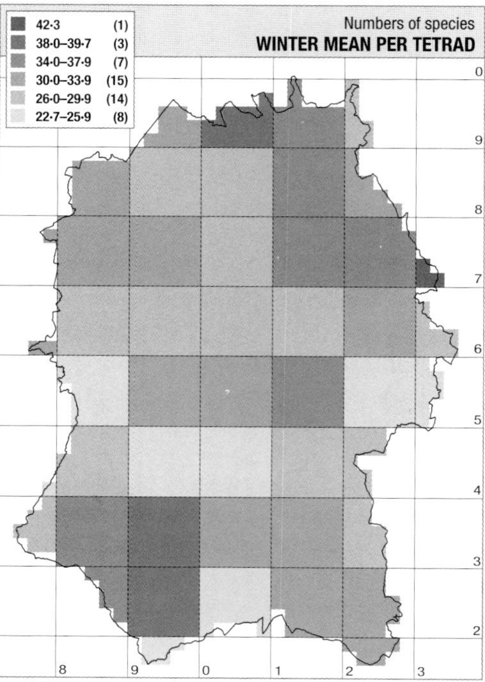

Figure 12. Numbers of species recorded in Wiltshire during the winter tetrad surveys 1998/99–1999/00

each tetrad is shown in appendix 2). Counts of 44 of the species exceeded 1000, and many of the most numerous birds are large, conspicuous, and often gregarious (table 12). (Note, however, that such counts do not always directly reflect true population size, and see also 'Calculating population estimates of Wiltshire's birds'.)

Winter

The pattern of species diversity in winter was similar to that of summer – whether summed at the 10-km square level, or allowing for the varying number of sample tetrads surveyed in each 10-km square (figure 12) – with obvious concentrations in the 10-km squares containing CWP, Swindon, and the upper tributaries of the Salisbury Avon. The range of species diversity at a 10-km level was similar to that of tetrads in summer though, as was to be expected, totals for 10-km squares were less variable, with most containing between 50 and 70 species. The highest total (82 species) was in SU09 – the 10-km square containing CWP – despite only part of that square falling in Wiltshire.

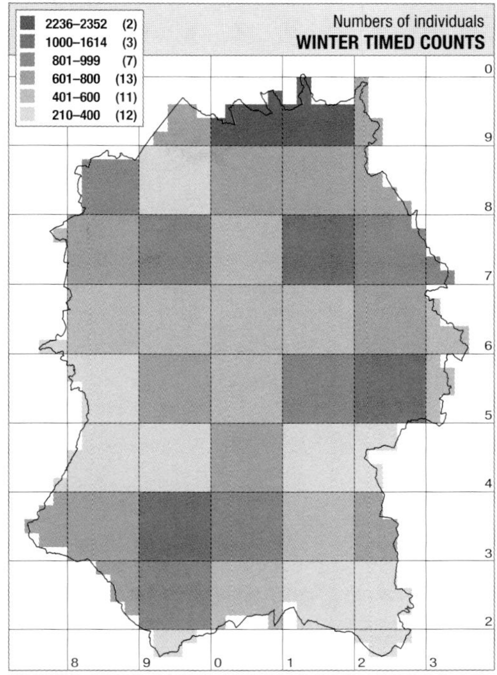

Figure 13. Numbers of individual birds per tetrad in Wiltshire during the winter surveys 1998/99–1999/00
The number of birds per tetrad is calculated as the mean of the numbers counted in the tetrads sampled in each 10-km square

The numbers of individual birds in winter – calculated as the average count per tetrad in each 10-km square, because not all tetrads were covered during the winter survey – were generally higher than in summer (figure 13). The highest recorded totals were again in the northeast of the county (notably at CWP, along the Thames valley and on the Marlborough Downs) and in the southwest (around the Salisbury Avon tributaries). The large numbers in the region of the upper Bourne valley are perhaps noteworthy in view of the markedly low species diversity recorded in that 10-km square during the winter surveys.

Some 318,000 birds of all species were counted in the 443 sample tetrads, and equate to an extrapolated figure of almost 630,000 in the 879 tetrads that comprised Wiltshire for the purposes of the winter survey. (The total of winter tetrads differed from the 915 surveyed in summer because the criterion for the latter had been that at least 20 per cent of any boundary tetrad must lie within Wiltshire, whereas in winter the centre of the tetrad had to fall inside the county: see 'Atlas organisation, methods and mapping 1995–2000'). It should, however, be understood that in all these calculations, the actual numbers, particularly of the smaller and more unobtrusive passerines, would have been much higher than could be found by making simple transects through the main habitats (see 'Calculating population estimates of Wiltshire's birds').

Species of conservation importance

The assessment of the conservation importance of Wiltshire's avifauna might be assessed in a wide variety of ways – many lists of priority species are identified under various national and international agreements and legislative instruments. For simplicity, we have chosen to use the assessment of the 'Birds of Conservation Concern' (BoCC) (Gregory *et al* 2002). This identifies three tiers of importance: a Red list (those most in need of urgent conservation action), an Amber list, and a Green list. The BoCC assessment takes into account both international conventions and a UK perspective, particularly national trends. Thus, the species on the Red list are those which are threatened, either globally or within Europe, or those which have shown rapid declines or contractions in their British breeding populations. The BoCC listing therefore acts as a good overall synthesis of the range of relevant factors when assessing conservation need. Moreover, the assessment is revised on a regular basis, allowing the changing fortunes of British populations – particularly the decline of such widespread and common farmland birds as Sky Larks and Corn Buntings – to be incorporated into updated revisions.

The Wiltshire List as a whole includes 38 species on the Red list and 115 on the Amber (see table 9). At the end of the 20th century, 21 of the former (table 13) and 38 of the latter could be regarded as regular breeders, while corresponding figures for the regular winterers were 18 and 48 respectively.

During the summer fieldwork of 1995–2000, all 915 Wiltshire tetrads were found to have at least one species on the Red list; moreover, 242 tetrads held ten or more of these, and almost 90 per cent held five or more (figure 14). There is, perhaps, no obvious overall pattern in the county to the diversity of species on the Red list – certainly, the more obvious geographical features are not readily discernable – although some central areas, particularly in the west, appear to support a higher density. The distribution of those species that are on the Amber list (figure 14) is more readily linked to geographic features, with watered areas – several river valleys, CWP and the lakes in the southwest – supporting higher densities of species.

Table 13. Numbers of tetrads in which species on the BoCC Red list (see text) were seen, and recorded as breeding, in Wiltshire during the summer surveys 1995–2000

Species	Seen	Per cent	Breeding	Per cent
Common Starling *Sturnus vulgaris*	822	89·8%	669	73·1%
Sky Lark *Alauda arvensis*	809	88·4%	602	65·8%
Yellowhammer *Emberiza citrinella*	792	86·6%	574	62·7%
Linnet *Carduelis cannabina*	776	84·8%	481	52·6%
Song Thrush *Turdus philomelos*	775	84·7%	514	56·2%
House Sparrow *Passer domesticus*	740	80·9%	644	70·4%
Bullfinch *Pyrrhula pyrrhula*	532	58·1%	213	23·3%
Spotted Flycatcher *Muscicapa striata*	432	47·2%	227	24·8%
Grey Partridge *Perdix perdix*	361	39·5%	114	12·5%
Corn Bunting *Emberiza calandra*	295	32·2%	160	17·5%
Marsh Tit *Poecile palustris*	284	31·0%	123	13·4%
Reed Bunting *Emberiza schoeniclus*	217	23·7%	106	11·6%
Turtle Dove *Streptopelia turtur*	142	15·5%	43	4·7%
Quail *Coturnix coturnix*	139	15·2%	23	2·5%
Grasshopper Warbler *Locustella naevia*	90	9·8%	33	3·6%
Willow Tit *Poecile montanus*	85	9·3%	27	3·0%
Stone-curlew *Burhinus oedicnemus*	76	8·3%	70	7·7%
Tree Sparrow *Passer montanus*	75	8·2%	37	4·0%
Lesser Spotted Woodpecker *Dendrocopos minor*	47	5·1%	10	1·1%
Nightjar *Caprimulgus europaeus*	16	1·7%	8	0·9%
Wood Lark *Lullula arborea*	3	0·3%	1	0·1%

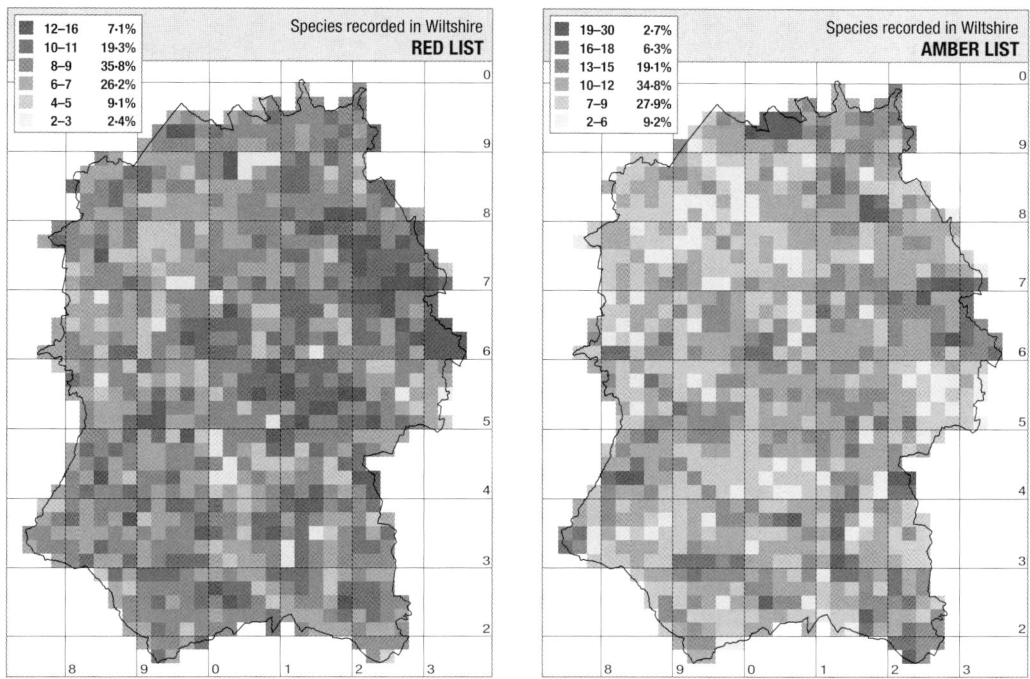

Figure 14. Numbers of species on the BoCC Red and Amber lists (see text) recorded in Wiltshire during the summer tetrad surveys 1995–2000

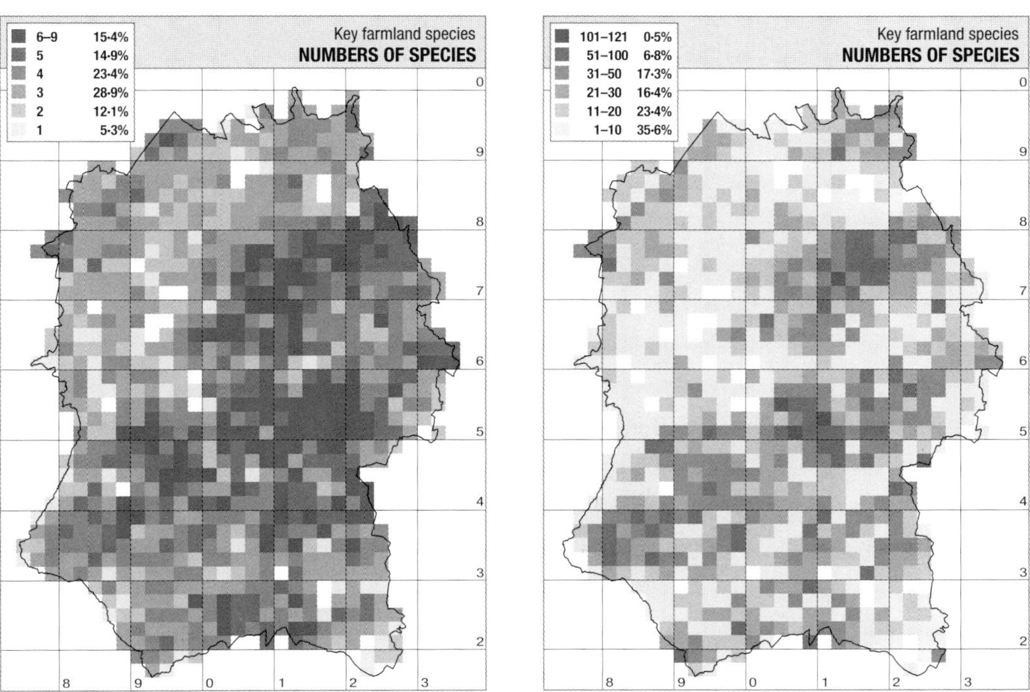

Figure 15. Numbers of key farmland species on the BoCC Red list (see text) recorded in Wiltshire during the summer tetrad surveys 1995–2000

Despite large declines nationally, some species of conservation concern are still faring reasonably well in Wiltshire. The combination of pastoral and arable, and relatively large areas of perhaps less intensively farmed downland, typify much of the county. The distribution and abundance of some key Red list species found primarily in farmland or grassland habitats – Grey Partridge, Quail, Stone-curlew, Sky Lark, Grasshopper Warbler, Tree Sparrow, Linnet, Yellowhammer and Corn Bunting (figure 15) – show how such areas dominate much of the Wiltshire landscape and also the important role of its lasting character for both the local and national avifauna.

Guide to presentation and abbreviations

Birds of Wiltshire contains numerous maps, figures, tables and other data. Full details of how these were derived are provided in relevant chapters and appendices. This section provides a brief overview, and an explanation of conventions, abbreviations and other terms adopted within the book, to act as a simple guide and quick reference for the reader.

General

Birds of Wiltshire aims to be a complete avifauna for the county. We have sought to cover all significant historical occurrences, and provide a summary of changing abundance and distribution, since records began. Data are inevitably more complete for the period since 1974, which marked the formation of the Wiltshire Ornithological Society and the first publication of its annual report *Hobby*. Given the existence of several previous publications, notably Buxton (1981) and Palmer (1991), this book focuses upon status in the 1990s, and in particular 1995–2000, the period of fieldwork on which the various species maps are based. Thus, *Birds of Wiltshire* aims to provide a complete picture up to the end of 2000 and, for example, records of rarities and earliest and latest dates of migrants in the county listed in the species accounts are only for that period. Changes to status and occurrences of vagrants since 2000 are deliberately omitted from the main species accounts, but these and other significant records during 2001 to 2005 can be found in a separate chapter following the species accounts; in such cases, '(See also page …)' is included in the main text.

Nomenclature

The sequence of species and the scientific nomenclature follow the recommendations of the BOURC, including recent changes in certain genera (*eg* the tits) and Latin endings. The only exception is that we have treated the Caspian Gull *Larus (argentatus) cachinnans* as a distinct species.

Against a national trend of giving every species a frequently complicated vernacular name unique to it, we have in general kept English names to their simplest forms. Only when two or more species with the same English 'surname' are on the Wiltshire List have we adopted a 'modifier'. For that, we have often applied 'Common' to the name that is frequently used alone: this is at least innocuous and a word that might be used in the field to distinguish, say, a Green-winged Teal among what are sometimes called 'Eurasian' Teals. We have, however, often dropped any modifier within the species account itself.

We have used hyphens when the English 'surname' is misleading: thus, 'Honey-buzzard' because that is not a buzzard; and, similarly, 'Stone-curlew'. On the same basis, we have followed Ferguson-Lees & Christie (2001) in adopting 'White-tailed Fish-eagle' for what is often called 'White-tailed Eagle' or 'Sea Eagle', because it is not a true eagle (see page 267).

Abbreviations and standard publications

The following abbreviations are used in *Birds of Wiltshire*:

AONB Area of Outstanding Natural Beauty
APEP Avian Population Estimates Panel
BBRC *British Birds* Rarities Committee
BBS Breeding Bird Survey
BOURC British Ornithologists' Union Records Committee

BTO	British Trust for Ornithology
CBC	Common Birds Census
CWP	Cotswold Water Park
Dstl	Defence Science and Technology Laboratory
ESA	Environmentally Sensitive Area
FWAG	Farming and Wildlife Advisory Group
IUCN	World Conservation Union (formerly International Union for the Conservation of Nature)
MAFF	Ministry of Agriculture, Fisheries and Food (the functions of MAFF have been taken over by the Department for Environment, Food and Rural Affairs)
MCNHS	Marlborough College Natural History Society
MoD	Ministry of Defence
NNR	National Nature Reserve (see page 742)
RBBP	Rare Breeding Birds Panel
RSPB	Royal Society for the Protection of Birds
SAC	Special Area of Conservation (see page 742)
SPA	Special Protection Area (see page 742)
SPTA	Salisbury Plain Training Area
SSSI	Site of Special Scientific Interest (see page 742)
STW	sewage treatment works
TAG	WOS Tetrad Atlas Group
WANHS	Wiltshire Archaeological & Natural History Society
WBS	Waterways Bird Survey
WeBS	Wetland Bird Survey
WOS	Wiltshire Ornithological Society
WWT	Wiltshire Wildlife Trust (the name of the Wildfowl & Wetlands Trust is always given in full)

A number of frequently cited major publications have also been abbreviated as follows:

1875–1900 Atlas	Holloway, S. 1996. *The Historical Atlas of Breeding Birds in Britain and Ireland, 1875–1900.* Poyser, London.
1968–72 Atlas	Sharrock, JTR. 1976. *The Atlas of Breeding Birds in Britain and Ireland.* Poyser, Calton.
1981–84 Winter Atlas	Lack, P. 1986. *The Atlas of Wintering Birds in Britain and Ireland.* Poyser, Calton.
1988–91 Atlas	Gibbons, DW, JB Reid & RA Chapman. 1993. *The New Atlas of Breeding Birds in Britain & Ireland 1988–91.* Poyser, London.
BWP – The Birds of the Western Palearctic	Cramp, S, & KEL Simmons (eds). 1977–83. *The Birds of the Western Palearctic.* Volumes I-III. Oxford University Press, Oxford.
	Cramp, S (ed). 1985–92. *The Birds of the Western Palearctic.* Volumes IV-VI. Oxford University Press, Oxford.
	Cramp, S, & CM Perrins (eds). 1993–94. *The Birds of the Western Palearctic.* Volumes VII-IX. Oxford University Press, Oxford.
CBWP	Snow, DW, & CM Perrins. 1998. *BWP Concise Edition.* 2 volumes. Oxford University Press, Oxford.
EBBC Atlas	Hagemeijer, WJM, & MJ Blair (eds). 1997. *The EBCC Atlas of European Breeding Birds: their distribution and abundance.* Poyser, London.
Seabird 2000	Mitchell, PI, SF Newton, N Ratcliffe & TE Dunn. 2004. *Seabird Populations of Britain and Ireland.* Poyser, London.

In a similar vein, for the frequently cited annual reports of several bodies, we have used that body's abbreviation in italics as a reference. Thus, BOURC, as the abbreviation for the British Ornithologists' Union Records Committee, is given as *BOURC* to signify one of their annual reports. In general, we have not specified the year of publication on the assumption that a record for a particular year will be found in the relevant year's report. Where the individual report is not obvious – for example, where a record was, following a review, published several years after the event – then the volume number has also been specified. A list of abbreviations so used, and other commonly cited annual reports, is given below, with the reference to a recent report where relevant.

APEP	periodic report of the Avian Population Estimates Panel, providing definitive estimates for British and UK bird populations (see Stone *et al* 1997, Baker *et al* 2006)
BB	*British Birds*
BBRC	annual report of the *British Birds* Rarities Committee, documenting occurrences of rare birds in Great Britain (see *eg* Rogers *et al* 2002)
BBWC	annual report *Breeding Birds in the Wider Countryside*, summarising British bird population trends based on national monitoring data (see *eg* Crick *et al* 1997, Baillie *et al* 2002, Crick *et al* 2004). Summary results are also available via the BTO web site
BOURC	annual report of the BOU Records Committee (see *eg* BOURC 2004)
DSBL	Dauntsey's School Bird List
EBR	*European Bird Report*, a summary of significant records (including, for example, breeding range extensions) in European countries, frequently published during the 1990s in *British Birds*
Hobby	annual report of the Wiltshire Ornithological Society
RBBP	annual report of the Rare Breeding Birds Panel (see *eg* Ogilvie *et al* 2002)
WANHM	*Wiltshire Archaeological & Natural History Magazine*
WeBS	annual report of the Wetland Bird Survey (see *eg* Cranswick *et al* 2005)

Tabulated data

For many species, numbers of indiviuduals (but also, for example, nests and broods) have been tabulated by years or months for individual sites. In some cases, particularly involving wildfowl, data are presented by winters; then counts are drawn from the months August to March inclusive. Note that many counts of large waterbodies (groups of gravel pits or stretches of rivers) will rarely have been co-ordinated or be a complete count of the whole site (which would have inevitably resulted in higher figures). Thus, for rivers, tabulated counts are generally the highest of individual stretches. Where several points along a river regularly hold large numbers of a particular species, numbers at each are listed separately.

In many cases, it is often difficult to distinguish between genuine zeros (an absence of birds) and an absence of data. Although zeros have been used on occasion (where we are reasonably confident that no birds were present), dashes have generally been favoured in view of the uncertainty, but inevitably a degree of subjectivity is involved in deciding which to use. Dashes for sites which normally hold large numbers are likely to represent missing data (or are used instead of obviously incomplete counts), whereas for sites that usually hold relatively few birds, dashes probably represent no (or very small numbers of) birds.

Maps

A number of map types, in most cases based on fieldwork during 1995–2000 (see 'Atlas organisation, methods and mapping 1995–2000'), are used to depict species distribution and relative abundance.

Summer distribution

Data from timed and casual visits, and in some cases particular surveys, during summers 1995–2000 show where each species was seen in the county, and where evidence of breeding was established.

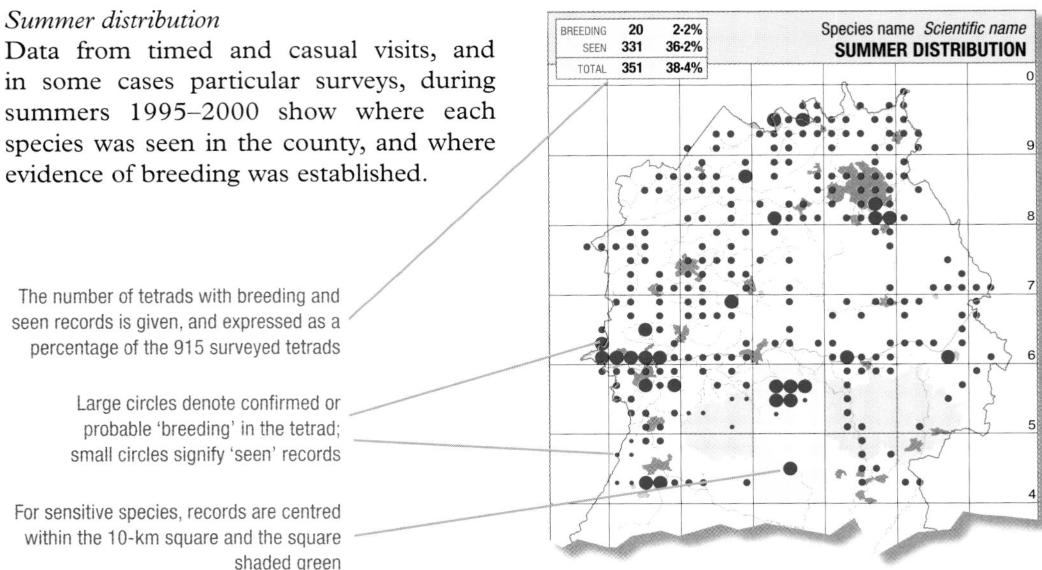

The number of tetrads with breeding and seen records is given, and expressed as a percentage of the 915 surveyed tetrads

Large circles denote confirmed or probable 'breeding' in the tetrad; small circles signify 'seen' records

For sensitive species, records are centred within the 10-km square and the square shaded green

Summer abundance

Relative abundance is shown using the counts from 2-hour visits to each tetrad during 1995–2000.

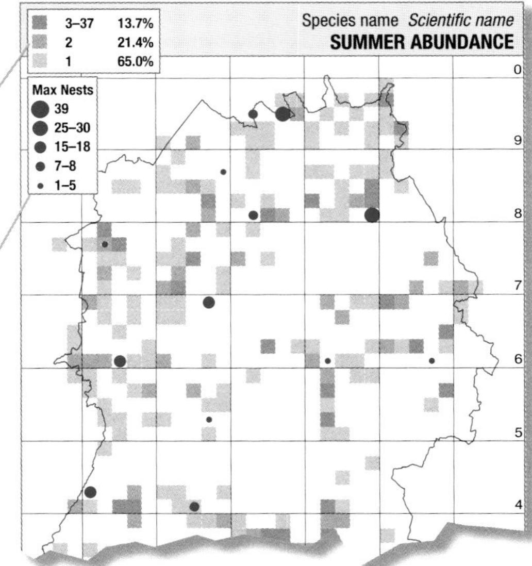

Categories denote the number of individuals of the species concerned counted in each tetrad. Percentage values are the number of tetrads in each category, as a proportion of the number of tetrads in which the species was found during timed visits

Note that, because of rounding, the percentage values may not total 100 per cent exactly

For two colonial species (Grey Heron and Sand Martin), colonies (counted in either casual or timed visits) are overlain as differently sized circles (relative to the numbers of nests) on the summer abundance maps

Winter abundance

Relative abundance is depicted as the mean of the counts of the species concerned from 2-hour visits to a sample of tetrads in each 10-km square during winters 1998/99 and 1999/2000.

Categories show the mean number of individual birds per tetrad; figures in parentheses are the numbers of 10-km squares in each category

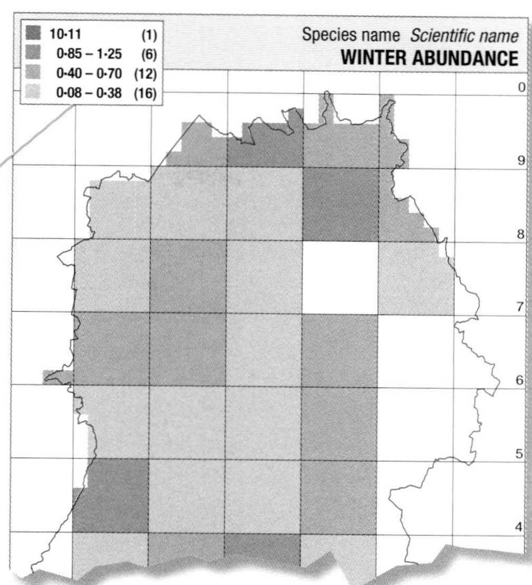

Bird-winters

For species which occur regularly in the county, but whose status is considered to have been greatly undervalued by the winter fieldwork, these maps show the numbers recorded during casual visits in 1995–2000.

Circles denote bird-winters (the sum of the highest count in each winter) for each location at which the species was found in that period

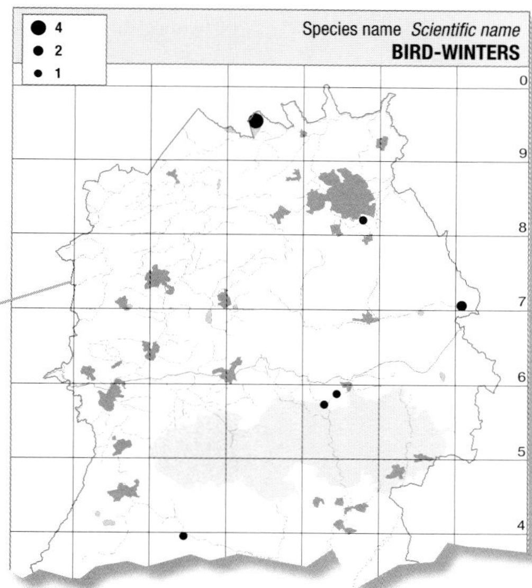

Histograms

Many histograms simply plot numbers of birds against year, winter or month. For some species, particularly scarcer waders – where determining the numbers of individuals is greatly complicated by turnover during passage periods – numbers are given as 'bird-days'. (Note that, for example, 'five bird-days' can mean one bird present for five days or five birds for one day). For more numerous species (again mainly waders), histograms show mean counts, which have been calculated as the average of the peak counts during the relevant period; the minimum and maximum peak counts in that time are indicated using error bars.

Sites

Lists of sites, in tables and the text, are given in a sequence running from north to south through the county, thus often beginning with CWP and ending with the lower reaches of the Salisbury Avon. All locations named can be assumed to be within Wiltshire; sites elsewhere are followed by the relevant county or country in parentheses, with the exception of some large geographic features (such as the Severn Estuary and the Wash) whose locations are assumed to be widely known. Other counties in Great Britain generally follow the names and extent of the pre-1970s counties or districts. The precise location of all named Wiltshire sites are given in the gazetteer.

Authors and artists

Authors of individual species texts are identified by their initials at the end of each account as follows:

GDP	GD Pictor	MVJ	MV Jackson	PCo	P Combridge
GLW	GL Webber	NPA	NP Adams	RT	R Turner
IJF-L	IJ Ferguson-Lees	PAC	PA Cranswick	SBE	SB Edwards
KJG	KJ Grearson	PEC	PE Castle	WEQ	WE Quantrill

Artists of the vignettes that accompany each account are also identified by their initials (see page 26).

Miscellaneous

The Cotswold Water Park (CWP) consists of a large number of lakes, each designated individually with a number (see page 841). Where relevant, these lakes are identified in the text as, for example, CWP68. References to CWP alone, particularly for counts of wildfowl in tabulations, refer specifically to the lakes that lie in Wiltshire. (Note that part of CWP West falls in Gloucestershire, and the eastern part of CWP is entirely within Gloucestershire and Oxfordshire.)

Species texts frequently refer to Wiltshire's '33 core 10-km squares', for example, to assess changes in distribution between the national atlases and fieldwork in 1995–2000. These are the squares for which all or the majority of their area falls within Wiltshire (see page 775).

WOS fieldwork during 1995–2000 involved timed visits to assess relative distribution. These counts were, in most cases, considerably smaller than the true number present (see 'Calculating population estimates of Wiltshire's birds') but are often quoted in the species accounts. Note that, because the winter fieldwork involved a sample survey, visiting only a proportion of tetrads in each 10-km square, the actual count was extrapolated to provide a figure comparable to that of summer, as if counts had been made in every tetrad. Unless specifically stated, the 'winter count' frequently referred to in texts is the 'extrapolated count', to allow comparison with the figure from the summer survey.

Mute Swan

Cygnus olor

Widespread and increasing resident, mainly from long-established feral stock

The Mute Swan is one of Great Britain's most charismatic and familiar birds. It features in stories and entertainment for both adults and children, has starring roles that include a famous ugly duckling, and is portrayed by graceful ballerinas. It is a royal bird, exuding regal poise and elegance, most evident when courting or repelling intruders from its territory, but most famously because Mute Swans are widely believed to be the property of the monarch.

The association between Mute Swans and humans stretches back for over a millennium. In historic times, swan ownership was a mark of status; they were also provided as gifts and, most importantly, used for food (Birkhead & Perrins 1986). The birds were effectively farmed, pinioned to prevent them from flying but free to move along watercourses to feed. At one time, the monarch claimed possession of all swans in England, and Yarrell (1856) maintained that 'anciently the Crown had an extensive swannery annexed to the Royal Palace or Manor of Clarendon, in Wiltshire'. By 966, ownership was already being transferred to others, usually important landowners, and a complicated custom evolved of engraving a pattern on the bill to identify the owner of birds caught during 'swan-upping'. Around 900 swan-marks were registered during the reign of Elizabeth I (Ticehurst 1957); an extensive series of laws was established, and people found guilty of killing swans not belonging to them, or of stealing eggs, were punished with fines or even imprisonment.

The Mute Swan's natural world distribution comprises three general areas, all with a somewhat restricted and patchy range: the most easterly winters primarily by the Caspian Sea, breeding locally there and across central Asia to China; another is restricted to locations around the Black Sea; and the third is found in northwest Europe, where it has spread somewhat in recent decades (Scott & Rose 1996). This last population is resident in Great Britain, Ireland, France, Germany, the Netherlands and Austria; and in summer is also widespread in Poland, the Baltic States and southern Fenno-Scandia, moving in winter from those countries to the Baltic Sea and adjacent ice-free wetlands (*EBCC Atlas*). Elsewhere, the species has become established through introductions in northeastern North America, South Africa, Australia, New Zealand and Japan.

Mute Swans are found nearly throughout Great Britain, except in uplands and parts of the far north of mainland Scotland (*1988–91 Atlas*). Although often regarded as having been introduced here by the Romans or after the crusades, archaeological evidence suggests that they were present in a wild state from prehistoric times, probably breeding wild in East Anglia until the 10th and possibly the 13th century (Ticehurst 1957). By then, however, their persecution for food was great and through the second millennium the species undoubtedly owed its survival to semi-domestication, thriving in the 'swan parks' established since at least 966 (*1875–1900 Atlas*). The 'water-poet' John Taylor (1623), in his journey up the Salisbury Avon, wrote that 'as I passed up the river at the least 2000 ... swans like so many pilots swam in the deepest places before me, and shewed us the way'. By the time swan-keeping waned in the early 18th century, numbers and range had increased substantially as a result of escapes from the now widely dispersed semi-domesticated flocks and through supplementary feeding in winter. Poaching probably limited the population

Table 14. Mute Swans *Cygnus olor* in Wiltshire: totals recorded in national censuses 1955–1990

	1955	1961	1978	1990
Breeding pairs	117	128	134	102
Non-breeders	274	464	384	591
Total birds	508	720	652	795

thereafter, except on private lands where gamekeepers provided indirect protection. Mute Swans received comparatively little attention from 18th century naturalists because they were generally perceived as being feral, but their main distribution was clearly south of a line from Lancashire to Lincolnshire, and they were common in all south coast counties and in Somerset and Wiltshire.

Mute Swans occur widely on many wetland habitats, favouring rivers, small ponds and, in Great Britain and western Europe, man-made wetlands and even urban environments. Such tolerance of people presumably results from the semi-domesticated relationship: eastern populations tend to avoid close human contact. This association also has its costs, however, and vandalism is cited as one of the major causes of nest failure in a 25-year study in the Midlands (Coleman *et al* 1991).

The aggressive and strongly territorial behaviour of Mute Swans, particularly during the breeding season, is well known. It is surprising, then, that they nest semi-colonially in two sites at opposite ends of Great Britain: Abbotsbury (Dorset) and Loch of Harray (Orkney). Apart from these locations and one site in Norfolk, the highest density recorded during the national survey in 1990 was on the Hampshire/Salisbury Avon and its tributary, the Wylye, with 188 pairs and 1052 non-breeders (Delany *et al* 1992): the numbers from the Wiltshire part of this area have been included in the county totals set out in table 14.

Comparison between national breeding atlases indicates stability in Wiltshire at the level of the 33 core 10-km squares, though a slight decline in peripheral squares. The further range contraction shown by the summer tetrad survey contradicts the national trend of an increase by roughly a quarter since the mid 1980s (*WeBS*, based on winter counts). The summer distribution map shows breeding is concentrated along rivers and canals, with an almost continuous distribution along the Salisbury Avon and its major tributaries, as well as the Kennet and the Kennet & Avon Canal, but only patchily along upper reaches of the Bristol Avon between Bradford-on-Avon and Malmesbury. There is also a marked concentration around CWP, on upper reaches of the Thames, and on urban lakes in and around Swindon. Although territory size may vary considerably between habitats (Birkhead & Perrins 1986), this species is strongly territorial and it is

Table 15. Mute Swans *Cygnus olor* in Wiltshire: peak winter counts at key sites 1990/91–1999/00

	90/91	91/92	92/93	93/94	94/95	95/96	96/97	97/98	98/99	99/00
CWP	124	87	50	68	34	74	84	88	82	69
Ramsbury Lake	29	35	42	51	58	55	72	29	50	35
Wilton Water	9	9	2	10	11	9	6	24	15	6
Longleat lakes	9	5	6	3	12	15	12	8	11	7
Fonthill Lake	8	27	2	12	27	17	16	9	14	10
River Wylye	77	56	150	200	60	–	–	–	–	–
Langford Lakes	53	24	60	62	–	–	–	–	–	–
Salisbury Avon	120	71	88	72	115	52	46	45	69	83
Petersfinger Gravel Pits	–	20	8	11	13	29	14	14	12	25

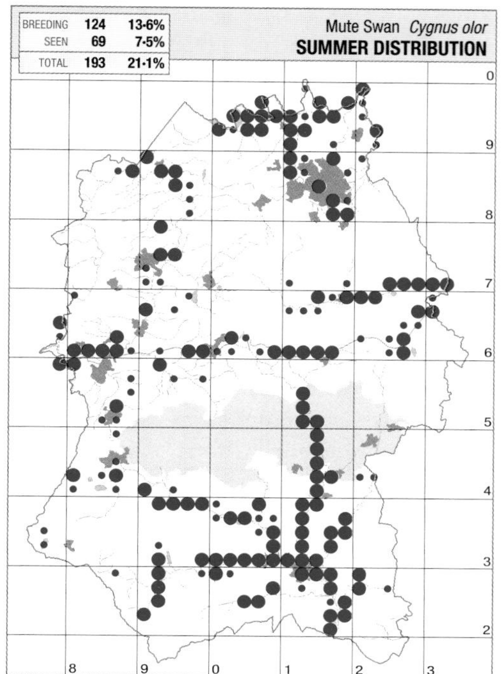

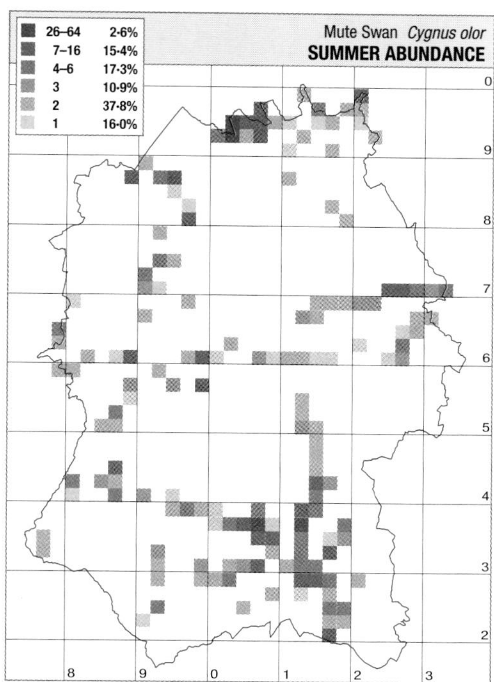

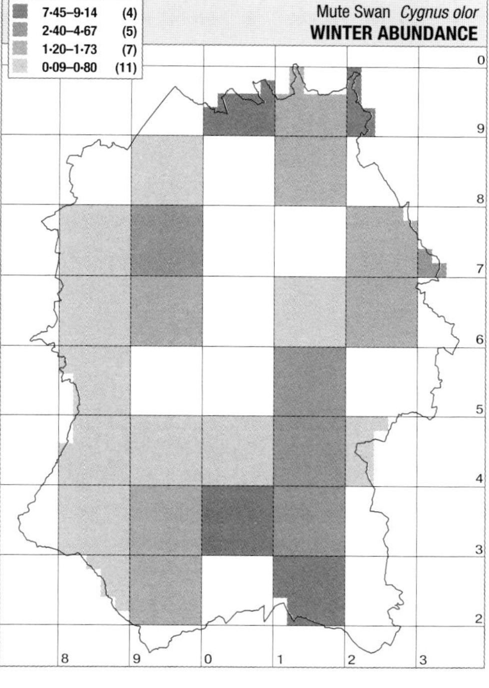

reasonable to expect that the 124 tetrads in which breeding was recorded equate to a similar number of breeding pairs in the county; in this connection, Trump *et al* (1994) found an average territory of 1·75 km along the Wylye. The winter tetrad survey suggests a similar pattern of distribution and abundance and, although the absences in the centre and north are probably an artefact of coverage and methodology rather than a reflection of the true picture, a total winter estimate of 1200 is perhaps reasonable, given the national increase. On 2 February 1984 as many as 280 were counted along the Wylye between Wilton and Wylye itself (*Hobby*). In the late 1990s, favoured sites were CWP (peak of 137) and the Salisbury Avon, in both of which areas counts regularly reached 75, and Ramsbury Lake, where grain is fed daily to the swans and 40–60 were often recorded (table 15); although few co-ordinated counts along the Salisbury Avon and its tributaries are available, totals there are likely to under-represent the true number. The importance of Wilton Water appears to have dropped in recent decades, peak winter counts there having ranged between 25 and 50 throughout most of the 1960s.

The popularity of Mute Swans extends to ringing. Many local schemes catch and mark large numbers with engraved plastic rings that result in frequent re-sightings. A total of 1386 was ringed in the county during 1965–2000, largely in a long-running study in the Hampshire/Salisbury Avon valley, where the oldest survivor recorded in 2000 had been ringed in August 1976 at Weymouth (Dorset). Whilst seasonal movements occur in some regions, notably the congregations in late summer at such traditional moulting sites as the Tweed Estuary, evidence shows that British Mute Swans are largely sedentary. Of the 256 recoveries or sightings of Wiltshire-ringed individuals, only five had travelled more than 100 km. It is, however, worth adding that one colour-ringed at Reading (Berkshire) in 1980 was seen at Corsham in November 1984; and another colour-ringed in moult at Abbotsbury (Dorset) in 1980 and found breeding at Fonthill Lake in 1984 was particularly interesting because most of the Mute Swans that moult at Abbotsbury come from Devon and south Somerset, and there is little evidence of interchange with Hampshire or Wiltshire (*Hobby* 12). Indeed, movements are sufficiently limited that birds in Great Britain and Ireland are now considered as separate populations, distinct from each other and from those in continental Europe (Wetlands International 2002).

These extensive studies, and the relative ease of monitoring such a conspicuous species, mean that the Mute Swan's fortunes have readily been tracked. In 1955 and 1956, when the first national census was undertaken, and in the mid 1980s, numbers remained relatively constant at around 20,000 (Ogilvie 1986). The population fell after hard winters, but the lack subsequently of any real increases comparable with those of other species that occupy similar habitats, such as the Great Crested Grebe, pointed to the existence of additional problems. By the 1980s, the impact of lead poisoning through the ingestion of discarded anglers' weights was well known (Goode 1981) and resulted in the sale of these weights being banned in January 1987. Just three years later, a new national census then showed a sharp increase, to over 26,500 (Delany *et al* 1992, CJ Spray), aided in part by a run of mild winters; and by the late 1990s an estimate based on WeBS data indicated that the increase had continued, to as many as 37,500 (Kershaw & Cranswick 2003).

Yet human factors continue to cause problems for Mute Swans. Flying accidents, particularly collisions with overhead powerlines, and vandalism are the two main causes of mortality (Brown *et al* 1992); and, at least in the Swindon area, fights with dogs are a frequent cause of injury and death, particularly of cygnets (SB Edwards). Furthermore, the increasing numbers of Mute Swans in some areas bring them into conflict with human interests: in the Wylye valley, there have been complaints of damage to crops and also to the aquatic vegetation that provides cover for brown trout; illegal control is thought to occur by egg removal, and there was an unlicensed cull of 70 Mute Swans in the Steeple Langford area in 1978 (Trump *et al* 1994). It is conceivable that management of the population may come to the fore in the future, should this conflict with fisheries or other interests continue to grow.

PAC

Sponsored by Linda Cady in memory of Jennifer Cooper-Wait

Bewick's Swan

Cygnus columbianus

Scarce passage/winter visitor, breeds arctic Russia, winters west Europe

The fact that it nests in the high Arctic from north European Russia across northern Siberia, and at comparable latitudes in North America, gives Bewick's Swan its other, more global, name of 'Tundra Swan'. The race *bewickii* is restricted to Eurasia, and in winter is split into roughly equal numbers between western Europe on the one hand and Japan and eastern China on the other (Scott & Rose 1996), except for relatively few, probably around about 500, that winter around the southern Caspian (Delany *et al* 1999).

The countries bordering the Baltic, particularly Estonia, Denmark and Germany, are heavily used by Bewick's Swans on passage, but the European and west Siberian population winters almost exclusively in the Netherlands and England, apart from smaller numbers in Wales, Ireland, France and Belgium. The British total has grown from 1500 in the 1950s to 7100 in 1999/2000 – which broadly matches increases in the European wintering population as a whole largely through the development since the mid 1960s of the major concentration on the Ouse and Nene Washes (Norfolk/Cambridge) (Rees & Bowler 1997), but has remained generally stable since the mid 1980s (*WeBS*). Although the biggest flocks are found in East Anglia, significant numbers regularly winter at Slimbridge and Walmore Common (both Gloucestershire), on the Somerset levels and, even if currently much reduced, on the Hampshire Avon near Ringwood. Any in Wiltshire are likely to be on their way to, or wandering from, these traditional haunts.

With the national increase from the mid 1950s, it was appropriate that Wiltshire's first record came in February 1954, when eight were seen at Fonthill Lake; in 1955 one appeared at Coate Water; and in February/April 1956 there was a marked 'influx of nearly 40 on six waters' (Buxton 1981) – though the recorded figures in *WANHM* totalled almost 50. At least one bird and sometimes several small parties were then recorded annually through to winter 1973/74, except in the years 1958, 1962 and 1969 (*WANHM*), and from 1975/76 to 1987/88, but subsequently rather less regularly with records in only just over half the winters up to 1999/2000 (figure 16). Regional and national totals fluctuate according to the severity of weather on the Continent, and most Bewick's Swans in Wiltshire do not stay for any length of time. Indeed, it seems that few ever actually alight in the county: in general, records have involved parties of up to 30 in flight, often in October or November as they

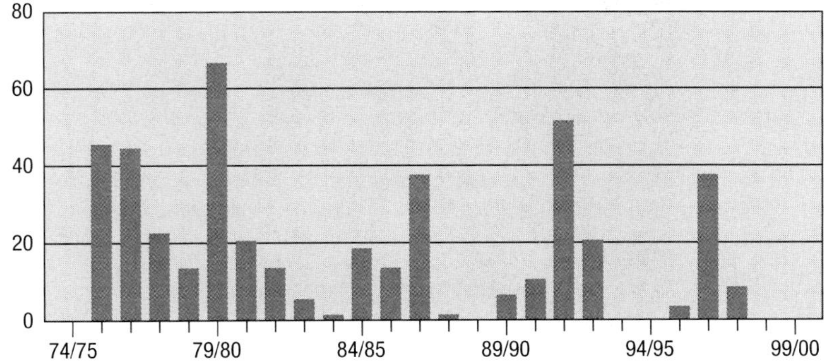

Figure 16. Bewick's Swans *Cygnus columbianus* in Wiltshire: annual totals 1974/75–1999/00

move to their wintering sites; in those months the species may occur almost anywhere in the county. Genuine winterers do occur at the more important waterbodies, however, CWP perhaps being the most frequented. Occasional large numbers at Langford Lakes suggest movement to or from the Hampshire Avon to Somerset or Gloucestershire, so it is perhaps surprising that more are not seen on the Salisbury section of the river. The recent paucity of records reflects an increasing concentration of the population in East Anglia, fewer reaching Ireland and other western locations.

(See also page 726.)

PAC

Whooper Swan

Cygnus cygnus

Winter vagrant (23 records) from north Britain/ Ireland, breeds Iceland/north Europe

The Whooper's breeding range is the most extensive of any swan, stretching from Iceland to far eastern Russia, and extending throughout the steppe and boreal zones from the southern edge of the tundra to central Asia. Small numbers bred in Orkney in the late 18th century, and nesting has been attempted annually in Scotland since 1978, though few pairs are successful (*1988–91 Atlas, RBBP*). Whooper Swans winter in Japan and eastern China, patchily around the Caspian, Black and Adriatic Seas, from the western Baltic and Norway to the Low Countries, and in Britain and Ireland (Madge & Burn 1988).

Those in Great Britain are derived almost exclusively from the Icelandic breeding population, although small numbers of colour-marked individuals from mainland Europe confirm a degree of mixing. Icelandic birds occur widely in lowland Scotland and northern England, and patchily elsewhere in England and Wales. Although they use a wide range of wetland habitats, they also favour pasture and, increasingly, arable. Regular counts as part of international censuses show an increase from around 5000 in the 1960s to almost 21,000 in January 2000 (Cranswick *et al* 2002). Whoopers in England are highly concentrated, notably at Martin Mere (Lancashire) and the Ouse Washes (Norfolk/Cambridgeshire), although the use of these areas by large numbers is a relatively recent phenomenon. Sporadic small numbers in Wales, Oxfordshire and Gloucestershire, often with Bewick's Swans, are usually the nearest to Wiltshire. Consequently, this species is very irregular in the county.

Smith (1887) listed six records for the 19th century. Three of these were dated: 'a dozen…on the Draycot Pond' in 1838 during an especially hard winter (Marsh 1842–62), one in flight west at Clyffe Pypard on 9 February 1877, and one shot at Bowood in 1885; those undated were 'one brought to Lord Radnor at Salisbury', four (two shot) at Britford, and one 'killed at Trafalgar'. (Smith referred to the last of these as a 'Whistling Swan', which was then an alternative name for the Whooper – *eg* Saunders 1899 – but which is nowadays often applied to the nominate North American race, *columbianus*, of Bewick's Swan.)

No more Whoopers were recorded until the mid 20th century, when there were two runs of records associated with the cold winters of that time: three records between 1946/47 and 1950/51 involved 11 birds, and 11 records between 1962/63 and 1965/66 involved 19 or 20. All were on the Salisbury Avon or Wylye, except for one at Erlestoke and two, one and one at Coate Water in three successive winters (*WANHM*, Kennedy 1966). The majority was in mid winter, although some late departing stragglers occurred in March and April. One adult and two juveniles which stayed variously at Alderbury, Longford and Britford from 16 January to 16 February 1947, a family party of two adults and five young at Stratford sub Castle on 16 April 1951, three on the Wylye at Upton Lovell on 10 February 1963 and five nearby at Boyton seven days later were the only groups of more than two (*WANHM*). (Five swans at Fonthill Lake on 15 November 1965 were listed under Bewick's although 'Whooper not excluded'.)

Whooper Swans remain a notable rarity in Wiltshire, with only one record in each decade from the 1970s:

1976	8 February	CWP24	Two adults
1984	25 Feb–15 Mar	Floods near Silbury Hill	Two adults
1993	7 March	CWP26	One adult

(See also page 726.)

PAC

Bean Goose
Anser fabalis

Now only winter vagrant (3–4 records since 1954), breeds arctic Eurasia, winters west Europe

Bean Geese nest in taiga and tundra zones from northern Fenno-Scandia to eastern Siberia, and winter discontinuously from Iberia to Japan. Two of the five generally accepted subspecies, taiga-breeding nominate *fabalis* and tundra-breeding *rossicus*, occur in Europe. In Great Britain, a few hundred nominate *fabalis* regularly winter in East Anglia and Scotland, while *rossicus* is more irregular and usually associated with hard weather movements into eastern England in particular.

Smith (1887) described the Bean as our 'commonest wild goose' and stated that it occurred 'in various parts of the county almost every winter'. None of the subsequent authors on Wiltshire's birds referred to its 19th century status, perhaps implying that they discounted Smith's view. Given, however, that Smith was clearly aware of the differences in the bill and leg colours of the grey geese, and that for most of the 19th century this species was clearly more common than at present (*eg* Owen *et al* 1986) – although previous claims that it was the commonest goose in some other areas, particularly Scotland, are now disputed because of problems with separation from the Pink-footed Goose (*eg* Bourne & Ralph 2000, Bourne 2002) – its former regular occurrence in Wiltshire seems likely. It should be added that Kennedy (1966) considered six geese seen at Yatesbury in January 1887, reported by Smith as 'presumably' Beans, more probably to have been Pinkfeet, but he gave no evidence to support his view.

One 'probably of this species' was reported at Clyffe Pypard on 14 December 1933 (*WANHM*). There followed two records, both considered to involve escapes, of singles near Amesbury in December 1966 (*WANHM*, Buxton 1981) and at Corsham Lake in June 1983 (*Hobby*). Since then, there have been three or four others, all multiples resulting from a large influx into eastern England between late December 1996 and February 1997:

1996	28 Dec–11 Jan **1997**	Downton	Three *rossicus*
1997	7–11 January	Stratford sub Castle	Two, not identified to race
	29–30 January	CWP Kent End	16, some identified as *fabalis*
	7–14 February	CWP74	Up to 21

It seems likely that the flock of up to 21 'mostly seen in flight over CWP74, on several dates between 7th and 14 Feb' (*Hobby*) included the same 16 as had been found at CWP Kent End on 29–30 January.

Sangster & Oreel (1996) presented various arguments, including reproductive isolation, to suggest that *fabalis* and *rossicus* (the latter then as a race of *A. serrirostris*) are best treated as separate species. They also suggested that, because of hunting pressure and indications of declining numbers, this treatment had conservation implications for *fabalis*. If valid, this view makes the (sub)specific identification of Bean Geese in Wiltshire of more than academic interest.

(See also page 726.)

PCo

Pink-footed Goose

Anser brachyrhynchus

Winter vagrant (15 records), breeds Greenland/ Iceland, winters Britain

The Pinkfoot was formerly considered a subspecies of the Bean Goose. It breeds in eastern Greenland, Iceland and Svalbard. While the Svalbard population winters along the North Sea coast from Denmark to Belgium, those from Greenland and Iceland do so in northern and eastern Great Britain as far south as Norfolk. At Slimbridge (Gloucestershire) there used to be as many as 500 to 1200 in the 1930s, falling to about 100 until the early 1960s and generally fewer than ten thereafter, though sometimes up to 20 in the 1990s. The species is now merely a straggler to Wales and southern England, where many records relate to escapes from wildfowl collections.

The only seven Wiltshire records (at least 19 birds) before 1974 comprised an adult male shot at Imber on 12 February 1952; three on the ground at Broad Hinton on 6 February 1955; one at Coate Water in January 1960; one at Chitterne from January to April 1961; one, 'with injured leg, flew away north from near Maiden Bradley' on 16 January 1964; a flock of 11–14 which foraged on two farms at Little Bedwyn during 7–28 January 1964; and one at Corsham Lake in October 1970 (all *WANHM*). Since 1974, leaving aside those considered escapes, the following are likely to have been wild:

1983	13 November	CWP37	Two in flight
1986	10 December	Stourhead	One
	20 & 28 December	CWP29	One
1992	13–16 February	CWP29	Five
	5 March	CWP68	One flying west
1996	3 February	SPTA Chirton Gorse	28 flying east
1998	20 December	CWP68	Nine circled, then flew north
1999	3–6 December	Corsham Lake	One

PCo

White-fronted Goose

Anser albifrons

Scarce and declining passage/winter, breeds arctic Greenland/Russia, winters Europe

Whitefronts breed in western Greenland and around the Arctic Ocean eastwards from the Kanin peninsula and Novaya Zemlya to Canada's Northwest Territories. They winter in eastern Asia and discontinuously from the Middle East to Britain and Ireland, where two subspecies occur: *flavirostris*, from Greenland, in north and west Scotland, north Wales and Ireland; and nominate *albifrons*, from Russia, in England and, until recently, south Wales. Since the 1960s, the numbers of nominate *albifrons* have roughly halved in Great Britain while increasing tenfold on the Continent. Slimbridge (Gloucestshire) remains the British stronghold and the most likely source of those recorded in Wiltshire, especially since their virtual disappearance from the Hampshire Avon area of Ringwood. Although not all in Wiltshire have been identified to race, there are no documented records of *flavirostris*. Escapes of both subspecies are encountered in small numbers in Great Britain (*eg* Delany 1993).

Although knowing of only one report – 'the very reliable testimony of the Rev. G. Powell, who tells me he has seen it in South Wilts' – Smith (1887) thought it 'most probable that so regular a winter visitor to our island frequently favours Wiltshire'. Smith was unaware of a report of a flock of 20 in flight over Marlborough on 11 February 1886 (Hart Smith 1887), although Meyrick (1895) later insisted that these were 'not certainly identified'. Peirson (1959) knew of just one definite 20th century record, of four shot at Marlborough in January 1940, though he shared Smith's earlier suspicion that they were under-recorded and stated 'It is likely that most of the grey geese seen flying over in the winter' were White-fronts. But he had overlooked four other observations: some in a flock over West Lavington on 10 January 1945 (*DSBL*), one also at Ramsbury in 1945, and singletons at Coate and Wilton Waters in 1956 (*WANHM*, Kennedy 1966); and from 1959 to 1969 there were no fewer than 26 records, including five flocks of 20–70 in 1959, 1963 and 1968 (*WANHM*).

Both Buxton (1981) and Palmer (1991) considered that Whitefronts occurred in most winters. Excluding individuals thought to have been escapes, analysis shows that the species was recorded in 13 of the 17 winters from 1973/74 to 1989/90, any bigger numbers coinciding with spells of hard weather in December and January. During that period, flocks exceeded 50 on 13 occasions, the three largest being 800 in flight over Porton on 16 November 1974, 120 at South Wraxall on 23 January 1979, and 110 at Steeple Ashton on 16 January 1986.

It must be added that, during 1929–34, 1936 and 1946–49, a total of 11 years in times when the flight identification of geese was often thought difficult or impossible, *WANHM* published over 100 winter reports of unidentified 'grey geese' (*ie* genus *Anser*) in or, more often, flying over the county, especially between November and March. Many involved parties of no more than 20, but some were larger flights of 50–100; moreover, the severe weather of 1946/47 produced at least three skeins of 100–200, and the cold winters of the 1960s nine flocks of 100–500. Increasingly, a proportion was considered to be 'probably' Whitefronts and the majority may well have been this species – though particularly in the 1930s, some could have been Pinkfeet (*qv*). Bearing in mind that in those days there were many fewer experienced observers and, especially before the late 1950s, recording was more haphazard, it seems possible that the numbers of Whitefronts flying over Wiltshire were at least as high then as was found to be the case in the 1970s and 1980s.

It is probably a reflection of the declining wintering numbers of nominate *albifrons* in Great Britain, and the tendency towards milder winters, that there were many fewer in the 1990s. The species was recorded in only four of the winters after 1992/93 and the largest group was just ten at Corsham Lake in January 1996. Most were present for just one day and there were only two instances of long-stayers involving more than one bird: five associating with the flock of Bean Geese that visited the Wiltshire part of CWP on a number of occasions in January and February 1997; and another party of five at Westbury from 10 January to 7 February 2000. Most were in January or February, although records occurred in all months from October to March. Perhaps the majority go undetected: flocks were heard calling at night over Chippenham, Cricklade and Swindon in February and March 1993, no doubt having just initiated their spring migration from Slimbridge and, given their propensity to depart *en masse*, may have involved several hundred birds.

PCo

Greylag Goose

Anser anser

Scarce/local resident following releases in southern Britain, recent vagrancy from other populations unproved

Greylags breed in boreal and temperate habitats from Iceland across Eurasia to the Pacific, and winter as far south as North Africa, the Middle East, northern India and China. In Great Britain, the indigenous population is nowadays confined to the north and west of Scotland's Great Glen (Thom 1986), but, before the drainage schemes of the 17th, 18th and early 19th centuries, the species bred as far south as the fens of East Anglia (*eg 1875–1900 Atlas*). The Icelandic population, numbering some 80,000–90,000, winters almost entirely in Scotland and northern England, and a few marked individuals from Fenno-Scandia have wandered to Britain.

Greylags have been in domestication in Wiltshire since the early Iron Age (Bramwell 1970); archaeological remains of this species have also been found at a late Bronze Age settlement at Potterne (Coy 1983), and of a goose egg dating from the Pleistocene at Fisherton (Blackmore 1854). In the late 1960s and early 1970s more than 1000 Greylags, chiefly from eggs laid in southwest Scotland by birds translocated from the Hebrides, were released by wildfowling clubs to re-establish the species in many areas from Cumbria and Yorkshire to Anglesey and Kent (*eg* Owen *et al* 1986, WWT unpublished). Aided by further releases (mainly through wildfowling interests) and an increase in the number of reservoirs and flooded gravel pits, the southern population has expanded dramatically since the 1970s, increasing almost 50-fold in that time (*1988–91 Atlas, WeBS*), to around 28,500 presently (Kershaw & Cranswick 2003). Greylags are a familiar sight on many waters in south and east England and the great majority, if not all, of those in Wiltshire nowadays are undoubtedly from this population.

Montagu (1802) referred to Greylags being 'frequently killed upon the Downs in the south of England, feeding on green wheat' and 'one ... shot in the wing ... in the neighbourhood of the Wiltshire Downs, was kept alive many years'. Marsh (1842–62) knew of only one 19th century record: 'two or three ... killed on the river Avon by Mr. Ferris, of Sutton Benger, in the very severe winter of 1838'. Nearly 90 years later, some were identified at Allington, near Devizes, in February 1929 (*WANHM*), but Peirson (1959) was somewhat dismissive of that observation. Five, slowly reducing to one, were then seen on the Bristol Avon at Dauntsey in February–April 1963, and a pair near Fonthill Lake in March 1967 (*WANHM*), but 'these records may refer to escapes' (Webber 1968).

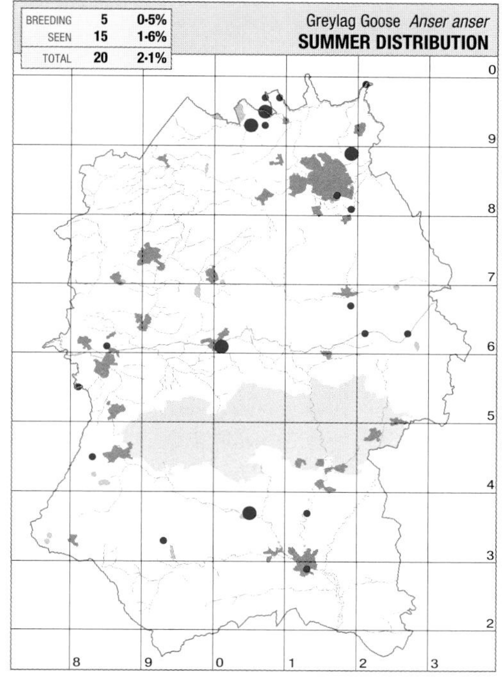

None was noted during the *1968–72 Atlas* survey, but a change in status began when in 'winter ... 1975/76 a small flock arrived at CWP ... apparently escaped from ... Gloucestershire' (Buxton 1981). Since then, Greylags have been present continuously in the Wiltshire part of CWP and more irregularly at various other sites, such as Coate Water, Wilton Water, Corsham Lake, Lacock Gravel Pits, Fonthill Lake, and Langford Lakes. Four young were raised at CWP in 1976 and a further three in 1977, but no more breeding was reported until four young in 1994. The *1981–84 Winter Atlas* recorded the species in four 10-km squares, and the *1988–91 Atlas* in six, with breeding proved in two – at CWP and in the southeast near the Hampshire border. Since then, the Greylag's range has apparently increased, the summer tetrad map showing records in a dozen 10-km squares and breeding in four. Captive-bred Greylags were released at CWP in 1991, and subsequently, to provide quarry for wildfowlers; the current population may be in the range of five to ten pairs, though only one pair was reported as breeding successfully in 2000.

The winter distribution is roughly similar to that of the summer and, although flocks usually do not exceed 20, the total is sometimes boosted through incursions by some of the larger numbers in the Gloucestershire part of CWP and at Buscot (Oxfordshire). For example, there was a record Wiltshire count of 115 at Inglesham on 21 February 1997; and 103 there on 9 November 1998. These influxes aside, Wiltshire's standard maximum of 20–30 is a surprisingly small share of the national total and there seems scope for increase in the future.

PCo

Canada Goose

Branta canadensis

Common resident following releases since 17th century, origin North America

The indigenous range of the Canada Goose is restricted to North America, where it breeds from Alaska to the eastern seaboard and winters as far south as Mexico. Wild individuals have occurred as transatlantic vagrants in Ireland and western Scotland, accompanying flocks of Greenland White-fronted and Barnacle Geese (*eg CBWP*), but those on lakes and ponds in Wiltshire are part of Great Britain's thriving introduced population.

Following releases in the late 17th century, this largest of the 'black geese' (*ie* genus *Branta*) was breeding freely in British wildfowl collections 100 years later (Witherby *et al* 1938–41). Its distribution was, however, limited until the mid 20th century, when translocations designed to alleviate agricultural problems in some areas and provide shooting for sport in others increased both its range and numbers (*eg* Owen *et al* 1986). National surveys have documented the exponential increase, from 3906 in 1953 to 10,510 in 1967–69 and then 19,190 in 1975–76 to 63,581 in summer 1991 (Delany 1992, 1993), by which time the species was widely distributed throughout lowland England wherever there was open water (*1988–91 Atlas*). It has also been introduced to the Continent – where it breeds discontinuously from Fenno-Scandia to western France – and to New Zealand too (*eg CBWP*).

The earliest Wiltshire record involved a flock of seven in January 1867: first seen at Britford, and later at Homington, the flock then evidently moved to the adjoining village of Coombe Bissett (Blackmore 1867b), where Smith (1887) noted that 'their reception was a warm one', one being shot on the 21st and another on the 26th. Blackmore conjectured that the seven were wild since 'I cannot learn that these birds were kept on any ornamental water or lake in the neighbourhood', but Smith commented that this species was 'frequently' so kept and it was 'difficult to say' whether the seven were 'mere tourists... come to visit this inhospitable country of their own free will, or... escaped convicts, involuntarily transported'; Hony (1915a) concluded that they must be escapes. Smith also reported a singleton killed at Enford Manor Farm in September 1870; and Morres (1878–85) referred to breeding at Bemerton in the 1880s. One was reported at Poulton in 1927 (*MCNHS*, Peirson & Walford 1930) and another in 1935 at Marlborough (Peirson 1939), but Peirson (1959) still considered the species an infrequent visitor to Wiltshire. Buxton (1981) commented that, although several introductions were made during the first half of the 20th century, no nesting was recorded until 1968, when a pair raised two goslings at Wilton near Salisbury. The *1968–72 Atlas* showed breeding in three of the 33 core 10-km squares and presence in a further two; a decade later the *1981–84 Winter Atlas* recorded this goose in 17 core squares.

The 1980s saw a threefold increase in Wiltshire, and breeding was established at 22 sites in 1988 (Palmer 1991); by 1989 it was reported that 'The species is now of pest proportions in Swindon', where control measures were taken in 1990, 75 per cent of eggs being sterilised (*Hobby*). Totals of 713 adults and 235 juveniles were recorded at 29 sites in the county during the national census in 1991, when CWP (92 adults), Coate Water (63), Liden Lagoon (108), Kennet at Axford (53), Bowood Lake (76) and Corsham Lake (58) held the greatest concentrations (Rolls 1992). Then, although numbers remained high during the 1990s in north Wiltshire and included a record count of 639 at CWP in August 1993, the expansion there was apparently stemmed. Elsewhere, however, the population continued to grow into the mid 1990s, resulting in counts of 318 on the Salisbury Avon in December

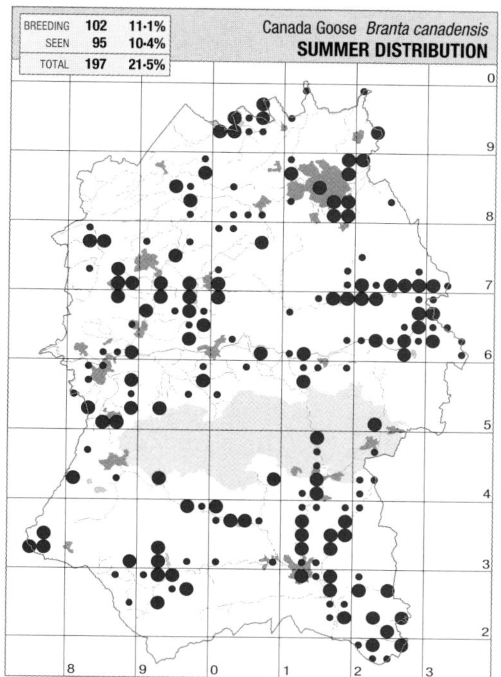

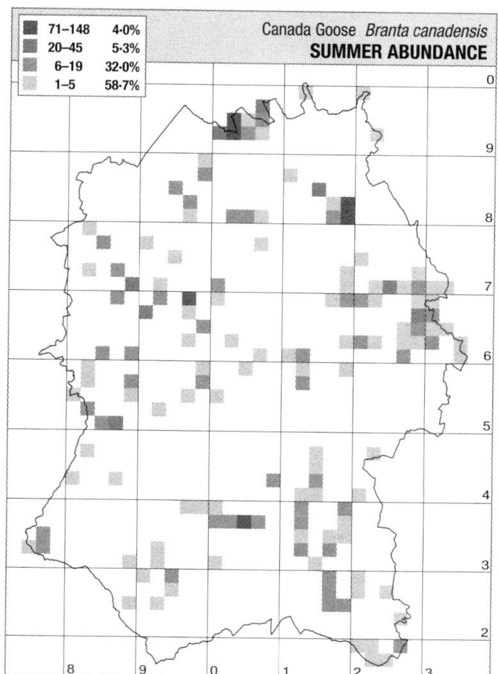

1994 and 238 at Wilton Water in November 1995. Whilst recent data in *Hobby* have suggested that numbers may have stabilised at some of the major sites, the 1995–2000 surveys indicated an ongoing increase in the county as a whole.

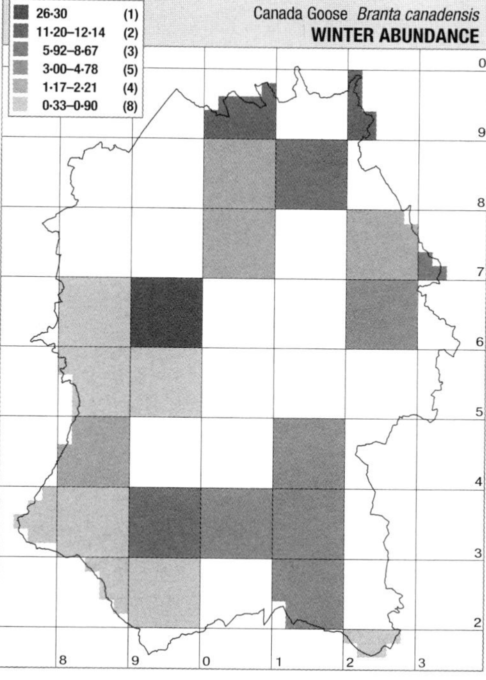

Canada Geese breed in a wide variety of wetland habitats, though favouring urban and parkland lakes, particularly those with islands and short-cropped areas for grazing. The summer tetrad survey showed them present in roughly one fifth of tetrads, and breeding in just over half of those, a far greater number than suggested by the annual average of about 20 localities for which reports have been provided by casual observations in recent years; this underlines their continued expansion into previously unoccupied sites, *eg* estate lakes in the far southeast. The Salisbury Avon and its tributaries, and the upper reaches of the Bristol Avon and the Kennet, are obvious features in the distribution map, but the summer abundance map highlights the greater numbers on lakes and gravel pits, particularly at CWP, Swindon, Bowood, Westbury and Langford Lakes. The summer distribution map suggests that the breeding population currently lies in the region of 150 to 200 pairs, a figure in keeping with a steady increase since the 1991 survey.

Table 16. Canada Geese *Branta canadensis* in Wiltshire: peak winter counts at key sites 1990/91–1999/00

	90/91	91/92	92/93	93/94	94/95	95/96	96/97	97/98	98/99	99/00
CWP	521	275	300	639	213	214	280	91	418	224
Coate Water	51	158	162	68	124	129	243	280	149	350
Liden Lagoon	336	133	307	246	58	109	130	172	167	208
River Kennet/Ramsbury Lake	180	245	186	206	205	–	173	140	120	237
Wilton Water	15	145	170	190	220	238	80	58	109	105
Calne Sand Pits	–	–	–	210	350	140	–	–	–	–
Bowood Lake	126	192	113	279	358	251	169	121	262	294
Corsham Lake	170	116	69	166	111	164	235	223	174	204
Lacock Gravel Pits	4	12	28	90	35	65	73	169	139	85
Langford Lakes	193	250	200	120	57	–	–	–	–	–
Salisbury Avon	128	111	116	250	318	173	320	128	58	86

Timed counts, however, put the summer total at almost 1600 birds which, even allowing for non-breeders (and perhaps some fledged young included in error), would indicate something in the region of 500 to 600 pairs.

Whilst Canada Geese in Great Britain are considered to be a closed population, there are regular movements within the country – for example, a well-marked moult migration from Yorkshire to the Beauly Firth (Highland) in late summer (*eg 1981–84 Winter Atlas*) – while the 20 recoveries in Wiltshire during 1987–99 of Canadas ringed at Chew Valley Lake (Somerset) appear to show that some from this county regularly move westwards to moult there or at least come here afterwards (ringing reports in *Hobby*). There have been two other inward ringing returns: one colour-ringed at Fewston Reservoir (Yorkshire) in July 1995 was seen at Corsham Lake in October the same year; another marked at Chiswick House (London) on 24 October 1993 was sighted on the River Lea (Essex) exactly two years later and afterwards at Corsham Lake that same day, a movement of 152 km in a matter of hours. In contrast, four recoveries from the 92 Canada Geese ringed in Wiltshire have involved easterly or northerly movements: three from Coate Water were recovered in Norfolk, Suffolk and Rutland, while one ringed at Corsham Lake was sighted in Staffordshire.

The winter survey map shows a consolidation of the species' range, lakes in the northeast, the Bowood area and the Salisbury Avon forming the key concentrations. Eleven sites in the county regularly hold 100 or more in winter (table 16), and another eleven have held this number at least once in the last ten winters: Queens Park Swindon (121), Froxfield (245), Shalbourne (200), Whaddon near Trowbridge (200), Bradford-on-Avon (250), Edington Lake (120), Stourton lakes (176), Fonthill Lake (138), River Wylye (100), Clarendon Lake (144) and Petersfinger Gravel Pits (108); many of these maxima were, in fact, in 2000/01 – and accompanied by record counts at Calne Sand Pits (390), Corsham Lake (300) and Lacock Gravel Pits (190) that winter – again suggest continuing growth in numbers. Extrapolations from timed winter counts produce a Wiltshire estimate of 2000, a sizeable proportion of the national population, which was put at 96,000 in the late 1990s (Kershaw & Cranswick 2003).

As their numbers have increased, Canada Geese have given rise to several conflicts, principally damage both to amenity grasslands and to agriculture, and water eutrophication and health problems resulting from the large mass of their faeces (including the possibility of disease transmission at urban sites); the potential risks of collisions with aircraft have also recently been highlighted (Hughes *et al* 1999b). Although the careful design and management of wetlands can alleviate some of these problems, further growth of the population will continue to give cause for concern.

PCo

Barnacle Goose

Branta leucopsis

Escapes/released wanderers not infrequent, vagrants from Arctic very rare

Barnacle Geese breed in Greenland, Svalbard and, in arctic Russia, from the Kola to the Yugos peninsulas and Novaya Zemlya, and winter in north and west Scotland, around the Solway Firth (Dumfries & Galloway/Cumbria), in Ireland, and along North Sea coasts from Denmark to France. In recent years, breeding has been reported in Iceland and the Baltic region, and populations are well established in northwest Europe, including Great Britain, following escapes and releases from collections.

Smith (1887) knew of two killed at Enford on 25 February 1865 and another, undated, killed at Britford. The first 20th century records involved three at Compton Chamberlayne on 21 March 1923, one at Bowood Lake in January 1957 and five above Longford in April 1959 (all *WANHM*). One then stayed at Wilton Water throughout the winter of 1969/70, from 1 November to early April (*WANHM*). Buxton (1981) referred to just two more singletons (one found dead) up to the end of 1975, and then continued that there had been 'Since 1976 ... a number of records at the [Cotswold] Water Park ... and several hybrids'. Both the *1981–84 Winter Atlas*, which mapped Barnacle Geese in five of Wiltshire's 33 core 10-km squares, and Palmer (1991), who noted 'annual feral occurrences in recent years', confirmed this trend, which continued through the 1990s.

Although Great Britain's expanding breeding population included 100 or more in both Gloucestershire (up to 175, but mostly removed in the mid 1990s) and Hampshire (*eg* Delany 1993), numbers in Wiltshire remained small. There were no indications of breeding until 1993, when a pair with a gosling was seen at Ramsbury Lake, and the only double-figure counts by the end of 2000 were at Wardour Castle (20 in January 1970), at Ramsbury (a peak of 33 in August 1993 that fell sharply by early winter), and on the Avon north of Salisbury (ten in winter 1993) (*WeBS*). The summer tetrad survey recorded Barnacles in seven of Wiltshire's core 10-km squares, and breeding in two out of thirteen tetrads. In line with populations of other introduced wildfowl, numbers seem likely to increase in the county in future.

PCo

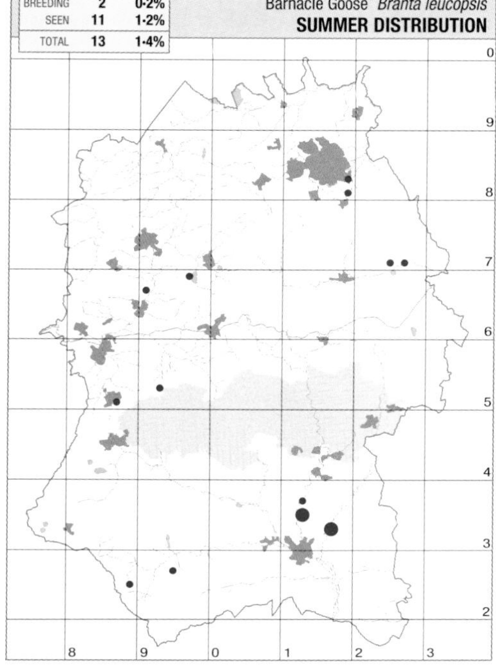

Brent Goose

Branta bernicla

Winter vagrant (26 records) from coasts, breeds circumpolar high Arctic

Brent Geese winter on the coasts of the north Atlantic and north Pacific, and breed in the Arctic on mainland tundra coasts and all major islands. Three forms, sometimes now treated as separate species (*eg* Sangster *et al* 1997), are currently recognised: dark-bellied nominate *bernicla* in western Siberia; *nigricans* (known as the 'Black Brant') in eastern Siberia, Alaska and western Canada; and pale-bellied *hrota* in eastern Canada, Greenland and Svalbard. In addition, evidence for a fourth, 'grey-bellied' form in northwest Canada (Boyd & Maltby 1979) is currently being closely scrutinised.

All Brent Geese recorded in Wiltshire apparently relate to nominate *bernicla*, which winters on coasts of the North Sea, English Channel and Atlantic, between Denmark and western France, and is the form most likely to occur in the county. In Great Britain as a whole, this race is most numerous from the Solent to the Wash. Common in the 19th century, the numbers of nominate *bernicla* wintering in western Europe fell by an estimated 75 per cent to 16,500 by the mid 1950s, of which 7400 were in Great Britain (*eg* Ogilvie & St Joseph 1976). Since then, numbers have recovered, and counts exceeded 100,000 in several winters during the 1990s (*WeBS*). Records of this maritime goose in Wiltshire reflect its changing status.

Table 17. Brent Geese *Branta bernicla* in Wiltshire: records by five-year totals 1976–2000

	1976–80	1981–85	1986–90	1991–95	1996–00
Records	0	2	2	8	7

Smith (1887) – who, from his description, was clearly referring to nominate *bernicla* – knew of records from Salisbury, Corsham, Calne (February 1870), West Lavington (October 1881), Collingbourne (winter 1881/82, spring 1887) and Britford (April 1884). There were no further reports until one at Clarendon in December1933 (*WANHM*), and then no more for another five decades until one at Boscombe Down in November 1982 became the first of three records in the 1980s. Those included the largest flock ever reported in the county, when an estimated 200–300 were heard at night over Wick Down, near Downton, in March 1985. Frequency of observations then increased in line with the national winter population: a further 16 records during 1990–2000 (table 17) totalled 36 birds. The earliest in autumn

Table 18. Brent Geese *Branta bernicla* in Wiltshire: monthly totals of records 1982–2000

	Jul	Aug	Sep	Oct	Nov	Dec	Jan	Feb	Mar	Apr	May	Jun
Records	0	0	0	2	2	2	4	2	5	0	1	0

was one at CWP on 3 October 1998, and the latest in spring two there on 26 May 1991; eight of the records were from CWP and a majority of the rest in, or north of, the Salisbury Avon valley. Most records were in March (table 18) and the larger parties were all flying north on return passage, but others may simply have been wandering disoriented. Unfortunately, although distinction is straightforward, few were identified as being adult or first-winter.

(See also page 726.)

PCo

Egyptian Goose

Alopochen aegyptiaca

Occasional wanderer from southeast England, where introduced from Africa

Egyptian Geese once bred in parts of the Middle East and southeast Europe, but nowadays occur naturally only in Africa. Introduced populations have long been established in France, Germany and the Low Countries, as well as in Great Britain. Recent estimates for Flemish Belgium (300–450 pairs in 2000) and the Netherlands (2500–3300 pairs in 1998–99) indicate thriving populations there (F Hustings, A Ovaa, D Vangeluwe, G Vermeersch).

Present in British wildfowl collections from the 1600s, free-flying breeding groups of Egyptian Geese were established in Devon, Bedfordshire, Norfolk and East Lothian in the 19th century (*1875–1900 Atlas*), but by the time the species was formally added to the British List in 1971 it was confined mostly to Norfolk. A national survey of introduced and escaped geese in summer 1991 found 906 Egyptian Geese in ten counties and proved breeding in three (Delany 1993), and Ogilvie *et al* (2000) reported 82 breeding pairs in six counties in 1998.

Smith (1887) noted that the first for Wiltshire were 'two ... killed at Corsham Court some years back', whereas Morres (1878–85) wrote, somewhat overenthusiastically, 'This peculiarly plumaged bird is also occasionally met with in our district [Salisbury], and though some may possibly be escaped birds, a sufficient number of undoubtedly wild specimens have been procured to authorise its admission into our list'. The first 20th century record was of one at Great Durnford in March 1982 (Palmer 1991). In 1988 the species was seen at Coate Water, Corsham Lake, Longleat and Salisbury and has been recorded almost annually ever since, mostly in the Salisbury and Swindon areas, though no group has exceeded four individuals and breeding has not been reported.

PCo

Ruddy Shelduck

Tadorna ferruginea

Former possible vagrant, perhaps from southeast Europe, now rare escape

Dispersive and nomadic, Ruddy Shelducks inhabit lakes and rivers on open steppe and semi-desert from Manchuria west to Turkey, sparingly also in Greece and around the Black Sea, with outposts in northwest Africa and Ethiopia. In Great Britain, their status has long been clouded by escapes from wildfowl collections (*eg* Saunders 1899). Rogers (1982) concluded that no record 'during at least the last 50 years has definitely related to a wild vagrant'. Although an apparent influx in 1994 may have involved wild individuals (Vinicombe & Harrop 1999), the BOURC later considered the evidence insufficient to confirm this view (*eg* Harrop 2002), but their origins remain hotly debated (Vinicombe 2002).

The first Wiltshire records came from the south of the county: singles near Longford Castle for a few days in April 1928 (*BB* 22: 24) and a male nearby at Clarendon Park for several days from 26 April 1946 (*WANHM*, Peirson 1959). The vast majority of the 33 subsequent observations, beginning with one at Coate Water in November 1968, have been in north Wiltshire. Since 1979, when four were found at CWP on 30 September, the species has clearly occurred more often, and there were records in 12 of the 21 years of 1980–2000. Apart from a group of 18 at Ramsbury on 28 June 1988 (which had escaped from a wildfowl collection), and the four at CWP, all have involved only one or two individuals.

Too few data exist for any firm conclusions to be reached on patterns of occurrence, though March with six records and April with seven show a slight peak. Increased reports in Wiltshire during the last two decades of the 20th century probably reflect creeping naturalisation in Europe rather than vagrancy from wild populations.

PCo

Sponsored by Center Parcs UK

Common Shelduck

Tadorna tadorna

Local passage/winter from British coasts/northwest Europe, breeds irregularly

Although mainly estuarine in Europe, where they are confined largely to the northwest, west and south, Common Shelducks also breed around lakes and inland seas from Turkey eastwards across central Asia to China. Migratory and dispersive, they winter discontinuously from western Europe and northwest Africa to eastern Asia. In most of Europe the breeding numbers have increased and, excluding Russia, a total of 28,000 to 45,000 pairs has been estimated (*EBCC Atlas*). The *1988–91 Atlas* put the summer population of Great Britain at 44,200 birds, including 10,600 breeding pairs, attributing the increase mainly to colonisation of inland sites in England (earlier estimates by Yarker & Atkinson-Willes 1971 and the *1968–72 Atlas* were considered too high by Owen *et al* 1986). A midwinter peak of around 78,000 has recently been suggested (Kershaw & Cranswick 2003), though there were signs of declines in both wintering and breeding numbers in the 1990s (*WeBS*, *BBWC*).

In Wiltshire, Smith (1887) knew only of single Shelducks killed at Alderton in 1856 or 1857, at Overton in September 1868, and of others undated at Britford and Bowood. One was then seen at Potterne in winter 1897 (*WANHM*, Hony 1915a). Seven records in the 1930s and 1940s were also in winter, all bar one in January or February and three of them at or near Britford, the others widely scattered; all involved ones or twos except for a party of five 'for a few hours' on Shear Water on 7 February 1932 (*WANHM*). By the 1950s, though perhaps more frequent, the species was still irregular in the county: Peirson (1959) reported that 'one or two have been seen in most of the last ten years'; and Kennedy (1966) noted six records in the Marlborough area since 1960, the last at Wilton Water in 1965; but

Table 19. Common Shelducks *Tadorna tadorna* in Wiltshire: peak winter counts at CWP 1990/91–1999/00

	90/91	91/92	92/93	93/94	94/95	95/96	96/97	97/98	98/99	99/00
CWP	7	6	12	4	7	4	8	13	16	18

the summers of the *1968–72 Atlas* produced no Wiltshire records at all. Buxton (1981) found this species to be 'More usual in winter', a view confirmed by the *1981–84 Winter Atlas,* which showed presence in nine of the 33 core 10-km squares.

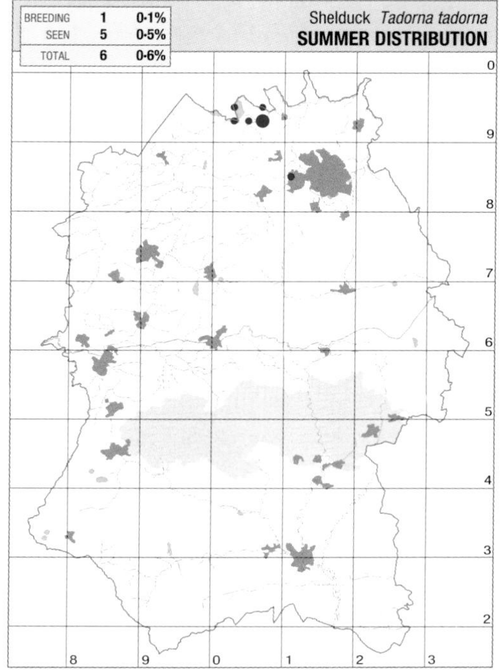

Nowadays, however, Shelducks occur annually in Wiltshire and in all months, though the only consistent locality is CWP, where numbers usually reach a peak in late winter, decline as the summer progresses, and increase again from early winter. In the late 1990s the winter peak was always well into double figures and the highest count of all was 18 in March 2000 (table 19). The species is recorded at around half a dozen other sites each year, usually in late winter or autumn, but generally stays only briefly.

One at Coate Water from autumn 1976 paired with a female Mallard in 1977 and 1978 (Buxton 1981). Pairs displayed at CWP from 1987 onwards, and breeding was proved for the first time in 1990, when eight young were reared. One or more pairs were recorded in all subsequent years up to 2000, and five pairs in spring 1992, but only breeding by single pairs was confirmed and on only five occasions, in 1990–92 and 1998–99. The summer distribution map illustrates the importance of CWP for this species.

The majority of Shelducks in northwest Europe migrate to moult in the Helgoland Bight, northwest Germany. A female ringed there in August 1969, and killed near Cricklade in October 1972 (*Bird Study* 21 supplement: 23), is the only recovery to have involved Wiltshire.

PCo

Sponsored by Center Parcs UK

Mandarin

Aix galericulata

Local resident, introduced to Britain from east Asia since 18th century

Drake Mandarins appear incredibly decorative, more like adornments from stylised Chinese paintings than anything that might exist in the wild. This picturesque exoticism has made them favourites with landscape gardeners and estate owners since the mid 18th century when they were first introduced into Europe from the Far East. Initial attempts to breed them in Europe were unsuccessful, probably because the Chinese exporters castrated the males to protect their markets (*1875–1900 Atlas*). In Great Britain, London Zoo bred two pairs in 1834, but it was not until early in the 20th century that wild populations became established following releases in parts of southern England (Delacour 1954–64), and the species was not added to the British List until 1971 (*BOURC*, *1968–72 Atlas*).

The Mandarin is a native of eastern Asia, including the islands of Sakhalin and Japan. Partly because of the huge numbers exported in the past, to meet the demands of European and American collectors, but also because of extensive deforestation and hunting pressures there, the mainland stock declined markedly. Indeed, it was believed even as recently as the *1988–91 Atlas* that the introduced British population, calculated to number as many as 7000 (Davies 1988), 'almost certainly exceeds the whole of that in the Orient outside Japan … and probably equals the total in the latter country'. Subsequent data have, however, enabled previously pessimistic Asiatic estimates to be revised upwards to 70,000 (Callaghan & Green 1993). Small numbers of escaped or released Mandarins are regularly recorded living in the wild in other European countries, but only in Germany, where in 1991 there was an expanding population of over 50 pairs near Berlin, and possibly in the Netherlands and Belgium (*CBWP*), are there anything approaching sustainable numbers.

In eastern Asia, Mandarins nest around forested lakes or along rivers with dense bankside cover, and migrate in winter to flooded rice fields, marshes and more open waters. In Great Britain, however, they are essentially sedentary, based on flowing or standing freshwater with dense growth of marginal trees and shrubs. They usually nest in holes in trees, often 6–7 m up, but sometimes under a bush or fallen tree, not necessarily in woodland and often several hundred metres from water (*eg* Savage 1952, Campbell & Ferguson-Lees 1972). They have also been found nesting in Barn Owl boxes along the Avon north of Salisbury and the Wylye. In England, their 'autumn and winter diet [is] mainly acorns, chestnuts … and beechmast … and in summer chiefly insects … off water and aquatic plants' (*BWP*, based on Savage 1952). Their stronghold is in the Thames Valley, 'in Buckinghamshire and Windsor Great Park on the Berkshire/Surrey border', but the species is now scattered over much of central and southern England (*1988–91 Atlas*). Elsewhere, in Wales, northern England and Scotland, small local populations may have arisen from separate releases from captivity.

The first records in Wiltshire were an immature at Coate Water in November 1962, another on the Kennet at Marlborough on 27 January 1963, and a male at Shear Water on 7 January 1963 (*WANHM*). The *1968–72 Atlas* did not show Mandarins in Wiltshire at all and the next published records were not until 1974, when a pair at Cole Park were dismissed as 'no doubt escapes' (WOS record card), and 1975, when three males were found at Corsham Lake and a female at Coate Water. Several more years passed before the next records, a female at Longleat on 7 January 1979 and a female at Corsham in December 1980. From 1981 onwards, however, Mandarins began to be reported with increasing frequency, particularly on the Salisbury Avon and its tributaries, on Half Mile Pond at Longleat and on Fonthill Lake, and the *1981–84 Winter Atlas* found them in five of Wiltshire's 33 core 10-km squares. In 1986 came the first reported breeding: a pair reared six young at Langford Lakes, and nesting was attempted unsuccessfully both at Little Durnford and near Broad Chalke. Numbers continued to increase, and on 18 September 1991 some 50–60 were 'disturbed from' Compton Chamberlayne Lake (*Hobby*). The *1988–91 Atlas* reflected this spread in the county, showing breeding in five core 10-km squares and presence in a further six.

In the late 1990s, Mandarins were reported from between ten and 17 sites in Wiltshire annually, the majority in the south but including occasional small numbers, mostly ones and twos, at CWP, Braydon Pond, Coate Water and other places in the Swindon area,

Table 20. Mandarins *Aix galericulata* in Wiltshire: peak winter counts at Fonthill Lake 1990/91–1999/00

	90/91	91/92	92/93	93/94	94/95	95/96	96/97	97/98	98/99	99/00
Fonthill Lake	19	19	16	14	12	18	18	19	16	23

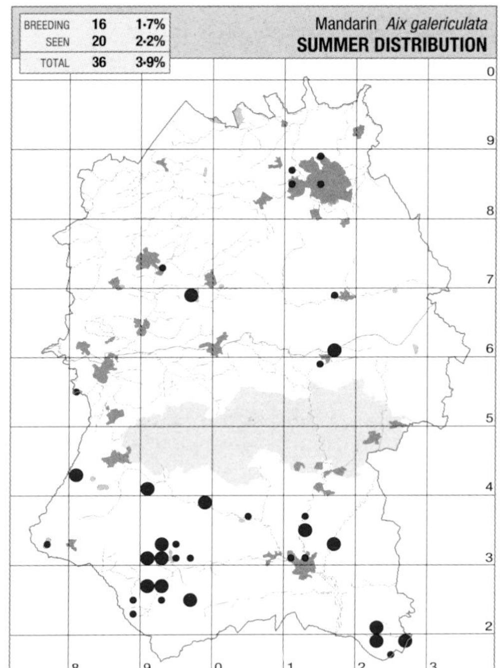

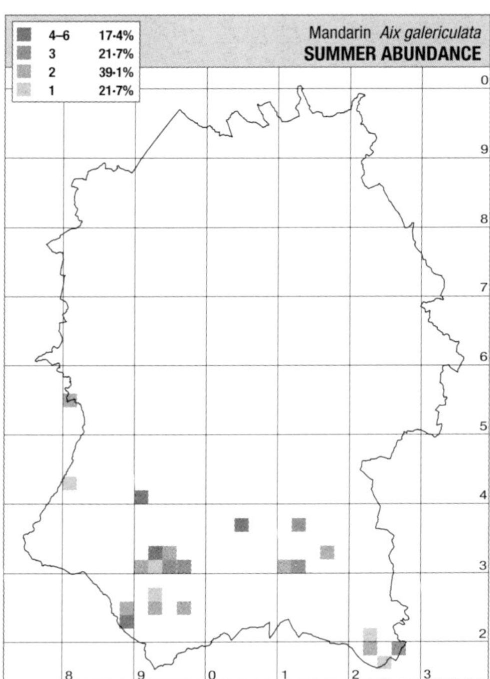

Little Bedwyn, along the Kennet, Bowood Lake, Corsham Lake and Half Mile Pond at Longleat. Fonthill Lake has consistently provided the most, with annual peaks of between 12 and 23 (table 20), and two or three broods seen each year.

The summer distribution and abundance maps emphasise the importance of southern Wiltshire for this exotic species, particularly the extreme southeast and, in larger numbers, the southwestern region of Fonthill Lake and the upper reaches of the Nadder together with its tributaries. The breeding in eight core 10-km squares, and occurrence in five others, supports the prediction in the *1988–91 Atlas* that the 'range and population will probably continue to expand and increase, but slowly, being limited by competition for nesting sites ... by the species' relatively sedentary nature in Britain ... and by its reliance on an adequate supply of nuts ... to see it through hard winters'. The first confirmed breeding for north Wiltshire came in 2000, when a pair with four ducklings was seen at Calne.

Wiltshire's colonisation may have been the result of spread from strongholds in neighbouring counties, as two young Mandarins ringed at Slimbridge (Gloucestershire) in September 1991 were shot in this county later that year, and the species' presence in the southeast is likely to have been influenced by the thriving New Forest population (*eg* Clark & Eyre 1993). On the other hand, the increase in sightings in the Salisbury area in 1987 was 'due to deliberate releases' (*Hobby*) and it is probable that these, too, may have been a factor. Whatever the explanation, the Mandarin is clearly now firmly established here as a breeding resident. The timed summer tetrad counts totalled 57, but the species' secretive nature, often in private woodland, makes numbers prone to underestimation. It seems reasonable to suggest a breeding population of at least 30 pairs at the turn of the millennium, and perhaps a minimum of 100 birds in winter, though the true figures may be much larger.

WEQ

Sponsored by Center Parcs UK

Wigeon

Anas penelope

Locally common winter visitor from Iceland/Fenno-Scandia/Russia

The Wigeon breeds right across northern Eurasia, from Iceland to the Pacific, and winters south to the Mediterranean, along the Nile valley to sub-Saharan Africa, and in southern and eastern Asia. The total population of northwest Europe in winter is estimated at 1·5 million; a further 300,000 spend that season in the Mediterranean and Black Sea areas; and large numbers also in temperate Asia (Wetlands International 2002).

Wigeons were not proved to breed in Great Britain until the 19th century, when a nest was found in Sutherland in June 1834, but by 1900 they were known to do so regularly in several areas of eastern mainland Scotland and the Northern Isles, and to have nested also in Merioneth, Yorkshire and Lincolnshire (*1875–1900 Atlas*). The *1988–91 Atlas* showed that they breed in many parts of Scotland and in the uplands of northern England, and that some are also present in summer farther south, notably in the East Midlands and East Anglia, but nesting south of the Humber is rare. Although the species has been recorded occasionally in summer in Wiltshire, there has been no evidence of nesting, apart from a brood of four at Wilton Water in 1989, but some observers considered that the accompanying adult female showed characteristics of an American Wigeon, or even that it could have been a hybrid; whatever the case, it is likely to have been an escape (*Hobby*). Breeding numbers in Great Britain are thought to have remained stable at 300 to 500 pairs between the *1968–72* and *1988–91 Atlases*, but this figure represents well under one per cent of the summer population of Europe, excluding Russia, which has been estimated at 93,000 to 116,000 pairs (*EBCC Atlas*).

On the other hand, Great Britain is of considerable importance for Wigeons in winter, and the evocative whistling of dense feeding flocks is a familiar experience around our coasts and at large waterbodies inland. This winter population is drawn from a broad northerly breeding range that stretches from Iceland to east of the Urals, and numbers normally reach a peak in January. Most are concentrated on a relatively small number of estuaries, where they graze in particular on eelgrass *Zostera* and the green seaweed *Enteromorpha*: the Lancashire Ribble alone held over 110,000 in 1995 (*WeBS*). Numbers had decreased nationally in the 1930s, following a wasting disease of *Zostera*, but subsequently recovered (Owen *et al* 1986) and, following a general increase from the mid 1980s, the current estimate of just over 400,000 suggests that this is now Great Britain's most numerous winter wildfowl species (Kershaw & Cranswick 2003). Its use of inland sites has spread in recent decades, and sensitively managed reserves, with the right combination of suitable grasses and water levels, have attracted large numbers: counts on the Ouse Washes (Cambridgeshire/Norfolk) and the Somerset Levels both regularly exceeded 20,000 in the late 1990s (*WeBS*).

In Wiltshire, the Wigeon has long been a familiar winter visitor, but im Thurn (1870) considered it generally 'not common'. Morres (1878–85) associated this species with hard winters, when it 'appears in our meadows [around Salisbury] in flocks varying from ten to twenty'. Smith (1887) wrote that it was 'as common as' the Teal (which he described as 'well known throughout the county'). This status probably changed little in the first half of the 20th century, though in 1929 the species was described as a 'rather occasional winter visitor' (Peirson & Walford 1930) and in the early 1930s the very few reports were itemised annually (*WANHM*). Peirson (1959), too, noted the Wigeon only as 'regular... in small numbers to the larger waters'. In recent decades, however, bigger flocks have often been recorded, which is consistent with the national trend for this species to become more numerous inland as the creation of managed wetland reserves has resulted in an increase in suitable habitats.

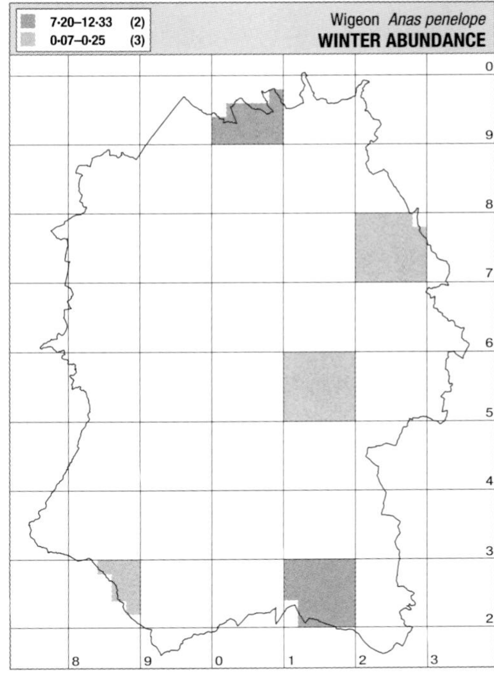

Until the 1970s, though occasionally holding sizeable flocks in flood conditions, CWP was of little importance for these ducks, but it is now the Wiltshire stronghold: a record 2000 were present there in December 2000. The Salisbury Avon is the only other area regularly holding significant numbers (winter map, table 21). Elsewhere, although they may occur at almost any waterbody of adequate size, they are usually recorded no more than sporadically and in very small parties. In the fairly recent past, a few sites have supported reasonable numbers for short periods: 30 to 150 were regular at Braydon Pond for four winters in the early 1960s; maxima at Chilton Foliat generally ranged between 20 and 125 throughout the 1970s and 1980s; peaks at Coate Water exceeded 20 in six of the winters between the late 1970s and early 1990s, including counts of 132 and 150; and peaks of between 50 and 100 were recorded at Clarendon Lake in six winters in the 1980s and early 1990s. Away from the above sites, the 1990s produced double-figure counts only at Bowood Lake and Longleat lakes.

Wiltshire's normal winter total is likely to be in the order of 500 to 2000, depending on the severity of the weather. In view of the shortage of suitable habitats in the county, it is no surprise that this number is of little importance, even at a regional level, against significant concentrations at Slimbridge (Gloucestershire), the Fleet (Dorset), the Solent estuaries (Hampshire) and the Somerset Levels. Given the rapid increase at the last site in recent years, larger flocks might be expected *en route* through Wiltshire in hard weather, but any such influxes are likely to be only transient in the absence of appropriate habitat management. There have been just two recoveries of ringed Wigeons in Wiltshire, one

Table 21. Wigeons *Anas penelope* in Wiltshire: peak winter counts at key sites 1990/91–1999/00

	90/91	91/92	92/93	93/94	94/95	95/96	96/97	97/98	98/99	99/00
CWP	400	300	554	328	320	300	420	700	482	1400
Salisbury Avon	300	73	203	35	220	101	500	48	350	61

marked at Slimbridge in February 1948 and shot at Braydon Pond the following November, the other ringed in Lincolnshire in December 1958 and shot at Codford that same month.

WEQ

Sponsored by Center Parcs UK

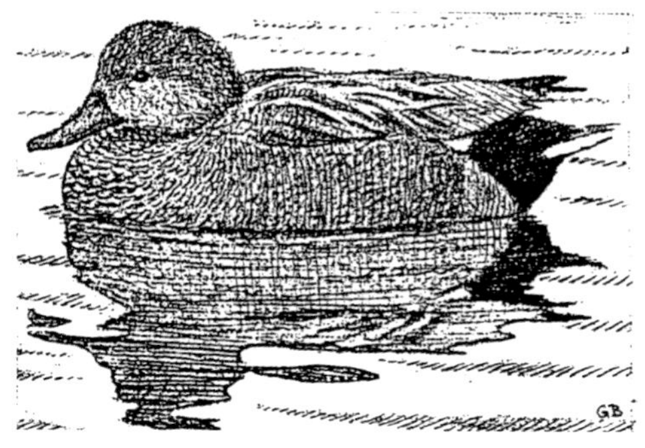

Gadwall

Anas strepera

Local winter visitor from Iceland/central Europe, rare breeder

Gadwalls breed in North America and from western Europe discontinuously east to northern China and Japan; the North American population winters as far south as Central America, and the Eurasian reaches Africa and southern Asia. In Europe, the species' range has been expanding for over two centuries (*EBCC Atlas*) and wintering numbers have increased markedly in western and central countries since the mid 1970s (Delany *et al* 1999).

For most of the 19th century Gadwalls were no more than scarce or rare visitors to much of Great Britain. In 1849, a pair trapped near King's Lynn (Norfolk) was pinioned and released on a lake in Breckland, at Narborough. From this pair, a local breeding population built up around the Norfolk/Suffolk border, and was apparently reinforced by wild stock's joining the naturalised (*1875–1900 Atlas*). Gadwalls were also proved to breed in Scotland in 1909, at Loch Leven (Kinross), and during the 20th century spread slowly to other parts of Great Britain, though the *1968–72 Atlas*, which estimated a population of some 260 pairs, found Breckland still to be the stronghold. Then, after a dramatic expansion in England and parts of Scotland over the following 20 years, the total was put at 770 pairs (*1988–91 Atlas*), some three to four per cent of the calculated 21,000 to 25,000 pairs in Europe as a whole, excluding Russia (*EBCC Atlas*).

In Wiltshire, Gadwalls were unusual until the 1950s. Smith (1887) knew of only one 'shot at Amesbury at the latter part of 1871'. Another was shot on 7 January 1893 on the Wylye near Stockton House (*WANHM*, Hony 1915a). A third was shot at Highworth in 1926, and there followed a singleton in each of the next two decades, one shot at Clarendon in March 1936 and a drake seen at Fyfield, near Marlborough, from February to June 1945 (*WANHM*). Peirson (1959) referred to a further eight in ten years, which seem to have been four in 1947 and four again in 1955, the latter involving a female in February and three the following December, all at Britford (*WANHM*). Records became almost annual from then onwards, usually singletons between September and March, predominantly at Coate Water, Clarendon Lake, Wilton Water and Longford, but few lingered for more than a day (*WANHM*). Although found more widely throughout the county in the 1960s, 'most records were of single birds or of small parties of up to four', with the exception of regular double-figure counts at Fonthill Lake in the latter half of that decade (Rolls 1975b). Pre-1970 increases probably resulted from the expansion of the introduced population at Chew Valley Lake (Somerset), founded by escapes from Slimbridge (Gloucestershire) (Harrison *et al* 1969). In the 1970s, a marked increase at Fonthill saw early winter numbers regularly exceed 50, reaching a peak of 92 in November 1973. Longleat lakes were also favoured, by up to 30, though only during the winters of 1969/70 and 1970/71. Rolls estimated that Fonthill supported '80–90% of all Gadwall

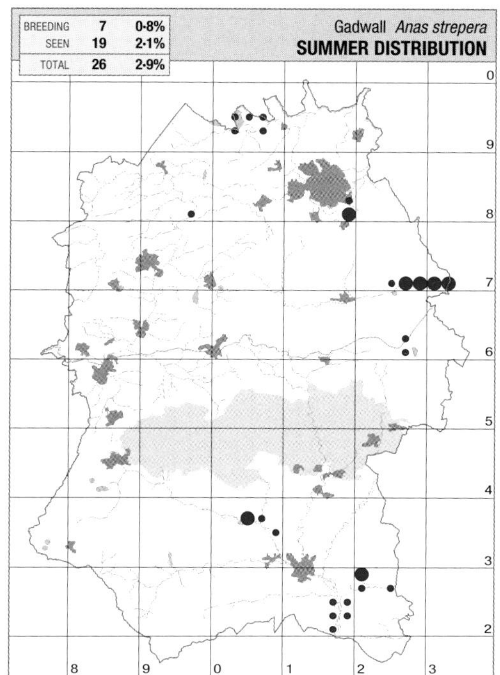

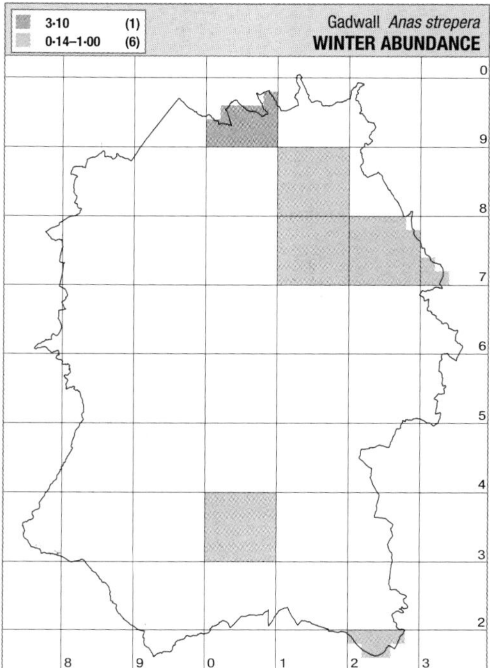

recorded in Wiltshire following a countrywide trend of large, isolated populations' in the mid 1970s, but numbers declined there shortly afterwards.

The Wiltshire picture matches the national, the numbers wintering in Great Britain having shown the fastest growth since the 1960s of any wildfowl apart from introduced Greylag Geese – doubling during the 1990s alone (*WeBS*). Numbers 'increased through the decade' of the 1980s (Palmer 1991), rising rapidly at CWP from 16 in 1984 to 105 by December 1989. The CWP count surpassed 100 again in two of the following three winters, including a peak of 127 in February 1992. There was then, however, a rapid decline to less than half of that figure just three years later, seemingly influenced by the partial back-filling of CWP25, a favoured lake. CWP totals recovered to their former high levels in 1997/98, although it remains to be seen whether these will be consistently maintained.

The winter abundance map shows the continuing importance of CWP and adjacent parts of northeast Wiltshire, including the Kennet. There have been obvious increases at several of the key sites in the 1990s, including Clarendon Lake and Chilton Foliat (table 22), and markedly so on the Salisbury Avon with notable counts at Trafalgar (32) and Standlynch (80). Elsewhere, double figures have been noted infrequently at Coate Water (maximum 18 during 1990–2000), Bowood Lake (11) and Fonthill Lake (14). Yet the county total, now normally around 200, represents only a small proportion of the 17,000 nationally (Kershaw & Cranswick 2003). Five ringing recoveries in Wiltshire during 1965–2000 – two shot and three found dead, all in winter – showed inward movements from Essex (three), Norfolk and Gloucestershire.

The first confirmed nesting of Gadwalls in Wiltshire was at Clarendon Lake in 1984. There was evidence of breeding activity at CWP, Fonthill Lake and other sites in subsequent years, but no more confirmation until 1988, again at Clarendon. During the 1990s, however, breeding was noted in all but two years, though at a maximum of only two places in any one year and with a peak of just six pairs; Langford Lakes became a regular site, holding up to four pairs. The summer distribution map demonstrates the

Table 22. Gadwalls *Anas strepera* in Wiltshire: peak winter counts at key sites 1990/91–1999/00

	90/91	91/92	92/93	93/94	94/95	95/96	96/97	97/98	98/99	99/00
CWP	70	127	101	73	45	48	63	102	78	36
Chilton Foliat	6	3	5	4	–	20	37	33	36	24
Langford Lakes	13	6	14	10	–	–	–	–	–	–
Salisbury Avon	8	9	15	–	34	20	–	–	80	–
Clarendon Lake	17	15	31	10	10	9	32	23	31	28

increase along the Salisbury Avon, seemingly colonised from Hampshire, while the marked 'invasion' of the Kennet from Berkshire during the 1990s was perhaps a consequence of improved water quality. Nesting has not yet been proved at CWP, where it has been suggested that feral American minks limit the chances of success; and the record at Coate Water on the summer map relates to an observation of 'breeding behaviour', rather than of a nest or young – proof of breeding for wildfowl is not easy unless ducklings are seen, but it seems likely that some 10–20 pairs nest annually in Wiltshire.

WEQ

Sponsored by Center Parcs UK

Common Teal

Anas crecca

Locally common winter visitor from Iceland and Fenno-Scandia/Russia, has bred

Until recently treated as conspecific with the Green-winged Teal *A. carolinensis* of North America, the Common Teal has a vast breeding range right across northern Eurasia from Iceland and France to the north Pacific. Most of the population is migratory, wintering west and south of the breeding range as far as western Europe, the Mediterranean, some parts of sub-Saharan Africa and the Middle East, and southern and eastern Asia. Excluding Russia, Europe holds between 325,000 and 381,000 breeding pairs, the large majority in Fenno-Scandia (*EBCC Atlas*). Northern parts of the European breeding range are abandoned during winter; about 400,000 are then estimated in more temperate regions of northwest Europe, and a further one million in central Europe and around the Mediterranean and Black Seas (*CBWP*).

Teals probably nested in small numbers throughout much of Great Britain before widespread drainage of agricultural land in the 18th and 19th centuries greatly reduced suitable habitats. By 1900, breeding was concentrated particularly in damp upland areas, but there were still substantial numbers in East Anglia and, more locally, in other lowland regions (*1875–1900 Atlas*). The population then remained stable until the late 1960s, but the estimate of the number of pairs in Great Britain subsequently declined from 2800–4700 to 1700–2900 over the next two decades (figures recalculated from data in *1988–91 Atlas*).

In Wiltshire, im Thurn (1870) noted that 'Its nest has never been found as far as I know, but from its having several times been seen in May and even June, I fancy that they sometimes breed on the Kennet'. Smith (1887) generalised that this species was 'well known throughout the county' and, in his chapter on 'Nesting', added that 'Occasionally, but rarely, a nest has

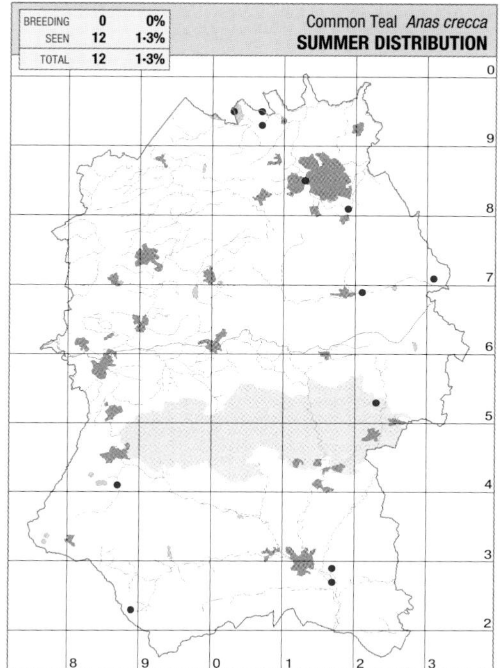

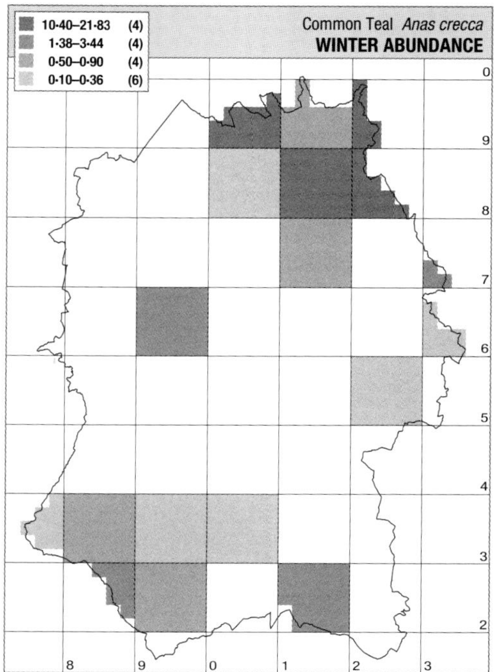

been found in Wiltshire'. Otherwise, the first documented records involved broods at Fonthill in 1936, in the southwest of the county in 1947, and near East Grimstead in 1949, though 'young birds' had also been seen at Longford in July 1930 (*WANHM*). Breeding was proved, 'probable' or 'strongly suspected' in eight other years up to 1965 (*WANHM*, Webber 1968), as well as 'near the Salisbury Avon' in 1969, and a nest was found near Chilton Foliat in 1976 (Buxton 1981). Though the annual averages of summer reports of this species in the county increased from less than one per year in the 1970s to six in the 1980s and over 25 in the 1990s (*Hobby*), there have been no subsequent confirmed records of nesting. (Indications of reproductive behaviour did come from various localities, including 'several pairs displaying' at Leckford crossroads in April 1996, but none of these provided convincing evidence of breeding activity.) The summer distribution map shows a wide but sparse presence and, though many of these records may refer merely to late migrants or summer wanderers, it is possible that a few pairs do nest. Wildfowl are difficult to confirm breeding unless broods of young are seen, and an estimate of 0–5 pairs in Wiltshire during the survey period seems not unreasonable.

In winter, Teals are found on all suitable waters, their numbers varying according to weather conditions both locally and elsewhere. Rolls & Tyler (1971), in their analysis of National Wildfowl Count data between 1949/50 and 1969/70, showed that December to February was the period of peak occurrence. Combined totals for the 'ten most important and/or most regularly covered' Wiltshire waters exceeded 400 Teals only once during the period, though the whole county total was presumably significantly higher. Coate Water and Longford Castle Lake were the only sites to 'contain Teal regularly and in any numbers', peak winter counts at the former usually reaching 200 in the 1950s and a high of 350 in December 1962 (Rolls 1976a). By the winter of 1964/65, however, a leaking outlet there which had caused the water level to fluctuate considerably was repaired, and counts remained below 50 for the rest of that decade, seldom surpassed 20 in the early 1970s, and did not exceed 100 again with any regularity until the mid 1980s.

Table 23. Common Teals *Anas crecca* in Wiltshire: peak winter counts at key sites 1990/91–1999/00

	90/91	91/92	92/93	93/94	94/95	95/96	96/97	97/98	98/99	99/00
CWP	469	423	767	498	210	200	200	550	229	400
Swindon STW	–	–	–	200	280	248	240	260	250	220
Coate Water	250	145	118	225	110	286	180	165	269	190
River Kennet	–	–	–	–	–	–	70	44	73	47
Salisbury Avon	250	135	115	–	61	70	100	–	140	–

Meanwhile, Wardour Castle became the foremost site in Wiltshire from the mid 1960s to the mid 1970s, numbers exceeding 100 in half of those winters and a peak of 210 in January 1973 (*WeBS*). Fonthill Lake was the other key site at this time, with around 100 in early winter, but there, too, higher water levels resulted in a sharp fall in numbers in the mid 1970s.

The winter map shows the northeast of the county supporting by far the greatest numbers in the late 1990s, although the species' use of smaller waters is demonstrated by the continuous distribution in the southwest; indeed, its absence from central areas and the northwest is somewhat surprising, and perhaps an artefact of the survey methods. Extrapolation from the tetrad counts suggested a winter total of around 1250 in Wiltshire, though regular counts at key sites indicate that 1500–2000 may be a more likely range. Though small numbers are found widely on many waterbodies, four sites have for many years held the great majority (table 23). Teals eschew colder weather, so numbers have fluctuated between winters, and, because these ducks sieve in the shallows for the seeds of the aquatic plants that form the bulk of their diet, changing water levels are also likely to affect counts. Their ability to exploit favourable conditions is exemplified by totals of over 300 at Swindon STW during 1983/84 and 1984/85. Few other sites hold significant numbers; only at Bowood Lake (maximum 57), Littlecote (73), Whaddon near Trowbridge (100), Fonthill Lake (77) and Clarendon Lake (54) did they exceed 50 during 1990–2000. Winter numbers have increased steadily in Great Britain as a whole in recent decades, and the late 1990s estimate of just over 190,000 (Kershaw & Cranswick 2003) is probably an all-time high.

All but two of the 51 recoveries of Teals in Wiltshire up to 2000 had been British-ringed, but single males shot near Salisbury in December 1980 and January 1981 originated, respectively, from Denmark in September 1977 and the Netherlands in September 1980. These are likely to have been migrants from Fenno-Scandia or north Russia, which comprise the majority of the British winter population (*Migration Atlas*).

WEQ

Sponsored by Center Parcs UK

Green-winged Teal
Anas carolinensis

Vagrant (2 records), breeds North America

Treated by the BOURC as specifically distinct from the Common Teal *A. crecca* since August 2000, the Green-winged Teal breeds in Canada and the northwest USA and winters as far south as Central America. Vagrants have been recorded in some 16 countries of Europe, as well as in Morocco and the Canary Islands. In Great Britain, where the species occurs regularly, there were 480 records during

1958–2000, with an annual average of 23 new arrivals through the 1990s, mostly in winter and spring, but 47 in 1999 and 42 in 2000 were the two biggest totals known (Fraser & Rogers 2002). All British records relate to drakes, readily identified by the vertical white line at the side of the breast instead of a horizontal white scapular stripe; the females are considered to be indistinguishable from female Common Teals.

Once they have crossed the Atlantic, many wildfowl and waders are believed to migrate south and north in the Old World, and the occurrence of a rarity at the same locality in different years is often thought to involve the same individual's faithful return to a particular site. Thus, the only two Wiltshire records of Green-winged Teals may relate to just one bird in successive winters:

1992	4–11 January	CWP40	Male
1993	30 Jan–4 Apr	CWP68/74	Male

(See also page 726.)

PEC

Sponsored by Center Parcs UK

Mallard

Anas platyrhynchos

Common resident (some released), and winter visitor from north Europe

Mallards have a circumpolar distribution that extends from the Arctic to the subtropics; they have also been introduced widely elsewhere, even in Australasia. In Europe – where, excluding Russia, between 2·1 million and 2·4 million pairs breed (*EBCC Atlas*) – they are found from Iceland, northern Fenno-Scandia and Russia south to the Mediterranean; those from the northernmost and eastern parts of this range migrate southwest and south in autumn to escape the harsh winters of the Arctic and the eastern Continent. It is estimated that, in winter, there are 4·5 million in northwest Europe and 3·0 million in central Europe south to the Mediterranean and Black Seas (Wetlands International 2002). Domesticated at an early stage in human history, they are the common ancestors of most types of 'farmyard ducks'; this has led to naturalised stock in many areas outside the original range, and to unusual and varied plumage forms where escapes have interbred with the wild population.

In Great Britain, resident Mallards declined from the 18th century onwards through loss of wetland habitats which, coinciding with the development of improved firearms for wildfowling, resulted in their becoming a comparatively scarce breeding species, particularly in southern England; there was then some evidence of an increase at the beginning of the 20th century, as a number of protection acts, banning shooting during the nesting season, took effect (*1875–1900 Atlas*). The *1968–72 Atlas* confirmed breeding in over 90 per cent of 10-km squares and estimated the summer population of Great Britain at over 50,000 pairs, but added that the actual figure could be twice as high. The *1988–91 Atlas*, which likewise found Mallards to be almost ubiquitous, used the estimates of Owen *et al* (1986) – derived from winter counts and a calculated late summer population of 500,000 birds – to put the breeding numbers in Great Britain at about 100,000 to 130,000 pairs, although all calculations for this widespread species necessarily include a fair degree of guesswork.

Table 24. Mallards *Anas platyrhynchos* in Wiltshire: peak winter counts at key sites 1990/91–1999/00

	90/91	91/92	92/93	93/94	94/95	95/96	96/97	97/98	98/99	99/00
CWP	531	555	285	515	300	269	469	193	156	144
Braydon Pond	–	–	171	77	48	240	96	52	60	65
Stanton Lake	267	104	40	255	–	–	16	20	43	28
Coate Water	147	122	110	133	99	176	128	147	124	128
River Kennet	–	–	–	–	350	450	400	315	325	170
Ramsbury Lake	292	466	109	183	149	314	250	367	267	218
Chilton Foliat	143	101	40	52	117	240	225	190	103	120
Wilton Water	317	47	167	100	66	85	185	112	175	65
Bowood Lake	211	148	47	131	96	167	85	87	85	47
Corsham Lake	100	65	64	73	103	314	106	169	67	64
Drew's Pond	150	100	70	130	60	100	60	–	–	–
Longleat lakes	350	256	255	264	270	288	210	202	162	251
Shear Water	297	159	128	153	120	140	145	180	90	189
Stourton lakes	221	290	119	112	–	185	158	145	254	148
Fonthill Lake	534	360	128	103	200	80	139	317	145	300
Langford Lakes	482	165	80	48	–	–	–	–	–	–
Salisbury Avon	52	418	334	105	259	310	160	80	115	80
Clarendon Lake	141	72	64	45	344	187	172	90	80	127

For Wiltshire, although im Thurn (1870) listed the Mallard as a winter visitor, with small flocks occasionally found at Ramsbury and Swindon Reservoir, he added that one or two instances of its remaining to breed had been reported and that a nest was found in 1857 'in Poulton Copse, at least half-a-mile from any water'. On the other hand, Smith (1887) wrote, 'Though rapidly becoming more scarce under the present system of draining, this is still too common a bird to require comment on its appearance and habits'.

In the 20th century, Peirson (1959) merely noted it as 'widespread and usually common', with numbers increasing 'considerably in winter'. The near-annual (from 1929) 'Wiltshire Bird Notes' in *WANHM* paid scant attention to numbers of Mallards throughout the three decades of the 1930s to 1950s. In those publications 'several hundreds seen on Coate Reservoir' in 1933 (with the added comment 'General reports show an increase') and 'several hundred flighting on to stubble fields at dusk for about a week from Sept. 27 near Semington' in 1948 were perhaps the only significant items.

Through the 1960s, however, maxima were given inconsistently from a number of sites, the highest each year being in the 350–800 range from, usually, Coate Water, Bowood Lake, Ramsbury Lake or Shear Water, while WeBS data reveal similar numbers then at Chilton Foliat and Wardour Castle. There were also occasional large counts of 200–400 at Braydon Pond, Tockenham Reservoir, Corsham Lake, the Longleat lakes, Fonthill Lake and Clarendon Lake, as well as on various stretches of the Salisbury Avon (regularly including 700–800 at Amesbury) and the Wylye. Analysing winter wildfowl counts in Wiltshire from 1954/55 to 1969/70, Rolls & Tyler (1971) demonstrated a marked increase in 1959/60 and a general upward trend thereafter, although there were considerable swings in numbers: these they attributed largely to the severity or otherwise of the winter, but also to breeding success in the preceding summer and to variations in the numbers of artificially reared birds released for wildfowling. Peak numbers generally occurred between October and December, followed by a marked decline from January until only a small proportion remained by March. Rolls & Tyler estimated the total in the county at about 3500. Updating the analysis to the mid 1970s, Rolls (1977) noted a marked decline in 1974/75 and the following winter, but a partial recovery in 1976/77. He highlighted Bowood Lake as the only site where over

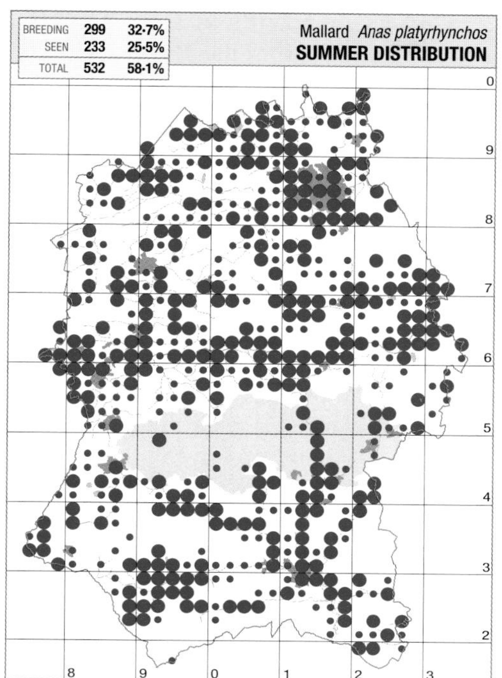

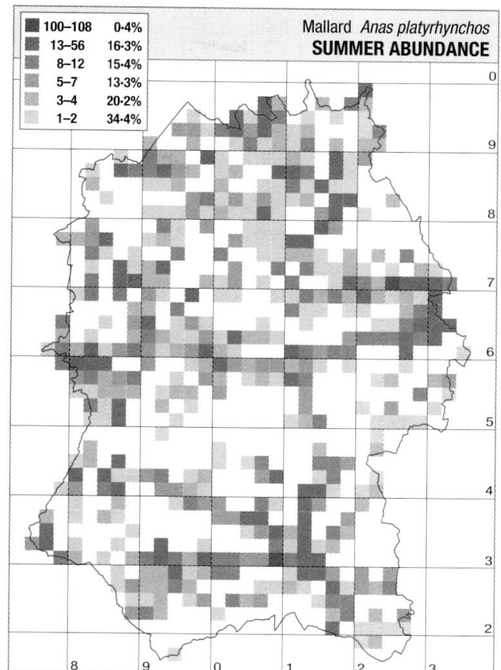

1000 had been recorded (peak 1600 on 16 September 1973), and noted that a proportion of those were released stock; but a count of 1350 was also recorded at Wardour Castle in September 1971 (*WeBS*). Rolls put the Wiltshire breeding population in the mid 1970s at 600 to 800 pairs.

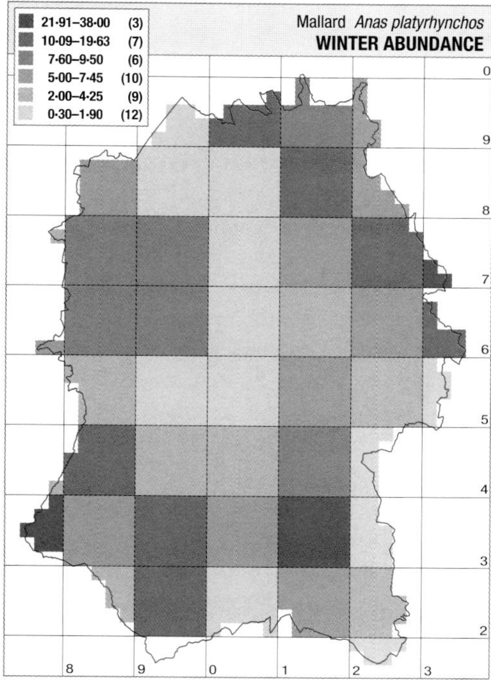

The shortage of detailed information continued initially in the 'Wiltshire Bird Reports' in *Hobby* that succeeded those in *WANHM*, and the Mallard did not even rate separate entries during 1974–80. Indeed, it was only in the last decade of the 20th century that counts were published systematically. WeBS data show numbers to have been maintained at broadly the same level – though varying somewhat between years, no doubt influenced at least in part by releases – at key sites from the mid 1970s to late 1980s: Coate Water (winter maxima normally in 200–400 range during this period), Liden Lagoon (100–255 from the mid 1980s onwards), Ramsbury Lake (250–693), Bowood Lake (200–650), Longleat lakes (150–440), Stourton lakes (150–326), Fonthill Lake (120–500) and Langford Lakes (100–321). Perhaps surprisingly, 460 at CWP in October 1978 was the first triple-figure count there by WeBS, and it was not until the end of the 1980s that that site became prominent for this species.

By 2000, Mallards were occurring in sizeable numbers on many waters in Wiltshire, although the figures were still variable – as shown by the maxima from the 18 sites with the highest counts (table 24) – and, with the exception of CWP, generally lower than 30–40 years previously. Another seven sites held 100 or more during the last ten winters of the 20th century: Swindon STW (270), Queens Park, Swindon (143), Liden Lagoon (147), Marlborough College Ponds (148), Ram Alley (110), Edington Lake (120) and Compton Chamberlayne (100). The winter abundance map demonstrates the importance of urban areas, where feeding by the public no doubt greatly influences numbers and distribution, including high densities around Swindon, Salisbury and several towns in the west. Concentrations were also found on the Salisbury Avon and its tributaries, and on the Kennet, CWP and various estate lakes. Over 3000 were counted during the winter tetrad survey, and the extrapolated total is fractionally under twice this number, suggesting a winter estimate of 6000 and indicating the widespread occurrence of Mallards away from the larger wetland sites.

It is likely that autumn numbers are higher still and the largest counts nowadays – for example, 531 at CWP in 1990, 555 there in 1991, 515 in 1993 and 433 in July 1997, all in August; 310 on the Salisbury Avon in August 1995; and 317 at Wilton Water in August 1990 – are sometimes in late summer. It is likely that the reasons postulated by Rolls & Tyler – that numbers are swollen by the presence of that year's young, but also bolstered at some sites by releases for wildfowling (and then aided by supplementary feeding) – still apply, and that the latter in particular may account for the highly variable numbers between years at some sites.

The summer maps reveal a picture not unlike the winter one, showing Mallards widely distributed across Wiltshire and breeding in roughly a third of all tetrads. Nests with eggs or females with small ducklings were recorded in a few tetrads that contain no ponds or streams at all, for some clutches may be laid 2km or more from the nearest water, on hillsides or in tree hollows or old Carrion Crow or Common Buzzard nests up to 10m above ground (Campbell & Ferguson-Lees 1972). On the summer abundance map, however, the higher densities again pick out the major rivers, estate lakes and urban areas – especially Bradford-on-Avon – as well as the Kennet & Avon Canal, particularly around Wilton Water and the Bedwyns. An assumed average of five pairs per tetrad in which breeding was recorded would give a total of 1500 pairs: as the timed counts yielded 3900 birds, a figure of 1500–2000 appears a reasonable estimate, and would represent an equitable proportion of the British population.

Numbers of Mallards in Great Britain have shown mixed fortunes in recent years: BBS and WBS data suggest small or moderate increases during the late 1990s, but WeBS indices show a steady decline in wintering numbers by around 40 per cent since the mid 1980s, a pattern seemingly reflected by counts at CWP and on the Salisbury Avon in particular (table 24). Whilst the majority of British Mallards are resident (all recoveries from the 70 ringed in Wiltshire during 1965–2000 have, bar two in the Netherlands and one in France, been within Great Britain), numbers are augmented in winter by eastern European and Russian breeders (*Migration Atlas*). Relatively few of those reach western England, however, and only six foreign-ringed Mallards have been recovered in Wiltshire – from Belgium (two), Denmark, Germany and the Netherlands (two) – five of them shot in winter. Current estimates suggest that just over 350,000 Mallards winter in Great Britain (Kershaw & Cranswick 2003), which means that this species is no longer our most numerous duck (now surpassed by Wigeon). Milder winters reducing the number of immigrants from the Continent and smaller numbers being released by shooters (*eg BBWC*) have been postulated as explanations for the decrease, given continuing increases in breeding numbers (*BBS*), but the causes remain a matter of conjecture.

WEQ

Sponsored by Center Parcs UK

Pintail

Anas acuta

Scarce passage/winter visitor from Iceland/north Europe

Pintails are famously elegant and mobile ducks. Although in Great Britain the majority occurs on estuaries, particularly in northwest England, they also favour shallow freshwater marshes and are quick to take advantage when temporary flooding creates suitable conditions, as in February 1990 when a group of 98 – Wiltshire's record count – appeared on flooded meadows at CWP. On the world scale, they are among the most abundant of wildfowl, their numbers running into millions. They breed right across the northern latitudes of North America and Eurasia and are highly migratory, wintering in lowland marshes, coastal wetlands and estuaries of temperate and tropical regions as far south as northern South America, northern tropical Africa, the Indian subcontinent and the Philippines.

Great Britain is on the southern fringe of the breeding range, and Pintails have nested here only sporadically and in small numbers since the late 19th century (*1875–1900 Atlas*). As few as 22–37 pairs were recorded in 1999, and only 10–26 in 2000, the majority in Scotland (*RBBP*) – these represent minute proportions of the European total of, excluding Russia, 23,000 to 33,000 pairs (*EBCC Atlas*). On the other hand, although this is one of the few ducks to have declined in recent decades (*WeBS*), numbers wintering in Great Britain are currently estimated at 28,000 (Kershaw & Cranswick 2003) and so form a significant part of northwest Europe's 60,000 (Wetlands International 2002).

Pintails evidently used to be rare in Wiltshire. Smith (1887) listed just four records: at Clarendon Park (undated), Mildenhall (February 1870), Axford (January 1871) and Lockeridge (February 1886). In the 1920s, and perhaps earlier, the species used to be seen 'at Coate, though it has not occurred there during the last few years [up to 1930]' and in the next decade the only four reports were all of singletons, in March 1933 and 1936 at Clarendon (all *WANHM*) and in 1939 at Ramsbury (Peirson 1939) and Coate Water (Halliday & Randolph 1955). One was then found at Erlestoke Lake on 11 January 1942 (*DSBL*). Peirson (1959) noted that the Pintail was once 'considered rare', but that 'one or two' had been reported 'almost every year' since the 1939–45 War; in fact, only three records were published in the late 1940s, but there was quite a series – of three to five observations each winter – in the early 1950s (*WANHM*) and the species has been annual since 1960. Kennedy (1966) stated that it had been seen just three times in the Marlborough College reporting area, at Coate Water and Ramsbury (perhaps as above) and at Wilton Water, usually in the coldest part of the year. Rolls (1980) described the Pintail as a 'scarce but regular winter visitor and passage migrant' during the 1960s and 1970s, recorded three to four times every year, mostly in November–February, and usually involving one to three staying for only short periods; he also noted its status as largely unchanged during the period.

A record of ten standing on ice at Coate Water on 26 January 1950, as well as what was presumably the same group there on 11 February, and another ten on ice at Wilton

Table 25. Pintails *Anas acuta* in Wiltshire: peak winter counts at key sites 1990/91–1999/00

	90/91	91/92	92/93	93/94	94/95	95/96	96/97	97/98	98/99	99/00
CWP	3	10	32	19	20	4	2	21	16	50
Whaddon near Trowbridge	–	–	–	–	5	5	–	5	2	–

Water in November 1963 were the only counts in double figures up to 1985, since when Pintails have been widely recorded in small numbers. Even so, only at CWP have they been regular, although two to five have appeared at Whaddon near Trowbridge in several recent winters (table 25). Elsewhere, double figures have been encountered only at Longford Castle (18 in October 1987) and at Inglesham (45 flying west on 27 December 1999). In the 1990s, most Pintails occurred in mid winter, but they were seen in all winter months, sometimes also early arrivals in late August and others lingering into mid May. Indeed, a male summered at CWP in 2000, from 14 April to at least 31 July. The normal Wiltshire total of just 10–30 may be compared with regular counts of over 500 at Slimbridge (Gloucestershire), the nearest major concentration. Noteworthy, however, were over 2000 present in the Gloucestershire Severn Vale early in 2002 (P Marshall), and a total of just over 1700 on the Somerset Levels in December 2000 (*WeBS*), which indicate the potential for large numbers to exploit suitable conditions as they arise, even in southwest Britain.

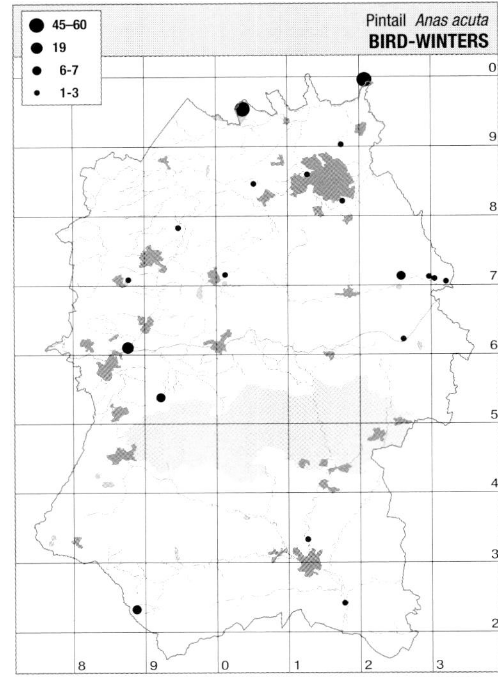

WEQ

Sponsored by Center Parcs UK

Garganey

Anas querquedula

Scarce passage/summer visitor, breeds much of Europe, winters Africa (first bred 2003)

Garganeys are summer visitors right across temperate Eurasia; they winter mostly in the northern tropics of Africa and from the Indian subcontinent to south China and southeast Asia. The breeding population of Europe (excluding Russia), which declined sharply in the 1970s, has been estimated at between 79,000 and 92,000 pairs (*EBCC Atlas*). In Great Britain, these small ducks nested scarcely, and only sporadically, in eastern England during the 19th century, their numbers possibly limited in spring by shooting (*1875–1900 Atlas*). They increased, however, at the beginning of the 20th century and nowadays have a scattered breeding distribution west into Wales and north into Scotland, though most are still found in eastern and central England (*1988–91 Atlas*); at least 30 and possibly up to 109 pairs nested in 2000 (*RBBP*).

Table 26. Garganeys *Anas querquedula* in Wiltshire: annual totals of individuals 1990–2000

	90	91	92	93	94	95	96	97	98	99	00
Birds	6	3	7	12	4	8	7	6+	4	3	6

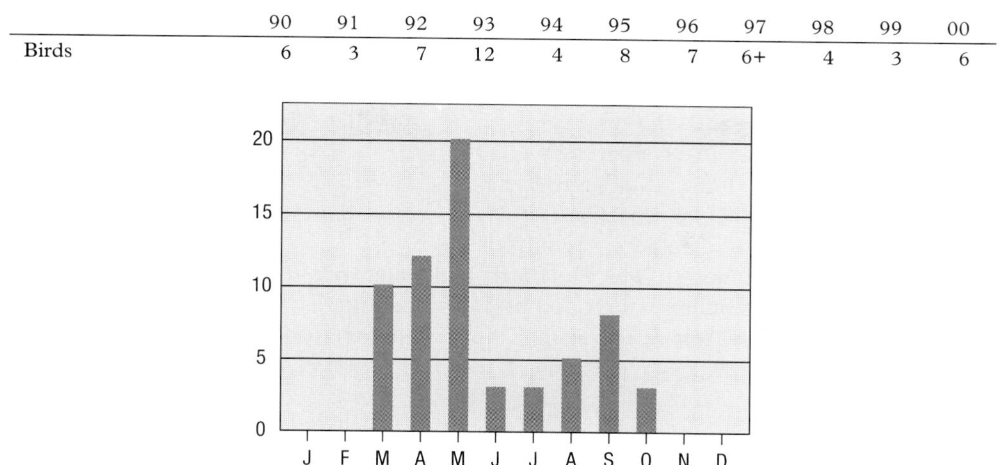

Figure 17. Garganeys *Anas querquedula* in Wiltshire: numbers by arrival months 1990–2000

In Wiltshire, Smith (1887) mentioned several that had been shot and concluded that the Garganey 'may be said to occur in this county, but sparingly', although Marsh (1842–62) had described it as 'by no means uncommon' in the Sutton Benger area during the 1850s. Hony (1915a) considered it a rare visitor and was able to add just two further records, both of single pairs at Downton in April 1911 and 1912. Only two published records have been traced for the 1930s and 1940s, the second at Axford in 1944 (*MCNHS*), but there were several in the early 1950s, including two on Clarendon Lake on the late date of 9 November 1952 (*WANHM*). Peirson (1959) thought this species 'a scarce passage migrant seen in most years, usually in spring but sometimes in autumn', and Buxton (1981) described it as 'an uncommon migrant... mainly in March and April'. Rolls (1980), however, found that only 42 per cent of Garganey records during the 1960s and 1970s were during March to May, the majority – primarily single males in August – being seen from June to October, and 90 per cent of the total in the north of the county. Palmer (1991) noted that Garganeys had occurred in eight years during the 1980s – 13 records in March–June and four in September–October – and that pairs had summered at CWP in three of those years. They were also suspected of having attempted to nest at CWP in 1992 and 1997 (*Hobby*) (but see also page 724).

Of the approximate total of 66 Garganeys recorded in Wiltshire during 1990–2000 (table 26), 45 were at CWP, which hosted the species in all but one of those years. The other 21 were at Swindon STW, Coate Water, Pewsey, Bowood Lake, Corsham Lake, Whaddon near Trowbridge, and Charlton-All-Saints, but at no more than two of those localities in any year. Garganeys are nowadays apparently far more numerous in spring (figure 17): 47 of the 66 were seen in March–June, reaching a peak in May, although from late May and June onwards some in eclipse plumage are doubtless overlooked. The extreme dates of arrival and departure have been 14 March 1971 and 9 November 1952 (*WANHM*).

WEQ

Sponsored by Center Parcs UK

Shoveler

Anas clypeata

Local passage/winter visitor from north and east Europe, has bred

Only one of the world's four shovelers – a subfamily of dabbling ducks that gain their name from their distinctive spatulate bills specially adapted for filter-feeding – is found in the northern hemisphere. The 'Northern' Shoveler breeds across much of North America and Eurasia, and in winter occurs as far south as Central America and the Caribbean, sub-Saharan Africa, the Indian subcontinent and southeast Asia. Numbers in Europe increased in the early decades of the 20th century, but have since fluctuated widely, making trends uncertain; excluding Russia, the breeding population has been estimated at 34,400 to 39,600 pairs, the majority in Finland and the Netherlands, but continuing drainage and agricultural intensification, notably in east Europe, are predicted to have an adverse effect (*EBCC Atlas*).

In Great Britain, the population was thought to have been limited by uncontrolled wildfowling in the 19th century; breeding records were scarce then, being sporadically reported from eastern England and parts of Scotland (*1875–1900 Atlas*). The introduction of a number of protection acts in the 1880s and 1890s provided some respite, however, and populations expanded from strongholds in Norfolk and southeast Scotland until, by the 1930s, Shovelers were nesting regularly in all but eight English counties, in most of Scotland and in south Wales and Anglesey (*1875–1900 Atlas*). Since then, drainage and agricultural improvement have meant a reduction in rough pasture with open water, their preferred breeding habitat, though numbers in protected refuges have actually increased. The *1968–72 Atlas* estimated the population at about 1000 pairs and, despite a contraction in range over the next 20 years, the *1988–91 Atlas* put it at between 1000 and 1500 pairs, the majority again in eastern parts of both England and Scotland.

Shovelers have become regular visitors to Wiltshire only relatively recently. Smith (1887) stated that they had 'been met with from time to time in various parts', but mentioned only Britford and Bowood as localities. Hony (1915a) quoted one shot 'about 1904' at Bishopstone and a female shot in October 1912 at Braydon, where 'the keeper…had occasionally seen the same species in other years'. *WANHM* then ably documented their increasing regularity from the late 1920s onwards with records, generally of ones and twos, from two or three sites each year, though 12 at Fonthill Lake in 1931 was a notable gathering. The first recorded breeding in the county was at Britford in 1932 (*WANHM*). In line with the general increase in western Europe at that time, Shovelers were reported more widely in the 1940s and early 1950s, occurring in small groups on many of the larger lakes. Most were seen in winter, but several remained into summer and the county's second and third breeding records were 'on the Salisbury Avon' in 1946 and 'by Avon at Britford' in 1947 (one assumes that both were at the same site).

Rolls (1976a) noted that Shovelers had 'become quite common to most of the larger lakes' by the 1960s, and that the species often remained for extended periods at some places, even summering in 1964 and 1966 at Coate Water, where nesting was suspected (but not proved) in the latter year. Breeding was again suspected in the county in 1972, at an unnamed site, but the young recorded as reared at CWP that year (Buxton 1981) were, in fact, in Gloucestershire 'a few yards from the county boundary' (*WANHM*). Although Shovelers are primarily winter visitors, Rolls (1976a) highlighted a small increase on passage

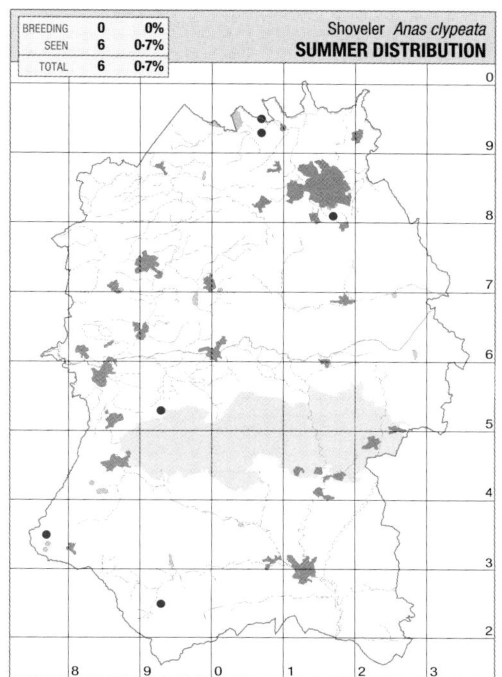

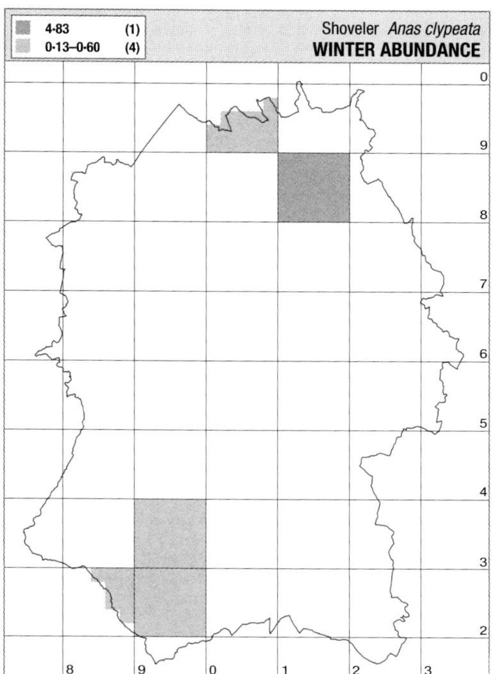

in April and, from intensive counts at Corsham Lake, noted a frequent turnover throughout the winter. Larger groups were seen with increasing regularity in the 1970s, mostly in mid or late winter, including 40 at Coate Water, 41 at Corsham, 67 at Fonthill, 35 at Langford Lakes and 23 at Clarendon Lake. The 1980s, however, saw Coate Water become the predominant Wiltshire site, including a peak of 79 in 1980, but in a matter of just a few years in the late 1980s the importance of CWP increased dramatically and 72 were recorded there in 1990.

Since that time, these two areas – along with lesser numbers at Swindon STW which, perhaps significantly, lies midway between them – have remained the key Wiltshire localities for Shovelers (table 27); although they are recorded widely elsewhere, numbers at other major waterbodies have stayed relatively low. The winter abundance map identifies the extreme north and the southwest as particular hotspots, and allowance for uncounted tetrads places the current winter population at about 150, perhaps a rather generous estimate in view of the counts at the key sites but still representing no more than one per cent of the British total of just under 15,000 (Kershaw & Cranswick 2003). The peak numbers nationally are often during spring and, particularly, autumn passage, and this is reflected in Wiltshire. Of the seven Shovelers ringed in the county during 1965–2000, no fewer than three, remarkably all trapped near Malmesbury on 1 September 1969, have been recovered: one was found dead at the same site in February 1970; the other two were

Table 27. Shovelers *Anas clypeata* in Wiltshire: peak winter counts at key sites 1990/91–1999/00

	90/91	91/92	92/93	93/94	94/95	95/96	96/97	97/98	98/99	99/00
CWP	32	63	88	43	15	33	61	15	12	16
Swindon STW	–	–	–	8	24	14	9	18	46	16
Coate Water	32	24	31	22	14	29	70	60	23	38
Corsham Lake	7	9	–	–	–	6	6	6	7	3
Fonthill Lake	4	10	4	–	–	–	25	10	7	6
Clarendon Lake	18	16	7	5	9	10	9	11	2	13

shot – in Gloucestershire in October 1970 and Lincolnshire in October 1971 – perhaps further confirmation of the high turnover of Shovelers during passage periods. Numbers are influenced by water levels and suitable feeding conditions, and these factors are thought to have been largely responsible for the fluctuating numbers at CWP in recent years.

The summer distribution map shows Shovelers to be regular then, although some records may relate to migrants lingering in spring or returning early in autumn. Nevertheless, the county's fourth breeding record came in 1994, when six ducklings were seen at CWP, although, like the young of many wildfowl there, they were not thought to have fledged successfully.

WEQ

Sponsored by Center Parcs UK

Red-crested Pochard

Netta rufina

Introduced local resident at CWP, rare elsewhere, breeds central/south Europe

Red-crested Pochards – adult males in particular – are striking, if rather incongruous-looking, ducks with something of a 'tainted' status in Great Britain. Whilst genuine vagrants from the Continent doubtless do occur here, and nesting in the wild is now regular at several sites south of a line from the Severn to the Wash, most of this scattered British breeding population relate to a background of escapes.

In their main range, from the Black Sea to Mongolia, Red-crested Pochards favour fairly large, reed-fringed, eutrophic lakes in lowland steppe, and winter in southwest Asia and northern India. Several thousand pairs also nest in Iberia, chiefly in Spain (a few south also into Morocco) and in Turkey; and a total of some hundreds in more isolated pockets north to the Netherlands, south Denmark and north Germany – occupying less typical habitats, generally small lakes and fishponds. This species first colonised central Europe in the late 1800s, spreading north almost to its present limits from the 1920s, and, although several areas have subsequently been abandoned, a slow increase and expansion appears to be continuing – so much so that the population of Europe, excluding Russia, has been estimated at 8000 to 11,800 pairs, the majority of which winters either in Spain or in the Black Sea region west into the Balkans and south into Turkey (*EBCC Atlas*).

Although escapes from collections were known in Great Britain from the 1930s, small numbers in eastern England in the 1950s – principally at Abberton Reservoir (Essex) – were associated with the annual departures to the wintering grounds in southern Europe of a moult flock of several hundreds which had built up at the Zwarte Meer in the Netherlands (Pyman 1959). The subsequent decrease in British records of genuine vagrants has been linked both to the disappearance of these moult gatherings in the 1960s (by then up to 1600 strong) – because of water pollution and the loss of stonewort, a favoured food – and to the decline of the small Danish breeding population after an outbreak of botulism in the 1970s (*EBCC Atlas*, Baatsen 1990).

In Great Britain, breeding was first recorded in 1937 in Lincolnshire, and then in Essex in 1958 (Pyman 1959). Red-crested Pochards have nested regularly since 1968, and now do so at scattered localities in East Anglia, in southeast England and on both sides of the

Wiltshire/Gloucestershire border at CWP, the last site having become a nationally noteworthy stronghold in recent decades (*1988–91 Atlas*). This species is easy to breed in captivity, and all these small populations have probably been founded by escapes from wildfowl collections (Pyman 1959, *1988–91 Atlas*).

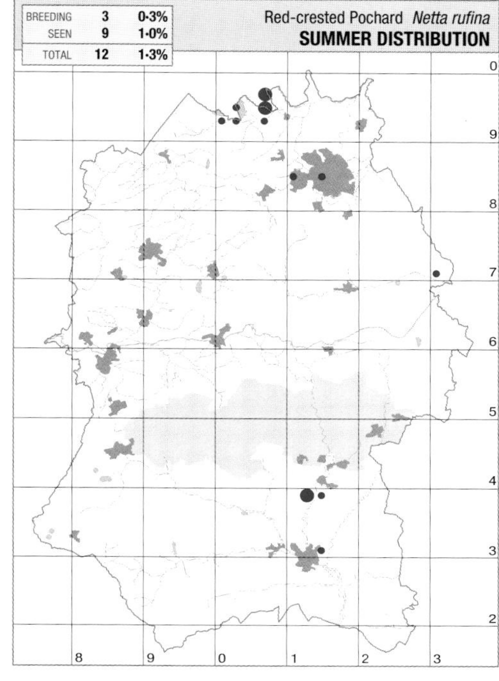

The first Wiltshire record, a male seen on Braydon Pond for half an hour in December 1954, 'may have been an escape'; and the next, two males at Westbury during 23–28 March 1958, were 'very tame, and behaviour suggested semi-wild birds' (*WANHM*). On the other hand, Pyman (1959) did comment on the occurrence of small numbers in western Britain during the 1950s and suggested that these might have been overwintering vagrants. The 1960s produced 11 county records, including three singletons for just one day apiece in autumn or early winter – an immature male at Upavon on 31 October 1961, a female at Corsham on 23 November 1968, and 'another bird' at Wilton Water on 29 November 1969 (*WANHM*) – fitting the suggested pattern for genuine vagrancy. Most of the 11 were, however, in late winter or spring, and two juveniles in 1968 were known to have escaped from a collection at Wootton Bassett.

The 1970s saw the beginning of a new chapter in the county's Red-crested Pochard story, with the first record from the Wiltshire side of CWP in 1973 – though the species had on several occasions in the 1960s been recorded in the Gloucestershire part (Baatsen 1990) where, also in 1973, breeding was first noted in the Poole Keynes area (Mardle & Ogilvie 1975). Numbers have since grown steadily on both sides of the county boundary (figure 18). Many of the larger counts in the late 1980s and early 1990s were in late summer: the moult gathering at that season perhaps enables a better assessment than at other times of year when the birds are more dispersed.

Elsewhere in Wiltshire, Red-crested Pochards have remained very scarce, even the 1990s producing only one or two records a year. Most have been singletons for just one day, generally in the Swindon area, on the Kennet at Littlecote, at Corsham Lake, or on the Salisbury Avon, though there were records for Langford Lakes in the early 1980s and for Braydon Pond, Tockenham Reservoir and Castle Combe in the 1990s.

Despite the increasing numbers at CWP, records of breeding on the Wiltshire side there have been few. During 1974–2000, young were noted in just five years: a brood of three in 1976, one of five in 1987, two broods in 1988, one in 1990, and one of three in 1997. (The more northerly record on the summer distribution map appears, in fact, to relate to a pair on the Gloucestershire side.) Two adults and three juveniles at Wilsford, on the Salisbury Avon, on 29 July 1997 were exceptional and the only evidence of breeding away from CWP, although, given the number of other escaped wildfowl on that stretch of river, they may have originated from local escapes.

Such 'feral' populations now cloud the status of the Red-crested Pochard in Great Britain as a whole. In 1996, excluding CWP, around 250 were reported, including a minimum

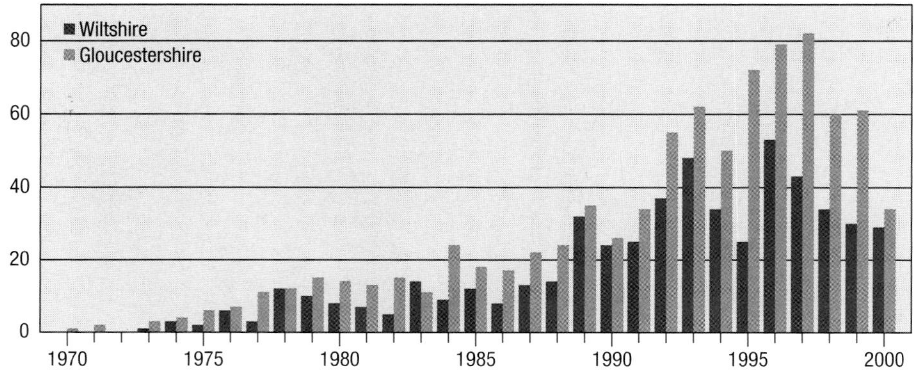

Figure 18. Red-crested Pochards *Netta rufina* in Wiltshire: numbers at CWP 1970–2000

of ten in every month and a peak from autumn to mid winter (Fraser *et al* 1999a); the species was found in 32 counties that year and in 42 in 1997 (Fraser *at al* 1999b), but was not included subsequently in these annual assessments of scarce migrants. It appears that those at CWP are relatively sedentary, although Baatsen (1990) suggested that a flock of eight noted in both Hampshire and Suffolk in January 1982 – which were believed to be of wild origin – might have wandered from CWP, given the departure of a similar number from there during a particularly cold spell. Unsurprisingly, the total of only 48 Red-crested Pochards ringed nationally (four of them in Wiltshire) has produced no recoveries involving the county.

Autumn counts suggest a total of 30–40 in Wiltshire, the number then falling slightly in winter. Breeding remains infrequent at best, but may be expected to increase as the CWP population continues to grow, albeit slowly, and perhaps as the habitat at the older lakes matures. Though long on the British List as a vagrant, this duck was admitted to Category C in 2005 as a result of regular nesting at CWP and elsewhere in southern England, the population now being regarded as self-maintaining without further introductions or escapes.

PAC

Sponsored by Center Parcs UK

Common Pochard

Aythya ferina

Common autumn/winter visitor from Baltic/north Europe, rare breeder

Common Pochards breed widely in temperate latitudes from western Europe across to northeast China. Although essentially birds of freshwater in steppe country, with the highest numbers and densities in the centre of their range, particularly eastern Europe, they have expanded over the last two centuries to nest, albeit rather sparsely, as far west as Iberia, Ireland and, sporadically, even Iceland (*EBCC Atlas*, Scott & Rose 1996). The westerly spread matches those of several other wildfowl that coincided with the desiccation of lakes in southwest Asia and the increase of man-made waterbodies in Europe.

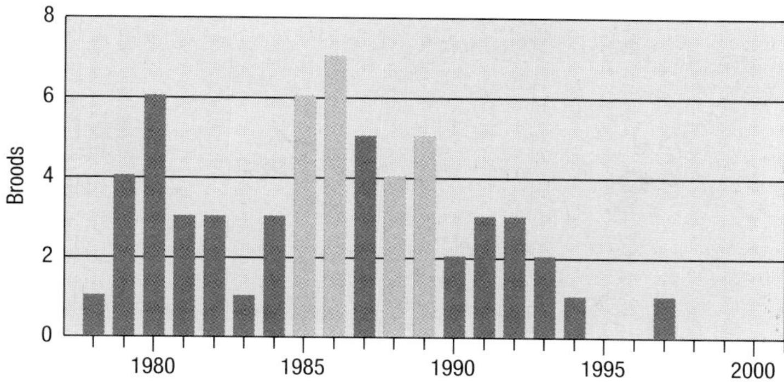

Figure 19. Common Pochards *Aythya ferina* in Wiltshire: broods reported 1978–2000
When the number of broods is uncertain, the recorded total of breeding pairs is shown in pale grey, but the latter is always likely to be slightly higher because it does not allow for failures at the egg stage

In Great Britain, Common Pochards were first recorded breeding in Norfolk in the early 1800s and had reached Scotland by the end of the 19th century (*1875–1900 Atlas*). Numbers increased steadily until they became quite widespread by the 1930s. Nowhere, however, are they really numerous, remaining thinly distributed in nutrient-rich 'oases', particularly in Essex and the London area, stretching into the east Midlands, Yorkshire and parts of eastern Scotland (*1988–91 Atlas*); low breeding success and susceptibility to disturbance may be limiting further increases (Fox 1991). Only about 400 pairs nest in Great Britain, a minuscule proportion of the European population that, excluding Russia, has been put at 202,000 to 241,000 pairs (*EBCC Atlas*).

Very few Common Pochards breed southwest of a line from London to the Dee Estuary. The abundance map in the *1988–91 Atlas* suggests that CWP holds the most significant concentration in the southwest, but, whilst small numbers regularly oversummer, there has been little evidence of nesting there and none at all on the Wiltshire side. Instead, breeding in the county is restricted to a handful of reed-fringed lakes in, mainly, the south. Although it was mooted that a Pochard at Clarendon Lake in May 1934 'may possibly have nested' (*WANHM*), the evidence – purely, a single bird seen twice in that month – is far from compelling, and the first records of breeding in Wiltshire were at Clarendon Lake in 1962, and again in 1965 when two, possibly three, broods were seen (*WANHM*). No further reports were published until 1978, but four broods at three sites in 1979 heralded the onset of a regular pattern that continued throughout the 1980s: between three and six broods were noted in most years, almost exclusively at Corsham Lake, Fonthill Lake, Langford Lakes, and Clarendon. After a slight decline during 1990–93, however, and just one brood in 1994, the six summers of the tetrad survey, 1995–2000, produced only a single further breeding record (figure 19).

In winter, Pochards vacate the colder northern and eastern parts of their range for more southerly areas: those from Fenno-Scandia and much of eastern Europe migrate west and southwest to western Europe, Mediterranean countries, and north and east Africa, while easternmost European and central Asiatic populations winter mostly in a band from southwest Asia across the Indian subcontinent to southeast Asia and Japan. On the other hand, many west European Pochards remain within or near their breeding range.

Numbers start to build up in Great Britain from late summer when moult concentrations are established in southeast England, notably at Abberton Reservoir (Essex), on waterbodies in southwest London (Owen *et al* 1986) and, increasingly, at CWP. Nationally, wintering numbers peak at around 60,000 (Kershaw & Cranswick 2003) and the species is then

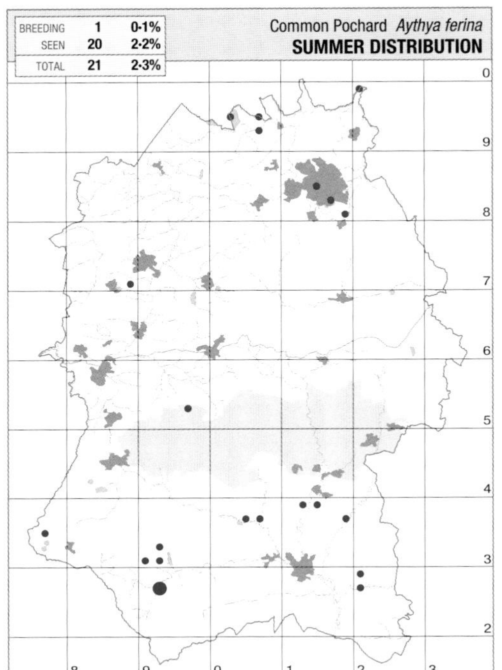

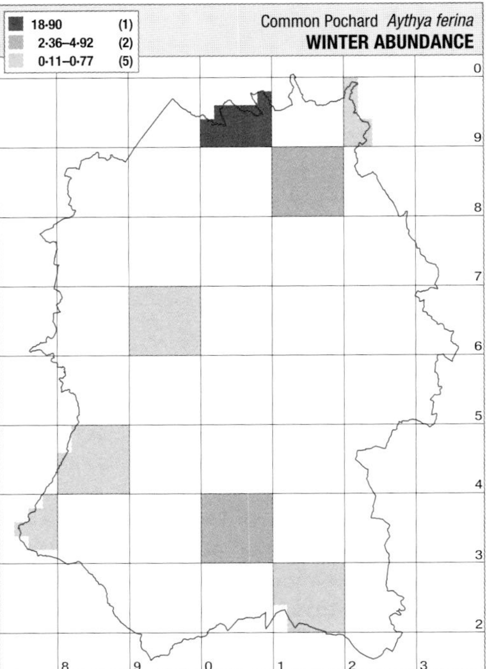

widespread on lowland fertile lakes, gravel pits and reservoirs throughout much of England, in the south-central lowlands of Scotland, and in northern Wales (*1981–84 Winter Atlas*). These Pochards are primarily from the breeding populations of Fenno-Scandia and elsewhere around the Baltic, but some are known to have travelled much greater distances. British-ringed individuals have been recovered in summer on the upper reaches of the River Ob in western Asia, and even one just north of western Mongolia (*Migration Atlas*). The only foreign-ringed recovery in Wiltshire, shot on 25 November 1972 at Ashton Keynes, had been ringed as an adult female in Latvia in June 1970. The three recoveries of British-ringed Pochards in the county, all in winter, included two ringed in Peakirk (Cambridgeshire), in December 1981 and January 1985, the former shot at Woodford in December 1982, the latter found dead at CWP in November 1989; the third was ringed at Abberton Reservoir (Essex) in May 1986 and shot at Fonthill Lake in January 1989.

The winter status of the Common Pochard in Wiltshire shows a general and gradual increase since regular records began. Smith (1887) noted that 'it occurs ... frequently in all parts of the county' and Peirson (1959) summarised it as 'A regular winter visitor in small numbers to the larger waters'. Through the 1930s, however, records in *WANHM* referred to only four or five sites and, apart from such statements as 'considerable numbers were seen on Coate Water' (in 1933), counts were generally small. Notable maxima included 20 at Ramsbury, and double figures were otherwise reached only at Braydon Pond, Coate Water and Clarendon Lake. These four sites, together with Bowood and Chilton Foliat, produced the majority of records, but it was not until the late 1940s that *WANHM* referred to an increase in numbers. Over the next five years up to and including 1952, around 10 sites were mentioned regularly, with notable maxima at Braydon Pond (60), Coate Water (40), Corsham Lake (50), the Longleat lakes (40), Fonthill Lake (30) and Clarendon Lake (30). As previously, the largest numbers were in January and February, although the species was now being encountered during an extended period from October to April.

Table 28. Common Pochards *Aythya ferina* in Wiltshire: peak winter counts at key sites 1990/91–1999/00

	90/91	91/92	92/93	93/94	94/95	95/96	96/97	97/98	98/99	99/00
CWP	585	183	252	391	488	515	306	573	352	250
Coate Water	13	13	21	25	60	24	42	53	63	37
Liden Lagoon	36	45	14	21	2	20	11	12	5	26
Wilton Water	6	3	10	23	30	43	13	5	12	18
Corsham Lake	44	33	47	43	34	108	66	41	34	–
Westbury Ponds	30	25	26	8	–	–	50	15	12	19
Fonthill Lake	151	64	100	98	105	220	133	42	33	55
Langford Lakes	94	111	84	42	48	–	–	50	–	–
Clarendon Lake	42	42	33	42	9	50	110	32	21	28

Rolls & Tyler (1971), analysing National Wildfowl Counts from the then ten key Wiltshire sites, noted considerable fluctuations during 1949/50 to 1969/70, but a general increase in line with the national picture. A then record count of 210 at Coate Water in January 1961 was followed by generally large numbers in the county during the cold winter of 1961/62, including 209 at Braydon Pond in February 1962 and 75 at Fonthill (*WANHM*). Large numbers persisted for the next three winters to 1964/65 at Braydon Pond (140), Longleat lakes (117), Fonthill Lake (100), Clarendon Lake (100) and Longford (110); but, thereafter, few exceeded 50 (*WANHM*). A notable exception was Wardour Castle, where there was a remarkable count of 435 in January 1965, and where numbers remained high until the mid 1970s, usually ranging between 200 and 400 (*WeBS*). Rolls & Tyler (1971) estimated that the Wiltshire total did not normally exceed 800–900, and was usually fewer than 500.

From the late 1960s onwards, three sites became prominent for Pochards in Wiltshire. Langford Lakes regularly held over 100 from the early 1970s to the early 1990s, and peaks at Fonthill normally numbered between 100 and 200 throughout this period (*WeBS*). Counts at the third site, CWP (particularly the Ashton Keynes lakes), also increased notably, including 200 in 1969 and 'approaching c.1000... in the Water Park' in November 1973 (*WANHM*); and the 1980s and 1990s saw a continued gradual increase as the complex of lakes grew. Elsewhere in the county, however, numbers appear to have remained broadly similar at most localities over these last two decades, and few sites regularly hold over 50 Pochards (table 28); the increases apparent at some sites in 1995/96 coincided with a particularly cold spell in February. Numbers reach a peak mostly in mid winter, although highest counts at CWP are often between August and October, following the build-up of a moult flock from June onwards. This distribution is reflected in the winter map, the concentrations at CWP, Corsham Lake, Fonthill Lake and around Swindon being prominent. Extrapolation from the winter tetrad counts suggests a total of 500 in Wiltshire, a figure that appears consistent with counts from individual sites in recent years, although numbers, as in the past, continue to fluctuate on a regular basis.

PAC

Sponsored by Center Parcs UK

Ring-necked Duck

Aythya collaris

Vagrant (5 records), breeds North America, where extending range

The North American equivalent of the Eurasian Tufted Duck, the Ring-necked Duck breeds extensively across southern Canada and some northern American states, and winters along the coastal plains of the USA, Central America and the Caribbean. It is a rare vagrant to Europe, normally during winter months. The first British record involved a drake that appeared at Slimbridge (Gloucestershire) in 1955, but there were then no fewer than 373 during 1958–2000 (Fraser & Rogers 2002), which might suggest that the species had been overlooked previously, perhaps through its superficial resemblance to the Tufted Duck. On the other hand, the upsurge in recent decades, including some 225 in the 17 years of 1977–93 alone (after which it was removed from the official list of rarities considered by the BBRC), coincided with a large increase in North America. Many British records now involve individuals returning to the same locations in successive winters; and separating genuine new arrivals from those that, presumably, ply an annual south-north migration on this side of the Atlantic is a difficult, if not impossible, task.

Wiltshire had five records during 1978–2000:

1978	11 Jan–26 Feb	Corsham Lake	Male
1980	17 Oct–1 Dec	Corsham Lake	Female
1981	27 Jan–7 Feb	Corsham Lake	Assumed same female
1989	14 October	CWP73	Female
1998	16 January	Coate Water	1st-winter male
1999	15–16 April	Corsham Lake	Male

There is some contradiction in published references to a record of a male at CWP at AK2 (now CWP41) on 16 April 1978, variously described as the same individual as at Corsham (*BBRC*) and 'Another, or the same' (*Hobby*), that was seen in Gloucestershire from 8 April to 3 May (Swaine 1982), apparently paired with a female Tufted Duck (*Hobby*), and what was believed to have been a hybrid male Ring-necked × Tufted Duck was also found there (*BBRC*). The following year (although again a degree of confusion surrounds the published records), a male Ring-necked, considered to be the same bird (*BBRC*), reappeared on the Gloucestershire side from January to March 1979 (Swaine 1982), and what was presumably the same 'hybrid' likewise reappeared in February, but, despite the 1978 record being listed in *Hobby* and Buxton (1981), there is no evidence that either ever crossed into Wiltshire.

(See also page 726.)

PAC

Sponsored by Center Parcs UK

Ferruginous Duck

Aythya nyroca

Vagrant (6 records), breeds south/east Europe, where generally decreasing

Apart from small pockets in western Mediterranean countries south to northwest Africa, Ferruginous Ducks have a somewhat fragmented breeding distribution from eastern Europe to western Mongolia, favouring reed-fringed lakes in steppe, semi-desert and steppe-forest. In winter, the primary concentrations are around the Black and Caspian Seas and in the Indian subcontinent, but small numbers are found in southwest Europe, West Africa, northeast Africa south to Kenya, and the Arabian peninsula (Scott & Rose 1996, Wetlands International 2002). Since the early 1980s there has been a marked decrease throughout much of Europe, where between 14,250 and 23,400 pairs now breed, mostly in Romania (*EBCC Atlas*). The decline has been even more catastrophic farther east in Europe, where the population in Ukraine, Moldova and parts of adjacent Russia fell from around 75,000 pairs in the 1960s to just 6000 in the early 1990s. These decreases are thought to have been caused largely by wetland drainage, exacerbated by natural droughts in parts of the range, but also by hunting (Krivenko *et al* 1994, Bankovics 1997). Although recent estimates for southwest Asia and southeast Asia suggest numbers there are higher than thought previously, the species is considered near-threatened by the IUCN (Wetlands International 2002).

Ferruginous Ducks are traditionally regarded as rare winter visitors in Great Britain, mostly in eastern England, but the large number presumed to be escapes has long complicated any assessment of their status in this country, and no national totals were published during 1969–85. Their increasing rarity, with an average of just ten records annually in the 1990s (Fraser *et al* 2000, *BBRC*), coupled with increasing concern over the plight of the species internationally, prompted a resurgence in interest and a return to the list of species considered by the BBRC in 1999; 15 records were accepted for Great Britain in 2000 and the total since 1958 was then put at 252 (*BBRC*).

In Wiltshire, Smith (1887) noted two records, involving three birds: 'two . . . shot by Mr. W. H. Stagg, of Netheravon, on December 9, 1875' and another, undated, reported by the Reverend E Duke as 'captured on the river' at Lake House, which lies by the Salisbury Avon in the Woodford valley. Peirson (1959) stated, without supporting evidence, that they might all have been escapes, but Ferruginous Ducks were more numerous in the wild in Europe in the 19th century, which could suggest that these were genuine vagrants. The species was, however, clearly also popular in 19th century wildfowl collections and captive breeding was reported in France as far back as 1870 (Delacour 1954–64). The first 20th century record, not until nearly a hundred years later, came from the Kennet, between Axford and Mildenhall, in February 1971 (*WANHM*) and, though it was again noted that this 'may well have been an escape', that is likely to have been a reflection of perceived wisdom at the time. From 1974:

1983	11 Nov–31 Dec	Corsham Lake	Female
1987	6 January	Corsham Lake	Male
2000	16–18 November	Corsham Lake	1st-winter male

All five dated Wiltshire records have occurred during November–February, matching the national picture which, it has been suggested, verifies the likelihood of genuine vagrancy since more random occurrences would be expected if escapes were involved (Vinicombe 2000).

(See also page 726.)

PAC

Sponsored by Center Parcs UK

Tufted Duck

Aythya fuligula

Common resident and winter visitor from Iceland/ north Europe

The Tufted is perhaps our second most familiar duck, partly because the male's black-and-white pattern is instantly recognisable, but also because this species is, like the Mallard, tolerant of human beings and found throughout the year in many urban areas. This familiarity is, however, relatively recent. It is only 150 years since the first report of Tufted Ducks breeding in Great Britain, but by the mid 1980s the population was estimated to be between 7000 and 8000 pairs (*1988–91 Atlas*). They are found primarily in lowland England south of a line between the Ribble and the Humber Estuaries, being largely absent from the southwest and from Wales, but, while they occur only in pockets in Scotland, there is a marked concentration in Fife and Tayside (Owen *et al* 1986, *1988–91 Atlas*).

Although Tufted Ducks breed across Eurasia – in a wide band between 50° and 70° N, from Iceland and France in the west to Kamchatka and northern Japan on the Pacific coast – their colonisation of most of west and northwest Europe took place only in the late 19th and 20th centuries. The success of this expansion, perhaps triggered by climatic changes that led to the desiccation of many lakes in the southwest of their Asiatic breeding range (Voous 1960, *BWP*), has been attributed to the growth in number and size of man-made wetlands, particularly reservoirs and gravel pits, as well as to the increasing eutrophication of freshwater habitats and the spread of the zebra mussel – not recorded in Great Britain until 1824 – which features highly in their diet (*BWP*, *1875–1900 Atlas*). An estimated 253,000 to 310,000 pairs of Tufted Ducks now breed in Europe as a whole, excluding Russia (*EBCC Atlas*).

Tufted Ducks are highly migratory across most of their range. They winter mainly in northwest Europe, east Africa, northern India, southeast Asia and Japan. Great Britain is one of the few countries in which large numbers can be seen throughout the year, and those that breed in southern Britain are some of the only resident populations in the species' entire range. Numbers are augmented in late summer by a distinct and substantial moult migration of east European breeders, mainly males, into Great Britain (*Migration Atlas*). Peak numbers at CWP often occur at this time – for example, 313 in August 1996 and 217 in August 1997 – and are indicative of regional moult gatherings. Winter numbers are swollen by immigrants arriving from September onwards in northwest Europe, including major concentrations in the western Baltic, the Netherlands and several central European lakes, especially in Switzerland and southern Germany. Tufted Ducks that come as winter visitors to both Ireland and Great Britain between late September and late February are primarily from Iceland, Fenno-Scandia and north European Russia; these islands receive relatively few extra during severe winter weather elsewhere in Europe (Ridgill & Fox 1990). Two foreign-ringed Tufted Ducks shot in Wiltshire support those origins: one, at Lacock in November 1967, had been ringed as an adult female in Finland in July 1962; the other, at Langford Lakes in December 1971, as a duckling in the Netherlands in July 1967.

In Wiltshire, Morres (1878–85) noted that Tufted Ducks 'are to be seen [in the Salisbury area] ... every hard winter, and ... are shot frequently here', but that was likely to have been a relatively recent development. Two other reports of this species being locally common were quoted by Smith (1887), but, apart from his earliest record of one 'killed ... in 1856 ... at Grovely', all the others for which he gave dates (mostly 'shot') related to the 1870s and early 1880s, suggesting that it was still quite rare. Yet by the 1920s it was 'a fairly common winter visitor' (*WANHM*) and in 1926 the first breeding was recorded, at Wilton Water, where there were later two pairs in 1928 and again in 1929. Nevertheless, reports in *WANHM* remained relatively few, Tufted Ducks being seen at only three or four sites each year, apparently no more than a handful at each and often on just one or two dates; thus, a record of 50 at Braydon Pond in 1931 and counts of 50, 60 and 100 at the same place in 1934 – where, incidentally, this species is nowadays a relative rarity – were particularly noteworthy. Even so, despite an increase in observations in April and the quoted comment in 1934 that LG Peirson 'notes it as still spreading and breeding', only two further breeding records – both close to the Berkshire border, at Wilton Water and Dodsdown Pond – had been published in *WANHM* by the 1939–45 War. But Buxton (1981) stated that the first breeding in 1926 was 'closely followed by one or two pairs on the Kennet at Chilton Foliat', and that new areas south to Clarendon Lake and Britford were colonised around 1940.

By the late 1940s, Tufted Ducks were being reported from up to eight or nine sites annually, though in 1947 no count exceeded ten, and the largest total in 1949 was 17 at Corsham Lake. From 1948, breeding was noted at one or two places each year; and summering at several others extended to the south and west of the county (Rolls 1978). (Yet a report in *WANHM* for 1952 that 'a female with seven ducklings was seen on April 17th' at Chilton Foliat was surely a misidentification: that would have been at least six weeks too early for this characteristically late-nesting species to have had even small young.)

There was also a marked jump in winter numbers, particularly in 1951/52 when double figures were recorded at several such larger waters as Braydon Pond, Coate Water, Corsham Lake and Clarendon Lake, as well as 75 on the Longleat lakes, 120 at Shear Water and 60–70 on Stourhead's Garden Lake. This led Peirson (1959) to summarise the species as 'a regular winter visitor to many waters, usually in small but occasionally in fairly large numbers'. Breeding continued to spread: in 1957 it was estimated that there were no fewer than 18 occupied nests at Longleat, and in 1959 Clarendon held at least six pairs (*WANHM*).

Rolls & Tyler (1971), analysing winter counts in Wiltshire for the 1950s and 1960s, considered Tufted Ducks to be primarily midwinter visitors, and believed that the county total rarely exceeded 1000, though marked influxes associated with the severe winter of 1962/63 had led to high maxima at Ramsbury Lake (42), Chilton Foliat (145), Wilton Water (140), the Longleat lakes (71), Fonthill Lake (50), Clarendon Lake (50) and Longford (200). But the most significant Wiltshire site in the late 1960s was Wardour Castle, where maxima ranged between 230 and 346, although numbers declined there in the early 1970s (*WeBS*). Rolls & Tyler also noted an apparent decrease towards the end of the 1960s, but, conversely, Buxton (1981) reported a marked increase at most key sites between the 1960s and the 1970s; for the summer, too, he thought that, as a result of expansion along the Kennet, 'probably all suitable stretches of this river are now occupied during the breeding season' and suggested a total of around 100 pairs in 1976 in the county as a whole; Rolls (1978) raised this figure to 'in 1977 about 150 pairs summered and the majority bred'. Extending the analysis of Rolls & Tyler (1971), Rolls (1978) calculated that wintering numbers doubled in the period from 1970/71 to 1976/77. Several sites, including Chilton Foliat, Longleat, Fonthill and Langford

Table 29. Tufted Ducks *Aythya fuligula* in Wiltshire: peak winter counts at key sites 1990/91–1999/00

	90/91	91/92	92/93	93/94	94/95	95/96	96/97	97/98	98/99	99/00
CWP	127	188	181	234	251	286	313	198	246	205
Liden Lagoon	74	73	6	2	0	1	1	0	0	0
Coate Water	30	55	25	28	30	14	30	20	13	27
River Kennet	200	101	54	–	71	21	27	21	8	19
Ramsbury Lake	90	69	109	104	71	39	21	28	35	28
Chilton Foliat	20	51	44	30	46	23	26	30	40	24
Wilton Water	29	18	39	40	56	34	25	33	47	44
Bowood Lake	26	28	10	24	27	46	58	49	86	42
Longleat lakes	35	36	20	22	59	87	41	50	53	82
Stourton lakes	30	47	40	35	–	47	50	26	54	140
Fonthill Lake	136	85	80	78	93	230	137	69	72	80
Langford Lakes	150	105	78	80	–	–	–	–	–	–
Salisbury Avon	200	178	160	–	72	22	78	40	38	22
Clarendon Lake	76	76	33	40	81	40	63	55	56	37

Lakes, regularly held over 100 wintering Tufted Ducks in the middle of that decade (*WeBS*), and CWP in particular became a prominent area for them at that time.

In the 1980s, numbers regularly exceeded 100 at these same sites, and also Wilton Water, while occasional large counts also came from Coate Water and Corsham Lake, as well as on both the Kennet and the Wylye. Table 29 shows continuing increases on some waters in the 1990s, but also a levelling off at others and apparent declines at many more. Indeed, some previously key sites are not listed at all in the table, either because of the paucity of counts or because they have decreased in importance. It may be that some localities with initially favourable conditions – perhaps in the period shortly following excavation (*eg* Liden Lagoon was expanded in 1976 and consistently held more than 50 from the early 1980s to early 1990s) – have become less attractive to diving ducks as they have matured. On the other hand, declines on the major rivers may reflect cleansing of those waterways if the previous concentrations were associated with organic inputs, *eg* from sewage treatment works or by artificial feeding.

The summer distribution map reflects the Tufted Duck's liking of eutrophic lowland lakes, ideally at least 1 ha in size and less than 5 m deep, although this species does also nest by rivers and other wetland habitats which have adjacent rank vegetation and high densities of chironomid midges (*BWP*). Breeding was recorded at the majority of the bigger waterbodies, along the eastern parts of the Kennet & Avon Canal, and by some rivers, including the Salisbury Avon, the Wylye and, particularly, the long-favoured Kennet. There was also a marked concentration on various small lakes around Tisbury, but the species was largely absent from the northwest of the county, and breeding was not noted along either the Bristol Avon or the Ebble. Perhaps surprisingly, too, CWP produced relatively few records but, in recent years, virtually no young have fledged there – thought to be attributable to high predation of broods by mink (Wildfowl & Wetlands Trust). Comparison with the *1968–72* and *1988–91 Atlases* suggests that the increase in the number of Wiltshire's core 10-km squares that hold breeding Tufted Ducks has slowed since the early 1990s (rising from ten to 18 between the atlases, but to just 20 in 1995–2000), although the number of summer squares where the species is simply seen has continued to grow (from 20 to 23 to 29) – as is consistent with a long-term national increase on waterways (*WBS*).

The summer distribution map shows breeding in nearly 60 tetrads, but the larger lakes in particular will have supported several pairs apiece and, given that this species is a late

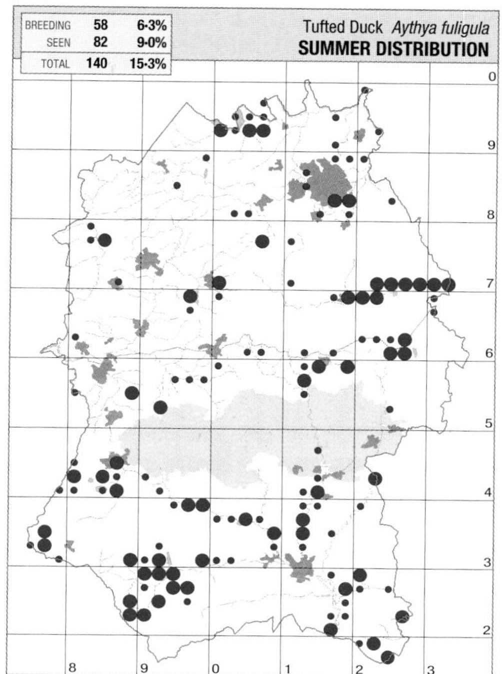

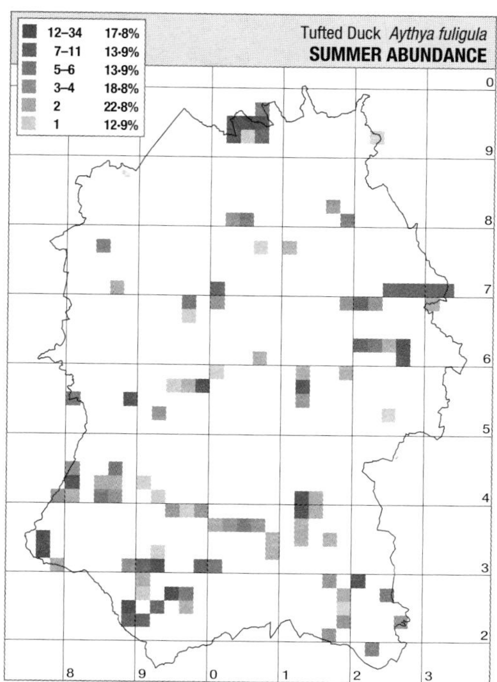

breeder – ducklings seldom hatch before mid June – many of the 80–odd tetrads in which it was noted only as present may have held pairs that nested after the April–May survey visit or had quickly lost broods of small young to predators before the June–July visit. Moreover, as one pair has bred successfully on a pond less than 10 m by 10 m in the middle of a Swindon golf course, it is very possible that what might be regarded as a relatively obvious species of duck may have been overlooked. The timed tetrad counts in summer totalled 789 and, though that figure will have included many non-breeders, it indicates a nesting population of, say, 150–300 pairs. This figure represents a rise – since estimates of 100–150 pairs in the mid 1970s – that is consistent with recent increases recorded by both WeBS and BBS.

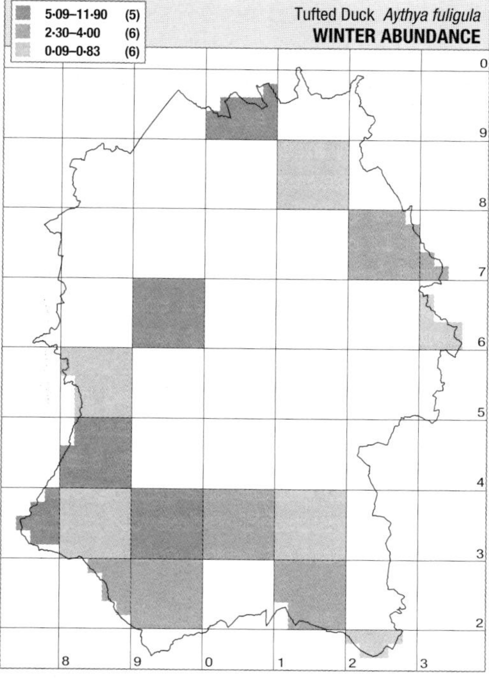

The winter map shows a distribution broadly similar to that of summer, though perhaps more restricted to major wetlands. Whilst concentrations throughout the south and west persist, Tufted Ducks were limited to just six 10-km squares in the north of the county, notably CWP, Swindon, Bowood Lake and the easterly sections of the Kennet, although the last may have been an artefact of the surveyed tetrads having missed the more notable sections of river. In recent years, most sites have held only small numbers, and fewer than ten have regularly supported 50 or more; of these, CWP is by far the most important (table 29). Higher counts away from these sites are unusual, though there have been marked concentrations on rivers – for example, 200 on the Salisbury Avon in December 1990 and 77 at Upper Woodford in January 1997 – but coverage is poorer there than on open waters. Extrapolation from the winter tetrad counts gives a Wiltshire total of about 1000, suggesting that the status of the Tufted Duck in the county at that season has changed little over the last 40 years. Nationally, there was a rise of around 50 per cent between the early 1960s and early 1980s, but numbers have remained relatively stable at around 90,000 since then (Kershaw & Cranswick 2003, *WeBS*).

PAC

Sponsored by Center Parcs UK

Scaup
Aythya marila

Rare winter visitor from coastal waters, breeds Iceland/north Europe

The Scaup has a low-arctic circumpolar breeding distribution, favouring tundra and wooded tundra zones. Between 7800 and 10,700 pairs nest in north Europe, excluding Russia (*EBCC Atlas*), mainly in Iceland and northern Fenno-Scandia, while in Great Britain this species ranks as the rarest breeding duck, not even nesting annually (*RBBP*).

Predominantly coastal in winter, the majority of the European population is then split between the western Baltic and the Dutch IJsselmeer. Small numbers also winter in the Caspian and Black Seas, along the coasts of northern France, and around Britain and Ireland (Scott & Rose 1996). Most of those in Great Britain are restricted to traditional, mainly northern, sites where they may occur in very large numbers: for example, over 30,000 were recorded around the distillery outfalls in the Firth of Forth until these discharges were cleaned up in the late 1970s (Campbell 1984), but current British numbers total only around 7500 (Kershaw & Cranswick 2003). The *1981–84 Winter Atlas* showed a predominantly coastal distribution and only a scattering of inland records, largely in the Midlands.

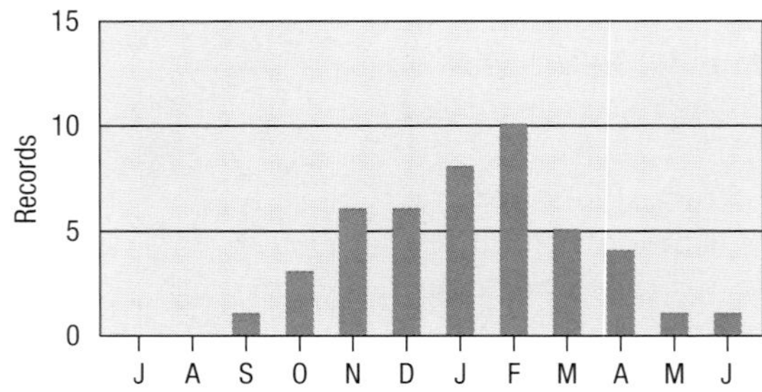

Figure 20. Scaups *Aythya marila* in Wiltshire: records by arrival months 1862–2000

The first Wiltshire record was reported by Hony (1915a): 'Mr. E Cambridge Phillips writes that he shot a female at Rowden about 1858'. A further five singletons in the 19th century – in 1862, 1864, 1870, 1873 and 1896 (Smith 1887, Hony 1915a) – were followed, after a long gap, by a total of 12 records involving 17 individuals during 1945–73 (*WANHM*) and then 29 records involving 35 birds during 1974–2000. It must be added that, in connection with a record in January 1959, the *WANHM* report for that year stated that 'What appeared to be the same [Scaup] has been seen again at Ramsbury and Chilton Foliat... early in 1960', but it was not mentioned in the report for 1960 and so has been omitted from these totals. Also, three at Stourton in January 1948 and a female at Ashton Keynes on 14 December 1969, each recorded at the time in *WANHM*, were respectively misdated as 1958 and 1970 by Buxton (1981).

Wiltshire's largest gathering was just four, a drake and three females at CWP on 7 May 1993. Most records have related to singletons that stayed for a week or less, mainly between November and February. Ten were seen between late March and June, suggesting passage movements (figure 20). Some of these later arrivals lingered, two of them for three months or more: a male at Wilton Water from 16 February to 16 May 1985 and, the county's latest date, an immature male at CWP from 5 April to 22 July 1994. The earliest date was 15 September 1997, at Swindon STW.

Though the Scaup is far from annual in Wiltshire, eight winters have each produced two records, three arrived in less than a month from mid January 1987, and there were four between early February and the end of March 1991. The majority of observations have been at CWP (11 records), Coate Water (eight) or Corsham Lake (six), and only nine of the 29 records since 1974 have been elsewhere.

PAC

Sponsored by Center Parcs UK

Eider

Somateria mollissima

Vagrant (2 records: 19th century) from British coasts, where mainly resident

With an almost circumpolar distribution – nesting in groups or colonies in northern Europe, mainly from the Netherlands and Germany north to Iceland, Svalbard and Franz Josef Land, as well as in northeast Asia, Alaska, Canada and Greenland – Eiders are almost entirely coastal ducks throughout the year and, except for leaving the high Arctic, make only partial or dispersive migrations. The European breeding population has been calculated at between 780,000 and 935,000 pairs (*EBCC Atlas*). In Great Britain, breeding is restricted almost entirely to Scotland, apart from a few in Northumberland and a colony at Walney (Cumbria). The latter indicates a southwards expansion from the Hebridean islands over the last few centuries, and the first breeding on Anglesey, in 1997, suggests this may be continuing. The *1988–91 Atlas* estimated the British total at 31,200 pairs. Movements are limited in winter and, although there are large concentrations at traditional sites, still mostly in Scotland, only small numbers are encountered around the English coastline; some of the most southerly of these may originate from Dutch colonies (Scott & Rose 1996).

With the exception of the recent development of some wintering regularly on Swiss and German lakes, Eiders are very rare inland. The only two Wiltshire records were both in the 19th century: one was killed 'a few years back... at Lyneham', and the other 'killed at Bottlesford, near Woodborough, in March, 1866' (Smith 1887). Even during a national 'wreck' in October 1993 – when 200 were found inland in Great Britain, mainly in a band from Northamptonshire to Yorkshire (Dennis 1994) – none was recorded in this county, and it seems that the species is destined to remain an extremely rare wanderer here.

PAC

Sponsored by Center Parcs UK

Long-tailed Duck

Clangula hyemalis

Winter vagrant (c10 records), breeds north Europe, winters North Sea/Baltic coasts

Long-tailed Ducks have a circumpolar breeding range that extends as far north as northernmost Canada and Greenland. They are among the most numerous of all wildfowl, with a world population of around 7·6 million (Wetlands International 2002), though their marine habits in winter, when they may disperse many tens of kilometres offshore, make monitoring difficult. Small numbers are encountered at many sites around the British coastline, though favoured haunts are off the more remote Scottish coasts and islands, and only around Orkney and the Moray Firth do concentrations exceed 1000 (*WeBS*). Inland records, generally in mid winter, usually involve single immatures or females which sometimes stay for protracted periods.

Smith (1887) included this species on 'the Wiltshire list without hesitation... on the authority of that excellent ornithologist, the late Rev. George Marsh', but apparently knew no date or locality. Interestingly, Marsh did not include this in his notes (1842–62), so it was almost certainly not a personal record. The next three, around a century later – all drakes and the county's only definite records of males – were on the gravel pits at Petersfinger in October 1950, on the Kennet & Avon Canal near Grafton in November and December 1962, and at Corsham Lake from 2 December 1967 to 9 January 1968 (this last was thought to be probably the same bird later seen at Bowood Lake on 14 January) (*WANHM*). From 1974:

1974	5 January	Corsham Lake	Female
	2 Mar–5 May	CWP	Female
1980	5–22 November	Liden Lagoon	Immature
1982	12 December	Longleat lakes	Female
	31 December	Fonthill Lake	Female
1983	1–8 January	Langford Lakes	Immature
1991	8 Nov–5 Dec	Corsham Lake	Adult female and 1st-year

The two records in December 1982 'probably' related to the same individual (*Hobby*).

PAC

Sponsored by Center Parcs UK

Common Scoter

Melanitta nigra

Rare visitor, mostly on passage, from coasts, breeds Iceland/north Fenno-Scandia/Russia

Common Scoters have an extensive arctic and subarctic distribution, breeding mainly throughout the tundra zone of Eurasia and east into Alaska, but also in isolated pockets in Canada, Iceland, Scotland and Ireland (*BWP*, Scott & Rose 1996). The populations of eastern Siberia, Alaska and Canada winter along Pacific and western Atlantic coasts, while those from northern Europe and western Siberia collect primarily in the southern Baltic – often in massive concentrations – apart from smaller numbers in the North and Irish Seas and off eastern Atlantic coasts as far south as Morocco.

The European breeding population, excluding Russia, has been put at 4900 to 14,000 pairs (*EBCC Atlas*). In Britain and Ireland, however – where this species is a relatively recent colonist, first recorded in 1855 – a comprehensive survey in 1995 estimated the breeding population at 95 pairs in Scotland and 100 in Ireland (Underhill *et al* 1998), yet there are indications of declines in some regions in recent decades, for instance in the flow country, and breeding sites in Northern Ireland have been abandoned.

In winter, Common Scoters generally favour sandy bays, and the majority of the 50,000 that winter around British coasts are concentrated off Wales, northwest England and eastern Scotland (Kershaw & Cranswick 2003). A few coastal areas hold some non-breeding scoters all year, numbers then building at traditional sites from late summer. The species is known to migrate overland through the Baltic and, though its movements are poorly understood, it must do so at least to a small degree across Great Britain also to account for the frequent occurrence of this otherwise essentially coastal species far inland, often in groups numbering ten or more, especially during passage periods.

Smith (1887) gave three dated 19th century records for Wiltshire: the first, rather curiously phrased, was 'met with … on Salisbury Plain in 1849', and the second shot near Devizes in 1871; the third involved two birds, one of which was 'caught', at Marlborough in February 1873. He also noted that Yarrell (1856) had recorded being informed by Sir Richard Colt Hoare that his keeper had shot one on what was presumably Garden Lake, Stourhead; no date was given, but it was certainly before 1850. One 'killed at Marlborough during the fog on the night of April 2nd 1911' (*MCNHS*, Hony 1915a) was the only further record until 1949 when sightings became more regular, totalling 31 records of 59 individuals from then to 2000.

These ducks have been recorded in Wiltshire in all months but few have been seen in winter and the only two known January occurrences were during the severe weather of 1962/63, one of them 'in a very weak condition, alongside the West Lavington–Erlestoke

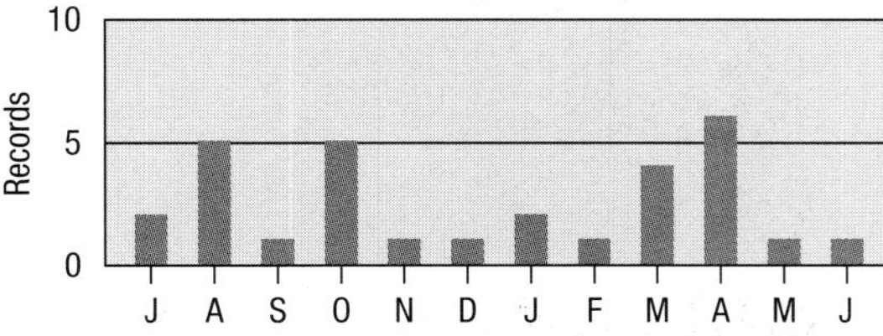

Figure 21. Common Scoters *Melanitta nigra* in Wiltshire: records by arrival months 1949–2000

road, was caught, revived and freed' (*WANHM*); indeed, most have been in spring and autumn (figure 21). While the numbers might indicate a protracted autumn passage, it could be speculated that the two, admittedly very small, peaks in August and October actually represent distinct waves, the first involving scoters moving to, or on from, British moult sites and the second those that have moulted elsewhere.

Most records are of singletons present for just one or two days, although a party of 11 (four males, seven females) was seen at Coate Water on 11 July 1967 (*WANHM*) and another of nine (three adult males, three immature males, three females) appeared at CWP on 23 May 1994. Half of the 24 records during 1974–86 were at Coate Water, Corsham Lake or Langford Lakes, and none at CWP; but all six from August 1996 to the end of 2000 were at that last site.

PAC

Sponsored by Center Parcs UK

Velvet Scoter

Melanitta fusca

Vagrant (4 records) from coastal waters, breeds Fenno-Scandia/north Russia

Velvet Scoters have an almost continuous circumpolar breeding distribution, from Fenno-Scandia eastwards to central Canada, favouring small freshwater bodies in boreal forests and southern tundra (*BWP*, Scott & Rose 1996). The population of Europe, excluding Russia, has been estimated to be between 21,000 and 31,000 pairs (*EBCC Atlas*). Those from Fenno-Scandia east to the Yenisey (85°E) winter primarily in the southern and eastern Baltic. At that season, these ducks are almost entirely coastal; some may occur in shallow waters many kilometres offshore. They are mainly winter visitors to Great Britain and about 3000 are concentrated at just three traditional sites in Scotland, while small numbers can be encountered widely around the coastline (*1981–84 Winter Atlas*, Kershaw & Cranswick 2003).

Against this background it is not surprising that Velvet Scoters are rare inland. The first two for Wiltshire were both shot towards the end of the 19th century, the first at Mildenhall on 28 October 1885 (Hart Smith 1887) and the second, 'a young bird', near Marlborough Mill on 14 October 1889 (Meyrick 1895). (Peirson 1919 stated 'Three records, the last in 1899', but Hony 1915a, Peirson & Walford 1930 and Peirson 1939 all show that there were only the two.) Another 70 years passed before a male was found at CWP – 'on a gravel pit near Ashton Keynes' – on 12 December 1959 (*WANHM*). Nearly two decades later, an adult male appeared at Liden Lagoon on 23 January 1979 'after a night of driving snow had blanketed southern Britain' (*Hobby*), then moved to Coate Water later the same day.

PAC

Sponsored by Center Parcs UK

Goldeneye

Bucephala clangula

Locally common winter visitor from Fenno-Scandia/Russia, rare summer

The Goldeneye has a widespread breeding distribution in a broad band across north-central Eurasia and North America, occupying temperate latitudes in the forest zone between steppe and tundra. In Europe its main range is in Fenno-Scandia and Russia, but there are sizeable populations in Germany, Poland, the Baltic States and Belarus, and small numbers south to the Czech Republic and Ukraine; excluding Russia, the European total has been estimated at 227,000 to 283,000 pairs (*EBCC Atlas*).

This species favours coniferous habitats with largish areas of cold, open water generally free of vegetation (*CBWP*). In 1970 a pair bred near Aviemore (Inverness-shire/Highland), the first known successful nest in Great Britain. Because potential breeding sites are limited in this country – Goldeneyes frequently use the holes of Black Woodpeckers on the Continent – a nestbox scheme was started the following year. As a result, the population grew rapidly to around 100 pairs by 1990 (*1988–91 Atlas*) and had reached about 185 by 1998, the most complete of recent estimates (*RBBP*). Although nearly all are still in Speyside, where this has become one of the commonest breeding ducks, small numbers now nest elsewhere in Scotland, and pairs or individuals have even summered in England south to Hampshire (*RBBP*).

On a world basis, winter distribution is more restricted. Goldeneyes are then found across much of the USA, but their range is far patchier in Eurasia where most move to coastal areas: notable concentrations occur in eastern China, Japan and, in northwest Europe, particularly in Denmark and the western Baltic. In Great Britain the winter distribution shows a strong northern bias and, although Goldeneyes may at that season be found anywhere in lowland Scotland and in many parts of northern England, the majority occupy coastal sites; few inland sites regularly support large numbers (*WeBS*). They are more thinly distributed inland elsewhere in England, favouring reservoirs and gravel complexes in the Midlands and the London area.

Goldeneyes have, until recently, been only scarce winter visitors to Wiltshire. The first dated specimen was killed near Salisbury in 1830 (Marsh 1842–62), and fewer than ten others were known to Smith (1887); Hony (1915a) could add only two, one

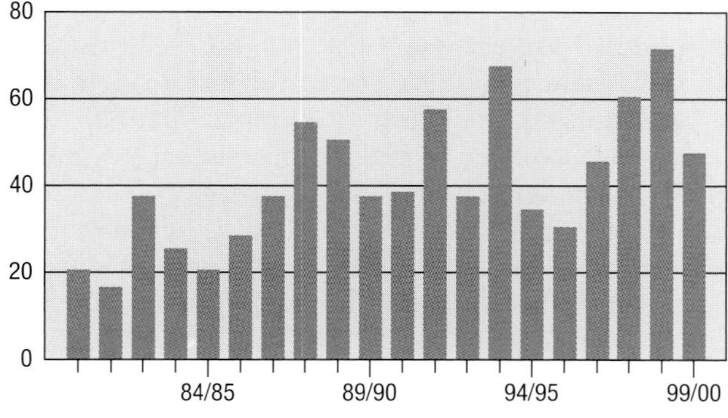

Figure 22. Goldeneyes *Bucephala clangula* in Wiltshire: peak winter counts at CWP 1980/81–1999/00

in January 1885 at Blackland and the other at Britford, reported by Rawlence but undated. Records remained less than annual in the early part of the 20th century, and in 1936 the species was still a 'very rare visitor occurring at times during very cold weather' (*WANHM*). Six at Coate Water on 25 January 1947 (*WANHM*) was the county's largest gathering up to that date and, indeed, no higher numbers at a single site were specifically listed until 1979, although greater totals may have been distributed across the Wiltshire side of CWP in the mid 1970s. Nevertheless, Goldeneyes were recorded annually in the county from the mid 1950s: one to three at up to three sites – predominantly Braydon Pond, Coate Water, Corsham Lake and Bowood Lake – and more often than not in December or February. Five records in 1962/63 were followed by six the following winter, but it was not until the early 1970s that any Wiltshire site could boast this species as regular: then numbers at CWP were noted as 'rising to *c.*15 in winter usually 1 or 2 birds on the Wiltshire waters' (*WANHM*). Coate Water, Corsham Lake and Langford Lakes regularly hosted Goldeneyes during the latter part of that decade (Rolls 1979). Nevertheless, CWP remained the county's only site of significance in the early 1980s (*1981–84 Winter Atlas*) and a general increase continued until the end of that decade when up to 50 were using the lakes on the Wiltshire side (Palmer 1991). Indeed, peak numbers there have continued to increase, albeit slowly and falteringly, in line with the national trend since the mid 1970s (figure 22). The highest counts in recent years have been in March, when what seems to be a passage influx is concentrated almost entirely on Lakes 68 and 74; numbers at Chew Valley Lake (Somerset) similarly peak in late March or early April (*Avon Bird Report*).

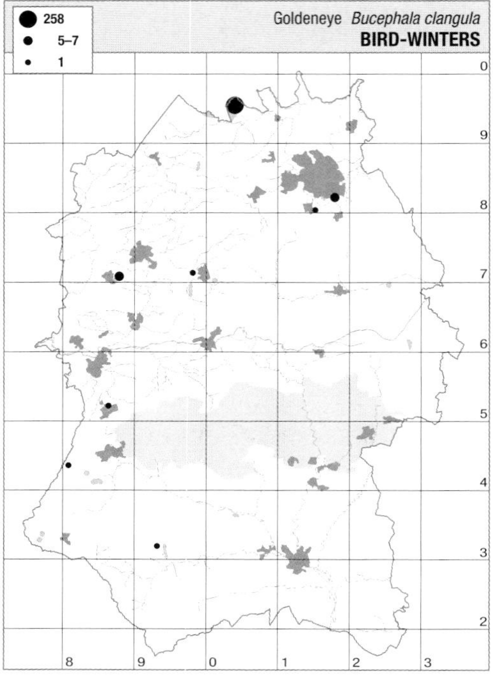

Goldeneyes occur widely, but in small numbers, elsewhere in Wiltshire and have been seen on most major waterbodies at some time in recent decades. They were, however, more numerous in the early 1980s, when records came from six to ten sites each winter and often involved three or four individuals for extended periods. Since 1990, with the exception of four at Fonthill Lake early in 1991, two has been the highest count at any of 14 sites other than CWP, and most have stayed for just a single day. Coate Water and Corsham Lake have been the most regularly used in this period. Although many occur during mid winter, there has also been a large number in early winter, these presumably being new arrivals in Great Britain that are still on passage.

A noticeable trend towards progressively earlier arrivals began in the 1990s. Previously, although records in August were not unknown, the first on return passage were generally in October, but this changed to September in the mid 1990s. Moreover, during 1997–99 the first records each year were during 13–25 June, and in 2000 on 30 July. These dates coincide with arrivals in Denmark of non-breeding Goldeneyes from Fenno-Scandia, though the main movement to the wintering grounds does not take place until November (*Migration Atlas*). By contrast, the latest Wiltshire record each spring has consistently been in the last week of April or, occasionally, the first week of May. A female at CWP on 3 June 1993 is difficult to classify as either a very late departure or an early return.

PAC

Sponsored by Center Parcs UK

Smew

Mergellus albellus

Scarce and local winter visitor from north Fenno-Scandia/north Russia

The strikingly white-and-black adult drakes of this smallest of the three 'sawbill' ducks are among Wiltshire's most attractive winter visitors. The infrequent appearances of Smews in the county usually coincide with the onset of hard weather in the Netherlands, where up to 10,000 occur at that season. This species nests in tree holes, mainly in the boreal taiga across northern Eurasia from northern Fenno-Scandia east to Kamchatka. In Europe the range slowly contracted northward during the 19th and 20th centuries, primarily because of habitat loss; it has been estimated that 1100 to 2100 pairs breed in Fenno-Scandia and between 7000 and 15,000 pairs in European Russia (*EBCC Atlas*). In winter, some 40,000 Smews are spread between the western Baltic and the Netherlands, while many others move to the Black Sea and eastern Mediterranean (Wetlands International 2002).

In Great Britain, the westernmost outpost of their regular winter range, Smews are most frequent in southeast England, and uncommon or rare west and north of the Midlands. They favour open fresh water, particularly gravel pits, where they dive for small fish, but will move to rivers in freezing weather. In the 1950s, the London reservoirs held about 100, representing 'a third to a half of the British winter population', which in the severe weather of early 1963 was as many as 'a few hundred', but the next 20 years saw a marked reduction: by the early 1980s, the London annual average was just seven and the national only 62 (*1981–84 Winter Atlas*). More recently, however, particularly during and after colder weather in the mid and late 1990s, numbers have been higher again and the British total has been estimated at 370 (Kershaw & Cranswick 2003). Although this is a conspicuous species, it must be added that its mobility – with the resulting risk of duplication of records of the same individuals – means that numbers can be difficult to judge.

Smith (1887) reported the first Smew in Wiltshire on the authority of Reverend G Marsh, but did not give place, date or sex, and added two subsequent records, both likewise 'killed', at Fifield, Enford, in January 1876, and at an unspecified locality in December 1879. Sixty years were to pass before the first 20th century observations, at Coate Water in 1939 (Kennedy 1966, Buxton 1981) and at Erlestoke Lake in February 1942, the latter a drake (*DSBL*). Another Smew appeared at Coate Water in January 1945 (*WANHM*, Kennedy 1966), but the following 30 years then produced just seven more records in only four winters: two, or possibly three, drakes at Coate Water in December 1952; a 'redhead' (female or immature male) at Longleat in March 1958, and a drake there in January 1962; and, in the severe winter of 1962/63, two redheads at Corsham Lake in November, a drake and two redheads on the Bristol Avon at Dauntsey on separate dates in January and February, and what may have been the same trio at Longleat in March (all *WANHM*).

The next was not until February 1976, when Wiltshire's first long-staying Smew was a redhead at CWP, a site that was to become increasingly important and, by the 1990s, the principal location for this species in the county. In the late 1970s and early 1980s, occurrences became more regular and, though still not annual, up to three in a winter were recorded. Consistent with the movement of female and immature wildfowl farther west and south than adult males, nearly all were redheads, which usually stayed for no more than one or two days at some time between November and March, the majority in February. Most of the others seen in this period were at Tockenham Reservoir, Coate Water and Corsham Lake; and, as it is strongly suspected that individuals sometimes return to the same sites in successive winters, it is perhaps significant that the only records at Liden Lagoon involved a redhead in February and March 1978 and again in February 1979.

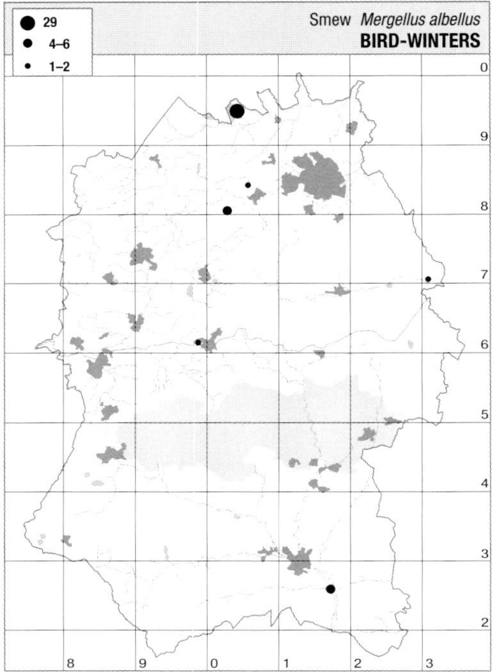

The beginning of 1985 saw a marked influx (figure 23): five at Bishopstone, Salisbury, in mid January; five others (this time including three adult males) at Coate Water a week later; and two at CWP and one at Corsham in February. Five more records followed in the next winter and five again in January 1987, spread fairly widely around the county and including not only the traditionally favoured lakes but also the Salisbury Avon.

With milder weather, the next eight winters produced just eight records, all bar two of them at CWP. Then blizzards in December 1995 saw a marked arrival and what was at that time a county record total of eight (all redheads) at CWP on the 9th. Such numbers, however, became a regular feature there over the next four winters – paralleling an increase of Goosanders (*qv*). Although the Smews were spread between several lakes (especially 68/74, 29, and 82/83), judging the total number involved a fair degree of guesswork: at least nine, possibly 13, but only one adult drake, were thought to have been present between January and March 1997; and a group of nine or ten, again including only one adult male,

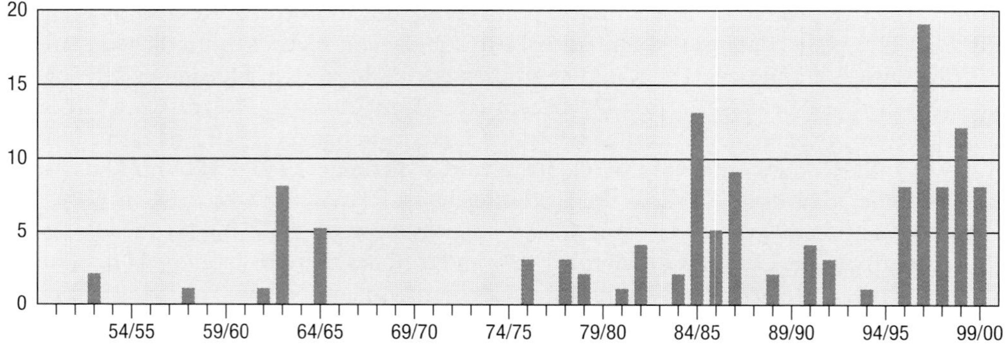

Figure 23. Smews *Mergellus albellus* in Wiltshire: estimated winter totals 1950/51–1999/00

Table 30. Smews *Mergellus albellus* in Wiltshire: numbers by arrival months 1952–2000

	Jul	Aug	Sep	Oct	Nov	Dec	Jan	Feb	Mar	Apr	May	Jun
Birds	0	0	0	1	9	23	54	37	25	2	0	0

then favoured the area around Lakes 68/74 in January 1999. As the species is now present at CWP from mid October to March in most years, it is likely that many observations relate to the same long-staying individuals, but it is also possible that turnover goes undetected and that considerably more Smews visit the site than peak counts indicate.

Despite the general increase in numbers since the mid 1970s, relatively few have been found away from CWP in recent winters. Indeed, during 1990–2000, Smews were otherwise recorded only at Queen's Park, Swindon; at Littlecote; on the Kennet & Avon Canal Ponds; on the Salisbury Avon at Bodenham (no fewer than six in January 1997); and, in two consecutive winters, at Tockenham Reservoir (two). Very few arrive before December, and most have departed by mid March (table 30), but the earliest and latest records are 20 October 1997 at CWP and 16 April 1987 on Garden Lake, Stourhead.

PEC

Sponsored by Center Parcs UK

Red-breasted Merganser

Mergus serrator

Rare and local winter visitor from coastal waters, breeds north Britain/north Europe

Red-breasted Mergansers nest by shores and rivers of the arctic and boreal zones, and winter along temperate coasts within or south of the summer range. They have a vast circumpolar distribution across northern Eurasia and northern North America, extending to Greenland and Iceland. Though they breed throughout much of the northwest of Great Britain, often far from the sea, they are almost entirely coastal in winter. Very few are seen inland in southern England, but in the 1990s the species became more regular at CWP, even if only in ones and twos, often associating with Goosanders, and sometimes roosting with them.

Confined to northwest Scotland until a southward expansion in the latter half of the 19th century, the British breeding distribution extended to northern England in 1950, to Wales in 1953, and to the Derbyshire Peak District by 1973 (*1875–1900 Atlas*), but the *1988–91 Atlas* then showed declines in Scotland – the results of both licensed control and illegal persecution. The British total was then put at a minimum of 2150 pairs, a small proportion of the estimated 59,800 to 84,500 pairs in Europe, excluding Russia (*EBCC Atlas*).

The *1981–84 Winter Atlas* showed that most British Mergansers are at that season concentrated on northern coasts close to the breeding areas. Numbers are also supplemented by migrants from Iceland – and, probably, some from Fenno-Scandia and north Russia, too – raising the total in Great Britain to about 10,000 (Robinson 1999, Kershaw & Cranswick 2003). More may arrive when hard weather on the Continent pushes them west from the Baltic and eastern North Sea shores, and it is then that some tend to appear inland (*1981–84 Winter Atlas*).

Table 31. Red-breasted Mergansers *Mergus serrator* in Wiltshire: numbers by bird-months 1864–2000

	Jul	Aug	Sep	Oct	Nov	Dec	Jan	Feb	Mar	Apr	May	Jun
Birds	0	0	0	0	8	8	10	18	79	1	0	0

Smith (1887) listed just five Wiltshire records for the 19th century, all singletons and all shot. The first, at Great Bedwyn, was 'presented to the Wiltshire Archæological and Natural History Society ... in the year of its inauguration, 1853'. (Although Smith did not make it clear that the bird was shot in 1853, *MCNHS* always noted the record as referring to that year.) The other four were found at Quemerford about 1860, at Trafalgar in December 1864, at Trowbridge in March 1873, and at Spye Park on 5 February 1881.

Over 60 years passed before the county's first 20th century record: a drake and two 'redheads' (females or immature males) seen on the Salisbury Avon near Charlton on 16 February 1947 (*WANHM*), in what was a particularly severe winter. But the species became more regular thereafter, there being 26 further published observations by the end of 2000, no fewer than 17 of them since 1990. All but five of those 17 were at CWP, where the only previous record had been in 1983. Indeed, Red-breasted Mergansers were found there in all ten winters from 1990/91 – some possibly the same individuals returning in successive years – often roosting with the growing numbers of Goosanders (*qv*). In 1993, 1999 and 2000, drake Mergansers were also frequently noted displaying to redhead Goosanders.

The most remarkable Wiltshire observation involved about 70 in flight at Idmiston on 11 March 1961: 'The birds were a little too high to be definite but were either Goosander or Merganser and are much more likely to be the latter, as numbers of Merganser winter on Poole Harbour' (*WANHM*); at that time, Goosanders were much rarer in Wiltshire than they are now, although an exceptional total of 43 was recorded at Chew Valley Lake (Somerset) early in 1963 (Palmer & Balance 1968). Except for that Idmiston observation, the three in 1947, three at CWP in February 1996 and two during the winter of 1997/98, all records have involved singletons. The earlier ones were all of short duration, suggesting hard weather movements or migration, but stays at CWP have lengthened, the longest having involved a redhead from 23 November 1997 to 19 March 1998, and all observations in the county, bar one, have fallen during these five months (table 31): the earliest arrival was on 12 November and the latest departure on 2 April, both at CWP in 2000. Away from that site, Red-breasted Mergansers have been recorded on more than one occasion only on the Salisbury Avon and its tributaries (four times) and at Coate Water (also four).

PEC

Sponsored by Center Parcs UK

Goosander

Mergus merganser

Local but increasing winter visitor from northern Fenno-Scandia/Russia

The commonest of the three 'sawbill' ducks that winter in Great Britain, Goosanders are an increasingly regular sight on Wiltshire's lakes and rivers at that season, the handsome adult drakes outnumbered by females and immature males, or 'redheads'. Since this species colonised Scotland in the 19th century, its summer distribution has spread steadily southward, but the late December arrival of most of the winter visitors to Wiltshire points to their having a north Continental origin.

Nesting Goosanders favour large, clear, inland lakes in forest or mountain regions, but are tolerant of both deep waters and fast-flowing streams provided that these hold fairly high densities of fish (*CBWP*). The species occurs throughout much of the northern hemisphere, but in Europe breeds commonly in Iceland and Great Britain, around the Baltic and throughout Fenno-Scandia and much of northern Russia, as well as in isolated pockets south to the Alps, Balkans and Ukraine.

During the 19th century, though regular in Scotland, Goosanders were only occasional winter visitors to many English counties (*1875–1900 Atlas*). First proved breeding in the Scottish Highlands in 1871, they subsequently spread southwards and, no doubt aided by reduced persecution during the 1914–18 and 1938–45 Wars, colonised England in 1941. Between the *1968–72* and *1988–91 Atlases*, their range showed a marked expansion into the central and south Pennines, Wales and the Welsh Marches, and since 1980 they have nested regularly in Devon. Though there were some losses in Scotland as a result of both licensed control and illegal persecution, the *1988–91 Atlas* estimated the British breeding population at 2700 pairs. Subsequent further spread included nesting in Somerset (1993) and Hampshire (1998).

In winter, most European Goosanders move to areas around the western Baltic and countries bordering the North Sea, then variably farther west in accordance with the onset and extent of ice. Those that nest in Iceland, Great Britain, southwestern Scandinavia, Germany and Poland south to the Alps are believed to be entirely or largely resident, or to move only short distances to sheltered estuaries, although the majority of the males of northwest Europe make a remarkable moult migration to northern Norway (Little & Furness 1985). The British breeding population is considered to be distinct from those on the Continent (Scott & Rose 1996), but is joined in winter by Goosanders from Fenno-Scandian and Russian breeding populations (*Migration Atlas*); the species then becomes widespread on inland waters, not only in the breeding areas but also in central and southeast England (*1981–84 Winter Atlas*).

The first Wiltshire Goosanders were a pair shot 'on the river [probably Salisbury] Avon' in February 1838, as noted by Marsh (1842–62) and then quoted by Smith (1887) who, in all, was able to list 15 records in the 19th century – including two small parties in the meadows at Britford – to which total Hony (1915a) was able to add a further two, the second reported by Reverend FCR Jourdain on the Bristol Avon, near Lacock Abbey, on 24 December 1892.

A male shot at Britford on 28 November 1936 was believed to be the county's first in the 20th century (*WANHM*) and no more records were published until 1948. In the first half of the 1950s, however, Goosanders were recorded annually, mostly in January, nearly always at Coate Water or Corsham Lake, and usually seen for just a single day, though one pair stayed at Longford Castle 'for about six weeks from March onwards' in 1956 (all *WANHM*). There were then few further records until remarkable groups of 26 on the Bristol Avon at Dauntsey and 23 on the Salisbury Avon at Longford in January 1963, undoubtedly as a result of the particularly severe weather that winter; smaller numbers lingered at both sites for over a month (*WANHM*). Singletons or small parties at Coate and Corsham continued to be the norm until the early 1970s, but dates from November to, in extreme cases, April became more frequent (*WANHM*).

Goosanders were found at six sites in 1973/74; thereafter records at such lakes as those at Bowood, Fonthill and Westbury became increasingly regular, while at CWP there were often several observations at the same place in the course of a winter (*WANHM*, *Hobby*). In the late 1970s and 1980s, the highest counts were 16 at Coate, 14 at CWP, and 11 at Corsham, but, in all, Goosanders were recorded at around 20 localities, including Braydon Pond,

Edington Lake, Shear Water and Langford Lakes. The cold winter of 1981/82 alone produced observations at ten sites, though maximum numbers were lower. Since 1989 the species has become more regular.

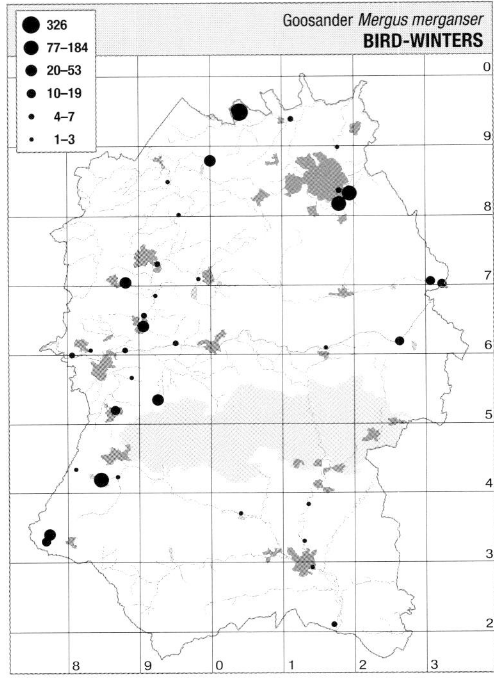

Table 32 shows winter peaks at eight key sites through the 1990s. Except at Corsham Lake and Shear Water, where numbers built up during the first half of the decade, the increase was more marked from the mid 1990s, especially at CWP where counts grew spectacularly after the discovery of a roost in 1995. These ducks gather there at night on undisturbed waters, dispersing to feed on other lakes and rivers during the day. Observations of Goosanders flying over several areas of Swindon confirmed that numbers at both Coate Water and Liden Lagoon involved a roving group that regularly moved the distance of 18km between those sites and the CWP roost, while 26 at Braydon Pond in January 1997 were also part of the same movements. The highest counts elsewhere in the second half of the 1990s included ten at Littlecote, 11 at Chilton Foliat and 20 on the Bristol Avon near Melksham. Exactly how many groups were involved is not clear, though it is conceivable that there may have been just one in the northeast of the county and another in the west, the latter perhaps roosting at Chew Valley Lake (Somerset).

Goosanders were mapped in ten of Wiltshire's 33 core 10-km squares in the west and northeast of the county in the *1981–84 Winter Atlas*, but in only three, centred on CWP, during the two winters of the tetrad survey. That observers were asked to cover only a random selection of tetrads in the winters of 1998–2000 – and, since most Goosanders do not arrive here much before the end of the year, perhaps also the timing of those visits – may well have led to this species with its localised habitat requirements being under-recorded. Even at its peak in the mid 1990s, the Wiltshire total probably numbered no more than 175, a relatively small proportion of the 16,100 in Great Britain as a whole (Kershaw & Cranswick 2003), although annual numbers are always influenced to a degree by the severity of the weather, particularly in the Netherlands.

Table 32. Goosanders *Mergus merganser* in Wiltshire: peak winter counts at key sites 1990/91–1999/00

	90/91	91/92	92/93	93/94	94/95	95/96	96/97	97/98	98/99	99/00
CWP	12	21	16	20	32	49	85	88	88	26
Coate Water	–	–	–	–	–	23	22	70	31	39
Liden Lagoon	–	–	1	–	–	2	2	44	24	17
Corsham Lake	3	27	18	44	11	16	9	5	16	1
Edington Lake	–	–	–	–	1	2	6	20	9	8
Longleat lakes	1	2	3	4	15	1	8	–	–	–
Shear Water	6	20	20	17	27	1	26	33	9	7
Stourton lakes	–	–	–	–	–	–	7	17	3	5

Another recent phenomenon has been an increase in the proportion of adult drakes, which made up 36 per cent of the CWP roost on 30 December 1998 and no less than 52 per cent on 13 December 1997. The fact that large numbers of Goosanders rarely arrive in Wiltshire before late December supports a Continental origin; in contrast, those at Somerset's Chew Valley Lake build up from October (*Avon Bird Report*). Most leave by the end of March. The earliest recorded arrival in Wiltshire is 21 September 1995 and, with one exception, the latest departure 25 May 1992. That one exception, a singleton on the Frome in June 2000, was perhaps not a surprising development, given recent breeding records in southern England.

PEC

Sponsored by Center Parcs UK

Ruddy Duck

Oxyura jamaicensis

Locally increasing resident following escapes in Britain in 1950s, origin Americas

Ruddy Ducks occur naturally in south Canada, much of west-central USA, and the West Indies, wintering in southern North America and south into and beyond Mexico. (The population of much of the Andes of South America is now generally considered to be a separate species.) Some were first imported into Europe in 1936 (Delacour 1954–64). In 1948, three pairs were brought to the then Wildfowl Trust at Slimbridge (Gloucestershire), where they readily bred. Mainly during 1956–63, about 70 unpinioned juveniles escaped into the wild, subsequently establishing a successful naturalised population, initially around Chew Valley Lake (Somerset) but later mostly in the West Midlands, and by 1975 numbering 'fifty or more' pairs (*1968–72 Atlas*).

While the West Midlands remained the stronghold over the following 20 years, Ruddy Ducks had, by exploiting a vacant niche and having high survival rates among ducklings, spread to many other parts of England, as well as to Wales and Scotland, and the population was estimated at some 570 pairs (*1988–91 Atlas*). Although the initial exponential increase had slowed, numbers continued to grow at 6–7 per cent annually through the 1990s (Kershaw & Hughes 2002), and in winter 1999/2000 British counts peaked at a new high of 4565 (*WeBS*). By this time, too, there had been over 900 records, involving some 1500 birds, in 19 other western European and North African countries (Hughes *et al* 1999a), including Spain, where some hybridised with that country's population of the globally endangered White-headed Duck. In response to the threat of genetic swamping of their Spanish congener, trials into the feasibility of controlling Ruddy Ducks in Europe were initiated in the mid 1990s, though this proved controversial (*eg* Zonfrillo 2000); just over 1600 had been killed by the end of 2000 (Central Science Laboratory 2002).

Corsham Lake produced all of Wiltshire's first few Ruddy Ducks: in 1966 an immature or female on 27 December (*WANHM*); in 1970–72 a prospecting male – presumed to be the same individual – on several occasions during March–July each year (*WANHM*); and in 1976, after a four-year gap, one male in June and two immatures in September. Thereafter, Ruddy Ducks were recorded annually as the national expansion reached Wiltshire, and numbers also increased. Observations in 1977 included no fewer than six at Coate Water in January and also the first breeding – itself only the eighth county record – when a female with five ducklings, along with seven other Ruddy Ducks, was seen at Tockenham Reservoir in August although, with the lake partially drained later that summer, it is not known if they fledged (*Hobby*, Buxton 1981).

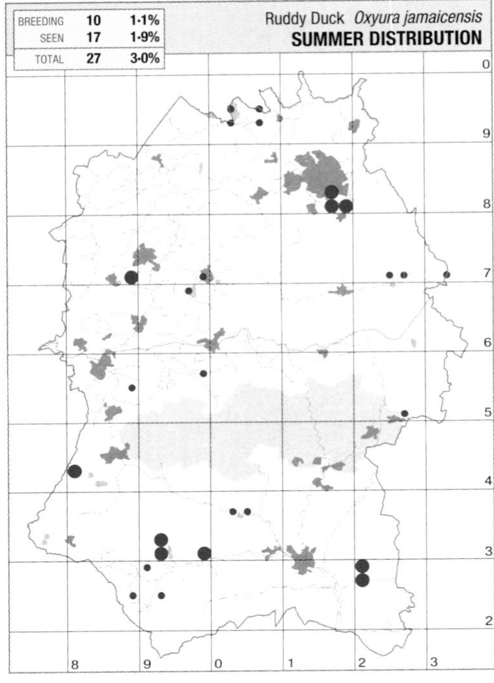

There were, however, still only half a dozen records each year into the early 1980s, often of males in the first part of summer, particularly at CWP, Coate, Tockenham and Corsham, but a male at Clarendon Lake in August 1980 signalled the arrival of the species in the south of the county. In 1982 the first Ruddy Ducks were seen at both Fonthill Lake and Langford Lakes. In 1983 they were found in five different months at CWP alone, and monthly maxima there of 13 in February and 11 in March and April 1984 were exceptional, particularly in the absence of any notable cold period that might have caused an exodus from the core wintering areas in the Midlands. In the late 1980s, Ruddy Ducks became regular (recorded in roughly half the months) at CWP, Coate, Corsham, and Langford Lakes, though usually no more than two or three at each.

Despite such increased presence, breeding was not proved in Wiltshire for a second time until 1988 – 11 years after the first – when a brood of four was noted at Langford Lakes on 9 August (though all the young had disappeared by the 22nd). After a blank in 1989, however, Ruddy Ducks nested successfully somewhere in the county in every subsequent year through to the end of the century, particularly favouring three reed-fringed lakes in the south: at Clarendon in 1990–94 and 1998, usually two broods annually; at Langford Lakes in the four years 1990–93; and at Fonthill Lake, now the most significant site, in all but three years during 1990–2000. Breeding was also proved at least once in the 1990s at each of Coate Water, Corsham Lake and the Longleat lakes, and near Teffont Evias. This is reflected in the summer distribution map, although that probably overstates the species' presence in any one year, and the county's breeding population may not be more than five or six pairs. The Ruddy Duck's wide distribution and use of small lakes suggest that room for limited expansion remains and it is, of course, likely that some breeding goes undetected. As this species 'Avoids flowing fresh water unless very sluggish' (*CBWP*),

Table 33. Ruddy Ducks *Oxyura jamaicensis* in Wiltshire: peak winter counts at key sites 1990/91–1999/00

	90/91	91/92	92/93	93/94	94/95	95/96	96/97	97/98	98/99	99/00
CWP	11	–	1	3	4	17	17	1	10	29
Coate Water	–	–	–	–	6	6	3	2	5	2
Corsham Lake	1	–	–	–	–	–	–	7	6	–
Fonthill Lake	25	3	4	28	17	30	35	14	23	23
Langford Lakes	12	10	11	6	5	–	–	–	–	–
Clarendon Lake	4	1	4	8	4	7	7	15	6	11

it seems worth adding that one and a sometimes a pair have been seen feeding on both the Kennet at Ramsbury (SB Edwards) and the Wylye near Teffont Evias (IJ Ferguson-Lees).

The winter picture mirrors that of summer reasonably closely and, among the data in table 33, the decline at Langford Lakes accurately matches the loss of the breeding stock there. Winter counts at many of those key sites presumably involved the local breeding populations; indeed, the largest counts at Fonthill and Clarendon were often in late summer and early autumn, presumably before the dispersal of the young. The significance of Fonthill is immediately apparent in the table, and rivalled only by CWP. Breeding at the latter site is, however, extremely rare – as is the case with many other species of wildfowl – and it is likely that the Ruddy Ducks that winter there originate from other areas. During cold winters, the centre of the national distribution appears to switch from the favoured reservoirs in the Midlands, and larger numbers then frequent Chew Valley and surrounding sites (*WeBS*). Increases at CWP in 1995/96 and 1996/97 lend weight to the outside origin of Ruddy Ducks there. The tetrad counts suggested a winter total of 45 in Wiltshire, probably an average figure for recent years that, depending on winter weather and local breeding success, may vary between 40 and perhaps as many as 60.

Should the control of Ruddy Ducks in Great Britain be deemed feasible, as appears likely at the time of writing, their tenure in the county may well be relatively short-lived.

WEQ

Sponsored by Center Parcs UK

Red Grouse

Lagopus lagopus

Former vagrant (5 old records) from Wales or, more probably, from attempted introductions

Long treated as a separate species, but now usually regarded as a race of the circumpolar subarctic Willow Grouse – distinguished by its white wings and white winter plumage – the Red Grouse *Lagopus lagopus scotica* is found only in northern and western Britain, south to Wales, and in Ireland, normally on heather-dominated moorland. The British population has been put at 250,000 pairs (*1988–91 Atlas*).

Montagu (1802) told of a female taken alive at Wedhampton in the winter of 1794, and Smith (1887) listed four further Wiltshire records: singles at Compton Bassett and Devizes, both undated, as well as one at West Knoyle in 1848 and another at Wedhampton in 1866. The time of year was given only for two of the five – 'August' and 'winter' – but Smith assumed that all were 'stragglers from Wales ... probably driven out of their course by the prevalence of high winds'. In the 19th century the closest populations to Wiltshire were indeed in the uplands of the Welsh Marches from Gwent to Shropshire, but most old records in south and east England have been attributed to introductions (*1875–1900 Atlas*). These have been attempted in the past in several counties from Devon and Somerset to East Anglia (Witherby *et al* 1938–41), but were successful only from 1915–16 onwards on both Dartmoor and Exmoor (Sitters 1988). By the end of the 20th century the species was almost extinct on the Somerset side of Exmoor (*Somerset Birds* 2000). Morres (1878–85) mentioned that it 'has been tried more than once to introduce them on the Quantock Hills, in Somerset'.

In view of the long-term decline in range and numbers of the Red Grouse during the last century, most noticeable in the south and west, so that, for example, relatively few now remain in south Wales (*1988–91 Atlas*), and its largely sedentary nature in Britain – the vast majority of movements are of less than 1·5 km (*Migration Atlas*) – it seems highly unlikely that this bird will be recorded again in Wiltshire in the short or medium term.

Finally, the following intriguing but inconclusive entry in *WANHM* for 1936 seems worth quoting: 'The under tail covert feathers of this species were picked up on the Plain near Stonehenge, but this does not prove that the bird was there, as the feathers might have come from a hat, but do people put a bunch of these feathers in a hat?' – which all brings to mind the case of the feather near Stonehenge in 1864 that proved to be a Great Bustard's (*qv*).

MVJ

Black Grouse

Tetrao tetrix

Bred locally until mid 19th century, subsequently straggler, last 1906

Mainly resident in subarctic, boreal and temperate zones across Eurasia, the Black Grouse decreased markedly in the 19th century over much of Europe except the north, though it remains locally common south to the Alps and north Balkans (*CBWP*), and the European population, excluding Russia, was in the 1990s still estimated at 578,000 to 878,900 pairs (*EBCC Atlas*).

In Great Britain, this decline was very significant in the 19th and early 20th centuries, and the species eventually became extinct in southern England. It had once been common from Lincolnshire and Norfolk south to Hampshire and Cornwall (*1988–91 Atlas*), though numbers were sometimes temporarily bolstered by introductions in such counties as Sussex, Surrey, Berkshire and Buckinghamshire (Witherby *et al* 1938–41). In the *1988–91 Atlas*, the British population was estimated at between 10,000 and 15,000 breeding females 'with perhaps a slightly higher population of cocks' – mainly in Scotland and the north Pennines, apart from a few in Wales – but numbers subsequently halved during the 1990s, prompting serious conservation concern, though small signs of recovery then followed targeted action (Gregory *et al* 2001).

Peirson (1959) noted that Black Grouse used to breed sparingly in the south of Wiltshire and believed that they became extinct about 1820, but game books from Longford Castle in the extreme southeast, on the border with the New Forest, show that they were still shot in small numbers in the 1840s, became rare after 1850, and vanished about 1860. After that, there appear to be only three stragglers on record for Wiltshire: one killed at Compton Bassett in 1866 (Smith 1887); a female shot at Dinton on 12 November 1880 (Morres 1878–85, Smith 1887); and a female 'killed against wire' near Warminster on 8 April 1906 (Hony 1915a).

In the fourth edition of Yarrell (1871–84), Howard Saunders stated that Black Grouse 'are found, although sparingly, in Wiltshire'. Smith (1887) slightly misquoted this and, while acknowledging that the occurrence of wild individuals in the county was credible, given neighbouring populations in the New Forest (Hampshire) and Somerset, concluded: 'I am afraid, however, that we can only lay claim to the visit of a very rare and accidental straggler, seen from time to time after an interval of many years'. Nevertheless, Saunders (1889) persisted that Black Grouse 'still maintain themselves in Wiltshire' and he repeated it in his second edition (1899). Hony (1915a, 1916a, b) then took Saunders to task and further blamed him for the continuing errors quoted both by Hartert *et al* (1912) and by the 'new B.O.U. List'. Because Hony found it difficult to believe that such a distinguished ornithologist as Saunders could be so mistaken, he even asked Eagle Clarke, who had access to Saunders's notes, whether there was any explanation, but he too could be of no help. So Hony (1916b) rightly continued with the assertion that the 1906 record was 'absolutely the last Wiltshire specimen' and there has been no later evidence to the contrary.

The Wiltshire records should be considered against the history of the Black Grouse in Hampshire, where it was 'formerly found in great abundance in the New Forest, but had become much scarcer' by 1834. 'By 1905, it had "not quite died out", but the surviving population included stock introduced by [Gerald] Lascelles…The species hung on until the 1930s' (Clark & Eyre 1993).

MVJ

Red-legged Partridge
Alectoris rufa

Locally common resident, introduced from France/ Iberia, also bred for shoots

Endemic to Europe, where it has a now limited natural distribution in France, Iberia, Corsica and northern Italy, the Red-legged Partridge has been introduced into Great Britain as a quarry species since the late 18th century and also, rather unsuccessfully, into parts of Ireland, as well as into Madeira (before 1450), the Azores, the Canary Islands, and one island in Greece. Both its range – it once extended naturally to Germany, Switzerland and the Channel Islands – and its numbers have declined over the past 400 years, not least as a result of agricultural intensification. The European breeding population is now put at between 2·5 and 4·4 million 'pairs' (*EBCC Atlas, CBWP*), though either sex may sometimes be bigamous. In Great Britain, the species is found mainly in southern, central and eastern England as far north as Yorkshire; it is scarcer and more widely scattered in the southwest, and in Wales and Scotland, preferring areas of arable cropping to open grassland.

Although Marsh (1842–62) noted captures in the Winterslow area, probably in or before the 1830s, which would be the earliest records for Wiltshire, Red-legged Partridges were little known in the county in the mid 19th century and Morres (1878–85) regarded their occurrence as 'isolated and infrequent'. Smith (1887) wrote that 'A few stragglers from time to time have made their way into Wiltshire' and listed only about 16 records, the first dated specimen having been 'killed at Erlestoke' in November 1861; but he included this species in his summary of the county's nesting birds and it seems likely, from the localities he mentioned, that introductions were already fairly widespread in both north and south Wiltshire by then.

The Red-leg ideally requires a dry climate and light soils with low or open vegetation in which it can run freely. In cereal fields, it seems to prefer (and is, of course, more visible) on the edges than in the centre, though large coveys do go right inside blocks of ripe maize grown for feed. Besides agricultural land and downland, ones and twos are occasionally

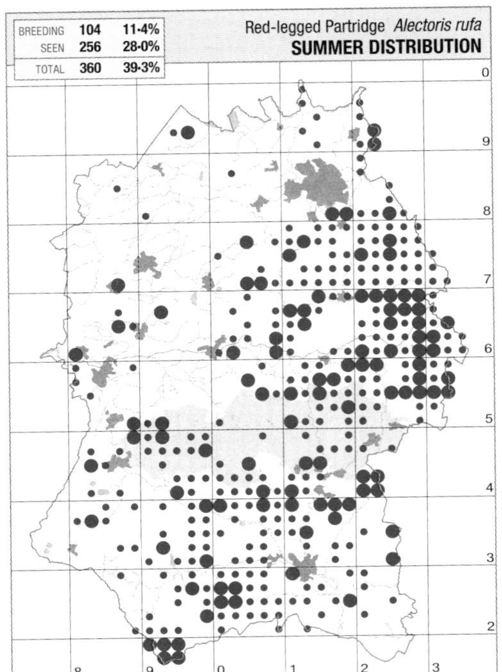

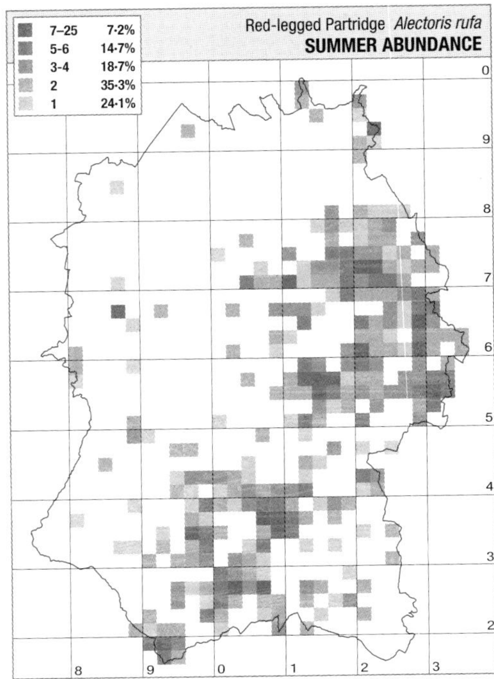

found in woods and near human habitation, such as in private gardens, and have even been recorded in Marlborough High Street and the centre of Swindon.

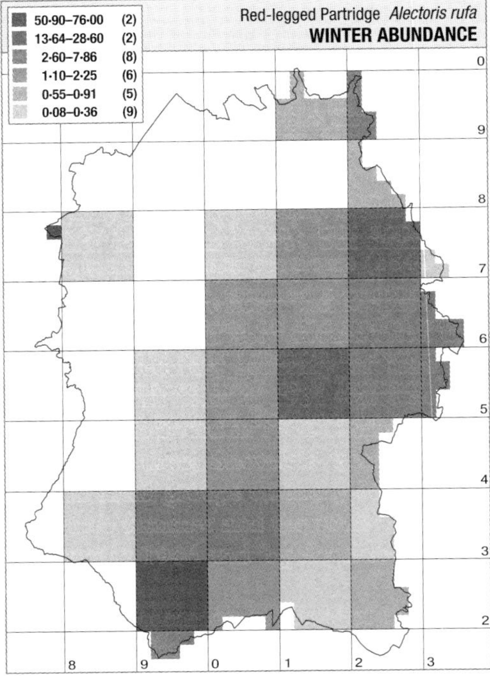

The *1968–72 Atlas* mapped Red-legged Partridges in 26 of Wiltshire's 33 core 10-km squares, with confirmed breeding in 14 and 'probable' or 'possible' nesting in the other 12, but had no records in parts of the north and the west; and the *1981–84 Winter Atlas* found them in only 25 of the core squares, most numerous in the east and south. In the *1988–91 Atlas*, however, the number of core squares had grown to 30, with evidence of breeding in 21, and in the summer tetrad survey these figures increased still further to 32 and 26. Thus, there seems to have been some spread in both range and breeding, though the summer distribution and abundance maps here still show Red-legged Partridges to be found predominantly in the south and east – demonstrating good correlation with the pattern of arable chalk downland – and largely absent from the southwestern and southeastern fringes and from large tracts in the centre, west and north. This distribution is repeated in the winter abundance map (even though records were received then for only 21 of the core squares) and is doubtless influenced by the locations of releases for shooting. Indeed, the *1968–72 Atlas* noted evidence that this partridge might have difficulty in maintaining its numbers naturally without continued introductions.

The status of this species has been complicated in the past by releases of the related Chukar Partridge and various hybrids, mainly between Red-legs and Chukars but perhaps also involving others of the same genus which are all broadly similar in pattern. The hybrids, known in the trade as 'Ogridges', were being bred in East Anglia and generally released in England in increasing numbers during the three decades from the early 1960s, apparently proving fertile and able to interbreed with pure Red-legs, the progeny 'slightly larger, blue-grey (instead of red-brown) on the back, and with less chestnut on underparts and flanks' (Payn 1991). In fact, Chukar Partridges and hybrids do not figure at all widely in *Hobby*, and seem highly likely to have been overlooked and reported as Red-legs. Apparently pure Chukars were first identified at Bay Bridge, near Marlborough, in 1988; and subsequently at Hackpen and Baydon in 1989; Rough Down, Marlborough and Baydon in 1990; Baydon in 1991; and Hackpen and Baydon in 1992. Two instances of Chukars pairing with Red-legs were reported, in 1989 and 1994.

Trends in game bag numbers in Wiltshire show few or no Red-legs shot from 1960 to 1970, but then rising to a peak in 1990 (Game Conservancy Trust, National Game Bag Census), though the increase was not as steady as that of Pheasants. A decline from 1991 must be partly accounted for by the banning of releases of Chukars and hybrids after 1 September 1992, since many of those will simply have been mis-identified as Red-legs and their banning will perhaps have meant a reduction in the total number of *Alectoris* partridges released. Given its dependence on releases, the county population of Red-legs must vary greatly from year to year, but extrapolation from the winter counts suggests a Wiltshire total of only about 3300. Yet the Game Conservancy Trust estimates that around 160,000 are released in Wiltshire annually for shooting, in addition to a wild population very roughly estimated at about 4000 (R Sage). The winter figures indicate a ratio of roughly six Red-legged to one Grey Partridge, but an RSPB survey of SPTA in summer 2000 showed 217 'territories' of Red-legs and 261 'pairs' of Grey Partridges (Stanbury *et al* 2000). This may imply that winter numbers of Red-legged Partridges, swollen by releases, are poor guides to the size of the breeding population, which could be some 500–1000 pairs (thus, in the range suggested for Grey).

Annual summaries in *Hobby* show considerable fluctuations in the numbers of Red-legged Partridges over the last quarter of the 20th century, a dry summer and a good breeding season seemingly reflected in more observations and larger numbers. As examples: 1976 was a good year and, while 1979 was poorer, 1980 showed sight records down by at least a further 50 per cent; a cold spring and heavy rain in 1981 may have made that a very poor year because of heavy chick mortality, though it appears that numbers released then were also smaller; sightings increased in 1985, whereas 1991–93 produced few records. Covey sizes may not be very useful, in view of varying releases, but, for what they are worth, have ranged from fewer than ten to over 100. A mixed covey of one Red-leg and 11 Grey near Netheravon in November 1980 (Edwards 1981) perhaps resulted from the fact that this species will 'sometimes' lay eggs in the other's nests (Campbell & Ferguson-Lees 1972).

There was a decrease in the national CBC index for the Red-legged Partridge over the last quarter of the 20th century, which may have been linked to the declining quality of farmland habitats, but has been thought more likely to be a result of the banning of the Chukar and hybrid releases (Crick *et al* 1997). The *1988–91 Atlas* estimated that, whereas up to the 1950s Grey Partridges outnumbered Red-legs nationally by about 20:1, wild stocks of both species 40 years later were approximately level (at around 750,000 individuals, post-breeding), a salutary reflection on the massive national decline of the Grey.

None of only five Red-legs ringed in Wiltshire during 1965–2000 has been recovered.

MVJ

Grey Partridge

Perdix perdix

Fairly common but long decreasing resident, some released/naturalised stock

Widespread from western Europe to central Asia, Grey Partridges have also been successfully introduced into North America. They were very common in Wiltshire in the 19th century (Smith 1887), the greatest numbers being on the most intensively farmed land. Two examples give some idea of their relative abundance then. In a single year, 1882, as many as 84 were killed flying into newly erected telegraph wires along a six-mile stretch of railway between Porton and Grateley (*WANHM*); and the game bag records of the Ferne estate, Donhead St Andrew, showed 366 shot in 1897, 191 in 1898, and 161 in 1899.

In Great Britain as a whole, Grey Partridges are still well distributed, except in western Scotland and much of Wales, but the two decades between the *1968–72* and *1988–91 Atlases* saw them nearly disappear from large areas of southwest Scotland, northwest England, Wales, Devon and Cornwall, and from parts of Dorset. Numbers are presently highest from East Anglia north to eastern Scotland, locally in central England and, not least, 'on some traditional ley farms on Salisbury Plain' (*1988–91 Atlas*).

In the 19th century, Grey Partridges were, in fact, increasing in Great Britain, especially in England and southern Scotland, apparently as a result of favourable changes in farming practices (*1875–1900 Atlas*). Numbers began to decrease during the 20th century, however, and in England this was particularly evident from the 1960s. The effects of herbicides on the food plants on which the young chicks depend for insect prey, and loss of cover leading both to increased predation and to a shortage of nest-sites, have been blamed (*eg* Potts 1980, 1986, *BBWC*). Conservation concerns have been prompted by long-term declines: CBC data showed a fall of 84 per cent between 1966 and 1999 in Great Britain as a whole, and the BBS revealed a 26 per cent drop between 1994 and 2000 in England. Estimates in the early 1990s put the British population at 140,000 to 150,000 'territories' or 'pairs' (*1988–91 Atlas*), but the most recent calculations now reduce these to 70,000 to 75,000 (*APEP*). These figures may be compared with a European total, excluding Russia, of 1·7 to 3·0 million (*EBCC Atlas*).

In Wiltshire, the *1968–72 Atlas* showed Grey Partridges to be present in all of the 33 core 10-km squares, and evidence of breeding in 31; the position was similar in the *1988–91 Atlas*, except that there were then three squares in which breeding was not recorded, all in the north of the county. In between, the *1981–84 Winter Atlas* found the species in only 26 of the core squares, and the highest numbers mainly in the eastern half. The summer tetrad survey recorded Grey Partridges in all 33 core squares and breeding in at least 25, but the sample winter survey found them in only 18. Nevertheless, this species is sedentary – none of the three adults ringed in Wiltshire during 1965–2000 has been recovered, but few movements anywhere of more than 1 km have been recorded (*Migration Atlas*) – and so it is not surprising that the summer and winter maps here are broadly similar despite some slightly confusing differences, notably in the west. All three maps show that Grey Partridges are largely absent from the clay vales of north, west and southeast Wiltshire, but have strongholds on the arable farmland and unimproved grassland of the chalk downs in the south and east, in particular on Salisbury Plain and the Marlborough Downs. This pattern is very similar to that of Red-legged Partridges and no doubt reflects the distribution of shooting interests, which provide suitable terrain and also release some Grey Partridges.

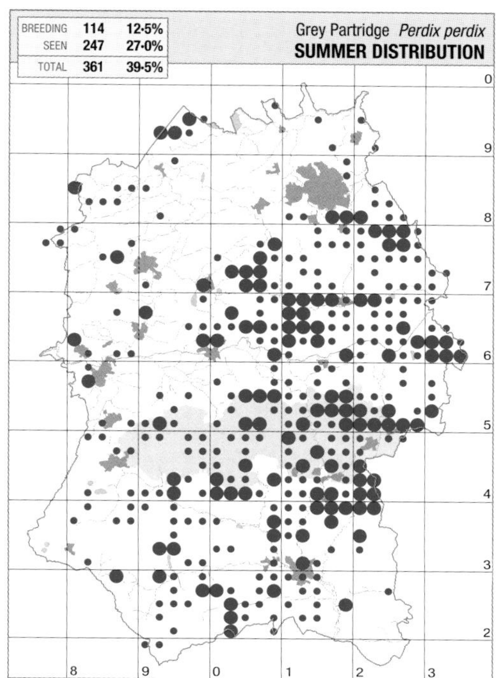

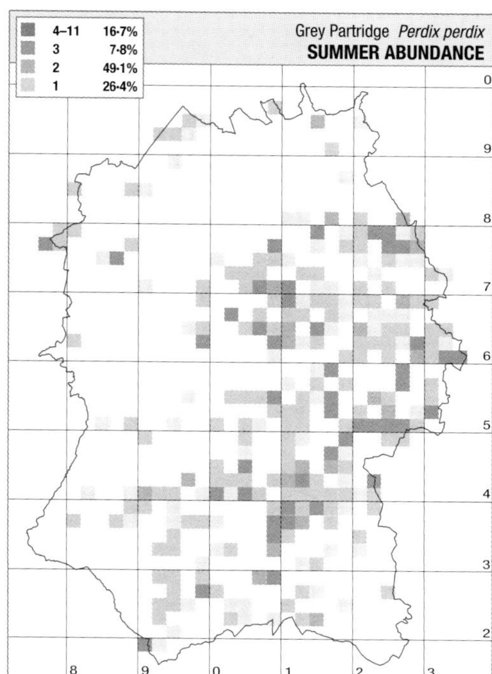

Despite the clear patterns shown by the surveys, Grey Partridges were certainly under-recorded and all the maps give an incomplete picture for Salisbury Plain. Estimates derived from the RSPB sample survey of SPTA by 1-km squares in 2000 indicate a total there of 261 pairs, 44 more than the corresponding figure for Red-legged Partridges (Stanbury *et al* 2000). This perhaps suggests that the indigenous species survives the better in semi-natural grasslands. (It may also imply that Red-legs are not self-sustaining; releases on farmland certainly boost their winter numbers, but many do not survive to breed.)

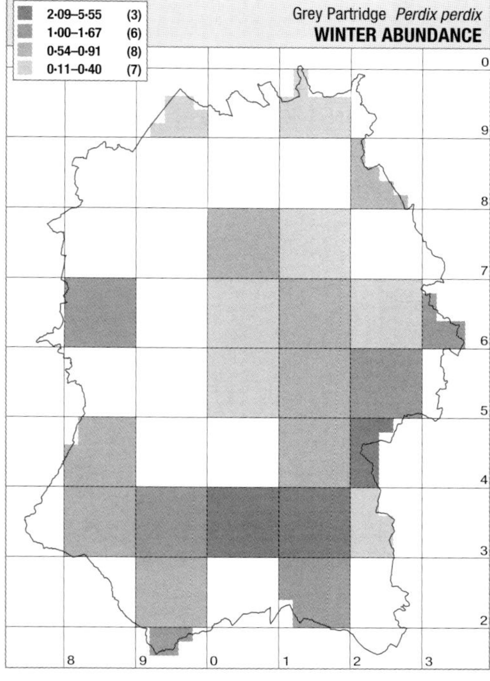

In Wiltshire, as elsewhere, numbers are a reflection of several factors, including breeding success and releases. Fortunes have fluctuated. As examples, based on *Hobby*, 1975 and 1976 produced some large coveys of up to 30, and this trend continued until 1979. Fewer were then reported from 1980 to 1982, but an increase was apparent in 1983: on one 800–ha estate at Tollard Royal, where no hand-reared birds were released for shooting, around 400 were counted; and other large coveys that year included 28 at Roundway and 40 at Ablington Furze. Numbers were generally low in 1988, reflecting national CBC results, but a small

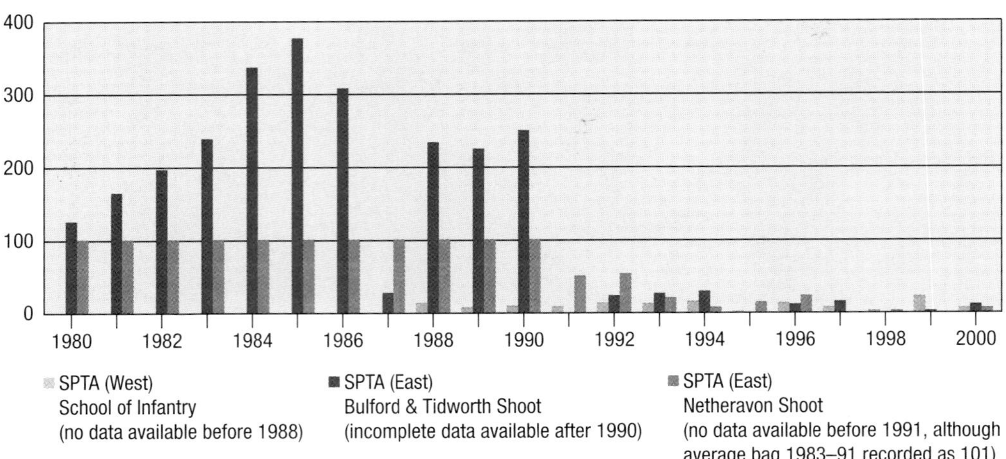

Figure 24. Grey Partridges *Perdix perdix* in Wiltshire: annual bags on the SPTA shoot 1980–2000

increase in 1990 resulted in reports of 12 coveys in the 10–22 range. In 1993 rather more large coveys than usual were seen, but in 1994 and 1995, although the species was widely reported, no coveys exceeded 20.

Trends in game bag numbers in Wiltshire have shown considerable fluctuations since 1960, from highs in 1961, 1962, 1976, 1984 and 1986 to a crash in 1963 after the extremely cold winter, and further lows in 1968 and 1969 (Game Conservancy Trust, National Game Bag Census). These trends could indicate greater dependence on wild populations than hand-reared releases in areas where Grey Partridges are shot. Figure 24 sets out the SPTA shoot bag from 1980 to 2001 (CAG Wells). Trends are difficult to determine as these data are incomplete, but the peak bags on SPTA (East) in the 1980s coincided with a study between 1985 and 1990 by the Game Conservancy Trust to investigate the effect of an experimental reduction in predator pressure on the breeding success and population density of Grey Partridges (Tapper *et al* 1996). Two experimental plots were established on SPTA (East) to test the effects of predator control: at Collingbourne (564 ha), the spring density of pairs/km² varied between 2·66 and 11·35; at Milston (496 ha), the corresponding figures were 6·05 and 13·71 pairs. At both sites, predator control significantly increased the proportions of partridges that bred successfully and the average sizes of their broods, although both the peaks and troughs in spring densities coincided with years when there was no predator control, suggesting that other factors, such as weather, habitat, and food, were also significant.

Just 653 Grey Partridges were recorded in the county during WOS timed summer counts, in a total of only 361 tetrads; the Game Conservancy Trust estimates the current Wiltshire population to be 2500 pairs (E Darling), which equates to less than two pairs per square kilometre and, given the known higher densities on SPTA, is perhaps a conservative figure. Extrapolation from the winter tetrad counts suggests a Wiltshire total at that season of only about 540, clearly again an underestimate, but a ratio of roughly 1:6 in favour of Red-legged Partridges, although this discrepancy may be exaggerated by differences in visibility: whilst more frequently heard, Greys are generally harder to see than Red-legs, especially in winter.

The future of the Grey Partridge in Wiltshire lies largely in the hands of landowners with an interest in shooting. The Biodiversity Action Plan target for increasing the population of this species in this county is to reach 5790 pairs by 2010 (E Darling), around double the current number. Such measures as leaving unsprayed headlands round cereal fields, managing hedgerows to provide food sources and nesting cover, leaving winter stubbles and growing root crops will, it is hoped, aid this and other farmland birds.

(See also page 725.)

MVJ

Sponsored by Henry Edmunds (Cholderton Estate)

Quail

Coturnix coturnix

Summer visitor from Africa/south Europe in fluctuating numbers

Male Quails summering in Wiltshire utter their distinctive *kwic-we-wic* ('wet-me-lips') mainly in long grass and cereal crops, particularly barley and winter wheat, on the calcareous soils of sheltered downland slopes and valleys. The summer distribution map shows Salisbury Plain and the Marlborough Downs to be the most obvious strongholds, while apparently suitable downland habitats in the southwest remain unoccupied. 'Probable breeding' was based almost entirely on song heard at the same site on dates at least 14 days apart, whereas unmated birds may wander over considerable distances.

These are our smallest and only migratory gamebirds and are widely distributed in continental Europe, western Asia and parts of Africa. The European population, excluding Russia, has been estimated at 642,000 to 876,500 'pairs' (*EBCC Atlas*), which presumably equates to 'calling males'. Those from Europe winter in the western Mediterranean basin or, quite separately, in the Sahel and arid steppe just south of the Sahara. Abundant in southern England until the late 18th century (*eg* White 1789), they then suffered a major decline, becoming 'comparatively rare' in Wiltshire by the 1880s (Smith 1887). Apart from occasional bigger influxes, notably in 1870 and 1893 (Hony 1915a, *1968–72 Atlas*), this decline continued into the early 1940s, though pre-war Wiltshire comments in *WANHM* varied from 'a rare summer visitor' (1929) to 'present in good numbers' (1936). Enormous totals used to be trapped on Mediterranean coasts until the regulation of spring hunting in 1937; the 1939–45 War then provided diversions, and the subsequent spread of arable farming helped further (Moreau 1951).

In Great Britain, something of a post-war resurgence has included invasions of various sizes in 1947, 1952–53, 1955, 1964, 1970, 1983, 1989 (*1988–91 Atlas*) and the five successive summers of 1994–98 – all of these being reflected in the annual bird reports in *WANHM* or *Hobby*, as too were 1954 ('over 30 on Downs south of Beckhampton', 'at least 20…in cornfields by the Ridgeway between Overton and Totterdown') and 1965. All these years involved higher totals nationally, of several hundreds each (2600 calling males estimated in 1989, the biggest number to date), and latterly have also extended much farther northwest and north than earlier influxes, reaching the Welsh Marches and Scotland. Indeed, even in non-invasion years, the British population is now put at 100–300 'pairs' annually (*RBBP*), though it must be added that almost all records are simply of males heard between May and the end of July. These birds may, or may not, be mated and the species can be monogamous, bigamous, polygamous or promiscuous (*BWP*).

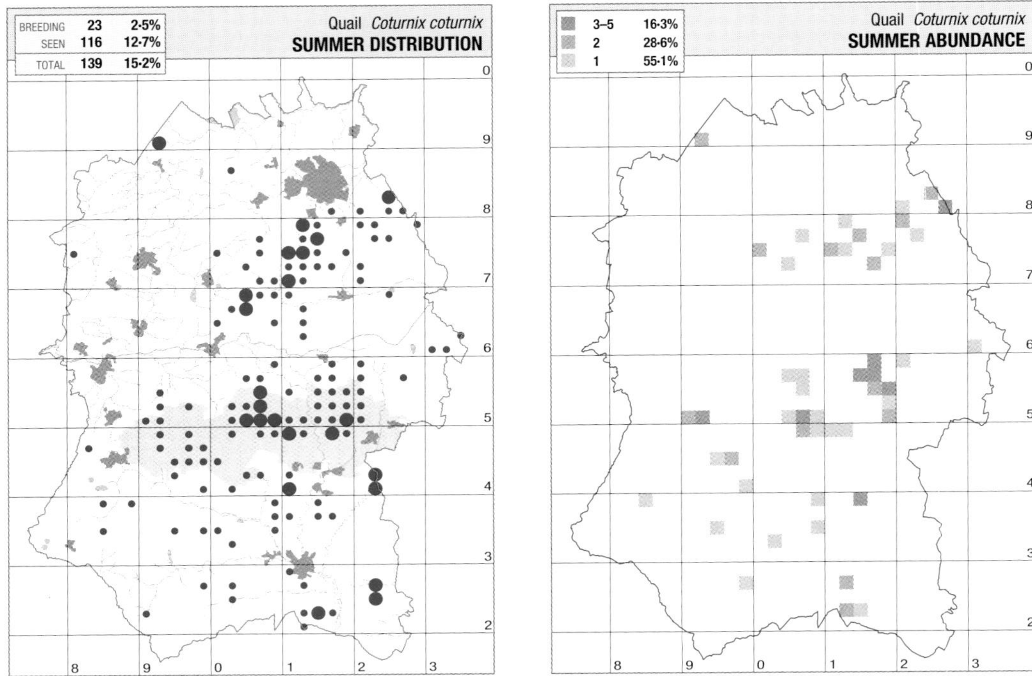

Wiltshire has long been one of the main traditional counties for Quails: of its 33 core 10-km squares, the *1968–72 Atlas* recorded them in 23, the *1988–91 Atlas* in 21, and the 1995–2000 summer survey in 25. During 1986–89, when the RBBP showed the national statistics on a county basis, Wiltshire was the most important of all in three of the four years. The annual numbers in the county during 1986–2000 are shown in figure 25, which also illustrates the difficulty of proving breeding: only seven records in the 15–year period. There were similarly only six certain nesting records during 1947–57 (Peirson 1959).

In the course of a general bird survey by 1-km squares on SPTA in 2000, the RSPB found 36 singing Quails, a figure that was considered probably to be an underestimate because a full study was not undertaken (Stanbury *et al* 2000). This was calculated to represent 12 per cent of the average British population and emphasises not only the importance of SPTA for this species, but also infers that, without dedicated surveys, Quails are under-recorded. As a demonstration of this, just 34 were reported to *Hobby* for the whole of Wiltshire in that year (figure 25), though 21 of those (nearly 60 per cent of the RSPB figure) were casual records from SPTA.

There has been evidence to suggest overwintering in the past: one was shot near Salisbury in December 1884 (Smith 1887) and another near Westbury in December 1930 (Peirson 1959). Morres (1878–85) also mentioned 'several... instances' of Quails in December in the neighbourhood of Salisbury, including 'on one occasion several being seen at the same time', and also one shot on Christmas Day at Mere, but he gave no years. In winter 1960/61, however, a bird seen several times in a kale field at Charlton-All-Saints was positively identified on 17 March (*WANHM*). Otherwise, extreme dates in Wiltshire in recent times have been the 'last week in March' in 1957 (*WANHM*) and 25 October in 1988.

It now appears that long-distance migrant Quails – those that fly directly from the Sahel into Europe – have declined in numbers, while the short-distance travellers have increased through the spread of irrigated land in northwest Africa, where they mostly winter and remain to breed as early as March or April; males of this latter population then leave

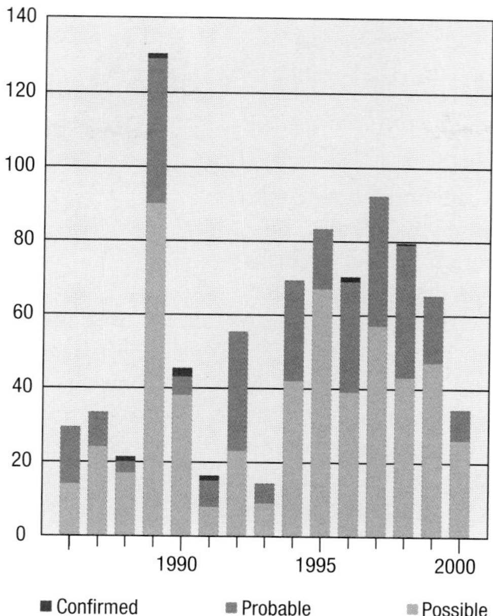

Figure 25. Quails *Coturnix coturnix* in Wiltshire: annual totals of records 1986–2000
To be comparable with the others, the figures for 2000 do not include the 36 males found by the RSPB survey on SPTA, though 21 of the 34 shown above for that year were casual records from SPTA (see text)

females on the nest and migrate north into Europe, followed later by females and young of the year, which may both be involved in renewed breeding (Tucker & Heath 1994). Thus, those that reach Wiltshire in May or earlier may be from the population that winters in the African Sahel, while the bulk, arriving from late June onwards, originate from the western Mediterranean area where they may have bred before moving north. As the grass and cereals are harvested there, they then come to this country to nest a second time.

Shooting on passage through Mediterranean countries must continue to affect the species, though not to the same extent as the former wholesale trapping. Changes in climate, both here and in the Sahel, and future developments in land use and farming practice in Europe as a whole, may also play their part. It is encouraging that Quails are found in a wide range of vegetation in Wiltshire, including set-aside, linseed and even oilseed rape.

(See also page 725.)

SBE

Sponsored by Linda Cady in memory of Keith Rupert Cady

Pheasant

Phasianus colchicus

Common naturalised resident, and bred for shoots, origin east Europe/Asia

The Pheasant, particularly the handsome cock and its noisy crowing in early spring, has long been a feature of much of the British countryside. It is indigenous to the Volga delta and northern Caucasus, and thence right over to China, Korea and parts of southeast Asia, but in the rest of its range across the middle of Europe – as in North America, Japan, New Zealand and elsewhere – it is present only as a long-introduced species. The European population, excluding Russia, has been estimated at a huge 3·8 to 4·7 million 'pairs' (*EBCC Atlas*), though numbers must varyenormously wherever the species is released for winter shooting and 'pairs' is a loose term as the males are often bigamous, polygamous or promiscuous.

In Great Britain, birds of the nominate *colchicus* group of races ('Caucasian or Black-necked Pheasants'), from the west of the natural distribution, were 'quite likely ... introduced towards the end of the Roman occupation ... But whether the bird was introduced by the Romans or not, it was certainly here well before the Norman conquest' (Vesey-Fitzgerald 1946). Since the late 18th century, birds of the far eastern *torquatus* group ('Ring-necked Pheasants') have been the forms mostly released here (*1968–72 Atlas*). The British stock now shows mixed characteristics of these and other subspecies (Fisher 1967). As a result, the plumages are very variable; melanistic Pheasants are not uncommon, and even all-white individuals occur occasionally.

Pheasants are widely distributed throughout Great Britain, except in the Highland and Grampian regions of Scotland and the more mountainous parts of Wales. Their preferred habitats are farmland with hedges, copses, woodland and parkland, and odd individuals are not infrequently seen in private gardens abutting open country, or even within villages, but they are rarely found on downland unless there is cover nearby. The population is supplemented annually on many estates and farms in Wiltshire, as elsewhere in Great Britain, by the release of large numbers artificially reared for shooting. The Game Conservancy Trust estimates that 650,000 to 700,000 Pheasants are released annually in Wiltshire, in addition to a 'wild' population of around 15,000 (R Sage); as an example, the total of chicks reared on the Longleat Estate alone in 1984 was 'put at 14,000' (Ferguson-Lees 1984). Clearly there will be considerable fluctuations and great seasonal variations, particularly between late summer and early spring as birds are released for, and later depleted by, shooting. (It must be remembered that, if up to 700,000 are released annually in Wiltshire, the equivalent of that number must be shot in the winter, or otherwise die naturally, for the basic population to remain anywhere near constant.) For what it is worth, the total number of Pheasants counted – not least as crowing males heard – during the summer tetrad surveys was a relatively low 5200.

The *1968–72* and *1988–91 Atlases*, as well as the *1981–84 Winter Atlas*, mapped Pheasants in every 10-km square in Wiltshire. The 1995–2000 summer survey similarly recorded them in all 33 core squares (breeding in 32), but the greater detail of the summer distribution map here shows evidence of breeding in only two-fifths of all tetrads. Nevertheless, taking account of tetrads where the species was only 'seen', the spread was fairly uniform except for a scarcity in parts of north Wiltshire and on SPTA, and the densities shown by both the summer and the winter abundance maps are likely to reflect the distribution of estates where Pheasants are bred or released for shooting. The winter counts again suggested a total of only just over 5000, but, as fieldwork began in November, after the start of the shooting season, and continued to the end of February, numbers would on average be far

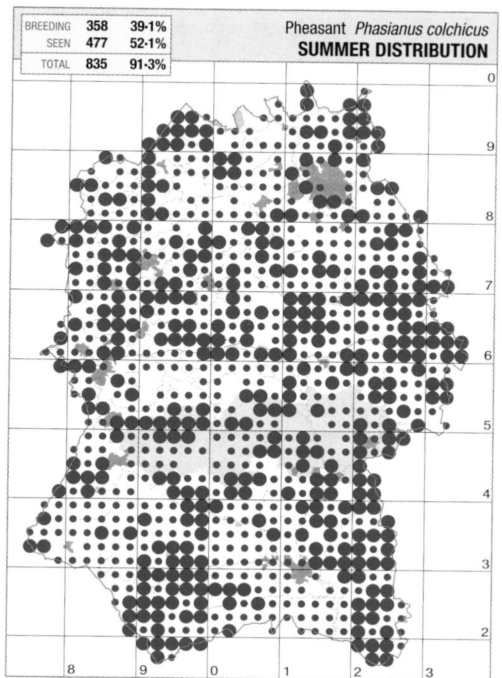

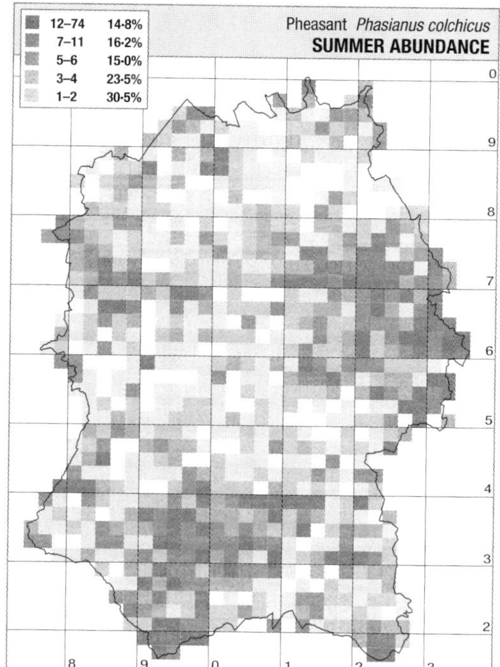

below their peak and many Pheasants have by then learnt to keep in cover.

Trends in game bag numbers in Wiltshire show a fairly steady increase from 1960 to a peak in 1991, followed by something of a decline (Game Conservancy Trust, National Game Bag Census). The peak in 1991 cannot be explained easily for, although weather conditions during the early part of that breeding season were not good, May was pleasant, June was one of the coolest, dullest and wettest on record, but August and the first half of September were good, which would tend to favour stocks released then; perhaps it was simply that more Pheasants were released in 1991? Nationally, populations increased during the last quarter of the 20th century (*BBWC*), but levels are related mainly to releases of captive-bred stock (Marchant *et al* 1990); there was a 17 per cent increase over the 26–year period of 1974–99 (*CBC*). In Wiltshire, as elsewhere, such practices as the removal of hedgerows – needed as cover for nesting by this and many other species – may limit numbers of the 'wild' population.

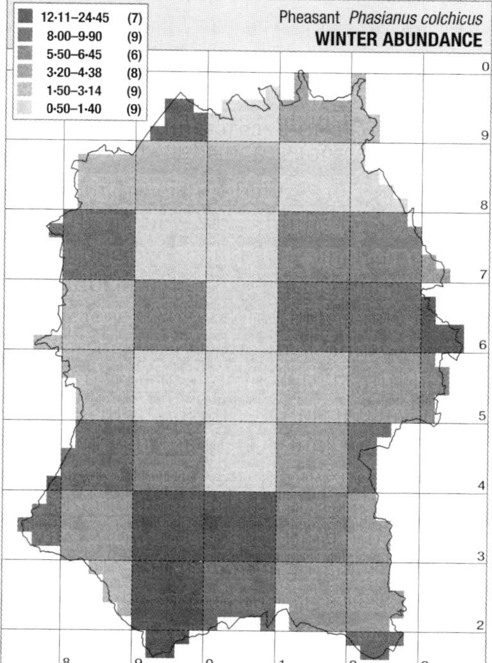

MVJ

Sponsored by Linda Cady in memory of Rupert Cady

Red-throated Diver

Gavia stellata

Winter vagrant (26 records) from coastal seas, breeds Scotland/north Europe

Red-throated Divers are circumpolar arctic and subarctic waterbirds that also breed as far south as lochs in north and west Scotland. It has been estimated that in Europe, excluding Russia, there are some 7000 to 10,500 pairs (*EBCC Atlas*), of which 935 to 1500 pairs nest in Scotland (*APEP*). In winter, apart from small numbers in the southern Baltic, the Bay of Biscay and the Black Sea, sometimes also the Mediterranean, the European population is found mostly in Atlantic and North Sea coastal waters from Iceland and western Norway south to northwest France, and the species is then rather rare inland. Birds ringed in Greenland and Fenno-Scandia have been recovered in British waters (*Migration Atlas*).

Wiltshire's 26 records have all involved singletons in the five or so months from November to the beginning of April. Smith (1887) stated that 'The first [though undated] was captured after a severe storm on Knoyle Down... so exhausted' that it was 'struck... down with a riding-whip'. Earlier, however, im Thurn (1870) had reported that one was 'said to have been obtained' at Ogbourne St George in 1856 – which may thus perhaps have been the first – and an immature killed at the same place in January 1866. Smith also noted one shot in 1866, at Lyneham, and another in November 1876, at Erlestoke. There were no more published records until one picked up injured by the railway line at Wylye in February 1909 (*WANHM*, Hony 1915a). Next came a juvenile at Britford on 15 January 1934 and one 'in non-breeding plumage' at Alderbury on 1 April 1947 – both oiled and, even in those more enlightened times, both shot – and then followed a run of ten seen in 1950–53, 1956, 1958, 1961 and 1963, including two apiece in 1958 and 1963 (all *WANHM*). One at Ashton Keynes for over three months from 27 December 1971 to 2 April 1972 (*WANHM*) was the first record for the CWP area; that same winter another stayed at Erlestoke Lake from 30 January to 7 April (*WANHM*). From 1974:

1977	8 December	Chippenham	Adult winter, grounded on playing field
1979	7–31 March	Coate Water	Juvenile, often absent (see below)
1981	3 December	Netheravon	Grounded on road
1986	1–8 January	Shear Water	Juvenile, slightly oiled on belly
1999	27 January	Marlborough	Juvenile, grounded
	30 Oct–7 Nov	CWP83	Juvenile

Of the trio grounded, the 1977 adult was released that same day at Purton (Gloucestershire) and the 1999 juvenile was taken to the Wiltshire Wildlife Hospital and released the next day at Portland (Dorset); the one in 1981 was taken to RSPCA Salisbury. The 1979 juvenile, often absent, was once seen returning from, probably, Liden Lagoon.

(See also page 726.)

RT

Black-throated Diver

Gavia arctica

Winter vagrant (11 records) from coastal seas, breeds Scotland/north Europe

Found in summer right across northern Eurasia into Alaska, Black-throated Divers otherwise have a small British population of around 175 pairs restricted to the larger lochs of the Outer Hebrides and the north and west Scottish mainland. There, in contrast to the more numerous Red-throated, they nest essentially by clear, fish-holding lakes and rarely feed at sea (*1988–91 Atlas*). But in winter the European breeding population – estimated at 19,000 to 26,500 pairs, excluding Russia (*EBCC Atlas*) – moves to coastal waters of the southern Baltic, the North Sea, and south to the Bay of Biscay, the northern Mediterranean and the Black Sea; small numbers are seen at that season around many British coasts, but this is then the rarest of our three regular divers, especially in the Irish Sea area and inland.

The only two 19th century records in Wiltshire, both 'killed', were in December 1872 near Salisbury and, undated, 'on the water at Corsham Court' (Smith 1887). Just two more were noted in the first three-quarters of the 20th century: one killed when it flew into overhead wires during a snowstorm at Aldbourne in January 1942; and a juvenile at CWP30 for several days in December 1972 (*WANHM*). From 1974:

1978	1–2 February	Coate Water	Adult winter
1979	17–24 February	Winterslow Corner	Injured at Dunstable pond, died
	18 Feb–18 Mar	CWP29/30/32/37	At least two adult winter
1981	24–31 October	Langford Lakes	Juvenile
1985	21 January	Melksham	Juvenile, grounded
1991	2–3 January	Stourton lakes	Adult winter
	9–12 January	Shear Water	Adult, possibly same as Stourton

There were probably three, rather than two, winter adults on several lakes at CWP in 1979. The juvenile grounded in 1985 was taken to the Wildfowl & Wetlands Trust, at Slimbridge (Gloucestershire), but died in care.

RT

Great Northern Diver

Gavia immer

Winter vagrant (21 records) from coastal seas, breeds Iceland/Greenland

Found mainly in North America, breeding from the Great Lakes northwards, this largest of our three more familiar divers nests also in Greenland and Iceland, and Great Northerns from those areas regularly winter along northwest European coasts from Norway to the Bay of Biscay. British and Irish coasts, particularly in the north and west, hold an estimated winter population of 3500 to 4500, about three times that of Black-throated Divers. Despite its tendency to favour deeper water and to remain farther offshore than the other divers, the Great Northern is generally the most frequently seen inland (*1981–84 Winter Atlas*) – although Wiltshire's all-time total of Red-throated (*qv*) is slightly the higher.

Smith (1887) listed five Wiltshire records from 1831 ('in the river at Salisbury') to 1877, and five more undated, mostly on estate lakes and all 'shot' or 'killed' (including the not inappropriate statement that 'Lord Nelson has one killed at Trafalgar'). Hony (1915a) was able to add only one undated report from Salisbury, but another four were noted during 1946–70: at Coate Water in March 1946 and November 1952 (the latter found dead), at West Kennett on 22 November 1962, and at CWP30 from 24 November to 20 December 1970; also a diver 'perhaps belonging to this species' seen at Shear Water on 14 February 1953 (all *WANHM*). From 1974:

1977	10 Dec to 'end of month'	Fonthill Lake	Adult winter
1988	1 Dec–1 Jan **1989**	CWP68	Juvenile
1989	19–28 December	Shear Water	Juvenile
1998	13 Dec–31 Jan **1999**	CWP68/82	Juvenile
1999	30–31 October	CWP82	Adult
	25 December	CWP74	Juvenile

The juvenile at Shear Water in 1989 was part of a considerable influx into southern English counties after gales (*BB* 83: 320).

(See also page 726.)

RT

Pied-billed Grebe

Podilymbus podiceps

Vagrant (1 record), breeds Canada/USA, moving south to winter

Pied-billed Grebes breed throughout the Americas, except in the extreme north and the far south. In North America, the more northerly populations move south to winter and these are the source of the individuals that turn up in Europe, probably via Greenland and Iceland (*BBRC* 1992); a recent flush of spring records, 'suggestive of northbound migrants' (*BBRC* 2001), perhaps indicates that some vagrants are now travelling south and north again within the Old World.

The first ever seen in Europe was discovered as close to Wiltshire as Blagdon Lake (Somerset), on 22 December 1963; and it found that area so much to its liking that it remained there for five years. By the end of 2000 as many as 35 had been recorded in Great Britain (*BBRC*), including the only one in Wiltshire – an adult still in summer plumage with black-banded white bill, black face and white-eye-rings – at CWP68 during 1–15 August 1997 (Buchanan 1998).

WEQ

Little Grebe

Tachybaptus ruficollis

Common resident, some nomadic and dispersive in winter

The only member of its genus in Eurasia, the Little Grebe is the smallest of the five grebes that occur regularly in Great Britain, and it lacks the decorative crests, ear-fans and tippets that characterise the others in summer plumage. Frequenting both still and slow-moving waters, often quite shallow, with ample submerged and emergent vegetation, it inhabits big lakes to smallish ponds, as well as canals, rivers and streams. In the breeding season it feeds chiefly on invertebrates, predominantly insect larvae, and also more molluscs than the other grebes, but small fish become important in winter (*BWP*).

Little Grebes are found from western Europe and northwest Africa eastwards to Japan and New Guinea, south through sub-Saharan Africa, Madagascar and the whole Indian region. They are mostly sedentary, although those breeding in central and eastern Europe and the colder parts of Asia migrate south or east to escape the hard winter weather. In Great Britain they were historically commonest in southern England and Wales, and there is evidence of expansion in northern England and into Scotland from the mid 19th century (*1875–1900 Atlas*). An increase in their numbers in the south corresponded with the proliferation of man-made waterbodies and a general amelioration in climate, but, being particularly susceptible to cold weather (Dobinson & Richards 1964), there were declines following the hard winters of the 1940s and 1960s and a retraction in range from western Wales and southwest peninsular England. The species is currently widespread throughout most of lowland Great Britain, with the breeding population stable at between 5000 and 10,000 pairs (*1988–91 Atlas*), a sizeable proportion of the European estimate of 75,700 to 91,800 pairs (*EBCC Atlas*).

Wiltshire contains a number of prime Little Grebe habitats, notably the upper reaches of the Bristol Avon, the Kennet, and particularly the Salisbury Avon and its tributaries. The earliest county reference to the species was to 'Considerable numbers all year living in a withy bed opposite the Master of Marlborough College's garden' (Bosworth Smith 1863). Smith (1887) described this as 'the commonest and best known of all the [grebes] ... which may be generally seen on every retired river or large pond'. Peirson (1959) agreed that it was 'common on most rivers, lakes and canals'. Buxton (1981) described Little Grebes as 'Widely distributed', breeding 'on both ... Rivers Avon, including their major tributaries, being commoner on the Salisbury Avon. The River Kennet supports a number of pairs from Marlborough ... to the county boundary in the east'. Buxton noted, too, that 'stretches of the Kennet & Avon Canal are also used, particularly in the Great Bedwyn area', but that the 'Thames and its tributaries are much less popular ... only a few pairs attempting to breed'.

The summer tetrad survey confirmed the species' strong preference for rivers, particularly the Salisbury Avon and its tributaries, and the Kennet, which hold some of the highest densities of Little Grebes nationally (*1988–91 Atlas*). Ponds and lakes are used in some areas, particularly in the north and west, and there is a marked concentration at CWP. The abandonment of the Kennet & Avon Canal after it fell victim to competition from the railways during the second half of the 19th century led to the establishment of new Little Grebe breeding areas as the disused stretches were invaded by vegetation: at one time there were said to be breeding pairs every 200 m along some parts (*1875–1900 Atlas*). During the last two decades of the 20th century, however, the restoration of the canal and its

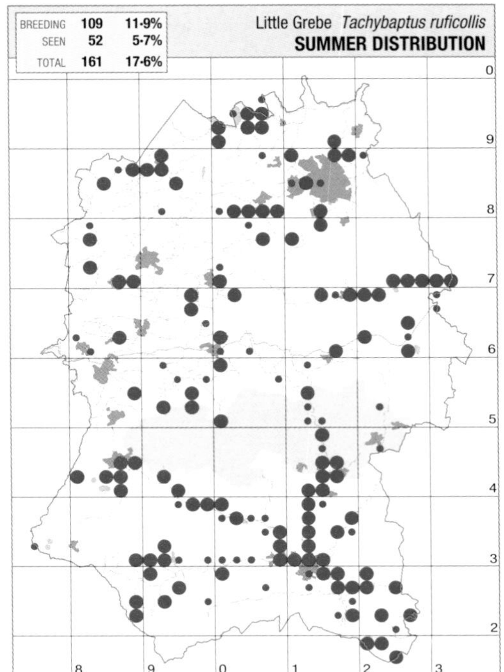

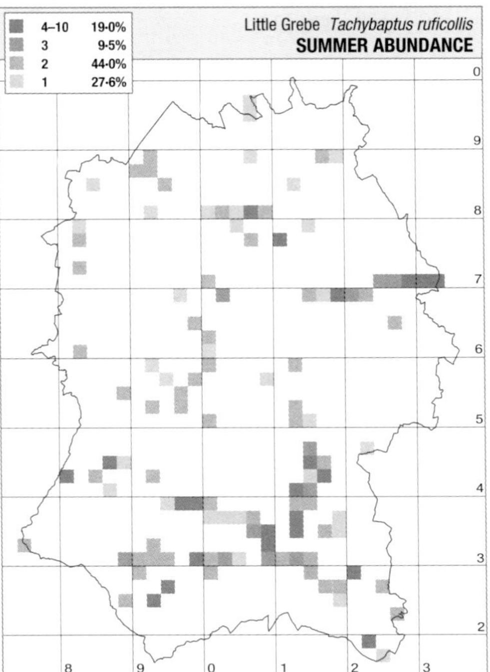

reopening to boat traffic reversed the position; the species no longer breeds there and is now very rarely even seen. Happily, the loss of the canal habitat has coincided with an increase in the numbers breeding on the county's lakes, notably CWP, and the population as a whole has remained healthy.

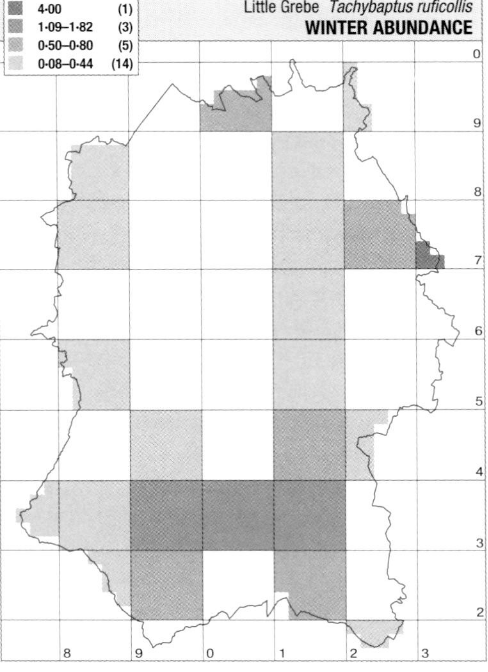

It is difficult to obtain any accurate picture of how the status of this species has developed in Wiltshire because it was not recorded systematically in the past, summaries in *Hobby* being restricted to such comments as 'No apparent change in status at regular breeding sites' and 'Status much as usual'. There is little suggestion of any alteration in summer distribution by 10-km squares between the national atlases and the tetrad surveys, though local fluctuations are evidenced by a decline from eight pairs to just one between 1994 and 1995 on a particular stretch of the Wylye – but certainly not on some other stretches of that river – and perhaps reflected by national figures also; the CBC, WBS and BBS have shown markedly differing trends – from large increases to large decreases over the last 30 years – though all suffer from relatively small sample sizes. In the late 1980s and early 1990s, records were

Table 34. Little Grebes *Tachybaptus ruficollis* in Wiltshire: peak winter counts at key sites 1990/91–1999/00

	90/91	91/92	92/93	93/94	94/95	95/96	96/97	97/98	98/99	99/00
CWP	4	4	6	6	4	–	4	13	42	21
River Kennet:										
Littlecote/Knighton	–	–	–	–	–	–	2	16	10	17
Chilton Foliat	5	8	7	8	7	3	3	11	11	16
Fonthill Lake	19	11	10	10	12	4	5	4	9	6
Salisbury Avon:										
West Amesbury	–	–	–	12	10	20	16	20	24	28
Salisbury/Fordingbridge	–	–	–	4	2	2	5	2	12	6
Clarendon Lake	8	2	2	8	6	5	4	5	5	5

received for 45 to 58 breeding pairs each year in Wiltshire (*Hobby*). The summer survey in 1995–2000 gave a minimum of 109 pairs, but allowing for there being more than one and often several pairs within good quality tetrads, as well as, inevitably for such an elusive species, some individuals or pairs missed altogether, a figure of 200 pairs seems a more realistic estimate for the county.

Little Grebes are known to be susceptible to cold weather: this results in widespread dispersal and even migration during the winter, contrary to the traditional perception of a sedentary nature (*1981–84 Winter Atlas*). They remain concentrated in lowland southern Britain, but significant numbers switch to coastal waters, and ringing recoveries have demonstrated that, while some move south into France, others arrive as immigrants from farther east in Europe (*Migration Atlas*). The winter tetrad survey showed that the core summer areas remain populated, but that there was an apparent desertion of, presumably, smaller ponds and tributaries in central and northwest Wiltshire. This may, however, have been an artefact of the sampling methods used, for the *1981–84 Winter Atlas* suggested a distribution almost as extensive as in the summer.

CWP and the Salisbury Avon at West Amesbury have consistently been the key sites, where counts of Little Grebes have regularly reached 20 and where post-breeding concentrations as high as 42 and 28 respectively were recorded in the late 1990s (table 34); there was also a remarkable count of 60 in August 1985 on the Avon nearby, between Amesbury and Upper Woodford (*Hobby*). WeBS data for Wiltshire suggest winter numbers of around 75, which is undoubtedly a considerable underestimate, not least because that survey does not cover this rather secretive species of rivers, ponds and lake edges as effectively as it does many wildfowl that feed and rest on open water. Allowing for suitable wetlands not included in the winter tetrad survey in 1998/99 and 1999/00, the WOS results indicate a winter population three times higher, at 229, but even this figure may be only a half, perhaps even less, of the true number. That would represent a significant proportion of the national total, recently estimated at 7770 (Kershaw & Cranswick 2003) – although previously put as high as 25,000 to 50,000 (*1981–84 Winter Atlas*). Numbers both nationally and locally doubtless vary as a result of weather conditions, immigration and breeding success, although the run of mild winters in the 1990s meant that the population was probably at a high level by 2000.

WEQ

Great Crested Grebe

Podiceps cristatus

Common breeder, in winter congregates on larger waters or moves to coasts

In the 19th century, this most elegant of grebes was driven almost to extinction in Great Britain by the activities of egg collectors, river keepers (who saw it as a threat to fish stocks) and the fashion trade (which used its feathers and under-pelts for decoration and as accessories). By the 1860s no more than a few dozen pairs remained, but a succession of Bird Protection Acts introduced in the 1870s reversed the decline, and by the end of the 1890s the species had returned to most of the places where it had nested previously (*1875–1900 Atlas*). Censuses in the 20th century tracked the continuing recovery, finding some 1240 pairs in 1931 and 4130–4730 individuals in 1965, by which time Great Crested Grebes were established over much of lowland England, in parts of Wales, and in lowland Scotland (*1968–72 Atlas*). By the late 1980s, despite little change in this range, the importance of central England had been consolidated as numbers almost doubled and the British population was estimated at 8000 individuals (*1988–91 Atlas*). This may be compared with some 270,000 to 315,000 pairs in Europe as a whole (excluding Russia), nearly one fifth of them in Finland (*EBCC Atlas*) at the northwestern limit of a breeding range that covers much of temperate Eurasia, and extends discontinuously through sub-Saharan Africa, Australia and New Zealand.

The Great Crested Grebe was in the 19th century 'only an occasional straggler in Wiltshire, where we have no large lakes suited to its habits' (Smith 1887). Maton (1843) mentioned one shot in the immediate vicinity of Salisbury and that he himself had seen one only during a hard winter. Of just four records known to Smith (1887), all 'shot' or 'killed', the only two dated were in February 1838 'on the Avon' and in February 1839 on the Kennet & Avon Canal near Devizes; Morres (1878–85) also mentioned one shot at Norton Ferris in 1860. Hony (1915a) cited just one further record, at Braydon Pond on 3 April 1912. In 'about 1912', however, the species was breeding at Coate Water and in 1914 at what may have been the same but unnamed locality in 'North Wilts'; by 1929 there were at least 22 pairs at ten lakes; and the 1931 national census found 21 pairs on 11 lakes (all *WANHM*). Later national censuses revealed 34 pairs in 1965 and 38 in 1975 (Webber 1968, Buxton 1981), and the position remained largely unchanged through the 1980s, when the population was estimated at 30–40 pairs (Palmer 1991). During 1990–2000, the breeding numbers reported through casual observations have varied between 20 pairs in 1997 (when they were certainly under-recorded) and 47 pairs in 1994 (table 35). The summer survey 1995–2000 found breeding in 44 tetrads and, though not all will have been occupied every year, many of the sites will have held two or several nesting pairs. Timed counts showed 230 individuals in all, but that figure will have included non-breeders and, erroneously, perhaps even some juveniles. Consequently, a Wiltshire

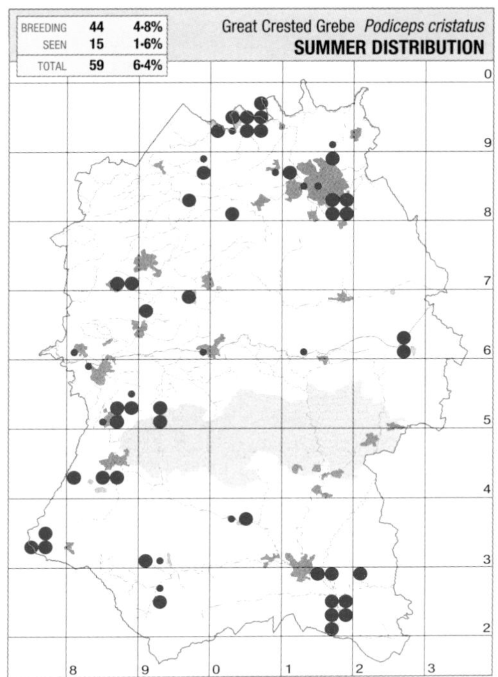

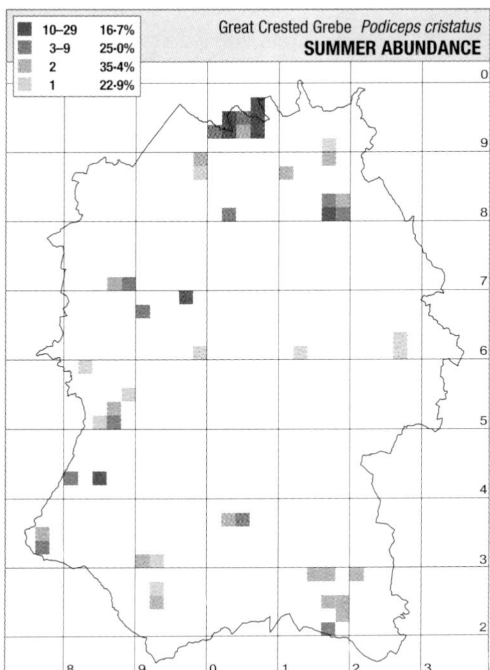

breeding population of 50–60 pairs is suggested – a relatively small proportion of the national total – plus up to 100 non-breeders.

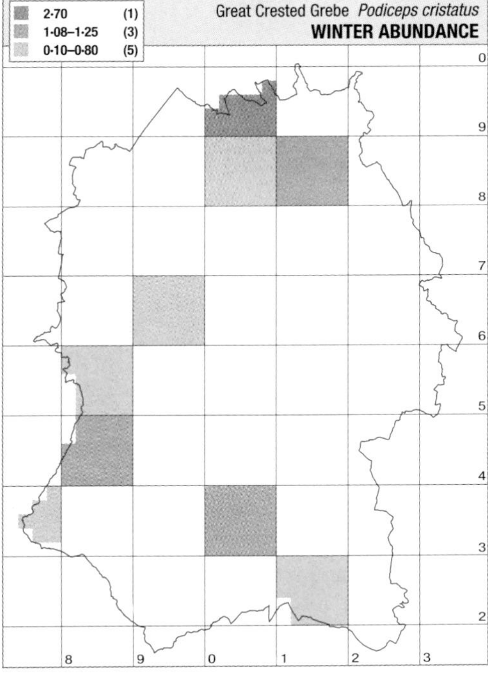

Great Crested Grebes favour relatively large areas of open, still water with emergent vegetation. They prefer eutrophic sites and have benefited from the increase in reservoirs and gravel pits, particularly when these have matured and once populations of fish, the grebes' main diet, have become established (*CBWP*). Although the species now nests at the majority of suitable sites in Wiltshire, particularly in the Thames valley/Swindon area and on estate lakes in the west, the general absence of such habitats in many other parts of the county was reflected in the *1988–91 Atlas* by the large distributional hole in the region of the downs and Salisbury Plain. Highest counts of breeding pairs during 1995–2000 were at CWP (seven), Coate Water (seven), Liden Lagoon (three), Bowood Lake (eight), the Longleat lakes (five), Shear Water (six), the Stourton lakes (five), Langford Lakes (five) and Downton (three), and nesting was regular on about 15 other waters. Great Crested Grebes' use of rivers for nesting was reported at the national level in the 1960s when preferred habitats became saturated (Harvey 1979); in Wiltshire, this development was apparently first noted in the late 1980s on the Salisbury Avon, at

Table 35. Great Crested Grebes *Podiceps cristatus* in Wiltshire: breeding pairs 1990–2000
Based on data recorded annually in *Hobby*, not on full surveys, so the totals simply indicate trends

	90	91	92	93	94	95	96	97	98	99	00
Pairs	35	33	44	38	47	37	35	20	38	36	34
Sites	12	15	23	22	18	17	16	16	14	16	20

Table 36. Great Crested Grebes *Podiceps cristatus* in Wiltshire: peak winter counts at key sites 1990/91–1999/00

	90/91	91/92	92/93	93/94	94/95	95/96	96/97	97/98	98/99	99/00
CWP	85	68	37	61	152	121	151	94	173	105
Braydon Pond	–	8	11	15	11	10	13	8	8	12
Tockenham Reservoir	–	–	–	9	10	8	7	4	5	5
Coate Water	33	53	41	41	51	33	32	35	38	34
Liden Lagoon	3	7	10	7	12	9	6	10	5	8
Bowood Lake	14	13	13	22	16	16	15	15	21	24
Corsham Lake	4	9	10	6	4	10	9	4	3	3
Westbury Ponds	2	4	6	4	–	2	7	–	7	15
Longleat lakes	4	4	13	7	8	11	5	14	12	9
Shear Water	17	23	23	21	28	21	23	22	22	25
Stourton lakes	1	16	4	13	10	12	8	6	7	6
Langford Lakes	12	19	14	20	–	–	–	–	–	–

Charlton-All-Saints and Standlynch, and spread to at least four other sites in that general area in subsequent years. Though river-nesting is still not nearly as common as, for example, on the Thames in Oxfordshire (Brucker *et al* 1992), it might be concluded that the Wiltshire population as a whole had reached a plateau, a picture supported by table 35 and by BBS data nationally, which both suggest stability over the 1990s. Nevertheless, numbers at Shear Water and Longleat lakes increased during that period, and the potential surely exists for CWP to support more.

Although Great Crested Grebes are present all year in Great Britain, the species is migratory and dispersive. Most of the breeding range in Europe east of Germany is vacated in winter in favour of more southerly or westerly areas, and there is then an influx into this country (*CBWP*, *1981–84 Winter Atlas*). Habitat preferences in winter are broadly similar to those of summer, but large numbers of Great Crested Grebes then also make use of coastal waters. A dozen Wiltshire waters regularly hold five or more between late summer and late winter (table 36), these sites being generally the same as those favoured for breeding. Smaller numbers are found then at most other suitable waterbodies and the midwinter total, based on these counts and the tetrad survey, is estimated at 250, again a tiny proportion of the 15,900 in Great Britain as a whole (Kershaw & Cranswick 2003).

In Wiltshire, however, the largest numbers occur during late summer and early autumn: as many as 152 were recorded at CWP in October 1994 – considerably more than the previous highest counts and double the normal midwinter peak – and totals ranging from 120 to 173 were found in August or September in subsequent years. These late summer influxes are a result of moult migration: Great Crested Grebes (like many wildfowl) move to large waterbodies in late summer to shed all flight-feathers simultaneously, which renders them flightless for up to six weeks. It appears likely that CWP plays host to a congregation immediately after the moult, at which time the Wiltshire total probably exceeds 300; many of these have left again by early winter. Yet at Coate Water most of the peaks in the 1990s were in late winter and early spring, especially March, presumably as the species returned to establish breeding territories.

WEQ

Red-necked Grebe

Podiceps grisegena

Winter vagrant (26 records) from European coasts, breeds central/east Europe

Found in two discrete populations, one extending from central Europe and the Baltic region into western Asia, and the other in eastern Asia and western North America as far east as the Great Lakes, Red-necked Grebes breed on reed-fringed fresh waters and winter mainly along coasts. The European breeding population – which, excluding Russia, has been estimated at 31,000 to 37,000 pairs (*EBCC Atlas*) – migrates mostly to the western continental seaboard from Norway and the southern Baltic south to Biscay. The small numbers on the British east coast in winter have been put at about 150, but up to 500 may occur during influxes in severe weather (*1981–84 Winter Atlas*) and it is then that the species is most likely to be found inland. During 1980–2000, a scattering of summer records in various parts of Great Britain included several nesting attempts but, as yet, no proved success (*RBBP*).

The first two published Wiltshire records of Red-necked Grebes appeared in im Thurn (1870): 'During the floods at Manton some years ago, one of these birds was seen swimming close to the road in a kind of bewildered state. It was captured in an open umbrella used as a fishing net'; and another was 'taken, in a regular fishing net, in September 1868'. Smith (1887) noted eight 'killed' in the 19th century, the first near Devizes in 1840 and the last at Westbury in 1874; he did not refer to im Thurn, and so it has to be assumed that all his eight were additional to those of the earlier author, though one of them was likewise in 1868. Over 50 years passed before the next report, and even that referred to two grebes seen at Wilton Water on 12 October 1930 which were only 'probably of this species' (*WANHM*). Three were then satisfactorily identified on the Salisbury Avon between Britford and Harnham by two separate observers 'during the end of January' 1934 and on 1 February (*WANHM*), but the only other record before the mid 1970s was one at Coate Water in February 1955 (*WANHM*, Peirson 1959). Seven in the ten years 1978–87 involved eight individuals, three of them at Coate Water and two at CWP. Apart from one in summer plumage on the Salisbury Avon, at Netheravon, from 7 May to at least 15 June 1986, all dated arrivals up to the end of the 1980s were between 13 November and 10 March. Indeed, most were associated with cold weather influxes in winter, but two of the seven in the 1990s first appeared in October, and one in September:

1991	21–27 Sep & 19 Oct–8 Dec	CWP68/69	Juvenile, moulting to 1st-winter
1993	20 & 30 October	CWP69/38	Adult winter
	15–24 December	Corsham Lake	1st-winter
1994	15–23 January	CWP68	Adult winter
1995	11 Jan–5 May	CWP68/74	1st-winter, summer by April
	25 Mar–1 Apr	Coate Water	Adult, partial summer
1999	31 October	CWP82/83	Adult winter

WEQ

Slavonian Grebe

Podiceps auritus

Winter vagrant (21 records) from coastal waters, breeds north Britain/Europe

Found in summer right across Eurasia and North America, along the northern edge of the temperate zone, Slavonian Grebes migrate to sheltered coastal areas in winter. The European breeding population, excluding Russia, has been estimated at 6000 to 9300 pairs (*EBCC Atlas*). The first British nesting record was in Scotland in 1908, and the population there reached a maximum of 86 pairs in 1990, subsequently declining to 41 pairs by 1999 (*RBBP*). The *1981–84 Winter Atlas* put the British winter population at around 400, including no more than 10–15 found inland, but over the seven seasons 1986/87–1992/93 Evans (2000) calculated a midwinter mean of 648 in British coastal waters.

In Wiltshire, five 19th century records, the first in 1864, included a remarkable account in winter 1877 by a policeman who, in Warminster 'on a cold, dark night, when it was snowing heavily, heard a flight of birds passing overhead, and shortly after was startled by hearing a heavy thud behind him, which turned out to be a Sclavonian [*sic*] Grebe, its plumage and wings…so encrusted with frozen snow that it could no longer use them' (Smith 1887); Morres (1878–85) added that the bird 'was apparently dead, but, on being held to the fire, the warmth partially restored it'; to little avail, however, as the unfortunate was then dispatched to the local taxidermists, J&S King. Nine more before 1974 included the only one in summer, an adult in full plumage, 'presumably injured', on the Kennet near West Overton from mid May to early September 1947 (*WANHM*, Peirson 1959). From 1974:

1979	Feb–Apr	CWP32	One (see below)
1982	1–4 January	Coate Water	One, winter plumage
1989	9–28 January	CWP26	One, winter plumage
1994	5–6 February	CWP62	One, winter plumage (see below)
	2 November	Fonthill Lake	Two juveniles
1996	19 March	Corsham Lake	One, winter plumage
	15–16 January	Langford Lakes	One, winter plumage

Those in February–April 1979 and February 1994 crossed into Wiltshire from the Gloucestershire side of CWP: the first appeared occasionally over the three months, and the second, which spent most of that winter on the other side, was recorded in Wiltshire on only the two days.

WEQ

Black-necked Grebe

Podiceps nigricollis

Passage/winter vagrant (28 records), breeds and winters Britain/Europe

In summer, the Black-necked Grebe's widespread range extends across temperate parts of Europe, western Asia and western North America east to the Great Lakes, as well as, more locally, in eastern Asia and eastern and southern Africa. The European breeding population, excluding Russia, has been estimated at 31,000 to 37,000 pairs (*EBCC Atlas*). Small numbers nesting in northern England have spread south to the Midlands and north into Scotland; in 1999 there were possibly as many as 53 pairs, and in 1998 one pair nested as close to Wiltshire as Somerset (*RBBP*). Most northerly Black-necked Grebes migrate to warmer areas to winter along coasts or on inland waters; in Europe, they are then found chiefly in the west and south. The British winter total, especially along the English south coast, has been estimated to number no more than 120 individuals (Prater 1981, *1981–84 Winter Atlas*).

Until the 1970s, Black-necked Grebes were apparently very rare in Wiltshire, but Smith (1887) accepted seven 19th century records (and was clearly aware of the differences between this species and Slavonian); the six of these that had published dates were all in the period 1864–78. The first noted in the 20th century were 'a probable' at Coate Water in September 1945 (*MCNHS*); two on the Salisbury Avon near Britford on 11 March 1947; and one at Coate Water again on 30 November 1949 (*WANHM*). A grebe that was again only 'probably of this species' was seen at the last site on 5 November 1955, and there were then three records of single Black-necked in the 1960s, one at Bowood Lake and two at Corsham Lake; one of the last two stayed for two days in May (all *WANHM*). Sixteen records (21 birds) during 1974–2000 involved four in winter, six (11 birds) in spring, five in August, and one in October. Six of these 16 records (11 birds) were at CWP and five at Coate Water. Those in August have been juveniles, presumably heading for west European and Mediterranean coasts – possibly from Great Britain, possibly from the eastern Continent – and those in spring have been adults in summer plumage on the reverse journeys. From 1990:

1993	14–15 August	Fonthill Lake	Juvenile
1995	6 February	Corsham Lake	One, winter plumage
1996	20 & 24–25 May	CWP68/74	Five, summer plumage
1997	4–5 August	CWP68	Juvenile
	26 October	CWP68	Adult, winter plumage
1999	29 Aug–5 Sep	CWP82	Juvenile
2000	20 May	CWP68/74	Two, summer plumage
	22–24 May	Swindon STW	One, summer plumage

Although the Black-necked Grebe is currently no more than a vagrant to Wiltshire, the Somerset nesting record of 1998 shows that it is not beyond the bounds of possibility that a pair may one day breed in Wiltshire.

WEQ

Fulmar

Fulmarus glacialis

Vagrant (7 records) from coasts or seas, breeds Britain/Iceland/northwest Europe

Fulmars nest in huge numbers on islands and coasts of the north Atlantic, Arctic and north Pacific Oceans, typically on cliff ledges, and winter both inshore and far out to sea. The European breeding population, excluding

Russia, has been estimated at between 2·2 and 3·5 million pairs. Now that they are familiar sights around virtually the whole coastline of Great Britain, it is easy to forget that St Kilda (Outer Hebrides) was their only known colony in these islands until breeding was proved on Foula (Shetland) in 1878 (Fisher 1952). The subsequent massive expansion to an estimated 516,000 pairs by the late 1980s (Lloyd *et al* 1991) along Scottish, Welsh and English coasts clearly helps to account for the small modern increase in occurrences inland.

Until the 1950s the only Wiltshire record involved an immature picked up in Savernake Forest during a heavy storm in October 1897 (*MCNHS*, Hony 1915a), but during severe gales in late August 1957 what must surely have been a Fulmar was seen swimming near Longford Castle (record card in WOS files). From 1974:

1978	30 January	Boscombe Down	Adult on airfield, died next day
	28 June	Coate Water	One swimming on lake, looked sick
1991	1 June	CWP68	One flying east
1996	17 March	over Bentley Wood	One flying northeast, fog to south
1997	27 June	CWP74	One flew from west, circled, flew off

It seems curious that three of the last four should have been in the summer month of June, not the time usually associated with inland records of pelagic birds.

RT

Cory's Shearwater

Calonectris diomedea

Vagrant (1 record) from Atlantic, breeds on Atlantic/Mediterranean islands

This is perhaps one of the most remarkable of the county's vagrant records. Cory's Shearwaters nest on many islands and some continental coastlines in the eastern north Atlantic (Azores, Madeira, Selvagens, Canaries) and the Mediterranean (though the latter population is sometimes considered a distinct species, *eg* Sangster *et al* 1998). They disperse west across the Atlantic, many reaching the coast of North America and some wintering off the shores of Namibia and South Africa (*BWP*). Late summer movements are regular off southwest England, and adverse weather conditions sometimes bring feeding flocks close inshore.

The sole Wiltshire record was of one found grounded amongst chickens in a large garden at Woodfalls, south of Salisbury, on 3 September 1984 (*Hobby* 11). It was later released at Mudeford (Dorset), where it flew strongly out to sea. (Coincidentally, one of the two finders also discovered a grounded Manx Shearwater at Salisbury in 1977.) Although an inland record is exceedingly unusual, it is not without precedent, one having been picked up exhausted in Staffordshire on 2 October 1971 (*BBRC*).

RT

Manx Shearwater

Puffinus puffinus

Vagrant (32 records) from open seas, breeds Britain/North Atlantic/arctic islands

Manx Shearwaters are strongly colonial seabirds that nest in burrows on smaller islands of the eastern North Atlantic. Great Britain holds between 280,000 and 310,000 pairs (*Seabird 2000*) on a couple of dozen offshore islands, most notably Rum (Inner Hebrides) – the largest colony of all – and Skomer and Skokholm (Pembrokeshire); including these last two, Wales alone has some 168,000 pairs on five islands (*Seabird 2000*). The British total represents more than 75 per cent of the world population of 284,000 to 323,000 pairs (*EBCC Atlas*), which – apart from small numbers south to Madeira and the Canaries – are otherwise largely confined to Iceland's Vestmann Islands, the Faeroes and, especially, certain offshore Irish islands. In winter, many spread south and west across the Atlantic, even as far as coastal waters off eastern South America.

Any Manx Shearwaters found inland are generally disoriented or storm-driven juveniles, some at least of those in Wiltshire having originated from the large Welsh colonies. Smith (1887) knew only of two: one, undated, 'taken at Market Lavington from a hole in a hayfield' and another found 'apparently wounded' at Avebury in early September 1879. But Hony (1915a) was able to add several more: in the late 19th century, singletons were 'picked up' on Mere Down on 6 May 1888 and near Calne on 1 September 1899; and, early in the 20th century, two males and a female were 'received ... from Bishopstone about 1904' (presumably three separate records), and one each were found at Wootton Bassett and Alton Barnes on 29 August 1910. Next came a remarkable record of 'one which flew over Wilts territory ... from north-east' on 15 November 1934: 'The characteristic call "Kitty Nock" "Kitty Nock" made when the bird was flying over, disturbed the dogs in the neighbourhood' (*WANHM*); although this description of one of the Manx Shearwater's varied calls is phonetically accurate, this species is normally silent away from its breeding colonies – yet the observer was a much-respected Dorset ornithologist.

One found at Brinkworth on 7 September 1948 had been ringed on Skokholm (Pembrokeshire) five days previously. In July 1951, one of a number taken from the Skokholm colony and, in homing experiments, released at Cambridge on the 5th was unfortunately shot at Westbury on the 8th, presumably *en route* back to its nesting burrow (Peirson 1959). Two of four found dead or grounded in the 1960s – at Colerne, Highworth, Lyneham and Market Lavington – had also been ringed in Pembrokeshire; the one from Market Lavington was regrettably being treated as a household pet eight days later.

The extreme dates of the 16 records during 1974–2000, mostly grounded, were 30 August and 18 October, and all but three were in September; any critically examined were juveniles. From 1990:

1992	1 September	Rowde	Released Severn Estuary (Glos)
	2 September	Salisbury	Found dead
1997	30 August	Liden, Swindon	Released Coate Water next day
	8 September	Durrington	Taken into care
1998	22 September	Warminster	Released Shear Water next day
	18 October	Chippenham	Released Portland (Dorset)

(See also page 726.)

RT

Wilson's Storm-petrel

Oceanites oceanicus

Vagrant (1 old record) from open Atlantic, breeds coastal Antarctic

Among the world's most numerous seabirds, nesting in cavities and burrows on the coasts and offshore islands of Antarctica, Wilson's Storm-petrels penetrate into northern seas, particularly the Atlantic, during the southern winter. Until 1986 the total recorded for Great Britain was just six, the second of which – and one of only two ever found inland – was picked up freshly dead at Sutton Benger in November 1849 (Smith 1887). This remarkable record was almost lost since 'the labourer who found it took it home... with the intention of taking it to the Vicarage; but on his wife persuading him that it was only a Swift, he threw it out into the road. But happily another labourer passed by... and satisfied in his own mind that a Swift did not possess webbed feet... took it to Mr. Marsh' (Marsh 1842–62).

This essentially oceanic species remains an extreme rarity close inshore in European waters, but frequent pelagic trips to the Southwestern Approaches have shown it to be regular and, at times, almost numerous there in at least the northern summer, so much so that over 280 were recorded during 1986–2000, including over a hundred in 1988 alone (*BBRC*).

RT

European Storm-petrel

Hydrobates pelagicus

Vagrant after storms (12 records), breeds east Atlantic/Mediterranean islands

European Storm-petrels nest in often uncountable colonies in rocky crevices on small islands, and more rarely on mainland promontories, in both the northeast Atlantic (Iceland and Norway south to the Canaries) and the Mediterranean. They are especially abundant on certain islands off northern and western Britain and Ireland, which together probably hold between one fifth and three-quarters of the world population, rather broadly estimated at 347,000 to 639,000 pairs (*EBCC Atlas*); British numbers have been put at between 21,000 and 34,000 pairs (*Seabird 2000*). The nearest colonies to Wiltshire are off the Pembrokeshire coast and in the Isles of Scilly and Channel Islands. Otherwise essentially pelagic, the species winters at sea off the western and southern coasts of Africa (*Migration Atlas*). Individuals occur inland only when storm-driven, usually on migration and, even then, far less numerously than Leach's Storm-petrels.

Wiltshire's first record came from Somerford Parva in 1830 (Marsh 1842–62); and there were six more during 1859–93, at Ludgershall, 'Cherrington' (presumably Sherrington), Marlborough, Panterwick, Rushall Down and Salisbury (Smith 1887, Hony 1915a): four in November and one each in April and October. The first half of the 20th century produced a further four singletons: at Edington in December 1909, near Netheravon in January 1936 ('a very decomposed specimen... picked up on the downs'), at Redlynch in April 1951 (all *WANHM*), and at Marlborough in 1929 (only in Buxton 1981). The one record since then followed severe westerly gales that caused a large wreck of storm-petrels – several hundred Leach's (*qv*), but only six European – along the south coast and in the Bristol Channel (*Hobby*):

1989 21 December Biddestone Adult, found dead
This bird was at least ten years old, having been ringed as an adult on Cape Clear Island (Co. Cork) on 8 August 1980.

RT

Leach's Storm-petrel

Oceanodroma leucorhoa

Vagrant after storms (22 records), breeds North Atlantic/north Pacific islands

The only known British colonies of Leach's Storm-petrels are on seven remote, predator-free islands in the far north and northwest of Scotland. Like those of other tunnel-nesting storm-petrels, they are almost impossible to census, but the Scottish total probably lies somewhere between 37,000 and 65,000 pairs (*Seabird 2000*): this represents a large proportion of those breeding in Europe, estimated very broadly at 106,000 to 222,000 pairs (*EBCC Atlas*), but only a small fraction of the world population. In Europe, they otherwise nest only on one or two islands of each of Iceland, Faeroes, Norway and Ireland, but there are many more colonies on the other side of the north Atlantic, as well as in the north Pacific. The species is essentially pelagic for the rest of year, wintering south to West Africa and northern South America. In late autumn and winter, sometimes many are wrecked along the west coasts of Britain and Ireland, when severe westerly gales force them inshore, and they are then found inland much more frequently than are European Storm-petrels (*qv*).

Blackmore (1866) published the first two Wiltshire records of Leach's: one picked up by a railway porter on the Great Western Railway two miles from Salisbury on 27 October 1859, the other found near the railway embankment at East Grimstead on 25 November 1866; both had apparently been killed by flying into telegraph wires. Smith (1887) included these and added three further records of single corpses at Pewsey in January 1867, in Spye Park in February 1876, and in Savernake Forest in November 1884. A sixth and last for the 19th century, again found dead, was picked up in Grovely Wood on 10 October 1896 (Hony 1915a).

Much more recently, in autumn 1952, one of the two largest wrecks in a hundred years resulted in about 2600 being seen in Bridgwater Bay (Somerset) alone, and probably over 7000 dead nationally (Boyd 1954). At that time 12 Leach's Storm-petrels were reported in various parts of Wiltshire between 28 October and 14 November 1952, mostly dying or dead, including three 'found dead close together in water at Longleat'; another corpse, this one 'long dead', at Clarendon on 14 January 1953 brought Wiltshire's total recorded share of the 1952 wreck to 13 (Boyd 1954, *WANHM*). In the next decade, singletons were recorded at Keevil on 22 December 1962 and Longford on 5 March 1965 (Webber 1968). From 1974:

1979	28 December	Calne	One exhausted on golf course after gales
1987	15 November	CWP68	One very tired, not present next day
1989	25 December	Stourton	One dead (*cf* also European Storm-petrel)

The last was 'part of a large wreck of Petrels along the English south coast and the Bristol Channel involving several hundred Leach's but only 6 Storm Petrels' (*Hobby*).

RT

Sponsored by Professor W Estlin Waters

Gannet

Morus bassanus

Vagrant (24 records) from coastal seas, breeds Britain and North Atlantic islands

Breeding only in colonies on sea cliffs and small islands in the North Atlantic and North Sea, Gannets have increased steadily since the 1960s, probably as a result of favourable feeding conditions and a decline in persecution. Some winter in the North Atlantic and west Mediterranean, but many others, particularly those in their first year, migrate down to the seas off West Africa. Some 186,600 breeding pairs were estimated for Britain and Ireland in the mid 1980s, a high proportion of Europe's 230,000 pairs (*EBCC Atlas*) and, indeed, 70 per cent of the world population (*1988–91 Atlas*); numbers in Britain alone had risen to 219,000 by 2004 (*APEP*). The gannetries nearest to Wiltshire are those on Grassholm (Pembrokeshire) – among the largest of all – and on Alderney (Channel Islands); one on Lundy in the Bristol Channel was last occupied in 1909 (*1875–1900 Atlas*).

Wiltshire records show no clear pattern, but – like those of most other seabirds – nearly half have been during September–November. Marsh (1842–62) published an undated specimen from the county border near Bath. There were then six during 1856–81, those dated being in June, September and November (Smith 1887); but in the following 65 years only one more was recorded, in November 1909 (Hony 1915a). A further six between 1952 and 1972 included one each in April, June, July and September, and two in August; five of these were found dying or dead, and the other was shot (*WANHM*). From 1974:

1976	2 November	West Dean	Sub-adult, grounded in field
1977	April	CWP (mainly Glos)	One, shot by angler in Glos
1978	17 September	Shrewton	Sub-adult
1982	25 May	Ashton Keynes	Four immatures in flight
	16 September	Covingham, Swindon	Two immatures flying west
1987	17 October	Bradford-on-Avon	Adult, exhausted
1994	13 January	Salisbury	Adult flying north
	10 October	Southleaze, Swindon	Juvenile, taken into care
1997	21 June	Dean Hill	Sub-adult flying west
	24 September	Collingbourne Ducis	1st-year, taken into care

The one at CWP in 1977, seen in Wiltshire too, was present for several days before it was shot (Buxton 1981). The 1987 adult was picked up after the 'Great Storm' and later released.

(See also page 726.)

RT

Cormorant

Phalacrocorax carbo

Regular winter visitor from Britain/Europe, also local in summer, bred 1994

Traditionally regarded as seabirds, because of their largely coastal breeding distribution, Cormorants became increasingly familiar in winter at inland waters during the last third of the 20th century, and are now regular visitors to landlocked Wiltshire. At favoured roosts, branches of waterside trees become stained white with their droppings, and Cormorants can be seen arriving late on winter afternoons in ones and twos or, in the case of the larger gatherings that developed at CWP, in goose-like skeins of up to 20 with much raucous calling as they alighted. Elsewhere diurnal loafing sites, which may or may not also be used for nocturnal roosting, can be found on promontories and islands, in waterside trees and, along the Bristol Avon, on electricity pylons and cables.

Cormorants breed across Eurasia from Iceland to Japan. They are both resident and winter visitors in western Europe and the Mediterranean, but only summer migrants in the Baltic and inland in eastern Europe. The nominate North Atlantic race *carbo* nests mainly in colonies along rocky coasts in northwest Europe, including Great Britain where the majority of the 7000 pairs are found in the west and in Scotland (*1988–91 Atlas*). Although there were some regional declines here between the *1968–72* and *1988–91 Atlases*, numbers in most other European countries increased markedly in the last few decades, particularly those of the Continental race *sinensis* in the Netherlands and Denmark (*CBWP*). The total European population, excluding Russia, has been fairly precisely estimated at 140,000 to 146,000 pairs (*EBCC Atlas*). A recent phenomenon has been the marked and rapid increase in inland breeding in Great Britain, particularly in southeast England. The colonies there appear to be initiated by *sinensis*, but an increasing number of nominate *carbo* occur as they develop (Newson 2000) and intergrades between the two forms may be found.

Cormorants were heavily persecuted during the 19th century (*1875–1900 Atlas*), particularly on inland waters in winter, and so it is not surprising that they were only infrequent visitors to Wiltshire at that time. Smith (1887) was able to find a mere 11 records, involving 14 birds, the earliest dated being 1856, and all but four recorded as 'killed' or 'shot'. Hony (1915a) added just two more records: one at Salisbury in September 1896, and a remarkable (even by today's standards) 25 at Marden on 2 October 1902, of which 'several were of course at once shot'; but he also noted a further report in 1902 of a 'Shag or Cormorant' shot at Britford.

Table 37. Cormorants *Phalacrocorax carbo* in Wiltshire: five-year mean maxima and peak counts at key sites 1976–2000

	1976–80	1981–85	1986–90	1991–95	1996–00	Peak count
CWP	7	11	33	83	70	107 (1997)
Coate Water	2	5	6	8	13	16 (2000)
Salisbury Avon	9	5	27	33	36	62 (1990)

Peirson (1959) described this species as a 'now regular [visitor] and sometimes in fair numbers to the Salisbury Avon in winter. Occasional only at other times of year or to other waters'. Later, Buxton (1981) considered it 'a regular visitor to the county... mainly... single birds but double figures have been recorded at favourable sites'. Following protection, numbers increased considerably in the 1980s with the establishment of a major roost at CWP and occasional large concentrations on the Salisbury Avon (table 37), though the latter were often short-lived because of continued illegal persecution. With a wholly fish diet, Cormorants commonly use stillwater fisheries and are widely perceived by fishery managers to be responsible for significant economic losses – through consumption of, or injury to, fish – and a potential vector of diseases (Hughes *et al* 1999b), although evidence of the precise impact of Cormorants upon fish stocks is still a subject of debate. Whilst the furore generated by this conflict in the mid 1990s, when the tabloid press vilified Cormorants as 'black death', appears to have abated somewhat through changed management practices and increased liaison between interested bodies, these birds continue to be the cause of significant controversy throughout much of Europe.

The *1981–84 Winter Atlas* graphically illustrated the marked winter spread to inland waters that produced a more even distribution throughout Great Britain, but Cormorants were at that time recorded in only six 10-km squares in southern Wiltshire and three in the northeast. The winter tetrad survey amply demonstrates the subsequent spread in this county. CWP and the Salisbury Avon remain favoured locations, although the major roost at CWP was abandoned in 1999 when the lake concerned was drained for landscaping: these birds switched to a site just over the border in Gloucestershire. Other concentrations have developed around Swindon, along the Wylye and, to a lesser extent, along the Bristol Avon (peak 26 in 2000); there was also an increase on the Kennet in the late 1990s (peak 21 in 1997) though those particular birds roost in Berkshire. Significant roosts started to build up at Coate Water and at Whaddon near Trowbridge in 2000. Cormorants are frequently recorded at most major waterbodies in the county, but only at half a dozen are numbers of more than five at all regular (table 38). Extrapolation from winter tetrad data gives a total of 170, but coordinated roost counts are required for an accurate assessment of a species that may be widely dispersed along various watercourses by day; an estimate of around 200 is suggested for the county.

Cormorants were seen in fewer than one twentieth of Wiltshire's tetrads during the summer tetrad survey, mostly concentrated at or along CWP, Coate Water, parts of

Table 38. Cormorants *Phalacrocorax carbo* in Wiltshire: peak winter counts at key sites 1990/91–1999/00

	90/91	91/92	92/93	93/94	94/95	95/96	96/97	97/98	98/99	99/00
CWP	83	66	78	95	92	82	89	107	58	28
Braydon Pond	–	–	6	2	1	10	20	5	2	4
Coate Water	2	5	3	11	8	6	12	12	10	14
River Kennet	–	13	17	5	12	20	21	–	6	1
Bristol Avon: Whaddon	–	–	–	–	–	–	–	–	14	16
Salisbury Avon	28	33	40	33	34	28	61	23	28	22

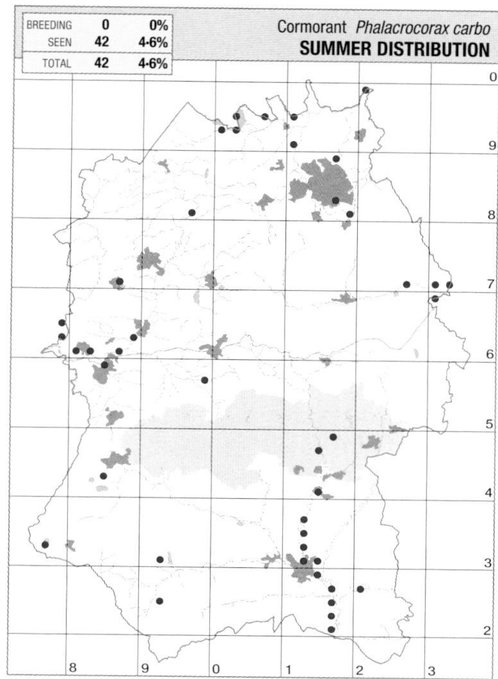

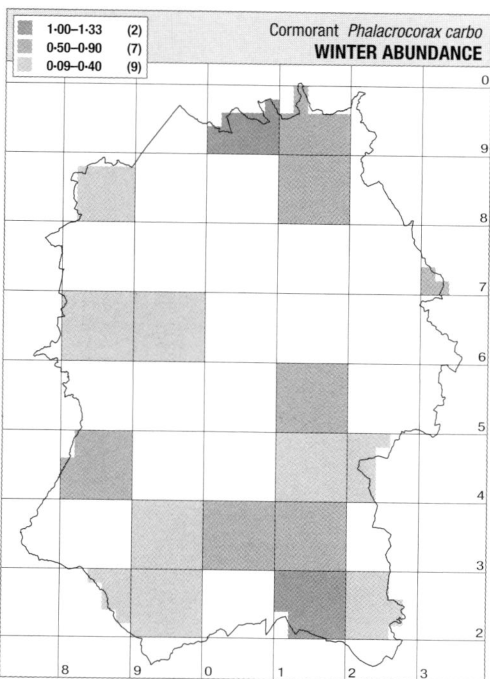

the Kennet and the Bristol Avon, the Longleat and Stourton lakes, and the Salisbury Avon. Allowing for repeat counts, particularly of those moving along rivers, the summer map suggests that no more than 20 are in the county at that season. No breeding was reported during 1995–2000; the one Wiltshire record was in 1994 when a second-summer female and an adult male nested in the top of a tall beech on an island at CWP and fledged three young. Although it is now established that 'some Cormorants breed in their second summers and that the majority have begun to breed by the time they are three years old... Many non-breeding second-year birds attend the natal colonies so most of the [summer] records away from the breeding colonies... are likely to be first-year birds' (*1988–91 Atlas*).

Most of the ringed or colour-ringed Cormorants recovered or recorded in Wiltshire have, not surprisingly, originated from the west coast of Great Britain, including Pembrokeshire, Anglesey, the Solway Firth and the west side of the Scottish Highland region. One seen at Coate Water in October 1987 had been colour-ringed as a nestling in Co. Dublin in June 1975. Single colour-ringed Cormorants at CWP in winter 1994/95 and at Britford in October 1996 had been marked as nestlings at the inland colony at Abberton Reservoir (Essex) in 1993 and 1996. Another seen at CWP during four successive winters – in October 1991, January–February 1993, January 1994 and February 1995 – had been marked as a nestling in Denmark in May 1990.

That last record shows that Cormorants from mainland Europe can reach Wiltshire and, with the inland spread into southeast England being initiated by Continental *sinensis* (see above), this race can be expected to occur here. Nevertheless, it is important to be cautious about the many sight records of *sinensis* that have been claimed in the county in various months from December to May, particularly at CWP (*eg Hobby* 23–25); in 1994 it was even stated that the numbers there of this form 'peaked in Feb'. Until recently, all '*sinensis*' at CWP were so identified because of their assumption of elongated white plumes on the head and neck. Long ago, however, Stokoe (1958) established that this feature also appears – if more ephemerally and dependent on age – in nominate *carbo* in Great Britain, and that some old *carbo*, even in north England and Scotland, show as many nuptial plumes as *sinensis*. Later Alström (1985) drew attention to the shape of the gular pouch, rather than the amount of white on the head, as the key feature for separating the two forms, but that too needs to be used objectively. Subspecific identification is further complicated by the increasing number of intergrades between the two races (Newson 2000). A Cormorant colour-ringed at Abberton and seen far inland in Limburg, in the Netherlands (van den Berg *et al* 2000), has been rejected as a certain record of nominate *carbo* because it could not be regarded as 'genotypically pure' (van der Vliet *et al* 2001), and it may now be that subspecific identification of at least some (even well-observed) Cormorants in the field is probably unsafe.

PEC

Shag

Phalacrocorax aristotelis

Vagrant (26 records) from British or Irish coastal waters

Confined to rocky coasts of Europe, Asia Minor and North Africa, Shags nest colonially from western Iceland and northern Fenno-Scandia south to the Black Sea, Mediterranean region and Atlantic Morocco. In Great Britain, they have a markedly northern and western distribution; some 35,500 pairs were estimated in the mid 1980s – a significant proportion of the European total, excluding Russia, of 85,000 to 88,000 pairs (*EBCC Atlas*) – although numbers had fallen to 26,600 by 1998–2002 (*Seabird 2000*). Though they disperse to some extent along coasts, their winter distribution is similar to that of summer, and there is little movement away from rocky shores (*1981–84 Winter Atlas*); unlike Cormorants, they are almost entirely marine, any occurring inland usually being sick or storm-driven.

Wiltshire's 24 dated records of Shags have all involved singletons between August and April, 12 of them during October to December (table 39). Smith (1887) listed three in the 19th century, the two with dates having been shot at Durnford Mill in September 1871 and at Avebury in October 1876. The first noted in the 20th century was at Ogbourne in October 1922 (*BB* 16: 167, Kennedy 1966) and, four years later, another was found 'near Salisbury in 1926' (*WANHM* 57: 139). One seen fishing at Stockton 'in the autumn of 1944 and again in January, 1945' (*WANHM*) was, assuming it was correctly identified, either a most unusual long-stayer or, perhaps more likely, involved two separate individuals.

There followed a further seven records during 1957–71 (*WANHM*); of these, one picked up dead at Goatacre in March 1962 had been ringed on the Farne Islands (Northumberland) in June 1961 (BTO). Eleven more during 1975–89, mostly seen at rivers and lakes, included a juvenile found near Redlynch in November 1977 that had been ringed 355 km away on Little Saltee (Co. Wexford) in June that year, and another caught at Etchilhampton in

Table 39. Shags *Phalacrocorax aristotelis* in Wiltshire: monthly totals 1871–1996

	Jul	Aug	Sep	Oct	Nov	Dec	Jan	Feb	Mar	Apr	May	Jun
Birds	0	2	2	4	4	4	2	2	2	1	0	0

February 1984 that had been ringed as a nestling 536 km away on the Isle of May (Fife) in June 1983 (*Hobby*). This, and another in February 1984, followed a major wreck of Shags in south and east England. Only two were recorded during 1990–2000:

1992 1 September Coate Water 1st-winter
1996 27 August Dauntsey Adult

The 1996 adult had been ringed as a nestling at Ousdale (Highland) in June 1989 and was thus seven years old (BTO).

(See also page 726.)

RT

Common Bittern

Botaurus stellaris

Scarce winter visitor from England or, mainly, continental Europe, nested in 1930s

Common Bitterns – the males of which have a far-carrying, foghorn-like, territorial call known as 'booming' – breed across much of temperate Eurasia from England and Iberia to Japan and north China, and also in southeast Africa. Northeast European and most Asiatic populations are migratory, wintering south to Africa, the Indian subcontinent and southeast Asia. In Great Britain, drainage and persecution resulted in the extinction of the breeding population by 1900, but small numbers recolonised early in the 20th century and reached a peak of about 80 booming males in the 1950s (*1988–91 Atlas*). Thereafter, a continuous slow decline has reduced the total to no more than 24 boomers in 1999, though these included two in the southwest (*RBBP*). Common Bitterns have also been declining since the 1970s elsewhere in Europe, partly through habitat loss and disturbance, and numbers die in severe winters. Excluding Russia, the European population has been put at 10,000 to 12,000 'pairs' or, more properly, booming males (*EBCC Atlas*).

The British population does not emigrate, so far as is known, and arrivals from the Continent in December onwards, especially during hard weather, probably account for the majority of Wiltshire records, which have been most frequent in January and February (table 40). The first reference to this species in the county appears to have been by Aubrey (1656–91), who wrote of 'Bitterns in the breaches at Allington, &c'. Maton (1843) recorded that considerable numbers were found near Britford in the very hard frost of January 1795, though im Thurn (1870) mentioned two occurrences 'killed many years ago'. Smith (1887) noted that the species was becoming a rarity in Wiltshire as early as 1820 and could total only 14 records (17 birds) between 1836 and 1886. On the other hand, Hony (1915a) listed 23, of which 20 were from dates later than Smith: five in 1892, one in 1897, seven in 1900, three in 1902, one in 1903, and three in 1908. A Bittern was also shot near Westbury in 1914, another in a Codford water meadow in January 1918 'in mistake for a Heron', and a third probably by the Kennet, opposite Mildenhall,

Table 40. Common Bitterns *Botaurus stellaris* in Wiltshire: monthly totals 1974–2000

	Jul	Aug	Sep	Oct	Nov	Dec	Jan	Feb	Mar	Apr	May	Jun
Birds	0	0	0	0	2	5	17	13	5	0	0	0

about the beginning of January 1924 (all *WANHM*).

The picture then changed dramatically. In winter 1928/29 the species was found in no fewer than nine localities – though, as three were shot, there was irony in the comment that it was making 'a gallant effort' to recolonise England (*WANHM*). Next came a series of references to 'reported breeding in the county in 1930'; 'undoubtedly breeding' on the Salisbury Avon in 1933, 'birds being seen all year for the last three years [presumably 1931–33] near Downton'; and still seen for 'most of the year', and heard, near Downton in 1934 (*WANHM*). In a letter to the *Salisbury Times* in February 1939 about Bitterns at Britford, CMR Pitman wrote, 'Apart from these migrants, however, a resident pair is still with us in the usual haunts' – which suggests that summering, and presumably breeding, continued into the late 1930s.

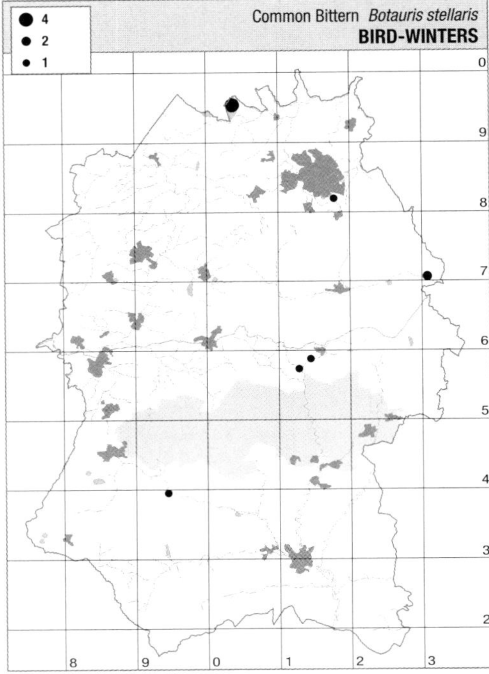

Peirson (1959) made no mention of this earlier breeding and described the Common Bittern simply as a rare but fairly regular winter visitor, one or two being seen in most winters, often on the Salisbury Avon. Indeed, apart from an absence between 1952 and 1957, Bitterns were noted in Wiltshire in all but two years from 1945 to 1971, many in the south of the county at sites along the Salisbury Avon, at Longford in particular, although of the 40 or so records during this period, all but four stayed for a only few days (*WANHM*). There were apparent small influxes associated with the cold winters in the early 1960s, but only five records during April–September. Booming was heard at Coate Water in the early 1950s, when the reedbeds were more extensive (Buxton 1981) and a Bittern

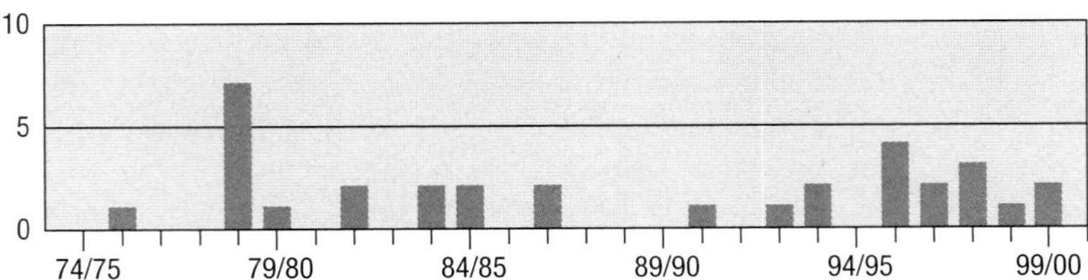

Figure 26. Common Bitterns *Botaurus stellaris* in Wiltshire: totals by winters 1974/75–1999/00

was seen in the Clarendon district in summer 1952 (*WANHM*). One ringed at Longford in January 1962 was later found dead there in April that year (*WANHM*). From 1974 to 2000 the species continued to be a rare winter visitor, with a total of 33 records (figure 26); Bitterns were found more than once at CWP (in six winters), Littlecote and Langford Lakes (in three apiece) and Broad Chalke, Coate Water and Westbury Ponds (in two each).

(See also page 726.)

RT

Little Bittern

Ixobrychus minutus

Overshooting vagrant (6 records), breeds south/ central Europe, winters Africa

Apart from resident populations in sub-Saharan Africa, Madagascar, the northern Indian subcontinent and Australia, Little Bitterns occur across much of southern and central Europe and into southwestern Asia, but only as summer visitors that winter in Africa. Being small and secretive inhabitants of reedbeds, these tiny herons have had a somewhat mysterious history in this country, mainly as overshooting spring vagrants, with breeding suspected on several occasions over the past two centuries but proved only once, in Yorkshire in 1984 (*BBRC* 1985).

A few are still recorded in Great Britain in most years – a total of 190 during 1958–2000 (*BBRC*) – but a widespread decline throughout Europe in the second half of the 20th century has been attributed mainly to drought in Africa (*CBWP*) and all Wiltshire's six records precede that period. Montagu (1802) wrote of one near Bath, probably in Wiltshire. Smith (1887) listed four singletons, at Stourton in 1820, at Seend in 1850, at Britford in June 1851, and at Wilton near Salisbury on 8 September 1869; the first was an adult male, but he gave no further details for the others. Then, 70 years later, the county's only 20th century record involved one found at Gore Cross, on the northern edge of Salisbury Plain, on 18 March 1940; it was caught on the 19th, died on the 20th and is now preserved in the Natural History Museum at Tring (Hertfordshire) (*BB* 33: 339). The specimen is labelled an adult female.

RT

Night Heron

Nycticorax nycticorax

Spring–summer vagrant (11 records), breeds southern Europe, winters Africa

Almost cosmopolitan in range, breeding in all continents except Australia, Night Herons are summer visitors to southern Europe north to Belgium and, less regularly, the Netherlands; the majority of this European population winters in Africa. Vagrants occur annually in Great Britain – a total of 418 records during 1958–2000 (*BBRC*) – but few have been found in Wiltshire. Smith (1887) reported one killed at Lake near Salisbury 'many years ago' and the Rawlence collection contained one reputedly taken near Downton. A bird 'probably one of this species' was seen at Longford in early May 1954, but the first accepted record in the 20th century was an immature at Longford in October 1956 (*WANHM*). Since 1974 there have been a further eight, those in 1983, 1987 and 1990 occurring in years when there were particularly notable influxes nationally (*BBRC*):

1978	20 April	Coate Water	Adult
1983	17 June	CWP40	3rd-year
1985	3–10 February	Dinton	Adult
1987	4 July	Coate Water	2nd-summer
1988	6–24 April	Longbridge Deverill	Adult
1990	7 May	Coate Water	Adult
1994	25 May	CWP68	Adult
1997	7 August	CWP68	Adult

The February dates in 1985 were unusual at that time. A colour-ringed juvenile that stayed at Downton from 29 December 1987 into 1988, before moving to Somerset, was apparently an escape from a free-flying population at Edinburgh Zoo (*BBRC*).

RT

Squacco Heron

Ardeola ralloides

Overshooting vagrant (3 records), breeds south Europe, winters Africa

Squaccos breed from southern Spain and northwest Africa eastwards to southwest Asia and winter mainly in sub-Saharan Africa, where there are also resident populations. Habitat destruction and plume-hunting caused a serious decline in the numbers of these magnificent but scarce little herons in the late 19th and early 20th centuries, estimates for the whole Eurasian and north African population crashing from 16,400 pairs in 1850–1900 to 6000 pairs in 1920–40, but then slowly increasing again to 8200 pairs in 1940–60 (*BWP*, based on Józefik 1969–70); there have been further decreases in eastern Europe since the 1970s, but numbers have been more stable in the west, and the Spanish, Italian and southern French populations were actually increasing in the early to mid 1990s (*EBCC Atlas*). Overshooting from Iberia or southern France is thought to be responsible for the majority of occurrences in Great Britain, and the period 1989–2000 produced 26 records, exactly half the national total of 52 since 1958 (*BBRC*).

For Wiltshire, Smith (1887) noted that one was shot at Boyton in 1775; and the Rawlence collection reputedly contained another taken by the Salisbury Avon (Peirson 1959), which would probably have been in the third quarter of the 19th century. (Peirson also referred to one, undated, at Britford, but his reference in *WANHM* appears untraceable and so that record is omitted here: perhaps there was confusion with Rawlence's.) Despite the increase nationally, the county's only 20th century record was an adult at CWP68 on 24–25 June 1997 (Grearson 1998a); this bird then moved over the border into Gloucestershire, where it stayed until 1 July, and was also assumed to be the same individual as had been seen at Rode (Somerset) on 13 June. It was one of five records in Great Britain in a good year for the species.

RT

Little Egret

Egretta garzetta

Scarce but increasingly regular visitor from Continent and now established southern Britain (first bred 2003)

Little Egrets have a wide distribution, breeding from western and southern Eurasia south to Africa and Australia, and are represented by a very similar congener, the Snowy Egret in the Americas. The European breeding population of Little Egrets, excluding Russia, has been estimated at 24,000 to 34,000 pairs (*EBCC Atlas*). In Europe, they were long confined to the far south and, indeed, did not nest even in southern France until 1931, yet they had spread to the Loire estuary by 1949 (*BWP*) and have been continuing north ever since along the northwest and north coasts of France. Now they are steadily beginning to colonise the Netherlands and southern England (*CBWP*/*RBBP*). It has recently been argued that the 'Egretys' of medieval banquets were Little Egrets and that they must have been breeding commonly in England in the 15th century (Bourne 2003, Andrew 2004) – on which basis current events should be looked upon as *re*colonisation – but no archaeological or paleontological remains of this species have ever been found in northwest Europe (Stewart 2004).

In the 1940s Little Egrets were among the rarest of vagrants to Great Britain and Ireland (Witherby *et al* 1938–41), and the grand total up to 1958 was just 23; 30 years later they were still primarily spring wanderers, but by then averaging nearly 15 a year. In 1989 over 120 occurred (*BBRC*), largely as a result of an unprecedented early autumn influx (Combridge & Parr 1992). Autumn influxes involving several hundreds, many then overwintering, are now the norm, and breeding was confirmed in Dorset in 1996 (Lock & Cook 1998). In 1999, when at least 30 pairs nested at nine sites, as many as 1650 Little Egrets were estimated to be present in Great Britain in September (Musgrove 2002), concentrated primarily on estuaries in southwest England and Wales.

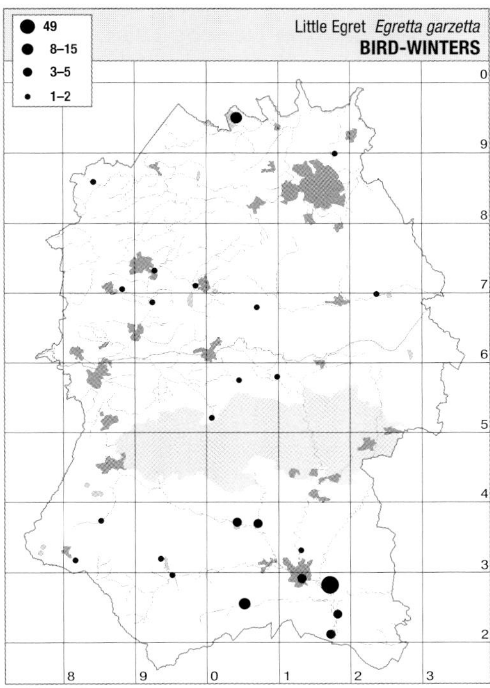

Wiltshire's first ever record was at Britford during 13–19 January 1992. Little Egrets have occurred annually at Britford ever since, up to a maximum of 25 in 2000. The distribution map shows a concentration of records there and at other localities on the Salisbury Avon and its tributaries, and it is likely that many of these birds follow the Hampshire/Salisbury Avon north from the coast. The map shows another concentration at CWP, where the species has similarly been annual since 1993. The wide scatter of records indicates that wanderers are likely to occur wherever suitable habitat exists, and suggests that they may be overlooked on waterways that have restricted public access.

One, presumed to be the same individual returning, was regular in winter in the Sherston-Luckington area between January 1993 and December 1996. There was a total of least 30 at six sites in Wiltshire in December 2000. Numbers will clearly continue to grow in the county.

(Particularly see page 724.)

RT

Sponsored by Joan and John Brown

Great White Egret

Ardea alba

Vagrant (1 record), breeds south/east Europe, now spreading to north/west

Almost cosmopolitan in range – breeding in the Americas, Africa, Australasia and central, southern and eastern Asia, as well as in parts of Europe where it was long confined to isolated colonies in the southeast – this largest of the egrets suffered greatly from the plumage trade in the 19th and early 20th centuries. The species has never been known as more than a vagrant in Great Britain. Indeed, up to 1958 only ten Great White Egrets had ever been found here, but by 2000, in which year no fewer than 25 were recorded, the total had risen to 143 (*BBRC*).

This much greater frequency reflects major increases in the European population and range since the late 1970s, first northward in Russia and Ukraine to Belarus and Latvia, then significantly westward. The species was rare in Bulgaria in the 1970s and had decreased to seven pairs by 1993, but a census in January 1999 showed 799 individuals; it is now of annual occurrence in the Baltic States and Fenno-Scandia, and began nesting in several western countries in the 1990s, including Italy (34–42 pairs by 1998), France (breeding north to Loire Atlantique, wintering at various localities on all coasts and along river valleys including the northeast) and the Netherlands (ten pairs nesting by 2000, 42 pairs in 2002, well over 100 individuals wintering), while breeding is expected soon in neighbouring Belgium (20–30 wintering, two or three pairs summering) (*CBWP*, *EBR* 2000–02, L Marion, G Vermeersch). Such a spread is reminiscent of that of its smaller congener, the Little Egret (*qv*), even if it began from a different direction.

By 2000, just one had been recorded in Wiltshire, at Britford from 3 September to 1 October 1999 (Blamey & Greenough 2000). It had a distinctive combination of colour-rings on the left tibia and a conventional metal one on the right, which later showed that it had been ringed as a nestling on 9 May 1999 at Lac du Grand-Lieu, in Loire Atlantique, northwest France (L Marion). It also briefly visited Worcestershire on 11–12 September, but was back again at Britford on the evening of the 12th; and four days after its last sighting in Wiltshire, it appeared at Radipole Lake (Dorset) on 5 October. Eight other Great White Egrets were recorded in Great Britain that year, three in April–June and five in July–August, and three in Ireland (*BBRC*).

(See also page 726.)

RT

Grey Heron

Ardea cinerea

Common resident/migrant, breeds in colonies, found widely by most waters

Long-necked and dagger-billed, Grey Herons are familiar and distinctive shapes by lakes, rivers, streams and ponds in Wiltshire, where they feed on fish, amphibians, small mammals, insects, reptiles and even ducklings. While they usually stand at the water's edge and stalk sedately in the shallows, they will also occasionally snatch items from water surfaces in flight, swim in search of food and even plunge-dive to catch fish, foraging methods that have all been noted in the county (*Hobby* 10, 17, 19, 21, 27).

Grey Herons have the most northerly distribution of any European heron, breeding locally in Mediterranean countries and much more commonly in north-central Europe, extending as far north as 69°N in ice-free coastal Norway (Voisin 1991). Elsewhere, they nest in parts of Africa, in Madagascar and through much of Asia. Early in the 20th century, the species was severely persecuted in Europe, and cold winters also took a heavy toll, so that by about 1970 it was, in some parts of the range, threatened or even extinct. Pollution, habitat destruction and pesticide poisoning probably also contributed to the decline. Since then, however, numbers have increased significantly, perhaps as a result of lessening persecution and milder winters, and the European population is now estimated at between 117,000 and 128,000 pairs (*EBCC Atlas*). In winter Grey Herons are far more widespread, being found in much of the Mediterranean area and throughout most of Africa, wanderers regularly even reaching such islands as Madeira and the Seychelles.

In Great Britain, following the first national census of heronries organised by EM Nicholson in 1928, nests have been counted annually at a large number of colonies, and the full national census was repeated in 1954, 1964 and 1985; this is now the oldest and longest-running bird survey anywhere in the world. Grey Herons are resident and widespread, the highest densities being recorded along major river systems and in some coastal areas (*1988–91 Atlas*); the number of British 10-km squares in which they were nesting increased by nearly two-fifths between the *1968–72* and *1988–91 Atlases*. The national census of 1985 estimated 9570 nests in Great Britain (Marchant *et al* 1990) and it was thought that this total had increased to 10,300 by 1991 (*1988–91 Atlas*); *CWBP* considered that the latter 'figure should be treated with some caution', but noted that the population in the 1990s 'has certainly increased significantly, with probably about twice as many as in late 1960s'; in 2003 the number of nests was put at 13,430 (*APEP*).

Numbers are reduced in severe weather. For example, over 80 per cent of first-year Grey Herons survive the mildest winters, but almost none came through the prolonged cold of 1962/63 (North 1979). The *1981–84 Winter Atlas* estimated the midwinter population at about 30,000, not including an unknown number of Continental immigrants, which arrive in late autumn and early winter. Many Grey Herons return to their breeding sites by the end of February (*1981–84 Winter Atlas*), indeed as early as January at some Wiltshire heronries in recent mild winters, but some do not lay their eggs until April and, with nearly four weeks for incubation and about seven for fledging, the young may still be in the nest well into July.

In Wiltshire, Aubrey (1656–91) wrote that 'Herons bred heretofore... about 1580, at Easton-Piers, before the great oakes were felled down near the mannour-house; and they doe still breed in Farleigh Parke'. Interestingly, too, im Thurn (1870) described the Grey Heron as 'a common and tolerably plentiful species, though it is certainly very much rarer

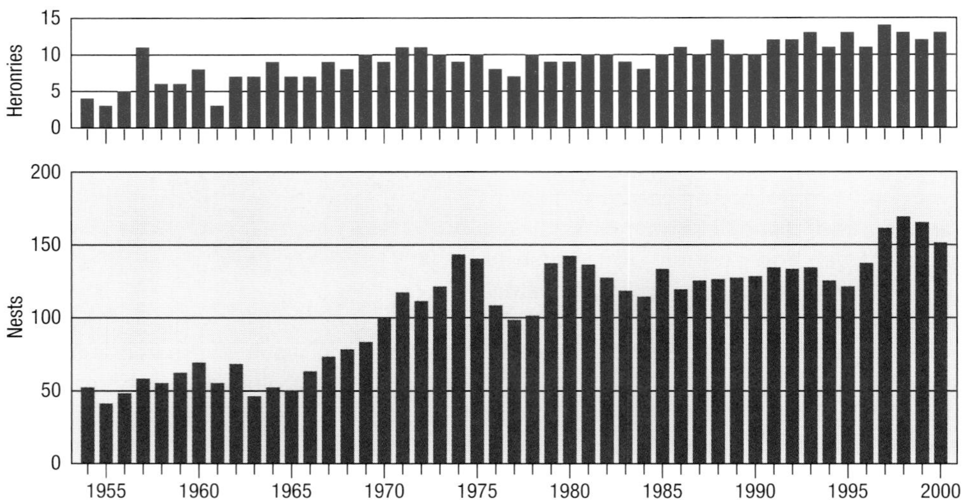

Figure 27. Grey Herons *Ardea cinerea* in Wiltshire: numbers of colonies and totals of nests 1954–2000
The 1977 figures are certainly incomplete, three regular heronries having apparently not been counted: it is estimated that these would have added 23 to the total, making 10 heronries and 120 nests more realistic (see also note to table 41)

than it has been', and stated that the only heronry near Marlborough was at Bowood; later (1876) he admitted to being wrong and that a few bred in Savernake Forest, about three or four nests every year. Smith (1887) described Grey Herons as 'known to everybody' in 19th century Wiltshire and listed seven main heronries: Crouch Wood, Bowood, Savernake, Longleat, Fonthill, Compton Park, and Longford Castle. Shaw (1929) detailed the history of the Savernake heronry: MCNHS reported nests intermittently from 1879 and each year since 1916. The 'normal site [was] at the western end of Ouselett, the next open space south of that in which the Eight Walks lie'; in 1926 most herons moved to Three Oak Hill Drive, near the Column, but returned the following year and 'in 1928 two nests at the Column site had young and ten at the Ouselett site'. Nests had also been reported in Noke Wood and near Tottenham House. Curiously, Colquhoun (1941) made no mention of Herons at all in Savernake, and Kennedy (1966) stated that by 1964 the number of nests was down to two – the lowest recorded figure since that site was first reported by im Thurn.

Peirson (1959) found that 54–59 nests had been counted at seven heronries in the first national census year of 1928, when Fonthill (14–18 nests) and Great Bradford Wood (13) were the most important. A 'decrease' was noted in 1929 and then counts were published rather erratically during 1930–34 and 1943–53 (*WANHM*): heronries were inconsistently noted for different years at Savernake (up to 9 nests), New Warren (up to 6), Bowood (up to 18), Great Bradford Wood (up to 14), Longleat (up to 4), Compton Chamberlayne (up to 2), Hurdcott House (up to 20), and Clarendon (erratically, 0–2).

From 1954 and through the 1960s the data are more complete, but there are small discrepancies between published totals and thus Boyle (1970) is followed for that period in the 47-year summary (figure 27), rather than Peirson (1959) or Webber (1968). Boyle found most of the county's heronries to be of 'moderate size, made up of less then ten nests each'. Only Bowood and Great Bradford Wood held over 25 nests during 1954–68, but the county total rose swiftly in the early 1970s, reached a peak of 142 in 1974 and then fell to 100 in 1978 (Buxton 1981), but probably not lower still in 1977 (see heading to figure 27). Through the 1980s numbers varied between 113 and 141. A general increase continued into and through the 1990s to 2000 – totals of nests ranging from 120 to 168, in up to 14

Table 41. Grey Herons *Ardea cinerea* in Wiltshire: colony sizes 1990–2000

Dashes do not necessarily mean that there were no nests: not every site has been visited every year, especially before 1994, and it is not always possible now to distinguish nil counts from unknowns. Some 160 nests were found at Longford/Britford in 2004, following better access to the colony for observers; larger numbers may have been present during the 1990s than shown below (see also page 724)

	1990	1991	1992	1993	1994	1995	1996	1997	1998	1999	2000
CWP29	14	17	14	14	15	7	2	5	7	6	7
CWP68/74	1	3	6	12	10	18	28	27	30	25	27
Braydon Pond	–	–	–	–	–	–	–	5	2	3	3
Hillocks Wood	8	5	6	8	8	6	7	7	7	8	–
Coate Water	11	8	12	8	9	12	15	17	25	24	19
Wilton Water	0	0	0	0	0	0	1	3	2	2	3
Wilcot	–	–	–	–	–	1	–	5	5	3	3
Castle Combe	–	–	–	–	–	1	–	–	–	–	–
Bowood	13	15	15	14	13	15	14	11	18	14	12
Lacock Gravel Pits	0	0	0	0	0	0	0	0	0	0	1
Great Bradford Wood	23	25	3	2	3	6	–	9	10	10	15
Gripwood, Bradford-on-Avon	–	–	–	5	–	–	–	–	–	–	6
Erlestoke	–	2	6	6	6	4	3	2	–	–	–
Longleat	10	9	12	12	13	14	15	18	13	14	15
Shear Water	–	1	1	1	0	0	0	0	0	0	0
Wardour	8	8	8	9	10	10	9	14	11	16	9
Boyton	9	9	7	6	6	6	8	6	6	0	1
Longford/Britford	30	31	42	36	31	20	34	36	32	39	30
Total nests	127	133	132	133	124	120	136	165	168	155	151
Heronries in use	10	12	12	13	11	13	11	14	13	12	14

heronries in any one year of the 18 variously occupied in that period (table 41) – this being somewhat at odds with a slight decline recorded in southwest England as a whole since the mid 1990s (*BBS*).

In Wiltshire, nearly all current and former heronries are by or near lakes, gravel pits or rivers, but a few, most notably Savernake, have been far away from water. Nests have been recorded in oak, beech, poplar, alder, willow, spruce, pine, and larch. Most are 7–25 m above ground, but some have been at water level, for example at Coate Water and Wilton Water.

The summer abundance map shows not only the positions of the colonies, but also gives an indication of how far the breeding birds travel to feed, though the records will, of course, also include non-breeders and, from June onwards, fledged juveniles may not always have been distinguished from adults. Grey Herons are found extensively along almost all watercourses in the county, avoiding only the higher ground between the Wylye and the Nadder and the Marlborough Downs and Salisbury Plain, although even these last two areas are bisected by their regular feeding along the Kennet and the Salisbury Avon. The summer tetrad survey realised a total of 413, a not unreasonable figure given the known number of nests.

Winter distribution broadly matches that of the breeding season, both nationally and in Wiltshire, although Salisbury Plain is no longer an obvious gap because of the 10-km scale of the winter abundance map. The apparent absence of Grey Herons in a strip down the east side of the county is largely an artefact of the sampling methods used, although the general paucity of suitable habitat there is likely to lead to genuinely smaller numbers, a fact also reflected in the *1981–84 Winter Atlas*. Outside the breeding season, Grey Herons are often seen singly, but large numbers are sometimes found at favoured sites, particularly along the Salisbury Avon, including counts of 116 at Charlton-All-Saints on 17 November

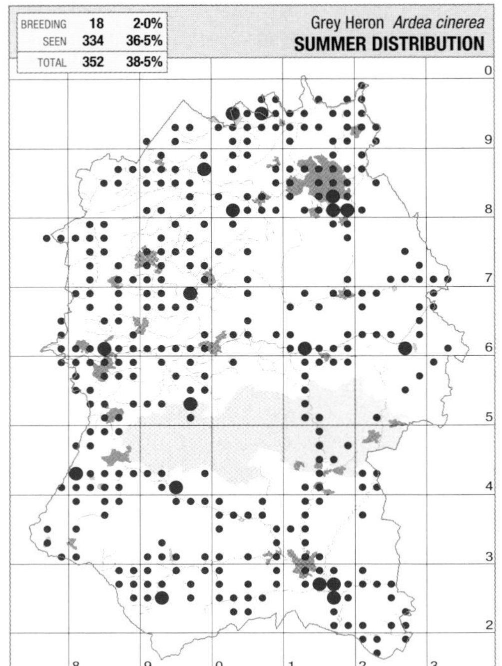

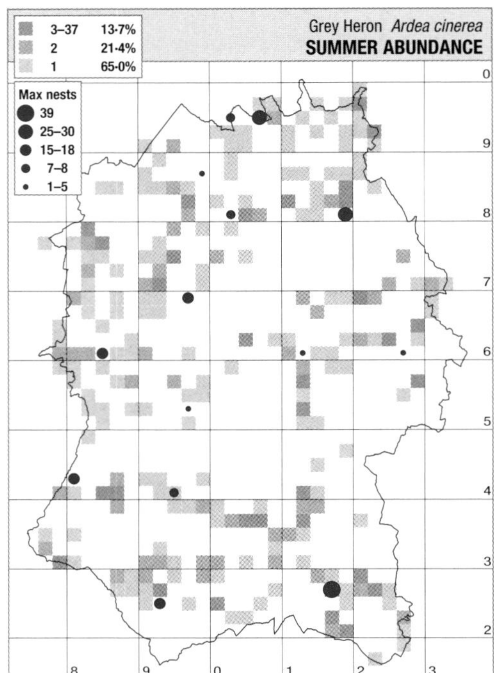

1989 and 104 at Trafalgar on 6 February 1990, and a remarkable total of 324 from Salisbury over the county boundary to Fordingbridge (Hampshire) in October 2000. Winter tetrad counts indicated a Wiltshire total of 557 and, this being such a relatively conspicuous species, that is probably a reasonably accurate figure; indeed, a projected estimate of, say, 600–750 in winter compares favourably with the national population.

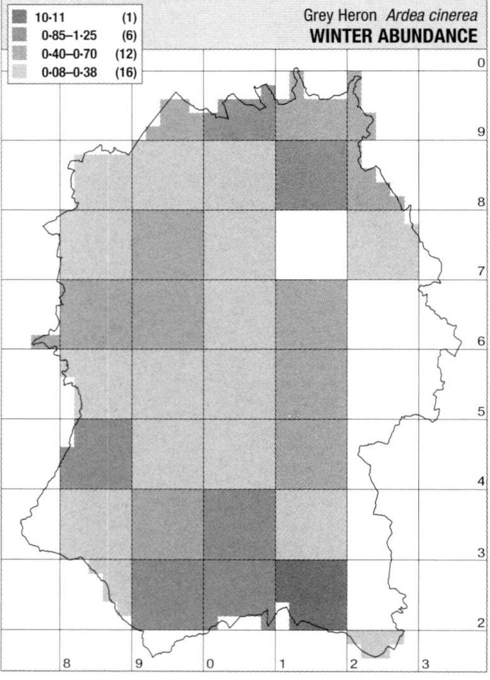

During 1965–2000, a total of 56 Grey Herons was ringed in Wiltshire. No recoveries of these have been reported, but five foreign birds have been found in the county, all ringed as nestlings, in Denmark (two, including one in 1910), Norway, France and Belgium.

So long as the current run of milder winters continues, the future for Grey Herons in Wiltshire seems assured, with no shortage of potential breeding sites and the recent creation of additional lakes, notably at CWP, increasing available feeding areas. Although now fully protected, they are still persecuted, even if to a lesser extent than in the 1970s when thousands were killed nationally by fish farmers. Practical solutions other than shooting were produced in the early 1980s and have reduced problems at fish farms.

SBE

Purple Heron

Ardea purpurea

Overshooting vagrant (6 records), breeds south Europe, winters Africa

Widespread and mainly resident in Africa, Madagascar and southern Asia through to Indonesia, Purple Herons are also not uncommon, but decreasing, summer visitors in southern Europe north to central France and the Netherlands. The European population has been estimated at between 7800 and 8600 pairs. These winter in sub-Saharan Africa and the majority of British records involve returning migrants overshooting to southern England in April and May. The annual average of records in Great Britain during 1970–2000 was 20 (Fraser & Rogers 2002). The total in Wiltshire to 2000 was six, none of which was seen on more than one day:

1981	16 May	Coate Water	1st-summer
1987	27 June	CWP Waterhay Bridge	Immature
1988	1 May	Shalbourne	Adult
1991	4 May	Trowbridge	2nd-year
1994	23 July	SPTA South Down Farm	Sub-adult
1998	25 August	CWP26	1st-summer, north over CWP73

Fraser & Rogers (2001) also included two Wiltshire observations for 1999, but neither of those was accepted by the WOS Records Panel (*Hobby* 26: 89).

RT

Black Stork

Ciconia nigra

Vagrant (3 records) breeds east/central/south Europe, winters Africa

Although they have a huge summer distribution across Eurasia to the Pacific, Black Storks are generally scarce in Europe west of a line from eastern Germany to the Balkans. Indeed, the breeding range in western Europe shrank markedly in the first half of the 20th century, leaving an isolated outpost in Iberia, until a subsequent reversal in this trend led to Belgium, Luxembourg, Denmark, France, Italy and Sweden being colonised, or recolonised, in recent decades. The European population has been estimated at between 5500 and 6100 pairs (*EBCC Atlas*). Some Black Storks are resident in Iberia and the eastern Balkans, but most from Europe winter south of the Sahara (where there is also a separate breeding population in southern Africa), while many from Asia travel down to the area between Pakistan and southern China.

In Great Britain, few were recorded before the late 1960s but, coinciding with the species' reappearance in western Europe, vagrants have occurred almost annually since the mid 1970s, the total during 1958–2000 being 115, including a remarkable 22 in 1991

(*BBRC*). The three seen in Wiltshire have all been in good years nationally (eight, eight and 14 records, respectively) and in the typical spring period between mid April and mid June:

1989	26 May	Pound Bottom	In flight only (see below)
1990	15 April & 27 May	Pound Bottom	Adult in flight (see below)
1995	18 May	Longbridge Deverill	In flight

The one in 1989 was probably the same as that seen in the Isle of Wight on 28–29 May, while the adult in 1990 stayed in the New Forest and Avon valley area of Hampshire from 7 April to 17 June and was seen to fly over Wiltshire on the two occasions. The coincidence of locality and dates raises the possibility of its being the same individual in 1990 as in 1989, though the Hampshire/Salisbury Avon is a clear funnel for any waterbirds heading north.

RT

White Stork

Ciconia ciconia

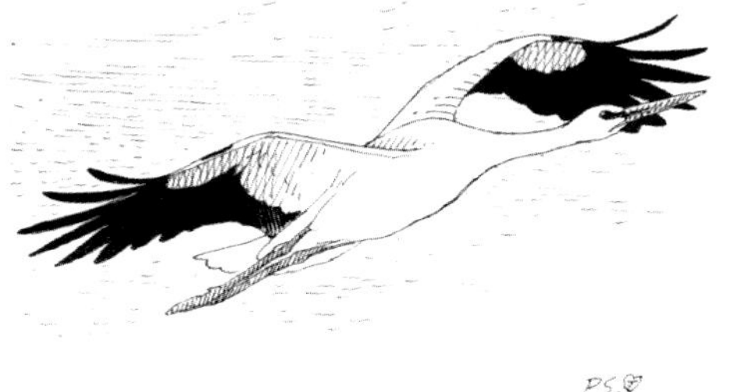

Vagrant (12 records), breeds Europe, some winter in south, most in Africa

Wintering mainly in sub-Saharan Africa and to a lesser extent the Indian subcontinent, White Storks breed only in Europe east to western Russia, in Turkey and the Middle East, and in North Africa, apart from isolated populations in central Asia and, sporadically, South Africa. The *EBCC Atlas* put the breeding population of Europe, excluding Russia, at 101,000 to 108,000 pairs. Vagrants to Great Britain occur mostly in spring, but there is a secondary peak in September. The status of this conspicuous bird is often confused by the movement of individuals between counties, which can inflate the number of reports, as well as by the problem of escapes. Despite a general population decline in much of western Europe, British records have increased since the 1970s, notably in the 1990s when the annual average was 21 (Fraser & Rogers 2001); perhaps this is linked to the situation in France, where 133 pairs in Alsace in 1958 had dropped to only 10 pairs plus a few elsewhere by 1973 (*BWP*) but a 'Recent increase followed marked decline' led to 315 nests nationally in 1995 (*CBWP*).

For Wiltshire, Yarrell (1856) had an undated report of one killed at Salisbury, evidently some time between 1808 and 1830, and Smith (1887) noted an immature shot at Downton in August 1789 and one shot on a chimney stack at Codford on 5 September 1882. Seventy years were to pass before the next, in early June 1952, when one joined a flock of white turkeys at Downton (*WANHM*). Singles at Upavon on 27 May 1967 and East Knoyle on 5 June 1971 were followed by one in the Ashton Keynes area from 6 September 1972 until the 14th, when two were present (*WANHM*, *BBRC*); one or both then moved over the border into Gloucestershire (Buxton 1981 wrongly gave the dates as 7–22 September). Earlier, one in poor condition captured at Hullavington on 26 December 1970 was considered to be an escape (*WANHM*). From 1974:

1975	14–20 August	Stockton	One
1996	17 September	Eldene, Swindon	Flying high to northwest
	22 September	Salisbury	Flying to southeast
	24 September	Downton	Circling low (see below)
1999	5 September	CWP Waterhay Bridge	Circled and then flew south

The comment in 1975 (*Hobby*) was 'may have escaped from a collection', perhaps because the bird stayed for a week and the species was at that time even rarer than now in Great Britain. Similarly, those in 1996 were at the time linked to a report of two escaping from Bristol Zoo, but additional evidence published the next year (*Hobby*) made it likely that the Swindon record could not relate to one of those; the Salisbury and Downton observations two days apart were assumed to involve one individual. The 1999 bird is known to have been the same as was seen at Andover (Hampshire) later the same day (Fraser & Rogers 2001).

(See also page 726.)

RT

Glossy Ibis

Plegadis falcinellus

Vagrant (2 old records), breeds south Europe, winters Mediterranean/Africa

Although almost cosmopolitan, breeding in all continents of the Old World as well as in eastern North America (and represented in other parts of the Americas by a closely related species), Glossy Ibises in general have a very patchy distribution, dependent on rather precise wetland requirements and a lack of human disturbance. Most of the very local European populations, estimated at 7300 to 9100 pairs (*EBCC Atlas*) and largely confined to the southeast from the Balkans eastwards, are summer visitors wintering in sub-Saharan Africa, though some from the northwest Caspian migrate to the Indian region and a few winter in Spain, North Africa and the Middle East. The European range has contracted markedly over the past century, through drainage and hunting, but, since the mid 1980s, higher winter numbers and the first modern breeding have been recorded in southwest Spain (roost of 226 in October 2000), south France, Italy (16–23 pairs in 1998, mainly Sardinia) and Morocco (*EBCC Atlas*, *CBWP*, *EBR*).

Against this background, the status of the Glossy Ibis in Great Britain over the last 100 years has changed from an annual vagrant in small parties to an exceptionally rare vagrant with just 70 records during 1958–2000 (*BBRC*). The only Wiltshire records, involving two or three individuals, are old. The first was killed near Calne in 1825 (Smith 1887); then in September 1915 one was seen at Draycot Foliat and another (or the same) was shot and preserved at Burderop Park, Chiseldon (*BB* 9: 252, *WANHM*).

(See also page 726.)

RT

Spoonbill

Platalea leucorodia

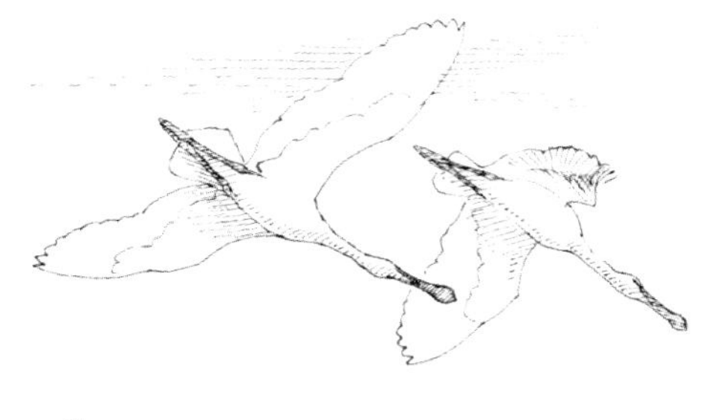

Vagrant (11 records), breeds Europe, winters Mediterranean/tropical Africa

Spoonbills are mainly summer visitors to southern Europe and central Asia, from Iberia to the Pacific, wintering in the Mediterranean basin, parts of northern tropical Africa, and southern Asia; there are also resident populations in West Africa and from the Red Sea to India. The European population, excluding Russia, has been estimated at only 2600 to 3200 pairs (*EBCC Atlas*), and it is patchily distributed, extremely so west of the Balkans, after earlier declines through drainage and other human pressures. But marked increases to 700 or more pairs apiece in Spain (1400 pairs in 1997–98), the Netherlands and Hungary in the last part of the 20th century (*EBCC Atlas*, *CBWP*) led to breeding being established or re-established in Denmark, Germany and France (*EBR*). In 1998–99 single pairs nested in England, the first for over 300 years; and in 2000, although none bred, pairs summered and built nests at several sites, including southern Scotland (*RBBP*). West European Spoonbills winter mainly from southern Spain and the west Mediterranean south to West Africa, especially on Banc d'Arguin (Mauritania), but in mild years some stay as far north as south and southwest England.

All Wiltshire Spoonbills have been found between 4 April and 8 August, the majority in April and May. None had been recorded here before 1978, and the increased number of vagrants in the 1990s probably reflected the recovery and subsequent growth of the Dutch population, after pollution and pesticides had caused a serious decline from the late 1950s:

1978	28 April	Coate Water	Two adults
	9 July	CWP Ashton Keynes	Adult
1982	9 June	CWP40	Adult
1989	4 April	River Bourne, Leckford	One
1991	26 May	CWP68	Two adults over, landed Glos
1992	28 May–1 Jun	CWP68	Adult
1996	20–23 April	CWP74/82	Adult
1997	13–14 April	CWP68/83	1st-year
	16–21 June	CWP74	Adult
1998	5 May–8 Aug	CWP68/74	1st-summer (not seen June)
	8 July	CWP68	Adult

That in 1996 was part of a large national influx involving 40 in April and 80 in May, most stemming from the Dutch colonies (Nightingale & Allsopp 1997), and 1998 was another record year with clear influxes in spring and autumn, southwest and eastern England attracting the largest numbers (Fraser *et al* 2000).

A spoonbill on a Devizes school field on 13 September 1988 may have been of the African species or even a hybrid (*Hobby*): just two days beforehand two spoonbills at Abberton (Essex) had been identified as African and earlier that summer two hybrid African × European had escaped from Birdworld (Surrey).

RT

Honey-buzzard

Pernis apivorus

Rare breeder as elsewhere in Britain, also vagrant from Europe, winters Africa

The Honey-buzzard – which is not a buzzard at all, but more closely related to the kites – is one of the most widespread raptors in the western half of Eurasia (and is replaced by a closely related species across central and eastern Asia). It is also polymorphic, and the most individually variable of all raptors. In summer it inhabits woodlands from southern Fenno-Scandia, France and Iberia east to western Siberia and south to the Balkans, Turkey and Caspian Iran. Ferguson-Lees & Christie (2001) calculated that the numbers of Honey-buzzards breeding in western Eurasia might exceed 500,000 pairs, of which the European total, excluding Russia, has been estimated at 41,000 to 48,000 pairs (*EBCC Atlas*); they are scarcest along the Mediterranean and Atlantic fringes. On migration, tens of thousands are recorded regularly at various traditional European and Middle Eastern landbridges and flyways on their way to and from winter quarters in the forests, woodlands and wooded savannahs of sub-Saharan Africa.

Within written ornithological history, Honey-buzzards have always been rare summer visitors to Great Britain; there were 19th century breeding records in Hampshire, the Welsh marches, the Midlands, northeast England, and north and east Scotland (*1875–1900 Atlas*). As far back as 1780, Gilbert White's *The Natural History of Selborne* (Letter XLIII to Thomas Pennant) recorded that a female was shot and her single egg taken at Selborne (Hampshire). Sadly, handsome sums were paid by egg- and skin-collectors for British-taken specimens, and the species was nearing extinction in the New Forest (Hampshire) by about 1870 (Saunders 1899). In the 17 years from 1856 to 1872, 24 nests were recorded there, 'of which at least 20 were plundered of eggs or young and the adults killed'; in contrast, the 35 years from 1880 produced only two known breeding records (Clark & Eyre 1993), though CR Tubbs (quoted in the *1875–1900 Atlas*) suggested that Gerald Lascelles withheld information about this species during his tenure as deputy surveyor from 1880 to 1915. At the other end of the country, Baxter & Rintoul (1953) recorded that nesting Honey-buzzards were killed and eggs collected in Scotland during the 19th century.

Against this background, it is perhaps not surprising that there has long been much secrecy about Honey-buzzards nesting in Great Britain, though small numbers have bred regularly since at least the 1940s. The *1968–72 Atlas* considered the British population unlikely to exceed a dozen pairs in any year, but that was clearly far too conservative: the *1988–91 Atlas* revealed that the New Forest alone held six to nine pairs annually during 1961–80 and estimated the total British population at perhaps 30 pairs. The first national census in 2000 showed 33 confirmed and 36 other probable or possible breeding pairs (*RBBP*, updated by Ogilvie 2003), although this apparent increase may, at least in part, have been a result of improved coverage and co-operation by observers in the 1990s.

For Wiltshire, Smith (1887) listed eight records of Honey-buzzards dated from 1847 to 1882, all shot or trapped by gamekeepers, though what was taken to be the specimen from near Marlborough that he included for 1855 was later found to be labelled 1885 (Hony 1915a). Most were collected on sandy soils and, though the only one of Smith's records with the month quoted – at Lavington Sands in October 1882 – is likely to have referred to a migrant, an adult destroying a wasp nest at Roundway Park around 1847 and a juvenile at West Lavington 'at about the same date' suggest the possibility of breeding. The Nethersole-Thompsons (1986), in an aside to discussing Stone-curlews in Wiltshire in the 1920s and early 1930s, noted mysteriously that 'In the largest wood…honey buzzards were reported although no nest was found' – an indication that at least summering had taken place.

More recently, Honey-buzzards were regularly found in suitable breeding habitat in Wiltshire from 1961, but only since the late 1970s have they been documented. Single pairs summered in the county throughout 1978–91 and bred successfully in 1978–80, 1982 and 1985–91, producing a total of 22 young. Perhaps in part a result of the formation of a Wiltshire Raptor Group, records increased during 1992–2000: the number of pairs found varied from two to four – though no more than two nested in any one year – and, in all, 27 young fledged. The best year was 1997 when four pairs and three singletons were found, though only one pair bred. There were also one or two unpaired birds in 1996 and 1998–2000.

Generally arriving in mid May and departing from late August onward (most in Wiltshire have departed by mid September), nesting Honey-buzzards occur in deciduous, coniferous and mixed woodlands, favouring areas where light soils make their excavation of wasp nests easier. Home ranges can extend up to 40 square kilometres and are possibly related to wasp densities: the larvae of social wasps are important food items for young Honey-buzzards. In a recent poor wasp year in southern England, however, common frogs and fledgling birds were enough to sustain them without loss of productivity (PE Castle & P Combridge).

Dates or habitats of all Wiltshire's other published records in the 20th century suggest migrants:

1940s	(no date)	near Wishford	One shot
1963	16 May	Tilshead	One
1978	3 September	Swindon	Two adults, third very dark, flying northeast
1992	24 May	Knook, near Warminster	One flying north
1998	17 July	near Amesbury	One flying southeast, mobbed by Buzzard
	18 October	Redlynch	One
2000	23 September	SPTA (Centre)	Dark juvenile flying southwest
	23 September	SPTA (West)	Dark juvenile flying west
	30 September	Lower Woodford	Rufous juvenile flying south
	30 September	Lower Woodford	Dark juvenile flying south 30 mins later
	8 October	CWP Lower Swillbrook	One circling towards Ashton Keynes

The very dark Honey-buzzard with the two adults in 1978 may have been a juvenile. The actual localities on 23 September 2000 were Honeydown Ridge and Berril valley.

A general increase in presumed migrants through Great Britain in both spring and autumn in the 1990s showed peaks in 1993, 1995, 1998 and 1999 (Fraser & Rogers 2001). In 1998, the first year in the above Wiltshire list to have two records, a total of 166 was recorded nationally away from known breeding sites, most in coastal counties from Yorkshire south and west to Cornwall, including a peak of 74 in September and October when many are likely to have been Continental migrants (Fraser *et al* 2000). The five in 2000 formed part of the biggest influx ever recorded in Great Britain. Between 20 September and 6 October, an estimated 1905 Honey-buzzards were blown across the North Sea by strong easterlies to make landfall along the whole length of the east and southeast coasts from Shetland southward (Fraser & Rogers 2002). Some continued well inland, or right across to northwest and southwest England, but the biggest numbers were seen in the southeast from Essex round to Dorset, especially in Sussex where the recorded total was 680. Apart from odd individuals on 18–19 September, the vast majority arrived in a series of waves in the last 11 days of that month, including a spectacular peak between Sussex and Dorset on the 29th and 30th, before departing southward over the English Channel; by 8 October, it was all but over.

PEC & PCo

Black Kite

Milvus migrans

Summer vagrant (8 records), breeds much of Europe, winters Africa

Considered to be the most numerous of all the world's raptors (Ferguson-Lees & Christie 2001), Black Kites breed across much of temperate and tropical Eurasia, as well as in Africa, Madagascar, New Guinea and Australia, though the numbers in Europe (excluding Russia), calculated at between 25,900 and 29,000 pairs (*EBCC Atlas*), are relatively small and have decreased in some countries as a result of poisoning, pesticides and pollution. They are, however, still common enough summer visitors in much of Europe, extending north to the Arctic Circle in easternmost Finland and northwest Russia, but missing from Great Britain, Ireland and most of Fenno-Scandia. In Europe, these kites favour wetlands and cultivation for foraging and open forest edge for breeding; but elsewhere they are often urban scavengers.

The European and western Asiatic populations winter in sub-Saharan Africa, as does the central Asian in southern Asia, and many of the 294 vagrants recorded in Great Britain during 1958–2000 (*BBRC*) were spring overshoots. Indeed, the first five in Wiltshire all occurred between 17 May and 12 June, those in 1994 being part of a total national influx of 31 (*BBRC*). The recent increase in vagrancy may reflect a 100-km northward range expansion in France in the 1970–80s (Doumeret 1994):

1986	12 June	Franchises Wood	Adult, flew south
1994	4 June	Little Durnford	Adult, flew west
	12 June	near Aldbourne	Adult, flew SE
1996	3 June	Newton	Adult, flew SW
1998	17 May	near Salisbury	Adult, at 08·00
		Vernditch Chase	Same, flying north at 13·20
1999	20 August	Redlynch	Flew south (see below)
	4 September	north of Whitsbury	Juvenile (see below)
	9 September	south of Wick Down	Assumed same as on 4 Sep
2000	18–24 July	near Everleigh	Adult, twine/grass on legs
	18–22 July	near Everleigh	Juvenile also present

The two records in September 1999, which were assumed to relate to the same individual, represented incursions into Wiltshire by a juvenile that stayed around Dunberry Hill (Hampshire) from 26 August to 10 September; the one at Redlynch on 20 August, for which age-class was not recorded, was possibly different, but arguably the same as it was heading in the direction of the Dunberry Hill area. In 2000, both adult and juvenile were seen to follow a hay mower and catch rats disturbed by the cutting; the adult was also watched feeding on a dead rabbit.

PEC

Red Kite

Milvus milvus

Rare but increasing resident/wanderer, now breeds, mainly from recent releases in England

The graceful flight of this handsome, russet-plumaged raptor must once have been a common sight over Wiltshire as it scavenged over downland and village alike. Remains of Red Kites have been found by archaeologists at medieval sites at Salisbury and Yatesbury, and at a Middle Saxon one at Ramsbury. Moreover, two place and six field names in Wiltshire refer to 'kites': thus, Pitton is derived from the Old English *puttoc tun*, meaning 'kite enclosure', and in field names *puttoc* has become corrupted to both 'Petty' and 'Pit' (see 'Wiltshire's early birds').

Red Kites were persecuted to extinction in England in the 19th century, but, as a result of national re-introductions, a few have now come to breed in the county after 150 or more years. They have a catholic diet: carrion is important, especially road casualties, but they also take a wide range of birds and mammals, some snatched from other raptors, as well as various invertebrates. They are gregarious at good food sources, such as rubbish tips, and at communal roosts in autumn and winter. They need woodland for nesting, often in hilly country, and open land and riverine habitats for hunting.

The Red Kite is endemic to western and central Europe, apart from a remnant population in northwest Africa. Its breeding range extends from Great Britain to western Belarus and Ukraine, and from southern Sweden to Italy, western Mediterranean islands, and north Morocco. The biggest numbers are in Spain, France and, above all, Germany. Those in the west and south are sedentary or, especially in their first year, dispersive, but the majority of the population from north and east of eastern France migrates mainly southwest to winter in the north Mediterranean basin and North Africa. Historically, the range has otherwise contracted from the Balkans and Asia Minor, and decreased in Scandinavia and North Africa, mainly through persecution and, to a lesser extent, a reduction in available carrion.

At the end of the 18th century, even if already in decline, Red Kites were still widespread throughout Great Britain (though absent from Ireland), but 100 years later all that remained was a tiny population in mid Wales. The last dated breeding in England was in 1863, and in Scotland 1884 (*1875–1900 Atlas*). Being easy to shoot, trap or poison, they may have ceased to nest in Wiltshire by about 1840. For the Marlborough district, im Thurn (1870) noted (in square brackets) that 'A pair of these birds are said to have built some years ago on the further side of Martinsell, but I am not certain of the correctness of this "*on dit.*" [hearsay] A friend has also assured me that he saw one flying over Liddington Castle'. Smith (1887) wrote, 'Fifty or sixty years ago the nest of this species was well known in Wiltshire ... but now, not only is the nest never found amongst us, but the bird, too, is no longer to be seen within the county'. The last specimen for which he gave a date was 1864, but Halliday & Randolph (1955) referred to im Thurn's second-hand report from Liddington, which apparently related to 1867, and Hart Smith (1887) recorded one at Kennet Barrows in 1886. Hony (1915a) reported that 'a male was shot at Fonthill in Nov., 1896', the final record for the 19th century.

Well over 30 years passed before the next observation, between Salisbury and Amesbury in April 1932 (*WANHM*) and, beginning with one at Ashton Keynes in April 1951 (*BB* 50: 140, Peirson 1959), Buxton (1981) could list only eight for the 35 years following the 1939–45 War, five in spring and three in autumn. These were widely scattered and most did

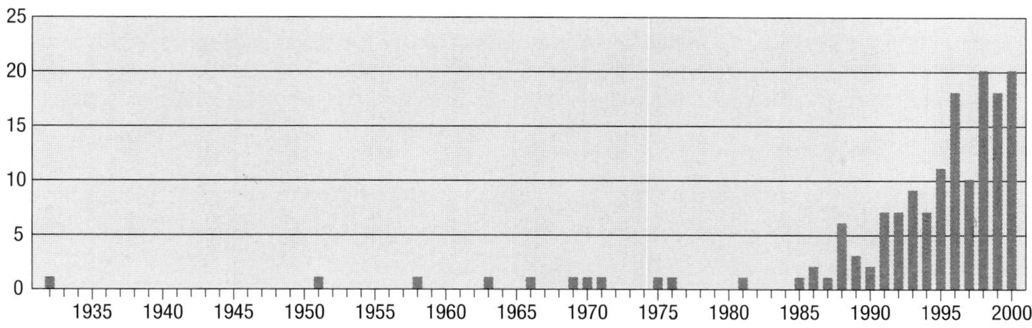

Figure 28. Red Kites *Milvus milvus* in Wiltshire: annual totals 1932–2000

not linger, but one stayed at Fyfield for more than seven weeks in September and October 1969. An immature at the same place for nine days in late March 1970 – the only sight-record of the period in which the age-class was ascertained – 'may have been the same one retracing its autumn route'; what was perhaps yet again the same individual, found dead nearby at Ramsbury in June 1970, had been ringed as a nestling in Wales 12 months earlier (all *WANHM*). Since 1985, however, records have been annual, initially reflecting a growth in the Welsh population, although five in spring 1988 were part of a national influx that was probably of Continental origin (Palmer 1991).

It is now accepted that numbers in Wales were at their lowest ebb in the 1930s (Davis 1993), but a gradual increase from the 1960s accelerated during the 1990s. With careful protection, the Welsh population had recovered to at least 249 pairs by 2000 (Wotton *et al* 2002a). The number of 10-km squares in Wales holding territorial pairs more than doubled in the 20 years after the *1968–72 Atlas*, and the year-on-year rate of increase averaged over 10 per cent in the early 1990s, even though egg-collecting remains a serious problem (*1988–91 Atlas*). The world breeding population, almost entirely European, has recently been calculated at between 18,240 and 24,240 pairs (Carter 2001), about 75 per cent higher than the estimate of Evans & Pienkowski (1991) even though the late 1990s saw reports of 'worrying' declines in each of the three stronghold countries, Germany, France and Spain (*eg* Seoane *et al* 2003, Mionnet 2004); much of the blame for such recent decreases has been directed at deliberate shooting and poisoning, agricultural intensification, and secondary poisoning by rodenticides.

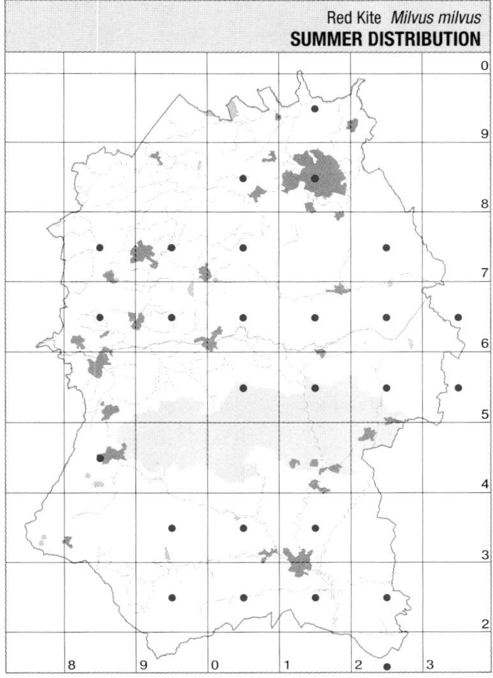

Figure 29. Red Kites *Milvus milvus* in Wiltshire: summer distribution 1995–2000 by 10-km squares, based on casual records, not 2-hour counts
Three breeding records have been downgraded to 'seen'

An ambitious conservation initiative to re-establish Red Kites widely in England

Table 42. Red Kites *Milvus milvus* in Wiltshire: totals by bird-months 1900–2000

Long-staying individuals inflate the monthly totals, particularly in autumn and winter, while spring records consist largely of birds flying over, especially since the national re-introduction scheme was started in 1989. The long first period 1900–88 preceded that scheme; the other two periods followed it, with 1999–2000 representing the years of Wiltshire's recolonisation

	Jan	Feb	Mar	Apr	May	Jun	Jul	Aug	Sep	Oct	Nov	Dec
1900–88 (89 years: total 23)	0	0	5	5	4	0	1	2	2	2	0	2
1989–98 (10 years: total 123)	3	12	11	15	21	11	8	10	5	8	9	10
1999–00 (2 years: total 99)	7	13	13	5	9	5	6	8	8	7	8	10
Combined	10	25	29	25	34	16	15	20	15	17	17	22

and Scotland began in 1989. Fledglings from Germany and Spain (initially, some also from Sweden) were imported, under licence, and by the end of 2000 a total of 395 had been released at five sites; as a result, England and Scotland respectively held 131 and 40 breeding pairs in the summer of 2000 (Wotton *et al* 2002a). Since those schemes started in 1989, the number of Wiltshire records has increased dramatically (figure 28). Juveniles from releases in the Chilterns began wintering in the county from the early 1990s, and summer records also increased in the late 1990s, the latter possibly also involving wanderers from Wales, so that this species was found widely across Wiltshire during 1995–2000 (figure 29). After a probable nesting record in 1999, the first breeding was confirmed in 2000: two young fledged, although one was later found dead, probably electrocuted; food remains and pellets at the nest showed, in order of frequency, rabbits, hares, corvids and brown rats to be the main foods, often scavenged as road casualties (*Hobby*).

In winter, young Red Kites tend to remain settled in a single area, centred on one or more communal roosts. Almost all long-distance movements are undertaken in autumn or spring, the months of April and May producing a peak in dispersal activity by one-year-old non-breeders (Carter 2001) – a pattern which is also suggested by table 42. During 1998/99 at least seven wintered in Wiltshire, and the winter survey 1998–2000 recorded the species in six tetrads across five 10-km squares, with an estimated total of 12 individuals. Extending this to the end of 2000, at least 20 were found in the county during the whole of that year, including the confirmed breeding pair and up to three more possible nesting pairs.

Red Kites generally nest within about 15 km of their birthplace and in England and Scotland most start to breed when two years old, but in Wales 'there is a significantly greater spread [and] many do not breed until their third or fourth year' (Carter 2001). Although those in Wales are largely sedentary, juveniles often move southeast to spend their first winter in England, as has also been shown by two ringing recoveries in Wiltshire in June 1969 (long dead) and December 1987. It is likely, too, that some winter records, especially in eastern England, involve Continental immigrants (*1981–84 Winter Atlas*), as did probably the 1988 spring influx. All released Red Kites, and a proportion of their offspring, are wing-tagged: three in Wiltshire have originated from re-introductions in the Midlands and another was the Suffolk-bred offspring of a migrant pair of Continental origin.

(See also page 724.)

PEC

Sponsored by Kay Austin

White-tailed Fish-eagle
Haliaeetus albicilla

Former vagrant (8–10 records, last 1935), breeds north/east Europe, reintroduced Scotland

Formerly more widespread in Europe west to Ireland and France, White-tailed Fish-eagles have long suffered serious decreases through persecution and pollution, and are now found mainly east of a line from western Norway to the Balkans. They still breed in Iceland, however, and, as a result of re-introductions and protection, are now again nesting in Scotland and some parts of central Europe where they had long been extinct. Even so, the total population of Europe, excluding Russia, is no more than 2500 pairs (*EBCC Atlas*). The breeding range otherwise extends west to Greenland, and right across the northern half of Asia, though there the species is only a summer visitor. In northwest Europe it is primarily coastal, but elsewhere it also favours large lakes and rivers; its diet includes fish, carrion, birds and mammals.

Once breeding probably in many parts of Great Britain, these large raptors – which, despite their huge size, are not true eagles but more closely related to kites and Old World vultures – were in long-term decline from Anglo-Saxon times because of persecution and the loss of forests and marshes. Historically, over 100 British eyries were known; the last recorded nesting in England was in the 1790s and the species became extinct in Scotland after 1916 (*1875–1900 Atlas*). Archaeological remains, dating from the late Neolithic near Stonehenge (Maltby 1990) and from the Bronze or Iron Ages at Potterne (Locker 2000), support a prehistoric presence in Wiltshire

A small population has now been re-established in west Scotland by the release of Norwegian juveniles during 1975–85 and 1993–98: in 2000, 19 pairs fledged 12 young from eight active nests (*RBBP*). Wanderers from the Continent, mostly immatures, sometimes cross the North Sea in autumn and winter: 25 were recorded in Great Britain and Ireland during 1958–98 (*BBRC*).

The county's own records are much older: the first was trapped at Stonehill Wood, near Minety, on 11 December 1841 (Marsh 1842–62); the next three were all shot, at Littlecote (*Berkshire Chronicle* January 1847, Anon 1847), at Savernake in 1859 (im Thurn 1870), and at Bedwyn Brail on 1 March 1864, the last having been seen in the Savernake area for two weeks (Rowlands 1864); and a fifth was found near Salisbury in 1887 (White 1887a). The one at Littlecote was first reported as a Golden Eagle, but was subsequently correctly identified. Smith (1887) also referred to two reports of single 'eagles', which he took to be this species: the first, from a mid 18th century edition of the *Salisbury Journal*, concerned an eagle that roosted for one night on the spire of Salisbury Cathedral; the other, related to him by 'a highly respected Rector of a Wiltshire parish', involved a similar incident in 1828 or 1829. Next, Hony (1915a) added a White-tailed Fish-eagle seen at Salisbury on 31 January 1897 (*Salisbury Journal* 1897) and others shot at Grovely Wood in March 1905 (*Wilts County Mirror* 1905, Anon 1905) and Marden on 24 February 1909 (*Marlborough Times* 1909, Goddard 1909), all originally reported in local newspapers but considered acceptable records.

Three reports of 'eagles' (published in *WANHM* as 'possibly' or even 'probably' Golden Eagles) in 1929 and 1930 seem most likely, in view of their 'autumn', April and June dates, to have been mis-identified Common Buzzards, which in those days were no more than 'occasional visitors' to Wiltshire. But there seems no reason to question an 'Eagle, probably White-tailed' – considered 'definite' by the observer, though treated with slightly more caution editorially – that was watched 'playing with a heron whilst high up on the wing' over Fonthill in March 1935, particularly as a White-tailed Fish-eagle was 'being seen many times in Dorset' at that time (*WANHM*, see also Prendergast & Boys 1983).

PEC

Marsh Harrier

Circus aeruginosus

Migrant, has summered, breeds Europe (local Britain), winters Mediterranean/Africa

The largest and easily the commonest of the harriers in Europe, this medium-sized raptor is, as its name implies, associated particularly with wetlands, although to an increasing extent sometimes also nesting in adjacent crops. Its breeding range extends right across Eurasia from Iberia to the Pacific, though the eastern populations are sometimes treated as a separate species (*eg* Simmons 2000). In Europe, Marsh Harriers nest in most countries from the Mediterranean to the Baltic, though the highest numbers are centred on the large reedbeds of the central plain from eastern France, the Netherlands and Germany to the Ukraine and south-central Russia. Those from north, central and east Europe are migratory, leaving for the Mediterranean region and Africa by October and returning in late March and April, but the breeding populations of south and west Europe are more sedentary, or dispersive and nomadic.

In the 18th and early 19th centuries, Marsh Harriers probably bred in many English and Welsh counties but loss of habitat through drainage, and also persecution, must have severely reduced numbers and distribution (*1875–1900 Atlas*). They were described in 1814 as common in Berkshire in the marshes around Newbury (Lamb 1880), and in neighbouring Oxfordshire 'may have bred in those days upon Otmoor' (Aplin 1889). Yet in 1899 a nest in Norfolk – at which the adults were trapped before any eggs were laid (Taylor *et al* 1999) – was to be the last in Great Britain until single pairs bred again in that county in 1911, 1915 and 1921, then up to four pairs from 1927 onwards (Witherby *et al* 1938–41). Suffolk was not recolonised until the 1940s (Payn 1978), but in the 1940s and early 1950s the species bred in four other counties west to Anglesey and Dorset (Nicholson 1957). Another decline in the later 1950s and 1960s probably resulted mainly from the effects of organochlorine pesticides, although, particularly in the Norfolk Broads, it was also variously attributed to disturbance by holidaymakers and by introduced coypus (*1968–72 Atlas*). By 1971 only a single pair remained, in Suffolk, but the restrictions on pesticides resulted in a remarkable recovery, with a mean year-on-year increase of 19·6 per cent through the next two decades (Underhill-Day 1984, *1988–91 Atlas*).

Most breeding is still in east coast counties of England, particularly East Anglia, although some pairs have now recolonised Somerset, Lancashire and Scotland. The species has

Table 43. Marsh Harriers *Circus aeruginosus* in Wiltshire: five-year totals 1971–2000

	1971–75	1976–80	1981–85	1986–90	1991–95	1996–00
Birds	0	4	1	7	16	21

Table 44. Marsh Harriers *Circus aeruginosus* in Wiltshire: totals by bird-months 1971–2000

	Jan	Feb	Mar	Apr	May	Jun	Jul	Aug	Sep	Oct	Nov	Dec
Records	0	0	0	8	16	5	4	10	13	0	0	0

also increased again in most other European countries, except in the south, and more are wintering in England, particularly in Kent and Norfolk (Clarke 1995, Taylor *et al* 1999). In 2000 the British breeding population was put at between 183 and 206 'pairs' (though males are sometimes bigamous or even polygynous) and at least 377 young were reared (*RBBP*); these figures are far higher than any in the preceding 150 or more years, but they are still minute compared with the calculated 26,000 to 34,700 pairs in Europe, excluding Russia, in the early 1990s (*EBCC Atlas*).

Smith (1887) wrote, 'Formerly it was not by any means uncommon…Montagu [1802] mentions Wiltshire as one of its haunts in his day; but now I seldom hear of its appearance'. He referred to three birds in the Rawlence collection and was able to list only four other 19th century records, all in the ten years from 1869 to 1878.

The first Wiltshire report in the 20th century was of one 'identified, "quartering a hillside" at Longleat on 25 May 1957 (G Bright): the observation has subsequently been ignored' (Ferguson-Lees 1984), but the observer was experienced and there seems no reason to question it. The next two records coincidentally happened to be that century's earliest and latest respectively, at Braydon Pond on 27 March 1960 and at Wylye Down on 23 November 1963; of the six during 1960–79, including those two, three each were at downland and valley or wetland sites and three each in spring and autumn; the only one that lingered was an immature on SPTA (West) from 29 August to 1 September 1979, and the first in 1960 was the only adult male (*WANHM*). Of eight during 1980–89, most were immatures in April–July and September and the majority at downland sites (Palmer 1991). After that, the numbers of records began to grow (table 43), in line with the national increase, but the species was still unpredictable and none was seen in the county in 1987 or 1996. There have been quite a few records in April and June–July, but May and August–September are the best months to see this harrier in Wiltshire (table 44), most regularly at CWP and often also on the chalk downs. As most nesting Marsh Harriers have eggs by the end of April, many of these migrants must be immatures. Relatively few adult males have been recorded, but one stayed on SPTA, in a downland area of cereals and grass with a large river nearby, from at least 27 June to 20 July 1989 and a first-year female was also seen in the same place on 27 June and again on the 29th. Three years earlier, a first-year male similarly resided on SPTA from 27 June to 13 July 1986. Although no reedbeds in the county are large enough to be suitable for breeding, the cereals and rough grasslands of the chalk downs provide ample habitat for hunting. One found dead near Upavon on 16 August 1958 had been ringed as a nestling at Poole Harbour (Dorset) on 10 June that year, whereas three in September 2000, the last on the 30th, were associated with a remarkable influx of Honey-buzzards (*qv*) from Fenno-Scandia.

PEC

Hen Harrier

Circus cyaneus

Scarce and local winter visitor, has bred, breeds Wales/Scotland/Europe

Over their range as a whole, Hen Harriers breed widely in open country right across Eurasia from Ireland to Kamchatka; and two similar species replace this one in North and South America respectively (Ferguson-Lees & Christie 2001). An estimated 8300 to 10,800 pairs nest in Europe, excluding Russia, the biggest numbers in Fenno-Scandia and, perhaps more surprisingly from the British angle, France (*EBCC Atlas*). North and east European birds mostly migrate to winter south of the Baltic, a few reaching as far as North Africa.

In Great Britain, Hen Harriers breed on upland moors and winter mostly on lowland heaths, downlands and wetlands. They used to nest in a number of areas of lowland England until the early 19th century (Watson 1977). Thereafter, intense persecution led to their extinction in England, Wales and mainland Scotland between 1850 and 1900, only Orkney and the Outer Hebrides ('very few') still holding regular breeding populations by the beginning of the 20th century and indeed up to the 1939–45 War (*1875–1900 Atlas*, Witherby *et al* 1938–41). Pairs returned to the Scottish mainland in 1939, however, after which the reduction in persecution during the War no doubt helped the recovery. Southern Scotland, northern England and north Wales had been recolonised by the 1970s, and the national breeding population has remained stable since then at about 570 pairs (DETR 2000), but including only 19 in England and 28 in Wales. Nevertheless, illegal persecution persists, especially on grouse moors.

In the 19th century Hen Harriers bred, or were reputed to have done so, in most of Wiltshire's neighbouring counties (*1875–1900 Atlas*), but, with the hindsight of 20th century status, the possibility of confusion with Montagu's Harrier has regularly raised doubts. In Berkshire and Oxfordshire, the Hen Harrier's 'breeding was suggested by some authorities' in the 18th and 19th centuries (Lamb 1880, Hewitt 1911); in particular, it 'was believed to have bred at Compton in 1844' (Hewitt 1844); but 'We will never know whether some of the early records in Oxfordshire refer to this species, or the Montagu's Harrier' (Brucker *et al* 1992). In Gloucestershire, the Hen Harrier was described 'as a former resident on open ground in the Forest of Dean "before the re-planting... ", about 1800; also on the Cotswolds where "it was still frequent about 1850", although perhaps not still nesting there' (Swaine 1982). In Somerset, the species 'probably bred fairly regularly on Exmoor, at least until about 1910; breeding possibly occurred about 1920 and in 1925'; a pair was also seen on Sedge Moor in May 1934 (Palmer & Ballance 1968). In Dorset, 'Breeding was claimed in the last [19th] century, and perhaps in 1922, but confusion with Montagu's Harrier is possible' (Prendergast & Boys 1983). In Hampshire, several nests in the New Forest, the last in 1893, were detailed by Kelsall & Munn (1905), but Cohen (1963) stated 'there is practically no evidence to substantiate' breeding and evidently believed that all the records referred to Montagu's; later, Clark & Eyre (1993) considered the subject 'open to debate'.

Because Hen Harriers now nest in Great Britain only from the uplands of Scotland south to north Wales, and are otherwise winter visitors to southern England – whereas Montagu's are annual, if rare and erratic, summer visitors to south and southeast England – it is easy to assume that any grey harriers breeding in the south in the late 19th and early 20th centuries are more likely to have been Montagu's. But it must also be borne in mind that – farther south still, just across the English Channel – some 7800 to 11,200 pairs of Hen Harriers nest throughout much of France (Millon & Bretagnolle 2004). The following records from Wiltshire should be considered against that background.

First, im Thurn (1876) wrote that 'I have seen a specimen of this bird, which was shot in Savernake Forest, in 1862. Six are said to have been seen together on Clench Common about 1864; one of which was procured…' – suggesting either a roost or a family party. Next, Morres (1878–85) noted that 'I can speak from personal observation, as scarcely a winter passes without its visiting our parish [Britford]…They are frequently to be met with also on the large downs between this and Cranbourne Chase, and without doubt occasionally breed there; and, owing to the great gorse covers which are to be found on many of our downs, they seem likely, I think, to hold their own amongst us, better than most other of our larger birds of prey'. Smith (1887), too, wrote of the Hen Harrier that 'Not many years since, this species used to breed regularly on Salisbury Plain; and it is not improbable that a nest still may be found in suitable localities; but that it is surely, if gradually, being exterminated from Wilts is only too certain'. He also reported that 'Mr. Stratton often saw them on the downs above Lavington, and thought it probable they bred every year in the gorse near him, but as the gorse was being taken up, the bird would probably soon be driven away'. Smith listed records of Hen Harriers in nine localities on Salisbury Plain and four each from south of the Plain and on the Marlborough Downs, but he gave the month in only one case (October) and, with the possible exception of 'a pair…killed in Clarendon Park in 1823', these seem likely to have related to non-breeders.

Hony (1915a) was able to cite only two additional records – the first shot on Urchfont Downs on 30 December 1879 and the second seen at Downton on 29 April 1912 – and the inaugural 'Report on the Birds of Wiltshire for 1929' summarised the status of the Hen Harrier as 'Formerly seen fairly frequently on the Plain, now a rare visitor', yet added that in that particular year they had been 'reported on Salisbury Plain, summer and autumn' (*WANHM*). Moreover, in 1936 'three records of breeding in the county were authenticated, two being on the New Forest borders and one on the Plain' (*WANHM*). CMR Pitman, who was evidently quite familiar with Montagu's Harriers, having reported that species nesting just outside the county boundary in 1932, was the editor of the annual report in *WANHM* at that time, but neither Peirson (1959) nor Buxton (1981) even mentioned these records. (Both also omitted many observations published on other species in the 1930s.) Although such records may seem remarkable, Hen Harriers certainly nested in Surrey in 1932 (Nethersole-Thompson 1992) and, as already noted, perhaps in Dorset and Somerset too in the 1920s or 1930s; Witherby *et al* (1938–41) also added 'in last thirty years Cornwall…and possibly Devon'.

A partial search in local museums has failed to produce any eggs of Hen Harriers from Wiltshire, Dorset or Hampshire, or any specimens taken in the breeding season, though there are some of each of Montagu's (P Combridge); but the words of Smith (1887) indicate that breeding had ceased before the last quarter of the 19th century and so before the heyday of collecting. It seems clear, however, that Hen Harriers became little more than uncommon winter visitors to Wiltshire from the late 1800s, apart from the above suggestions of breeding in 1929 and, more firmly, 1936 (and see page 724).

Long known as a scarce and mainly coastal winter visitor to East Anglia and southeast England, this species suddenly improved in status from the mid 1970s, at the same time as an increase in the Dutch breeding population; and there was a large influx during severe winter weather early in 1979 (*1981–84 Winter Atlas*). In Wiltshire, Hen Harriers had been scarcer in winter than Montagu's Harriers in summer through the 1950s and early 1960s, and were not recorded annually until 1967 (figure 30). The increase in the 1970s was also no doubt influenced by the formation of MoD Conservation Groups that provided access to areas of SPTA previously closed to birdwatchers. By 1981, Buxton could state that the species had become a 'regular winter visitor to more open and upland areas of the county from October to May. In recent years the total winter population has been at least twelve and probably nearer twenty individuals, and it is commoner now than in the 19th and much of the 20th centuries. Roosts have been located from time to time and up to seven birds have been observed at one of these'.

Since then, roosts have become annual on SPTA, at least three being in use in any one winter and the highest single count of individuals standing at 13 (figure 30). The county's first roost was located in October 1975, in a young conifer plantation at Grovely Wood, though the record cards for *Hobby* show that that site has not been used since 1984. Another was found in rough grassland on SPTA (West) in December 1977 (Turner 1978), but has since not proved to be annual, unlike SPTA (Centre) where roosts have been in use in every winter since 1979 (*eg* Howells 1986a, b, Castle 1993, Castle & Clarke 1995, *Hobby*). Others were located on SPTA (East) in 1987 and 1994 and, in southern Wiltshire, in a set-aside field in 1997/98. Clarke *et al* (1997) showed that Hen Harriers using the main Hampshire roost in the northern New Forest rely heavily

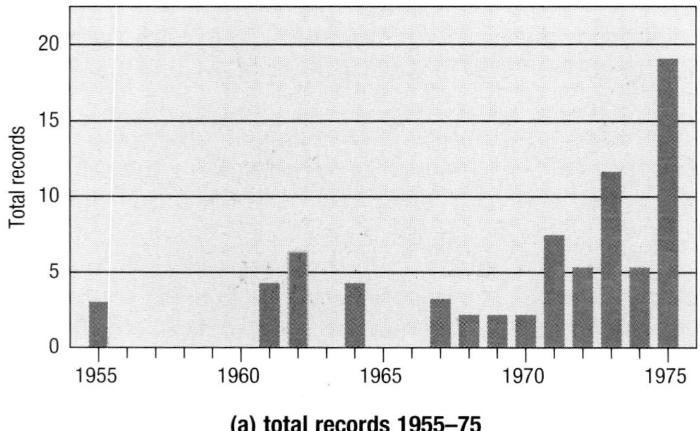

(a) total records 1955–75

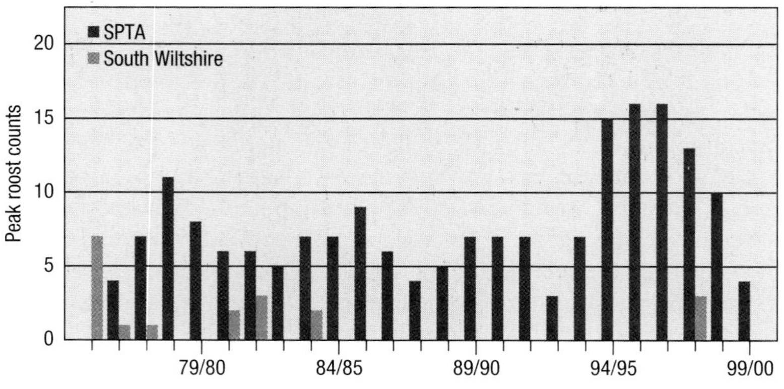

(b) maximum winter counts 1975/76–1999/00

Figure 30. Hen Harriers *Circus cyaneus* in Wiltshire

'Maximum winter counts' are the sum of the highest counts of males and of ring-tails (these will usually have occurred on different dates during the course of a winter)

on farmland for hunting. Most of the available farmland in that area lies within Wiltshire, which, as most other roosts in the New Forest have collapsed, is now of great importance in maintaining numbers there (P Combridge). The winter tetrad survey during 1998–2000 suggested that Hen Harriers were foraging widely over the whole of Salisbury Plain and, separately – possibly from the main Hampshire roost – over the downlands south of Salisbury.

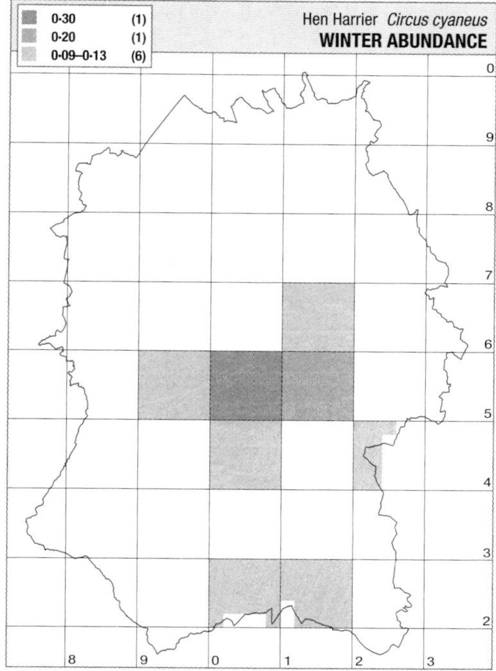

The availability of safe roost sites is a major influence on winter distribution, and SPTA – the largest unbroken expanse of chalk grassland in northwest Europe – provides ample choice, though the harriers spend much of the day hunting over farmland, especially weedy winter stubbles that attract flocks of passerines. A wing-tagged individual using the Larkhill roost in 1996 was also seen on the Marlborough Downs, 14 km to the north – evidence of the size of the diurnal hunting range. Analysis of pellets from SPTA roosts found that small passerines, especially Sky Larks and Linnets, dominate the midwinter diet (Turner 1978, Castle & Clarke 1995). There is a switch to rabbits and brown hares in spring, presumably as the young become available. Small mammals also form an important element of the diet throughout the winter, although their annual abundance can vary considerably.

The species was recorded in only seven of Wiltshire's 33 core 10-km squares in 1998–2000, as against no fewer than 17 two decades earlier (*1981–84 Winter Atlas*), but in that previous national winter survey each 10-km square received about twice as much fieldwork. Eleven Hen Harriers were found in nine tetrads in 1998–2000, and extrapolation to allow for uncounted tetrads indicates a Wiltshire total of 26 – a significant proportion of the English winter population, estimated at 300 in early 1984 (mild winter) and 753 in early 1979 (hard weather influx) (*1981–84 Winter Atlas*). Indeed, the National Hen Harrier Winter Roost Survey 1983/84–1994/95 showed that, on average, the Larkhill roost holds 2·5 per cent of the national count in January and 2·7 per cent in March (see also Castle & Clarke 1995). Moreover, whereas there was a steady decline in winter numbers of Hen Harriers in Great Britain over the last decade of the 20th century (Clarke & Watson 1997), Wiltshire's share probably started to increase in the mid 1970s and then showed a clear increase from the mid 1990s (table 45). (It must be added, however, that the quality of roost count data depends very much on observer effort and expertise, which have not always been constant.)

Records of wing-tagged Hen Harriers seen in Wiltshire give some indication of the origins of the county's wintering population. These have included at least three and – if one male and one female in each of three successive winters were different individuals – possibly as many as seven from north Wales, now the nearest breeding area, during 1994–99. (Wing-tagging in Wales ended in 1995 and the tags last only up to four years.) In contrast, although the numbers marked in this way in Scotland are much larger, just two from Dumfriesshire and one from Grampian have been seen in Wiltshire. It may be

Table 45. Hen Harriers *Circus cyaneus* in Wiltshire: five-winter mean maxima and single highest count at SPTA (Centre) 1971–2000

	1971–75	1976–80	1981–85	1986–90	1991–95	1996–00	Peak count
Mean maximum	0	1	4	4	6	8	13 (1996)

that many of the Hen Harriers in Wiltshire originate from the Continent – either the Netherlands or Fenno-Scandia. The presence of grey males late into April and even May supports this theory, because the British nesters are in their breeding territories by then. As in other western areas of Great Britain, a significant proportion of the Hen Harriers roosting on Salisbury Plain are grey males; moreover, the majority of ringtails can be identified as immature males (Castle & Clarke 1995). First-winter males from Scotland are more likely to migrate than females and, travelling down the western side of Great Britain, many winter in southwest France and northwest Spain. There have been no recoveries or sightings of Welsh first-winter males within Wales, and their main wintering areas appear to be southern and eastern England and the Biscay coast of France (*Migration Atlas*). In at least four years since 1987, first-year males have spent the summer on SPTA; grey adults return from September.

(See also page 724.)

PEC

Sponsored by John Pollard in memory of Audrey Pollard

Montagu's Harrier

Circus pygargus

Scarce migrant, irregular breeder, summers Europe, winters Africa

Colonel George Montagu – 'the worthy ornithologist whose residence in this county [Wiltshire] we are proud to boast' (Smith 1887) – is best known for clarifying the then long-standing confusion between the two British harriers whose adult males are predominantly grey and all other plumages mostly brown with dark-banded (or 'ringed') tails. In the first edition of his *Ornithological Dictionary* (1802), published after he moved to Devon, he described a male shot in Wiltshire under the name 'Ash-coloured Falcon *Falco cineraceus*', though it later became generally known as 'Montagu's Harrier *Circus Montagui*'. The adult male, however, had already been depicted, and captioned '*Pygargus*', by Eleazar Albin in his *A Natural History of Birds* (1731–38) and, on the basis of that coloured plate, the Swedish naturalist Carl von Linné (Linnaeus) named it '*Falco Pygargus*' in the tenth edition of his *Systema Naturae* (1758) – which is why the binomial *pygargus* (with the *p* in lower case by later convention) now has priority. Yet Linnaeus did not distinguish the male Hen Harrier until 1766 and, even then, confusion about the taxonomic positions of the 'ringtail' females and juveniles of both species remained for over three decades. George Montagu's part in investigating the differences between the two (Montagu's and Hen), each including plumages of what had been regarded as a third species ('Ringtail Harrier'), is celebrated by the use of his name in the English vernacular. Incidentally, all plumages of Montagu's Harrier do also occur in a rare dark morph.

Long-distance migrants, Montagu's Harriers breed from western Europe and northwest Africa across to Mongolia, and winter in sub-Saharan Africa, parts of Arabia, and India. In Europe, the biggest numbers are in Iberia, France and Russia. They used to nest regularly in parts of southern and eastern England at the end of the 19th century (*1875–1900 Atlas*), but do so rather less now. Smith (1887) wrote that 'This species, which I believe to have bred pretty regularly in Wiltshire in days gone by, still occasionally is found nesting in the county'. He gave some details of two undated breeding records: a pair and two young shot and trapped at their nest in gorse on a rabbit warren above Fifield Bavant; and, in the Rawlence collection, a pair of adults and three young not a week old – 'two of which are white and the third blue [dark morph]' – from 'property belonging to Lord Bath'. Smith noted four other records of single specimens killed between 1841 and 1885, and added that the species 'has visited Erlestoke'. Hony (1915a) listed three more records, from 1858, 1905 and one, undated, of a female and 'a young bird', indicating breeding.

The British population was at a low ebb from the late 19th century to the beginning of the 1914–18 War, but then grew slowly to 15–25 pairs annually by the 1930s, these being scattered across East Anglia, southern England and south Wales. Numbers increased during and after the 1939–45 War, and estimates for the mid 1950s varied from 'up to 30 pairs' (*1988–91 Atlas*) to an earlier 'at least 40–50 pairs (and perhaps 70–80) pairs' (*1968–72 Atlas*, based on Nicholson 1957). In this period, the species nested as far north as north Wales, northeast England and even Scotland (*eg* Thom 1986).

Numbers of Montagu's Harriers then declined nationally from the late 1950s onward, and the population has been low and fluctuating ever since (*1988–91 Atlas*). Similar decreases occurred in much of northwest Europe, probably as a result of agricultural intensification (*EBCC Atlas*), though other factors may well have been involved. In particular, circumstantial evidence strongly suggests a link between numbers breeding in Great Britain and drought conditions in the winter quarters in the Sahel zone of Africa. In the 1950s Sahel rainfall was high, but after 1957 was consistently closer to the average, and analysis of the period 1966/67–1994/95 showed a strong correlation between annual rainfall in the western Sahel and numbers of British Montagu's Harrier nests the following summer (Clarke 2002). In addition, nearly half of all nest failures in Great Britain during 1900–83 were attributed to egg-collecting (*1988–91 Atlas*).

In Wiltshire, Peirson (1959) considered Montagu's Harrier to be 'A rare but regular summer visitor... never seems to have been at all common... very few pairs nest in the county probably every year'. One WANHS record card in 1962 remarked that, were it not illegally persecuted and killed off, this harrier would become a regular breeding species on Salisbury Plain. Yet Webber (1968) noted that the species was 'Not proved to have bred during the past fifteen years', and Buxton (1981) referred to 'central areas of Salisbury Plain and in the extreme south-east, south and south-west of the county... last known breeding record concerned two pairs using traditional sites during 1953'. Although the only published records of *nests* over the whole period related to 1946 (four eggs and later three young, of which at least two fledged) and 1949 (one egg and two young, which had already been ringed by someone else), apparently both at the same site in 'S. Wilts', Montagu's Harriers (usually one, two or three pairs) were regular in summer at up to three sites in every year during 1946–53 – a peak time in Great Britain as a whole (Nicholson 1957a) – and there were again summer records in 1960–61 (*WANHM*).

More recently, in 1982, a pair that was not actually proved to nest was the first in an intermittent series of attempts and some successes by single pairs (Clarke 1996, *Hobby*). In 1985 young hatched but died in wet weather; in 1993 three young fledged, in 1995 one and in 1998 four, the last from a nest in rye grass intended for silage. Three pairs nested in 2000, though only one, which raised either one or two young, was successful; the other two pairs began nesting late in the season, and perhaps for that reason failed at the egg stage. The species was present at additional localities during most of the 1990s without breeding being proved. In 1998, a first-year dark-morph female and, in 2000, a first-year dark-morph male were among 'visiting' Montagu's Harriers seen at breeding sites.

During the 1990s, peak years for young fledged in southern Britain were 1990 (20) and 1995 (26), whereas only 12 young were raised in 1999 and just seven or eight in 1998 and 2000 (*RBBP*). In this period the number of breeding females recorded varied from three to 12, a tiny total compared with estimates of up to 11,000 pairs in Europe excluding Russia (Ferguson-Lees & Christie 2001).

Until 1968, Montagu's Harriers in Great Britain nested largely in semi-natural habitats, but since then have switched almost entirely to arable crops, especially winter wheat, barley and oilseed rape (*1988–91 Atlas*); without active steps to protect such nests, many are destroyed by agricultural operations. In Wiltshire, likewise, they evidently used to breed in rough grass on downs and heathland, whereas all recent records have come from either winter-sown barley or hay in areas of mixed habitats on chalk downland. Their prey consists mainly of passerines and small mammals. Analyses showed the remains of Meadow Pipits in two-thirds of pellets collected at one Wiltshire nest and Sky Larks in four-fifths at another; also small mammals in a third of each (Clarke 2002).

Montagu's Harriers arrive in the county in April and early May, and lay eggs in the second half of May. During 1974–2000, the earliest recorded arrival date was 17 April 1999 and the latest departure 31 August 1992. Previously, the earliest and latest dates were 26 March 1956 and 10 October 1961, although confusion with Hen Harriers cannot be ruled out for these extremes.

(See also page 724.)

PEC

Sponsored by Paul Castle

Goshawk

Accipiter gentilis

Now breeds, rare resident/local vagrant in Britain since earlier escapes/releases

Although females can be as large as Common Buzzards, these powerful raptors are elusive and often difficult to observe except during their display-flights in late winter and early spring. Goshawks have a circumpolar distribution, from the tree line southward, and are found almost throughout continental Europe, where they are largely resident, though northern populations may be partial migrants, some individuals dispersing south in winter. They live almost exclusively in forest and woodland, but also hunt over open ground, especially in winter. Corvids and Wood Pigeons are their principal prey, but they eat other birds and also mammals, notably rabbits and squirrels.

Three large raptor bones found in an excavation at Great Bedwyn, and dated to 300–500 AD, 'correspond with the available reference specimens' of the Goshawk (Allison 1997), indicating presence of the species in Wiltshire in the distant past. Goshawks became extinct in southern England before the 16th century, through persecution and the young being taken for falconry; deforestation also reduced the available habitat. According to the *1875–*

1900 Atlas, they may have bred in Scotland until as late as 1883, and were more regularly seen on passage in the 19th century than subsequently, but most occasional reports and odd nesting attempts were assumed to involve falconers' escapes. Nevertheless, Witherby *et al* (1938–41) believed that a female shot in Yorkshire in May 1893, with a nest and four eggs, was 'probably' wild, and noted that most recorded vagrants were juveniles on the east coasts of England and Scotland, adding 'elsewhere, and especially in W., extremely rare'.

Against this background, it is not surprising that Smith (1887) knew of only two Wiltshire records – one seen by a falconer while flying his own Goshawk near Salisbury, originally recorded by Morres (1878–85), and the other shot at Compton Bassett in September 1885 – both likely to have been escapes. In Great Britain as a whole, Goshawks became regular breeders again from the mid 1960s as a result of deliberate releases and falconers' escapes. A rapid expansion took place in the 1970s, and they were widespread by the time of the *1988–91 Atlas*, primarily in state-owned forests in Wales, the Pennines, and the Southern Uplands of Scotland. Breeding pairs are resident and juveniles (particularly males) disperse locally, so that there has been only a gradual spread from established areas; nest-robbing by egg-collectors or falconers and direct persecution remain serious problems. In 2000 the known British total was 237–322 pairs (*RBBP*), a tiny number compared with a calculated population for all Europe (including Russia) of between 145,000 and 161,000 pairs (Ferguson-Lees & Christie 2001).

Apart from a 'large hawk, said to be of this species… seen by a keeper at Stourton' on 7 October 1931, the first Goshawks recorded in Wiltshire in the 20th century were at Woodford on 19 October 1953 (the observer was also 'fairly sure that he saw one a day or two earlier near Lake') and at Little Durnford on 6 October 1958 (all *WANHM*). A further seven reports, in various parts of the county, preceded the first proved breeding in 1979, when a nest containing a single chick was found; the tree had been climbed and it was thought that a local falconer might have taken any other young. The next evidence of breeding did not come for another 20 years, but then a pair raised two young in 1999 and three more in 2000. This pair nested in mixed woodland and appeared to stay in the vicinity throughout the year. Apart from the three confirmed breeding records, there were at least 13 other reports of Goshawks during 1979–2000, many of them wandering immatures away from likely breeding habitats, but others in suitable areas, some even involving displaying pairs. The validity of several of these observations must, however, be questioned: displaying Sparrowhawks are sometimes confused with Goshawks.

Goshawks are now well established in neighbouring Gloucestershire, breeding in the Forest of Dean (estimates range from five to 20 pairs) and found 'in eight sites in the Severn Vale and fifteen in the Cotswolds' (*Gloucestershire Bird Report* 2000).

(See also page 724.)

PEC

Sparrowhawk

Accipiter nisus

Common and widespread resident, little movement apart from juvenile dispersal

Unlike most of the county's other raptors, the Sparrowhawk is secretive, elusive, and usually only glimpsed dashing along close to cover; it is also the scapegoat blamed, often wrongly, for almost everything from Pheasant failures to the decline of farmland birds and, nowadays in the popular press, even the disappearance of the suburban House Sparrow. As is typical of bird-eating raptors, females are bigger than males – indeed, they can be two or three times the weight – which means that, whereas males mostly catch small birds in the range of 5–80g, females regularly take prey 120–230g and up to 500g (Newton 1986). Prey items recorded in *Hobby* have ranged from tits, finches and martins to Moorhen, Lapwing, Wood Pigeon, Collared Dove, Great Spotted Woodpecker and Rook. But the effect the Sparrowhawk has on bird populations is tiny compared with present or past effects of losses of habitat and food, pesticides and pollution.

Although generally inconspicuous, and often overlooked, one or both of a pair will soar or indulge in more complicated aerial displays over the nesting area in the early stages of the breeding cycle, mainly from late February to early May. They can at times also be noisy, and it is the periodically uttered and pitiful *peeay* of the fledged juvenile wanting to be fed that sometimes also provides ready evidence of breeding. Although this is such a secretive species, it is also one of the most intensively studied of all raptors. The long series of papers by JH Owen (1916–32) was a ground-breaker, ahead of its time, while the many publications of Ian Newton and his colleagues since 1976 have thrown much light on every aspect of this bird and helped the understanding of the population ecology of raptors in general (*eg* Newton 1979, 1986).

Widespread and common throughout much of Europe (as well as south to northwest Africa and the Canary Islands), Sparrowhawks also breed right across Asia, mainly in the northern half, to Kamchatka and Japan; excluding Russia, the European breeding population has been put in the range of 148,000 to 168,000 pairs (*EBCC Atlas*). Many northern continental populations move south for the winter, some reaching as far as northeast Africa, Arabia and southeast Asia. Some from Fenno-Scandia and the Low Countries occur on passage down the east coast of Great Britain in autumn, others along the south coast when returning in spring, but there is no evidence of such migrants reaching Wiltshire. The British population is almost entirely sedentary; juveniles disperse when they become independent, but recoveries of those ringed in southern England indicate that only 23 per cent move more than 20km (*Migration Atlas*). During 1965–2000 the total of Sparrowhawks ringed in Wiltshire was 199, the majority as chicks in the nest; 25 have been recovered, only nine of them more than 9km away and the most distant just 99km.

It is not easy to trace the history of the elusive Sparrowhawk in Wiltshire, but Smith (1887) considered that this species was 'sparingly met with throughout, nowhere very numerous, and nowhere entirely wanting... But it is not by any means so common with us now as it was thirty years ago'. Persistent persecution by gamekeepers and landowners doubtless kept the numbers down in some areas in the late 19th and early 20th centuries, though Sparrowhawk populations always managed to weather the effects of this better than those of many other birds of prey.

Indeed, by the first full county bird report in *WANHM* in 1929 the Sparrowhawk was still a 'fairly common resident, but unevenly distributed'. Thereafter, it received very few significant mentions over the next 30 years: in 1933 there was 'a pair in most big woods on the Plain' and elsewhere different observers contradictorily described it as both 'scarce' and 'common'; in 1946 there was an 'Increase reported from Marlborough and Salisbury Districts'; and in 1949 the seven localities where the species had been reported were simply listed. But in most years – whether being too elusive to find or too common to report – it had no mention at all. Then a nationwide decline of Sparrowhawks – caused by their accumulation of the organochlorine residues in the bodies of their bird prey (Prestt 1965, Newton 1986) – became evident during 1959–60, and over the next few years all Wiltshire records were listed or summarised in *WANHM*. In 1961, for example, none was found at Bratton where 'four years ago several could usually be seen', but the species was still 'frequently about Maiden Bradley' (a favourable situation that continued to be reported in subsequent years) and in 1962 was 'Noted as holding its own on Salisbury Plain'. After Sparrowhawks were given legal protection in 1963, the number of sightings increased steadily each year, perhaps partly because observers had become much more aware of their status, until by 1968 there were 'Numerous sight records, well spread over the county, obviously much commoner than in recent years' and successive reports in *WANHM* and *Hobby* continued thereafter in much the same vein. By 1987 numbers were considered 'to have stabilised after the increase of recent years', but the totals of pairs reported to WOS continued to grow almost every year up to 1994. After that they dropped away, perhaps partly because the tetrad survey deflected a proportion of reports during 1995–2000, though it should be noted that *BBS* data showed a 37 per cent decrease in southwest England during 1994–2000, despite numbers nationally having remained stable over that period. CBC results during 1968–99 – thus, from soon after the beginning of the post-pesticide period of recovery – indicated that the population had almost trebled over three decades (*BBWC*).

The *1968–72 Atlas* recorded Sparrowhawks in 31 of the county's 33 core 10-km squares but breeding in only 21; in both the *1988–91 Atlas* and the summer tetrad survey the corresponding figures were 33 and 30. The *1981–84 Winter Atlas* also found the species in all 33 squares, but the winter tetrad survey in only 30 (though there the three blanks may have been artefacts of the sampling technique).

At the tetrad level, on the other hand, the distribution can be seen to be much more patchy: Sparrowhawks were recorded in little more than half of all tetrads in summer, and evidence of breeding came from only just over a quarter of those. There is an obvious link with the wooded areas that they mostly inhabit, especially dense conifers but also broadleaved, particularly in the south and east where more extensive woodland is broken by open country. Nowadays, too, they nest in leafy suburbia and in urban parks and cemeteries – as is evidenced by the concentrations in and around Swindon and several other urban areas. On the other hand, the species appears to be largely absent from agricultural areas with only relatively small patches of broadleaved woodland in, for example, the central-north and the southwest. There is also something of a link with lakes and rivers, though that is probably more a result of linear hunting than of nesting.

Overall densities of 10–72 pairs/100 km^2 (or one 10-km square) have been found in Great Britain – though small areas of suitably rich woodland have held nests less than 0·5 km apart and as many as ten territories in 3 km^2 (Newton *et al* 1977, *BWP*). This suggests that 0·4–3 pairs per tetrad might be a reasonable range: on that basis Wiltshire could hold anything from an absurdly small 50 pairs (applying the lower figure to tetrads in which breeding was proved) to a no less absurdly large 1400 pairs (applying the higher figure to all tetrads in which the species was seen). As shown by the summer abundance map, one sixth of all the tetrads in which Sparrowhawks were recorded in the course of 2-hour counts involved 2–5 sightings, which suggests that, in those areas at least, the population may now be near its limit, though non-breeders are likely to involve anything up to half the total. By considering the areas of woodland of appropriate age in different altitude zones in Britain against the known relationship between nest-spacing and altitude, Newton (1986) calculated the maximum number of pairs likely to be able to nest in Great Britain to be about 32,000. On a purely proportional basis, without taking account of the area of woodland in the county, Wiltshire's 33 core 10-km squares with breeding evidence might thus conceivably hold a population of, at most, 485 pairs. The highest number of possible breeding pairs reported to *Hobby* in a single year before the tetrad survey (and thus not the result of systematic coverage) was 90 in 1994. The total of tetrads in which breeding evidence was obtained over the six summers was 124, but the

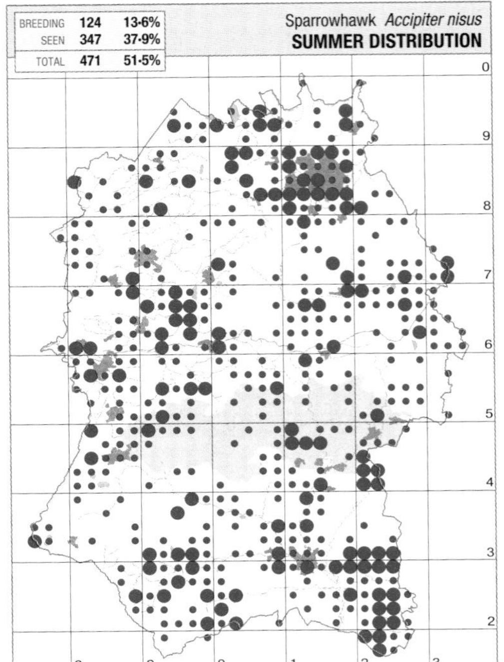

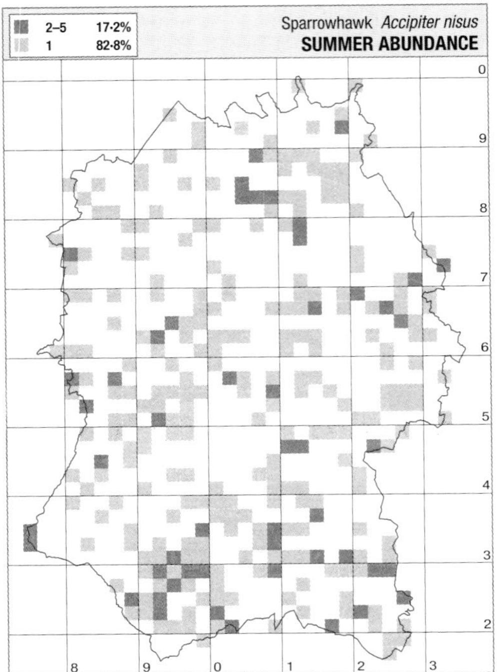

number of Sparrowhawks recorded in the summer 2-hour counts was 357, which should suggest that at least 200 breeding adults were seen, probably representing a similar number of pairs. It is difficult to know what proportion of the nesting population of this species in a tetrad is likely to be recorded within two hours, but on the basis of these calculations it seems fair to suggest that Wiltshire holds somewhere in the range of 200–500 pairs.

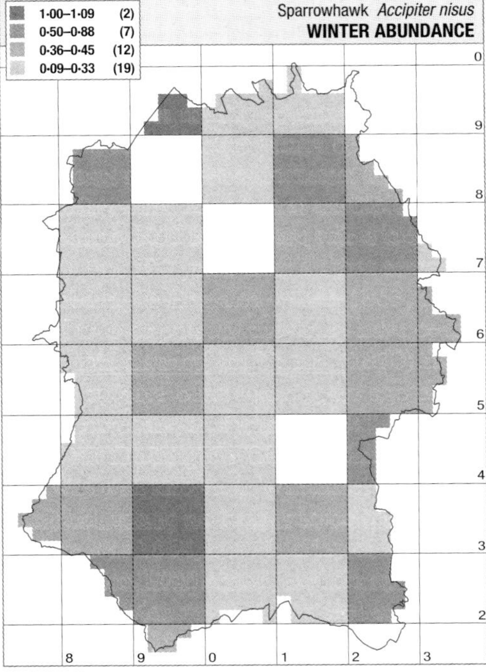

The 2-hour counts in winter yielded a total of only 152 Sparrowhawks, in just over a quarter of the sample of 443 tetrads surveyed. Extrapolation then gives a county estimate of only 285, whereas one would expect at least the early winter population, including both sedentary adults and the previous season's now wandering juveniles, to be higher than that of summer. This merely serves further to illustrate the elusiveness of these raptors, especially at a time of year when they are not displaying and are quite silent. But it is particularly in winter that individuals that live in or near towns and villages have learnt that potential prey congregates at bird-tables. The winter map reflects the summer one to some extent, with the higher densities in the east and southwest, but also, much more surprisingly, the far northwest (though not in the 10-km square that includes CWP, where easy pickings might be expected); the three blank squares are probably anomalous, unless the breeding population in the eastern part of Salisbury Plain, north of Amesbury, moves out for the winter.

IJF-L

Sponsored by Judith Hiller in memory of George F Hiller

Common Buzzard

Buteo buteo

Widespread and steadily increasing resident, also much wandering by non-breeders

With its vast range across temperate Eurasia from Iberia to Japan, not forgetting various island forms from the eastern Atlantic to the western Pacific, the Common Buzzard is one of the world's most numerous birds of prey, with a population of, probably, at least four million pairs, of which between 371,000 and 472,000 have been estimated in Europe, excluding Russia (*EBCC Atlas*); it is also one of the most individually variable in appearance, from largely white through rufous to the commonest brown, or even almost black (Ferguson-Lees & Christie 2001). In Wiltshire, where it was virtually extinct for some 50 years in the late 19th and early 20th centuries, it is now generally the most visible raptor, soaring on broad wings or hunting invertebrates on ploughed ground.

British Buzzards do best in farmland areas with grassy slopes broken up by scrub, timbered hedges and small woods. In Wiltshire, the favoured sites for their substantial stick nests are tall woodland or ancient hedgerow trees, often ivy-covered. Yet the distribution depends not only on small woods with adjacent pastures, but also on historical factors.

Numbers and distribution have changed greatly over the past 250 years, and fluctuations in Wiltshire reflect the national picture. In the 1700s Common Buzzards nested almost throughout Great Britain, but then the excessive practices of game preservation led to all-out persecution of any birds with hooked bills. By 1865 the British range was much smaller than today and, though a small residual population possibly still then remained in Wiltshire, Smith (1887) was able to give dates for only six records in the preceding 20 years and any others before 1930 (see below) are likely to have been just wanderers.

By 1915, British Buzzards had been cut back to a narrow broken strip from west Scotland south patchily to mid Wales, Devon and Cornwall (Moore 1957), and the estimate then of 12,000 pairs was later revised down to between 8000 and 10,000 (Tubbs 1974, *1968–72 Atlas*). But the nadir had been reached: increases in pasturage helped turn the tide, other priorities made gamekeeping irrelevant during two world wars, and attitudes to raptors were beginning to change. Buzzards built up slowly and started to spread. Where they extended into richer habitats, mostly in the lowlands, they fledged larger broods and the population increased more rapidly.

After single records in Wiltshire in 1918 and 1919 (*WANHM*), sightings became more regular in the southwest in the 1920s (Webber 1994), but even 1929 produced only three autumn-spring observations of what was still regarded as an 'occasional visitor' (*WANHM*). From June to August 1930 a pair frequented Lydiard Park and the following year four birds were seen there during the same months; in 1932, after instances of breeding in Hampshire just over the border, a nest was built and lined in Wiltshire but then deserted;

in 1934, five nests were found and breeding was suspected at two other sites, mainly in the Fonthill area or south and east of Salisbury; by 1936, the species was 'Definitely increasing throughout the county. Many breeding records have come to hand' (*WANHM*).

Things continued at similar levels in the late 1940s, and more landowners and gamekeepers were realising that rabbits and rodents form the species' main prey, but the problems were not over. In the 1950s and 1960s, organochlorine pesticides affected many raptors at upper ends of food chains; and for Buzzards this was compounded by the crash of the rabbit population through myxomatosis over several years from 1954. Nationally in that period, some Buzzards died from starvation and many more did not nest. In Wiltshire, in 1956: 'One definite record of nesting…no confirmation of successful rearing of young…a young bird almost fully fledged but not yet able to fly and weak for lack of food was picked up…Several observers reported that birds were seen less frequently'; there were two breeding records in 1957, but only one in 1958 when otherwise only 'several reports of birds seen throughout the year' (*WANHM*).

Wiltshire's Buzzards showed signs of recovery in 1959 when it was likely that at least seven pairs nested, possibly up to 12, but numbers apparently fluctuated through the 1960s, with records of confirmed breeding varying from none to, more usually, three to five or more with such comments as 'sightings widespread throughout most of county' in 1964 (*WANHM*). Prestt (1965), in his review of the British breeding status of various raptors, showed this species as 'local' in Wiltshire in 1963 and any change since 1956 as 'slightly negative'.

By the *1968–72 Atlas*, however, the species was breeding in 11 of the county's 33 core 10-km squares, and probably or possibly in another 15; that total of 26 'occupied' core squares was matched by the *1981–84 Winter Atlas*. Palmer (1991) demonstrated an increase to 45 recorded pairs during the 1980s. By the *1988–91 Atlas* Buzzards were found breeding or probably breeding in all but two of the core squares, and a total of at least 54 pairs was nesting in Wiltshire. Since then, numbers have risen rapidly: over 90 pairs estimated in 1992 (Webber 1994) and 'surely...approaching 200 pairs' in 1996 (*Hobby*). These higher figures were partly due to more extensive fieldwork, not least during the tetrad survey, but Buzzards are certainly on the increase in southern, central and northeast England, and in south and east Scotland (Clements 2000, 2002): there was a 46 per cent increase in England as a whole during 1994–2000 – although the equivalent figure for the southwest was only 19 per cent, suggesting the population here is nearing saturation (*BBWC*).

The tetrad surveys found breeding evidence in 32 of the 33 core squares, and winter presence in all of them. The summer distribution map indicates breeding in a quarter of all tetrads, and birds seen in a further half. Many of the latter, sometimes in tetrads without suitable nest-sites, will have involved either wandering non-breeders or soaring pairs from adjacent tetrads, but the winter map shows a very similar pattern. Adults in areas of low density may range over as much as 2–3 km^2, but nesting territories are often only 50–260 ha in extent and a mean density for optimum Buzzard habitat in Great Britain has been calculated at 1 pair/1·6 km^2 (see discussion and references in *BWP*), so it is not surprising that many tetrads (4 km^2) hold more than one pair, some even three or four.

On this basis, Wiltshire's 3485 km^2 could easily now be supporting 400 pairs: an average of eight to ten pairs per 10-km square, or one pair per two or three tetrads. The summer abundance map indicates that this figure is exceeded in many wooded parts in the south, where there may even be as many as 25 pairs per 10-km square, and probably in much of the western and east-central areas. But Buzzards are scarcer in the far northeast and on the Marlborough Downs – not surprisingly, because much of the recolonisation has been from the southwest – and there are also gaps on Salisbury Plain, where trees are few, and along the Kennet valley.

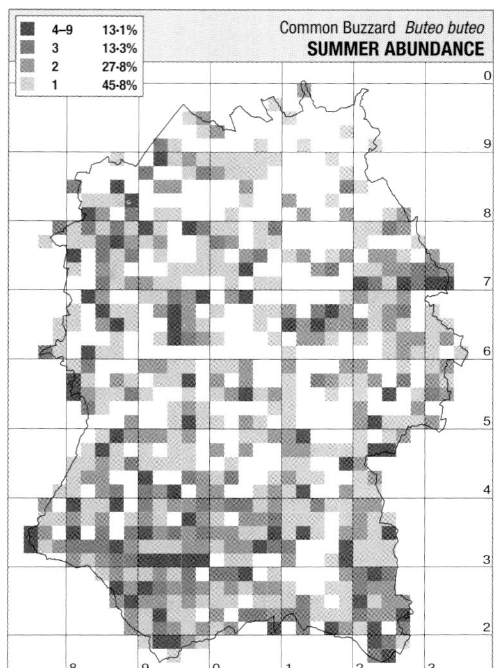

The position is complicated, however. The total of individual Buzzards recorded during 2-hour tetrad counts in Wiltshire in the six summers was 1175 and the extrapolated total for the two winters was 1287. R Prytherch, after comparing these figures and the maps with data from his 75 km^2 study area southwest of Bristol, has estimated the Wiltshire population by 2000 at a minimum of 385 breeding pairs – possibly considerably more – but has also drawn attention to the conclusion by others that there are likely to be as many wandering non-breeders as nesting birds. In Dorset, Kenward *et al* (2000) found a ratio of three non-breeders to each pair with eggs, but, as they took no account of established pairs that failed early or did not lay, a figure of less than two wanderers for each established pair seems more probable.

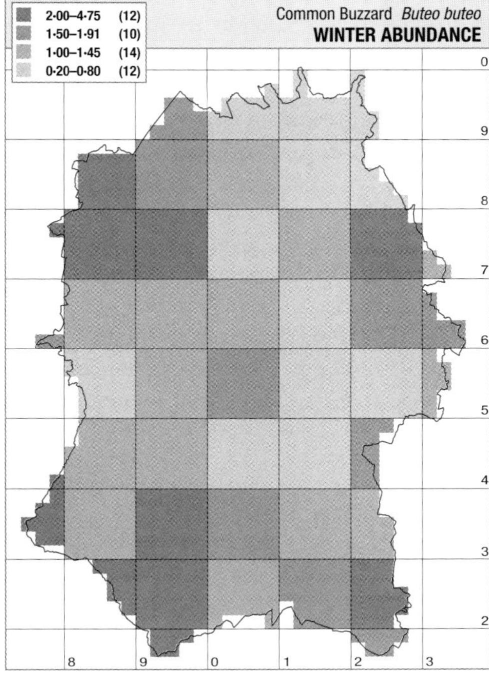

Palmer (1991) believed that migrants were regular through Wiltshire on passage, 'especially in October with birds moving south and west'; and Buzzards over Swindon, often juveniles, have been assumed to be on passage, while a trickle is sometimes evident moving southwest along downland scarps in October, but these are much more likely to be wanderers and any true migration must be on a tiny scale: adults in Great Britain are essentially sedentary, most remaining in their home ranges all year, while immatures wander only as far as they need to establish territories. None of 31 Buzzards ringed in Wiltshire during 1965–2000 has been recovered, but nationally three-quarters of recoveries show movements under 50 km and very few over 100 km (Picozzi & Weir 1976). Only three of more than 500 recoveries of ringed Buzzards have involved movements to or from the European mainland, and the radio-tracking of 114 juveniles confirmed that migration is rare in the British population; it is difficult to assess the origins of the regular winter influxes of Buzzards on the east coast (*Migration Atlas*).

In contrast, east European and Asiatic Buzzards do travel enormous distances, even down to southern Africa, but, in general terms, few cross the North Sea into Great Britain, where the winter distribution is broadly similar to that of summer (*1981–84 Winter Atlas*); in September 2000, however, 'substantial numbers' of this species did accompany the exceptional influx of Honey-buzzards (*qv*) (Fraser & Rogers 2002), and eight Buzzards seen passing over Swindon from the northeast in two hours on 8 October may have been some of these (PE Castle).

The single long-accepted British record of the highly migratory subspecies *vulpinus*, or 'Steppe Buzzard', which breeds from Finland and east Ukraine eastward, was a juvenile shot at Everleigh, Wiltshire, in September 1864 (Gould 1873, *Ibis* 1876: 366; 1878: 118). Recent examinations of the specimen, however – in the Natural History Museum, Tring (Hertfordshire) – have shown that, on current knowledge, the possibility of its being from the intermediate population of north Fenno-Scandia south to west Ukraine, or even an exceptional individual of the nominate race, cannot be excluded (Harrap & Collinson 2003). As a result, the record has now been officially deleted (*BOURC* 2004).

In Great Britain as a whole, the Common Buzzard is still most typical of western counties, but it is spreading rapidly eastwards to new areas. Taylor *et al* (1988) estimated the national population at 12,000 to 17,000 territories, but such was the subsequent growth and expansion that, little more than a decade later, the estimate was put at 31,100–44,000 territories (*APEP*), while Clements (2002) published calculations to indicate a total of between 44,000 and 61,000 territorial pairs. These last figures may be rather optimistic: applying the habitat density levels used in the latter study to the Wiltshire maps and counts, he subsequently proposed (*in litt*) that the Wiltshire level could be, or eventually reach, as high as 980 to 1300 territorial pairs, given an absence of persecution and a continuing plentiful supply of food, especially rabbits. All the tetrad survey evidence, however, indicates a population of around or slightly over 400 pairs at the end of the millennium. Illegal shooting and poisoning, the latter often aimed at mammal predators and crows, together with destruction of hedgerows, are probably still limiting factors, but most country people enjoy this spectacular raptor and its loud plaintive mewing call.

IJF-L

Rough-legged Buzzard

Buteo lagopus

Winter vagrant (42 records) from eastern Britain after influxes from Fenno-Scandia

Every few winters, one or more of these large, pale buzzards visits Salisbury Plain, often seen late in the afternoon hovering over a rabbit warren, or perched on a bush, in some remote downland valley. Rough-legs breed in the higher latitudes of Eurasia and North America, and mostly winter well to the south. In Europe, they nest on the arctic and subarctic tundra and, to a lesser extent, on northern uplands just above the tree line; and they winter in open country, mainly from the southern Baltic region south to the Alps and eastwards across Russia.

Relatively small numbers, chiefly juveniles, wander farther west in winter, into the Netherlands and eastern Britain, especially East Anglia and Kent. Like those of other tundra birds, Rough-legged Buzzard populations fluctuate in response to the abundance of their main prey – arctic lemmings and voles – and the year's breeding success is often reflected in the size of the periodic influxes into Great Britain. Larger national influxes since the 1960s have included 250 in 1974, 237 in 1994 and 110 in 1998 (Fraser & Rogers 2001, 2002), but these numbers represent a tiny proportion of the calculated Fenno-Scandian breeding population of 13,000 to 20,700 pairs (*EBCC Atlas*).

In Wiltshire, where Rough-legs hunt young rabbits and smaller mammals on downland, the records fall into line with the national pattern of a main arrival in October and a small return passage from mid March to the end of April. For the 19th century, Smith (1887) and Hony (1914a) listed 15 records between 1854 and 1885, mostly in winters when 'considerable numbers' occurred in Great Britain (Witherby *et al* 1938–41). The majority were either shot or trapped, including five at Fonthill in December 1876 (four trapped). Mr Rawlence, of Wilton, had told Smith 'that in 1882 a pair of these birds hatched out five young ones near Tisbury', but any such nesting seems highly improbable, even though the whole family was apparently killed and one of the adults made 'a very fine specimen'.

More than 80 years were to pass before the next Wiltshire records in winter 1966/67, again when there was a large influx in eastern England: one between Tilshead and Chitterne on 28 October 1966, and what was thought probably to be the same individual near Upavon on 4 November and 24 December; as well as another at Weavern on 7 March and again on the 19th (*WANHM*). Others were seen at Edington in October 1968 and near Rushall on 1 January 1972 (*WANHM*), followed by one at Warren Down on 21 April 1974 and again on the 29th (*Hobby*). Then at least 12 in winter 1974/75 (figure 31) included five in the Ham/Buttermere/Inkpen area and three at Imber, where one was subsequently 'well seen' on the surprising date of 3 July. Two were found in autumn 1977, but the only record in the whole of the 1980s was a juvenile on SPTA (West) from 29 March

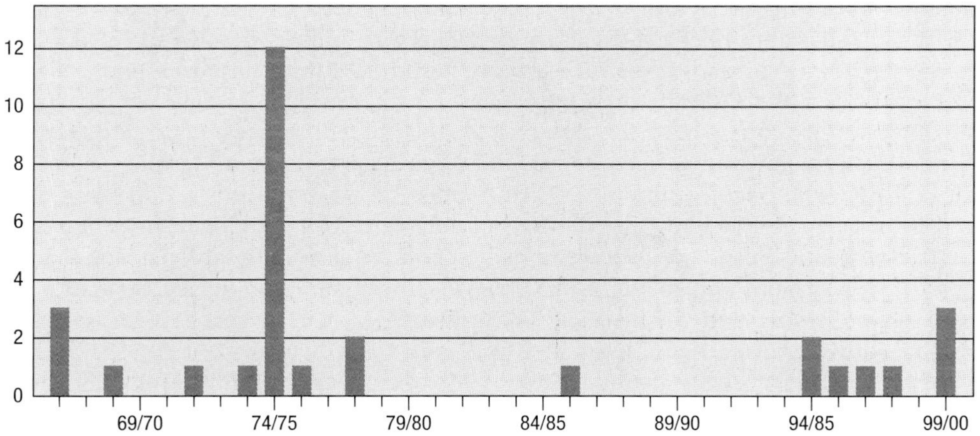

Figure 31. Rough-legged Buzzards *Buteo lagopus* in Wiltshire: winter totals 1966/67–1999/00

to 11 April 1986. In contrast, the 1990s produced six records (though the three in 1999 may possibly have related to the same individual):

1994	23 Oct–13 Apr **1995**	SPTA (West)	Juvenile
1995	23 March	Hippenscombe	(not aged)
1996	23 Mar–6 Apr	SPTA Water Dean Bottom	Juvenile
1997	10 March	Chippenham	(not aged)
1998	27 March	Lacock	(not aged)
1999	4 November	Cratt Hill and Great Ridge	Juvenile
	28 November	SPTA South Down	Juvenile
	5 Dec–11 Mar **2000**	Haxton Down	Juvenile

The singleton in the 1980s and the relatively high numbers in the 1990s reflect the national annual averages of 28 and 71 for those two decades (Fraser & Rogers 2002); indeed, the one in 1994 was part of the second biggest influx since the 1960s. The 1996 bird was also recorded wandering to SPTA (West).

Apart from the rather unlikely 1975 summer record (and the reputed nest in 1882), the earliest county date was 11 October 1977 and the latest 29 April 1974.

PEC

Osprey
Pandion haliaetus

Scarce migrant, breeds north Europe, including now Britain again, winters Africa

Ospreys feed almost exclusively on fish, caught in freshwater rivers or lakes and in estuaries or other coastal waters. They have a virtually cosmopolitan range, nesting or wintering on every continent except Antarctica. The world population was estimated at between 25,000 and 30,000 pairs in the 1980s (Poole 1989), but is increasing with protection and was probably higher by the late 1990s when regional estimates included 7000 to 9000 in north Europe and 7000 in Asiatic Russia (Ferguson-Lees & Christie 2001). Those that breed in Europe migrate south in September and October to winter mostly in Africa, south of the Sahara but north of the equator, and return in late March and April.

In the 19th and early 20th centuries, persecution by fishing interests and collectors almost eradicated the Ospreys of western and central Europe. As a result, apart from small numbers in Corsica and the Balearic Islands, breeding became largely restricted to Fenno-Scandia and the eastern half of the Continent from east Germany across the former USSR. The once common Scottish population was reduced to odd pairs by the early 1900s, and the last known nest was at Loch an Eilean (Highland/Inverness-shire) in 1916. But Fenno-Scandian Ospreys remained regular, if usually rare, passage migrants through Great Britain, and in the mid 1950s the first pairs recolonised Scotland, even though egg-collectors and disturbance by birdwatchers caused the best-known site at Loch Garten to be unsuccessful in its first four years.

Thirty-five years later, although collectors had stolen nearly a tenth of all clutches laid during 1955–90, British Ospreys were breeding in over three times as many 10-km squares as in 1972 (*1988–91 Atlas*), favouring wooded areas for nesting, not necessarily near water; indeed, sites now include electricity pylons. In the 1990s several started summering in

Table 46. Ospreys *Pandion haliaetus* in Wiltshire: five-year totals 1971–2000

	1971–75	1976–80	1981–85	1986–90	1991–95	1996–00
Birds	5	7	16	23	40	27

Cumbria and one pair raised young there in 2000, perhaps the first successful breeding in England since the 17th century. A project started in 1996 to establish a population at Rutland Water (Rutland), by releasing young brought down from Scotland, led to the first nest being built there in 2000. In that year alone, 147 pairs in Scotland and four in England raised a total of 209 young (*RBBP*). The species also recolonised mainland France in 1984 and has nested irregularly in Portugal since the 1970s, but, although it has increased in several central or north European countries, it has still generally decreased in the south.

For Wiltshire, Smith (1887) wrote, 'Notwithstanding the scarcity of large sheets of water in this county, this bird has been often killed in different parts of it, and not infrequently within the last few years'. He listed at least 11 Ospreys, all shot or trapped, in the latter half of the 19th century, and also referred to an account in the *Salisbury Journal* of two killed in Wilton Park in 1782.

There were no Wiltshire records of Ospreys from 1883 until 1951, when one spent the summer at Fonthill Lake (*WANHM* 56: 21, Peirson 1959), and only a further nine from then to 1973 (*WANHM*). Since 1974, even allowing for there being more observers and better recording following the foundation of WOS, numbers have increased substantially as the Scottish breeding population has grown (table 46), although annual totals do vary considerably: for example, only two were recorded in 1996, but 14 in 1992.

April and May are the best months to find an Osprey in Wiltshire (figure 32). Singletons have summered in four years, particularly in the Wylye valley. One which stayed at Shear Water almost continuously from 15 June to 29 August 1981 – except for two short breaks of two days each and, after a particularly severe thunderstorm, a gap of seven days – was carefully documented by Pollard (1982), who himself watched it catch fish on 51 occasions. At least 40 records have come from the Salisbury Avon and its tributaries, compared with only nine from CWP. One at Downton on 30 March 1990 had been ringed seven years earlier in a nest in the Scottish Highland Region on 6 July 1983. Reservoirs and lakes on country estates have produced 24. The earliest record was on 17 March 1996, and the latest on 18 October 1992.

Few have been found far from water in Wiltshire, but, remarkably, one remained centred on Larkhill – specifically, about 1 km north of the Bustard Hotel – during the four days of 22–25 September 1999 without apparently ever being seen anywhere in the county by any

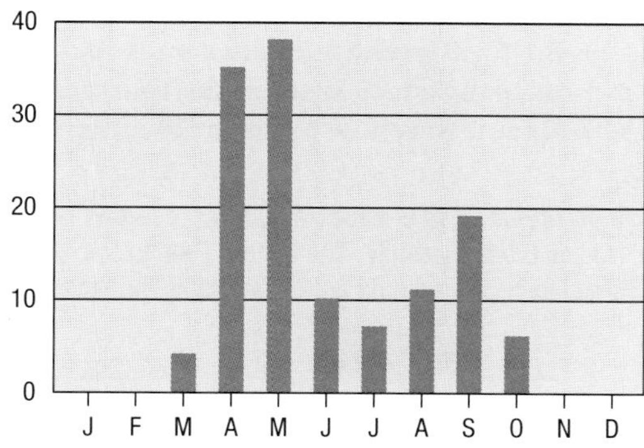

Figure 32. Ospreys *Pandion haliaetus* in Wiltshire: monthly totals 1971–2000

known observer. This was an 11–year-old male which, hatched in Strathspey (Highland/ Inverness-shire) in 1988, had returned to breed in its natal area since 1995 and, when trapped near Aviemore on 24 August 1999, was fitted with a transmitter that enabled it to be tracked by satellite. It left Aviemore on 13 September, was in the Dordogne (France) by 30 September, and had reached the coast of Mauritania by 19 October. Its stay in Wiltshire, during which it presumably fished along the Salisbury Avon, was the second longest stop of this migration (fuller details in *Hobby*).

PEC

Kestrel

Falco tinnunculus

Common but decreasing resident, also passage migrant and winter visitor

As motorways and bypasses proliferated from the 1960s onwards, Kestrels became particularly familiar sights in many parts of Great Britain – much remarked upon by motorists – as they hovered over the wide grass edges; by the mid 1970s the species had recovered from the effects of the worst organochlorine pesticides. Now, although still seen near roads, they are rather less conspicuous. This is partly because many edges have matured into scrub or been planted with decorative trees, but also, more seriously, because Kestrel numbers fell nationally by at least 25 per cent over the last quarter of the 20th century (CBC), the only British raptor to have declined over this period. This decrease has been linked to the effects of agricultural intensification on farmland habitats and subsequent declines in populations of small mammals. Although Kestrels rallied briefly during the late 1980s, there was a steady fall throughout the 1990s, and a decline of 15 to 20 percent – both in England as a whole and in the southwest (which includes Wiltshire) – during 1994–2000, the period of the Wiltshire tetrad surveys (*BBWC*).

Yet this is one of the world's most adaptable and widely distributed birds of prey, found throughout much of Eurasia and Africa, and replaced by allied species in the Americas, Madagascar, and Indonesia through to Australia. The European population alone, excluding Russia, has been estimated at 256,000 to 325,000 pairs (*EBCC Atlas*).

Kestrels occupy a wide variety of mainly open habitats, such as farmland and chalk downland, but have also learnt to live with human beings and not infrequently lay their eggs in church towers and on high ledges or crevices in other buildings – for example, for several years in the 1980s, on a warehouse roof in Swindon – as well as on electricity

Table 47. Kestrels *Falco tinnunculus* in south Wiltshire: breeding productivity 1992–2000

This table is based on Major NJ Lewis's results only. The Bulford Ornithological Group also studies Kestrels on SPTA (East), but full data are not available for all years

	92	93	94	95	96	97	98	99	00
Pairs	35	56	61	62	54	57	46	61	57
Young	145	207	221	203	224	195	102	232	155
Young per pair	4·1	3·7	3·6	3·3	4·2	3·4	2·2	3·8	2·7

pylons, all of which are the man-made equivalents of such more traditional breeding sites as ledges in quarries or cliffs, holes in trees, and old nests of, particularly, corvids. Rarely a pair will lay and incubate its clutch on the ground, as at Britford in 1934 (*WANHM*), and occasionally Kestrels have, like Peregrines, nested on Salisbury Cathedral.

Roadside Kestrels are hunting for small mammals, especially voles, in short grass. But these falcons also take small birds and, as witnessed by occasional entries in *WANHM* and *Hobby*, sometimes lizards, snakes, frogs, insects (which they commonly hawk on the wing), and even earthworms and other terrestrial invertebrates (for which they will forage on the ground). Occasionally, in a hard winter, a Kestrel may learn to attack small birds at a feeding table, as at Tockenham in the exceptionally severe weather of early 1963 (*WANHM*), but this behaviour is far more typical of Sparrowhawks.

Like those of other predators that depend largely on small mammals, the Kestrel's clutch size and nesting success – and, at times, even the numbers of breeding adults – vary in relation to vole numbers, though success can also be adversely affected by wet summers. These are the two main factors to which the fluctuations shown by the population using nestboxes on SPTA and elsewhere in south Wiltshire (table 47) are attributed.

The *1968–72* and *1988–91 Atlases* both recorded Kestrels in all of Wiltshire's 33 core 10-km squares, though breeding was only 'probable' or 'possible' in two of them; similarly, the summer tetrad survey found breeding evidence in 32 and the species was 'seen' in the only other. The summer distribution and abundance maps show Kestrels to be widespread throughout the county, though apparently more thinly spread in parts of the north and northwest. The cluster of proved breeding on SPTA (West) reflects the better coverage and greater density resulting from Major NJ Lewis's nestboxes – less obvious on SPTA (Centre), where his nestbox scheme is more for Barn Owls.

The *1968–72 Atlas* also estimated the British and Irish population at around 100,000 pairs, basing this on an arbitrary half of the 1972 average of 75 pairs per 10-km square over all CBC areas. Two decades later, however, wider studies had shown the density of Kestrels in Great Britain to vary from a comparatively low 36 pairs per 100 km^2 (or 10-km square) in grassland, in good vole years, down as few as only ten pairs per 100 km^2 in intensive arable farmland (Village 1990). From these figures the same author used a mean density of 'probably nearer 20 pairs per 100 km^2', to arrive at a likely average of 50,000 pairs in Great Britain. On that basis, Wiltshire's 3485 km^2 might be expected to hold about 700 pairs.

The 2-hour summer counts, plotted on the summer abundance map, resulted in a total of 915 Kestrels in two-thirds of the tetrads – six the most in any one (though the limitations of the record cards do not indicate whether that number may have represented three or more pairs or whether, incorrectly, the juveniles of a family party may have been included) – and, with casual records added, the distribution map shows the species was seen in just over four-fifths of all tetrads. At the time of many tetrad visits in April or May, one of each pair is likely to be with the eggs or small young, so it could be said that only half the population is countable in those months, whereas during visits in June or July the young may be out of the nest and, as juveniles closely resemble females, it could be argued that the numbers seen then would be likely to exaggerate the breeding population. Of all the tetrads in which Kestrels were found during 2-hour counts, however, only one tenth involved more than two birds. Breeding was established in 263 tetrads, and if it be assumed that each of these held only one pair and that the observations in half of the other 485 'occupied' tetrads also involved a nesting pair, a summer figure of just over 500 pairs is reached. But this may be too conservative. Breeding Kestrels defend only small areas, and sometimes pairs will breed only a few metres apart (*eg* Village 1990, *BWP*). Certainly a number of the county's tetrads held more than one pair, and the 50–60 pairs in nestboxes on SPTA and elsewhere in south Wiltshire (table 47) were all in a total of only twelve 10-km

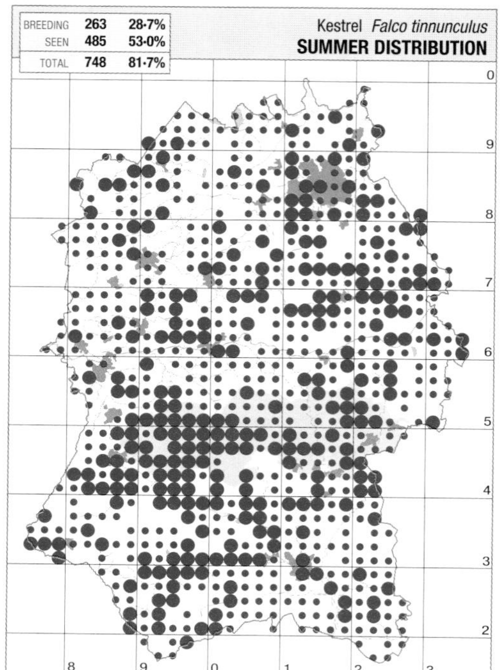

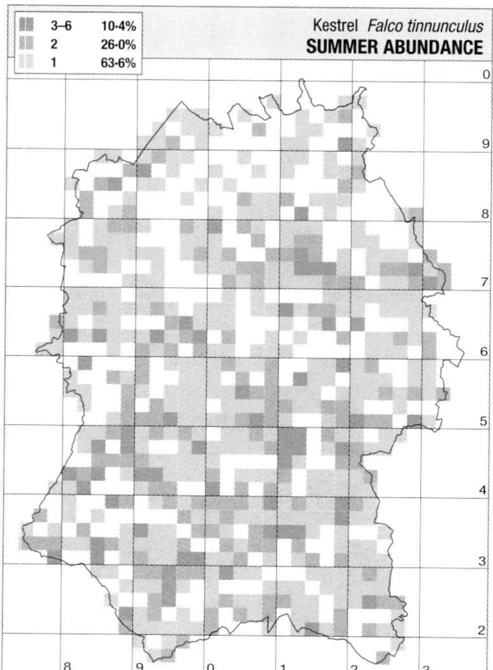

squares. Densities calculated from BBS in Wiltshire and the Cotswolds would suggest some 1240 to 2400 pairs in the county, but this is surely too large a proportion of the national total of 35,400 (*APEP*). Still, the county's population in 1995–2000 may well have been nearer that 'expected' from the national calculations of Village (1990), and a figure in the range of 500–700 pairs seems a reasonable conclusion.

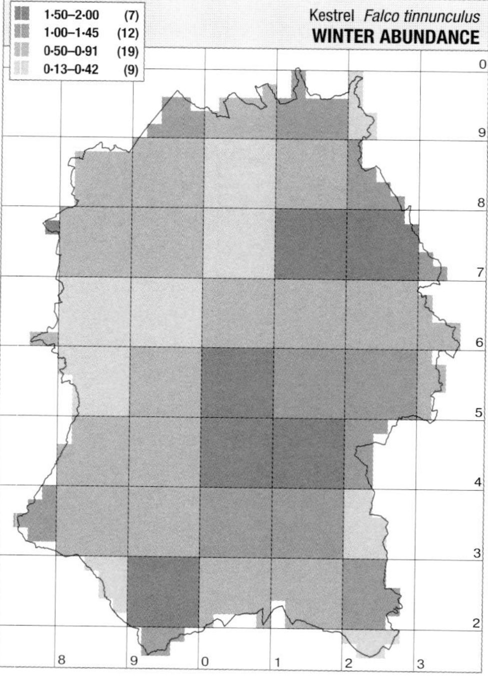

For one reason or another, numbers have fluctuated markedly over the past 150 years. Smith (1887) considered this 'the most common, the most harmless, and the most persecuted of all' Wiltshire's birds of prey, which 'abounds in vast numbers throughout the county', but then contradicted himself by adding, 'Where I used to see half a dozen in a morning's ride on the Downs forty years ago, I scarcely see one now'. This was, of course, the era when anything with a hooked bill was shot. Similarly, Morres (1878–85) wrote, 'This bird still remains common in our immediate neighbourhood [Britford, and wider Salisbury area], though, from my own observation, I should say it is scarcely to be so frequently met with as it was some ten or twelve years ago' and he went on to 'plead against its wholesale destruction'.

But pressure relaxed between the 1914–18 and 1939–45 Wars, and in the 1920s and 1930s the Kestrel was regarded as a 'common resident', if at times variously described as 'decreasing' and 'very common' in the same year (*WANHM*). In 1934 it was 'scarce' to 'rare' in north Wiltshire but 'seen more as one gets further south... where it is very common'; that pattern accords fairly well with the tetrad maps here, but the species is probably not so common now as it was then in the south. In the late 1940s and 1950s the annual bird reports included little or nothing about status or numbers, but the early 1960s saw references to slow deaths assumed to be caused by pesticides. By 1968, however, the Kestrel was 'holding its own and possibly spreading'; and, in 1973, 'apparently as numerous now as it was prior to the "pesticide" decline' (*WANHM*). In the 1980s it was often noted as 'widespread and common', but 1982 produced a 'Marked drop in numbers after the extremely hard weather in Dec'.

Many British Kestrels are sedentary or move only short distances – indeed, some pairs remain in their breeding territories throughout the year – but others are partial migrants, and juveniles in particular tend to disperse, often not very far. No fewer than 2805 Kestrels were ringed in Wiltshire during 1965–2000, mostly as chicks in the nest, and this is the county's highest ringing total of any non-passerine species. Of those, 124 had been recovered by the end of the 20th century, a good proportion as road casualties – perhaps not surprisingly in view of the risks of hunting close to speeding traffic – and a number of them in their first year; the oldest lived for 5 years 8 months. As many as 80 of these recoveries have been within Wiltshire, and some 50 of them less than 10 km from where they had been ringed, but there has also been a good sprinkling across southern Britain from Cornwall and Gwent to Suffolk and Kent, north to the Midlands; only 19 had moved 100 km or more. A small minority of British Kestrels crosses the English Channel to winter abroad, but five from Wiltshire have been recovered in France (1957, 1975, 1984, 1991, 1996) and one 917 km away in Spain in 1995, which is almost the southern limit ever achieved by Kestrels from Great Britain. Although some farther north in the country move south in autumn and winter – as shown by one ringed in Leicestershire in June 1959 and recovered at Pitton seven months later (*WANHM*) – passage-migrants and winter visitors (mostly in their first year) from Fenno-Scandia, the Low Countries and France also reach eastern and southern England (*Migration Atlas*), and one ringed at Limburg (Netherlands) in July 1985 was found dead at Edington that November. But we cannot be sure of the origins of loose concentrations, commonly of up to eight and sometimes 12–15 in July–October; once up to 30 were scattered over SPTA (Centre) on 9 October. Indeed, some such concentrations may just be the result of optimum feeding conditions.

The *1981–84 Winter Atlas* and the winter tetrad survey both recorded this species in all the core 10-km squares. The winter map here shows a wide distribution, but this time with the highest numbers concentrated in the open areas of the Marlborough Downs, Salisbury Plain (now especially the eastern two-thirds) and the smaller downland areas farther southwest and southeast. In winter, Kestrels were found in 58 per cent of the sample tetrads and extrapolation from the counts indicates a population then just short of 800. It may be that numbers are lower in the county in winter than summer.

IJF-L

Red-footed Falcon

Falco vespertinus

Overshooting vagrant (c10 records), breeds east Europe, winters Africa

Red-footed Falcons are long-distance migrants that arrive in May to nest, often colonially in deserted rookeries, across a strip of central Eurasia from east Europe to the upper Lena in east-central Siberia; and then in autumn depart to spend the northern winter in a relatively small region of southern Africa. In Europe, the biggest summer numbers are in northwest Kazakhstan, southern Russia and Ukraine, south to Romania and west to Hungary. Spring passage is on a more westerly track than that of autumn, resulting in now almost annual influxes into western Europe. These falcons' preferred breeding habitat is grassy and wooded steppe, although they often favour wetlands on passage. Adults live almost exclusively on insects, but feed their chicks on reptiles and amphibians, fledgling birds and small mammals.

Wiltshire's first report of a Red-footed Falcon was of a female at Littlecote Park in 1825, published 18 years later by Holme (1843). He had bought the bird alive 'from a countryman, who said he had seen it pursued and struck down by a raven'; the man had then 'caught it on the ground before it recovered, and according to his account it laid an egg…which was broken'. Holme continued, 'I was a tolerable ornithologist for a school-boy, but the yellow claws and strange markings of my bird puzzled me to identify it with any of the English hawks, and I made a drawing of it'. That was just as well because the bird escaped a few days later and it was not until, some years afterwards, he and an Oxford colleague, NC Strickland – who had a similar drawing of one shot in Yorkshire – were able to identify the species 'in the Zoological Gardens' (presumably London Zoo, as Holme was by then a Fellow of the Zoological Society of London).

At a time when there had been 'scarcely twenty' Red-footed Falcons in Great Britain as a whole, Smith (1887) referred to this observation and one other Wiltshire record, which involved an undated pair in the Rawlence collection, 'shot in a plantation on the downs at Kingston Deverell'; he considered the latter to be the 'More satisfactory because more undeniable' of the two. Many years later, one was reported near Coombe on 8 April 1934 'by Capt. Read, who was certain of identification' (*WANHM*); that would have been an unusually early date, though not unknown nowadays. Some may question whether any of these instances is good enough to stand as the first for Wiltshire and so, although it is the policy of this book not to attempt to reassess historical records by modern standards (see page 18–19), further discussion seems desirable.

In fact, the first of the three, at Littlecote Park in 1825, is arguably the most acceptable. In general, the claws of falcons are black, but those of two of the most gregarious – Lesser Kestrel and Red-footed – vary from pale brown to yellowish-white, and the 'yellow claws' (not quoted by Smith) appear to have surprised Holme as much as the 'strange markings' (which, if so strange, would exclude Lesser Kestrel). Also, since he referred to the bird as an 'Orange-legged Hobby', an old name for this species, it seems safe to assume that it had orange legs. Having kept it in his possession for several days and made a drawing, Holme must have studied the bird closely and, since he regarded himself as 'a tolerable ornithologist' when young and was to become a Fellow of Corpus Christi, Oxford, it is likely that he already had a clear-minded approach. If it be accepted that the bird did extrude an egg when caught (though that was not seen by Holme), then it must have been an adult female and the date, almost certainly, May. Holme's drawing evidently matched the female Red-footed plumage that, with contrasting black-barred slaty upperparts and reddish head and underparts, certainly has 'strange markings'. Although Peirson (1919) considered this observation doubtful and, perhaps because of all the unusual circumstances, Smith also apparently had some reservations, since he considered the pair from Kingston Deverill in the Rawlence collection to be the 'More satisfactory' of the two (even though completely undated), Holme's own published words make it much more convincing. And Hony (1915a), who long assessed Wiltshire bird records published in *The Zoologist*, did not question it. Finally, it should also be added for clarity that Naylor (1996) gave this record the wrong years of both observation and publication, and incorrectly listed it under Berkshire, as did Radford (1966), who also referred to 'the *specimen* [our italics] being in the possession of a Mr T. Holme of Corpus Christi College, Oxford'.

Turning back to the other 19th century record – the pair at Kingston Deverill – it must be pointed out that vagrants of many species tend to occur singly in Great Britain, often as inexperienced immatures, and that the high incidence of 'pairs' (usually adult males and females) in late 19th and early 20th century collections always raises the possibility of fraud (*eg* Nicholson & Ferguson-Lees 1962, Nelder 1962). Red-footed Falcons are highly gregarious, however, and one of the relatively few rare migrants that not infrequently appear in Great Britain in mixed-sex parties of two, three or even more. Also, it is the policy of this book not to reject records accepted by Smith and Hony. Finally, although the report near Coombe in 1934 is the only old one with a full date – unusually early but not impossibly so, as there have been rare modern British records in January–March – it is no more than an asserted sighting but no description; not even the sex of this 'certain ... identification' was given, whereas adult male and female Red-footed Falcons, and immatures in their first year, are all quite distinct from one another.

During the late 20th century, spring influxes of Red-footed Falcons into western Europe became more frequent, so much so that Great Britain amassed 614 records during 1958–2000, compared with only 100 before 1958 (*BBRC*). The biggest invasion, in spring 1992, involved up to 150, three times as many as in the second-best year, 1973, which saw the first of Wiltshire's modern records. Many have been in their first summer, and thus about ten months old. These falcons' most frequent haunt in the county has been CWP, where they have been watched hawking for insects over the lakes with the Hobbies that gather there in late spring. Most of Wiltshire's eight recent records (ten birds) have been in the second half of May:

1973	1–2 June	Orcheston Down	Female (not aged)
1988	16–23 May	CWP68	1st-summer male
1989	28 May	CWP Swillbrook	1st-summer male
	28–30 May	CWP Swillbrook	1st-summer female
1990	27–29 May	CWP68	1st-summer male
1992	16–21 May	CWP68	1st-summer male
	29 May–3 Jun	CWP Swillbrook	Two 1st-summer females
	2 June	Haxton Down	1st-summer male
1999	2 August	Redlynch	Female, flying south

Orcheston Down and Haxton Down are both on SPTA (Centre and East respectively). The male and female in 1989 were together on 28 May and so, even though the male then disappeared and the female stayed alone for two further days, they are treated as one record; some of the details of this observation were published incorrectly elsewhere (*BB* 83: 457–458).

(See also page 726.)

PEC & IJF-L

Merlin

Falco columbarius

Winter visitor from north Britain and Iceland (first bred 2005)

This aggressive, quicksilver raptor breeds farther north than any other small falcon, in a circumpolar distribution that encompasses the boreal, cool temperate and, to some extent, steppe and tundra zones of both North America and Eurasia. Numbers of Merlins have decreased over much of that huge range since the 19th century, as a result of human persecution, pesticide poisoning, habitat loss and disturbance. Most populations are migratory, wintering south to northern South America, North Africa and south-central Asia (Voous 1960, Ferguson-Lees & Christie 2001).

Some 10,000 to 16,000 pairs have been estimated to breed in Europe, excluding Russia (*EBCC Atlas*). Great Britain's population is found mostly from Shetland, Orkney and the Hebrides through mainland Scotland and northern England to the Welsh uplands, though a few persist on England's southwest peninsula (*1988–91 Atlas*). In the early part of the 19th century, the species still nested in north Lincolnshire and coastal Essex (*1875–1900 Atlas*). On slender evidence, the *1968–72 Atlas* reported a slow but steady decline in the first half of the 20th century, this becoming more marked in the 1950s, though, as the *1875–1900 Atlas* pointed out, it was apparently only in the early 1900s that Merlins colonised southwest England. The *1988–91 Atlas* showed further losses, but found also that, in certain areas, these raptors 'may now be in a phase of recovery, partly associated with their recent use of forest margins'; such a recovery is more than borne out by a subsequent 1993–94 survey estimate of 1100–1500 pairs (Rebecca & Bainbridge 1998), which doubled the 1983–84 figure of 550–650 (Bibby & Nattrass 1986). Merlins are increasingly breeding in trees in Great Britain, mostly in old crow nests, on the edge of moorland as conifer plantations mature (Parr 1994, *EBCC Atlas*).

In autumn through to early spring Merlins are far more widespread in Great Britain (*eg 1981–84 Winter Atlas*), and it is at that time that they become familiar to observers in Wiltshire. Smith (1887) knew of the species as a regular visitor, listed many occurrences across the county, and described it as 'arriving in October, and leaving us in the spring'. This better fits today's status than does Peirson's (1959) 'scarce visitor seen regularly in the autumn dispersal and also occasionally in winter'. Buxton (1981) considered Merlins to be regular on 'Salisbury Plain and other upland areas from late August to April'.

Buxton also stated that single birds, usually immatures, were occasionally seen in summer; and he included a remarkable report of nesting in 1971, when a pair was said to have laid eggs (subsequently taken by a collector) in an old Carrion Crow nest in a Scots pine. Oddly, these unusual events were not mentioned in *WANHM* for that year. Buxton added that 'A pair of birds reported at another site subsequent to the above record were present throughout the breeding season and were seen carrying prey but no young were seen'. Although undated and thus by implication also involving 1971, this second pair were 'almost certainly' in a following year (GL Webber), and thus may be the pair noted in *Hobby* as seen carrying food in 1974; *Hobby* also mentioned a nest located at another site in 1974, as well as pairs present in different areas in 1973 and 1975. As there are no reports of any summer Merlins in the WOS archive for 1971–75, let alone any mention of breeding, it is difficult now to know what to make of these observations, which were contained in two long-lost letters from a gamekeeper relating to unnamed localities on Salisbury Plain (GL Webber), nor why Buxton chose to include details of two pairs but ignore three or perhaps four others. It has been suggested, without any evidence, that these unusual events may have been the results of attempted introductions by falconers, though it could equally be that Hobbies were mis-identified. Given the murky and confused background, and the fact that there is no proper evidence to substantiate such important episodes, unreserved acceptance seems unwise.

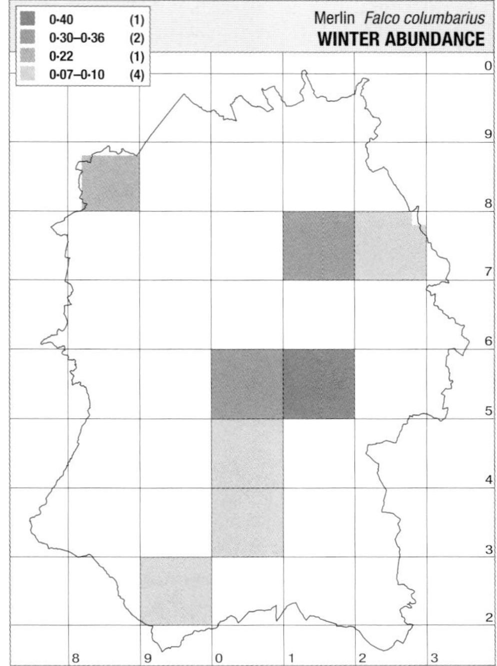

Discussing the 1980s, Palmer (1991) added no further summer records, but identified Salisbury Plain, with up to 'seven … each winter', as the 'most regular site … from September to April'. He also noted a large increase in observations away from traditional areas as a result of increased observer coverage; the *1981–84 Winter Atlas* recorded this species in 15 of Wiltshire's 33 core 10-km squares.

During 1990–2000, records as early as August came from SPTA (West) between the 8th and the 20th in four years; from SPTA (Centre) on the 5th in 2000; from Stonehenge on the 27th in 1994; from Beckhampton on the 30th in 1994; and from Devizes on the 27th in 1996. Merlins are never particularly widespread before October, however, and they are scarce after March, though the latest spring sightings have usually been in April (and once at Figheldean on 5 May 1997). None has been ringed in the county, nor are there any inward recoveries to suggest or confirm the origins of those that winter in Wiltshire, but it is likely that they come mainly from the British breeding populations; most of some 70 recoveries of Icelandic Merlins in these islands have been in Ireland and there have been very few of Fenno-Scandian origin (*Migration Atlas*). It is possible, too, that at least some of those seen in autumn and late spring are simply passing through.

Merlins hunt small passerines, such as Sky Larks, Meadow Pipits and Linnets, over downland, farmland and other open areas. On SPTA, they regularly attend foraging Hen Harriers, opportunistically pursuing any small birds that those flush (PE Castle). Thus, it was no surprise that the winter survey produced as many as 17 observations in 15 tetrads of largely open country – the map identifies the Marlborough Downs and SPTA as prime localities – though the records involved only eight of the 33 core squares (little more than half of the 15 in the *1981–84 Winter Atlas*). Extrapolation for uncounted tetrads indicates a Wiltshire winter total of about 40, though that figure may be too high as the numbers on downland are not typical of the county as a whole and those in the vicinity of roosts may also have added a bias. On SPTA, where these small falcons roost in elders and hawthorns in dry chalk valleys, no fewer than eight were found in December 1998, but, rather than there being unusual numbers of Merlins that winter, such a record count was probably because they were roosting close to the keenly studied Hen Harriers (*qv*). Not all Merlins roost within the county: like Hen Harriers, some of those hunting over Wiltshire's southern farmland overnight in Hampshire's New Forest (P Combridge). The only Wiltshire report of roosting away from SPTA involved one on the ground in set-aside in the south of the county on 21 November 1997; usually this species spends the night in a bush or low tree in winter.

The big increase in observers – and, consequently, sightings of Merlins – during the last quarter of the 20th century makes any trends extremely difficult to interpret. Regular monitoring of roost sites might help, but would not be easy: Merlins are far more challenging than Hen Harriers to watch at roost, often arriving later in the evening and departing earlier in the morning (PE Castle, P Combridge).

(See also pages 724 & 726.)

PCo & IJF-L

Sponsored by Paul Castle

Hobby

Falco subbuteo

Local summer visitor, mostly May–September, increasing nationally, winters Africa

The logo of WOS, the name of its annual publication, and the rarest of the four well-established breeding raptors in a county which has always been one its strongholds, the Hobby has long been closely linked with Wiltshire and its ornithology. Its comparative rarity, its elegant shape and its lifestyle, coupled with its being a summer visitor that migrates down to the southern quarter of Africa, have long combined to attract the attention of anyone interested in birds including, unfortunately, egg-collectors.

Hobbies have a wide summer distribution in Eurasia north to about the Arctic Circle, from Iberia, Great Britain and east Sweden across to Kamchatka, north Japan and China, south to North Africa, central Israel and the northern fringes of the Indian subcontinent. Most of the western populations winter in southern Africa, and the eastern largely in a band from Pakistan to south China. The world population has been put at 'approaching 200,000 pairs' (Ferguson-Lees & Christie 2001), more than three times the maximum suggested by Cade (1982), and the European – excluding Russia, where the species is thought to be much more numerous – at 19,700 to 22,800 pairs (*EBCC Atlas*).

This is one of half a dozen primarily insectivorous falcons that nest in Eurasia and North Africa, where they feed their young on birds, and winter in southern Africa and Madagascar or, in one or two cases, also southern Asia. Most of the others – such as the Red-footed Falcon (*qv*), a vagrant to Wiltshire – are commonly gregarious and often breed in colonies, whereas Hobbies, though sometimes roosting socially and congregating at insect swarms, are generally seen in ones and twos, except in the period when the young accompany their parents for four to six weeks after they leave the nest. In courtship or when they have well-grown chicks in the nest or recently fledged young, Hobbies can be quite conspicuous and even noisy, but at other times are surprisingly unobtrusive and easily missed, remaining quietly perched for long periods; they often hunt in the half-light of dusk, catching moths and other high-flying insects which they hold in their feet and eat in flight.

Hobbies lay their eggs in disused nests of Carrion and, elsewhere, Hooded Crows, nowadays even taking over old nests on electricity pylons (*eg* Trodd 1993, Catley 1994). Their breeding season is remarkably synchronised, 92 per cent of clutches, usually of three eggs, being completed during 6–25 June (Fiuczynski & Nethersole-Thompson 1980) and, as incubation and fledging each take around 30 days, and independence not much longer, the families typically hatch in mid July, fledge in mid August and leave in mid to late September. In Wiltshire, the first are usually seen in April and the last in September, but the earliest and latest dates have been 26 March 1997 and 22 November 1987; also, in 1936, one was 'caught at Salisbury during the end of November, probably attempting to winter in this country' (*WANHM*) – an unreliable assumption, because winter records anywhere in Europe are exceptional.

The rearing of nestlings in late July and early August coincides nicely with a plentiful supply of the flying young of small birds, especially juvenile hirundines and Swifts which, along with Sky Larks and roosting House Sparrows, form much of the Hobby's prey at that season. Insects become important again when the fledged young are themselves learning to hunt. Then a significant proportion of the food is made up of dragonflies: two species have greatly increased in England through the proliferation of reservoirs and gravel pits since the 1950s, and are now found abundantly around wooded areas as well as open water, especially from August onwards (see Prince & Clarke 1993). This increase may have been a major factor in the evident expansion of the British population of Hobbies over the last three or four decades of the 20th century.

In Great Britain, Hobbies were long particularly associated with heaths and downland in southern England, but they also breed commonly in farmland with scattered pine clumps or mature broadleaved hedgerow trees. In the 1940s and 1950s it was believed that there were only about 60–90 pairs in total (*eg* Brown 1957), largely restricted to seven counties from Dorset through Wiltshire and Hampshire to Berkshire, Surrey and West Sussex. Even in the 1960s and early 1970s, by which time breeding was being proved west to Cornwall, east into Kent and Essex, and up to and slightly beyond the Severn-Wash line, the British population was still put at 85–100 pairs (Parslow 1973) and 'probably close to, or may exceed, 100 pairs' (*1968–72 Atlas*).

By the end of the 1980s, however, Hobbies were found west and north to Gwent, Powys, Shropshire, Derbyshire and Humberside, and there had been more isolated breeding

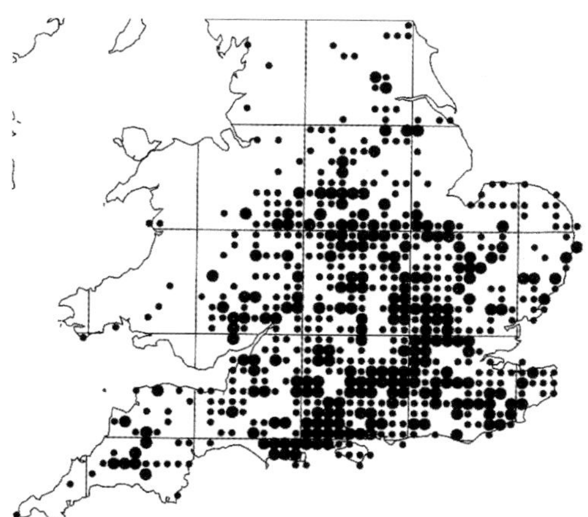

Figure 33. Hobbies *Falco subbuteo* in England and Wales: mapped by 10-km squares 1988–91 (from *1988–91 Atlas*)
Small dots: seen in nesting season
Large dots: evidence of breeding

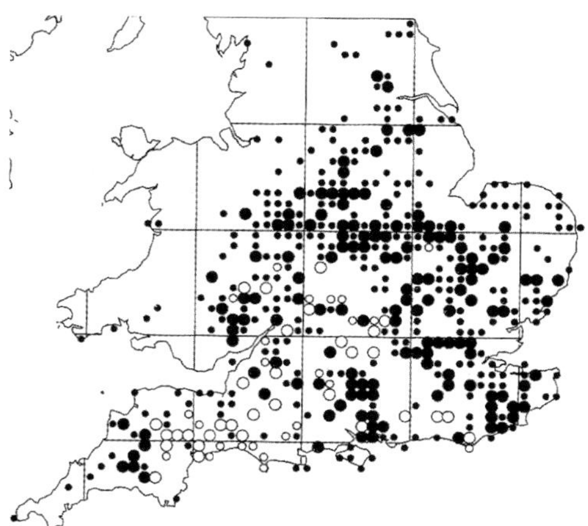

Figure 34. Hobbies *Falco subbuteo* in England and Wales: changes in 10-km distribution between 1968–72 and 1988–91 (from *1988–91 Atlas*)
Filled dots: not noted 1968–72 but seen (small dots) or evidence of breeding (large dots) 1988–91
Open dots: breeding possible (small dots) or probable/confirmed (large dots) 1968–72 but species not recorded 1988–91

records northward to north Yorkshire and Tyne & Wear (*1988–91 Atlas*, figure 33), though also some indications of a withdrawal from the base of the southwest peninsula (figure 34). Put more graphically, the 1968–72 distribution had been largely confined inside a southern English triangle enclosed by lines from the Wash south to Sussex's Beachy Head and southwest to the Severn estuary: the number of 10-km squares in which Hobbies were found to the east and north of these lines grew from 17 and 27 (*1968–72 Atlas*) to no fewer than 104 and 194 (*1988–91 Atlas*) – six-fold and seven-fold increases, respectively (Ferguson-Lees 1994). Most estimates by differing methods in the early 1990s variously put the British population in the range of 500–1000 pairs (*eg* Ferguson-Lees 1993, Parr 1994).

These figures apparently represented a huge boost over the previous 20 years, even though Fuller *et al* (1985) had considered that the estimate in the *1968–72 Atlas* 'took little account of the substantial populations north of the River Thames': they had found 3–4 pairs per 10-km square in the southern Midlands, which they believed showed 'no evidence of a recent increase'. Moreover, allowing for the fact Hobbies are easily overlooked when nesting, they proposed a 'conservative average of two pairs' for all 10-km squares in which the species had been recorded; on that basis, they suggested that even in 1968–72 the British population could have exceeded 500 pairs and by the early 1980s have been as high as 1122 pairs.

More recently, the British population has been put higher still. Chapman (1999) estimated it at between 948 and 1775 pairs; and Clements (2001), having arrived at a calculation of 2264 pairs, believed that 'the total number of breeding pairs in Britain probably exceeds 2,500, and is likely to increase still further as the species spreads north and west'. What can we conclude from this plethora of ever-growing numbers? First, the old figure of around 100 was surely well below the mark. Second, the species has undoubtedly spread and probably greatly increased, and may be doing so still. But how

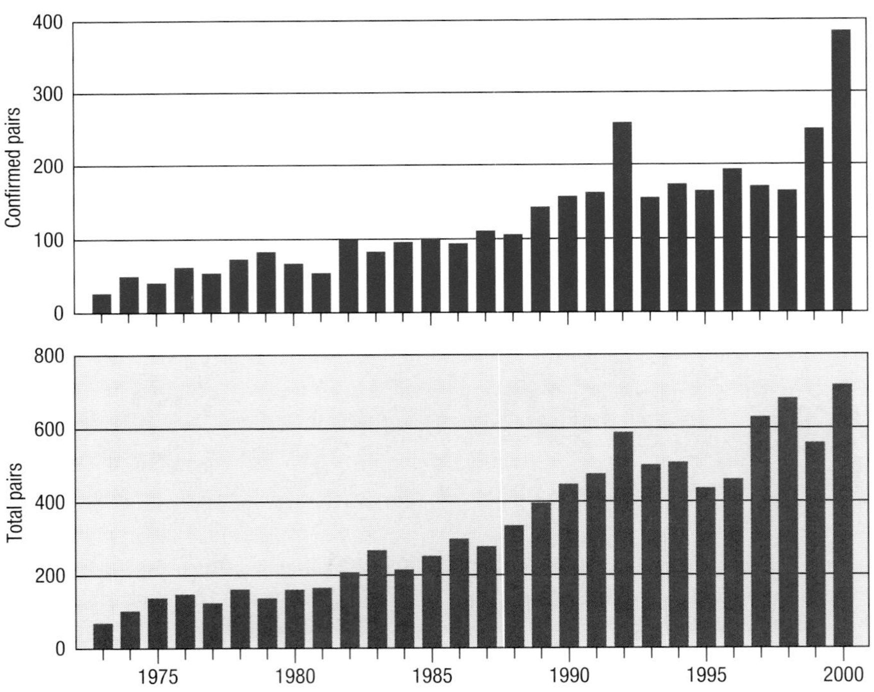

Figure 35. Hobbies *Falco subbuteo* in Great Britain: totals reported to RBBP 1973–2000
These cannot be regarded as anywhere near full counts, but illustrate steady upward trends in finding and reporting this species

Table 48. Hobbies *Falco subbuteo* in Wiltshire: pairs recorded 1990–2000

	90	91	92	93	94	95	96	97	98	99	00
Number of sites	23	38	36	38	34	30	24	30	26	40	31
Proved breeding	8	6	12	7	7	4	5	7	6	10	6
Probably breeding	9	14	18	12	6	14	12	11	8	7	6
Possibly breeding	8	18	13	20	21	12	7	12	12	23	19
Total pairs	25	38	43	39	34	30	24	30	26	40	31

much it was overlooked (and probably still is) remains guesswork. Numbers reported to the RBBP during 1973–2000 (figure 35) also show the upward trend.

It is difficult to find any indications of the numbers of Hobbies in Wiltshire in the days when this was regarded as one of the 'headquarter counties'. As early as the mid 17th century, however, Aubrey (1656–91) noted 'the hobbies doe goe away at... and return in the spring'. Bosworth Smith (1863) simply stated that the species was rare, and im Thurn (1870) that it was occasionally to be found at Aldbourne and on the Overton Downs. Smith (1887) believed it to be 'sparingly distributed annually throughout' and had 'received many instances of its nesting... in various localities'; he went on to refer to adults and even whole families being shot, for which reason he thought it 'better not to describe them [the localities] too minutely', though quoting the Reverend AP Morres to the effect that 'in the immediate neighbourhood of Salisbury' the species 'is not uncommon'. Meyrick (1895) thought it 'not very uncommon' but 'at all times a great rarity'. There were then occasional references in *WANHM* over the years, and the first proper Wiltshire bird report, for 1929, summarised the Hobby as 'An uncommon summer visitor. Still breeds in a few localities. Fairly common in S. Wilts. on migration'.

Thereafter, what was published depended on who was sufficiently interested in Hobbies to find and report them, and it is impossible to obtain any clear picture from the annual entries. In 1933 they had 'increased considerably during recent years on the Plain since the... judicious taking of the Crow's eggs' to provide nesting sites; but in 1934, apart from 'Several nests on Salisbury Plain', there were reports of 'Not in evidence so much as during the last two years' and 'not so many as usual on the Plain'; and in 1936 simply 'good numbers' (*WANHM*). During 1946–53, only once were more than ten observations reported, and published breeding records were few apart from several references to nests being robbed (*WANHM*); undoubtedly, egg-collectors knew more than birdwatchers about nests of Hobbies on Salisbury Plain at that time. Even during the next 20 years, 1954–73, records remained sparse, the highest numbers of pairs referred to being six in 1954 and 1962, and seven in 1963; in four years there were no reports of nesting; and 1966 was regarded as a 'bad breeding season... known sites being unoccupied... The reported recovery of pesticides in a grasshopper may be significant' (*WANHM*). In fact, however, pesticides seem to have had little effect on British Hobbies (Fiuczynski & Nethersole-Thompson 1980).

With the establishment of WOS in 1974 and the increasingly systematic reporting of observations, particularly from the late 1970s, a clearer picture began to emerge. There were over 70 sight records of Hobbies in Wiltshire in 1978 and again in 1979. Through the 1980s the number of pairs reported each year varied from 11 to 29, at an annual average of 21 – though not all proved or even probably nesting – and during 1990–2000 the total of pairs varied from 24 to 43 (table 48), at an average of nearly 33.

These fluctuating data suggest an increase in the 1990s, while the numbers involved and the summer distribution map, indicate that the species may have become more widespread since the era when Wiltshire was considered one of the key seven counties: Hobbies were recorded in 31 of the county's 33 core 10-km squares in the 1995–2000 tetrad survey, compared with 26 in the *1988–91 Atlas* and only 19 in the *1968–72 Atlas*. Yet this may just be

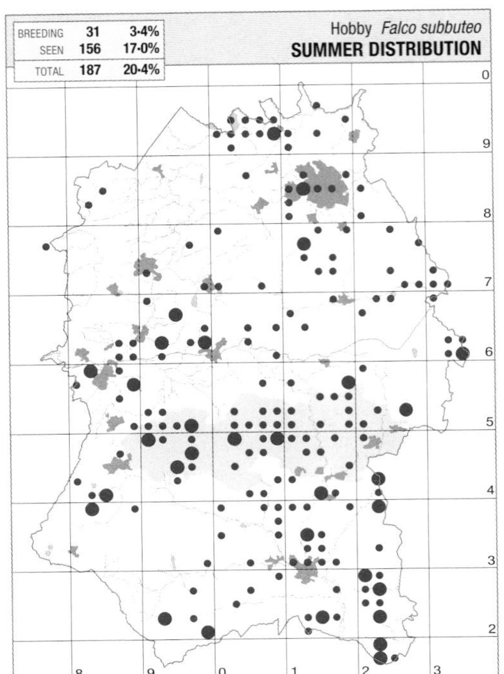

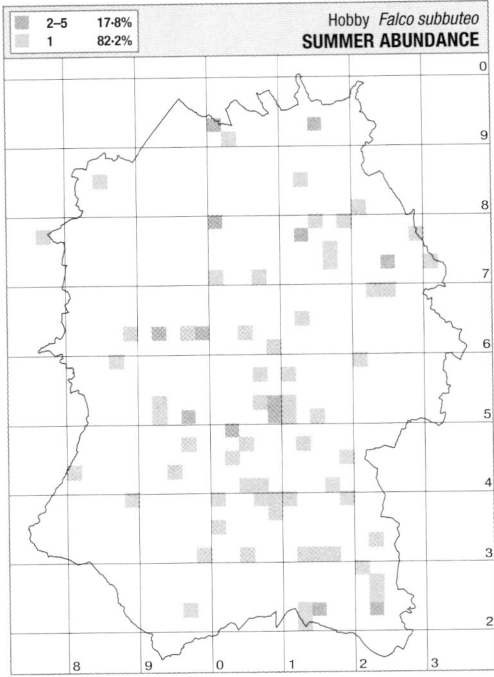

the result of more observation by more people, for the number of core squares with evidence of breeding remained in the 11–17 range through all three surveys, though, if we take the total of 48 squares that fall at least partly within the county, the number in which Hobbies probably nested in the 1968–2000 period grew from 12 to 18 and the total in which the species was seen increased from 28 to 38. But how incomplete are the reported numbers?

Clements (2001) calculated populations of 255 and 285 pairs in the 100-km squares ST and SU of the Ordnance Survey grid and, since 17·4 per cent of these two combined is taken up by Wiltshire, that might suggest a county population of some 94 pairs. That would be more than twice the highest number of pairs actually recorded in Wiltshire during 1990–2000 (table 48), but the two pairs per 10-km square postulated by Fuller (1985) would indicate a population of 62 pairs in the 33 core squares alone. The latter figure perhaps equates more closely with the 'more likely to be in the region of 70 pairs' suggested by Ferguson-Lees (1994) when publishing the Wiltshire distribution map by 10-km squares for 1993.

There are curious differences between that map for 1993 and the one published here for 1995–2000: if probable and confirmed breeding be combined for 1993, comparison shows that no fewer than seven of the 10-km squares (six of them in the northern half) had a higher level of evidence in that single year than in all the six years of the tetrad survey, whereas 16 (12 in the southern half) had a lower level. Does this demonstrate a shift in population, or simply underline the county's fluctuating numbers (1993 was the third best year for recorded pairs during 1980–2000), or emphasise that in no year are more than variable proportions of the pairs ever found?

The 2-hour summer counts resulted in a total of 91 Hobbies in 8 per cent of the tetrads – five the most in any one – and it is probably safe to suggest that there are normally at least 50 pairs of Hobbies in this county, in most years perhaps 70–80. But no longer is Wiltshire one of the seven most important counties for the species; instead, it is probably no more than one that is average for the whole southern half of England. Yet surely the numbers did increase here in the last third of the 20th century, and nowadays the concentrations of waterside insects and small birds (later in the season, especially dragonflies and young hirundines) make CWP – Britain's largest area of gravel pits, straddling north Wiltshire and south Gloucestershire – one of the best places in the whole country to find Hobbies. It is not difficult to see ten to twenty there in the course of a day through spring and summer, sometimes more than a dozen over a single pit. In April and May these are adults on passage, then from late May through July apparently mainly non-breeding yearlings, and in late August and September family parties.

One of only 27 Hobbies ringed in the county during 1965–2000 was subsequently reported, and three others had been recovered from earlier ringing: all four were marked as nestlings 'near Salisbury' or 'on Salisbury Plain'. Two of them, ringed on 9 August 1936 and 17 July 1953 respectively, were both shot less than eight weeks later – on their first southward migrations – at Landes (France) on 16 October 1936 and Espinho (Portugal) on 13 September 1953 (the latter detailed in *WANHM* for 1954). The other two, ringed on 19 August 1934 and 25 July 1976 respectively, were each recovered almost exactly one year later – presumably having spent the intervening winters in Africa and then wandered as yearlings in western Europe – appearing at Burrington (Shropshire) on 28 August 1935 and at Limburg (Belgium) on 22 July 1977 (the latter detailed in *Hobby* 4).

IJF-L

Sponsored by Linda Cady and Paul Castle in memory of John Pollard

---

Gyr Falcon
Falco rusticolus

Vagrant (2 old records) from Greenland/Iceland/ north Europe

With a circumpolar arctic or subarctic distribution, Gyr Falcons inhabit northern tundra, rocky coasts and mountains. In Europe, their breeding range extends from Iceland and Fenno-Scandia eastwards across northern Russia, but those populations are mainly sedentary apart from some juveniles dispersing south. In the New World these large falcons are more clearly migratory, though still travelling little south of the breeding range, and many of the wanderers to Europe originate probably from Greenland. In winter, they frequent coasts, wetlands and other open habitats. The species is polymorphic, with white and dark morphs and a wide range of intermediates, and nowadays the possibility of falconry escapes, which may even include hybrids, needs to be borne in mind.

During 1958–2000, no fewer than 116 Gyrs were recorded in Great Britain (*BBRC*), especially along northern and western coasts in spring – many of them white morphs, which predominate in Greenland – but none has been identified in Wiltshire since the early 20th century. Smith (1887) reported a large white falcon observed at Ram's Cliff, near Market Lavington, on 9 December 1842; it was initially mistaken for an albino Peregrine, but was subsequently concluded to have been a white-morph Gyr. The only other record was of an evident white-morph immature shot near Downton in April 1906: it 'was first seen in February… and was generally found near some lynches [terraces] on Newcourt Farm, half-way between Charlton and Downton', where it apparently lived 'chiefly upon partridges and pigeons' (Radnor 1910).

PEC

Peregrine

Falco peregrinus

Scarce year-round visitor, especially winter, from north/west/south Britain, rare breeder

Greatly admired by birdwatchers and falconers alike, this most cosmopolitan of all raptors breeds discontinuously from the High Arctic of North America and Eurasia to the southernmost parts of South America, Africa and Australia. It is, however, scarce or rare over much of this vast range and its strange absence from many archipelagos, and even islands as large as Iceland and New Zealand, has long been remarked upon (*eg* Voous 1960). Its breeding range is scattered over 40 per cent of the earth's landmass, yet its world population probably does not exceed five figures and is thus, for example, less than a third of that of the Kestrel in Europe alone (Ferguson-Lees & Christie 2001).

British Peregrines are thought to have declined during the 19th century as game preservation became more widespread and firearms more accurate (*1875–1900 Atlas*); they suffered also at the hands of pigeon-fanciers, egg-collectors and nest-robbing falconers. Then, under an emergency government order in 1940 and applied until the end of the war in 1945, nearly 600 adults and immatures were shot, and many young and eggs destroyed, because Peregrines were perceived to be a threat to carrier pigeons bringing messages from RAF airmen who had crash-landed at sea; as a result, Peregrine numbers were much reduced from some 800 pairs to fewer than 500 (Ferguson-Lees 1951, Ratcliffe 1980). The breeding population had still not fully recovered from these war-time depredations when, in the late 1950s and early 1960s, numbers fell again to 430–450 pairs because, at the top of the food chain, this predominantly bird-eating species was accumulating organochlorine pesticide residues from its prey (Ratcliffe 1980). Subsequent pesticide bans, coupled with national and local nest-protection, led to a remarkable recovery.

The national survey in 1991 found a total of 1283 pairs (Crick & Ratcliffe 1995), a notable increase from the previous lows; indeed, British numbers were then probably at their highest known level, forming between a fifth and a quarter of a European population which, excluding Russia, has been calculated at 5600 to 6100 pairs (*EBCC Atlas*). More recently, a national survey in 2002 found 1492 occupied territories and showed that, although numbers had risen in most of England, south Wales and southern Scotland, they had fallen in coastal north Wales, Northern Ireland and north and west Scotland. These regional decreases were attributed to a combination of food shortages, marine pollution, conflict with nesting Fulmars and, not least, human persecution (Crick *et al* 2003).

In 19th century Wiltshire, the Peregrine was a widespread visitor and a rare breeder. Smith (1887) noted a decline in sightings since 'thirty years ago' when it was 'almost… abundant', though he qualified this by adding 'I should mislead if I were to imply that it is by any means a rare bird even now'. He noted that Lord Pembroke had 'been assured by an old servant… that before his time Peregrines… used to build in the park at Wilton, until… driven away by the ravens' (though 'breed' would be a better word than 'build' as falcons do not construct nests for their eggs); and that nesting on Salisbury Cathedral 'is stoutly affirmed by some, though denied by others'. Smith also quoted the Reverend AP Morres as having seen up to 'four Peregrines soaring at one time' around the spire of the Cathedral, which offered 'an irresistible attraction as a secure resting-place', implying that this imposing medieval building was then used, as it is again now, for roosting. Morres himself (1882) had written 'About 1864 or 1865, I one day noticed no less than four Peregrines, all soaring round the spire at the same time…This certainly looked like the old ones with their young, but unfortunately I cannot remember the date or time of year, though I feel sure it was in the summer or early autumn'.

While noting that breeding Kestrels had occasionally been wrongly reported as Peregrines, Ratcliffe (1980) felt able to list nine 'fully authenticated nestings' on Salisbury Cathedral: in 1864 or 1865 (young reared), 1879 (eggs laid), 1880 (evidently nesting), 1896 (two young taken for falconry), 1929 (see below), 1932–34 (broods reared each year), and one of the years 1951–53 (two young fledged). There may, however, be confusion over one of these dates (1929) and possibly over a second (1880), while two others (1934, 1953) seem at best circumstantial; on the credit side, one certain (1931) and another circumstantial (1955) can be added.

Perhaps the most complicated of all these records involves a possible confusion between 1878 and 1880. In 1949, Major WM Congreve (*Oologists' Record* 21–22) reported the discovery of 'a volume of Seebohm's "British Birds and their Eggs" once in the possession of the Revd. Arthur P. Morres of Britford' into which had been pasted a photograph inscribed 'Photograph of two Peregrine eggs dropped in the gutters of Salisbury Cathedral Tower. Taken by Canon Swaine, 1878'. Congreve thought that these were probably 'the two still in existence in Salisbury Museum'. On the other hand, Morres himself (*The Zoologist* 1882: 18–20) referred to nesting attempts in 1879 and 1880 (the same years as Ratcliffe): in 1879 'the boy who rings the bell got up and took the eggs' and in 1880 'one of the Canons' took 'two eggs [laid] in two different gutters'. Thus, while 1878 may seem at first sight to have been an additional year, there were reports for both 1878 and 1880 of 'two eggs…in…gutters', each involving a 'Canon': it seems likely that both Congreve's '1878' and Morres's '1880' may have related to the same event, but in that case who wrongly noted the year – Morres, or the inscriber of the photograph in the book that had been in Morres's possession? And why did Ratcliffe's reference to 1880 not mention eggs at all?

The remaining amendments to the Salisbury Cathedral story are all based entirely on entries in *WANHM* for 1929–55. The early issues used the word 'nested' for two additional years, 1928 and 1931, the latter 'after an absence of [nesting for] two years' – which suggests that Ratcliffe's '1929', when the only observation was a pair seen daily in 'autumn', may have been a miscalculation – and also confirmed the rearing of broods in 1932 and 1933. For 1934, however, it was noted simply that Peregrines had been seen 'often, occasionally four at a time'. The only reference in the first two years of Ratcliffe's 1951–53 period was to three roosting in December 1951. In 1953, however, after a male was found dying on 3 May 1953, the 'Bishop of Salisbury reported that three [Peregrines] were seen circling' on 8 July, and a pair was seen on the 31st. Lastly, four were watched 'circling…and calling' on 20 July 1955. The four, three and four Peregrines in the summers of 1934, 1953 and 1955 may all indicate adults with one or two juveniles, bringing the number of nestings to eight or nine 'confirmed' and three 'circumstantial'; the last two are also of particular interest as by then Peirson (1959) considered Peregrines to be merely non-breeding visitors to the county, frequent in autumn but scarce in winter.

The catastrophic national decline of the British breeding population from the late 1950s was, not surprisingly, reflected in Wiltshire. In 1962, *WANHM* reported that an area of Salisbury Plain where Peregrines could always be found during autumn and winter was now deserted; and Webber (1968), summarising the ten years from 1957, could find just 16 records. Buxton (1981) noted that the species was seen 'most often…between October and March' and described it as 'uncommon and irregular', with zero to seven records a year during 1974–79 (*Hobby*). The *1981–84 Winter Atlas* showed Peregrines in just six of Wiltshire's 33 core 10-km squares, though even that was better than in large areas of inland central and southeast England, where none was noted at all.

Table 49. Peregrines *Falco peregrinus* in Wiltshire: breeding pairs and young fledged 1995–2000

	95	96	97	98	99	00
Pairs	1	1	1	2	2	2
Young	1	1	3	2	1	3

But the fortunes of the British population were changing. Palmer (1991) reported an encouraging 50 per cent increase in records during 1980–89, and the winter of 1988/89 saw the species roosting once again on Salisbury Cathedral; all except one sighting in that period were between August and April, most from November to February. Reports increased steadily in the early 1990s, and from 1993 became too numerous to be listed individually in *Hobby*. During 1998–2000, the annual totals of WOS record cards submitted for Peregrines in Wiltshire were 44, 56 and 35, and in each year a number of these held several observations apiece.

In 1995 a pair fledged a single chick in Wiltshire, the first known breeding in the county for some 40 years – but this time not on Salisbury Cathedral – and in the next five years raised a total of nine more (table 49). The second pair in the table attempted to nest but failed in 1998 when the female was in first-year plumage, was present throughout 1999 without evidence of breeding, and succeeded in raising a single chick in 2000. Adult Peregrines, which often roost as pairs, regularly winter at sites where they are not going to nest, such as Salisbury and CWP, but it is unclear whether these are individuals that have bred or been reared in the county (PE Castle).

A juvenile with a damaged wing, picked up near Burderop in mid-September 1989, was unusually pale and thought to resemble one of the arctic races, which are highly migratory and, in general, lighter-coloured at all ages. The wing-formula confirmed its identification as a Peregrine, but the measurements and a photograph taken are no longer available. Pale-plumaged juveniles do occasionally occur in the nominate race (*eg* Forsman 1999), which includes the British breeding population.

By the end of the 20th century, Peregrines could be encountered in Wiltshire at any time of the year and in any habitat, including such urban areas as Swindon, but there remained a bias towards winter. The standard winter map, based on 2-hour tetrad counts, is not reproduced here because it shows presence in only five of the county's 33 core 10-km squares and four of the 15 part squares, but this is misleading and an artefact of the survey method: a total of 86 casual observations submitted on WOS record cards for November–February in 1998/99 and 1999/2000 involved 23 core and five part squares have been mapped instead (figure 36). The 2-hour winter counts produced a total of ten observations

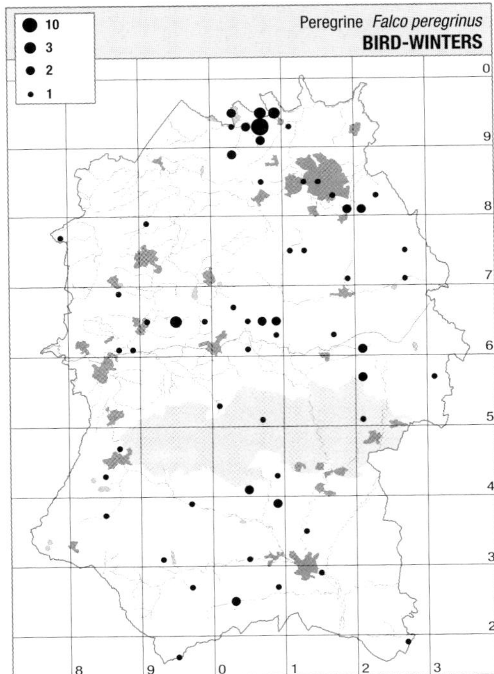

Figure 36. Peregrines *Falco peregrinus* in Wiltshire: winter distribution and numbers 1998/99–1999/00, plotted by tetrads but based on casual records, not 2-hour counts

in nine of the sample tetrads, and extrapolation to include the remainder suggests a winter population of 17 individuals. Casual records clearly show that the species is more widespread at that season and, although Peregrines are highly mobile, the total could lie in the region of 30–50. Starlings and Feral Pigeons are the favoured prey of Peregrines at Swindon – where long-stayers, usually immatures, occur from late summer to late winter – while Golden Plovers and Common Teals apparently predominate at CWP (PE Castle).

Given the generally improved fortunes of British Peregrines, and increased nesting in recent years in neighbouring Gloucestershire, Somerset, Dorset and Hampshire, it seems likely that more pairs will establish themselves in the county.

PCo & IJF-L

Sponsored by James Ferguson-Lees

Water Rail

Rallus aquaticus

Locally common winter visitor from Britain and central/east Europe, rare breeder

Their preference for thickly vegetated wetlands, and the secrecy of their behaviour, make Water Rails difficult to see. Indeed, they are more often heard, especially when 'sharming' – a combination of pig-like squeals and grunts which they may utter by day or night, at any time of year, though especially at dawn and dusk just before and during the breeding season. Both sexes also have a more rhythmic 'courtship song' of three or four syllables, which may or may not end with a harsh trill, but this and other groans and whistles are less well known.

Water Rails are found throughout much of Europe north to southern Fenno-Scandia and central Russia, and thence discontinuously across central Asia to Japan, south also to North Africa, the Middle East and China. Those that breed in the temperate zones bordering on the Atlantic, the North Sea, the Mediterranean and the Black Sea are mostly resident; elsewhere in Europe (as in much of Asia) the species is migratory and moves south and southwest for the winter. The European population, excluding Russia, has been estimated at between 130,000 and 240,000 pairs (*EBCC Atlas*) – and there are possibly twice as many in Asia (Taylor & van Perlo 1998) – but recent decreases, especially in eastern Europe, may be linked to agricultural intensification and the associated drainage of wetlands (*EBCC Atlas*).

In Great Britain, Water Rails occur in mosaics of static or slow-moving freshwater with tall emergent vegetation and usually some open expanses of mud, habitats that were once far more widespread. In the 19th century this was considered a common breeding species throughout much of the country, including Wiltshire, but drainage, shooting and egg-collecting – both birds and eggs were regarded as delicacies – led to local extinctions. Even so, the broad distribution was little affected until the 1930s, after which a general decline resulted in its loss by the 1960s as a breeding bird in much of Scotland and Wales, as well as in central, northeast and southwest England (*1968–72 Atlas*). The *1988–91 Atlas* put the British population at 450–900 pairs, and indicated nearly twice as many in Ireland, compared with the earlier and rather larger combined estimate in the *1968–72 Atlas* of 2000–4000 pairs, and attributed the apparent decrease to the canalisation of waterways, partial drainage of bogs, urban development on coastal marshes, and loss of waterside vegetation. In nature reserves, however, the creation of new, managed wetlands has partly compensated for the loss of natural habitat. The breeding population is then swollen in winter by immigrants from north and central Europe, and formerly perhaps Iceland.

The Water Rail was apparently once widespread in the county, has probably declined over the last 150 years, although reports on its status are sometimes conflicting. Smith (1887) described it as 'a very common bird in wet and marshy districts... especially numerous in the low lands near Salisbury... I have instances of its occurrence in all parts of the county', and he included it in his list of species known to breed. On the other hand, in the Marlborough area, both Bosworth Smith (1863) and im Thurn (1873) had earlier stated that it was found in small numbers in winter, but never stayed to nest. Meyrick (1895, 1906) gave it as a resident, not uncommon – if shy – on the Kennet, but that a nest and eggs had been found only once, in 1885. Peirson (1919) noted it as an uncommon resident, and Peirson & Walford (1930) also as an uncommon and irregular resident. In the second half of the 20th century, too, the species was variously summarised as 'a local resident, seemingly scarce, but perhaps only overlooked' (Halliday & Randolph 1955); usually in winter in osier beds, 'especially in the Kennet valley below Marlborough' (Kennedy 1966); 'Regular and locally common during winter with a very few records between May and August' (Buxton 1981); and 'locally common winter visitor and very rare breeder' (Palmer 1991).

It is important to look in greater detail at the records in *WANHM* over the 45-year period between the first and last of its annual reports on the birds of Wiltshire, though at times the picture is confused: in 1929, the Water Rail was considered 'a rather scarce resident in N. Wilts, though not uncommon in the southern half of the county'; in 1932, LG Peirson had 'the impression that this very shy bird is increasing', an impression supported by other observers the following year; in 1933, there were 'Breeding records from Stratford..., Britford... [and] Longford' (four observers); and in 1934, 'Breeding records at Britford' (three observers). While it might be argued that the last two entries could simply have been overenthusiastic interpretations of summer records – with no real proof of nesting – there seems less doubt about another 1934 observation, to the effect that the species was 'not infrequently seen at Orcheston but a pair nested there when the meadows were in flood'. In the 1930s, incidentally, there were also several references to Water Rails flying into overhead wires, including, in 1936, 'An extraordinary number of these birds was found dead in various parts of the county and in most instances death was due to contact with telegraph wires'.

Whereas the previous paragraph suggests a number of reports of Water Rails breeding in the county in the 1930s, it is surprising to find that the editors of *WANHM* for 1959 noted that there was 'only one breeding record for the county – that for 1951'; yet *WANHM* for 1951 mentioned simply that 'A juvenile was found dead... near Melksham on Aug. 23'. Moreover, the observation of a juvenile at Swindon STW on 25 July 1965 – a whole month earlier – attracted the editorial comment that it 'may indicate local breeding but there is still no Wiltshire record of nesting'. In between, 'Young were seen at Rodbourne sewage farm [Swindon STW]' in 1954 (no month given); and a juvenile trapped at Coate Water on 28 August 1964 was, at the time, reported as 'very early for passage'; and, later, 'An apparent juvenile seen in Jul. [1973] possibly indicating breeding nearby' (no locality given). It is not known how much of this evidence from *WANHM* Buxton (1981) took into account, but he still stated that it 'has not yet been proved to breed in the county'.

More recently, there has been an increase in summer sightings, as well as two definite breeding records: a chick seen at Coate Water on 5 June 1982; and a nest found at Granham near Marlborough on 30 June 1987. Water Rails were also recorded during every month in 1997, 1999 and 2000 at CWP, where breeding must surely occur. The summer distribution map shows Water Rails to be quite widely but very sparsely scattered across the county at

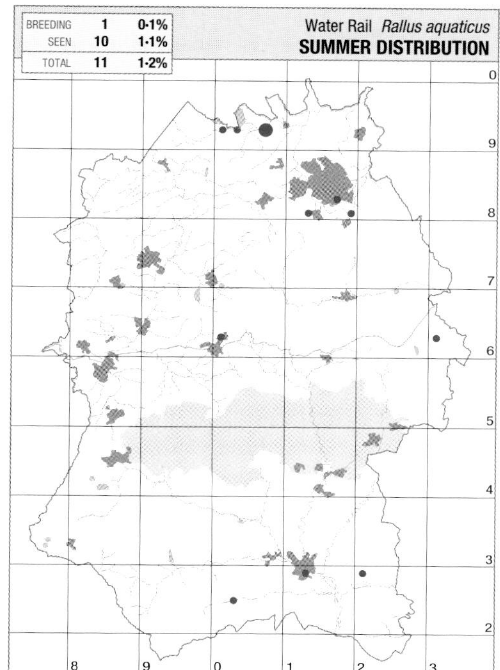

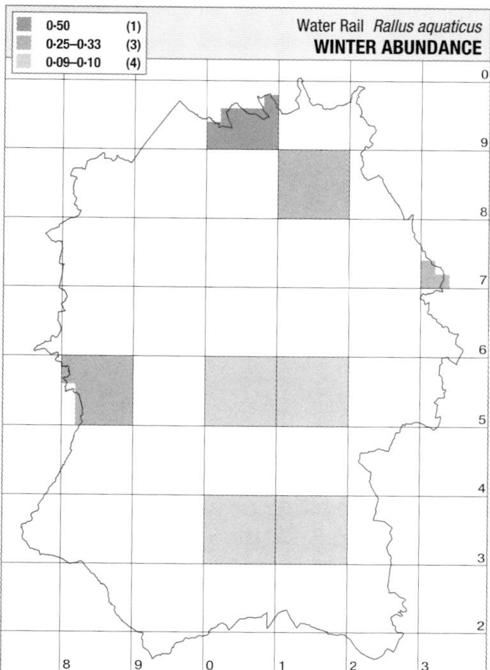

that season. Moreover, the number of the 33 core 10-km squares in which they have been found has remained at only five during each of the *1968–72 Atlas*, the *1988–91 Atlas* and the 1995–2000 WOS summer survey. On present knowledge, any estimate of the county's breeding population must be highly speculative but, even allowing that the summer map almost certainly underplays the distribution, it seems unlikely that the Wiltshire total exceeds more than a handful of pairs.

Most observations in the first three decades after the 1939–45 War, generally at six to ten sites a year, related to autumn and winter, usually October–February (*WANHM*). Favoured localities over this period were vegetated still-waters and rivers (particularly those along the Salisbury Avon): Corsham Lake, Swindon STW, Coate Water, Axford, Chilton Foliat, Figheldean, Idmiston, the Woodfords, Harnham, Petersfinger and Britford were mentioned regularly, as were watercress beds. Of 37 sight records 'widely distributed' in 1962, 21 were in November–December; and, of 16 in 1963, seven – in addition to 'Many seen in lower Kennet during the cold spell' – were in January–March (*WANHM*): the exceptionally prolonged hard winter of 1962/63 probably involved larger influxes from the Continent and the evidently declining numbers perhaps suggest mortality in the big freeze.

Turning to *Hobby*, over 100 Wiltshire records in 1976, all in January–April or August–December, may also have resulted from larger-than-usual influxes, from a general population growth or, simply, from more intensive observation, but reports from 28 localities in 1983 and 'numerous records' in 1984 reinforce the idea of real winter increases. Throughout the 1980s and 1990s, although records stayed concentrated in the winter months, often with marked influxes in November, there were usually reports from at least ten sites, and occasionally from over 20. Because of the difficulty of catching this species, only two Water Rails were ringed in the county during 1965–2000, but two from abroad have been recovered in Wiltshire: single adults found dead at Pewsey in April 1969 and Steeple Langford in February 1985 had been ringed at Hannover (Germany) in September 1966 and Moen (Belgium) in April 1982 respectively.

In Wiltshire, Water Rails are mostly seen singly, but counts of five have not been infrequent. Ten at Corsham in October 1965 were 'presumed to be grounded by fog' (*WANHM*), but seven on the Kennet between Axford and Marlborough in December 1995, eight at Swindon STW in early 2000 and, in particular, a noteworthy observation of 20 disturbed when an area of sedge was cut at Standlynch Meadows in November 1999 (*Hobby*) are all perhaps indicative of the numbers that simply remain hidden at most sites.

It seems clear that Water Rails are relatively common in Wiltshire in winter, in areas of suitable habitat. Numbers vary greatly from year to year, however, as can distribution: the 1998–2000 winter survey reported them in only seven of the county's 33 core 10-km squares, compared with no fewer than 24 in the *1981–84 Winter Atlas*. Possible reasons for such variation may include national breeding success, cold weather either in Great Britain and on the Continent, and local conditions: Water Rails become more visible when frost, snow and ice force them to venture into the open, where they may then feed on carrion or even kill small birds. The winter map demonstrates the importance of CWP for this species and probably reflects not only the amount of suitable habitat that some of the lakes there provide, but also the degree of observer coverage: many of Wiltshire's other waterways are private and so have restricted access. Extrapolation from the sample counts suggests a winter total of around 30, though the actual population of this essentially skulking bird is more likely to be as high as, or even exceed, 100.

(See also page 724.)

WEQ

Sponsored by Humphrey Kay

Spotted Crake

Porzana porzana

Vagrant, apparently nested 1881 and 1933, breeds Europe, winters Africa

Breeding in wet places with tangled cover across west and central Eurasia, from Norway, Great Britain (although now very locally) and Spain east to southwest Siberia and northwest China, Spotted Crakes winter mainly in sub-Saharan Africa and the Indian region, though a few go no farther than the area of the Nile delta. They were formerly fairly common and nested in most British counties, but the loss of favoured marshy habitats led to a rapid decline during the first half of the 19th century, and they became very local summer visitors by 1900 (*1875–1900 Atlas*).

A national census in 1999 found 46–77 singing males: these were concentrated mainly in eastern and northern England, and mid and north Scotland, but, although no Wiltshire sites were surveyed, some were as close to this county as Dorset, Gloucestershire and Somerset (Gilbert 2002, *RBBP*). Spotted Crakes also pass through Great Britain as scarce migrants: the annual average during 1986–2000 was 63, occurring almost anywhere though most often in southern and eastern England, chiefly in August–October but (excluding the singing males) some in April–May or late June–July and odd ones even in winter (Fraser & Rogers 2001, 2002).

The earliest recorded Spotted Crake in Wiltshire appears to be one killed at Devizes in June 1849, which was in the collection of Robert Cummings at the Albert Memorial

Museum in Exeter (D'Urban, in Aplin 1891). Smith (1887) believed this species to be 'not in reality uncommon... it escapes observation, and is supposed by many to be a rarer bird than it really is'. Beginning with one at Christian Malford in October 1849, he mentioned a dozen further records for the next 38 years – three involving individuals picked up dead under telegraph wires (*cf* Water Rail) – and also that an egg from a clutch of 12 in a nest 'cut out in a clover-field adjoining a marsh beside the stream at Mere' was identified at the office of *The Field* in June 1881 as belonging to this species. That identification was treated with some scepticism by Peirson (1959), though Buxton (1981) appeared more inclined to accept it. Spotted Crake eggs should be distinguishable from those of both Water Rail and Corncrake, the only conceivable alternatives, being generally smaller in size, lighter in weight and darker in ground colour, and one would expect that, in the late 19th century, *The Field* would have had ready access to competent oologists. If 'adjoining' a streamside marsh meant 'close to', the dry site is not unreasonable, though clover is a favoured habitat of Corncrake.

Seven others, all found dead under telegraph wires, were recorded between 1872 and 1924 (Hony 1915a, Halliday & Randolph 1955, Peirson 1959). There followed singletons at Lydiard Millicent in February and October 1929; one and sometimes two (believed to have bred) at Britford throughout April–August 1933; and, more recently, one caught by a dog near Stockton in November 1957, another by a cat at Idmiston in June 1969, and singletons calling at Corsham in August 1969 and October 1971 (all *WANHM*), these being the last Wiltshire records of the 20th century. (See also page 726.)

That this species is generally under-recorded is undeniable, and Wiltshire may be no exception. The distinctive 'song' – a rhythmically and rapidly repeated, upslurred *h'wit*, audible for at least a kilometre on a calm night – is variously likened to a whiplash at close range and to dripping water at a distance. But how many people regularly survey suitable habitats in the county at night in May and June? Mauro (1994) found that males stopped singing once they had mated, and that isolated males were less likely to sing, which must further exacerbate the problems of location.

WEQ

Corncrake

Crex crex

Nested to 1950s, now rare migrant, breeds north Britain/Europe, winters Africa

The unmistakable disyllabic 'song', or territorial call, of the male Corncrake – a rasping *crek-crek* – can still be heard in summer, mostly at night, in many areas from Ireland across Europe and central Asia to the vicinity of Lake Baikal in Siberia, but over much of western Europe this species has greatly decreased or entirely disappeared over the past 100 years. The decline was evident early in the 20th century, but its speed and associated contractions in range accelerated from the 1970s, and populations dropped by more than 50 per cent in many countries. In Europe, the largest numbers remaining are in Belarus, Russia and the Baltic States, these countries alone now holding at least three-quarters of the world breeding population, which has been roughly estimated at 100,000 to 200,000 pairs; some thousands of pairs are also found in Poland, Romania, Bulgaria and the Ukraine, and up to four figures in Sweden, Finland and Moldova; excluding Russia, the European total has been put more precisely at between 87,500 and 97,000 pairs (*EBCC Atlas*).

For nesting, Corncrakes favour hay and clover – rarely, other habitats such as cereals – and they winter entirely in grassland and savannah in sub-Saharan Africa, mainly from central Tanzania and Mozambique to eastern South Africa (Urban *et al* 1986). They used to be found in every county of Great Britain in the 19th century, and there was no evidence of falling populations until about 1880–1900, when a slight decline was linked to the mechanisation of mowing (*1875–1900 Atlas*). In the face of the spread of this activity, as well as the introduction of faster-growing grasses and the development of silage – both of which have allowed earlier and earlier cutting – and the loss of meadowland to permanent sheep pasture, numbers continued to fall throughout the 20th century. The *1968–72 Atlas* mapped most in the north and west, though there were isolated records elsewhere, but by the *1988–91 Atlas* virtually all were confined to the Hebrides and Orkney: national population estimates were 2640 'pairs' in 1968–72, 730–750 calling males in 1978–79 and 550–600 in 1988. In 2000, 622 pairs or singing males were recorded (*RBBP*).

Maton (1843), who was born in January 1774, wrote that 'This bird was very common in corn-fields about Salisbury in my younger days; but I have understood that they do not breed there now'. Bosworth Smith (1863) recorded that it appeared at Marlborough about 22 April and that in 1858 one was disturbed several times 'in the [Savernake] Forest', and im Thurn (1870) commented that 'this clever ventriloquist is in reality common... seldom seen though often heard. Its eggs are observed nearly every year... chiefly breeds amongst growing corn', adding that it was usually first seen around the third week of April. Smith (1887) observed that the Corncrake was 'familiar to the partridge shooter', 'common enough in our cornfields in summer', and 'very common at this day in all parts of the county'; he noted, too, that (a century earlier) 'Gilbert White speaks of it as having been abundant in the low wet bean fields of Christian Malford in North Wilts'. Morres (1878–85) had described this species as 'Known to everyone who has ever carried a gun in September' and, with limited foresight, considered that 'a cry raised that these birds were deserting our shores' was 'without foundation. Their numbers vary from year to year'.

Old 19th century gamebooks of the Goddard Estate at Swindon, Knoyle House near Mere, the Methuen Estate at Corsham, and Ramsbury Manor all support Morres's comment about September shoots (SB Edwards). At Stourhead, too, 16 were shot in September 1867, but none thereafter through to 1874, the last year for which the records are available; nevertheless, none was noted as shot on the Bentley Wood estate during 1757–61, the only period for which the gamebook records are available there (ID Collins).

Peirson (1919) referred to Corncrakes as common summer visitors that had decreased, but were recovering. A decade later, Peirson & Walford (1930) considered that they had almost vanished, but Peirson (1939) then noted that they had occasionally been recorded in the last few years and, 20 years later, the same author (1959) wrote, 'By 1906 it was scarce, by 1915 rare and by 1923 it had almost vanished. In the early 1930s it was a little less rare'. As a summary, however, this was perhaps misleading. *WANHM* reported a few pairs in the Wylye valley in 1927 and 1928, and in 1929 described the Corncrake as 'Scarce as a breeding species, but fairly common on Autumn and Spring migration in North Wilts; in South Wilts... seems to be on the increase'. In 1931 there were eight breeding records, and one observer described it as 'more numerous than for many years past'; 1932 also produced at least eight breeding records and others heard calling in summer, but reports from different areas ranged from 'more frequently' to 'now absent', an annually varying pattern that continued over the next few years, though 1936 still apparently had seven breeding reports. The only records in the 1939–45 War years, when little was published, were one heard near Marlborough in May, three seen in late August and one at Phantom

Wood on 10 July, all in 1944 (*WANHM, DSBL*). During 1946–73, however, Corncrakes were reported in every year bar two: there were ten records in 1949 and 1952, eight in 1953, six in 1950 and five in 1951, and from 1954 onwards the maxima were four records apiece in 1955, 1965, 1966 and 1972 (*WANHM*).

Buxton (1981) put forward a 'Recent average of one sight record per year' and, like Peirson, stated that there had been just two certain breeding records since the 1939–45 War. *WANHM*, however, documented no fewer than three in the post-war period: 'nesting near Draycot Cerne' in 1946; 'adult and five young at West Grimstead' on 18 July 1949; and 'family of adult and young birds… at the end of June near Trafalgar' in 1952. Palmer (1991) knew of only seven records of the species in 1980–89, four in spring and three in autumn, and 1990–2000 produced just five more: near Longleat on 29 September 1991; seen and heard at Swindon on 6 May 1992; singing from clover in the Nadder valley through 13–27 July 1993; at the edge of set-aside at Milston on 17 August 1995; and flushed during a shoot at Everleigh on 24 November 1999.

Peirson (1959) noted winter records at Salisbury on 20 December 1899 and at Chippenham on 18 January 1954; the latter was 'in first year plumage found dead in a public park' (*WANHM*).

There have been some improvements in the Corncrake's fortunes at the end of the 20th century – primarily as a result of sympathetic grassland management, particularly in western Scotland – but the future for this globally threatened species remains uncertain at best and to hope that Corncrakes might yet become more regular again in the county will require much change to the wider countryside throughout its range.

(See also page 726.)

NPA & PCo

Moorhen

Gallinula chloropus

Common and widespread resident, perhaps also winter visitor from Europe

This is the commonest of Wiltshire's rails, found almost anywhere there is water. Yet, although a Moorhen skittering across the surface, or two combatants sparring, are familiar sights, the species' presence is often betrayed only by occasional croaking, clucking and chattering calls or by characteristic flicks of laterally white undertail-coverts as one skulks around the edges of reeds. Thus, it is likely that many go undetected.

With a varied plant and animal diet, Moorhens are highly adaptable, breeding at a variety of lowland lakes, canals, rivers, streams and ponds, often very small ones, and even slurry pits, particularly where there is sufficient emergent or surrounding cover. Not infrequently they feed, and may occasionally nest, some distance from water, then becoming much less skulking. Particularly in autumn or winter, for example, scattered groups may regularly be seen feeding out in the open, in short-cropped fields that are no more than damp. At some sites, Moorhens have grown accustomed to people and then, in public parks and at riverside picnic sites, often come with tame Mallards to bread.

Moorhens typically nest low in waterside vegetation, but also not unusually up to 8 m above ground in bushes or trees (Campbell & Ferguson-Lees 1972). Reports in *Hobby* in

1995 included one pair nesting 2·5 m up in a tree at Westbury and another seen taking twigs up an inclined ivy-covered tree to a nest about 3·5 m above ground at Smallbrook, Warminster. More remarkably, back in 1934, one pair built in between the rafters in the roof of a barn, entering through a hole in the thatch, while that same year a pair at Pitton nested in a hawthorn hedge 'quite two and a half miles [4 km] from any river or pond', the birds being 'seen daily in the farmyard feeding and drinking with the chickens' (*WANHM*). Two other unusual Wiltshire nests have been on the ground 'in the middle of a bridle track... some distance from the nearest pond... in a tuft of marsh grass' in Spye Park in 1959, and in an 'open grassy meadow' near Chilton Foliat in 1973 (*WANHM*).

Found on every continent except Antarctica and Australia, Moorhens are distributed throughout Europe, where they may be resident, dispersive or migratory, those from the northeast moving west and south in winter. A susceptibility to cold and, often, a lack of suitable waterside cover account for their absence from upland waters. There are an estimated 240,000 breeding territories in Great Britain and most of the high densities are in the lowlands of central and eastern England from Lancashire and Yorkshire southwards, while the species is generally much scarcer in the southwest (*1988–91 Atlas*). This is a pattern that appears to have changed little over the last two centuries despite loss and drainage of many wetland areas (*1875–1900 Atlas*), and the numbers represent a sizeable proportion of the population of Europe as a whole, which, excluding Russia, has been put at between 904,000 and 1·2 million pairs (*EBCC Atlas*).

This waterbird's often secretive nature usually precludes anything like complete counts, so quantifying its abundance is difficult. Most early authors recorded it as 'abundant', 'common' or 'frequently met with'. Smith (1887) considered the Moorhen to be 'the most common species of the whole family', but made no specific remarks about its Wiltshire status. From the first regular 'Report on Wiltshire birds' in *WANHM* in 1929 through to the early 1960s, the only reference to numbers or status was a laconic comment in 1933 that 'this confirmed egg thief is increasing'. Peirson (1959) simply noted the Moorhen as a 'very common resident on all waters'. But then the prolonged severe weather in the first quarter of 1963 resulted in such observations in *WANHM* as 'High mortality', 'Badly affected', 'Missing from usual haunts', 'Twenty found dead along the Bybrook', and 'Feeding in gardens, farmyards, etc., during cold weather'; only a year later, however, comments on the species were already, 'Numbers recovering', 'back to normal' and 'common'.

BTO survey data for Great Britain as a whole show that the breeding population of the Moorhen has fluctuated along linear waterways – though with no long-term trend – whereas numbers nesting on farmland have declined since 1972, perhaps indicating a decline in farm ponds, but characterised by a significant reduction in breeding performance (*BBWC*). Buxton (1981) recorded that the species 'is common where suitable habitats are available', also noting that during the 1960s Moorhens showed a tendency to colonise drier habitats in Wiltshire but that 'recently numbers may have declined and reversed that trend'. This reversal clearly mirrors the national BTO survey data for farmland, where loss of waterbodies and poorer water quality may be to blame. Moorhens are not infrequent road traffic victims and also hold the dubious honour of being, in 1533, the first bird species known to have been shot with a gun (Gurney 1921).

The *1968–72* and *1988–91 Atlases*, and the summer tetrad survey in 1995–2000, all found Moorhens breeding in every one of the county's 33 core 10-km squares. The pattern in the greater detail of the summer distribution map corresponds well with the mosaic of rivers, streams, lakes and ponds in Wiltshire, and demonstrates the absence of this species from SPTA and the higher chalk downlands. The summer abundance map shows high concentrations along the Kennet & Avon Canal – a long-favoured site which, however, saw a reduction in Moorhen numbers as bank cover was lost from some stretches during

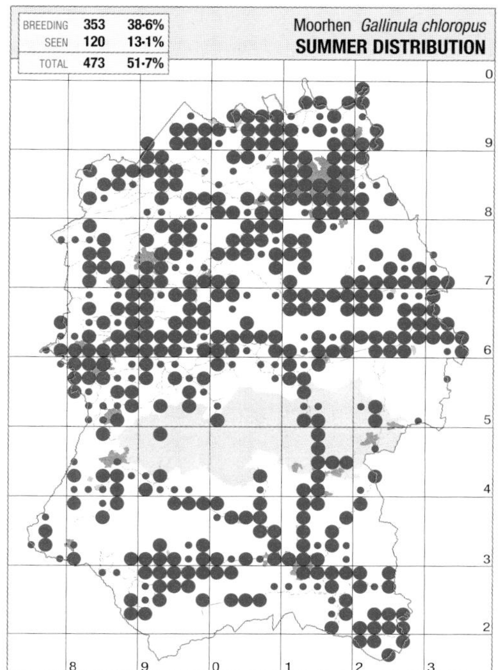

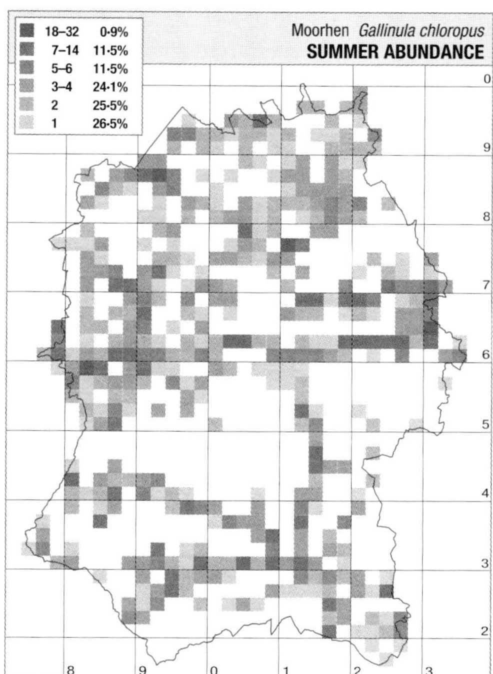

the restoration for boating – and along the Salisbury Avon and its tributaries, but also in some urban areas, particularly Swindon and towns in the west. The summer counts totalled only 1510 Moorhens; using BBS data from Wiltshire produces a figure of 6700 territories; and the *1988–91 Atlas* suggested an average density of 0·026 territories per hectare across farmland in Great Britain, which might indicate a total of just under 9700 'pairs' for Wiltshire's 915 tetrads, though a large part of this county's farmland – being chalk downland – is likely to support lower densities than the national average. A Wiltshire total of 2500 to 5000 territories is thus proposed, but any estimate for this often skulking species can be only a rough approximation.

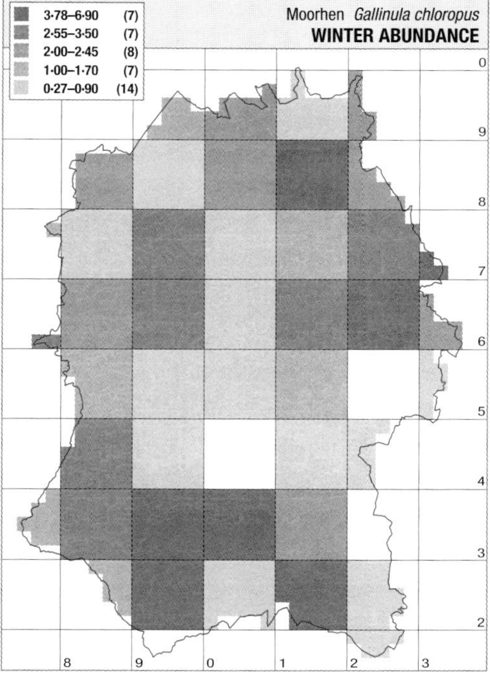

In winter, immigrants from the Continent swell numbers in Great Britain, but it has been suggested that, even without these migrants, the British winter population would be over one million birds (*1981–84 Winter Atlas*). Extrapolation of the winter tetrad counts would suggest a Wiltshire population of some 1900 Moorhens, perhaps as little as one tenth of the true total, here estimated at 5000–15,000 individuals. The similarity of the winter and summer maps might suggest that our population is largely sedentary, a picture confirmed by the fact that all of the 12 recoveries from the 139 ringed in the county during 1965–2000 have been within Wiltshire and only three of them had moved more than 9 km. On the other hand, two Moorhens ringed in Lincolnshire in October 1971 and August 1978 were, respectively, found dead in Wiltshire in February 1972 and picked up sick in Swindon in May 1981.

Not surprisingly, there have been relatively few reports of high numbers of Moorhens in Wiltshire, although counts for Corsham Lake exceeded 50 on five occasions in the late 1960s and early 1970s, including 116 in January 1972 (*WANHM*), still the largest figure for a single site in the county. Two more sites to have produced counts of over 50 are Bodenham (highest 94 in October 1992) and Wilton Water (75 in February 1994). The only other is CWP but even there, the highest WeBS total (for all Wiltshire lakes combined) was just 55 in October 1994.

PCo & IJF-L

Coot

Fulica atra

Common resident, also moult migrant and winter and hard-weather immigrant

'Bald as a Coot' is a common phrase, but only the forehead is a bare white shield extending up from the white bill of this otherwise nondescript blackish waterbird. Coots are far more conspicuous than other members of the rail and gallinule family, because, like ducks, they are often seen in flocks on open lakes and reservoirs; they also frequently announce their presence by harsh calls and aggressive behaviour.

This species has an extensive distribution in the Old World, from western Europe and parts of North Africa east through central Asia to Japan, as well as from India patchily to Australasia. The breeding population of Europe, excluding Russia, has been estimated at between 1·1 and 1·3 million pairs (*EBCC Atlas*). Western European Coots are basically sedentary or dispersive, but ringing has shown a number of long-distance movements from southeast England to southwest France and Spain, mostly involving juveniles ringed between mid July and the end of August and recovered in the same year (*Migration Atlas*). Coots that breed in Fenno-Scandia and countries east of the Czech Republic are largely migratory, and Brown (1955) suggested coastal passage along the southern Baltic, North Sea and north French coasts; he concluded that Coots moved into Great Britain to winter and probably also occurred on passage here. Cold-weather movements may bring Coots from Continental breeding populations into, particularly southeast, England (*Migration Atlas*).

The *1988–91 Atlas* estimated the minimum summer population of Great Britain at 46,000 birds (not translating that figure into pairs because of the difficulty of deciding the proportions of non-breeders). WBS and CBC data have indicated a consistent and moderate increase since the early 1970s (*BBWC*), a pattern reflected in Wiltshire by a rise in the number of the county's 33 core 10-km squares in which the species was recorded during the two national atlas periods and the WOS tetrad survey: 28 in 1968–72, 30 in 1988–91, and 32 in 1995–2000.

The Coot may have been relatively local and uncommon in Wiltshire in the mid 19th century, particularly in summer, though some of the references are conflicting. Bosworth Smith (1863) noted that it was seen occasionally in severe winters at Ramsbury, while

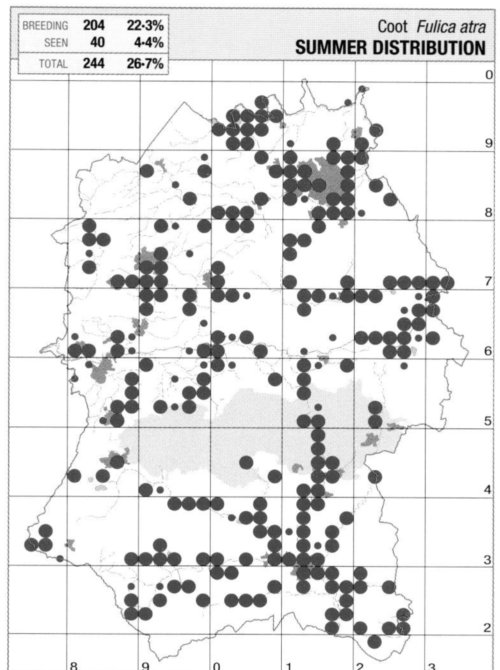

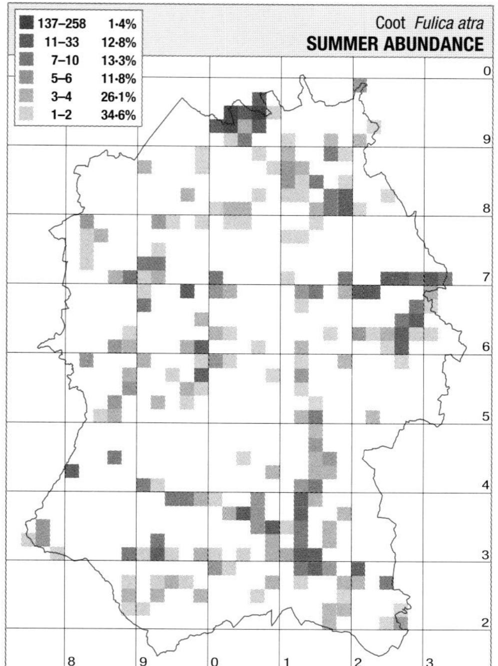

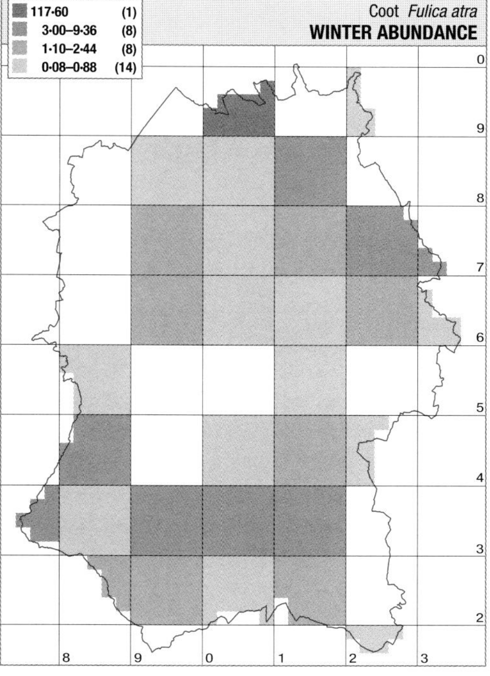

im Thurn (1870) recorded it as 'far from common' in the Marlborough area, though resident in some numbers at Swindon reservoir (now Coate Water), adding that only a few were to be seen at Ramsbury Chase where, however, two to three nests were likely every year; in winter, some would also appear on the Marlborough water meadows. Smith (1887) considered the Coot 'a common bird, generally to be found in the haunts of the Moorhen'. On the other hand, Meyrick (1895) regarded this as only 'a local species', in some numbers at Swindon reservoir and on the broad waters of the Kennet above Chilton, but elsewhere occurring only occasionally. Peirson (1919) wrote that the Coot was a 'fairly common but very local resident' in the Marlborough area and, forty years later, referring to the county as a whole, the same author (1959) reported it as a common resident whose numbers 'seem to increase in winter'. This seasonal change was endorsed by Buxton (1981), who recorded that 'Numbers increase considerably during the late autumn particularly in the Cotswold Water Park'.

Unlike Moorhens, Coots generally avoid small and overgrown ditches, streams and ponds, preferring larger and more open waterbodies. The summer tetrad survey reflected

Table 50. Coots *Fulica atra* in Wiltshire: peak winter counts at key sites 1990/91–1999/00

	90/91	91/92	92/93	93/94	94/95	95/96	96/97	97/98	98/99	99/00
CWP	1004	589	295	545	1637	1752	1436	1586	1721	1450
Coate Water	40	45	46	33	46	44	79	72	97	97
Ramsbury Lake	41	23	32	37	27	25	46	50	65	51
Chilton Foliat	51	49	47	88	20	62	44	47	65	48
Wilton Water	158	71	45	96	96	95	55	90	81	95
Corsham Lake	18	17	11	11	13	42	22	29	119	28
Longleat lakes	42	43	16	29	34	51	45	33	40	113
Fonthill Lake	84	110	60	87	89	48	100	50	150	104
Langford Lakes	251	225	85	59	–	–	–	–	–	–
Clarendon Lake	62	51	70	61	81	14	42	53	6	11

this preference, the majority being confined to the bigger lakes and gravel pits, but others were found along most of the major rivers; indeed, the Kennet, the easternmost Kennet & Avon Canal, and the Salisbury Avon and its tributaries supported some of the highest summer densities, rivalling those of CWP and Swindon. Coots will also exploit temporary floods, and in March 1979 a pair nested, albeit unsuccessfully, on floodwater on SPTA (West). The summer tetrad counts totalled 1826, but undoubtedly a good proportion of those – including the numbers that, at CWP in particular, build every year from July onwards, presumably to moult – were non-breeders or ones that had failed. Yet high breeding densities do occur at some sites: for example, Winter (1991) recorded 22 nests at Coate Water in 1990, at least ten of which were successful. Given that Coots were found nesting in over 200 tetrads during 1995–2000, the county's breeding population seems likely to be in the order of at least 400–600 pairs.

The ever-growing area of lakes at CWP has produced by far the largest non-breeding counts of Coots (table 50), and CWP West as a whole – including the Gloucestershire part – regularly holds in excess of 3500, which makes this one of the five most important sites for the species in Great Britain (*WeBS*). Numbers build there from late summer, and usually peak between September and December, presumably including arrivals from elsewhere in Great Britain. Few Coots are ringed, at least in Wiltshire (just one during 1965–2000), but two thus marked at Salisbury in February 1960 were later recovered at Bridgnorth (Shropshire) in June 1960, and at Keele (Staffordshire) in April 1962. Numbers at most other Wiltshire sites usually also peak in early winter, but counts at Wilton Water and Fonthill Lake are often high in late summer and then, curiously, have in several years dropped sharply by autumn (*Hobby*).

The Coot's favoured winter haunts in the county are, not surprisingly, the larger and well-established lakes, in keeping with the species' preference for still waters that are eutrophic with rich aquatic vegetation, and nine sites have held 50 or more on a number of occasions during the 1990s (table 50). Counts have sometimes also exceeded this number at eight other sites, seven of which are Bowood Lake (52), Westbury Ponds (72), Stourton lakes (150), Upper Woodford (78), Lower Woodford (50), Salisbury Avon (137 – counts there probably exceed this number regularly, but few are provided) and Standlynch (96). The eighth, Braydon Pond, was historically one of the most important Wiltshire lakes for this species – including records of 100 in 1949/50, 149 in 1955/56 and 340 in 1967/68 – but in only two winters during the 1990s did numbers reach double figures (*WeBS*). This accords reasonably with the winter abundance map, itself broadly similar to the summer distribution though with the marked concentration at CWP considerably higher than any in the rest of the county. Extrapolation from the winter counts indicates a

Wiltshire total in November–February of just over 3200 Coots, probably a realistic figure in view of the numbers at individual sites, though it may be that – as happens nationally (*WeBS*) – numbers are higher still in autumn.

SBE & IJF-L

Crane

Grus grus

Vagrant (4 modern records), breeds north Europe, winters southwest Europe/North Africa/Middle East

Cranes are summer visitors to their main breeding range, which extends from Fenno-Scandia and north Germany east through Russia and Ukraine to central Siberia. The north European population uses two distinct migration routes to winter quarters: southwest to France, Italy, Iberia and North Africa; and south and southeast to Asia Minor, the Middle East and northeast Africa. Smaller numbers that breed from Turkey eastwards are relatively sedentary.

This species was formerly more widespread in Europe, but its range decreased markedly from the Middle Ages, through drainage and disturbance, so much so that by the 17th century it had become extinct in most of the west and south. This trend continued into the 1960s, since when numbers have increased again in many areas, and the breeding population of Europe, excluding Russia, has recently been estimated at 22,800 to 28,000 pairs; isolated nesting occurs as far west as France and East Anglia (*EBCC Atlas*). Rather more also now pass through Great Britain on migration: the grand total recorded during 1958–2000 was nearly two thousand, but over one third of those came in a big influx of 685 in 1963; in only two other years were 100–200 noted and the annual average during 1990–2000 was 43 (Fraser & Rogers 2002).

Cranes used to breed commonly in the East Anglian fenlands, some until about 1600 (Witherby *et al* 1938–41, *BOU* 1971), but these elegant birds then became no more than scarce migrants or vagrants in Great Britain for the best part of 400 years. Since 1981, however, at least one pair – slowly increasing to four pairs – has attempted to nest each year in Norfolk, if only sometimes successfully. After eight consecutive years of failure, one of three pairs in 1997 and one of four pairs in 1998 and 1999 fledged one or two young annually, but the four pairs in 2000 all lost their eggs or young to predation (Taylor *et al* 1999, *RBBP*).

In Wiltshire, archaeological remains of Cranes were found at two sites dating from the Bronze and Iron Ages (table 5, page 69). In more recent times, Smith (1887) recorded 'In 1783 it was recorded in the Salisbury paper that a gentleman shot a Crane, on whose leg he found a piece of copper which he himself had attached in the year 1767, after having caught the same bird by means of a hawk: the copper plate bore his initials and the date 1767'. Smith (1887) noted, however, that the Grey Heron was 'generally known to the country people' as the 'crane', and many heronries were preserved for falconry (*1875–1900 Atlas*), so it is not unlikely that this event refers to a Grey Heron rather than a Crane. Yet there are some modern opinions (Yalden 1999) that, in instances of this kind, the people were well aware of differences between the species and it is not impossible that this bird was indeed a migrating Crane (Boisseau & Yalden 1998). The only modern records have been:

1969 11 June near Trowbridge Adult
1975 8–10 April All Cannings (no age-class)
1988 First 2 weeks November Odstock Down Three adults
1995 14–24 December Calne Adult

The adult in 1995 left at the onset of freezing weather and possibly moved to Cornwall, where one was seen at St Just on 28 December; earlier, a Crane flying west at Chichester (West Sussex) on 10 December may also have been the same individual.

(See also page 726.)

RT

Little Bustard

Tetrax tetrax

Vagrant (7 or 8 records), probably from southeast Europe, also breeds southwest Europe

During the late 19th century and the first half of the 20th, Little Bustards became extinct in central and much of eastern Europe, leaving a fragmented breeding range in two quite separate areas: a western group in Iberia, France, Sardinia, southern Italy and northern Morocco; and an eastern group from the Crimea and southern Russia to western Siberia and Iran. The whole western population is largely sedentary or, at most, dispersive and partially migratory. In contrast, those in the east move south to winter in Transcaucasia, central Asia, Iran and Pakistan.

Little Bustards breed on agricultural plains and steppes, and the population of Europe, excluding Russia, has been estimated at between 220,000 and 242,000 pairs (*EBCC Atlas*). The number of vagrants in Britain and Ireland as a whole before 1958 totalled 92, but, despite the great increases in the numbers of observers and the improvements in recording since the 1950s, only 18 were recorded in Great Britain during 1958–2000 (*BBRC*).

Wiltshire's first reported Little Bustards were a pair identified at Sidbury Hill on 4 April 1867, and described in a letter to 'the local paper' (presumably the *Salisbury & Winchester Journal*), by a man who claimed experience of both species of bustards in southern Spain but who wished to remain anonymous, perhaps because 'I hope no sportsman or naturalist will think it necessary to shoot them'. Morres (1878–85) doubted this observation because of the date – most British records have been during October–January, but there have been some in all other months (and the last two paragraphs below include one each in April and May in Wiltshire, both unquestioned) – and doubtless because the writer withheld his name: he even pondered that the man might have seen a pair of Stone-curlews. Smith (1887), on the other hand, was not quite so cautious and did not think that the species at that time was 'so rare in this country as some imagine'.

Smith also recorded two seen (by a named observer) on Salisbury Plain, near Netheravon, on 6 August 1877. One was then found on Salisbury Plain between Roche Court and Over Wallop – thus probably on the Wiltshire/Hampshire border – on 29 September 1897 (*Salisbury & Winchester Journal*, 16 October 1897, though Hony 1915a gave the date as the 27th) and what Hony regarded as 'presumably the same bird' near Market Lavington, still on Salisbury Plain, about mid October 1897 (*WANHM* 35, Hony 1915a, both based on *The Field* of 6 November 1897). The next two were shot, one near Chilmark in 1905 or 1906 (Hony 1915a) and a male in summer plumage at Avebury on 26 April 1909 (*WANHM*, Hony 1915a).

Nearly 40 years later, an adult male was seen at Little Wishford from 16 July to 20 September 1946 (*WANHM*, *BB* 40: 126–127). An adult female was at Northleach (Gloucestershire) from 20 May 1946 until shot on 30 July (Swaine 1982), but in subsequent literature this bird became wrongly confused with the Wiltshire record (Evans 1994, Naylor 1996). Finally, an adult male was shot on Salisbury Plain in mid May 1952: both *WANHM* and *BB* (47: 213) gave the locality as Salisbury Plain, but *MCNHS* noted it as 'Broad Town', which lies to the north of the Marlborough Downs.

RT

Great Bustard

Otis tarda

Nested to early 1800s, vagrant from Europe to 1891, re-introduction now begun

The magnificent Great Bustard had a bloody record in and around Salisbury Plain until the first decades of the 19th century and, as a vagrant from the Continent, even to the early 1890s. None has been seen truly wild in Wiltshire since then, but the species' traditional link with this area is demonstrated by the Arms granted to the County Council in 1937, these being dominated by a male Great Bustard on top of a shield. A big male is the largest, heaviest and – unfortunately for its own good – supposedly one of the most palatable landbirds to have nested in Great Britain within historical times, though Johns (1862) quoted Pliny to the effect that 'its flesh is very disagreeable, in consequence of the strong scent of its bones'.

This species is a highly gregarious, terrestrial omnivore that takes a wide variety of plant and small animal foods, but the early stages of the development of the chicks depend on a good supply of invertebrates. It is typical of undulating open grasslands, but adapts well to nesting in crops, especially cereals, mustard and oil-seed rape. Through the 1970s and 1980s, the former Great Bustard Trust attempted to re-establish the species by holding in an enclosure on Porton Down a small captive-breeding stock of Portuguese and Hungarian origin – also a vagrant sent down from Fair Isle (Shetland) where it was failing to thrive (Dymond 1991) – but conditions were not ideal and none of the total of only eight chicks that hatched over the years was strong enough to survive very long, let alone fly free. With hindsight, it is arguable that there were too few adults, that they had an inadequate female-to-male ratio and that, in an enclosed area, the pinioned birds lacked the necessary invertebrate biomass to reproduce.

Most conservationists these days approve of re-introductions – that is, of species lost from the landscape as a result of human activities – if they meet internationally agreed guidelines and have, in the light of present-day knowledge, a reasonable chance of success, such as, in particular, those developed recently for releasing flying juveniles of Red Kites and White-tailed Fish-eagles in Great Britain. Now, a successor to the Great Bustard Trust – the Great Bustard Group, set up in 1998 through the initiative of David Waters – has begun a new attempt; in this it is cooperating with the IUCN's Bustard Specialist Group and representatives of a number of national and local conservation bodies, both statutory and voluntary, including WOS. The story, as it has developed, has been published in *Otis* 1–18 (1999–2006).

A feasibility study (Osborne & Martin 2001) enabled the Group to put forward a licence application (Osborne 2002) that has been accepted by all the organisations concerned. DEFRA finally granted a licence for the annual importation of batches of chicks hatched in incubators in the Russian region of Saratov (a comparable latitude to southern England), the first batch arriving in June 2004; these chicks will always be from eggs saved when nests are exposed in the course of agriculture. Each year's batch of chicks will then be reared with minimal human contact in a special enclosure on Salisbury Plain so that, when old enough to fly, they may, it is hoped, begin to establish a wild population. This is a long-term project: females breed at 2–4 years old, but males take 4–6 years to mature; it may well be two or three decades before a viable, self-sustaining population can be established.

Male Great Bustards grow heavier with age and their normal weight range of 8–12 kg (extremes 5·75–18 kg) and wingspan of 2·1–2·4 m are comparable with those of Mute Swans; but females are much smaller at only 3·25–5·25 kg. Because of the species' size and palatability, we know more of its history in Great Britain than might otherwise have been the case. In former times, it nested in many parts of England – at least including the downlands of Wiltshire, Dorset, Hampshire and Sussex, the brecks and heaths of East Anglia west to Hertfordshire and Cambridgeshire, and parts of Lincolnshire and Yorkshire – and even southeast Scotland (FCR Jourdain in Kirkman 1912), while the earliest British fossil records came from south Wales and Cheddar (Somerset) (Reid-Henry & Harrison 1988). By the 16th century, however, it was already 'not very plentiful', and as early as 1534, under Henry VIII, Great Bustard eggs were protected by law 'upon paine of imprisonment for one yeare' (Smith 1887). Ray (1678) regarded the species as a rarity, but it was evidently still not uncommon on parts of Salisbury Plain a century later. Yet the historical reference of Coward (1920–26) – to 'the "droves" which roamed over the Yorkshire wolds, Salisbury Plain, and similar uncultivated areas were often immense' – may perhaps be a little misleading as, at best, any really large gatherings of, say, hundreds or even two or three thousand are likely to have represented whole local populations gathering in hard weather. Other early references to Bustards in Great Britain and their former culinary uses have been summarised by Waters (2001a, b).

The first published reference to Great Bustards in Wiltshire was actually among the food recipes of Muffett (1655). Soon after, Aubrey (1656–91) wrote, 'On Salisbury plaines, especially about Stonehenge, are bustards. They are also in the fields above Lavington: they do not often come to Chalke'. Pennant (1768) referred to 'flocks of fifty or more' in Wiltshire. Chafin (1818) told of 25 put up near Winterslow Hut in 1751, which 'flew very quietly over the hill called Southern Hill'. (This is assumed to be the now named Suddern Hill, just across the Hampshire boundary, but there is little doubt that the original sighting was in Wiltshire.) In the latter half of the 18th century 'it was the custom of the Mayor of Salisbury to have a bustard as a prominent dish at the annual inauguration feast' (Smith 1887, based on *Wiltshire Independent* 1854).

By the beginning of the 19th century, Great Bustards were probably confined to isolated groups on Salisbury Plain, the Norfolk/Suffolk Breckland, Lincolnshire, the Yorkshire wolds and, perhaps, the Sussex downs (Walpole-Bond 1938, Witherby *et al* 1938–41). The last British breeding records were in Norfolk in 1830 and Suffolk in 1832 (*BOU* 1971), but 'hen birds lingering until 1838… Possibly some indigenous hens until 1845 in Norfolk' (Witherby *et al* 1938–41). In 1900, 15 Great Bustards from Spain were pinioned in a wire enclosure at Elveden (Suffolk) until the summer of 1901 when, 'their wing-feathers having grown, all but four or five took their departure' (Rivière 1930); certainly two were shot shortly afterwards and, according to Coward (1920–26), the whole lot 'foolishly wandered and were soon accounted for'.

In 1887, Smith's account of this former 'pride of our Wiltshire downs...its stronghold in Great Britain' extended across 26 pages but, by then, the indigenous population had already been extinct in the county for well over half a century. He concluded that the species might have 'lingered on till about the year 1820'. The last recorded Wiltshire nest was in a wheat field above Market Lavington in 1801 (Yarrell 1837–43, Smith 1887); it is possible that the egg inscribed 'Wilts' in the Natural History Museum at Tring (Hertfordshire) – though undated, likely to be the oldest egg in the national collection there (Collar 2003) – came from that nest. 'At that date ... there were many Bustards haunting the flat between [Tilshead] and Shrewton ... also in some abundance ... near the Bustard Inn'; the following 11 years produced occasional suggestions of breeding, such as what was termed 'a young Bustard' being ridden down on horseback in 1806 and a flock of seven birds seen in June or July 1812 (Smith 1887), but no clear recorded evidence of nesting. At least 30 years after the likely extinction of the indigenous population, Waterhouse (1849) told of having seen a Great Bustard, probably a female, near Stonehenge on 9 August 1849. That same year one was shot in Savernake Forest, and in 1851 another near Chiseldon (Peirson 1959); in January 1856 one was shot flying over Hens Wood (Smith 1887).

In 1864 Mr Francis Brown, of Wylye, picked up a fresh feather about a mile from Stonehenge, which later that same week, on 5 October, was identified at the British Museum as a contour feather or covert from a Great Bustard; documented in a letter, the details came to light when the feather was presented to the Salisbury Museum (Stevens 1921). Mr Brown had concluded his report on the feather with 'Last February our carters saw one morning a bird which they described as brown in colour and near two feet in height standing on the knowl ... they never mentioned the circumstance to me until the April following'.

The few subsequent Great Bustards in Wiltshire were certainly only winter vagrants from the Continent, which, like many of their predecessors, came to sticky ends: at least two, one a male, from a party of seven were shot near Maddington in January 1871 (Blackmore 1871, Stratton 1871, Smith 1887, Anon 1926), a male and female at Winterbourne Stoke in February 1871 (Newman 1871), one 'reported shot at Salisbury' in January 1880 and, finally, one near Chippenham on 4 February 1891 (Harting 1891a, 1891b, Hony 1915a). In each of those three winters (1870/71, 1879/80 and 1890/91) a 'number of migrants occurred' in Great Britain; in the last of them records came 'from Norfolk, Suffolk, Essex, Sussex, Hants, Wilts, and Wales' (Witherby *et al* 1938–41). Though wanderers turned up rarely in Great Britain during the 20th century – 29 in all, chiefly from Kent north to Shetland (*BBRC*) – no more were found in Wiltshire.

Now classed as 'Vulnerable' and still decreasing, Great Bustards have a highly fragmented, mainly European and Asian breeding range, in northwest Morocco, Iberia, northeast Germany, parts of central and southeast Europe (especially Ukraine and south Russia), and from Turkey across to Turkestan, Lake Baikal and Mongolia; the world population is currently put at 31,000 to 37,000 individuals, half of them in Spain and the majority in Europe, including some 8000 in Russia (BirdLife International 2003). European Russian and Asiatic populations are generally considered to be migratory, moving south in winter to Ukraine, the Caspian area and Transcaspia to Tadzhikistan, as well as into China and North Korea. At least in European Russia, however, such movements are perhaps better regarded as responses to the snow cover that makes it impossible for these essentially terrestrial birds to find food. Similarly, a few reach Romania and Bulgaria in hard weather and at least part of the Turkish population moves to north Syria and Iraq. During heavy snowfalls in central Europe, the 'resident' German and Hungarian birds may also shift westwards, sometimes as far as the Netherlands, France and, very rarely, Great Britain – but there is no chance of natural recolonisation here.

These huge, stately birds are majestic in flight, with much white on the wings and underbody, but on the ground they look brown, grey and rufous – flocks sometimes likened to big geese, or even small deer – until the breeding adult males blow up their large gular pouches and turn their plumages inside out, appearing almost all white in their astonishing 'balloon-displays'. With the skills of the conservation organisations, and not a little luck, such sights might again be seen around Salisbury Plain in the next decade.

(See also pages 726–727.)

IJF-L

Sponsored by David Waters on behalf of the Great Bustard Group

---

Oystercatcher

Haematopus ostralegus

Annual migrant from within Britain or north Europe (first bred 2002)

With pied plumage, orange-red bill and pink legs, this is among Great Britain's most easily recognised waders, and also one of the most successful – though feeding on cockles, mussels and, inland, earthworms, rather than oysters. In the 19th century, nesting Oystercatchers in Great Britain were almost entirely confined to coasts (*1875–1900 Atlas*). From around 1900, however, the population began to increase, spreading inland along larger rivers in Scotland and northern England. Nowadays, inland breeding is fairly widespread as far south as north Wales and northern East Anglia, though the species is still mostly coastal in south Wales and southern England (*1988–91 Atlas*). The British breeding population rose from between 19,000 and 30,000 pairs in the early 1960s (Dare 1966) to between 33,000 and 43,000 in the mid 1980s (Piersma 1986, *1988–91 Atlas*).

This coastal-breeding habit is common among Oystercatchers throughout northern Europe – from Iceland, Fenno-Scandia and north Russia south to northwest France – as well as, very locally, in the Mediterranean, but from the Black Sea east into western Siberia and central Asia they breed far inland along river systems. The same species is also found along the Pacific coasts of Asia south to northeast China, and other rather similar-looking oystercatchers (some all black) replace it in much of the rest of the world. The European breeding population, excluding Russia, is considered to be in the range of 220,000 to 260,000 pairs (*EBCC Atlas*).

Most Eurasian Oystercatchers are largely migratory, wintering along the coasts of western Europe, northern Africa, the Middle East, the Indian subcontinent, and south and east China. The British population, however, appears mostly to remain within Great Britain (*Migration Atlas*) and the species is also essentially coastal at that season (*1981–84 Winter Atlas*). Arrivals from Iceland, Faeroes and Fenno-Scandia swell autumn numbers to around 315,000 (Rehfisch *et al* 2003). Those from northern Britain winter mainly around the Irish Sea, with many from Iceland, the Faeroes and Norway, while others from, particularly, Norway again and the Low Countries, together with some from other parts of Fenno-Scandia and north Russia, winter along the east coast (*Migration Atlas*). Only five Oystercatchers were ringed in Wiltshire during 1965–2000, but the lone recovery involving the county was an adult caught on 23 February 1957 near Malmesbury and found dead 11 years later, on 15 March 1968, at Perth (Perth & Kinross).

Table 51. Oystercatchers *Haematopus ostralegus* in Wiltshire: monthly totals 1981–2000

	Jan	Feb	Mar	Apr	May	Jun	Jul	Aug	Sep	Oct	Nov	Dec
Records	3	5	10	11	17	4	30	37	8	4	3	3

Wiltshire's first records involved one caught at Bradford-on-Avon in September 1859 and another killed at Enford in August 1877 (Smith 1887). One was found dead on the Marlborough Downs in 1904 (Hony 1915a), and singles were seen in 1915 (*MCNHS* 1915) and 1946, the latter at Bay Bridges, near Marlborough (Halliday & Randolph 1955). A marked increase in numbers saw 30 records spread over 19 of the years between 1950 and 1980 (five records in 1977 the most in one year), all involving just one or two birds (*WANHM*, *Hobby*), 'the majority in spring and autumn' (Buxton 1981). Palmer (1991) noted 'a trend of increasing records', which has continued: Oystercatchers were found annually in the county during 1981–2000 – a reflection of the increasing British breeding population – with a total of 135 records involving 179 birds. Few have stayed more than one or two days, and the largest numbers have been five together on three occasions: 25 August 1985, 1 August 1986 and 9 September 1988, all at CWP.

Most Oystercatchers in Wiltshire are still found in spring and early autumn, but some have been seen in every month (table 51). CWP has produced the majority, though a few have occurred at other wetland sites, such as Swindon STW, Calne Sand Pits and Corsham Lake; the species has appeared at Langford Lakes in five years and there have been no fewer than eight records at Boscombe Down. Singletons heard at night over Salisbury in February and March 1997 were following the river valley, as was one flying west along the north scarp of Dean Hill in July 2000.

In 1998, a pair prospected for a nest-site at CWP during 4–21 May, and were even seen mating, but abandoned the site without laying eggs.

(See also page 724.)

NPA & PEC

Black-winged Stilt

Himantopus himantopus

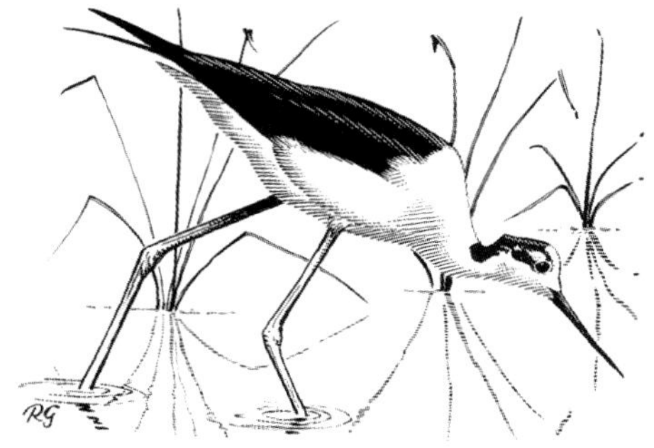

Overshooting vagrant (2 records), breeds south Europe, winters Africa

One of the most distinctive of all waders, Black-winged Stilts are unmistakable with their strikingly black and white plumage and exceptionally long, bright red legs. They are found in every continent, but almost entirely south of 50°N in Eurasia and North America; certain races, particularly those in the Americas and New Zealand, are sometimes considered distinct species. In Europe – where they are largely confined to shallow marshlands in southern countries – the breeding population, excluding Russia, has been estimated at 15,400 to 16,800 pairs (*EBCC Atlas*), the great majority in Spain and many of the rest in southern France, Italy and Greece.

But this species is an opportunist breeder that nests only when conditions are right; in years following winter droughts, particularly in Iberia, many do not even attempt to breed and may then wander, occasionally nesting as far north as north Germany, the

Netherlands and Belgium, as well as in England where there were four records of nesting in half a century: three pairs bred in Nottinghamshire in 1945 (Staton 1945) and one raised two young in Norfolk in 1987 (*RBBP*); single pairs also laid eggs in Cambridgeshire in 1983 and in Cheshire in 1993, but both of these failed.

Apart from small numbers in southern Spain, the European population is migratory, wintering in sub-Saharan Africa. A total of 193 Black-winged Stilts was recorded in Great Britain during 1958–2000 (*BBRC*), many the result of overshooting on spring passage, especially in May. In 1987, the year of the Norfolk nest, an exceptional influx of at least 40 included three in Wiltshire:

1987	3–8 May	near Collingbourne Ducis	Adult
	26 May	CWP68	Two adults

NPA & IJF-L

Avocet

Recurvirostra avosetta

Vagrant (4 records), from south/east English coasts or nearby Europe

Widely known as the emblem of the RSPB, Avocets – and their recolonisation of Great Britain – are a major conservation success story. Until the late 18th and early 19th centuries these dainty white and black waders used to nest regularly, if perhaps never commonly, along the east and south coasts of England from the Humber to Sussex, but then dwindled to extinction by the 1840s (Witherby *et al* 1938–41, *1875–1900 Atlas*). Their disappearance is often attributed to the land-claim of coastal marshes and the taking of eggs and adults by collectors, but must have been more complicated than that because the period of extensive drainage and the heyday of collecting both came later (*1968–72 Atlas*). Although both eggs and adults certainly used to be harvested for food, it is likely that the improvement of sea defences deprived the Avocets of the brackish and saline pools, in which they feed on insects, crustaceans and annelid worms by sweeping from side to side with their long upcurved bills.

Almost exactly 100 years later, when much of the English east coast was closed to the public during the 1939–45 War, and some marshes were flooded, Avocets are known to have nested in Essex and Norfolk, and they became established in Suffolk from 1947. Thanks to conservation work, particularly by the RSPB, the population has grown until in 2000 at least 980 pairs were spread mainly down the east coast from the Humber to Kent (*RBBP*). This is still, however, only a small proportion of the 26,800 to 29,400 breeding pairs estimated for Europe as a whole, excluding Russia (*EBCC Atlas*).

Avocets in western Europe nest by or in brackish coastal lagoons and deltas, from the Baltic area to western France, Iberia and locally around the Mediterranean, but elsewhere – from central and eastern Europe across the central Asian steppe and semi-desert, and in eastern Africa – their breeding range extends far inland in suitable saline habitats, even to 3000 m in mountains. The Eurasian populations are largely migratory, wintering mainly in the Mediterranean area, sub-Saharan Africa and parts of southern Asia, more locally too in Portugal, western France and the Netherlands, as well as increasingly along some coasts of southern England, East Anglia and the Humber estuary; there has been a three-fold increase in UK wintering numbers during the 1990s (*WeBS*). Colour-ringing has shown those that winter (from August to March) in Devon and other parts of the southwest are largely of English east coast origin. Indeed, most of the winterers in Great Britain are thought to be from the British breeding population, though they include some from the Continent (*Migration Atlas*).

The only four Wiltshire records were all at CWP between 1987 and 1992:

1987	19–23 July	CWP68	Two adults
1988	1 May	CWP Swillbrook	Adult
	16–24 June	CWP68	Two adults
1992	4 May	CWP68	Adult

These wanderers to Wiltshire may have been in their second summers, or failed nesters: Avocets occupy their breeding sites on the English east coast from March to September, but do not nest until they are two or even three years old.

NPA & IJF-L

Stone-curlew

Burhinus oedicnemus

Local summer visitor (formerly commoner, now increasing again), winters south Europe and northern Africa

The haunting cries of 'Great Plovers' – as they used to be known in Wiltshire (Smith 1887) – can still be heard across parts of Salisbury Plain. They are survivors from an era when, like Great Bustards (*qv*), they inhabited a treeless landscape of unimproved and unfenced downland that stretched uninterrupted to the horizon, except for the occasional furze brake, rabbit warren, or wandering flock of grazing sheep. They are not, however, 'plovers', any more than they are 'curlews', but representatives of a family, widely distributed in the Old World, of large-headed, big-eyed, longish-legged waders, elsewhere known as 'thick-knees', that are seen mostly on dry land.

Stone-curlews have an extensive, but often somewhat patchy, breeding range from the Canary Islands, North Africa, Iberia, France and southern England eastwards to central and southern Asia. They are summer visitors to the more northerly parts of this range, those from Europe wintering in Iberia, the Mediterranean region and, to an uncertain extent, sub-Saharan Africa south to southern Niger and northwest Kenya. Although the population of Europe, excluding Russia, is still estimated at 32,700 to 45,700 pairs (*EBCC Atlas*), they declined markedly from the late 19th century through the 20th, becoming extinct in Germany, Belgium and Poland, and seriously decreased in, for example, England and France.

In Great Britain, until the mid 19th century, Stone-curlews extended from Dorset to Kent and north to Yorkshire, mainly on limestone and sandy soils, and were widely distributed in Wiltshire (*1875–1900 Atlas*). Although im Thurn (1870) simply recorded eggs taken on Overton Down in 1868, Smith (1887) reported that the species 'was once very generally known in Wiltshire', and quoted various contacts to the effect that 'up to

1840 it was still common on the downs near Salisbury' and was 'becoming more scarce, but still occasionally to be seen on Ellbarrow and the higher hills'. He added that the 'Rev. A. P. Morres ... used to consider it by no means uncommon on the downs near him [Salisbury]; but he laments, what I fear is also the case in North Wilts, that it is rapidly decreasing in numbers'.

From that time, conversion of semi-natural grassland and heath to arable and conifer plantations caused a steady decline in Great Britain. Breeding ceased in Nottinghamshire in 1891 and in Lincolnshire in the early 1900s (*1875–1900 Atlas*) and, though a few hung on in Yorkshire to 1937, subsequently the species became limited to 13 counties – from East Anglia through the Cambridge/Essex borders, Hertford, Buckingham, Oxford, Berkshire and Wiltshire to Dorset and thence along the south coast shires to Kent – having formerly also nested in Gloucester, Surrey, Essex and Bedfordshire' (Witherby *et al* 1938–41). In fact, it was 'rediscovered' in Essex in 1949, having probably not 'ever completely deserted this district' (Hudson & Pyman 1968), and a few pairs again bred in Gloucestershire during 1950–54 (Swaine 1982). Nowadays, most of the population is found in just five of those counties (irregularly nesting in three or four others) in two separate regions, the East Anglian Brecks and the 'Wessex' downs of Berkshire, Wiltshire and Hampshire.

In Berkshire, 'Annual reports ... in the 1930s showed that there were fair numbers breeding regularly on the Berkshire Downs, much of which is now in Oxfordshire' (Standley *et al* 1996); by 2000, just seven pairs of Stone-curlews were found in Berkshire and breeding was irregular in Oxfordshire (*RBBP*). In Hampshire – where 'At the beginning of the [20th] century, there were several hundred pairs breeding ... and this was probably still the case in the 1930s ... the population still numbered considerably in excess of 100 pairs in the early 1960s' (Clark & Eyre 1993) – only 20 pairs were recorded in 2000 (*RBBP*). Indeed, whereas the estimated total in England was still 1000–2000 pairs in the 1920s and 1930s (*EBCC Atlas*), this had fallen to 300–500 by the early 1970s (*1968–72 Atlas*) and to just 150–160 two decades later (*1988–91 Atlas*), but more recently, with protection and habitat management, the numbers are rising again. So what has been happening in Wiltshire?

In the 1930s, the annual reports in *WANHM* made it clear that Stone-curlews were not uncommon in this county. In 1934, for example, they were 'well up to the standard and breeding freely throughout ... particularly on Salisbury Plain and the barren downs near Salisbury'. Sizeable autumn flocks were also recorded: in 1930, in one locality, 26 on 2 September grew to 55 on the 15th, to 70 from 18 September to 10 October, and then to 'a very large flock of not less than 90' on 19 October; and in 1931 flocks of 20, 40, 40 and 70 were reported.

The two decades after the 1939–45 War saw considerable changes, but these were not always reflected in *WANHM*. Although the autumn flock sizes quoted were only in the range of four to 20, comments about breeding were generally optimistic apart from a smattering of references to agricultural damage. Thus, in 1946, 'Slight increase, but many nests on arable are destroyed by harrowing, rolling, etc.'; in 1947, 'loses its early layings to some extent from ploughing and harrowing'; and, in 1950, 'The records of successful nesting and the size of the autumn flocks suggest that it was a good breeding season for this species'. Yet there was no comment on the effects of the spread of myxomatosis among rabbits in 1954, as a result of which the vegetation on the remaining fragments of chalk downland was no longer grazed and became unsuitable for Stone-curlews.

Indeed, Peirson (1959) wrote that in Wiltshire this species was 'locally not uncommon. Breeding has been somewhat disturbed by the ploughing up of downland and the sowing of leys'. Later, however, Webber (1968) found that that 'unfortunately is no longer true for most of the county. It is distinctly uncommon in the majority of its original breeding haunts'. Between 1953 and 1965 there were still about six pairs on the Marlborough Downs, but the number there then declined to one or two pairs and the last successful breeding was in 1976 (WOS record cards). In 1974, in the county as a whole, 'at least 20 pairs were still showing evidence of breeding' (*Hobby*).

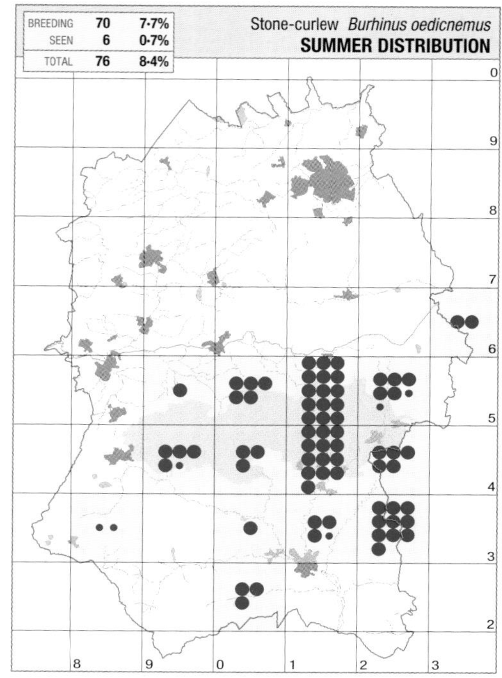

Buxton (1981) recorded that 'breeding still takes place on Salisbury Plain, Porton Down and in the south and south-west and possibly on the Marlborough Downs. Since 1975 there has been a slight increase in the number of sight records which perhaps indicates a real increase in numbers. During the last three years there have been ten to eighteen pairs occupying breeding sites'. It is probable, however, that the increase noted was in part the result of improved recording on Salisbury Plain from the mid 1970s, when the formation of MoD conservation groups allowed access to birdwatcher members for the first time.

Stone-curlews nest on open, flat or gently sloping ground with short, sparse vegetation, or on bare, stony areas. Chalk downland grazed by livestock and rabbits holds the highest densities, up to seven pairs per 1-km square at Porton Down (Austin 2002). The largest surviving patches of this type of habitat are on military training areas, but reduced grazing there has resulted in much of the grass being too tall and thick. Populations persist at lower densities on spring-sown arable land, but many nests there are destroyed when the young wheat is rolled. Moreover, the switch from spring- to autumn-sown crops has reduced the availability of bare ground for breeding, few sites being available after early May. Whilst Stone-curlews favour bare ground for breeding and roosting, they feed on invertebrate-rich pasture, likewise a declining resource in today's farmland. In 1998, however, RSPB and MAFF developed an option in the Countryside Stewardship Scheme to create and manage suitable 2–hectare plots on farmland. It is largely thanks to the enthusiastic co-operation of farmers that Stone-curlews survive in Wiltshire today, but, before this initiative, their efforts were undertaken with little, if any, financial incentive.

A national project initiated in the 1990s aimed to achieve the UK Biodiversity Action Plan's target of 200 pairs by 2000: this figure was reached in 1998; in 2000 a total of 253 pairs was proved to be breeding in Great Britain and another 17 pairs ranked as 'probable/possible' (*RBBP*). The next goals are 300 pairs by 2010 and the re-establishment of the species in former breeding areas.

Meanwhile, since 1985, an RSPB team has monitored and protected the Wessex population, finding 22 pairs that year in Wiltshire. Subsequently the recorded numbers increased steadily, at first through better coverage and then, from 1991 (table 52), through habitat creation and the protection of nests from agricultural and military operations. With a total of 44 pairs proved to nest in 2000, and 13 other pairs located, Wiltshire held 17·4 per cent of the breeding population of Great Britain, and 21 per cent of the total pairs, making the Stone-curlew one of this county's most 'important' birds.

The Wiltshire population is confined now to the chalk downland of the southern half of the county, concentrated on the MoD ranges of Salisbury Plain and Porton Down. The *1968–72 Atlas* showed the species as breeding in seven of Wiltshire's 33 core 10-km squares and seen in nine others; the corresponding figures in the *1988–91 Atlas* were eight and one, and in the 1995–2000 summer tetrad survey ten and one. Stone-curlews are active at night and difficult to find by day, but the summer distribution map shows that they were found breeding in 70 tetrads during 1995–2000, and seen or heard in a further six (plotting all records over a 6–year period for such an intensively studied species thus overstates the number of breeders). There were no certain records from the Marlborough Downs on the tetrad cards, though the earliest report in 2000 came from there on 5 March (*Hobby*). In Wessex in 1998, 24 pairs attempted to breed on grazed downland and 37 on bare ground within grazed downland. Of the 41 pairs that nested on farmland, 23 were on set-aside and 18 either on specially created bare plots or among crops of linseed, maize or peas. By 2000, more than two-thirds of the national population were nesting on spring-sown crops on arable farmland (RSPB).

Stone-curlews usually arrive in March and depart in October, the earliest recorded date being 13 February 1953 and the latest 13 November 1954; one near Imber on 28 January 1952 may have been overwintering (all *WANHM*). Clutches are laid from the end of March, sometimes two broods are raised, and chicks can fledge as late as October, making the breeding season the longest of that of any summer visitor. From July, Stone-curlews start to form communal roosts, initially of failed breeders, but subsequently including both adults and fledged young. Using traditional sites, they moult at the roosts and remain in flocks until they leave in October, perhaps *en masse*. Seven roosts were used in 1998, though the highest count, of 58 on 16 September 2000, was divided between three of these sites.

A total of 322 chicks was ringed in the county during 1965–2000, mostly as part of the RSPB project, resulting in a number of recoveries. A juvenile colour-ringed on Salisbury Plain in June 1990 was seen in South Glamorgan during 20–22 August 1990. There is a regular interchange between the breeding populations of Wiltshire and the rest of England: one fledged on SPTA in 1982 bred in the Brecks (Norfolk/Suffolk) in 1985 and 1986; two more ringed on SPTA in 1997 and 1998 nested in the Brecks and at another site in East Anglia in 2000. In 1995, 1997 and 1998 Stone-curlews colour-ringed in Berkshire, Oxfordshire and Breckland were identified at roosts in Wiltshire. On the other hand, there is also firm evidence of site faithfulness to Wiltshire: the oldest ringed Stone-curlew was found breeding in 1998 only a mile away from where it was marked in 1982.

Recoveries of Wiltshire-ringed Stone-curlews in southern France in September 1974, October 1980 and November 1984 illustrate passage to winter quarters; others in Portugal in December 1996, in Spain in January 1980, 1983 and 1996, and in Algeria in March

Table 52. Stone-curlews *Burhinus oedicnemus* in Wiltshire: breeding pairs and fledged young 1991–2000
No attempt was made to distinguish young of undiscovered pairs before 1995

	91	92	93	94	95	96	97	98	99	00
Total pairs	30	35	35	32	36	38	41	44	49	57
Pairs proved breeding	25	29	31	29	34	32	37	39	41	44
Breeding attempts	39	46	47	53	55	47	65	61	64	60
Total fledged young	22	15	24	21	32	17	25	30	38	29
Young of undiscovered pairs	–	–	–	–	3	0	3	1	4	1

1983 probably show wintering grounds. Ringing results also indicate that young birds travel farther than adults, and Wiltshire holds the record for the southernmost recovery of any Stone-curlew ringed in Europe: a juvenile ringed near Salisbury in June 1981 was found dead in Sierra Leone in January 1982. The dearth of any other first winter recoveries of British-ringed Stone-curlews south of the Mediterranean 'suggests that a high proportion may migrate to arid, sparsely populated parts of North and West Africa' (*Migration Atlas*, based on Green *et al* 1997).

This species is rarely found in Wiltshire away from the breeding areas, but singletons at Swindon STW on 23 August 1965 and at CWP from 27 July to 3 August 1980 showed post-breeding dispersal.

(See also page 724.)

PEC

Sponsored by John Austin in memory of Peter Austin

Cream-coloured Courser

Cursorius cursor

Vagrant (2 old records) from north Africa/Middle East

This plover-like wader – rather small and inconspicuous as it sits or runs on sandy ground, but much larger in flight with long wings boldly black-ended above and all black below – breeds in sandy deserts and semi-deserts across northern Africa, also in a narrow strip along the southern fringes of the Sahara to Kenya, and through the Middle East and Arabia into southwest Asia, as well as on the Cape Verde and eastern Canary Islands; the more northerly populations move south into the Sahara, Arabia and Pakistan in winter. It has been recorded only as a rare vagrant in about 20 countries of Europe, but in 2001 six with a chick were seen in southern Spain (*eg* van den Berg 2001).

Only some 30 records of Cream-coloured Coursers are now accepted for Great Britain, including 'about a score of specimens' by the end of the 19th century (Saunders 1899). With roughly two-thirds of all records in the 1800s it was clearly more frequent in the past. The total of just six in 1958–2000 (*BBRC*), all before 1985 – despite the huge increase in birdwatching from the 1950s onwards – perhaps suggests declines in the source populations. With the exclusion of the unlikely 'pairs' in East Sussex in May 1911 and on the Kent/Sussex border in February 1913 – which were among the 'Hastings Rarities' (Nicholson & Ferguson-Lees 1962) – all have been singletons in September–December, the great majority in October.

Wiltshire's two old records fit the national picture well. Both were shot, the first at Elston, near Tilshead, on 2 October 1855 (Smith 1887), the second 'on the Downs above Erlestoke' on 10 October 1896 (Smith 1896, *WANHM* 29: 70; Hony 1915a). Interestingly, another was shot in Bouley Bay, Jersey, only nine days later (Harting 1896).

NPA & IJF-L

Collared Pratincole

Glareola pratincola

Overshooting vagrant (2 records), breeds south Europe, winters Africa

With short, wide-gaped bills, long wings and forked tails, pratincoles are curiously attractive waders that behave somewhat like plovers on the ground, and hunt insects on the wing in the manner of the 'marsh terns' (genus *Chlidonias*). The Collared Pratincole has a discontinuous breeding distribution from southern Portugal and north Morocco east through mainly coastal countries of the Mediterranean and Black Sea regions into west-central Asia, the Persian Gulf and Pakistan, and an even more fragmented range over much of sub-Saharan Africa, where all Eurasian populations also go during the northern winter. It is nowhere abundant and the numbers in southern Europe, excluding Russia, have been estimated at a mere 5600 to 6600, though weather and water levels result in marked fluctuations from year to year (*EBCC* Atlas). Its preferred habitats are sun-baked mud in dried-out marshlands, semi-deserts with low herbage, and lowland steppes, particularly where grazing animals keep the vegetation down and encourage insects; nests are often, but not essentially, near water, which the pratincoles visit to drink, bathe and hunt flying insects.

Returning north to breed, a few overshoot in April–June and, particularly then, have occurred north to Fenno-Scandia; in 1997 one even reached Iceland (*EBR*); fewer still wander north in July–November. The total of Collared Pratincoles recorded in Great Britain during 1958–2000 (*BBRC*) was only 53, mostly in southern and eastern England, and there had been no more than about 30 from the 19th century to 1957. Thus, these waders have remained consistently rare vagrants here, and Wiltshire has done well with two records, the first having been shot at Tilshead in mid November 1852 (Smith 1887) – misquoted as 'October' by Buxton (1981) – and the second, more than a century later, which was seen hawking insects with Common Swifts over the Thames at Cricklade on 30 May 1968 (*WANHM*, *BBRC*).

GLW & IJF-L

Little Ringed Plover

Charadrius dubius

Local summer visitor/passage migrant, breeds Britain/Europe, winters Africa

Until 1938, when a pair nested at Tring reservoirs (Hertfordshire), these small plovers were no more than rare vagrants to Great Britain (Witherby *et al* 1938–41), but six years later two pairs bred at Tring and a third in Middlesex, after which numbers increased steadily. Over 400 pairs summered in England and Wales in 1972 (*1968–72 Atlas*), 608 in 1984 (Parrinder 1989) and an estimated 825 to 1070 by 1991, also occasionally a pair or two in Scotland (*1988–91 Atlas*). In Great Britain, the vast majority of Little Ringed Plovers (over 90 per cent in 1984) breed in such artificial habitats as gravel pits, waste dumps and reservoirs, making scrapes for their eggs on bare or sparsely vegetated ground near water. Elsewhere in their huge summer range from North Africa north to southern Fenno-Scandia and across much of Eurasia to Japan, Philippines and New Guinea, many

Table 53. Little Ringed Plovers *Charadrius dubius* in Wiltshire: breeding pairs 1990–2000

The numbers for 1997–2000 all related to confirmed breeders, but some of the earlier totals involved pairs that only probably or possibly nested; in 1990, for example, all eight pairs attempted to do so though very few young were recorded, whereas in 1993 just one of the total of 11 pairs was actually proved to nest

	90	91	92	93	94	95	96	97	98	99	00
Pairs	8	3	4	11	4	3	3	1	4	4	4

nest on sand or gravel banks by or in rivers or lakes. It has been estimated that 66,000 to 87,000 pairs breed in Europe, excluding Russia (*EBCC* Atlas). But for small numbers around the southern Mediterranean, all European populations winter in sub-Saharan Africa from Senegal to Somalia and Kenya; and 'judging by the spread of autumn and spring recoveries… most British breeders are likely to winter in the western Sahel' (*Migration Atlas*).

Little Ringed Plovers were not recorded at all in Wiltshire until 1959, when 'At a gravel pit [Kent End, Ashton Keynes] birds were present during spring and might have nested but for being continually disturbed'; that same year, at Coate Water in August, an adult and a juvenile were present on the 16th and 18th, and as many as ten there on the 17th (*WANHM*). Occasional records followed through the 1960s: singles at Coate in 1960 (April) and 1962 (August); one at Swindon STW in 1963 (September) and three in 1965 (juvenile July, two adults August), becoming an annual series there from 1967, mainly in August–September but including a peak of ten on 26 July 1970; and two at Seagry Gravel Pits on 18 April 1969 (*WANHM*). In 1970, for the first time at CWP since the original record in 1959, 'Two pairs attempted to breed and 3 young were reared'; there was no report of breeding in 1971 or 1972, but in 1973 two pairs nested (unsuccessfully) and breeding has been regular there ever since, the population reaching peaks of ten pairs in 1987–88 and eleven in 1993, though by no means all laid eggs (table 53). Nesting has also been attempted at Coate Water, Calne Sand Pits, and Swindon STW and rubbish tip, successfully at the last site during 1998–2000; and in the Steeple Langford area in several years from 1979, but only in 1980 – when two pairs reared six young in, more unusually, a partially flooded arable field adjacent to the gravel pits – were they known to be successful.

Wiltshire's breeding population of Little Ringed Plovers fluctuates in accordance with the availability of suitable habitat: the largest numbers were at CWP68 during 1987–93 when that was still a working gravel pit, the highest count of adults and juveniles there being 42 in July 1987. But even these totals are relatively low for the county's share of the largest gravel pit complex in England and, unless a reserve with managed shallows and bare gravel can be established there, the continued nesting of this species will depend on the availability of

working pits, an ephemeral environment that may eventually cease to exist. The map illustrates the Little Ringed Plover's breeding opportunism: different parts of the CWP complex were occupied temporarily during the six years of the summer tetrad survey – depending where conditions were suitable – so the overall picture exaggerates the situation for any one year.

The first migrants arrive in Wiltshire usually during the second or third week of March, the earliest recorded date being 11 March 1989 at CWP. The protracted autumn passage begins with juveniles in early July and adults moving through from later that month; most have departed by early September, but the latest recorded date is the 28th, in 1975 and 1998.

None of the total of 53 chicks ringed in the county during 1965–2000, mainly in the early 1970s, has been recovered.

(See also page 724.)

GLW & PEC

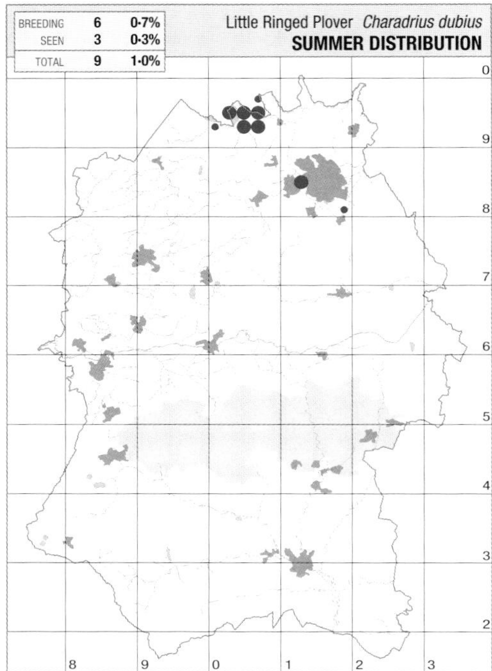

Ringed Plover

Charadrius hiaticula

Uncommon passage migrant from within Britain/Iceland/north Europe, has bred

Common year-round on many coasts of Great Britain, Ringed Plovers have now become regular visitors inland, the increasing availability of such man-made habitats as gravel pits helping to influence this spread (*1988–91 Atlas*); indeed, by 1984, 17 per cent of the total English population was nesting inland, mostly in eastern and central counties (Prater 1989).

The species breeds mostly on arctic tundra from northeast Canada, Greenland and Iceland across Fenno-Scandia to Siberia, but in more southerly parts of its range in northwest Europe, from Ireland and north France to the Baltic, it traditionally favours sand or shingle coasts. The European population, excluding Russia, has been estimated at between 82,700 and 105,800 pairs (*EBCC Atlas*) – of which something of the order of 8500 pairs, perhaps 10 per cent, nest in Great Britain (Prater 1989, *1988–91 Atlas*). These last are largely resident, but in winter the numbers are boosted by migrants, arriving mainly from the Wadden Sea (Netherlands/Germany/Denmark) and Baltic coasts, which bring the total in winter to an estimated 32,450 birds (Rehfisch *et al* 2003). Most of the world's Ringed Plovers, including those from Canada, Greenland and Siberia, winter in western Europe, the Mediterranean and, not least, Africa, the most northerly populations travelling the farthest.

In the 19th century Ringed Plovers were rare visitors to Wiltshire (though the *1875–1900 Atlas* mapped them as rare breeders here, apparently erroneously). Smith (1887) and Hony (1915a) together were able to list just nine records of 16 birds between 1838 ('killed' near Malmesbury) and 1889 ('Mr. Ward shot one at Blackland in June'). But these included an interesting series in mid August 1881, when singletons were 'shot at Kennet' on the 12th and 'killed at Lavington' on the 13th, on which date also 'Mr. C. A. Tanner's shepherd… knocked down three' of a flock of seven at Yatesbury.

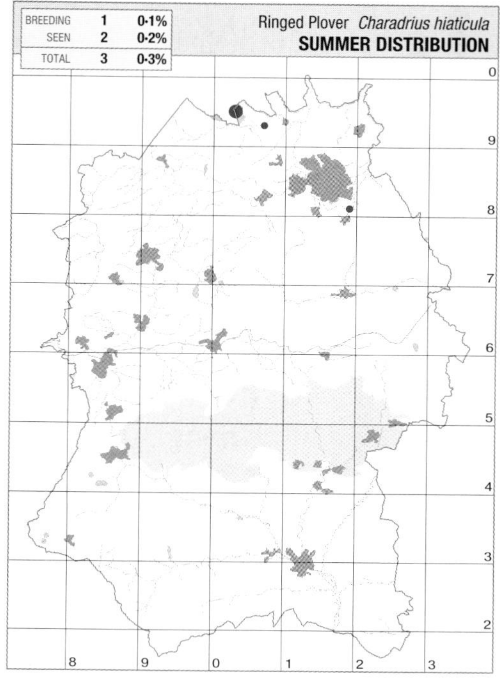

By the middle of the 20th century, Peirson (1959) described the species as 'A rare visitor usually in bad weather', but there had been more than a dozen records during 1934–59 (*WANHM*) and his last four words seem surprising as all, bar three in October–January, were during April–May or July–August. The nine years 1960–68 produced at least another 15 records, all in March–April or June–September, as well as a fascinating report of 'Between midnight and 0200 hours, Mar 31st [1960], large flocks heard flying over Melksham; waves of birds appeared to pass at about 10 minute intervals. The calls mostly 2 syllable but occasional "pit-a-lee-o" and "rolling" calls heard (R.J.S[pencer].)' (*WANHM*). Webber (1968) considered this species to be 'Regular, especially in the Swindon area'.

The development of CWP saw a significant increase in records of many waders, and Ringed Plovers were found there annually from 1973, the numbers reported varying according to the habitats available. As recently as 1985 there were only seven bird-days per year at CWP, but numbers increased considerably during the 1990s (table 54) after the construction of the Cleveland Farm complex and the drainage and extension of CWP29. Most records in the first half of the year occur from mid March through to a peak in May. Autumn passage starts in July and peaks in August, usually finishing after mid September, though stragglers occur through October into November (but not December, at least during 1974–2000). Ringed Plovers passing through in late May are heading much farther north, as by then the British birds are already on their breeding territories. Apart from those heard overhead at night in March 1960, the largest flock recorded in Wiltshire was 30 at CWP on 18 May 1988. Although Ringed Plovers usually occur in wetland habitats, up to seven (at Stonehenge on 18 November 1990) have been reported associating with Golden Plovers on downland and, once, one with a Dotterel in a pea-field at Westdown Range, above Market Lavington, on 19 May 1991.

Table 54. Ringed Plovers *Charadrius hiaticula* in Wiltshire: annual totals of bird-days 1990–2000

	90	91	92	93	94	95	96	97	98	99	00
Bird-days at CWP	230	271	96	165	95	42	59	107	126	201	78
Rest of Wiltshire	8	7	0	0	1	1	1	0	0	0	3

Ringed Plovers have nested at CWP on several occasions. In 1989, 1994 and 1998 the eggs were taken by predators, but in 1991 one chick fledged and in 1999 four. The summer map shows the species in three tetrads, but confirmed breeding in just the one. The southernmost dot, relating to Coate Water, involved singletons in spring 1995 and again in 1996 that were certainly migrants.

Only four Ringed Plovers were ringed in the county during 1965–2000 (all in 1968 or 1969, over 20 years before the first successful breeding, so presumably caught as adults or at least full-grown) and Wiltshire has had no inward or outward recoveries of this species.

NPA & PAC

Kentish Plover

Charadrius alexandrinus

Overshooting vagrant from adjacent Continent (4 records), winters Mediterranean area

As their vernacular name suggests, Kentish Plovers were once not uncommon breeding birds in extreme southeast England, but the 19th century quest for specimens and, later, coastal development and human disturbance all contributed to their decline and eventual extinction. Moderate numbers, decreasing to a handful, bred locally in Kent until the mid 1930s (Harrison 1953) and, much more irregularly, in Sussex (Walpole-Bond 1938), occasionally thereafter until 1956; nesting has been only sporadic since, the last record in Lincolnshire in 1979 (*RBBP*).

The species is widespread in coastal or temperate inland regions of the Americas, Africa and Eurasia. In Europe – where the breeding population, excluding Russia, has been estimated at 16,300 to 18,300 pairs (*EBCC Atlas*) – the Kentish Plover is largely a coastal nester in the Mediterranean area westwards round to southernmost Sweden. There, as in England in the mid 20th century, increased human disturbance and habitat loss are likely to have been key factors in declines in several countries over recent decades. But from Hungary east to the Caucasus and Turkey, and in a band across central Asia, it also nests far inland.

British vagrants originate from those that breed on the northwest European mainland and winter along the Mediterranean coastline, especially in Spain. Although a few have wintered in Great Britain, most of those seen here are spring overshoots to southern England, the annual average during 1986–2000 being 33 (Fraser & Rogers 2002). The four Wiltshire records (the first rather marginal) fall into this spring category, all in the first third of May:

1975	10 May	CWP7/11	Glos, but overflew Wilts
1977	1 May	CWP43	Glos, but overflew Wilts
1980	5 May	CWP26	Male
1988	3–4 May	CWP68	Female

NPA & IJF-L

An article by JC Laidlaw entitled 'The War and its effects on Birds', published in *Country Life* on 2 September 1916, claimed that Kentish Plovers had been nesting not far from the Wiltshire 'camp near some downs' where he was stationed: 'on manœuvres there [I] had sometimes one or more of these strange little birds quite close to me, circling round, showing great signs of distress at their formerly lonely nest-site being so frequently disturbed'. This was quoted in *WANHM* (40: 365) in June 1919 under the heading 'Kentish Plover in Wilts?' with speculation whether the birds could have been Dotterels. Another possibility might have been Ringed Plovers, which at that time bred commonly on the East Anglian Brecks and, although there is no published record, certainly could have done so on Salisbury Plain. No description was given and this seemingly most unlikely report is mentioned only for completeness. Eds

---

Dotterel

Charadrius morinellus

Migrant (now rare), breeds north Britain/north Eurasia, winters northern Africa

Dotterels have rather precise requirements for nesting, favouring flat and sparsely vegetated uplands, and northern lowlands, above or beyond the treeline but below the snowline. They summer widely, if patchily, on arctic tundra in Fenno-Scandia and from Novaya Zemlya and the Urals in two discrete bands across Siberia, as well as in isolated pockets in alpine regions of southern Europe. The population of Europe, excluding Russia, has been estimated in the broad range of 17,900 to 39,100 pairs (*EBCC Atlas*) and that of Great Britain, at the western limit of the species' distribution, at 510–750 pairs (*APEP*).

British Dotterels nest mainly in the Scottish Highlands, but include a handful in southern Scotland and northern England (*1988–91 Atlas, RBBP*). Numbers were greatly reduced in the second half of the 19th and early 20th centuries by shooting and egg-collecting, but have apparently recovered to some extent since the 1970s. Even so, Watson & Rae (1987) argued that more birdwatchers detect more Dotterels: Scottish estimates of only 60–80 pairs from the 1940s on, rising to 100–150 by the 1970s, were probably inadequate for such birds of inhospitable uplands.

Apart from a few in Spain, all Dotterels winter in semi-desert in northern Africa and the Middle East, from Morocco to Iran, and the north-south migration is on a broad front. The species has been ringed in many countries, but, interestingly, every recovery in Morocco has originated from Scotland. It is likely that the Wiltshire records have always involved the British population. There is, however, some interchange of individuals between Scotland and Scandinavia, including a female that, having failed in north Scotland, 'initiated a replacement clutch' in Norway in the same season (*Migration Atlas*).

Migrating Dotterels tend to alight every year on traditional sites, and were once 'so common and regular... that in parts of Hertfordshire and Cambridgeshire May the 10th used to be known as Dotterel Day' (Vaughan 1927a). Chafin (1818) told of killing five from a flock of ten to 12 close to Winterslow Hut in November 1751. Smith (1887) recorded that, early in the 19th century, they were commonly seen on the Wiltshire downs in both autumn and especially spring, when they were often shot in some numbers – 'sportsmen now alive have killed from forty to fifty' – but well before the 1880s they were 'rarely to be met with'. Hony (1915a) was able to list only four records during 1900–05, three of them in September, but added that the species 'is sometimes seen on the Plain in the second week in May'.

Peirson (1919) described the Dotterel as 'a very rare bird of passage, usually in the spring'. Vaughan (1927a) reported a trip of five near Collingbourne Kingston on 10 September 1923 and, after remarking on their tameness, commented on the decline of this species since the mid 19th century: 'It had the misfortune to be a good bird for the table... so was mercilessly butchered to make a dainty dish... it has suffered much from

Table 55. Dotterels *Charadrius morinellus* in Wiltshire: five-year totals 1971–2000

	1971–75	1976–80	1981–85	1986–90	1991–95	1996–00
Records	0	3	2	2	3	2
Birds	0	11	7	4	6	6

the depredations of egg collectors, and still more...from the demand for its feathers for making artificial flies'. Eight years later, in 1931, another trip of 'about a dozen, one of which was shot, was seen at Laverstock in the early spring'; and, after a further 20 years, there were two records in 1951 – one by an observer who had also seen a Dotterel at the same place 'some ten years ago' – and another in 1955 (*WANHM*). After that, despite the great increase in numbers of birdwatchers, no more were noted for another two decades and there were still only 12 records during 1976–2000 (table 55).

Those 12, involving a total of 34 birds, were all on chalk downland, especially on Salisbury Plain, favouring bare spring-sown crops such as peas and linseed. With the decline through the 19th century, and the long gaps between records in the first 75 years of the 20th, Wiltshire's traditional migration sites possibly became 'forgotten', and no new ones seem to have been established during the recent resurgence in the Scottish population. In the 25 years from 1976, two at Stoford on 22 April 1990 were the earlier of just two records in April, and four at Casterley Camp on 28 May 1984 were the latest of nine records in May. Two at Tan Hill on 28 September 1996 were the only ones in autumn. The largest trips were five at Pitton on 2 May 1976 and five at Hill Deverill during 1–3 May 1980. From 1991:

1991	19 May	SPTA Westdown Ranges	One female
1992	3 May	Chain Hill	One female
	7 May	Berwick St James	Four
1996	28 September	Tan Hill	Two
1997	27 April	SPTA Quebec Farm	Four males

NPA & PEC

Sponsored by Derek Lyford

Golden Plover

Pluvialis apricaria

Locally common winter visitor/passage migrant from Iceland/north Europe/Britain

Golden Plovers nest mainly on moors, heaths, peatlands and tundra from Iceland and Ireland across northern Europe into western Siberia, and winter in western Europe and parts of the Mediterranean and Caspian regions. In Great Britain, they breed on uplands in southwest England (few), Wales and, especially, northern England and Scotland, but in winter generally avoid land above 200 m: they are then much more widespread, occurring from the Isles of Scilly to Shetland, preferring to feed on grasslands, especially permanent pastures, and to roost on arable (*1981–84 Winter Atlas*). The *1988–91 Atlas* estimated some 22,600 pairs in Great Britain, a decline of roughly a fifth since the *1968–72 Atlas*, though that still represented as much as three to five per cent of the 474,900 to 621,800 pairs in Europe as a whole, excluding Russia (*EBCC Atlas*).

During the winters of the 19th century, the Golden Plover was widely, if sparingly and uncertainly, distributed in flocks throughout Wiltshire, and Marsh (1842–62) noted it as 'plentiful in Salisbury market at a penny a head'. Smith (1887) described this species as a migrant on the downs, 'which favours our county when frosts and snows drive it from more northern latitudes', adding that 'Its flesh is very highly esteemed by epicures, and therefore it is diligently sought for by the fowler'. In 1929 it was described as 'Fairly common on the Downs in winter' (*WANHM*) and – as Golden Plovers were probably established as breeding birds on Dartmoor (Devon) at that time, even though that was not proved until 1950 (Sitters 1988) – it is noteworthy that, in Wiltshire, 'A pair about for several weeks in nesting season' in 1929 and 'Seen during the summer months near Chilmark, but not apparently breeding' in 1930 (*WANHM*). Peirson (1959) did not mention these observations, but wrote that Golden Plovers sometimes formed considerable flocks in winter, either alone or with Lapwings, and 'that of late years many more have been reported but it is doubtful if this represents a real increase'.

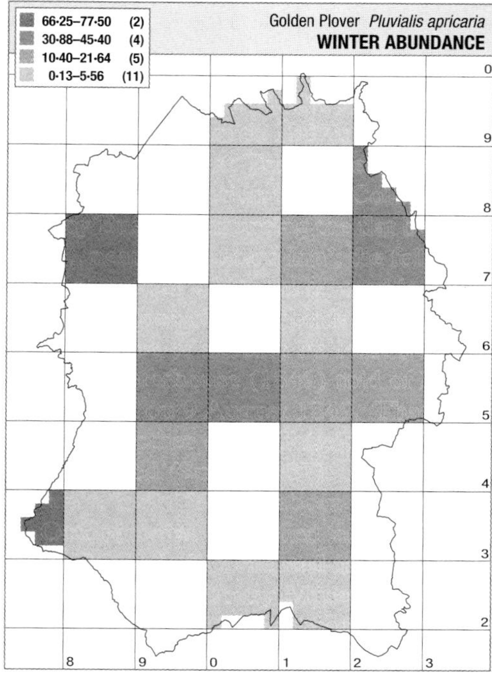

The winter tetrad survey recorded this species in only 23 of Wiltshire's 33 core 10-km squares, compared with a much wider spread of 31 in the *1981–84 Winter Atlas*. This apparent marked drop may have represented a real decrease, or it may have been at least partly a result of either the exclusion from the WOS winter map of casual records – the submission of which was actively encouraged for the *1981–84 Winter Atlas* – or the sample methods adopted for fieldwork during 1998–2000. Flocks tend to range over large areas and have secure roost sites, much movement taking place at dusk and dawn. Former and present-day airfields, including those at Keevil, Old Sarum, Netheravon and Zeals, are greatly favoured for roosting. At CWP Golden Plovers roost, often with Lapwings, wherever suitable islands and spits are exposed.

The earliest recorded dates of Golden Plovers in Wiltshire have been singletons on 19 June 1997 and 1 July 1992, and a party of seven at Barton Stacey on 23 June 1963 (*WANHM*, *Hobby*), though arrivals are more usual from September onwards and they become widespread during October–November. Most winter flocks are present from November to February, but hard weather causes large movements to the south and west, some then deserting Great Britain until the following winter. The spring passage is on a smaller scale than the autumn, mostly during March and the first half of April; the latest recorded dates having been in early May, one on the 6th in 1991, two on the 7th in 1992, and no fewer than about 50 at Marden on the 7th in 1979.

There were marked fluctuations and redistributions of numbers in the county as a whole during the last 25 years of the 20th century (figure 37). During the 1990s, counts of more than 1000 became regular at CWP – where at least 2000 were recorded in most winters – and flocks exceeding 500 were notable elsewhere in the county, but there were no more than six such records in any one winter. There were just nine records of between 1000 and 1300 Golden Plovers in Wiltshire away from CWP during that decade, and 3000 at North

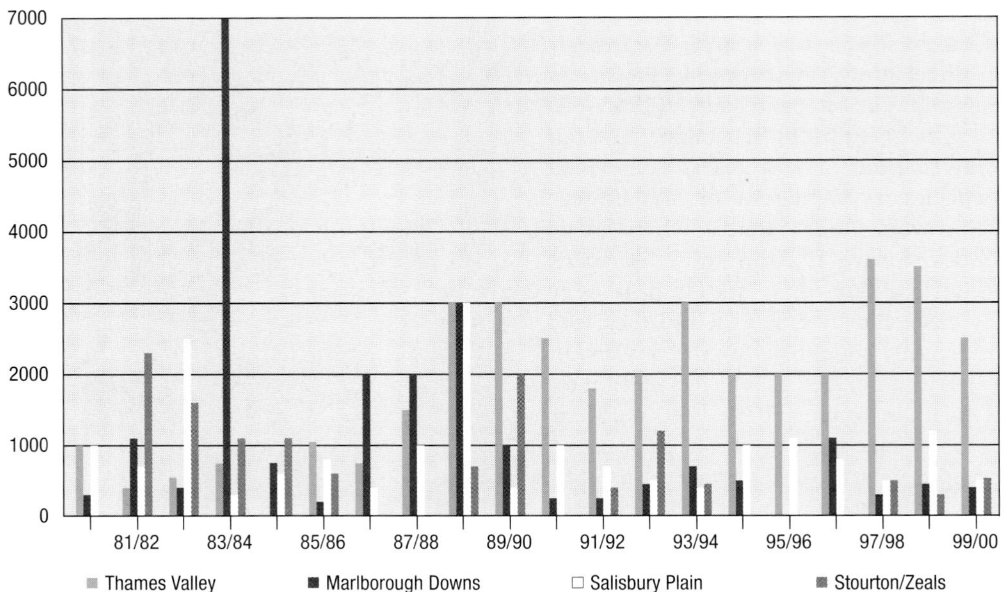

Figure 37. Golden Plovers *Pluvialis apricaria* in Wiltshire: peak counts in four key areas July–June 1980/81–1999/00

Meadow (January 1994), the same number at Stert (December 1998) and 2200 again at North Meadow (November 2000) were the only counts higher. Flocks of 700 at Ramsbury on 1 April 1994 and of 800 at Everleigh on 18 April 1997 and, again, on the 25th were noteworthy, given the late dates.

The increase at CWP was probably largely because of the creation of safe roosts on silt-beds and dry gravel pits, although greater coverage by birdwatchers may well have played a part. Declines on the Marlborough Downs and in the southwest corner of Wiltshire were perhaps results of the loss of permanent pastures to arable crops, whereas an increase in grazed permanent pastures on SPTA may explain the recent positive trend there. The number of Wiltshire sites with counts of 500 or more has increased from, usually, two to four in the early 1990s to, generally, five to seven at the end of that decade. This may be indicative of warmer winters, so that large numbers of Golden Plovers have remained farther east, rather than leaving for westernmost Britain or Ireland; certainly, analysis of WeBS data has shown a recent increasing trend for some other wader species to occur in smaller numbers on British west coast estuaries in favour of eastern ones (Austin *et al* 2000).

During the WOS winter survey, a total of 4090 was counted across all tetrads and the maximum in any one was 630. But numbers at CWP must surely have been underestimated, as the morning timed visits will have missed the exodus of the large flocks that roost there. Extrapolation gives a total county estimate of 8158 – a seemingly not unreasonable number, in view of the counts set out in figure 37 for four key areas – between 2·5 and 4 per cent of the estimated 200,000 to 300,000 wintering in Great Britain as a whole (*1981–84 Winter Atlas*). Even so, as this species shows marked and rapid responses to changing weather, the numbers in Wiltshire will vary between winters.

Those that winter in Great Britain are of Icelandic, north British and Fenno-Scandian origins (*Migration Atlas*).

PEC

Sponsored by Rosemary Hart

Grey Plover

Pluvialis squatarola

Uncommon migrant, breeds arctic Russia, winters along British coasts

Grey Plovers summer in the high Arctic from Canada and Alaska westward across Asia, but extend into Europe only in northernmost Russia. In winter, their breeding areas freeze and, some travelling vast distances, they migrate to temperate and tropical coasts in the Americas, Africa and southern Asia down to Australia, as well as in increasingly significant numbers in western Europe, when they are essentially waders of mudflats and beaches, seldom found inland. Estimates of the European winter population grew from 61,200 in the mid 1980s to 103,000 in the early 1990s, the British share rising at the same time from 21,300 to 38,500 (*CBWP*) and subsequently to 52,750 by the late 1990s (Rehfisch *et al* 2003). Thus, Great Britain – about as far north as this species occurs regularly in winter – apparently hosts around a third to a half of all the Grey Plovers that spend the non-breeding season in Europe.

Before 1980, Wiltshire had had only six records of Grey Plovers, scattered over the previous 50 years. The county's first were two at Coate Water on 4 November 1934, followed by singletons at High Post on 4 April 1958 and at Hodson on 9 December 1962, and then no fewer than four near Biddestone on 2 March 1963 (*WANHM*). (It was also reported in *WANHM* that a juvenile, 'probably of this species', was seen by a much respected observer at Keevil aerodrome on 20 October 1950 – but perhaps he was being overcautious because at that time it would have been only the second county record.) The 1970s similarly produced just one at CWP24 (formerly Kent End, now filled in) in June 1975 and two at CWP30 in May 1977.

Since 1980, on the other hand, Grey Plovers have been recorded annually (figure 38), the vast majority at CWP, but others have been found at Corsham Lake (one), Lacock Gravel Pits (one), Cherhill Down (one), Lavington Folly (one), Boscombe Down (two together) and Langford Lakes (one), and flying over Swindon (two singletons) and Salisbury (one). Most are seen during their migrations north in May (only two records in early June) and south in September–October (one in August), but there have been six records in November, four in December (one a party of five), four in January, and two each in February, March and April.

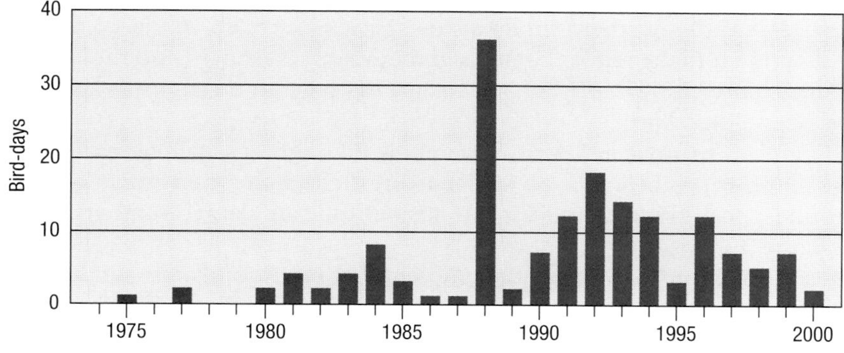

Figure 38. Grey Plovers *Pluvialis squatarola* in Wiltshire: annual totals of bird-days 1974–2000

As the figure shows, the totals were unusually high in 1988, when probably at least 23 birds were involved, but not necessarily more than about 13 of them in September–October, the rest being in January, February, May, and the five together in December. The peak came during mid September, seven at CWP68 on the 15th being the county's largest ever single count, followed by three, five and three there during the 16th–18th, though it is impossible to know how many of these were the same individuals. There was some overlap at that time with the first part of an exceptional influx of Curlew Sandpipers (*qv*) – a species whose breeding range coincides with the Grey Plover's in western arctic Siberia – but the peak of the Curlew Sandpiper passage was a week to ten days later, so it seems unlikely that there was any close connection other than the likelihood that the breeding season had been generally successful for waders in that region.

GLW & PEC

Lapwing

Vanellus vanellus

Decreasing breeder, common late summer/autumn/ winter visitor from north/east Europe

With rolling display-flights and plaintive calls, Lapwings are familiar to anyone with an interest in the British countryside, even though they have disappeared from many areas where they used to be common. They also nest widely in Europe – eastward from Iceland (irregularly), the Faeroes (very few), Ireland, France and, locally, Spain and Morocco – and continue in a narrower band right across southern Siberia and north-central Asia. The breeding population of Europe, excluding Russia, was estimated at 1·2 to 1·5 million pairs in the early 1990s (*EBCC Atlas*), but the major part of that total was made up by around 200,000 or more pairs in each of Great Britain, the Netherlands, Germany and Belarus, and some of those populations – particularly that of England and Wales – have since declined drastically.

Lapwings are mainly, or at least partially, migratory and the entire populations from much of Europe (those of Scandinavia, Germany and Switzerland eastward), move northwest, west and, later, predominantly southwest in summer and autumn, some adults starting in June or even as early as the end of May. Britain and Ireland – and, if the weather remains mild, the Low Countries and the coastal hinterland of extreme southwest Norway and Denmark – are the northern limits of the species in winter, but large numbers move across the Continent to the milder climates of the Atlantic seaboard and the Mediterranean down to North Africa (*BWP*, *Migration Atlas*). They start to travel north again in January through to March and April.

At CWP, after a marked influx in November, the highest totals occur in mid winter, decreasing in February before a rapid departure in March when many return to their nesting grounds; post-breeding movements start in June and larger numbers gather in July to moult (figure 39).

The general directions of immigration and emigration in southwest England are hinted at by a small number of ringing results involving Wiltshire. Two Lapwing chicks ringed at Höyland (Norway) on 21 May 1951 and at Pampus Haven (the Netherlands) on 26 May 1968 were both found dead here towards the ends of their first winters, respectively

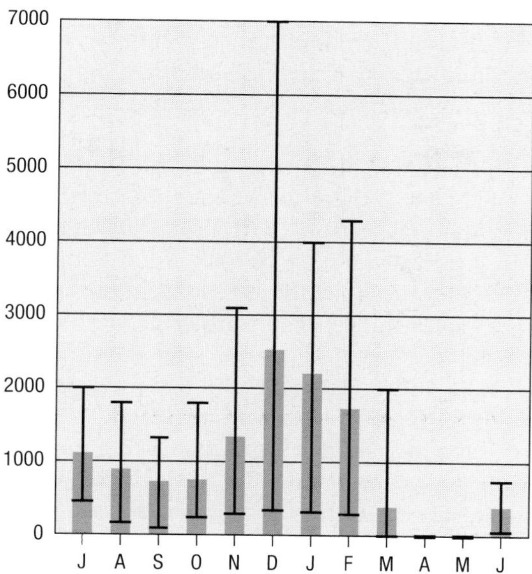

Figure 39. Lapwings *Vanellus vanellus* in Wiltshire: monthly means (shaded columns) and maximum and minimum peak counts at CWP 1990–2000

near Malmesbury on 1 April 1952 and in Savernake Forest on 30 March 1969. Of the 26 recoveries from 508 Lapwings ringed in the county during 1965–2000 (and an unknown number earlier in the 20th century), mostly as chicks in May or June, 17 were later found within Great Britain, six in France, and three in Spain. The French recoveries included one ringed as a chick on Salisbury Plain as far back as June 1912 and shot in Finistère in January 1914. One of the Spanish trio survived rather longer, ringed at Old Sarum in May 1959 and shot near Madrid on 27 January 1963 – at a time when many Lapwings will have left Great Britain in the harshest winter of the second half of the 20th century. Except for one in March, most of the recoveries abroad were shot or found dead in December or January between 7 months and 3½ years later, but two in France had survived 5½ years and 8½ years.

In former times, the species was evidently much commoner in Wiltshire. Chafin (1818) recorded that in November 1751 he had been informed by 'a servant, who had been sent to Winterslow Hut' that he had seen 'a very large flock of Green Plovers' land on a large cultivated area where the turnip crop had failed. Bosworth Smith (1863) noted that 'Great numbers of this bird breed upon the large fields and open downs between Marlborough and Aldbourne', adding that they were also found in smaller numbers in all open country around Marlborough. Similarly, im Thurn (1870) found Lapwings 'abundant on all of our downs', a few remaining all year. Smith (1887) described this species as 'the true Plover of the downs … what Wiltshireman does not know the peculiar call-note of the Peewit … ?' He also wrote that 'Mr. F. Stratton … had noticed a most extraordinary increase … at Gore Cross, on Salisbury Plain: for whereas he used to see five or six pairs breeding there annually, that year [1875] there were hundreds'.

Over half a century later, reports in *WANHM* during 1929–36 began with 'A common resident which is increasing as a breeding species in many parts of the county' and continued with repeated references to 'further evidence of increase', apart from a blip in 1934 when a 'great deal of movement has been noticed … most particularly the autumn passage and the absence of this species from their regular breeding haunts'. In the report for 1931: 'Attention was drawn at a meeting of the Wiltshire Agricultural Committee to the great increase in the number of plovers in the county, and to the influence of a resolution, passed by that committee, in bringing about the legislation which has secured this. Certainly the increase of this species as a breeding bird has been most marked during the past three seasons'.

In the *WANHM* reports for 1946–48, Lapwings were evidently considered too common to be worth mentioning, but in 1949 there were references to their comparative scarcity around Marlborough, where this was attributed to 'the taking of eggs by ploughmen, etc.', and around Chisenbury. In contrast, in 1951, 'Small colonies and single pairs nested in areas near Corsham where there were none three years ago'. Over the next few years most entries related to the larger observations of autumn and winter flocks (including some in the 1000–1500 range) and feeding methods (among them, 11-day old chicks eating tadpoles at Lacock Gravel Pits, quoted from *BB* 49: 502), but in 1955 'many nests were destroyed by gang mowers' on Overton Down and at Keevil.

Peirson (1959) regarded Lapwings as 'common', remarking that they moved 'away from the breeding areas ... to form flocks about July; the flocks increase in size in early autumn and leave the exposed country for the water meadows and lower farmland during the late autumn'. He thought that this species had increased generally from about 1930, then decreased during and after the 1939–45 War, and increased again 'since 1953' – though this last status change was not apparent from the entries in *WANHM*, which either simply listed the Lapwing without comment or concentrated on winter flocks and weather movements. These flocks seem to have become larger through the late 1950s and 1960s, including an observation near Wroughton in January 1959 of 3000 to 4000 flying south during the morning and 2000 west in the afternoon (*WANHM*). Several other flocks of between 1000 and 2000, and even of 'several thousand birds', in various years grew to one of 7000 in 1967, which in turn was beaten by 11,000 near Tilshead on 26 October 1971 (*WANHM*). Buxton (1981) noted flocks 'numbering 2000/3000' during autumn and winter.

The *1968–72 Atlas* noted that the severe weather of 1961/62 and (especially) 1962/63 had 'drastically' reduced numbers of the Lapwing in Great Britain as a whole – though neither of those winters caused any particular comment for this species in *WANHM* – and that otherwise 'the general trends seem to be a gradual decrease in southern areas and an increase in the north'. It quoted a CBC estimate in 1972 of an average density of 3·4 breeding pairs per km^2 on British farmland, and continued, 'Even one-fifth of this, over all the occupied 10-km squares, would give a total British and Irish breeding population of over 200,000 pairs'. Applied to Wiltshire's 3485 km^2, this might indicate a county population at that time of some 2370 pairs, albeit a very rough calculation. In 1987, Shrubb & Lack (1991) estimated 123,000 (110,000–138,000) pairs in England and Wales, which – allowing for 75,000–100,000 pairs in Scotland – the *1988–91 Atlas* used as the basis for its figures of 185,000 to 238,000 breeding pairs in Great Britain. Only 11 years later, however, in 1998, a national breeding survey found just 63,000 in England and Wales, a fall of almost 49 per cent (Wilson *et al* 2001). Changes in agricultural practice, particularly the increase in autumn-sown cereals, drainage of wet areas, ploughing of permanent pastures, and high stocking rates on remaining permanent pastures appeared to be the major problems.

The *1968–72 Atlas* mapped Lapwings as breeding in all 33 of Wiltshire's core 10-km squares (and in all the other 15 squares that have only small parts in the county); this total fell to 30 in the *1988–91 Atlas* and rose again to 32 during the summer tetrad survey 1995–2000. The summer distribution map for 1995–2000 shows Lapwings to have been more widespread in the higher east of the county, where the majority of arable farming is found, and only sparsely scattered in the lower-lying west, which is mainly devoted to

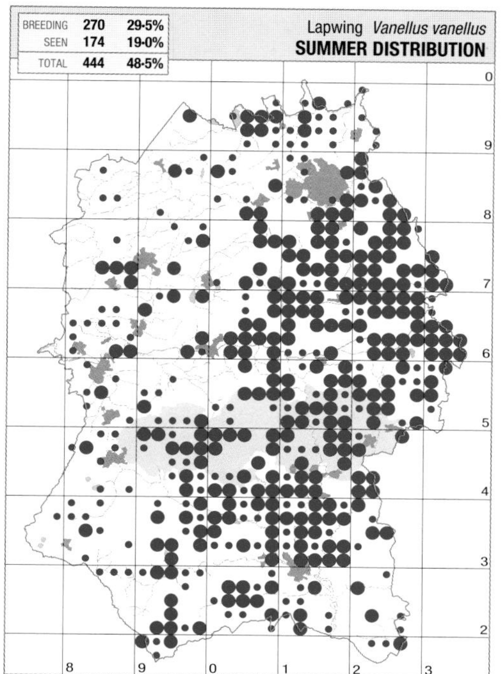

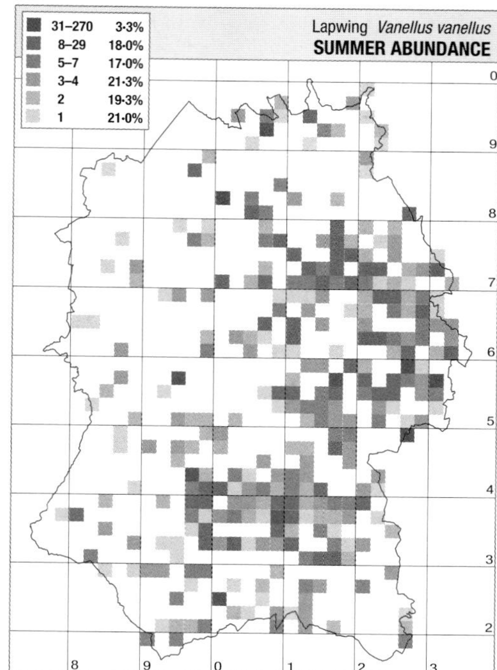

dairy farming. The ideal habitat for this species – mixed farmland where spring-sown cereals and grazed permanent pasture exist side by side – is still to be found on the Wiltshire downs, though it is declining.

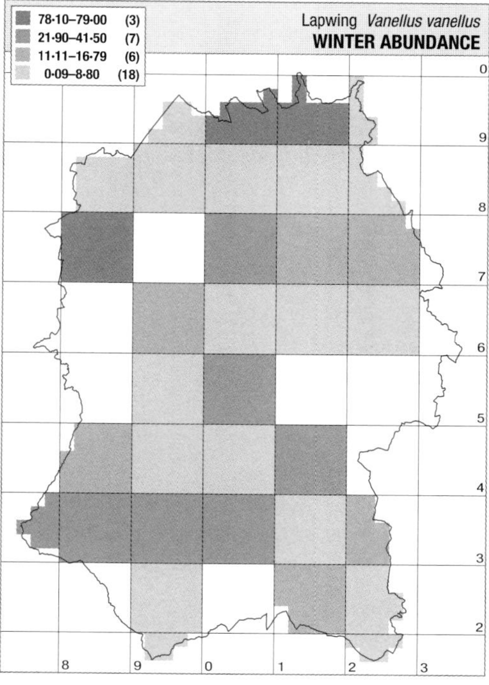

There was evidence of Lapwings breeding in just under a third of all tetrads and the species was seen in a further fifth; many 'breeding' records may, however, have related to displaying birds that, because of agricultural operations or other disturbance, subsequently failed to nest at all, let alone successfully. The summer abundance map shows the highest densities to the south of Salisbury Plain and from the east side of the Plain up to the Marlborough Downs. The counts of Lapwings on timed visits totalled 2277, but the inclusion of some large numbers – the highest single tetrad count was 270 – show that some counts must incorrectly have included post-breeding flocks, particularly in July, and the true summer population of this early migrant is likely to be well below that total. The breeding bird survey of SPTA by RSPB found 71 pairs (Stanbury *et al* 2000). This included casual records but is likely to have been a minimum figure, since only around two thirds of suitable habitat was surveyed, yet the distribution and the

Table 56. Lapwings *Vanellus vanellus* in Wiltshire: peak counts at CWP July–June 1990/91–1999/00

	90/91	91/92	92/93	93/94	94/95	95/96	96/97	97/98	98/99	99/00
Peak count	3000	3000	4300	2000	3000	1700	4500	4000	7000	2500
Peak month	Dec	Feb	Feb	Jul/Dec	Jan	Dec	Dec	Feb	Dec	Dec

number of tetrads in which birds were found (around 30) matched findings of the WOS survey quite closely. Were this density (around 2·5 breeding pairs per occupied tetrad) repeated across the county's 270 occupied tetrads, a population of some 675 pairs would be estimated but, given that SPTA represents a relatively unfavourable area – with much higher densities recorded directly to the south and north and on the Marlborough Downs – a figure of 750–1000 pairs might be suggested for the period 1995–2000. This would represent a considerably larger population than the 200–250 indicated in a recent review of breeding waders in southwest England (Jeffs & Lock 1998). Nevertheless, that report identified that, like Somerset, Wiltshire remained a regional stronghold for the species and held, in most cases, several-fold more than counties farther to the south and west.

Not surprisingly, Lapwings are more widely distributed in winter, when concentrations occur at CWP (table 56) and in the Thames valley, in the peripheries of Salisbury Plain, and in the southwest. During the winter months, flocks favour such short grass habitats as airfields, playing fields and sheep-grazed downland, and they also bathe and roost by day at gravel pits. Many of these flocks exceed 1000, but really hard weather reduces their numbers dramatically. The *1981–84 Winter Atlas* found this species in all 33 of Wiltshire's core 10-km squares, whereas the tetrad survey of 1998/99 and 1999/2000 recorded them in only 27. The winter map suggests a rather patchy distribution – including some notable absences, such as to the northeast of SPTA – and it is likely that habitat preferences at that season are to an extent obscured at the 10-km square level. The total of the 2-hour counts was 6556, which may be extrapolated to 12,684, and on which basis some 12,000–20,000 are estimated for the whole county, although numbers are likely to vary in different weather conditions.

(See also page 725.)

GLW & PAC

Sponsored by Boyton Farms Warminster

Knot

Calidris canutus

Rare migrant (31 records), breeds Canada/Greenland/Siberia, winters coasts of Britain/west Europe/Atlantic Africa

Knots have a very discontinuous arctic breeding distribution in Alaska, Canada, Greenland and Siberia, and migrate huge distances to winter on coasts as far south as the tip of South America, southern Africa, Australia and New Zealand. An estimated 450,000 winter in west Europe (Stroud *et al* 2004), some 283,600 of those in Great Britain (Rehfisch *et al* 2003) where most are concentrated at a few key sites, such as the Wash (Lincolnshire/Norfolk) and Morecambe

Table 57. Knots *Calidris canutus* in Wiltshire: monthly totals of bird-days 1974–2000

	Jan	Feb	Mar	Apr	May	Jun	Jul	Aug	Sep	Oct	Nov	Dec
Bird-days	0	0	1	3	24	1	1	5	14	2	0	0

Bay (Lancashire). Although some may originate in Siberia, the vast majority comes from Greenland and northeast Canada. The numbers reaching western Europe dramatically halved after disastrous breeding seasons in those regions in the mid 1970s, but partially recovered during 1977–85 through better nesting success and survival, and have remained more or less stable since (*Migration Atlas*, Boyd & Piersma 2001).

Wiltshire's first Knot was a male 'killed' at Langley in 1850, and other singletons met similar fates at Seend in February 1870 and at Langford on 10 December 1879 (Smith 1887); a female was then captured half a mile from Salisbury on 27 February 1906, very weak and thin with part of one wing missing (Bankes 1906), but 50 years were to pass before the next. (Until the 1940s small waders, particularly of the genus *Calidris*, were – in the post-gun and pre-telescope era – often considered almost unidentifiable.) Then came a little flush of records: one was found feeding with Lapwings at Coate Water on 3 November 1956, two in first-winter plumage were seen there during 7–9 September 1960 and one on the 12th; and one watched at Coombe Bissett watercress beds during February 1963 was 'presumably the same bird found dead in observer's garage' on 10 March (*WANHM*).

After that, however, no more Knots were recorded for nearly another two decades, until increased numbers of birdwatchers and the more extensive habitat available at CWP resulted in their being found in 14 of the 20 years 1981–2000. This species is now a rare – less than annual – passage migrant in Wiltshire, seen almost exclusively at CWP, the only observations elsewhere during those 20 years having been two flying east over Trowbridge on 1 April 1981 and one at Swindon STW on 24 October 1997. A total of 24 records involved 51 bird-days (figure 40). While most of the records up to the 1960s related to the winter months of November–February, those during 1981–2000 were all in July–October, apart from nine records in March–June, including one to three daily at CWP during 7–12 May 1993 (table 57). The largest gatherings have been parties of three on 25 September 1988 and 10 May 1993.

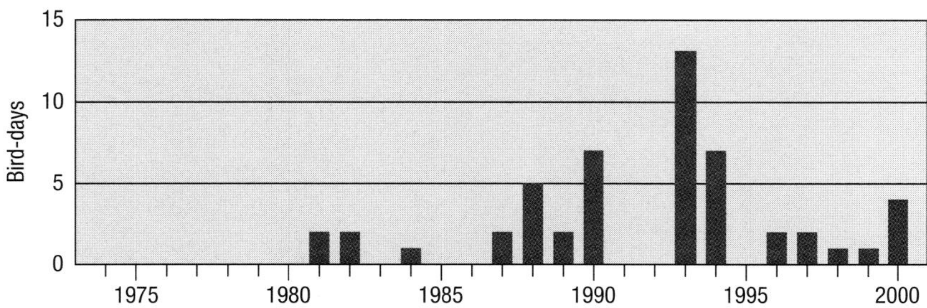

Figure 40. Knots *Calidris canutus* in Wiltshire: annual totals of bird-days (mainly CWP) 1974–2000

NPA & PAC

Sanderling

Calidris alba

Scarce migrant, breeds Canada/Greenland/ Siberia, winters Europe/Africa

Familiar visitors to sandy shorelines virtually worldwide, Sanderlings breed in the northernmost regions of North America and Asia, in a fragmented arctic distribution not unlike that of the Knot (*qv*). Around 20,000 winter in Great Britain (Rehfisch *et al* 2003) – very roughly half the total of western Europe – where they are mainly concentrated at a handful of estuaries but also spread thinly along sandy coastlines (*1981–84 Winter Atlas*). These come from both Greenland and Siberia, but it is not known whether any from arctic Canada winter on eastern Atlantic shores (*Migration Atlas*). Typically, large numbers occur on autumn and, especially, spring passage.

The first reported Sanderlings in Wiltshire – a party of four by the By Brook at Ford on 24 April 1960 – were published as 'probably of this species' (*WANHM*). There is, however, no question about the flock of 11, all bar one in summer plumage, seen at Kent End (later CWP24, now filled in) on 14 May 1973 (*WANHM*). At CWP also, two more were found in May 1976, five in May 1980, and one for four days in May 1982. During 1986–2000 the species was recorded there in every year except 1990 (figure 41). Meanwhile, three had also been seen at Liden Lagoon on 7 June 1977 and one at Coate Water on 14 August 1977, but these were the only records away from CWP up to and including 2000.

The distinct peak in Wiltshire in May (table 58) is consistent with the highest numbers on spring passage through Great Britain as a whole. Numbers in the county vary greatly between years and can be linked to weather patterns, but – even though the strongest passage of this species in spring is on the west coast (*Migration Atlas*) – a brisk easterly or southeasterly wind in May is the key time to look for Sanderlings at CWP, as it is along the English Channel. The largest numbers were 12 on 17 May 1987, eight on 25 April 1997 and six on 25 May 1994, the last group part of a series of records at CWP74 from the 14th to the 28th, including five on the 15th–16th. The earliest were two on 10 April 1989, and the latest a singleton on 16 September 1987.

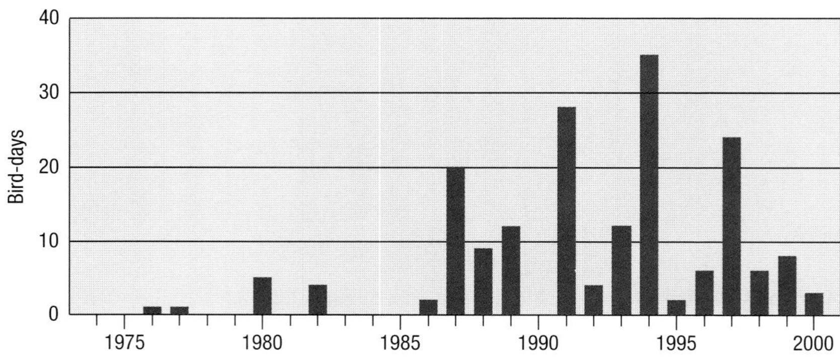

Figure 41. Sanderlings *Calidris alba* in Wiltshire: annual totals of bird-days (mainly CWP) 1974–2000

NPA & IJF-L

Table 58. Sanderlings *Calidris alba* in Wiltshire: monthly totals of bird-days 1974–2000

	Jan	Feb	Mar	Apr	May	Jun	Jul	Aug	Sep	Oct	Nov	Dec
Bird-days	0	0	0	16	141	4	10	13	1	0	0	0

The use of 'brown' in the brief published description of the four birds reported in 1960 as 'probably of this species' is not encouraging: Sanderlings in winter are palest grey above, and in summer their heads and breasts are markedly rufous, while the riverside locality, the behaviour, the lack of reference to black legs, and the emphasis on 'white outer tail feathers' all militate against that species. One obvious conclusion is that they might have been Common Sandpipers, particularly as 'each time they did not fly far, but kept low over the water', but they were watched for 1½ hours and 'approached within 20 ft' and it is difficult to believe that the experienced observer concerned was not familiar with Common Sandpipers in Wiltshire. Another possibility might conceivably be Temminck's Stints, but the behaviour was not typical of that species on passage. Eds

---

Little Stint
Calidris minuta

Uncommon passage migrant, breeds arctic Eurasia, winters mainly Africa/India

Little Stints are high arctic birds that nest in small numbers in northernmost Norway (200–500 pairs: *EBCC Atlas*), sporadically extending into extreme north Sweden or Finland; they are much more numerous across the far north of European Russia and western Siberia, and they winter chiefly in sub-Saharan Africa, Arabia and the Indian subcontinent, though in some years many thousands go no farther than the south Mediterranean basin and the Middle East. A few are even found in Great Britain in winter, but Little Stints are normally only passage migrants in this country, chiefly in autumn, when they migrate across Europe on broad fronts, occurring most commonly in September (Prater 1981); their 'Relative scarcity on western seaboard [of Europe] in spring suggests that… [their] main return route from West Africa is north-east across Sahara and Mediterranean' (*BWP*, and *cf* Curlew Sandpiper).

Remarkably – apart from one reported on 9 February 1886 (*MCNHS*), which was discounted by Hony (1915a) because the 'evidence is certainly not sufficient' – no Little Stints were identified in Wiltshire until two were found at Coate Water on 1 September 1956; thereafter, singletons were recorded at Coate Water in 1960 and at Swindon STW in 1963 and 1969, all in September (*WANHM*). One and then two were seen at Swindon STW in September 1974, and one each there and at Coate Water in September 1975. The exceptionally hot summer of 1976 saw, perhaps at least partly as a result of the lower water levels, what were then unprecedented numbers at CWP: three on 8 June (the county's first record of northward spring passage), one during 13–17 August and varying numbers, up to a maximum of eight, in September and the first three days of October. The species remained relatively scarce during the next ten years: up to four together were recorded at Swindon STW during 6–10 September 1978, one at CWP on 21 September 1980, two at Langford Lakes on 16 August 1984 (one remaining to the 20th), a series of observations of one to three at CWP from 26 August to 30 September 1984, and one at CWP on 25 September 1985.

Table 59. Little Stints *Calidris minuta* in Wiltshire: monthly totals of bird-days 1974–2000

	Jan	Feb	Mar	Apr	May	Jun	Jul	Aug	Sep	Oct	Nov	Dec
Bird-days	31	28	17	0	19	5	1	52	463	123	1	4

The next occurred in 1987, when Langford Lakes claimed only the county's second spring record on 25 May. Since then, Little Stints have been seen annually in autumn, mostly in September, and irregularly also in spring (figure 42). This is doubtless because of far greater observer coverage in the ever-extending wetland habitats at CWP – where, indeed, most are seen, including Wiltshire's highest autumn count of 29 on 21 September 1996 and largest (early) spring flock of eight on 21 March 1999. There had been, however, occasional records elsewhere by 2000, at Swindon STW and Langford Lakes, though none at Coate Water since 1975. The autumns of 1998 and, particularly, 1996 (*Birding World* 9: 333) produced the biggest influxes.

While water levels at CWP clearly play a part in the annual fluctuations in numbers, other factors are weather patterns – both British and Continental – and, most importantly in autumn, also breeding success. Unfortunately, age-classes are not always reported, but all in spring appear to have been adults and the vast majority in autumn juveniles. Although May and August–October are the most likely times to find Little Stints in Wiltshire, records now come from all months, and in 1988/89 one overwintered at CWP from 29 December to 5 March (this last accounting for the large values in those months in table 59).

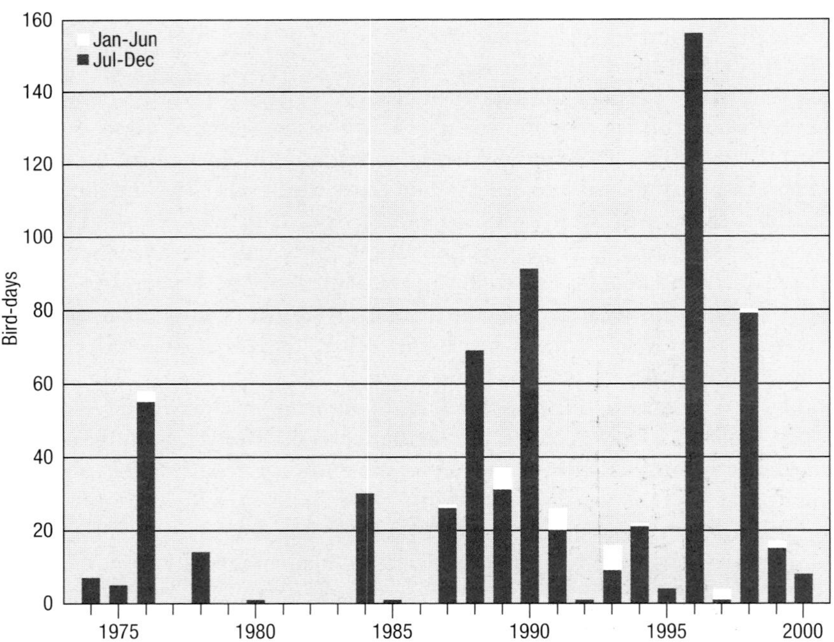

Figure 42. Little Stints *Calidris minuta* in Wiltshire: annual totals of bird-days (mainly CWP) 1974–2000

NPA & PAC

Temminck's Stint

Calidris temminckii

Vagrant (11 records), breeds north Eurasia (few Britain), winters Africa/south Asia

The Temminck's Stint is one of the most diminutive waders, with grey-brown to olive upperparts, white outer tail, dusky chest, and short pale legs. It breeds in the Arctic from Fenno-Scandia right across Siberia, favouring sheltered and often relatively rich habitats. The European population, excluding Russia, has been estimated at between 11,600 and 17,700 pairs (*EBCC Atlas*). Of this total, a tiny proportion – reaching a peak of nine adults at four sites in 1980 (*1988–91 Atlas*) – has maintained a nesting toehold in the Scottish Highlands since 1971, though only three males were present at two sites in 2000 (*RBBP*).

The species winters mainly in sub-Saharan Africa, India and southeast Asia, but small numbers, perhaps from Fenno-Scandian populations, are regular in Great Britain on passage, with annual average totals of 70 recorded in the 1970s, 105 in the 1980s and 95 in the 1990s (Fraser & Rogers 2002): although most are seen in English east and southeast coastal counties, others are found widely across Great Britain, including far inland. More than half appear in the middle two weeks of May (*cf* Little Stint). The more protracted autumn passage involves unsuccessful breeders returning south in July, followed by juveniles in August and September. Of the 11 Wiltshire records (12 birds), all from 1970 onwards, seven have been during the peak spring passage period:

1970	31 Aug–15 Sep	Swindon STW	Immature, ringed on 1st (*WANHM*)
1974	5–7 September	Swindon STW	(unaged)
1978	9–11 Sep	Calne Sand Pits	(unaged)
1987	9–10 May	CWP68	Two adults, summer plumage
	17 May	CWP Swillbrook	Adult, summer plumage
1988	17–20 May	CWP68	Adult, summer plumage
	18–20 May	CWP73/68	Adult, summer plumage
1989	13 May	CWP68	Adult
1992	7–9 August	CWP74	(unaged)
1993	12 May	CWP74	Adult
1998	19 May	CWP68	Adult

The two individuals in 1988 are treated as separate records because they were first discovered at different pits and the second was not found to have joined the first at CWP68 until the 19th and 20th.

Because it was published (Halliday 1956), and was later included without qualification by Kennedy (1966), a Temminck's Stint identified at Coate Water on 22 January 1956 must be referred to here, even though it was rejected at the time by the county records panel (GL Webber) and was not even mentioned in *WANHM*. This wader was briefly seen 'in the company of a small party of wagtails' by a number of observers who were in boats and 'able to get within a few feet... making identification a matter of certainty' before it towered away; a compilation of impressions concluded that it was stint-sized, uniformly plumaged and pale-legged. But this clearly cannot be substantiated now: the descriptions supplied were evidently inadequate for what would have been a first county record on an exceptional winter date. (See also the report of four 'Sanderlings' in April 1960.)

NPA & IJF-L

White-rumped Sandpiper

Calidris fuscicollis

Vagrant (2 records), breeds arctic Canada, winters South America

This vagrant wader from the New World, fractionally smaller than a Dunlin, breeds in the arid tundra zone of arctic and subarctic Canada, and migrates almost the total length of the Americas to winter by both estuaries and inland waters south to southern Argentina and, to a lesser extent, Chile. The White-rumped's southerly migration follows the Great Circle route through eastern North America and the western Atlantic, which accounts for its being one of the commonest Nearctic vagrants in Europe in autumn (though disproportionately rare in spring). It is annual in Great Britain, probably so in Ireland and Iceland, and has also occurred in at least a dozen other European countries, while small flocks have reached some of the Atlantic island groups.

During 1958–2000, 317 White-rumped Sandpipers were recorded in Great Britain (*BBRC*), the vast majority in autumn at almost any time between late July and late October, with a preponderance of adults over juveniles. Wiltshire's first was an adult on the old silt-bed at CWP68 during 25–29 September 1988 (*Hobby*, *BBRC*) – a year in which relatively few were seen in Britain. The second, also an adult, was found on the new silt-bed at the same lake eight years later, on 2 October 1996.

NPA & PEC

Pectoral Sandpiper

Calidris melanotos

Vagrant (6 records), breeds arctic Canada/Siberia, winters southern South America

Pectoral Sandpipers are relatively large among calidrid sandpipers, similar in size to female Ruffs. They are the commonest of all American vagrants to Europe, with records in many countries south also to Morocco and Egypt, and even in sub-Saharan Africa south to South Africa (Urban *et al* 1986). In Great Britain alone, no fewer than 1823 were recorded during 1968–2000 – an annual average of over 55 – including as many as 131 in 1984 and again in 1999 (Fraser & Rogers 2002).

Juveniles leave their arctic Alaskan and Canadian natal areas towards the end of August, following a route that crosses the western Atlantic where fast-moving depressions whip some of them over to Europe rather than down to their intended destinations in southern South America (*cf* White-rumped Sandpiper). Most British records thus involve juveniles in September, widely distributed but with the highest numbers in coastal southwest England, the Northern Isles and East Anglia. It is possible that some Pectorals also come from an easterly direction, since the species' breeding range has gradually extended westward across most of arctic Siberia – almost indeed to the northeastern border of European Russia – but these Asiatic populations are believed to migrate eastward and mostly to cross to Alaska and

Canada before likewise turning south to winter in the traditional regions of southern South America (*cf* Wheatear).

Wiltshire's six records fall nicely within the national parameters and illustrate the lure of CWP for vagrant waterbirds crossing the county:

1977	6–16 October	CWP29	Juvenile, often in Glos
1984	22–23 & 26 September	CWP24	Juvenile, also Glos 24th–30th
1987	17 May	CWP Swillbrook	Adult, flew in from Glos
1988	25 September	CWP68	Presumed juvenile
1992	28 September	CWP68	Juvenile
1997	4–7 September	CWP68	Adult

The one in 1984 was erroneously stated in *Hobby* to be 'The 3rd county record... the previous 2 being in 1976 and 77', but, in fact, none was reported in 1976.

The adult in May 1987 was accompanied by a Temminck's Stint (*qv*). The relatively few records of Pectoral Sandpipers in Great Britain in spring perhaps include vagrants from previous years now travelling north and south in the Old World with European waders.

NPA & IJF-L

Curlew Sandpiper

Calidris ferruginea

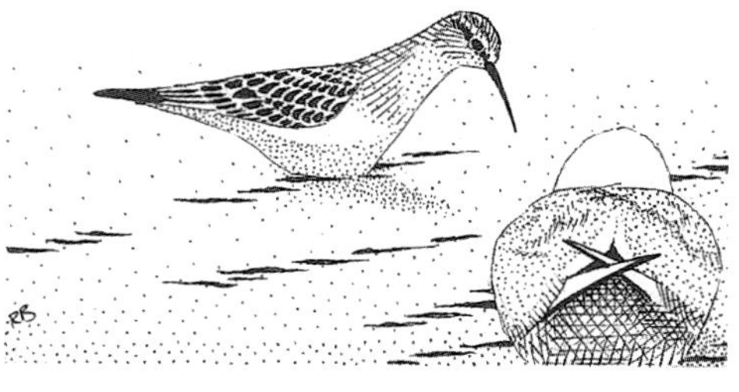

Irregular passage migrant, breeds arctic Siberia, winters Africa/Australia

Curlew Sandpipers breed on high arctic tundra in Siberia and, irregularly, Alaska. They are long-distance migrants, wintering in sub-Saharan Africa, Arabia, the Indian subcontinent, southeast Asia, and Australasia. Very variable numbers occur in Great Britain during spring and, more particularly, autumn passage, the peak usually in August–September. Occasionally there is an exceptional influx through western Europe, as in 1969 (Stanley & Minton 1972) and 1988 (Kirby *et al* 1989), but the species is rarely found here in winter (Prater 1981).

Wiltshire's first recorded Curlew Sandpiper was shot at Chippenham in July 1869 (Smith 1887). Nearly 90 years were to pass (note comments under Knot and Dunlin) before the next – one seen at Coate Water on 6 September 1958 – but then singletons were found there again in both the following two autumns, on 23 August 1959 and during 19–23 September 1960 (*WANHM*). As individual migrant waders will sometimes reappear at particular sites in successive years, perhaps this run of three records involved the same bird. Certainly no more were recorded at Coate during 1961–2000.

Indeed, the 1960s and 1970s produced only two more county records, both at Swindon STW where there were three on 30–31 August 1969, dropping to one on 1–2 September (*WANHM*), and a singleton on 5 September 1974. The autumn of 1969 had brought an unprecedented immigration of Curlew Sandpipers (Stanley & Minton 1972) and the paucity of Wiltshire observations then – compared with the numbers that would appear at CWP during the next big invasion, in 1988 – presumably reflected the county's relative lack of suitable wader habitats in the late 1960s.

The next at Swindon STW was not for another ten years, on 18 August 1984, but in the meantime CWP had had its first, on 12 September 1982; and its second appeared almost exactly four years later, on 10 September 1986. Thereafter, increases in available habitat

Table 60. Curlew Sandpipers *Calidris ferruginea* in Wiltshire: monthly totals of bird-days (mainly CWP) 1974–2000

	Jan	Feb	Mar	Apr	May	Jun	Jul	Aug	Sep	Oct	Nov	Dec
Bird-days	0	0	0	1	23	2	0	66	149	11	2	0

and observer coverage resulted in Curlew Sandpipers being reported almost annually (figure 43). Indeed, Wiltshire's first spring records came in 1987, when six were noted at CWP in May, including five together on the 1st, still the county's largest spring flock. In autumn, most arrive in September though they have been found from July through to early November (table 60), the latest date being two at CWP on 7 November 1998.

In the peak autumn of 1988, a large influx into Great Britain – attributed to a low-pressure system over Fenno-Scandia and the Baltic that coincided with the main migration after a season of high breeding success (Kirby *et al* 1989) – included a Wiltshire record total of 40 Curlew Sandpipers at CWP on 25 September, among them a flock of 34 which were seen to arrive together. Although this and some previous influxes followed successful breeding seasons, other years of high breeding productivity have not resulted in big autumn numbers in Great Britain (Kirby *et al* 1989). Thus, it appears that weather patterns and, of course, the availability of suitable habitat are the keys to this species' occurrence in Wiltshire.

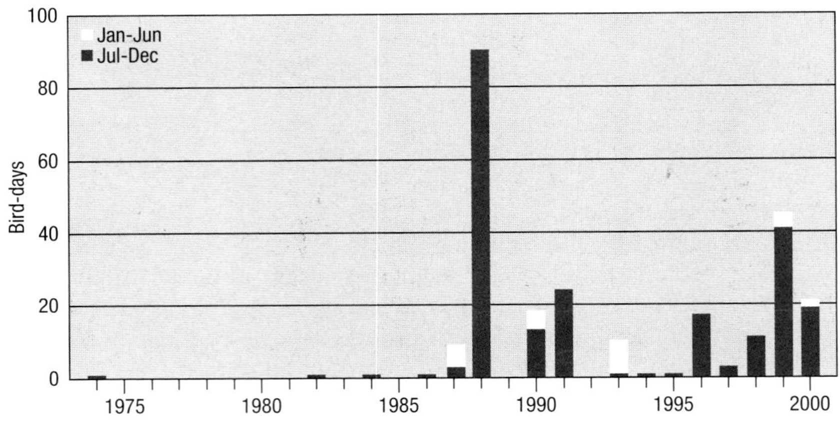

Figure 43. Curlew Sandpipers *Calidris ferruginea* in Wiltshire: annual totals of bird-days (mainly CWP) 1974–2000

Full details of records are not available for 1999: the five spring bird-days reported in *Hobby* have been attributed to May in the above figure, and the 41 autumn bird-days reported have been divided between August (20) and September (21)

NPA & PAC

Purple Sandpiper

Calidris maritima

Vagrant (1 old record) from British coasts, breeds Iceland/arctic Eurasia, winters northwest Europe coasts

Purple Sandpipers nest in subarctic to high arctic regions from Canada east to western Siberia, including Greenland, Svalbard, Iceland, Faeroes, Fenno-Scandia and northernmost Russia. Excluding the last, the European population has been put broadly at 27,700 to 52,000 pairs (*EBCC Atlas*). Since 1978 the species has also nested sporadically in Scotland (*eg* Thom 1986): during 1990–98 there were one to four pairs annually, but in 1999 and 2000 only a singleton was found in suitable breeding habitat (*RBBP*).

In winter, these dumpy, short-legged waders are characteristic of rocky coasts in eastern North America, southern Greenland and Iceland (including many migrants from east Greenland) and in northwest Europe from Norway and southernmost Sweden to Great Britain, Ireland and northwest France, occasionally south to Iberia. The British winter population has most recently been estimated at 17,530 (Rehfisch *et al* 2003).

Though there have been records in several central European countries, the species is 'Exceptional inland' in Great Britain (Witherby *et al* 1938–41). Thus, 'the arrival of a specimen in the heart of Wiltshire, at Everleigh Rectory, on February 3rd, 1881 (as I learn from Mr. Grant, who received it in the flesh and preserved it) must be looked upon as the single specimen which proves the rule' (Smith 1887).

GLW & IJF-L

Dunlin

Calidris alpina

Local winter and scarce passage visitor, breeds Greenland/north Eurasia/Britain, winters southwards from west Europe

Dunlins have a circumpolar breeding distribution, from arctic North America and Eurasia south in Europe to the southern Baltic, Ireland and Great Britain, where in Devon 'a few pairs... on the highest and remotest parts of Dartmoor' are the world's most southerly nesters (Sitters 1988). In Europe, excluding Russia, there are an estimated 294,900 to 396,300 breeding pairs (*EBCC Atlas*), some 9150 to 9900 of these in Great Britain, despite a decline of 44 per cent in the number of occupied 10-km squares between the *1968–72 Atlas* and the *1988–91 Atlas*. The species winters south to the northern fringes of Central America, West and northeast Africa, Arabia, northwest India, and around the Sea of Japan and the South China Sea. With about 555,000 Dunlins in winter, Great Britain holds the lion's share of the 1·3 million estimated to be in Atlantic Europe at that season (Rehfisch *et al* 2003), when they have a predominantly coastal distribution, particularly favouring large muddy estuaries.

Smith (1887) recorded just seven Dunlins 'killed' or 'shot' in Wiltshire: two at Chitterne, one at Market Lavington and one at Compton Bassett, all in February 1870; singletons at Avebury and Wedhampton in February 1873; and, the only one not in February, at Netheravon in December 1875. One was then shot 'near the river Ray' on 24 January 1907 (*WANHM*, Hony 1915a). The next traceable reports came in the 1930s: three at Grove Farm, near Axford on 27 January 1933; and a rather tantalising reference to 'quite a number seen on the downs near Devizes during migration' in 1934 (*WANHM*). No more were published for another 14 years and, even then, the conclusion of Peirson (1959) that Dunlins had 'been seen sometimes in small flocks in eight years since 1948, often as a winter visitor... occasionally in spring and autumn' was somewhat misleading – because the eight years 1948–55 produced only seven records of up to three, and just one of 10–20 'on the Whaddon reaches of the Bristol Avon in November' 1952. The paucity of 20th century Dunlins in Wiltshire before 1956 may have been partly because small waders were long regarded as 'difficult' (see under Knot), but also largely because Wiltshire had very few suitable wetland sites to attract birds that feed on open mud or sand.

From 1956, however – at times when the water level was low for repairs to the dam, usually in winter – Coate Water became a regular site for Dunlins: during 1956–64 it totalled 22 records, mostly of one to three, but including 30–40 on 28 January 1956, about ten on 15 December 1958, and up to four in September 1960 (*WANHM*). Other localities that held Dunlins from time to time in the 1960s and early 1970s included Swindon STW (even a 'series of autumn records' in 1970) and Lacock Gravel Pits (*WANHM*). These sites continued to produce Dunlins occasionally, but Kent End (later CWP24, now filled in) became the most regular source up to the late 1970s: there they were nearly annual, chiefly in March–May and July–September, and mostly in ones and twos, but up to maxima of six and eight in spring. Buxton (1981) regarded the species as mainly an autumn visitor that was 'not uncommon' in winter but scarcer in spring. Palmer (1991), covering 1980–89, considered it regular in winter and on spring and autumn passage, and noted that very few were recorded away from CWP, where numbers depended 'on suitable dry pits being available'.

The largest counts in Wiltshire – about 100 in December 1991, about 60 in March 2000 and 58 in January 1992 – have all been at CWP during 1991–2000 (table 61), but smaller numbers are still sometimes found at Swindon STW and other wetlands: there were 18 at

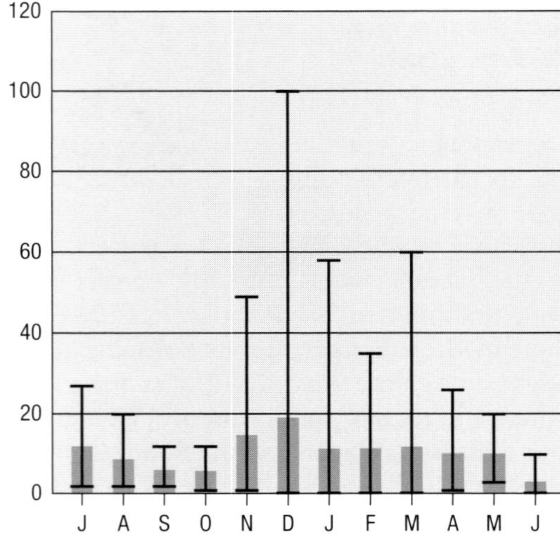

Figure 44. Dunlins *Calidris alpina* in Wiltshire: monthly means (shaded columns) and maximum and mimimum peak counts at CWP 1990–2000

Table 61. Dunlins *Calidris alpina* in Wiltshire: peak winter counts at CWP 1990/91–1999/00

	90/91	91/92	92/93	93/94	94/95	95/96	96/97	97/98	98/99	99/00
Peak count	19	100	29	20	22	17	20	21	49	60
Peak month	May	Dec	Feb	Jul	Dec/Jan	Jul	Apr	Nov	Nov	Mar

Coate Water in December 1991, as many as 39 at Inglesham in November 1998, and 13 on winter floods in North Meadow NNR, Cricklade, in November 2000. The counts of Dunlins at CWP during 1990–2000 (figure 44) show that the numbers are highest in the first half of the winter and to a lesser extent in spring, and then, after the summer trough, rise again in early autumn before falling away in September–October. The peak period of passage of Dunlins inland is considered to be October–November (*BWP*), but, even allowing that the figures in individual years are affected by water levels, the Wiltshire peak in November–January, especially December, appears to be six to eight weeks later.

Although the origins of the only two ringed as migrants in Wiltshire during 1965–2000, in 1966 and August 1974, are unknown, Dunlins on passage through Great Britain come from several regions: those from northeast Greenland pass through in August and September, winter probably in northwest Africa, and return through western Britain in late May; those from southeast Greenland, Iceland, Scotland and south Norway pass south in mid June to October (first failed adults, later juveniles), winter in northwest Africa, and return in late April and early May; and those from northern Eurasia winter in southern Eurasia west to the Mediterranean and north to Ireland, Great Britain, the Netherlands and Germany (*BWP*). It is some of the populations from northern Fenno-Scandia and Russia, and perhaps even Siberia, that make up the bulk of the large numbers that winter on British estuaries, arriving in the east from mid July (failed adults) and mid August (juveniles), moving across to western estuaries in winter after they have moulted, and returning from March onwards (*Migration Atlas*). There has been a recent trend for some waders wintering in Britain to abandon west coast sites in favour of those in the east (Austin *et al* 2000) and thus it may be expected that fewer will occur in Wiltshire at that season in future.

GLW & PAC

Broad-billed Sandpiper

Limicola falcinellus

Vagrant (2 records), breeds north Eurasia, winters Africa to Australia

Broad-billed Sandpipers nest in waterlogged but well-vegetated bogs in Fenno-Scandia, northwest Russia and discontinuously eastwards across northern Siberia, and migrate south on broad fronts to winter from eastern Africa to Australia. Some 14,000 to 19,600 pairs are estimated to breed in Fenno-Scandia (*EBCC Atlas*), but migrants are scarce or rare west of a line from the Baltic to Italy. Only 174 were recorded in Great Britain during 1958–2000 (*BBRC*).

Many British records involve spring adults, but Wiltshire's two were autumn juveniles, both at Swindon STW, during 23–28 September 1962 and on 21 September 1977 (*WANHM, BBRC*).

GLW & IJF-L

Buff-breasted Sandpiper

Tryngites subruficollis

Vagrant (1 record), breeds arctic Alaska/Canada, winters South America

This unusual wader, reminiscent of a small juvenile Ruff, breeds on dry, grassy tundra in high arctic North America, and migrates largely through the middles of USA and South America to winter on grasslands in Argentina and Paraguay. Some, however, follow a more easterly route across the Great Lakes, perhaps then flying directly from New England to South America, and it is these that are believed to be the source of the considerable numbers of vagrants which have reached some 25 countries of Europe, as well as the Atlantic islands and North Africa. The total found in Great Britain during 1958–2000 was 601, mostly in southwest England in September and often on golf courses or airfields; but annual numbers have declined in recent years – averaging just 15 during the 1990s – although there were 34 in 1996 and 32 in 2000 (Fraser & Rogers 2002).

Wiltshire's only record was a juvenile at the former CWP24 (formerly Kent End, now filled in) on 11 September 1975 (*Hobby*, *BBRC*). In all, 48 were recorded in Great Britain that year, the second highest annual total during 1958–2000 (Fraser & Rogers 2002).

GLW & IJF-L

Ruff

Philomachus pugnax

Passage migrant, rare winter visitor, breeds northern Europe, winters mainly Africa

For a few weeks every year, between late April and June, male Ruffs become the most individually variable birds anywhere in the world, as a result of their temporary development of long ear-tufts and the loose neck-ruffs that give them their name: these vary from black through every shade of chestnut, rufous and buff to white, and can be plain or lightly to heavily spotted, streaked or barred; also, tufts and ruffs may be the same colour or, often, quite different. The adornments have both marital and martial purposes as the males strut, posture, jump, compete for females ('Reeves') and joust with one another at communal leks.

Even in the 18th century these display grounds were a widespread, if decreasing, sight in fenland and other marshes from East Anglia to northeast England, but they were virtually extinct by the end of the 19th, the result of drainage and agricultural change (*1875–1900 Atlas*). Ruffs were also greatly prized for food and, although there is no evidence that they were ever more than stragglers to Wiltshire, Smith (1887) was moved to write in general terms, 'No birds were in old time more highly esteemed by epicures... the price they fetched was very remunerative, and they were caught in nets in great numbers'.

Ruffs nest in temperate and subarctic latitudes, mainly from the Low Countries and Fenno-Scandia south to Belarus and east across the northern half of Russia and Siberia. Some winter locally in Europe, the Middle East and the Indian region, but the

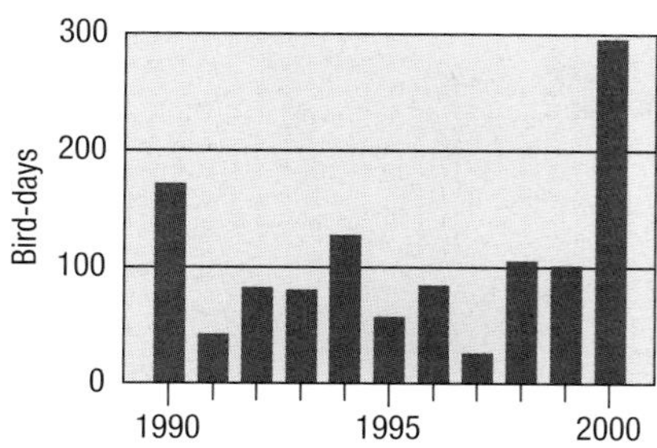

Figure 45. Ruffs *Philomachus pugnax* in Wiltshire: annual totals of bird-days 1990–2000

vast majority migrates to sub-Saharan Africa, where hundreds of thousands congregate at particular wetlands; some from northeast Siberia thus travel 15,000 km each way to and from South Africa. The breeding population of Europe, excluding Russia, has been estimated at between 105,700 and 139,200 pairs (*EBCC Atlas*), of which the British share is negligible. Ruffs nested sporadically in Great Britain in the early part of the 20th century and regularly since the 1960s (*1968–72 Atlas*), especially in Cambridgeshire and Norfolk (*1988–91 Atlas*), but always in tiny numbers, and probably decreasing from the beginning of the 1980s. Numbers fell through the 1990s from summer presence at nine localities in 1991 (four leks, and seven nests or broods recorded) and at 21 localities in 1992 (seven leks, but no nests or broods seen) to no more than five localities in 1998–2000, of which 2000 was the best year (four leks, one probable breeding record) (*RBBP*). But Ruffs are still quite common on passage, at both inland and coastal British wetlands, locally also in winter, though it seems unlikely that they ever total more than a thousand or two (*1981–84 Winter Atlas*, *WeBS*).

Wiltshire's first recorded Ruffs were one 'taken' near Salisbury in 1828 and another 'killed by a farmer' near Wootton Bassett in 1850, leading Smith (1887) to describe the species as 'a rare straggler to our county'. A female was then shot at Ramsbury on 22 December 1879 (*MCNHS*, Hony 1915a), but at least 65 years were to pass before the next. In early May 1945, a wader 'at Fyfield, near Marlborough… was watched closely on several days… most puzzling but I am practically certain it was a Ruff' (LG Peirson in *WANHM* 51: 217). At that time Ruffs had the reputation of being difficult to identify – as BW Tucker (in Witherby *et al* 1938–41) wrote, 'In its other [non-breeding] plumages the species lacks outstanding features and is apt to puzzle the inexperienced, though no other wader is quite like it' – but, as Peirson (1959) himself did not treat what was evidently his own observation as more than 'very probably' a Ruff, the first unqualified records of the 20th century must be those at Coate Water in September 1957, when one on the 7th–8th had been joined by two others by the 14th–15th (*WANHM*).

The 1960s then produced at least a dozen records at eight or more localities over seven of the ten years, mostly ones or twos and up to four, but including a flock of 14, possibly 17 or 18, at West Harnham – 'in various states of plumage' by late March 1961 – and others at a 'suitable breeding site until late May' in 1969 (*WANHM*). A decade later, Buxton (1981) considered the species near annual, sometimes associating with Lapwings, and usually in ones and twos, though a flock of 20 had been found at Swindon STW in September 1974. During 1973–82, spring passage was clearest in March, autumn passage chiefly in August–September (Edwards 1984a). Palmer (1991) noted that, through the 1980s, Ruffs were uncommon migrants, but that peak passage in spring was then during April–May; also that 'though not annual…Winter birds have often been recorded with Lapwing flocks in pasture and stubble'. In fact, Ruffs associate with autumn flocks, too, and

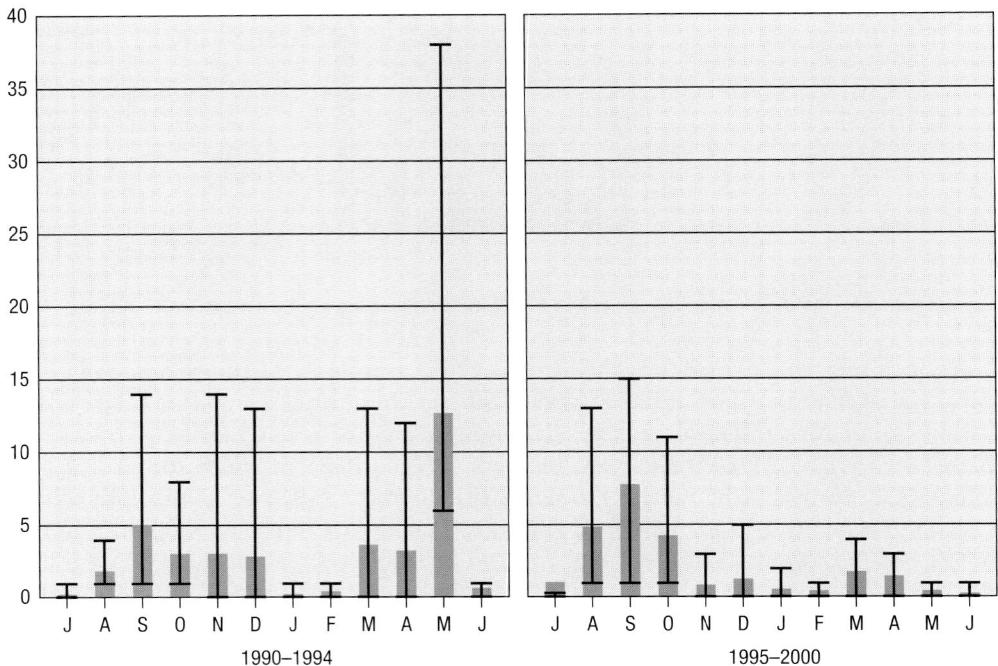

Figure 46. Ruffs *Philomachus pugnax* in Wiltshire: monthly means (shaded columns) and maximum and minimum peak counts at CWP 1990–1994 and 1995–2000

with Golden Plovers as well as Lapwings (Edwards 1984a). By this decade most Ruffs were being seen at CWP, where the largest flock reported was 42 on 18 April 1987. No larger flock than that had been recorded by 2000.

Throughout 1990–2000, this species was still regular in Wiltshire in spring and autumn, and also recorded in every winter, with large annual and seasonal fluctuations in numbers of individuals and bird-days (figure 45). In those years almost all Wiltshire's Ruffs were seen at CWP, although a few were found at 11 other sites, including two records each from Braydon Pond, from winter floods on North Meadow NNR at Cricklade (notably six on 2 January 2000 and 11 on 19 November that same year), and from Swindon STW. But in the five years to 1994 – when up to 38 at one time were seen at CWP in May – the numbers in spring (and early winter) were clearly higher than those in the same months in the following six years (figure 46). It might be thought that this decrease reflected the decline in the small numbers of British nesters, but they – like the Dutch population – should all be on their breeding grounds by the third week of April at the latest, whereas laying begins in mid May in Scandinavia and in June in the far north. Thus, it seems more likely that the few males seen in full plumage in Wiltshire during the 1990s, all in late May and June, were late migrants to the far north or non-breeders.

NPA & PAC

Jack Snipe
Lymnocryptes minimus

Scarce winter visitor, breeds north Europe, winters Britain/west and south Europe

Nesting in boggy, lightly forested areas from northern Fenno-Scandia and the Baltic States eastwards to the Kolyma delta in east Siberia, the Jack Snipe is a winter visitor to western and southern Europe, as well as to parts of North Africa and the Middle East, to sub-Saharan Africa mostly north of the equator, and to southern Asia from the Indian subcontinent to Vietnam. This small species sits much more tightly than the Common Snipe in its winter marshland habitats, usually not rising until almost trodden on, and so assessing the true numbers present is difficult. In Great Britain in the early 1980s, it was found widely scattered but under-recorded and, based on annual shooting totals, it was suggested that the winter population of Great Britain and Ireland could possibly be as high as 100,000 (*1981–84 Winter Atlas*), but 15 years later 'Probably several thousands... Decline suggested' (*CBWP*).

Because their unobtrusiveness makes Jack Snipe so easily overlooked, no census data are available and relatively few have been ringed. Nevertheless, foreign-ringed recoveries in Great Britain have all been from Fenno-Scandia and the Low Countries, and British-ringed recoveries abroad have been mainly in France but also as far south as Tunisia (*Migration Atlas*); *BWP* mentioned one British-ringed found as far east as Kaliningrad. As most of the European breeding population – which, excluding Russia, is broadly put at 13,500 to 24,000 pairs (*EBCC Atlas*) – are considered to migrate to the Atlantic countries from Great Britain and Ireland south to Morocco, this inconspicuous species is likely to remain a not uncommon, if very local, passage migrant and winter visitor. Nevertheless, there do seem to have been some fluctuations during the 20th century.

Bosworth Smith (1863) noted the Jack Snipe as 'occasionally met with in winter', and im Thurn (1870) recorded small numbers, chiefly at 'Swindon Reservoir' [Coate Water], though one specimen in his collection was 'shot on the Kennet, close to Marlborough'. Smith (1887) had remarkably little concrete to say about the Jack Snipe in Wiltshire, apart from quoting behavioural notes at second hand, though he did list its first arrival dates – among those of 'the common regular birds of passage' – as generally 15 September but ranging from 6 September to 30 October. In 1929 it was 'Numerous at Coate Reservoir [Water]' and in 1933 'unusual numbers' were seen there; in 1934 it was 'Common in the water meadows near Salisbury during January but soon disappeared. Not so many reported as in 1933' and in 1936 it was 'Reported many times from there' (*WANHM*). Yet 'Wiltshire Bird Notes', newly revived after the 1939–45 War, could muster only two single records during 1946–51, and mostly ones and twos in the next few years, but then as many as 15 at Coate Water in November 1958 and about 20 there in November 1960, as well as a 'dozen or more' at Maiden Bradley in January 1962 (*WANHM*). Peirson (1959) summarised this rather fluctuating status as 'A winter visitor usually scarce but occasionally in large numbers at a few places'.

Two decades later, Buxton (1981) found that the species was generally uncommon, though regular at a few localities, adding that it usually occurred in 'ones and twos... occasionally... in larger numbers at sites such as Swindon sewage farm [STW]. There are one or two records from downland areas'. From 1982 to 1989 they were annual at CWP, the maximum being seven in 1987. At least in the early 1980s, when cherry, Corsican pine and Norway spruce were being planted in damp, low-lying areas on the Longleat Estate, straddling the Wiltshire/Somerset border, these became a significant habitat for up to three Jack Snipe from late December onwards (Ferguson-Lees 1984), and the young plantations continued to produce ones and twos in subsequent winters.

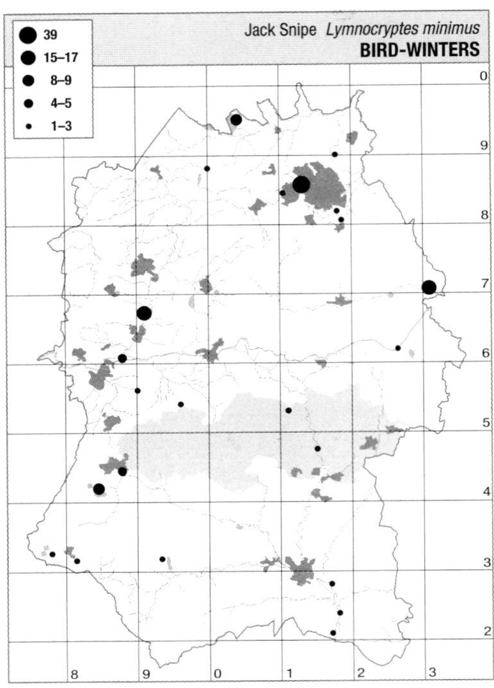

Nowadays the Jack Snipe is most regular at CWP, Coate Water, Littlecote, Lacock Gravel Pits, Smallbrook Nature Reserve and, not least, Swindon STW, which hosted Wiltshire's highest recent count, but only of 12, in February 1995. Elsewhere, one more than the highest figures from Littlecote and Lacock, the largest number recorded during 1990–2000 was six in the marsh by Shear Water in January 1997. The map plots the total of individuals recorded at each of the two dozen sites where the species was found during 1995/96 to 1999/2000, but, bearing in mind that they combine five winters in a time of far greater observer coverage, these numbers are small, so perhaps there has been a real decrease since the late 1920s and early 1930s, even since the late 1950s and early 1960s.

Most Jack Snipe are recorded in the county between October and March, and the recent extremes have been 23 September in both 1984 and 1995 (rather later than Smith's arrival dates a century earlier) and 30 April 1976. Because this species is so difficult to flush, it is not surprising that timed visits during the winter survey recorded no more than singletons in three tetrads; such data preclude deriving any meaningful county estimate. Recorded numbers in Wiltshire probably fluctuate as a result of various factors – such as observer effort, water levels, winter severity, and the previous summer's breeding success – but, although the highest winter total during 1990/91 to 1999/2000 was only 29 (table 62), it is likely that the average population is at least in the range of 30 to 50, perhaps many more. For example, a total of 13 was found at just four sites in January 2000, all in north Wiltshire, while many must go unreported in areas such as the Salisbury Avon, where birdwatchers are few and public access restricted.

A Jack Snipe ringed at Coate Water on 9 October 1962 was shot only 4 km away just ten weeks later, on 26 December 1962. Only one other was ringed in Wiltshire during 1965–2000.

Table 62. Jack Snipes *Lymnocryptes minimus* in Wiltshire: peak counts September–April 1990/91–1999/00

	90/91	91/92	92/93	93/94	94/95	95/96	96/97	97/98	98/99	99/00
Birds	7	8	13	13	22	23	29	15	13	22

GLW & SBE

Sponsored by Mike Hamzij

Common Snipe
Gallinago gallinago

Winter visitor from northern Europe, also former resident but nesting now rare

The Common Snipe breeds widely in arctic and temperate regions across the northern half of Eurasia, but in winter leaves most of this range for milder climates in western Europe, the Mediterranean region, the Middle East, southern Asia and sub-Saharan Africa. It is replaced by closely related forms in the Americas and in sub-Saharan Africa, most of which are now considered to be distinct species. In Europe, the breeding population, excluding Russia, has been estimated at between 862,000 and 991,000 pairs (*EBCC Atlas*) – of which Great Britain's share has been put at 8500 to 21,500 pairs (*1988–91 Atlas*). But several European countries, including Great Britain, have reported recent declines that are thought to be the result of loss of nesting and moulting areas to agriculture and drainage.

Common Snipe tend to avoid the warmer southern areas in summer, being found mainly north of a line from northern France to northern Ukraine. Across much of that range, however, they are only summer visitors that in winter are confined largely to the western maritime countries from the Low Countries, Great Britain and Ireland south to the Mediterranean. The southwesterly direction of autumn movements is well illustrated for Wiltshire by the recoveries in October–February of four that had been ringed when full-grown at distances of 966 to 1422 km away in Norway, Sweden, Denmark and Poland in August–October between three months and 7½ years earlier; also, one ringed at Britford in January 1962 was shot in West Flanders (Belgium) the following October. Only 13 were ringed in Wiltshire during 1965–2000 and none of those has as yet been recovered, but other ringing has shown that Common Snipe from Fenno-Scandia and northern Europe as far east as Russia occur in southern Britain outside the breeding season (*Migration Atlas*).

Bosworth Smith (1863) noted that the Common Snipe was only to be seen in winter, and im Thurn (1870) that it visited yearly but 'very few and in rapidly decreasing numbers', occurring occasionally in all the water meadows but chiefly at Swindon Reservoir. Smith (1887) considered that this species was 'Occasionally, but rarely, found breeding in Wiltshire', and was more of 'a true migrant, arriving in the autumn and departing in the spring'; he listed the mean date of first arrival as 15 September (range 12 August to 30 October), but 'becoming perceptibly scarcer every year' through 'the general increase of draining, and the reclaiming of fens and marshes; so that, like the Red Indian in America, the Snipe will soon be improved off the face of this country'. Even so, Meyrick (1895) recorded that it was not uncommon during the winter along the water meadows in the Marlborough district, and that one remained as late as May in 1873.

Single nests were reported in water meadows near Marlborough in 1909 and 1912 (Matthews 1909, *MCNHS*). After being quoted in an editorial note in 1909 about breeding at Downton, Penrose (1912) recorded an exceptionally early nest there on 15 March 1912. Hony (1915a) noted that the species 'almost certainly nested at Milton in 1913', and Peirson (1919) described Common Snipe as fairly common winter visitors that have 'probably bred regularly in the [Marlborough] district'. By 1929, the species was 'A fairly common resident' and 'Increasing', and by 1933 'a decided increase, records of large numbers of winter visitors and [like Redshank (*qv*)] breeding birds come in from all parts of the county' (*WANHM*).

Table 63. Common Snipes *Gallinago gallinago* in Wiltshire: reports of drumming 1990–2000

	90	91	92	93	94	95	96	97	98	99	00
Birds	11	5	5	1	8	3	0	0	0	0	0
Sites	6	3	4	1	4	3	0	0	0	0	0

By 1949, however, decreases were reported in the Marlborough district, and also in the Longford meadows where 'very few' at the turn of the century had become 'very plentiful in the years between the wars, the peak year being 1941', but 'for the past four or five years…only…in small numbers'. There were odd records of breeding in the next few years, though in 1956 'As many as six displaying at Bemerton during June evenings' and drumming – the sound of the outermost tail-feathers vibrating when held at right angles during aerial dives – 'up to July 3rd' (*WANHM*). Peirson (1959) considered that the Snipe was mostly a winter visitor and passage migrant, and wrongly stated that it did not nest in the county in the 19th century. He added that 'Thirty years ago it was breeding in small numbers chiefly in the Kennet valley near the Berkshire border but also in the Salisbury Avon and Bristol Avon valleys. This breeding population has since diminished'.

During the 1960s and early 1970s, a few pairs nested near Inglesham and display was noted in the valleys of the Bourne, Nadder and Wylye (GL Webber). By the late 1970s breeding had ceased along the Bristol Avon and in 1978 fewer than 20 breeding pairs were found in the county, mainly along the Kennet, and the Salisbury Avon and its tributaries (Buxton 1981). The BTO Waders of Wet Meadows Survey in 1982 recorded a total of 30 drumming, though breeding was confirmed only at Ramsbury (*Hobby*). Numbers continued to decline during the 1980s: improved drainage around Inglesham saw the demise of the few remaining pairs in the Thames valley and only 12 displaying males were located in the county in 1989.

About 11 in total were drumming at Britford, Chilton Foliat, Littlecote, Odstock, Petersfinger and Standlynch in 1990, but the next few years saw the species' rapid extinction as a Wiltshire nester: no drumming was recorded after 1995 (table 63), though a single Snipe was seen at Littlecote in June 1996 and one 'calling at night' there on 30 April 1997 was rather questionably taken to be a 'sign of breeding activity'. Snipe need high water levels and good growth of grasses and rushes. With improved drainage and major water abstraction by both Thames and Wessex Water combining to dry out riverside marshes, their nesting future in the county looks bleak. The meadows of the Kennet between Ramsbury and Chilton Foliat appear to be the only suitable habitats left; even those of the Salisbury Avon between Britford and Downton are now too dry.

The *1968–72 Atlas* found Snipe in summer in 16 of Wiltshire's 33 core 10-km squares and proved breeding in six; the corresponding figures for the *1988–91 Atlas* were 12 and seven, but during the summer tetrad survey, whereas the species was recorded in 13 of the core squares, breeding was proved in only one. The summer distribution map shows the two adjacent tetrads in the Kennet valley where the species nested at the beginning of the survey period, the small dots in a further 19 tetrads probably relating simply to late migrants.

Numbers of wintering Snipe have also fallen and it is now unusual for any site to hold more than 100, but at CWP and Swindon STW, in the Kennet valley between Littlecote and Chilton Foliat, and in the marshes at Whaddon near Trowbridge, they sometimes approach or even surpass that figure. A count of 135 at Swindon STW in December 1998 was no doubt encouraged by a new scrape created there by Thames Water. The winter map draws attention to these key areas, as well as to the Salisbury Avon and upper Wylye valleys. The species was recorded in all 33 of the core 10-km squares by the *1981–84 Winter Atlas*, but in only 11 during the winter tetrad survey.

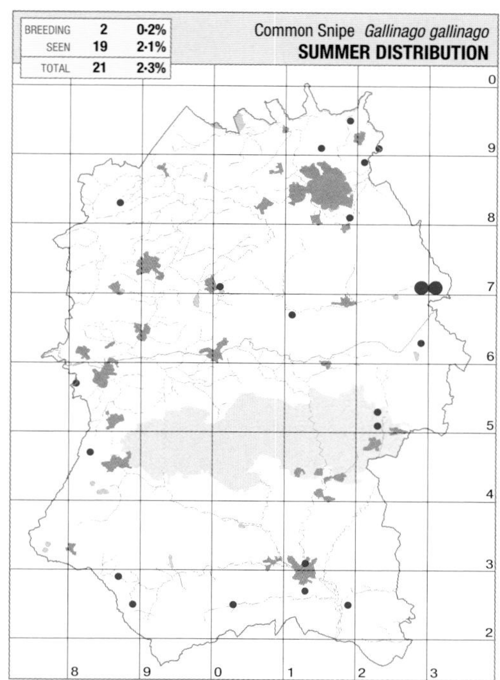

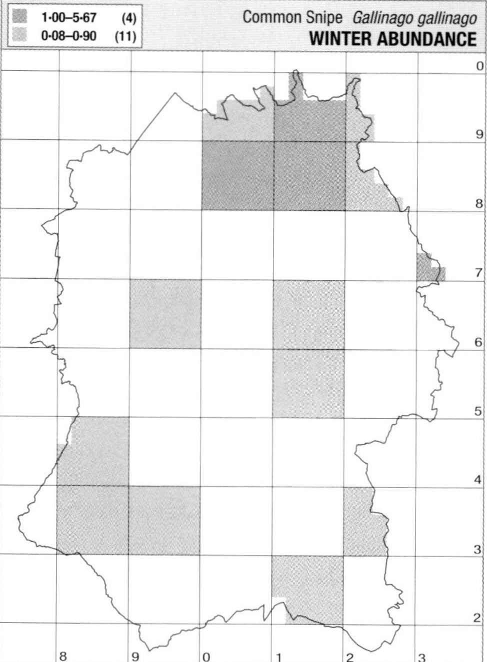

Timed visits produced a total of 90 and an extrapolated minimum county population of about 170, but that is clearly too low. In December 2000 just three sites accounted for 148 individuals (*Hobby*) and, allowing for marshy areas in river valleys where public access is restricted, it seems not unreasonable to suggest a current winter total of over 300, but many – perhaps the majority – of these cryptic and secretive birds are easily overlooked and the true total may be several if not many times larger. Nevertheless, it is likely that Wiltshire holds a small number compared with the estimate of 85,000 shot in the UK each year (Harradine 1983), from which the *1981–84 Winter Atlas* concluded that the national winter population 'must be many hundreds of thousands'.

GLW & IJF-L

Sponsored by Patrick Cashman

Great Snipe
Gallinago media

Vagrant (8+ records, last 1936), breeds north/east Europe, winters Africa

Though able to list only half a dozen or so Wiltshire records, Smith (1887) considered that 'the Great Snipe is found to be sparingly scattered over the country every autumn'. Indeed, Saunders (1899) described it as an 'annual visitor in small numbers to the eastern and southern portions of England' and, half a century later, Witherby *et al*

(1938–41) still regarded it as a 'Very scarce passage-migrant (Aug. To mid-Nov., chiefly Sept. and very rarely spring… and winter)', noting also that there had been over 50 in Scotland, mostly on Fair Isle.

Nowadays, however, it appears to be no more than a rare vagrant to Great Britain with, despite the great increase in numbers of birdwatchers, a norm of only two to three identified each year and a total of 111 during 1958–2000 (*BBRC*) – though it must be added that the grand total during the 19th and early 20th centuries (through to 1957), when the many fewer people interested in birds were often armed with guns rather than binoculars, was only about 180. Most Great Snipe are now found in the Northern Isles and, in smaller numbers, down the east coast. Wiltshire has not had a firm record for nearly 70 years.

There are probably two main reasons for the apparent change in status. First, a marked decline in numbers and a contraction in range began in the mid 19th century, at which time the species may even have nested as far west as the Netherlands. Since then, breeding has gradually ceased in Denmark, western Norway and much of Sweden and Finland, as well as in Germany and most of Poland. A stable population of perhaps no more than 10,000 pairs (*EBCC Atlas*) remains in the Scandinavian uplands, but the Great Snipe is now otherwise confined to eastern Europe and western Asia, east from eastern parts of the Baltic States, Belarus and northern Ukraine across Russia to the Yenisei. Even so, it remains more numerous – with a breeding population, excluding Russia, of 21,500 to 34,400 breeding pairs (*EBCC Atlas*) – and still has a more westerly distribution than the Jack Snipe (*qv*), which is regular in Great Britain. The difference is that the Great Snipe is a long-distance migrant, on a south-north basis (not southwest-northeast), to winter quarters almost entirely in sub-Saharan Africa, and evidently many fewer than before, mainly juveniles in autumn, travel through western Europe. Although this species often nests (and winters) on much drier ground, even at wood edges, than either Common or Jack Snipe, its decline is generally attributed to habitat loss or deterioration, also to shooting pressure and perhaps climatic change.

Virtually all of Wiltshire's Great Snipe have been specimens, obtained not necessarily by ornithologists or collectors, at least some probably in the course of Snipe shoots. According to Smith (1887), the first was 'killed' in 1831 in Winterslow Wood, followed by other singletons, similarly treated, in 1854 in 'South Wilts' (near Salisbury, according to Buxton 1981), in September 1868 at Pewsey on the 23rd and at Hurdcott on the 25th (or 24th, as in *The Zoologist* 1868 and *The Field* 3 October 1868: 273) and in October 1874 near Hungerford (wrongly 'Hungerdown' in Buxton 1981). Smith noted that 1868 was an exceptional year for Great Snipe when 'these birds were extraordinarily numerous in many parts of England' and continued 'I have notices of one killed on Salisbury Plain, another at Milton, near Pewsey, and of several others on the borders of the county'. He also mentioned that the Reverend G Marsh, who reported the 1831 specimen, had himself seen another 'in Christian Malford, though he was not able to obtain it', but the lack of even a date must make this second-hand observation questionable at best.

Sixty years after the last of Smith's records, singletons were shot at Britford 'during December' 1933 and on 23 January 1936 (*WANHM*). A sighting near Wick Farm, north of Marlborough, on 9 September 1951 was considered to be 'very probable' (*WANHM*).

NPA & IJFL

Long-billed Dowitcher

Limnodromus scolopaceus

Vagrant (1 record), breeds east Siberia/northwest America, winters south USA/Central America

Long-billed Dowitchers nest on the coastal plains and tundra of northeast Siberia, north and west Alaska and extreme northwestern Canada, wintering from California and Florida south through Mexico to Guatemala. Yet they are also regular, if rare, transatlantic vagrants that have been found in at least ten countries of Europe and the Middle East. In Great Britain, though a few have overwintered or appeared in spring – or even stayed, on and off, at one site for several years – most of the 156 recorded during 1958–2000 (*BBRC*) have been autumn juveniles associated with Atlantic depressions.

These waders favour shallow muddy freshwater pools on migration, although most of those found in Great Britain have been by estuaries. Wiltshire's only record was a juvenile seen at Swindon STW for ten days in September 1974, from the 14th to the 23rd (*Hobby*, *BBRC*), not quite accurately noted by Buxton (1981) as staying 'for some eleven days'.

GLW & PEC

Woodcock

Scolopax rusticola

Decreasing resident, under-recorded winter visitor from north/east Europe

Woodcocks are secretive and crepuscular waders that breed in moist woodlands from some of the Atlantic islands right across Eurasia to Japan, and winter in western Europe, the Mediterranean region and southern Asia. The male's display flight, known as 'roding', may not always have been as widespread a sight and sound in Great Britain as it is now: in the 18th century, Woodcocks were considered to be winter visitors that only occasionally nested, but by the end of the 19th they were known to be breeding in nearly every county (*1875–1900 Atlas*). The upward trend continued through the first two-thirds of the 20th century, reaching a peak in the 1960s, but since then there has been a steady decline until the *1988–91 Atlas* put the British breeding population at a 'minimal estimate' of 8500 to 21,500 pairs. This may be compared with the figure for Europe as a whole, excluding Russia, of 529,000 to 689,000 pairs (*EBCC Atlas*). It must be added that Woodcocks are difficult to census because they are largely nocturnal and, as males mate with more than one female, 'pairs' is a convenient rather than strictly accurate term.

Whereas earlier increases were attributed to climatic change and to the ban on shooting in the nesting season, the expansion in Great Britain in the 20th century resulted from the greater availability of the breeding habitat provided by new conifer plantations (Avery & Leslie 1990). Woodcocks nest almost exclusively in young woods with damp areas. In the 1980s, numbers declined as plantations matured, but the trees in many such areas will be harvested in the early part of the 21st century and it is hoped that restocked plantations will again be suitable (*1988–91 Atlas*).

In Wiltshire, Woodcocks were largely winter visitors in the 18th and 19th centuries, and many early records come from estate gamebooks: for example, 52 shot in Bentley Wood from November 1760 to March 1761; a hundred years later, 60 shot at Stourhead in the winter of 1865/66 and 133 the following winter (SB Edwards). Smith (1887) believed that they were 'becoming less abundant every year'; he reported nesting only at Winterslow (in 1830), Compton and Longleat, but added that it was 'strongly suspected' at Savernake. Peirson (1919) described this species as a fairly common winter visitor to the Marlborough district, 'a few sometimes staying to breed', and ten years later *WANHM* gave it similar status for the county as a whole, 'some staying to breed'.

The first coordinated survey of Woodcocks in Wiltshire was carried out in the springs of 1934 and 1935, as part of a national enquiry (Alexander 1945–47), and breeding evidence – perhaps mainly roding – was obtained in the remnants of Braydon Forest between Purton and Malmesbury (often); in Savernake (only twice); at Bradford-on-Avon (occasionally); along the Nadder valley west of Salisbury; and in the woods east and south of Salisbury to the Hampshire border (good numbers). It was also concluded that 'There is some evidence that the numbers breeding on the chalk are greater in seasons after wet winters. These remarks apply to the greater part of Wiltshire'.

Casual totals of sites where roding males were seen in spring or summer and where Woodcocks were found in winter, as recorded annually in *Hobby* (and previously in *WANHM*), are almost meaningless for such a crepuscular and nocturnal bird. The peak totals of casual observations of roding males were 41 in 1987 and 49 in 1992, but a much fuller survey in 1984 – 50 years after the completion of the first – yielded a total of 148 at 60 sites (though it was difficult to be precise about numbers at one locality on the Somerset boundary); and additional information from gamekeepers indicated a further 40 pairs; even so, that 1984 survey was still incomplete and five of Wiltshire's 33 core 10-km squares were not visited (Edwards *et al* 1985).

Woodcocks were found in 14 of those core squares in the *1968–72 Atlas*, in 15 in the *1988–91 Atlas*, and in 12 in the summer tetrad survey during 1995–2000, but this nocturnal wader is inevitably under-recorded by such general surveys, which are usually carried out in mornings (rather than evenings) because the majority of other bird species are at their most active then. The summer map shows Savernake and the Kennet valley, Bowood and Spye Parks, Chute Forest, Longleat, Great Ridge and Grovely Woods, Fonthill, Clarendon to Bentley Wood, and the New Forest fringes to be key areas. Sites apparently deserted since the 1984 survey include Braydon Forest and the woodlands around Stourton. In the 2003 national Woodcock survey, 17 Wiltshire woods were surveyed and suggested an estimate of 1·18 birds per 100 ha (A Hoodless); extrapolation from this figure for the 5185 ha of woods sampled to the 26,819 ha of this habitat in the county as a whole gives a total summer estimate of 316 individuals.

British Woodcocks are thought to be mainly sedentary (*1968–72 Atlas*) and, though few have been ringed in Wiltshire, one shot at Maiden Bradley in January 1962 had been marked as a chick the previous summer 'within half a mile' (*WANHM*). From November onwards, however, local populations are joined by much larger numbers of migrants from northern Europe – most of those that reach southern England having originated in Finland, Latvia and Russia – and British-bred Woodcock are thought to constitute only around 10 per cent of the wintering total (*Migration Atlas*). The origins of some of the wintering birds in this county are further shown by the finding of Wiltshire-ringed individuals in Sweden in May 1938 and July 1991, as well as by the recovery at Chilmark in January 1969 of one ringed in Finland in April 1968 and the shooting in Savernake in January 1992 of another marked in Sweden in May 1988; one shot at Bowood in December 1979 had been ringed on migration on Helgoland (Germany) just 19 days earlier.

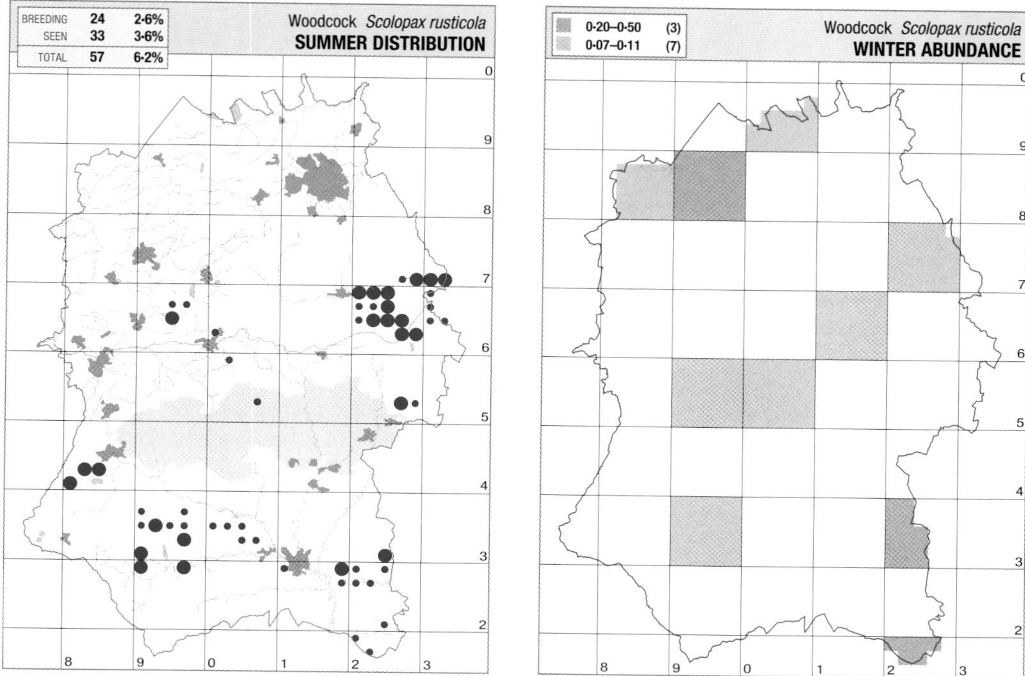

Alexander (1945–47) found that 'comparatively few Woodcocks spend the winter in the chalk areas, though they sometimes occur there in considerable numbers on their first arrival [in] adjacent woods of S.E. Wiltshire' and the species 'occurs [in the] lower woods N. and W. Wilts'. He also cited average Wiltshire shooting bags of 32 on 8000 acres (3200 ha) in the southwest, 38 on 16,000 acres (6400 ha) in the south, and 11 on 975 acres (390 ha) in the northeast.

Although a single count of 16 on SPTA (Centre) in December 1977 was notable for its size, casual observations by single observers are of even less help in assessing Woodcocks in winter than in summer. It has, however, been estimated that 'the British wintering population may number 800,000' (Hirons & Linsley 1989, quoted in the *Migration Atlas*) and, two decades earlier, that some 200,000 Woodcocks were shot annually in Great Britain (*1981–84 Winter Atlas*). The numbers recorded as shot on the three sections of SPTA during the 21 winters of 1980/81 to 2000/21 (based on figures from up to eight shoots, supplied by CAG Wells) varied from just over 70 (1981/82, 1994/95) to nearly 250 (1998/99), but are incomplete for almost two-thirds of those seasons (see notes under figure 47). These annual variations probably relate far more to the availability of shoot bag data than to fluctuations in the numbers of Woodcocks. If the data for the eight 'more complete' winters (1987/88–1991/92 and 1997/98–1999/00) be taken on their own, these give an annual average bag of 168 over the whole of SPTA.

Game Conservancy Trust spot-lamp estimates of densities of Woodcocks feeding on Wiltshire farmland at night during the early 1990s averaged 10 birds/100 ha on grass and 3 birds/100 ha on arable fields (A Hoodless); extrapolation from these densities for the 144,100 ha of grass and 133,900 ha of arable in the county as a whole gives a total winter estimate of 18,500. The *Migration Atlas* reported that 'the highest densities of wintering Woodcock are found in southwest England and Wales' and that 'a high proportion ... in these areas are foreign migrants', so it should be expected that Wiltshire is of some importance for this species. Clearly, however, there is a large degree of speculation in

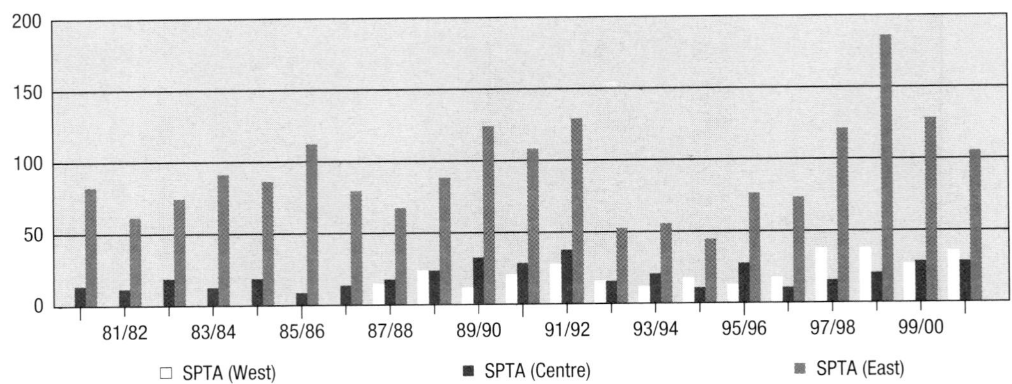

Figure 47. Woodcocks *Scolopax rusticola* in Wiltshire: numbers shot on Salisbury Plain November–January 1980/81–2000/01 (based on data supplied by SPTA Game Shooting Associations)
The SPTA (West) bags are available only from 1987/88, and data for one of the SPTA (Centre) shoots only from 1994/95. Also unavailable are figures for the SPTA (East) 'rough shoots' 1992/93–1996/67 and 2000/01

producing such figures for this species and there is the potential for significant errors at several steps of such a calculation.

The winter survey in 1998–2000 recorded the species in just eight of the 33 core 10-km squares, compared with 24 in the *1981–84 Winter Atlas*, and only 15 Woodcocks in total were seen, but the winter map indicates a distribution coinciding with some of the key breeding sites – though in many woods, such as Savernake, observers generally kept to footpaths and so failed to flush any. They also winter in open country on the Marlborough Downs and the Cotswolds – where worm-rich permanent pastures are available – as well as on SPTA.

NPA & PEC

Sponsored by Sean Dempster

Black-tailed Godwit

Limosa limosa

Scarce on passage, rare winter, breeds mainly Iceland, winters west Europe

Black-tailed Godwits breed in Iceland and, often quite locally, from Great Britain and France eastwards across the middle latitudes of Europe and western Asia, as well as in isolated areas of eastern Asia north to Anadyr and Kamchatka. The European population, excluding Russia, has been estimated at between 135,600 and 158,000 pairs; numbers have decreased in some countries, but increased in others, including Great Britain (*EBCC Atlas*). This species is migratory, wintering in western Europe, the Mediterranean region, Africa between the Sahara and the equator, and discontinuously across southern Asia to Australia.

Marshland drainage brought the Black-tailed Godwit to virtual extinction as a breeding species in Great Britain by the mid 19th century (*1875–1900 Atlas*). Nesting was thereafter only sporadic until recolonisation began in the 1930s on the Ouse Washes (Cambridgeshire/

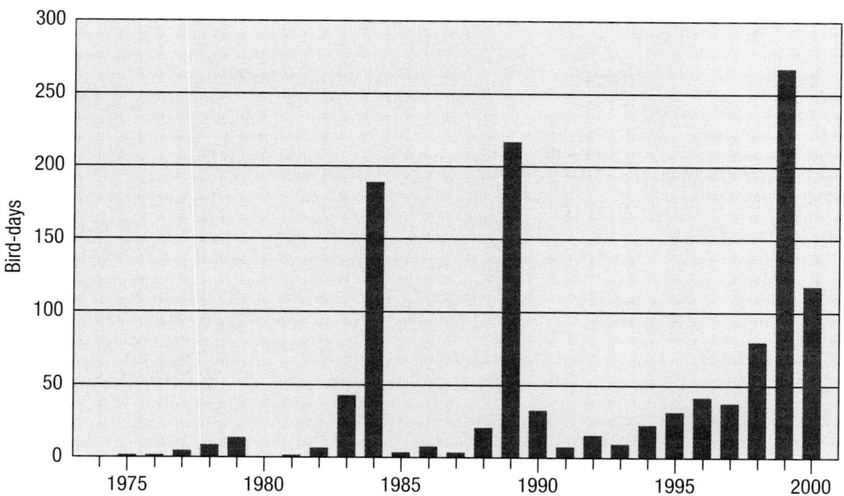

Figure 48. Black-tailed Godwits *Limosa limosa* in Wiltshire: annual totals of bird-days (mainly CWP) 1974–2000

Norfolk), where it has now been regular since 1952 (*1988–91 Atlas*). During 1990–2000 at least 20 pairs, and usually 28–45, up to maxima of 33–66, nested at 11–24 localities in eastern and northern England and on the Northern Isles (*RBBP*). Northern Scottish breeders are thought to be of the Icelandic race *islandica*, while those elsewhere in Great Britain are of the nominate Continental race (*1988–91 Atlas*), which nests from mainland Europe into Siberia. Numbers wintering in Great Britain, almost entirely of the Icelandic race, have also increased, particularly since the mid 1980s, to around 15,400 in the late 1990s (Rehfisch *et al* 2003).

Wiltshire's first records were of one at Coate Water in late August 1944 and two near Ramsbury on 19 April 1951 (*WANHM*, Peirson 1959). Two more in 1959 coincidentally each involved a party of seven, near Cricklade on 10 January and near Harnham (not 'Hornham' as Buxton 1981) on 3–4 April. But these two 'sevens' were totally eclipsed in early December 1965 by one of the county's more remarkable wader observations: a flock of about 250 at Durrington, which were filmed and then shown on local television (all *WANHM*). Two records each, of one to three birds, in 1967 and 1969, and then 'A pair in meadows near Coate Water' on 11 April 1971, were Wiltshire's only Black-tailed Godwits (*WANHM*) over the following ten years.

But from 1975 onwards the sole blank was 1980. Palmer (1991) showed a steady increase during 1981–89, all between March and September, mostly in June, August and September (figure 48). During 1990–2000, and by now nearly always at CWP, the species was noted with increasing frequency and in all months – though remaining scarce and irregular in winter – and the totals of bird-days recorded grew steadily, notably from the middle of the decade. That reflected a general increase in Great Britain (*WeBS*). It is worth noting that there are two sites of international importance for this godwit – Poole Harbour (Dorset) and Southampton Water (Hampshire) – in neighbouring coastal counties (*WeBS*).

During 1974–2000, Black-tailed Godwits occurred most often in August and the highest numbers were seen in July–September (table 64). (Unfortunately, age-classes were determined in only a few cases, and so it is not possible to comment on the proportions of juveniles.) The much smaller spring numbers, in March–June, showed a peak in April (largely because of a flock of 22 at CWP68 in 1999) and surprisingly few in May, while the June totals were inflated by a flock of 13, also at CWP68, in 1998; some parties or

Table 64. Black-tailed Godwits *Limosa limosa* in Wiltshire: monthly totals of bird-days 1974–2000

	Jan	Feb	Mar	Apr	May	Jun	Jul	Aug	Sep	Oct	Nov	Dec
Bird-days	5	18	30	52	27	99	187	358	182	78	15	19

individuals stayed ten days or more. None was recorded between November and February until 1997/98, the first of three successive winters in which one overwintered at CWP; it is tempting to suggest that the same individual was involved. The only five records away from CWP during 1990–2000 were singletons at Swindon in June 1993, at Coate Water in April 1994, at Whaddon near Trowbridge in September 1996, and at Swindon STW in September 1998; and then two at Stratford sub Castle in March 2000.

The largest flock recorded since 1965 was of 37 at CWP68c on 14 July 1999, one of which had been colour-ringed at Farlington Marshes (Hampshire); others colour-ringed in Hampshire have been sighted in Iceland in summer (Bell 2001).

NPA & SBE

Bar-tailed Godwit

Limosa lapponica

Scarce passage migrant, breeds arctic Fenno-Scandia/Russia, winters west Europe

This slightly smaller of the two European godwits is a summer visitor to arctic and subarctic zones of far northeast Sweden (very few) and Norway, and of northernmost Finland into northwest Russia, as well as across northernmost Siberia to western Alaska. Unlike the Black-tailed, it is almost exclusively a shorebird in winter: the European and west Siberian populations are then found mainly along the western coasts of Europe and Africa, apart from smaller numbers around the Mediterranean, Red Sea, Persian Gulf and Indian Ocean; and the east Siberian and Alaskan populations move down into southeast Asia and Australia. Excluding Russia, only 1300 to 3300 pairs nest in Europe (*EBCC*), but about 125,000 Bar-tailed Godwits winter in western Europe and almost half of those in Great Britain (*CBWP*) – the most recent estimate for this country being 61,600 (Rehfisch *et al* 2003).

Wiltshire's only Bar-tailed Godwit in the 19th century was shot near Marlborough in 1881, and sent to Smith (1887) on 6 November for identification. Another 77 years passed before the next record, of two at Coate Water on 16 July 1958; then, after a smaller

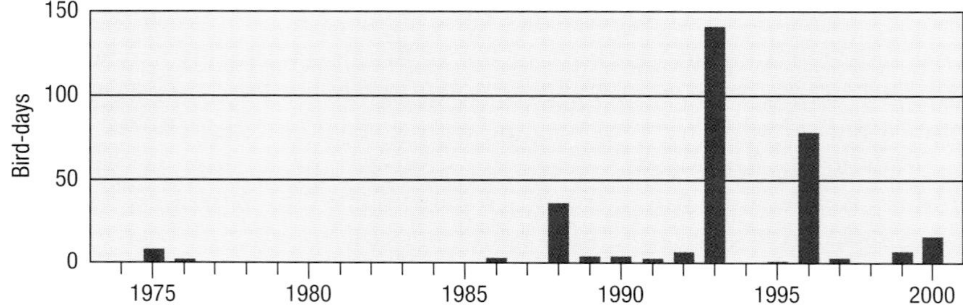

Figure 49. Bar-tailed Godwits *Limosa lapponica* in Wiltshire: annual totals of bird-days (mainly CWP) 1974–2000

Table 65. Bar-tailed Godwits *Limosa lapponica* in Wiltshire: monthly totals of bird-days 1974–2000

	Jan	Feb	Mar	Apr	May	Jun	Jul	Aug	Sep	Oct	Nov	Dec
Bird-days	7	0	3	28	151	0	0	107	10	1	0	2

gap, one was seen at Leckford Bottom on 3 April 1969, and five in flight over Avebury Down on 29 March 1970 (*WANHM*). Next came eight at Coate Water on 5 September 1975, and singletons there on 24 March and 18 October 1976 (*Hobby*), the latter the county's only October record in the 20th century.

A further decade later, Bar-tailed Godwits became almost annual during 1986–2000, being seen in every year bar three (1987, 1994, 1998) (figure 49). Most have been at CWP, though 1986 produced singletons at Liden Lagoon, Rushall Down and Boscombe Down, and 1996 two at Corsham Lake. Most have been in late March to May, but there were a few records in August and September, two in December, and one in January (table 65). Most, too, have involved singletons or small numbers up to five, but five bigger flocks were recorded: 31 at CWP68 on 30 August 1992, 56 at CWP74 on 5 May 1993 and 26 at CWP59 on the 10th, and 28 at CWP68 and 47 over CWP82, both on 10 August 1996. In 1993, the year of the largest of these flocks, the species was recorded at CWP on no fewer than 15 dates from the end of March to the end of May. It is doubtless the availability of suitable habitats at CWP that has led to the great increase in the county's sightings of this species.

GLW & PAC

On 12 September 1934, two flocks of waders, 'fairly high and flying west' near Chippenham, were identified as godwits on size, 'call and flight' by HCR Gillman, who was a contributor to *WANHM* for several years and who had elsewhere 'had opportunities of observing Godwits before'. The then editor was evidently quite satisfied, and included the sighting under Bar-tailed Godwit. Peirson (1959) and Buxton (1981) both overlooked or ignored this observation, but, as it was published, it must be mentioned here – even though there is nothing in the sparse details given to show why the observer or the editor decided in favour of Bar-tailed rather than Black-tailed.

Eds

Whimbrel

Numenius phaeopus

Scarce passage migrant, breeds Iceland/Scotland/ north Europe, winters Africa

Whimbrels have a circumpolar but patchy breeding distribution in the upper latitudes of North America and Eurasia, also very locally south to northwest Kazakhstan. They are long-distance migrants that winter mainly along the coasts of the central and southern Americas and sub-Saharan Africa (some reaching the extreme south of both continents) and of southeast Asia to Australia, though small numbers now travel no farther than Spain and the Persian Gulf. Excluding Russia, an estimated 184,000 to 289,000 pairs breed in Europe, where the population has recently increased (*EBCC Atlas*). Some 530 pairs nest in Great Britain (*APEP*), most in Shetland (*1988–91 Atlas*). A very few occur on British estuaries in winter, but the species is most familiar in spring and autumn, when it is a not uncommon coastal migrant that also occurs inland in small numbers.

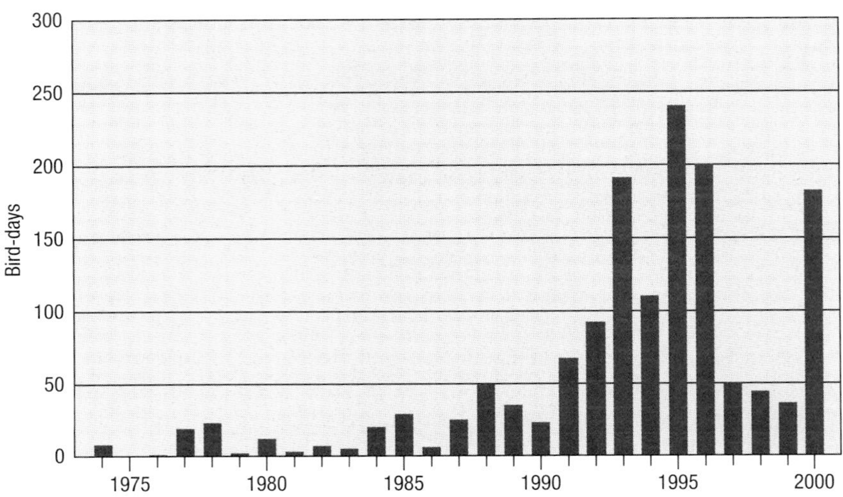

Figure 50. Whimbrels *Numenius phaeopus* in Wiltshire: annual totals of bird-days (mainly CWP) 1974–2000

The first of the seven or eight Wiltshire records of Whimbrels listed by Smith (1887) was, from Marsh's collection, 'obtained' in 1838 at Sutton Mead, 'where it had been observed alone for some time'. Two shot at Swindon in April 1865 were followed by a series of May records: one at Overton in 1873, six (one shot) at Berwick Bassett in 1876, and one at Enford in 1882. In October 1882 four or five were seen at 'Butteridge' (locality untraceable), and in October 1883 one was killed there. Smith's only other 19th century record was an undated specimen, in the possession of Lord Nelson, that had been 'killed at Trafalgar' (an estate in south Wiltshire), but Hony (1915a) added two more from *MCNHS*: 'One was caught wounded on August 20th, 1877, and on May 15th, 1890, five were seen and two shot on the Downs near Kennet'.

Peirson (1959) knew of 'only five records this [the 20th] century', but mentioned just the two seen at Wilton Water on 1 May 1951 and those heard calling on passage over Marlborough on 18 July 1953. The other three were presumably the records in the early 1930s, the first on 14 March 1931 near Swindon, the last a party of three in late September 1934 on Boscombe Down, and the other an intriguing series in 1933 of three separate sightings of what the then Wiltshire recorder considered 'undoubtedly refer to the same pair' on Salisbury Plain, the first on 3 May, the second on 18 June, the third undated (*WANHM*). Two further reports of this species in 1958 both involved birds heard calling on migration, near Box on 12 May and over Walcot on 26 July (*WANHM*).

Six more records were published in *WANHM* in the 1960s, and there was also a reference in Kennedy (1966) to another heard over Marlborough in 1961, bringing the total in the 20th century to 13 or 14. Probably because there were by then more observers, Buxton (1981) was able to add 'over twenty' Wiltshire records for the previous two decades – though the number published in *WANHM* and *Hobby* during 1960–80 actually totalled 31, or 32 with Kennedy's – and stated that the Whimbrel was 'now an annual migrant in small numbers'. Palmer (1991), in summarising the 1980s, noted a marked increase in records, and identified April and May as the peak months. During 1973–2000, like those of other waders, numbers rose markedly and this species was seen in every year except 1975. In 1973–86 only 28 (21 per cent) of the 132 bird-days related to CWP, whereas in 1987–2000 that site's share rose to 1009 (92 per cent) of 1098 – though increased coverage there doubtless played its part.

Table 66. Whimbrels *Numenius phaeopus* in Wiltshire: monthly total of bird-days 1974–2000

	Jan	Feb	Mar	Apr	May	Jun	Jul	Aug	Sep	Oct	Nov	Dec
Bird-days	0	0	1	613	641	5	110	102	3	1	0	0

Recorded numbers fluctuate between years, often widely. The data are shown here by bird-days for 1974–2000 (figure 50), though this form of analysis has its limitations, as particularly demonstrated in 1992 when one with a broken leg stayed at CWP29 from 29 April to 3 June, thus alone accounting for a total of 36 bird-days. Passage across Wiltshire involves more than eight times as many Whimbrels in spring as in autumn, with April and May by far the peak months (table 66). The earliest spring record since 1990 was 10 April 1995, and the latest (apart from the one with the broken leg) 31 May 1992. The earliest on return autumn passage was 19 June 2000 and the latest 4 September 1999. All but 74 (6 per cent) of the 1195 individuals recorded during 1990–2000 were at CWP, the highest count elsewhere being 27 flying northeast at Corsham Lake on 5 May 1993. At CWP, most parties involved fewer than ten, but 21 records were in the 11–20 range, two in the 21–30 and three in the 31–40. The only count over 40 was 47 on 5 May 1996 – part of an unusually large spring passage of 13, 33, 47 and 37 on the 3rd, 4th, 5th and 7th – and was Wiltshire's highest single-day spring figure until 66 in two flocks were seen over CWP on 1 May 2000. In contrast, the highest autumn count was a mere 11 on 27 August 1997.

NPA & PAC

Curlew

Numenius arquata

Local breeder, scarce passage from north Britain/Europe, some winter south to Iberia/Africa

Curlews breed in a variety of open habitats from upland bogs to damp lowland meadows in Great Britain, Ireland and France, and thence across Fenno-Scandia, Russia and, more patchily, central Europe, to western Siberia and north-central Asia as far as Amurland. Most populations are migratory and spend the winter mainly on coasts of western Europe, the Mediterranean, Africa, Madagascar and the whole of southern Asia from Arabia through India to western Indonesia and southern Japan. Some also winter inland, in Europe most notably in Ireland, parts of Great Britain and some Mediterranean countries. The breeding population of Europe, excluding Russia, has been estimated at between 123,000 and 148,000 pairs (*EBCC Atlas*).

From the 1860s nesting Curlews began to spread south and east from strongholds in the uplands of northern and western Britain (*1875–1900 Atlas*), though two decades earlier 'the REV. EDWARD BOWEN informed me that he once saw some of these birds on the plain not far from Salisbury' (Maton 1843). The early history of the species breeding in Wiltshire was summarised by Hony (1916a) and, 40 years later, reviewed in greater detail by Stanford (1955). The first reported nest, on Aldbourne Down, was published by Bosworth Smith (1863) and repeated by im Thurn (1870, 1876), but both the latter's original report and his later, slightly expanded version were subsequently disputed in reviews by E Newman in *The Zoologist* (1870: 2178–2180; and see Stanford). Also mentioned by im Thurn was a report in the *Marlborough Times* for 22–29 July 1876 when 'A curlew was rescued from the grasp of a hawk by Wm. Brown, gamekeeper, in the West Woods district, recently'.

Morres (1877a) wrote positively that he had been informed that Curlews bred regularly on the downs near Salisbury, but had to recant when eggs sent to him proved to be Stone-curlew's (Morres 1883). (The eggs of the two species are quite different in shape; normally also, the Stone-curlew's clutch is only two and the Curlew's four.) Smith (1887) noted that many sportsmen asserted that Curlews had been common on the downs in the first half of the 19th century and also, in his separate chapter on nesting birds, mentioned possible confusion with Stone-curlews, but he was satisfied 'that the true Curlew … does occasionally breed on the fallows of the open downs'. Hony (1916a), reviewing the above reports, concluded that all probably related to Stone-curlews and that the Curlew should not be included amongst the species known to have nested in Wiltshire. One day after that was published, Hony (1916b) found a pair of Curlews on 'typical downland' near Tidworth and, feeling sure that they had young, returned two days later, on 4 July 1916, to make a fuller search: he was proved right when his dog caught a young Curlew about a week old.

The next observations were scattered in both time and place, and generally rather inconclusive. In *MCNHS* (1925) Peirson wrote 'I have small doubt now that the Curlew nests in this district [Marlborough]'. In the very first 'Report on the birds of Wiltshire' in *WANHM*, for 1929, this species was considered 'An uncommon visitor, which may nest on the Plain'; in 1930 there were references to pairs seen at Manton and near Aldbourne in the second half of May; and in 1931 came a report of '10–12 pairs breeding near Chute' – but this was questioned when the birds did not reappear in either of the following two years, even though the observer considered their absence then to have been caused by 'the continued presence of men about the area all day' and 'the interference of machinery and the milking machines in the field adjoining' (*WANHM*). Also in 1931, two breeding pairs were reported near Hale (Hampshire) 'within a mile of the Wiltshire border', and in 1932 'Five pairs bred just outside the county near Redlynch'; the latter site continued to be occupied for at least the next four years, though all reference to Hampshire was dropped until, in 1936, 'the birds on the Wilts-Hants border were reduced to one pair' (*WANHM*). Nothing more was published until after the 1939–45 War, but during 1946–55 came several more records of breeding in south or southeast Wiltshire, mentioning 'at' or 'near' Redlynch on two occasions (*WANHM*). Stanford (1955) noted that CMR Pitman – the main observer involved, both before and after the War – 'tells me that though they have nested in boggy valleys just inside Wiltshire, they normally nest on heathy moorland on the Hampshire side of the county boundary, which is here the Redlynch-Bramshaw road'.

The fact remains that, as emphasised by Stanford (1955), no certain reports of eggs or young being seen within Wiltshire were published between 1867 (Bosworth Smith, repeated by im Thurn) and 1946, apart from the chick killed in 1916 (Hony 1916b). From 1946, however, 'the records became considerably more copious and clear and it seems probable that a definite new colonisation took place in the war years ... [when] I suspect a good deal of poor agricultural land here went back to rushy marsh' (Stanford 1955). The following summary is based on *WANHM*. In 1946 breeding was proved near West Lavington and two pairs also nested in south Wiltshire. Nearby, pairs were seen in the Patney-Etchilhampton area in 1948, 1949 and 1950, though breeding was not proved there until two nests with eggs were found in 1952; that year other pairs bred at Bulkington, Sandridge Park and Urchfont, probably also at Keevil and West Lavington. Additional breeding sites in 1953 were Ogbourne St George, Potterne Wick and Seend Cleeve.

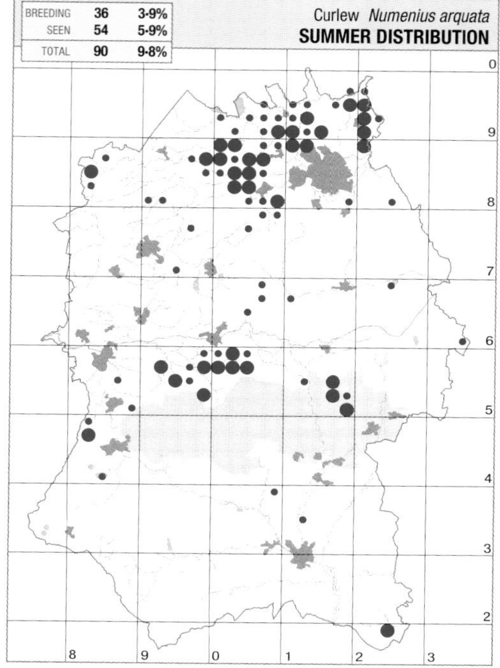

Stanford concluded that Curlews were slowly extending their breeding range in Wiltshire and that 12 to 20 pairs were nesting in the county in 1954. There appeared to be a steady increase during the rest of the 1950s and the early 1960s, including some new sites, but numbers of reports then decreased from about 1963 or 1964 (*WANHM*); this may have been a result, at least partly, of the high mortality of Curlews during the prolonged severe winter of 1962/63 (Dobinson & Richards 1964), though many of those that died would probably have been immigrants from Fenno-Scandia, whereas at least some southern English Curlews move to France and Iberia (Bainbridge & Minton 1978).

By 1969, however, there were estimated to be some 70 breeding pairs, mostly within three main areas: at least 15 pairs in the Pewsey Vale west to Trowbridge, South Wraxall and north to Bromham and Melksham; at least 40 pairs in a broad circle around Swindon, particularly in the meadows of the clay vale; and possibly eight pairs northwest of Chippenham around Yatton Keynell; there were also a few around Semley, at Corsley near Warminster, and near Landford (Webber 1993). Most sites at this time were unimproved, damp meadows, but some nests were in hayfields and occasionally in pastures grazed by cattle.

In 1970, several sites around Swindon were deserted as the town expanded. Drier summers from the mid 1970s, coupled with extensive drainage in the Pewsey Vale and Upper Thames, caused many traditional fields to dry out and the numbers of Curlews decreased further. Some of the dried-out meadows were planted with cereals, while others were artificially manured and cut for silage.

Palmer (1991) believed that, over the course of the 1980s, the species had increased from 7–9 breeding pairs to 20–29. Some increase might have been expected as a result of legal protection in 1981, and better coverage and recording possibly played a part. Yet the Upper Thames around Inglesham to Castle Eaton and east of Cricklade appeared to be deserted by the mid 1980s (Webber 1993); and a population of '5–6 pairs ... in the

Table 67. Curlews *Numenius arquata* in Wiltshire: breeding pairs reported 1990–2000

	90	91	92	93	94	95	96	97	98	99	00
Pairs	25	14	13	18	33	18	10	6	13	11	8

area between Chapmanslade, Upton Scudamore, Warminster and Corsley Heath' in 1984 (Ferguson-Lees 1984) had disappeared by the end of the decade.

The early 1990s also seemed to show a decline, and the late 1990s to 2000 even more of one, whereas 1994 saw a clear but somewhat artificial peak (table 67). That year, WOS and the Wiltshire Wildlife Trust jointly undertook a survey of Curlews in the Braydon Forest area, covering the Oxford Clay Vale from the Bristol Avon in the west to the Ray in the east, and from the Swillbrook and Thames in the north to the Brinkworth Brook in the south. That survey located 23 territories, of which mated pairs occupied 20 and 17 were thought to have bred (McGrath 1995), compared with 13–16 pairs in the area in 1991 and a maximum of ten recorded pairs in 1993 (Webber 1993). Records elsewhere in Wiltshire brought the county total in 1994 to a possible 33 pairs – a tiny figure compared with the British population of 105,000 pairs (*APEP*), which is mostly located in northern England and southern and eastern Scotland (*1988–91 Atlas*).

The number of pairs in Wiltshire apparently dropped again after 1994 (table 67). Although some decrease was to be expected in the absence of a dedicated single-species survey, the summer tetrad survey should have located a higher proportion of these obvious waders if they were still present elsewhere in the county. The *1968–72 Atlas* mapped Curlews as breeding in 15 of Wiltshire's 33 core 10-km squares and seen in another six, but the corresponding figures in the *1988–91 Atlas* – which also showed widespread losses in Devon, Dorset and the Midlands – were down to ten and five, and in the summer tetrad survey nine and nine. But, as the species was recorded breeding in 36 tetrads and seen in 54 others during 1995–2000, the county population may not in fact have changed much from the 33 pairs found in 1994: it is here estimated at 25–40 pairs.

The summer distribution map confirms that some traditional sites are still in use, including the stronghold in Braydon Forest, but underlines the decline in the Pewsey Vale and along the Bristol Avon, where only a few pairs remain. Most welcome are records east of Swindon in an area that had shown an alarming decrease; and it is possible that these are the result of colonisation from Oxfordshire, where the population is small but now

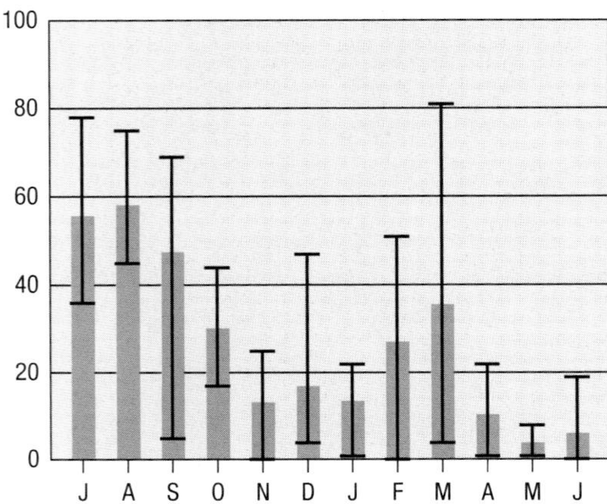

Figure 51. Curlews *Numenius arquata* in Wiltshire: monthly means (shaded columns) and maximum and minimum peak counts at CWP 1990–2000

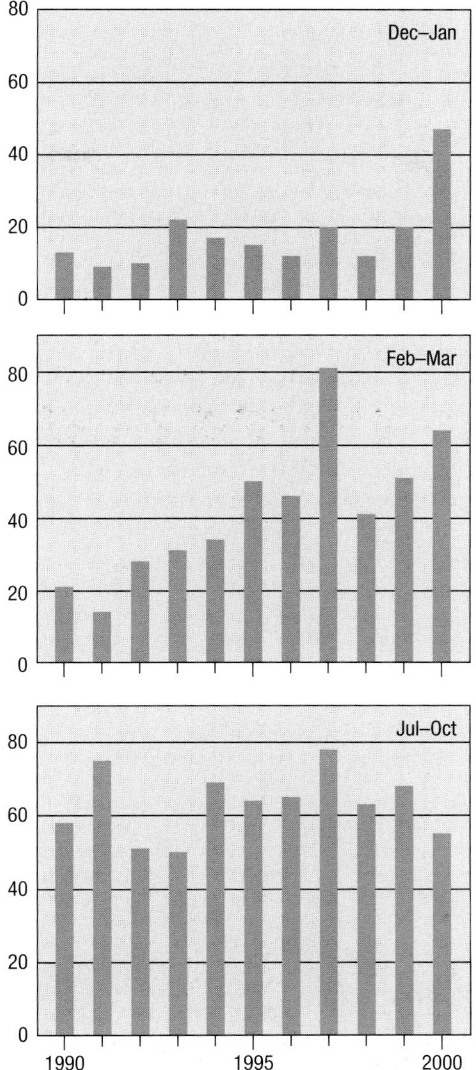

Figure 52. Curlews *Numenius arquata* in Wiltshire: peak winter and post-breeding counts at CWP 1974–2000

increasing (*Birds of Oxfordshire* 2002). Since the late 1990s one or more pairs have bred, or attempted to do so, on downland managed for hay on SPTA (East), the first reported on any downs in Wiltshire since Hony (1916b). Pairs still nest sporadically in the southeast near the Hampshire border, where breeding was proved in one year of the summer tetrad survey.

Curlews arrive back on their breeding grounds from mid February, the male establishing a territory up to two weeks before the female arrives. The chicks hatch, on average, in the last week of May and disperse from the nest-site after two to three days, being led to refuge and feeding grounds by the male. About a week later, the female departs and at this time, the beginning of June, a flock of mainly female Curlews builds up at CWP (McGrath 1995). The chicks fledge in early July and quickly move to CWP with other juveniles, the males and failed nesters, later transferring to coasts in the southwest.

The post-breeding moult flock during July–October became established at CWP from 1982 onwards. Generally rather fewer, but sometimes comparable or even higher numbers, appear there on return passage during February–March (figure 51).

Considerable numbers of Curlews – as many as 147,000 (Rehfisch *et al* 2003) – were wintering in Great Britain in the late 1990s. The *1981–84 Winter Atlas* found the species in six of Wiltshire's 33 core 10-km squares, whereas the winter tetrad survey during 1998–2000 noted it in only two, but overwintering became regular at CWP and in increasing numbers during the last decade of the 20th century (figure 52 and *cf* Palmer 1991), perhaps a result of the run of mild winters. Extrapolation from the tetrad data indicates a winter total of at least 24 Curlews, and it is probably in the range of 25–40 individuals. But spring and autumn passage numbers now exceed this figure: in 2000, for example, counts at CWP peaked at 64 in March and 55 in July (figure 52). Most Scottish and northern English Curlews move southwest to winter along the British west coast and in Ireland (*BWP*), and Wiltshire migrants and winterers are perhaps most likely to be of British origin, but could well involve some from Fenno-Scandia, Germany and the Low Countries (*Migration Atlas)*. The sole county ringing recovery involved a chick marked on 30 May 1961 at Appleby (Cumbria) and found dead only ten months later, on 6 April 1962, at Oare, near Marlborough. Only four Curlews, all chicks, were ringed in Wiltshire during 1965–2000.

It would be a great loss if the male Curlew's lovely spring song could no longer be heard bubbling over the meadows of Wiltshire. McGrath (1995) found the major hazards to be rolling and harrowing in spring and, increasingly, mowing in May and June for silage; he considered the future conservation of this species in the county to be inextricably linked with sympathetic agricultural management of suitable habitat.

GLW & PEC

Sponsored by Mike Jackson

Spotted Redshank

Tringa erythropus

Scarce passage migrant, breeds north Europe, winters southern Europe/Africa

Among the most elegant of British waders, Spotted Redshanks breed in arctic and subarctic regions from Lapland almost right across northern Siberia, and winter chiefly in sub-Saharan Africa north of the equator, as well as in the Indian region and southeast Asia, though some go no farther at that season than western Europe, the Mediterranean and the Middle East. The numbers breeding in Europe, excluding Russia, have been estimated at between 25,900 and 35,900 pairs (*EBCC Atlas*), but, apart from a range expansion in Sweden, population trends are little known. In Great Britain, the species occurs most widely and numerously on spring and, especially, autumn passage, when September is the peak month (Prater 1981). Numbers wintering here vary from year to year: the *1981–84 Winter Atlas* suggested a British and Irish total within the range of 80 to 200, which has more recently been more precisely estimated for Great Britain at 196 in the late 1990s (Rehfisch *et al* 2003), but even that was a comparatively recent development during the second half of the 20th century.

Table 68. Spotted Redshanks *Tringa erythropus* in Wiltshire: monthly totals of bird-days 1974–2000

	Jan	Feb	Mar	Apr	May	Jun	Jul	Aug	Sep	Oct	Nov	Dec
Bird-days	1	2	39	42	60	4	1	79	66	32	19	0

Before the 1939–45 War, the Spotted Redshank was far less regular in Great Britain, being 'Uncommon... autumn, scarce spring, exceptionally winter' (Witherby *et al* 1938–41). Thus, it is perhaps not surprising that Wiltshire had no records until 1947, when one picked up wounded at Charlton Mill on 1 February died later that day, and another was seen near Pitton on 25 April (*WANHM*). No more were found until two in 1960 (*WANHM*), but then – at least partly through better coverage of developing wetlands in north Wiltshire, particularly at CWP – there were at least a further 25 by the end of 1979, including seven records involving nine birds in 1976 alone, though none was seen in six others of those 19 years. A total of 33 was noted during 1980–89, 15 of them in August and eight in September, but they included two long-stayers at CWP, from 23 September to 19 November 1988 and from 11 March to 6 May 1989 (*Hobby*).

During 1990–2000, the species was reported in every year except 1997, but numbers varied (figure 53). While 1990 and 1996 produced the most individuals, those totals were boosted by parties of up to six during 1–6 May 1990 and of five on 9 September 1996. In this period, all Spotted Redshanks bar six singletons were seen at CWP, the exceptions being at Swindon STW, Coate Water, Lacock Gravel Pits, Collingbourne Ducis, Imber and Stratford sub Castle. Spotted Redshanks occur primarily on passage in Wiltshire (table 68); during 1990–2000, the highest totals were in September, August and May in that order – though the May observations were all in just two of the 11 years, 1990 and 1993. For comparison, the 19 in the 1970s comprised seven in spring (March–June) and 12 in autumn (August–September); and the 33 in the 1980s eight in spring (March–June) and 25 in autumn (July–November).

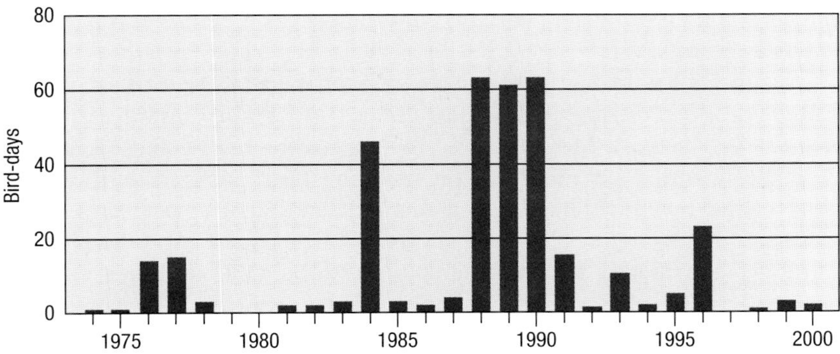

Figure 53. Spotted Redshanks *Tringa erythropus* in Wiltshire: annual totals of bird-days (mainly CWP) 1974–2000

NPA & PAC

Common Redshank

Tringa totanus

Virtually extinct as nester in Wiltshire, now scarce passage migrant from elsewhere in Britain/Iceland

How things change! In 1933 CMR Pitman, then editor of the 'Report on the Birds of Wiltshire' in *WANHM*, wrote of the Common Redshank: 'The extraordinary increase of this species and also the Dipper and Common Snipe as breeding birds in the county deserves special attention' and 'new' breeding sites for Redshanks that year were cited at Salisbury and nearby Laverstock on the Bourne, at Wilton on the confluence of the Wylye and the Nadder, at Harnham on the Nadder, and, in the Avon valley south of Salisbury at Britford, Longford and Barford, as well as at Bulford (though, in fact, nesting had also been recorded there in 1931) and, finally, at 'Martin and district'. (Martin is just inside Hampshire, so presumably the 'and district' referred to Redshanks on the Wiltshire side of the border.) Nor was 1933 an isolated year: since 1929 increases had been reported in the valleys of the Kennet and the Salisbury Avon; by 1931 the species was 'more common in the Wylye valley than by the Nadder'; in 1932 'increasing in the Salisbury district' and 'Still on the increase near Marlborough'; in 1934 it bred 'near Bowerchalke for the first time'; and yet again in 1936 'A very definite increase noticed throughout the county', including a pair near Salisbury that even 'succeeded in rearing a brood on the crest of a hill towering high above the water meadows' (*WANHM*).

Yet half a century earlier Smith (1887) had had 'but two instances of [the Redshank's] occurrence... both communicated to me by Mr. Grant, who received the two specimens in the flesh, the one on May 16th, 1865, the other in September, 1868, both, strangely enough, from the same locality, Whitley, near Melksham'. Hony (1915a) included this as a Wiltshire breeding species for the first time after a report of a nest at Downton in 1907 (*WANHM* 35: 150). And now, nearly 100 years later, the wheel has turned full circle: Redshanks have again all but disappeared from Wiltshire as breeding birds, and indeed are seldom seen away from CWP.

This rise and the fall is in line with what has happened to the British population as a whole. Numbers dropped during the first part of the 19th century, but increased from about 1865 to 1940 (*1968–72 Atlas*). More recently, the population has decreased again, especially inland, where the favoured breeding habitat has long been wet grassland and where the drainage of riverside meadows has been a marked feature of agricultural intensification (*1988–91 Atlas*).

Peirson (1959) considered the Redshank to be 'a regular summer visitor breeding locally in considerable numbers', but 'only rarely reported between October and March'. He added that it had colonised Wiltshire 'first up the Salisbury Avon', having bred at Downton in 1907 (*WANHM*, Hony 1915a) 'and then up the Kennet', where it first nested at Stitchcombe in 1920 (*MCNHS*); 'By 1940 it was breeding in the Thames and Bristol Avon valleys also', though 'Recently there has been a slight regression' with 'breeding in numbers' reported only from the Salisbury Avon and Kennet valleys.

Redshanks continued to be well established in the 15 years after the 1939–45 War. Despite Peirson's remarks, they seem not infrequently to have appeared in the second half of March, including in 1947 '30 to 40, Cheverell Wood, March 20th'. That same year two pairs nested by floodwater north of Pitton and, when the water dried up, 'one pair safely escorted their family, a day or two old, across the village, the old birds flying around and alighting on roads and rooftops, while the little ones scurried through gardens and along paths... evidently making their way to Clarendon Lake, 2 miles to the S'. In 1948 they 'bred on downs near Totterdown, an unusual site so far from water'. In 1949 'they seemed scarcer this summer in the Kennet valley', but in 1951 'About fifty pairs between Chilton Foliat and Knighton'. In 1953, apart from a scatter of summer records 'in usual haunts', including small young by the Kennet & Avon Canal near Seend Cleeve, the species was seen 'throughout December at Axford' and on two dates that month at Swindon STW. In 1957 'regularly heard or seen by several observers between February and June' and even 'four nests found at Chilton Foliat'. In 1959, 'This bird is quite a common breeder in the river valleys to the east, west and south of Salisbury as well as in the Amesbury area'. Kennedy (1966) regarded it as 'a summer visitor all along the [Kennet] valley. Most birds arrive in March and leave in September. It was first certainly recorded in 1911 ... the first nest was found in 1920'.

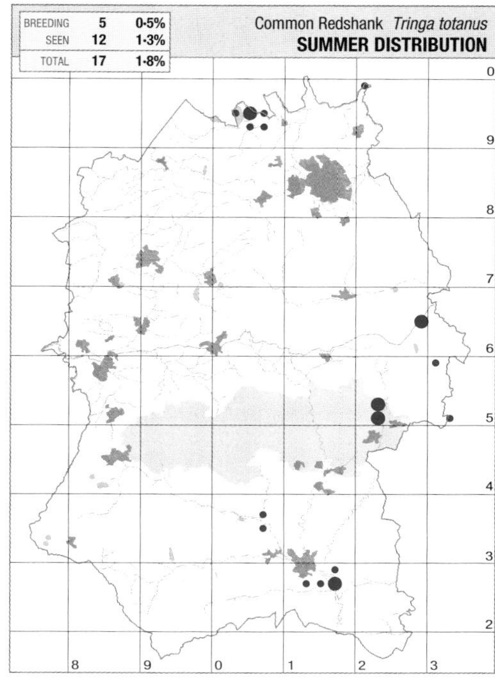

The species' fortunes fluctuated more during the 1960s and 1970s. At least 14 pairs were recorded in 1960 and similar numbers in each of the following two years, but then the unusually harsh winter of 1962/63 in Great Britain and western Europe apparently took a heavy toll: in 1963 Wiltshire held a maximum of only four pairs and, while numbers partly recovered in 1964 and 1965, the population slumped again for the following ten years. The early 1960s saw breeding season reports from at least 34 sites, but that figure had declined to about 21 in the 1970s. In 1976 Redshanks were recorded at 11 sites, and nesting was proved at Coate Water and Ashton Keynes; there were similar reports in 1978 and 1979. During those two decades, regular breeding areas included the valleys of the Bourne, the Kennet, the Thames, and the Salisbury Avon and its tributaries. The largest winter counts came from Britford on the Salisbury Avon in the 1970s, including 12 on 29 January 1977. (It should be noted that this summary, based on the annual reports in *WANHM* and *Hobby*, differs in a number of respects from that in Buxton 1981; also that the report in *Hobby* of 31 at Britford in January 1976 is incorrect: it should have been one on the 31st.)

Nesting Redshanks declined to an average of 20 pairs (Palmer 1991) in the late 1980s – though the data in *Hobby* show the actual average to be fewer than 18 pairs – and further still during the early 1990s, down to possible maxima of only one or two pairs in the late 1990s and 2000, though none has actually been proved breeding in the county since 1995 (table 69). The 17 tetrads marked on the summer distribution map, five of them

Table 69. Common Redshanks *Tringa totanus* in Wiltshire: reported pairs in summer 1990–2000
The 'possible pairs' attempt to summarise any reported during the breeding season, even though some were seen only once, and the figures include those subsequently 'proved breeding'

	90	91	92	93	94	95	96	97	98	99	00
Highest possible pairs	18	12	7	7	6	3	1	1	2	2	2
Peak proved breeding	0	4	1	0	0	3	0	0	0	0	0

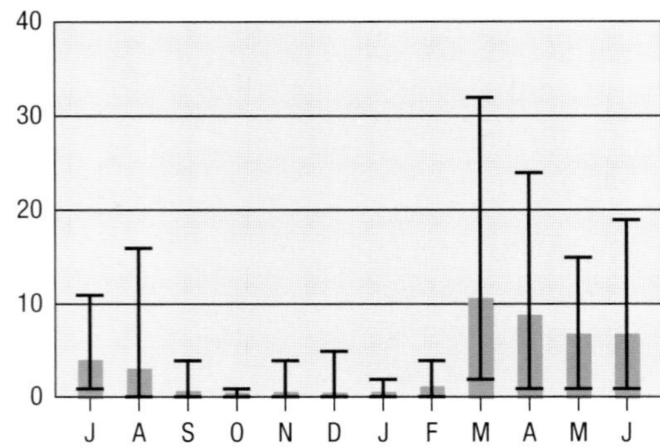

Figure 54. Common Redshanks *Tringa totanus* in Wiltshire: monthly means (shaded columns) and maximum and minimum peak counts at CWP 1990–2000

showing evidence of breeding, are the accumulation of the six years of the survey and give a greatly exaggerated impression of the Redshank's current nesting distribution in the county. Unless positive conservation measures can be taken, the future for this species in Wiltshire looks bleak.

Elsewhere, this is a common wader with a wide distribution across Europe and Asia. The telltale alarm calls of Redshanks can be heard in summer in a variety of marshy habitats from Iceland and Iberia to Amurland and China, but most of the population leaves much of this vast breeding range in autumn to winter along the coasts and certain major river valleys of western Europe, the Mediterranean area and southern Asia. Excluding Russia, some 317,000 to 386,000 pairs are estimated to nest in Europe (*EBCC Atlas*), 30,600 to 33,600 of them in Great Britain (Reed 1985, *1988–91 Atlas*). British Redshanks are partially migratory, and almost all move to coasts, mainly within Great Britain, some crossing to Ireland and others moving down Atlantic shorelines to western France. At the same time, many Icelandic (and probably Faeroese) Redshanks also winter on British coasts – raising the total at that season to around 116,000 (Rehfisch *et al* 2003) – but few from the north Continental populations apparently pass through this country and those probably only on autumn migration (*Migration Atlas*).

The monthly peak counts at CWP, Wiltshire's main wader site, during 1990–2000 (figure 54) emphasise that the numbers are highest in March and continue relatively high through to June: this protracted spring passage perhaps suggests that the first waves involve migrants returning inland to breed elsewhere in southern England, and that the later ones may be heading for Scotland, even the Faeroes or Iceland; though these counts also include Redshanks attempting to breed at CWP. But return movements are much smaller and confined to the early autumn, these possibly being failed breeders. Only 19 Redshanks were ringed in Wiltshire during 1965–2000, most as chicks in the late 1980s, and none has been recovered, but an adult that had been colour-ringed on the Taff estuary at Cardiff (South Glamorgan) on 14 February 1996 was seen at CWP68 on 14 March 1999.

IJF-L & NPA

Greenshank

Tringa nebularia

Local passage migrant, breeds Scotland/north Europe, winters west Europe/Africa

Greenshanks breed mostly in taiga and forest zones from Scotland across northern Europe and Siberia to Kamchatka, and winter south to sub-Saharan Africa and across southern Asia to Australia. Between 57,600 and 83,200 pairs are estimated to breed in Europe, excluding Russia, but, apart from three studies in Scotland which show that numbers and range contracted there during the 20th century, no information exists on trends (*EBCC Atlas*). The Scottish population has been estimated at 1000 to 1600 pairs, most nesting on blanket bogs, though some in wooded country (*1988–91 Atlas*). Only about 1100 individuals winter in the Atlantic countries of Europe (*CBWP*), 600 of those in Great Britain (Rehfisch *et al* 2003). The species is much more numerous in Great Britain on autumn passage, and maxima of 1800–2600 were recorded annually by WeBS in the late 1990s.

Wiltshire's first recorded Greenshanks were three that stayed for six or seven days in a flooded water-meadow near Salisbury in May 1865 (Morres 1878–85): the author bemoaned the fact that, despite his efforts over two days, 'they remained just out of shot of me'. Smith (1887) listed several other, less fortunate specimens, all 'killed' or 'shot': at the Knook meadows, Heytesbury, on 27 August 1868; at Foxhanger in August 1870; at Amesbury in August 1886; and, both undated, at Corsham Court and at Gombledon near Salisbury. Hony (1915a) did not add any, and the next references to Greenshanks in Wiltshire were mention of two records near Marlborough in 1937 and 1938 (Peirson 1939) and a brief statement that the species had been seen at Wilton Water in May and September 1944 (*WANHM*).

After a further gap of ten years, there came a series of nine records (12 birds) during 1954–58, more than half of them at Lacock Gravel Pits or Coate Water, but including singletons at Swindon STW, at Charlton-All-Saints and near Cricklade; four of the nine were in April–May and the other five in August–September (*WANHM*). On this basis, but presumably taking the 19th century records into account, Peirson (1959) regarded this species as a 'rare passage migrant, usually seen in autumn but sometimes in spring'. After a blank in 1959, the 1960s saw Greenshanks recorded in every year except 1968, often at least five in a year, at a total of nearly 20 localities, though mainly at Swindon STW, Coate Water and Lacock Gravel Pits.

The Wiltshire records for 1969–81 were tabulated by Edwards (1983a). In that time the species occurred annually, but numbers varied from just a singleton (in 1973) to totals of 41 and 40 (in 1975 and 1977); by far the peak month was August with 139 over the whole 13-year period, followed by 46 in September, 23 in July and 21 in May; the most regular localities were Swindon STW, CWP (increasingly after only two records during 1970–74) and Coate Water, but the species was found in at least 21 other places, although records at Lacock declined to only three in the whole of the 1970s. The largest flock ever recorded in Wiltshire was 22 seen at CWP24 (then known as Kent End) on 5 August 1975, and the same total, albeit in a number of parties, was recorded at CWP on 1 September 1985.

The county's only winter records came in the early 1980s: two at Britford on 21 December 1982, presumably the same two there on 30 January 1983, and one at Langford Lakes on 16 February 1985. As a result, Palmer (1991) was able to note that Greenshanks had been reported in every month, mostly at CWP and largely in May and July–September, adding that 'good spring passage is a fairly recent phenomenon'; indeed, the species was

Table 70. Greenshanks *Tringa nebularia* in Wiltshire: monthly totals of bird-days 1974–2000

	Jan	Feb	Mar	Apr	May	Jun	Jul	Aug	Sep	Oct	Nov	Dec
Bird-days	2	1	9	45	408	21	168	1097	603	43	7	2

recorded in only four springs in the 1960s, but in seven in the 1970s, in eight in the 1980s, and annually in the 1990s.

During 1990–2000, approximate annual totals of Greenshanks reported, still mostly at CWP, varied between 19 and 37 individuals. The larger numbers continued to be in May and in July–September, but August remained by far the most significant month (table 70). Earliest and latest dates in the 11 years were 26 March 1995 and 10 November 1997. Like those of other waders, numbers of Greenshanks recorded in the county have increased as a result of the development of CWP and better observer coverage, but vary between years according to water levels and weather patterns (figure 55). The species was added to the county's ringing list when one was caught at Swindon STW on 22 August 1999.

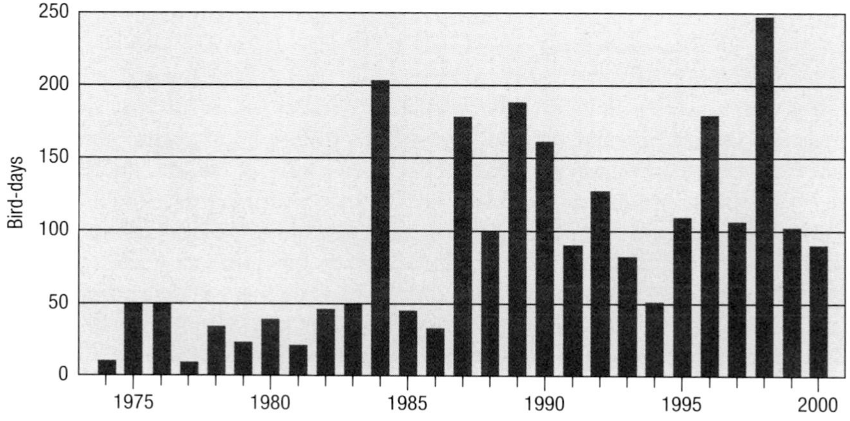

Figure 55. Greenshanks *Tringa nebularia* in Wiltshire: annual totals of bird-days 1974–2000

NPA & SBE

Lesser Yellowlegs

Tringa flavipes

Vagrant (1 record), breeds east Alaska/Canada, winters West Indies/South America

The elegant Lesser Yellowlegs nests in grassy meadows and bogs from eastern Alaska to James Bay in Canada. Although some winter in southern USA and Central America, most do so in the West Indies and in South America down to Chile and Argentina. Their autumn migration has a marked southeasterly component across Canada, which probably accounts for this species being one of the more frequent transatlantic vagrants: as many as 184 were recorded in Great Britain during 1958–2000 (*BBRC*).

Wiltshire's only Lesser Yellowlegs was an adult in summer plumage at CWP29 on 28 April 1992 (*Hobby*, *BBRC*). Interestingly, there were other reports just before that, in Northern Ireland (22–26 April), and just after, in Lancashire (5 May). Lesser Yellowlegs are found in Great Britain mostly in autumn, often in juvenile/first-winter plumage. American waders in spring may have crossed the Atlantic in autumn and then travelled south and north again in the Old World (*eg* Dymond *et al* 1989).

NPA & PEC

Sponsored by Martin Buckland

Nearly a century ago, another bird was published as Wiltshire's first record of this species: 'A specimen, shot by Mr. Carey Coles at Winterbourne Stoke, in 1908, has been preserved by Mr. White' (*WANHM* 35: 508). At the request of Hony (1915a), however, the specimen was taken to the British Museum and there identified by WR Ogilvie-Grant as 'a Common Redshank on which the beak and legs have been wrongly painted yellow' (*WANHM* 38: 641). Eds

---

Solitary Sandpiper

Tringa solitaria

Vagrant (1 record), breeds Alaska/Canada, winters South/Central America

A slightly smaller North American counterpart of the Green Sandpiper of Eurasia – likewise laying and hatching its eggs in old tree nests of thrushes and other birds – the Solitary Sandpiper breeds in wet coniferous forest from Alaska to eastern Canada. Wintering mainly in South America south to Argentina, but to some extent also in Central America and the West Indies, it then similarly occupies streams and ponds rather than open wetlands and, as its name suggests, mixes little with other species.

Compared with some other American waders, Solitary Sandpipers are particularly rare vagrants to Europe: only six had been recorded in Great Britain by 1957 and just 21 more during 1958–2000 (*BBRC*). Thus, Wiltshire is lucky to have hosted even one: a juvenile at Swindon STW, which was found on 13 September 1966, trapped and ringed on the 17th, and last seen on the 25th (*WANHM*, *BBRC*). It was the first of only three to have been ringed in Great Britain by the end of the 20th century.

GLW & PCo

Green Sandpiper

Tringa ochropus

Regular passage/winter, breeds north Europe, winters west Europe/Africa

Usually incubating their eggs in old tree nests of other birds – often thrushes – or in squirrel's dreys, Green Sandpipers have a breeding range that extends, if somewhat patchily, right across the northern half of Europe and much of the northern third of Asia, broadly from Fenno-Scandia and Germany east to the Sea of Okhotsk. They have also nested as far west as the Netherlands and Italy, as well as in Westmorland (now Cumbria) in 1917 and, more recently, in Scotland in 1959, 1999 and 2000 (*RBBP*). Some 153,000 to 193,000 pairs are thought to breed in Europe, excluding Russia (*EBCC Atlas*). Usually in freshwater habitats, the species winters in the Mediterranean area, sub-Saharan Africa, the Middle East and southern Asia; and also in small numbers north in western Europe to southern Britain and Ireland, where the *1981–84 Winter Atlas* estimated the combined total at 500 to 1000.

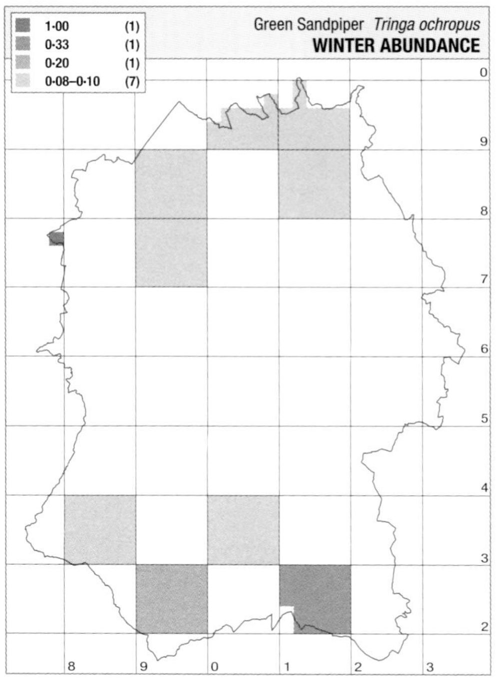

Smith (1887) considered the Green Sandpiper to be 'a far more common bird in Wiltshire than many suppose' and quoted the Reverend AP Morres as having seen the species in water meadows near Salisbury in every month except June. He added, too, that 'Mr. W. Wyndham writes that it is common at Dinton' and that 'Mr. Grant furnishes me with a goodly list of sixteen ... taken within a radius of ten or twelve miles of Devizes'; earlier, im Thurn (1870) had recorded that one of a flock of seven was shot on the Rockley downs and sent to him on 3 September 1867. Hony (1915a) did not mention the species, presumably because there were too many records, while reports in *WANHM* for 1929 considered it 'A not uncommon winter visitor'; 'Always 2–6 pairs from October to March' (from an observer based at Lydiard Millicent); and 'Regular visitor to water-meadows near Salisbury'.

Peirson & Walford (1930) noted this species as 'a passage migrant, irregular in appearance'. In the early 1930s, however, further reports in *WANHM* confirmed its frequency by the Salisbury Avon, including five at Longford in August 1930 and seven there in August 1932; in 1933, one observer recorded seeing Green Sandpipers 'on the Avon below Britford from November to June' and another, based at Longford, saw them throughout the year; in 1936 there were records of up to four in different parts of the county, 'chiefly during March, April and August'.

After the 1939–45 War, as the number of observers increased, Green Sandpipers were recorded in *WANHM* at eight sites in 1952, nine in 1953 and ten in 1954. They were seen at Swindon STW (then Rodbourne Sewage Farm) from July to December 1954, including eight in August that year. Peirson (1959) described the species as a 'regular but uncommon visitor in autumn and winter', mainly from 'mid-July to early February ... in gravel pits, small streams and sewage farms ... less frequently ... April and May ... only occasionally in the remaining months'. It was recorded in May in at least five years in the 1950s and in June in at least two. In the 1960s and 1970s the largest counts came from Britford (up to ten in September 1961), Seagry Gravel Pits (seven in August 1965), Longbridge Deverill (seven in September 1970), Swindon STW (11 in August 1969, up to 18 in autumn 1970, up to 16 in autumn 1971, up to 28 in August 1974) and later, as its area developed, CWP (20 in August 1974).

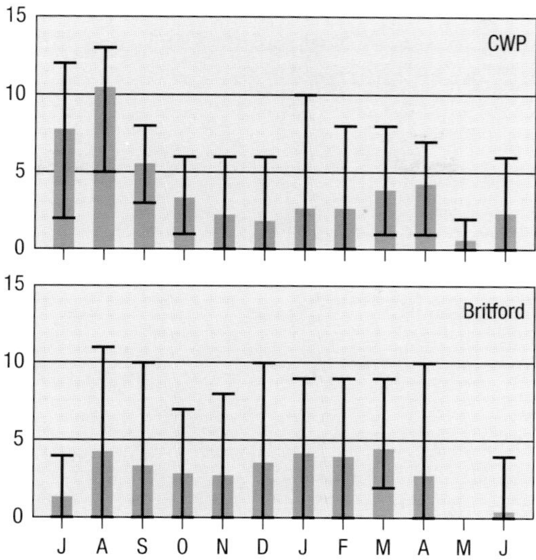

Figure 56. Green Sandpipers *Tringa ochropus* in Wiltshire: monthly means (shaded columns) and maximum and minimum peak counts at CWP and Britford 1990–2000
Data for Britford are only available for 1992–2000

Buxton (1981) painted a largely similar picture to that of Peirson (1959), considering the species to be common in autumn and scarce but regular in winter in north Wiltshire, adding that 'the less obvious' spring passage was more widespread. In the 1980s, however, Palmer (1991) noted that Green Sandpipers were absent from the county only in late May and early June, that passage occurred mainly in March–April and July–September, and that there was a wintering population from October to February. The peak monthly counts for 1990–2000 show that this continued to be the pattern at CWP, the most consistently watched site, and also that August was by far the peak month there (figure 56). Although there were casual records of the species in the county from around 10–15 localities annually during the 1990s, the other most regular site was Britford, where a good run of published counts during 1992–2000 revealed a slightly different pattern: the August peak was still clear, but the winter numbers were just as high; again, there was little evidence of spring passage after April (figure 56). In the last half of that decade, Swindon STW also featured with increasing regularity, showing peaks of at least six individuals and in some years 15–16.

Green Sandpipers are absent from Wiltshire as a whole for only a few weeks in spring and early summer. In each year during 1990–2000, the latest spring record fell between 18 April and 14 May, and the first of the return passage always came in June, between the 2nd and the 28th: these are some of the earliest of all 'autumn' migrants and are perhaps mainly females, which may leave the males to tend the chicks (*BWP*). The winter map reflects the species' preference for ponds, gravel pits, ditches and streams, and confirms the north around CWP and the lower Salisbury Avon, as well as Broadmead Brook, West Kington, as the most favoured areas at that season. Extrapolation from the winter counts suggests a total of 28, but that is undoubtedly on the low side for this secretive and often solitary wader, especially as it was found in only nine of the county's 33 core 10-km squares during the winter survey, compared with 14 in the *1981–84 Winter Atlas*. It may be that 40–60 is a more realistic figure – which would represent a significant proportion of the British winter total.

Only four Green Sandpipers were ringed in the county during 1965–2000, but one of those, caught near Malmesbury on 5 September 1965, was shot four winters later near Toot Baldon (Oxfordshire) on 18 January 1969.

NPA & SBE

Wood Sandpiper

Tringa glareola

Scarce passage migrant, breeds north Europe, winters Africa

This elegant species, superficially similar to the Green Sandpiper, is always a welcome sight for the county's wader enthusiasts. Wood Sandpipers nest in a broad swathe across northern Eurasia, mainly from Fenno-Scandia and Belarus to Kamchatka, but locally also in Poland, north Germany, Denmark, and Scotland. The population of Europe, excluding Russia, has been estimated at between 299,000 and 412,000 pairs, but is thought to be in decline (*EBCC Atlas*). In Scotland, the *1968–72 Atlas* showed confirmed or probable breeding in as many as 14 widely spread 10-km squares, but 20 years later the *1988–91 Atlas* could map only four, far less scattered squares; and in 2000 just two to six pairs nested at three sites (*RBBP*).

Wood Sandpipers are highly migratory, wintering in sub-Saharan Africa and in southern Asia through Indonesia to Australia. The Fenno-Scandian population moves to Africa in a south to south-southwest direction and relatively few pass through these islands, adults first and then juveniles over a more protracted period. The peak, involving both adults and juveniles, occurs during August (Prater 1981). The return migration in spring, when variable numbers overshoot here, is largely concentrated in May.

Wiltshire's first Wood Sandpiper was 'taken' at Lavington on 13 January 1879. Although a highly unusual date for a species that normally winters in the tropics, there are old December records for Essex and Northumberland (Witherby *et al* 1938–41) and, as a more recent example, one was seen at Ibsley on the Hampshire Avon from 23 February to 6 April 1984 (Clark & Eyre 1993). There were no more Wiltshire records until four or five in the 1950s: one at Lacock Gravel Pits on 22–23 August 1952; two at Lacock again on 16 May 1956, and one at Salisbury on the 17th; and two at Coate Water on 25–29 August 1957 and one there on 31 August and 7–8 September (*WANHM*). The species began to become more regular, if not quite annual, in the county in the 1960s and 1970s – although, as Buxton

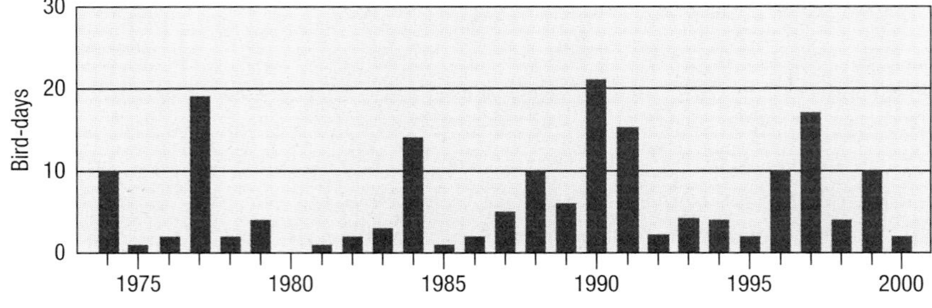

Figure 57. Wood Sandpipers *Tringa glareola* in Wiltshire: annual totals of bird-days 1974–2000

Table 71. Wood Sandpipers *Tringa glareola* in Wiltshire: monthly totals of bird-days 1974–2000

	Jan	Feb	Mar	Apr	May	Jun	Jul	Aug	Sep	Oct	Nov	Dec
Bird-days	0	0	0	2	46	6	8	70	24	4	13	0

(1981) pointed out, few were 'from areas south of the Marlborough Downs'. Those two decades produced a total of 30–36 records (*WANHM*), the actual figure depending whether observations a few days apart at the same site be treated as one record or two. The majority were seen in August and September – including the only Wood Sandpiper caught and ringed in Wiltshire, at Swindon STW in late August 1977 – but also one in April, three in May, and two each in June and July. In the 1980s the species was found in every year except 1980 itself, and again in every month from April to September, with peaks in May (seven) and August (ten); by then most of the 22 seen in that decade were at CWP (Palmer 1991).

Wood Sandpipers were recorded in Wiltshire in every year during 1990–2000, a notable increase (figure 57). Of 41 seen in that period, 34 were at CWP, three at Swindon STW, three at Coate Water, and one at Calne Sand Pits. The spring peak was concentrated in May – although the species was not found in that month in three of the 11 years – and the autumn one was spread over four months, a similar pattern to that since 1974 (table 71). One at CWP on 16 May 1999 was seen in song flight. An adult at CWP on 19 April 1986 was the county's earliest record in spring, and a juvenile there from 31 October to 13 November 1997 the latest in autumn.

NPA & SBE

Common Sandpiper

Actitis hypoleucos

Regular passage migrant, has bred, rare in winter when most travel to Africa

Instantly identified by its unmistakable call and distinctive wing-flicking flight low over the water, the Common Sandpiper is nevertheless something of a mystery in Wiltshire, at least as far as its past breeding and wintering status are concerned. This species nests by or near shallow streams and shingle-edged rivers, reservoirs and lochs over much of Scotland and in northwest England and Wales; it also does so very locally in Devon and has bred in Somerset, as well as sporadically in the past in a dozen other English counties. But how often has it nested in Wiltshire?

The Common Sandpiper's breeding range in Great Britain has contracted somewhat since the 1939–45 War, but the population has been put at 15,800 pairs (*1988–91 Atlas*). The species also nests commonly in mainly upland freshwater habitats in most countries of Europe – with, excluding Russia, a generally stable population of 505,000 to 665,000 pairs (*EBCC Atlas*) – and in a vast region across much of Asia to Kamchatka and Japan, south to Afghanistan, Tibet and China.

For Wiltshire, im Thurn (1870) noted that Common Sandpipers visited every summer, frequenting pools and rivers, but were not known to breed. Smith (1887) wrote that this species was 'frequently met with in summer' and was 'especially abundant in the neighbourhood of Salisbury', but he did not include it in his list of 106 species recorded as nesting in the county. Earlier, Morres (1878–85) had found Common Sandpipers 'scattered in the summer months along the banks of almost all our rivers [in the Salisbury area]...I see them every summer...but have never found their nest'. According to Meyrick (1895, 1906), 'pairs are not uncommon along the river [Kennet] in summer, and may be seen in the same localities year after year. It seems highly probable that they breed here'. Were these all late spring and early autumn migrants, or non-breeders, or did some nest in Wiltshire in the 19th century? The *1875–1900 Atlas* assumed that they did, and showed large areas of southern England in a former breeding distribution that exists no longer. Nesting was indeed proved sporadically in various southern counties, such as Hampshire, Sussex and Kent, but Witherby *et al* (1938–41) did not include Wiltshire in the list.

Even so, G Dent wrote to Hony (1915a) that the Common Sandpiper 'Probably breeds on the Kennet (near Marlborough); it is seen every spring, and this year (1912) my brother saw the old birds with young ones only just able to fly', though Hony still square-bracketed the record and, in his county bird list, put a question mark against the Common Sandpiper in the 'known to have nested' category. Peirson (1919) stated that it 'certainly breeds, but the nest had not been found'. In 1929 the species was described as a 'not uncommon passage migrant, some staying to breed' (*WANHM*). In 1933 'the nesting of a pair on the [Salisbury] Avon above Bulford' was reported, and in 1934 the same observer believed 'two pairs...nested...below Bulford but were disturbed', both then being 'seen eventually further up the river...near Milston, and...near Netheravon' (*WANHM*).

There were further indications of seemingly established pairs, or birds seen right through the summer, in the 1950s and 1960s, most notably in 1952 when three pairs were recorded, 'March–September inclusive', along sections of the Kennet & Avon Canal, the Bristol Avon and the Salisbury Avon, but 'No nest was traced'; and in 1962 'seen every evening throughout summer flying down R. Avon at Longford' (*WANHM*). But Common Sandpipers, like many other waders, probably do not normally breed until two years old (*BWP*) and, as no nest was ever confirmed, it may be that all these summer records, even stretching back into the 19th century, relate to non-breeders staying outside the normal range. The county's only certain breeding record to the end of the 20th century involved an adult with two downy young at Langford Lakes in July 1980 (Peart 1981a).

Peirson (1959), Buxton (1981) and Palmer (1991) all agreed that Common Sandpipers were regular and not uncommon passage migrants in spring and autumn, the last two authors adding that the species occasionally wintered. Over much of its range this species is strongly migratory, wintering throughout sub-Saharan Africa, and in southern Asia through to Australia, but small numbers now stay in western Europe, many of them in estuarine habitats, where the British and Irish winter total perhaps 'did not exceed 50' (*1981–84 Winter Atlas*, following Prater 1981). In Wiltshire – where this wader used to be known, inaccurately, as the 'Summer Snipe' – there seems to have been no suggestion of overwintering until 1934, when Common Sandpipers were reported as seen at Britford 'from January to the end of May', and then no more again until a passing reference to one in December 1966; but in 1972 'Several early spring records...may refer to overwintering birds', the first of which was at Longbridge Deverill on 13 February (*WANHM*).

During 1975–2000 there were November–February records in Wiltshire in no fewer than 14 of the 26 years and involving at least 13 different sites. The most were three on floodwater near Cricklade on 29 December 1979 and four at Langford Lakes on 11 December 1982. Long-stayers included one at CWP in January–February 1981, one at Swindon STW from 11 October to at least 6 December 1994 and, interestingly, two and then one at CWP29 through three successive winters from 1988/89 to 1990/91. As migrant waders are often faithful to particular sites, it is tempting to suggest that the same individuals were involved, one not surviving to return for the third winter. Five other 1990–2000 winter

Table 72. Common Sandpipers *Actitis hypoleucos* in Wiltshire: peak monthly counts at three key sites 1990–2000

	Jan	Feb	Mar	Apr	May	Jun	Jul	Aug	Sep	Oct	Nov	Dec
CWP	1	1	4	8	6	1	7	14	6	2	1	1
Coate Water	0	0	0	16	12	3	14	7	8	2	1	0
Corsham Lake	0	0	0	15	3	2	13	7	2	0	0	0

records were at Corsham Lake on 12 December 1990, at West Amesbury on 7 November 1991, at Longford Castle on 29 November 1991, at Swindon STW during 7–9 February 1994 and, finally, at CWP29 on 10 November 1997.

During 1990–2000, spring passage was noted between 12 March and 6 June, and autumn return movements from 21 June to 30 October, although for early and late dates it is difficult to distinguish migrants from winterers. Highest counts in spring are usually concentrated in the last ten days of April, and in autumn mainly in July and the first half of August (see table 72, showing the monthly pattern at three key sites). During 1955–2000 there were at least 24 counts in double figures, half of them from Coate Water, the most favoured site for this species. All seven double-figure counts during 1955–70 were in July and August, whereas of the 17 during 1971–2000 seven were in April, four in May and three each in July and August. The highest numbers were 18, 19 and 20 at Coate on 9 July 1956, 1 May 1986 and 2 July 1955; 25 at Bowood Lake on 2 August 1956; and 20–30 at Swindon STW on 28 August 1963. In general, maximum counts during 1990–2000 were slightly lower than they had been in the 1950s and 1960s, and even the 1980s, the highest being only 16 at Coate Water on 27 April 1998.

Although 23 Common Sandpipers were ringed in the county during 1965–2000, all as migrating adults or juveniles, none has been recovered. One at Corsham Lake on 24 April 1997 had been colour-ringed as a chick at Dewar Burn (Borders) on 4 June 1995; and another at Wilton Water on 20 April 1997 had been marked near Edinburgh. These two records may suggest a north British origin for those passing through Wiltshire, but Scandinavian – particularly Norwegian – populations may also be involved (see *BWP*, *Migration Atlas*).

GLW & SBE

Sponsored by Bob Blamey

Turnstone

Arenaria interpres

Scarce passage migrant, breeds northeast Canada/ Greenland/Fenno-Scandia, winters west Europe/ Africa

Turnstones have a circumpolar arctic and mainly coastal breeding distribution, extending south in Europe to southern Scandinavia and the Baltic – the most southerly anywhere in their range – yet neither eggs nor young have ever been found in Iceland or the Faeroes, or even in Scotland where the odd pair sometimes hangs around in summer (and 'probably' nested in Sutherland in 1976). An estimated 14,800 to 25,200 pairs breed in Europe, excluding

Table 73. Turnstones *Arenaria interpres* in Wiltshire: monthly totals of bird-days 1974–2000

	Jan	Feb	Mar	Apr	May	Jun	Jul	Aug	Sep	Oct	Nov	Dec
Bird-days	0	0	0	10	96	2	14	25	7	0	0	1

Russia, mostly in Norway, Sweden and Finland, many fewer in Estonia, Denmark and Svalbard (*EBCC Atlas*). These European birds migrate southwest in autumn along western Continental and British and Irish coasts, most moving on down to the shores of West Africa; while the considerable numbers that winter commonly on the coasts of western Europe from southern Iceland to Iberia, including Great Britain, come mainly from Greenland and northeast Canada (*BWP*, *Migration Atlas*). Turnstones are great travellers and other populations winter as far south as the coasts of South America, South Africa, Madagascar, Australia and New Zealand. Prater (1981) put the British winter population at about 25,000, but estimates for the late 1990s suggested a total of almost 50,000, just over 50 per cent of the northwest European total (Rehfisch *et al* 2003).

Wiltshire's first recorded Turnstone was in full summer plumage at CWP24, formerly known as Kent End, on 1 May 1973 (*WANHM*). There had been only ten more records by 1986, though involving at least 16 birds, and none was found in six of those 13 years: May, with a total of seven, was the most frequent month; otherwise three each were found in August and September, and singletons in April, June and July; three was the largest party, and none stayed longer than two days in that time. Since 1986, however, the species has been seen annually, at an average of four records a year (figure 58).

During 1973–2000, a grand total of 62 Turnstone records involved about 135 birds, all at CWP except for two at Coate Water on 5 September 1976 and one at Liden Lagoon on 22 August 1977, with an obvious increase in occurrence from 1987 (figure 58). Almost half were in May (table 73) and these are likely to have been heading north to Greenland and northeast Canada. The slightly smaller number of July–September records – though involving many fewer bird-days (and individuals) – probably included at least some from Fenno-Scandia. One at CWP68 on 13 December 1998 was exceptional. The two largest parties, of seven each, were both in May, on the 13th in 1994 and on the 23rd in 1999. Two of three parties of five were also in May, on the 12th in 1997 and on the 20th in 1999 (the latter at a different pit from the seven on the 23rd); there were also five on 22 August 1998. The vast majority of the records were apparently single-day visits, but at least eight of the records involved longer stays. In 1994, one Turnstone seen at CWP74 on each of the six days of 14–19 May was perhaps the same individual; indeed, were it a remnant of the seven there on the 13th, it could have been present for a whole week.

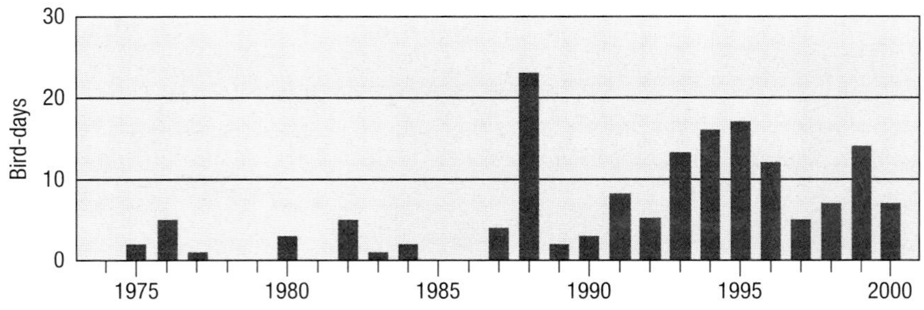

Figure 58. Turnstones *Arenaria interpres* in Wiltshire: annual totals of bird-days 1974–2000

NPA & SBE

Red-necked Phalarope

Phalaropus lobatus

Vagrant (2 records), breeds Iceland/north Europe, winters Arabian Sea

In summer, these hyperactive swimming waders, often conspicuously tame, have a circumpolar distribution in upper middle and low arctic latitudes, nesting in marsh tussocks and by shallow pools, frequently far inland and in Iceland even in sparsely vegetated heathland on lava desert. It has been estimated that in north Europe, excluding Russia, the breeding population of Red-necked Phalaropes is somewhere in the region of 65,500 to 94,300 pairs (*EBCC Atlas*), as many as 30,000 to 50,000 of them in Iceland (*CBWP*) and most of the rest in mainland Fenno-Scandia. The nesting range still extends south to the Faeroes and Great Britain – as well as to Ireland in the 1980s – but numbers in these countries have been decreasing since early in the 19th century. More recently, whereas there were still 54–65 pairs in Scotland and Ireland in 1968 (Everett 1971, *1968–72 Atlas*), the Scottish population had by 2000 – though that was a particularly poor year – been reduced to just 13 known nesting males in Shetland and a handful of mostly non-breeders elsewhere (*RBBP*), while no evidence of any nesting was recorded in Ireland in the 1990s, apart from a single phalarope seen at the last Irish breeding site in one year (*Irish Bird Reports*).

In winter, the world population of Red-necked Phalaropes is, so far as known, concentrated in three main marine areas: off western South America, in the Arabian Gulf, and around the East Indies. Those from Fenno-Scandia, north Russia and west Siberia make the long flights overland to offshore Arabia via staging posts on the Black and Caspian Seas and the Kazakhstan lakes, but whether the large numbers in Iceland migrate across the North Sea and Europe, or even join the Greenland population in heading for South America, is unclear.

In any event, surprisingly few are seen on migration in Great Britain (or in other eastern Atlantic coastal countries) at either season, and this species does not feature in coastal wrecks like the Grey Phalarope, though that may be partly because it generally migrates south earlier (predominantly July–September). During 1985–2000, there was an annual mean of only 34 British records away from known breeding sites, most in east coast counties in late May and August–October (Fraser & Rogers 2002).

These two phalaropes look very different in summer, but are easily confused in non-breeding plumages. A Red-necked listed by Smith (1887) as 'killed in a garden at Marlborough' in autumn 1869, 'turns out to be a Grey… (*M.C.N.H.*, 1904)' (Hony 1915a). Omitting that, and two others much more likely to have been Grey Phalaropes (both discussed under that species), there are only two sure records for Wiltshire, almost 150 years apart:

1841	May	Old Park brickfield, near Devizes	Male shot
1990	15 August	Lacock Gravel Pits	Juvenile

(See also page 727.)

RT

Grey Phalarope

Phalaropus fulicarius

Stormblown vagrant (50+ records), breeds Iceland/arctic Atlantic islands, winters western African seas

Grey Phalaropes are the more pelagic of the two European species of phalaropes, breeding on arctic islands and coasts of North America, Greenland and Eurasia, and migrating well offshore to winter at sea in the plankton-rich upwellings off western South America and western Africa. In Europe, where they nest regularly only in Iceland, Svalbard, Bear Island and Novaya Zemlya, there are no more than a few hundred breeding males – an estimated minimum of 145 or, at most, 1000 pairs (*EBCC Atlas*).

Though this species is highly adept at sea, numbers are sometimes wrecked on British and Irish coasts, driven inshore by the vigorous westerly gales of deep Atlantic depressions. During 1986–2000, the total of 2949 recorded in Great Britain was almost six times as many as that of migrating Red-necked Phalaropes (Fraser & Rogers 2002). Indeed, as the latter pass mostly down the east side of England, Wiltshire's ratio of records of Greys is, at more than 25:1, probably a better indication of the likely relative frequency of the two species in the west, particularly as late as October. Usually most Greys are seen on western and southwestern coasts in autumn and early winter, from September to December, but ones and twos often appear then on inland waters. In late September–October 1960, well over 7000 reached southwest England and southern Ireland (Ferguson-Lees & Williamson 1960): this still appears to have been the biggest number ever recorded in these islands, and represented far more than the combined breeding population of Iceland and arctic Europe – supporting the belief that many Grey Phalaropes from Greenland and at least northeast Canada migrate southeast across the Atlantic and travel down to wintering areas off western Africa (see discussion in *BWP*).

Smith (1887) described the Grey Phalarope as an 'accidental straggler' to Wiltshire and listed some 32 records, including no fewer than ten ('as well as several others') in the north and west of the county in 1870. (According to Witherby *et al* 1938–41, 1870 does not seem to have been as significant a year nationally for this species as were 1866 and 1869, but the Wiltshire list does include records for those also.) Smith noted, too, that the specimen from which Montagu took his description for his *Ornithological Dictionary* (1802) was obtained 'at a pond in Alderton'; that an adult in partial summer plumage had been 'killed in…August'; and that one had been 'knocked down with his oar by Mr. Edwards while rowing on the river near Salisbury'. Hony (1915a) added a further seven, including one from Downton 'in full summer plumage', but his only dated record was at Collingbourne Ducis in late September 1899.

No more were published until 1936, when one was found dead 'near Charlton' (it is not clear which one) on 17 September, another seen near Figheldean for several days at the end of that month, and a third found alive but exhausted near Martin (though Martin itself is just inside Hampshire) on 7 October (*WANHM*). Singletons were then seen at Lyneham from 28 October to 3 November 1954, at Fonthill Lake on 11 November 1960, and at Winterbourne Dauntsey in November 1963 (*WANHM*). In 1960, a phalarope near Maiden Bradley for two days in late September was not specifically identified, and the several observers of another at Coate Water during 4–9 October could not at the time agree on the species (*WANHM*) – but both of these occurred at the peak of the biggest ever recorded influx of Grey Phalaropes in southwest England (see above) and, indeed, the latter record is here now accepted as such.

During 1974–2000 there were only seven records:

1974	16–18 January	Poulshot	Eating earthworms in flood on green
1983	16 September	Fonthill Lake	Part of influx in southwest after gales
1984	4–8 October	Tidworth STW	Juvenile
	4–14 October	Coate Water	Juvenile
1987	16 October	CWP68	Two, after the Great Storm
1989	17–18 September	West Kennett	Juvenile, at farm slurry pit
2000	7 December	Membury	Dead on road in Wiltshire near M4 Services

Thus, six were seen in the 1980s, and none in the 1990s. It is worth adding that 1987 and 1989 were the two biggest autumns for Grey Phalaropes in Great Britain during the last 15 years of the 20th century, and that the annual mean number of records during 1987–89 was 351, twice that of the 1990s at only 167 (Fraser & Rogers 2002).

(See also page 727.)

RT & IJF-L

Pomarine Skua

Stercorarius pomarinus

Vagrant (1–2 records), breeds arctic Eurasia/America, winters at sea off West Africa

On its nesting grounds, the Pomarine Skua feeds almost exclusively on rodents; thus, it much depends on the population cycles of lemmings, whose abundance fluctuates regionally according to a three-year cycle, and so its breeding areas vary annually (Furness 1987). The species has a poorly defined and relatively restricted summer range in the coastal tundra from north Russia across Siberia to Alaska, Canada and west Greenland. Adults move south at the end of August, juveniles in late September and October. In the Atlantic, migrating Pomarine Skuas generally avoid coasts and so are only rarely seen from land. Key wintering areas are tropical waters north of the equator, and most of the migrants that pass near or over Great Britain are likely to winter off West Africa. First-year Pomarines often stay south, while adults pass through British waters in April–May.

Not surprisingly, Wiltshire has had just two records of this pelagic migrant. The first was originally square-bracketed by Hony (1914a) because he thought that the observer was 'not quite sure of the identification'. Subsequently, however, after details had been published (Robinson 1914), Hony (1915a) felt able to state that 'Mr. H. W. Robinson records an immature specimen which was shot at Sherstone [now Sherston] about thirty years ago [thus, at some date in the mid 1880s], and is preserved in a farmhouse at Common Wood'. Peirson (1959) also accepted this record without reservation.

The second came about 100 years later, when one of a party of seven skuas flying over Freshbrook, Swindon, on 11 November 1985, was clearly identified as a pale-morph Pomarine and, although the observer considered that five of the other six were probably also Pomarines, the record was accepted simply as one Pomarine and 'six skua species'. (One of these six was identified at the time as an Arctic Skua and has now been accepted as such.) This occurrence formed part of an influx that month of Pomarines along the coasts of Great Britain and to a lesser extent inland (Fox & Aspinall 1987).

KJG

Arctic Skua

Stercorarius parasiticus

Vagrant (10 records), breeds northern Britain/ Eurasia/America, pelagic in winter

Although all skuas will harry other birds to force them to drop or disgorge their food, the Arctic Skua is a year-round specialist in this form of food-piracy – known as kleptoparasitism – usually attacking smaller seabirds, particularly Kittiwakes, terns and auks. Its breeding range stretches across the higher latitudes of Eurasia, North America and Greenland, and extends farther south than those of other skuas. It is estimated that between 15,000 and 35,000 pairs of Arctic Skuas breed in the northeast Atlantic region (Stroud *et al* 2001).

One of the most southerly populations is in north Scotland, where some 3400 pairs were estimated in the mid 1980s, mostly in Shetland and Orkney (Lloyd *et al* 1991, *1988–91 Atlas*). But the collapse there by the early 1990s of stocks of sand-eels – a chief prey of the local seabirds, which Arctic Skuas then steal – caused a decline in the numbers of seabirds to parasitise, while an increase in Great Skuas, which compete with Arctics for breeding areas, saw a reduction in the latter's population to just over 2100 pairs in 1998–2000 (*Seabird 2000*).

Arctic Skuas generally winter off the coasts of South America, southern Africa and Australia. On migration they are commoner than other skuas along British shores, where southward movement is a leisurely affair, lasting from early August well into October, and shows some correlation with that of their Arctic Tern victims; the spring passage is most evident in April–May.

Most of those in Wiltshire have been in autumn. Three in the 19th century, all shot, were at Pewsey in November 1867 (Buxton 1981, though source unknown), at Heytesbury in October 1879 (Smith 1887), and an immature at Martinsell in 1881 (Hart Smith 1887). There were then no more until one was found dead under high tension wires at Wilsford (not 'Wishford' as in *BB* 32: 280 and Peirson 1959) in October 1938, after which another 38 years passed before the start of a spate of six records during 1976–91:

1976	4 September	Little Durnford	Four immatures flying south
1985	19 October	CWP	Dark morph
	10 November	CWP68	Pale-morph adult
	11 November	Freshbrook, Swindon	Pale morph with 1–6 Pomarines
1989	9 September	CWP68	Dark-morph adult, flew southwest
1991	9 September	CWP32	Harried gulls and tern, flew northwest

The one over Freshbrook, Swindon, on 11 November 1985 was seen with six other skuas, five of which were considered to be Pomarines though only one was clearly identified as that species (*qv*); the Arctic was queried by association at the time, but is now considered a valid record.

A juvenile skua on Boscombe Down airfield on 9–10 October 1978 'was reluctant to fly far and… walked to within 5 m' of the observer; it was published in *Hobby* as 'probably an Arctic', but there is no description to rule out the possibility of a juvenile Long-tailed. A dark-morph skua reported on the Wiltshire/Gloucester border on 27 January 1974 also cannot be identified to species and the observer is not certain that it flew over Wiltshire.

KJG

Long-tailed Skua

Stercorarius longicaudus

Vagrant (2 records), breeds north Eurasia/America, highly pelagic in winter

This is the smallest of the skuas, though the elegant adult has remarkably long central tail-feathers; it is also the least frequently seen in Great Britain. The Long-tailed Skua's breeding range is circumpolar in both high arctic and subarctic regions, extending south to southern Norway in Europe and to similar latitudes in eastern Asia and eastern Canada; its wintering areas are poorly known: although there are indications of general dispersal in the Atlantic and the Pacific between 40°S and 50°S, concentrations of immatures have been recorded close to both southern African and South American coasts (Furness 1987). In summer this species feeds largely on small rodents, but in the rest of the year is the most pelagic of the skuas, living by picking small fish and other items from the surface of the sea.

Long-tailed Skuas begin their autumn migration earlier than other skuas, passing through British waters from the beginning of August, but they are so highly pelagic away from the breeding grounds that they are rarely observed from land. Spring passage through British waters occurs mainly in May. The first Wiltshire record was of one picked up dead at Calstone in May 1881; shot marks were found when it was skinned (Hony 1915a). The second was in autumn, well over a century later: on 12 September 1998, one with damaged tail-streamers was watched descending from a considerable height during a sudden squall over Salisbury Electricity Depot and then flew only 30 m above the observer before climbing again and disappearing. Although the main published account (Blamey 2000) did not mention age, this bird was referred to as an adult in the systematic list in *Hobby*, but it has now been shown that it must have been in either second- or, possibly, third-summer plumage (Combridge & Edwards 2003).

KJG

Great Skua

Stercorarius skua

Vagrant (13 records), breeds Scotland/Iceland/ north Europe, pelagic in winter

The Great Skua, or 'Bonxie' to use its widely favoured Norse name, is the only native representative of the larger skuas in the northern hemisphere, where its breeding range is restricted to relatively few locations in the northeast Atlantic and around the North and Barents Seas. The world population was recently estimated at around 16,000 pairs, all but about 700 of them in Scotland and Iceland (*Seabird 2000*); indeed, most of the other areas involved – including Svalbard, Norway and northernmost Russia – were colonised only in the 20th century.

This species favours coastal moorland close to seabird concentrations, feeding extensively by predation, piracy and scavenging. Colonies on Foula and Unst (Shetland) were first documented in 1774, but persecution held numbers low during the 19th century – despite pleas by Shetlanders for these birds to be spared, because their aggressive behaviour towards other predators, especially White-tailed Fish-eagles, provided some protection for lambs (Furness 1987, *1875–1900 Atlas*). Conservation measures have since seen numbers increase markedly in parts of Scotland, so much so that the breeding population there reached 7600 pairs in the late 1980s and 9600 in 1998–2002, representing 60 per cent of the world total (*Seabird 2000*).

Some immatures wander as far south as West Africa and (particularly those from Iceland) even across the Atlantic to both North and South America, whereas adults winter 'mostly in the Bay of Biscay, on the Iberian coast and in the western Mediterranean' (*Migration Atlas*). The breeding population returns in late March and April. Migrants occur off all British coasts and occasionally far inland.

Wiltshire had nine records in the 19th century (Smith 1887), the first 'killed by Mr. Hooper, of Lavington' in December 1857 and the second killed at Wedhampton in 1861. A 'young female' was shot at Heytesbury in September 1863 and another individual there in the early 1880s. Meanwhile, one was 'taken' at Swindon in May 1864, the only recorded Wiltshire date that was not during August–January. One with a broken wing was being attacked by Rooks at Avebury in January 1872 and then there were no fewer than three quite separate records in 1882. In contrast, only four were recorded in the whole of the 20th century, although the species became far more numerous then in Scotland (even if it decreased somewhat in Iceland):

1987	16 October	White Sheet Hill	One in flight near Ansty
1990	4 February	Southwick	Moribund adult, died next day
1998	4 January	near Imber	Preening on ground, soon left
1999	3 July	Porton Down	One flying west

The last was an unusual date, so it is interesting to note that what was presumably the same individual had been seen a little earlier that same day, also flying west, about 65 km away at Eversley Gravel Pit (Hampshire). Those in 1987 and 1998 both followed periods of strong winds, in the first case the 'Great Storm' of October that year.

KJG

Mediterranean Gull

Larus melanocephalus

Scarce but increasing visitor, most months, breeds Europe/some in Britain, winters coasts of west Europe/Mediterranean

Mediterranean Gulls underwent a marked expansion in breeding range during the last decades of the 20th century, and became regular if rare visitors to north Wiltshire in the 1990s. In the early 1950s, the world breeding population was still largely concentrated on the Black Sea coast of the Ukraine, apart from smaller numbers in Turkey and the Balkans, and sporadic nesting in the Netherlands from 1933 (Voous 1960). The Ukrainian population increased to a maximum of 336,000 pairs in 1983, but in subsequent years severe flooding, and perhaps predation by foxes, caused major fluctuations and a general decline, so that by 1994 numbers had been reduced to about 60,000 pairs (Ardamatskaya 1998).

Table 74. Mediterranean Gulls *Larus melanocephalus* in Wiltshire: annual totals 1990–2000

	90	91	92	93	94	95	96	97	98	99	00
Birds	0	0	2	2	3	6	5	9	10	11	7

Table 75. Mediterranean Gulls *Larus melanocephalus* in Wiltshire: totals by arrival months 1990–2000

	Jan	Feb	Mar	Apr	May	Jun	Jul	Aug	Sep	Oct	Nov	Dec
Adults	1	7	5	0	0	0	10	0	0	1	0	1
1st-years	1	2	3	1	1	0	4	0	2	1	3	0
Juveniles	0	0	0	0	0	0	5	7	0	0	0	0
Totals	2	9	8	1	1	0	19	7	2	2	3	1

Meanwhile, however, irregular colonisation had started in Hungary and Germany in the 1950s, in the Czech Republic, France, Belgium and England in the 1960s, and elsewhere west to Spain, north to Denmark and east to the Sea of Azov in the 1970s and 1980s (*CBWP*). By 1999, about 1000 pairs were breeding in northwest Europe, 900 of them in the Netherlands and Belgium, the rest in Great Britain, France and Germany, mostly within Black-headed Gull colonies (P Meininger) and it is with flocks of that species that they are usually found in Wiltshire. Mediterranean Gulls first bred in Great Britain in 1968, and by 2000 no fewer than 90–109 pairs were nesting in southern England (*RBBP*). Outside the breeding season, they are found throughout the Mediterranean and Black Seas, and along North Sea and Atlantic coasts from Denmark to northwest Morocco.

The first Wiltshire record was an adult at Hilperton on 18 February 1973 (*WANHM*). Single adults were then seen at Langford Lakes on 18 April 1982 and at CWP on 2 April 1989, and a juvenile (or possibly two individuals, as one observer noted plumage differences) at CWP on five days during 24 August to 2 September 1989 (*Hobby*). There were no further records until 1992, after which the species was seen annually (table 74), the majority at CWP. The exceptions were single observations at Cricklade (Eysey Manor Farm), Liddington, Bradford-on-Avon and Britford, singletons at Corsham Lake in each of the five years 1994–98 (first-winter, 'immature', then adult in winter or summer plumage on the last three occasions) and four records at Swindon (Southbrook School playing field) during 1998–2000. All bar one were present for just a single day.

Numbers of adults reach a peak in February–March, perhaps as they are moving back to their nesting colonies, and again in July when they disperse after breeding, whereas immatures are more evenly distributed through the year, and juveniles appear only in July–August (table 75). Sightings at CWP of three Mediterranean Gulls with inscribed white rings on their legs have shown a direct link between Wiltshire and the Dutch breeding population (P Meininger):

1. Juvenile, 4 August 1998 – ringed as chick, Volkerakmeer (Zuid-Holland), 17 June 1998.
2. First-summer, 22 July 1998 – ringed as chick, Kreekak Oost (Zeeland), 2 June 1997. Also seen Lowestoft (Suffolk), 19 September to 26 December 1997 and 19 August 1998 to March 1999.
3. Adult, 27 February 1999 – ringed as chick, Volkerakmeer (Zuid-Holland), 16 June 1995. Also seen northern France, June 1997, April 1998, June 1999; Rye (Sussex), 10–18 April 1998; southern Ireland, 30 August 1998.

It proved impossible to read the inscriptions on two others at CWP with white rings, but both were considered to be different individuals from those above. These rings are used only in the Netherlands and Belgium, so it seems likely that many of our Mediterranean Gulls originate from that region.

KJG

Laughing Gull

Larus atricilla

Vagrant (1 record), breeds eastern North America, winters south to Brazil

As daylight faded on 9 August 1996, three dedicated gull-watchers in the WOS hide at CWP68 were rewarded by the appearance of a moulting adult Laughing Gull in the regular pre-roosting flock of Black-headed Gulls (Adams 1997). It was not present at dawn the following day. Laughing Gulls breed on west Atlantic and Caribbean coasts from the United States south to Venezuela, and locally on the Pacific coast of Mexico. Northern populations migrate south in winter, the range then extending from North Carolina south to northern Brazil and also northern Chile. Just over 90 vagrants had been recorded in Great Britain by the end of 2000 (*BBRC*), although there was no obvious seasonal pattern and several were long-stayers; 1996 was a bumper year nationally, including three others in August and seven in total.

(See also page 727).

KJG

Little Gull

Larus minutus

Regular migrant, rare winter, breeds northeast Europe, winters western coasts

Little Gulls nest mainly in northeast Sweden, Finland, eastern Europe and patchily across northern Asia, but also sporadically, or in tiny numbers, as far west as Great Britain and western France. On the other side of the Atlantic, a small breeding population in the Great Lakes region, established in 1962, has now extended to Hudson Bay (*CBWP*, Sibley 2000). Europe's Little Gulls winter mainly in coastal areas, from the Baltic and North Sea west around (including some Atlantic islands) to the Mediterranean, Black and Caspian Seas. The European breeding population is increasing and, excluding Russia (which probably holds a similar number), has been estimated at between 13,000 and 16,300 pairs, about two-thirds of them in Finland (*EBCC Atlas*), a country which this species did not colonise until 1879 and which still held only 200 pairs in the 1950s (Merikallio 1958).

That same period has seen a dramatic change in the status of Little Gulls in Great Britain. Pairs even attempted to nest on six occasions during 1975–91 (*CBWP*), though not apparently since (*RBBP*). Until the early 1950s, these gulls were no more than scarce passage migrants, largely in autumn, along the east and south coasts of England, though spring and autumn flocks of several tens, once even 135, had started to appear in the Firths of Tay and Forth from the late 1940s. A wider increase began in the 1950s along the North Sea and Channel coasts of England, and in the 1960s especially in eastern Scotland and the Irish Sea; in the early 1970s, annual totals of several hundreds were being recorded along various coasts, and even inland English counties together amassed three figures a year (Hutchinson & Neath 1978). Since then, as the Finnish and north Russian populations

Table 76. Little Gulls *Larus minutus* in Wiltshire: annual totals 1990–2000

	90	91	92	93	94	95	96	97	98	99	00
Birds	7	9	0	9	11	7	36	14	7	20	11

Table 77. Little Gulls *Larus minutus* in Wiltshire: totals by arrival months 1990–2000
Two long-stayers at CWP – one January to March 1995, the other February to March 1998 – have each been included only for the month in which it was first found

	Jan	Feb	Mar	Apr	May	Jun	Jul	Aug	Sep	Oct	Nov	Dec
Birds	1	1	5	88	18	0	3	2	11	1	1	0

have continued to grow, much larger concentrations have been seen, most spectacularly off Yorkshire coasts. Day-counts of 1000 and over 2000 in September 1982 off Flamborough Head (Dunn & Lassey 1985) were followed over the next 15 years by at least four counts of over 3000 or even 4000 there or in adjacent Bridlington Bay, mostly in October – only to be eclipsed by a 'remarkable gathering of 10,000+ during calm conditions on the evening' of 12 September 2003 off Spurn Point (Hartley 2004). Sizeable totals have been recorded elsewhere, including hundreds in Merseyside in the 1980s (Smith 1987, Messenger 1993) and several thousands off the coast of Co Durham in the early 1990s (*Durham Bird Report*).

On a very small scale, this increase has been reflected in Wiltshire, where Little Gulls were formerly very rare. Only three were recorded in the 19th century: at Rodbourne (Swindon) in 1848 (Marsh 1842–62), at Upton Scudamore in January 1869 (Smith 1887), and on Rockley Down on 14 February 1870 (im Thurn 1876), the last dated as 28 March 1870 by Smith (1887); though im Thurn also noted that 'About that time the species was unusually abundant throughout England'. Another 60 or more years were to pass before the next published record. After one at Knowle in 1935 (Peirson 1939), an immature was provisionally identified at gravel workings… between Marlborough and Hungerford for two or three days after 22 September 1936' and one was found dead by the Kennet & Avon Canal at Savernake Station in February 1950 (both *WANHM*). Fourteen years later, an immature that stayed at Coate Water from 19 December 1964 was beginning to moult into summer plumage when last seen on 6 March 1965 (*WANHM*, Webber 1968).

Thus, just seven Little Gulls had been found in Wiltshire before the 1970s when, however, observations began to be more regular and two of 11 records involved doubletons; all were during migration periods except for three in January and early February, which are likely to have been displaced inland by winter storms; nine were either at Coate Water or Liden Lagoon, and only two at CWP (*WANHM*, *Hobby*). The 1980s produced no fewer than 38 records (20 of them at CWP and 11 at Coate Water), involving a total of 48 birds, in every month apart from January, February and July, but with 19 in August–September the peak.

Despite marked annual fluctuations, Little Gulls clearly became much commoner during 1990–2000, when they were recorded in every year except 1992 (table 76); no fewer than 114 of the 131 were seen at CWP, and 79 (60 per cent) were adults. This status change is perhaps partly the result of better observer coverage and more extensive wetland habitats at CWP, but surely primarily because both breeding range and numbers are expanding in Europe. Although the monthly totals show a small peak in September, most now occur in spring, especially in April (table 77). In 1980–89 just 11 per cent of the total were in April, but in 1990–2000 as many as 67 per cent. The destination of these spring migrants remains unknown, but it seems likely that they are from the Fenno-Scandian population.

(See also page 727.)

KJG

Sabine's Gull

Larus sabini

Vagrant (2 records) from Greenland/Canada, pelagic in winter to South Africa

Sabine's Gulls, which have a distinctive three-tone triangled wing-pattern, nest mainly in the Arctic of Siberia, Alaska, northern Canada and Greenland. Outside the breeding season they are almost exclusively pelagic, the populations of Siberia and Alaska migrating to the Pacific side of South America, and those of Canada and Greenland wintering off southwest Africa. Always scarce in Europe, even in coastal waters, these smallish gulls are recorded mostly in the west during their southerly autumn migration. In Great Britain, they are generally found between mid August and early November, the majority in the first ten days of September: over 700 were seen in 1987, but the annual average of records during 1980–2000 was about 170; most occur in the southwest, particularly Cornwall, but also north to the Western Isles and small numbers regularly in the North Sea (Fraser & Rogers 2002).

The relatively few inland records generally follow periods of strong winds. Elkins & Yésou (1998) have shown that the largest numbers of Sabine's Gulls in western France and southern England, mainly adults, are associated with deep depressions moving across, or to the north of, the Bay of Biscay. Wiltshire's two records occurred in such conditions and are set out here against the background of relevant influxes noted by those authors. After severe westerly gales on the 2 September 1983, an adult was found at CWP26 on the 3rd (*Hobby*); about 100 were recorded at St Ives (Cornwall) that same day and a further 200 elsewhere in Great Britain that autumn. A similar weather pattern developed on 6–7 September 1995, and a juvenile was seen briefly at CWP68 on the 8th; although few were found in Great Britain at that time, over 850 were counted on the west coast of France on the 7th, at Les Sables d'Olonne (Vendée).

KJG

Black-headed Gull

Larus ridibundus

Local breeder, common winter/passage from Iceland/northwest Europe

Misleadingly named, as its head is no darker than chocolate-brown in the breeding season and mainly white in winter, the Black-headed Gull might better be termed the 'Laughing Gull' – its scientific name means just that, and it is known as such in most other European languages – but this particular English vernacular is already used for a North American species, *Larus atricilla*, which has occurred in Wiltshire as a vagrant. Here, as elsewhere in Great Britain, Black-headed Gulls are familiar sights in both rural and urban habitats, where, for example, they exploit farmland, rubbish dumps, parks and wetlands in their search for food.

These small, elegant gulls breed from Iceland, the Faeroes, Ireland and Iberia across the middle latitudes of Eurasia to Kamchatka and Ussuriland; also, since the last quarter of the 20th century, some have nested, and are increasing, in North America (Grant 1986,

CBWP). The European population, excluding Russia, has been put at about two million pairs (*EBCC Atlas*). In winter, many of those that nest in Eurasia move south, some reaching sub-Saharan Africa, southern Arabia, the Indian subcontinent and southeast Asia, though ringing recoveries indicate that post-breeding dispersal from British colonies, especially of juveniles, is largely restricted to Britain and Ireland (*Migration Atlas*).

Indeed, of eight recoveries in Wiltshire of Black-headed Gulls ringed elsewhere in Great Britain, six had been marked as chicks in June–July in Hampshire (three), Kent, Essex and Oxfordshire: five of those were found dead, and one 'sick', all but one in July–September of the same year and the other in June of the following year. The remaining two had been ringed as adults in Worcestershire and Warwickshire in January 1979 and January 1980, respectively, and found dead in north Wiltshire in December 1981 and May 1983: the second at least seems likely to have been of British origin.

Burton *et al* (2003) estimated that a minimum of 1·7 million Black-headed Gulls winter in Great Britain. Over two-thirds of those in England and Wales at that season are thought to come from the Continent, originating mostly from the Netherlands, Denmark, Fenno-Scandia and the Baltic States, but also others from Iceland or from Russia and elsewhere in eastern Europe (*Migration Atlas*). Nine marked abroad and found in Wiltshire had come from Estonia, Lithuania and the Netherlands (two each), and Finland, Latvia and Denmark (one each). The last of those had been colour-ringed as an adult in a Danish colony on 20 March 1997 and been seen subsequently in Denmark on a number of occasions during 1997–99 (K Pedersen), in which time it also appeared at CWP68 on 7 March 1998. One of the Dutch two, marked with green wing-tags at Westernieland (Noordholland) on 5 July 2000, was sighted just over 15 weeks later, also at CWP68, on 22 October.

The numbers of Black-headed Gulls breeding in England fell during the late 18th and early 19th centuries, mainly as a result of marshland enclosure and drainage, and the collection of eggs for food, a trend that was not stemmed until the Sea Birds Preservation Act of 1869. The population began to recover shortly before 1900, and in 1938 a survey found some 38,000 pairs in England and Wales (*1875–1900 Atlas*). Fifty years later, the *1988–91 Atlas* estimated a minimum of 147,000 breeding pairs in Great Britain as a whole, but demonstrated that just under one fifth of all colonies had disappeared since the time of the *1968–72 Atlas*. Movements of and between colonies do occur, however, in response to such factors as disturbance and changes in water levels, and, because of differing extents of coverage during national censuses, it is difficult to be precise about population trends in recent years. Thus, the latest estimate of 128,000 pairs in Great Britain (*Seabird 2000*) may well represent continuing stability in total numbers, although there had been a marked reduction in range and a 50 per cent decrease in occupied 10-km squares (mainly inland) since the *1988–91 Atlas*.

Smith (1887) wrote that the Black-headed Gull was 'Occasionally... found in North Wilts' but that 'It is often seen on Salisbury Plain and on the downs of South Wiltshire, following the ploughman... greedily devouring the grubs that are thus exposed'. In 1930, Black-headed Gulls were described as 'Quite common on the Plain and in S. Wilts', and a 'great increase' was noted in 1936 when they and Herring Gulls were 'well distributed in the county... particularly in the vicinity of Salisbury' (*WANHM*). The largest flock reported in the 1950s was of about 800 near Chippenham on 3 March 1952, but at least five other three-figure counts were recorded in that decade (*WANHM*).

Peirson (1959) knew of this species as 'A winter visitor mainly; at other times of year scarce and occasional'; he also noted that it was common from 'late October to April' along the Salisbury Avon, and that it was to be seen 'in good and increasing numbers up the Bristol Avon and of recent years quite commonly to Coate Water and the north-east... where it used to be distinctivly [*sic*] scarce'. In the 1960s and early 1970s, winter numbers continued to increase and a count of about 1000 near Cricklade in February 1968 was then a Wiltshire record; Corsham Lake also became a favoured site (*WANHM*). Buxton (1981) emphasised the 'large increase in the wintering population during the past 25 years'. A roost at CWP26 was considered to number about 10,000 on 28 February 1982 and other large winter totals were recorded with increasing regularity at CWP during the late 1980s, including estimates of 17,500 in January 1987 and 10,000 in February 1989. Elsewhere, there were notable counts of 4000 at Cricklade in January 1985, 2000 at Swindon refuse tip in December 1986, and 1500 at Castle Eaton in December 1989.

The maximum estimates of Black-headed Gulls at CWP over the ten winters from 1990/91 to 1999/2000 (table 78), like those at other places where concentrations occur, are hardly complete enough for any certainty about trends. Extrapolation from the winter tetrad counts suggests a Wiltshire daytime total of roughly 12,100 – a relatively small proportion of the 831,000 Black-headed Gulls found roosting at inland localities in England in a national survey in 1993 (Burton *et al* 2003) – but that may be in part because not all such major sites as landfills and rubbish tips happened to be in the sample tetrads covered by the WOS winter survey.

On the other hand, no counts of gull roosts (of any species) were made in Wiltshire during that 1993 national survey. Yet up to five gull species have long regularly roosted at CWP26 and probably also CWP68/74. Elsewhere, Black-headed Gulls in flocks exceeding 1000 were recorded during 1990–2000 at Cricklade, Swindon STW, Sevington, Calne, Corsham Lake (table 78), Melksham, Whaddon near Trowbridge, Bradford-on-Avon, Parsonage Down and Broad Chalke. A few such flocks may represent overnight roosts, but most are daytime or pre-roost gatherings, which vary from week to week and from year to year: some sites are not even regularly used and the numbers in the Wiltshire section of CWP are also affected by the gulls' choice of pits in the Gloucestershire part. Generally speaking, on both sides of the county boundary, only the larger pits attract high numbers.

For the winter tetrad survey, the map shows the highest numbers away from CWP to have been in the Swindon area, along the Bristol Avon, and in southwest and southeast

Table 78. Black-headed Gulls *Larus ridibundus* in Wiltshire: peak winter counts at two key sites 1990/91–1999/00

	90/91	91/92	92/93	93/94	94/95	95/96	96/97	97/98	98/99	99/00
CWP	5000	1000	5000	500	2250	800	1500	2000	3000	1000
	Feb	Mar	Jan	Jan	Oct	Jan/Mar	Sep	Aug	Dec	Mar
Corsham Lake	1000	2000	850	750	1000	600	800	425	520	955
	Feb	Jan	Feb	Feb/Mar	Oct	Feb	Mar	Jan	Oct	Feb

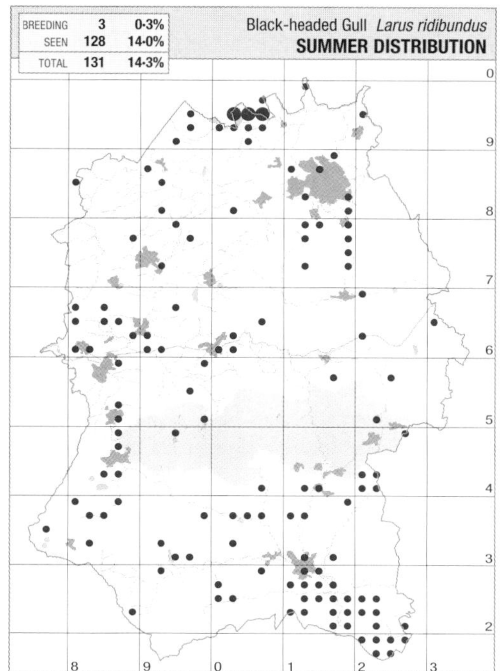

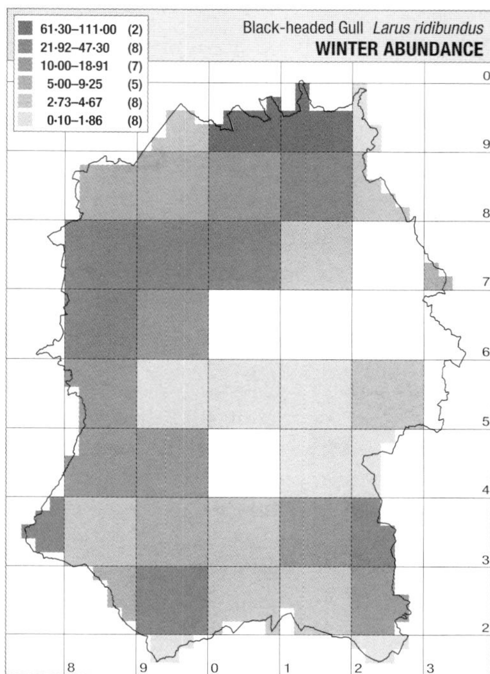

Wiltshire, whereas the species was scarce on the Marlborough Downs and Salisbury Plain, and was not recorded at all in the sample tetrads in some 10-km squares. It should be noted, however, that many of the gulls seen here roost outside the county, for example arriving and departing each day from the Severn Estuary, from Chew Valley Lake and other Somerset reservoirs, and also from Hampshire up the Test and the Salisbury Avon, to feed on Wiltshire's farmland and rubbish tips.

Wiltshire's first breeding attempt by Black-headed Gulls came in 1993, when two pairs laid eggs at CWP74, but the nests became flooded. In 1994, ten pairs established a colony, shared with Common Terns, on a gravel spit between CWP68 and 74, but only one was successful, raising two young; the remaining nine nests were deserted, probably because of disturbance or predation by the foxes that were regularly seen close by. Nesting was not attempted in 1995, but 11 pairs of Black-headed Gulls bred successfully in 1996 on a floating raft in CWP74 that had been provided in the previous year by WOS for Common Terns (*qv*).

A second raft built in 1997 (with a grant from English Nature) increased the numbers that year to 15 pairs, all of which fledged young. Also in 1997, some nested on gravel islands at CWP83 and CWP76, but those at the former site failed and only a single pair succeeded at the latter. The rafts on CWP74, shared with the Common Terns for which they were intended, have continued to provide safe sites for 18 Black-headed Gull nests in 1998, 26 in 1999 and 40 in 2000. Ten of the 18 Black-headed Gulls ringed in the county during 1965–2000 were nestlings on the CWP rafts in 1999, but none has yet been recovered.

The colonisation of the county is something of a contrast to the apparent slight decline nationally and those at CWP are the only Black-headed Gulls breeding inland in the whole of southern England, apart from 22 pairs in Berkshire (*Seabird 2000*) and about 150 in Oxfordshire (I Lewington). Although breeding was proved in only three Wiltshire tetrads during the summer distribution survey, the species was seen in just over 90 others. Summer records away from CWP probably related to individuals foraging inland from the coastal colonies around the Solent (Hampshire) and perhaps also Poole Harbour (Dorset), for these are the only other significant breeding areas within striking distance of Wiltshire.

(See also page 724.)

KJG

Ring-billed Gull

Larus delawarensis

Vagrant (5 records), breeds south Canada/north USA, winters south to Caribbean

This North American gull had never been identified in Great Britain until one was found in West Glamorgan in 1973, but there followed a trickle of records and then a huge upsurge in numbers from 1981. The annual average of new arrivals through the 1980s was 47, and through the 1990s no fewer than 76; this is now one of the two most frequent and regular of all transatlantic vagrants, so much so that over 1300 had been found in Great Britain, particularly in southwest coastal counties, by the end of 2000 (Fraser & Rogers 2002). The species was undoubtedly overlooked in the past because of its similarity to the darker, slightly smaller and thinner-billed Common Gull. Identification techniques and optical aids improved greatly during the last third of the 20th century, and many gull flocks are now regularly checked for vagrants.

But distributional factors have been involved in what is also a clear increase in vagrancy. Ring-billed Gulls breed in two large but discrete regions, both straddling southern Canada and the northern United States, and winter mostly along seaboards south to Mexico and the West Indies. During the 20th century, the eastern population, extending east from the Great Lakes and St Lawrence River, has shown dramatic increases in both numbers and eastward range expansions since the 1970s (*eg* Vinicombe 1985). By December much of this eastern population is at latitudes equivalent to Iberia and northwest Africa, and the hypothesis that many may cross the Atlantic at these levels is supported by the number of records in France, Spain, Morocco and the Azores; many then move north in Europe and this results in a spring passage in western Britain and Ireland (see discussions in Vinicombe 1985 and *1981–84 Winter Atlas*).

Some return to favoured sites for several years, and distinguishing new arrivals from individuals that have become established in Europe can be difficult. Most apparent new arrivals in Great Britain are recorded between December and April, and all the five in Wiltshire have been found in that period (though some, of course, may have reached this country earlier and then become caught up in seasonal movements of Black-headed and Common Gulls):

1989	1 April	CWP68	Adult
1992	9–16 February	CWP26	Adult
	27 Nov–27 Feb **1993**	CWP, especially 26/73	Adult
1994	22–27 March	Ferndale Fields, Swindon	2nd-winter
1998	21 February	CWP26	2nd-winter, in flight

The long-stayer in 1992/93 was possibly the same individual as in the previous winter.

KJG

Common Gull

Larus canus

Common winter/passage from north Britain/ Iceland/north Europe

In summer, Common Gulls nest widely right across mainly northern Eurasia – from Iceland, Ireland and northeast France to Kamchatka and Sakhalin – and in Alaska and northwestern Canada. They are essentially northern gulls that colonised France, and several other countries south to Switzerland, Hungary and Ukraine, only in the 20th century. The British breeding population (almost entirely in Scotland, but locally and erratically south to Hampshire and Kent) numbered some 48,000 pairs in 1999–2002 (*Seabird 2000*) – a notable decline from the 68,000 estimated in the mid 1980s, although that earlier survey had been incomplete for this species (Lloyd *et al* 1991). Even so, it is still a significant proportion of the 416,000 to 558,000 pairs in Europe as a whole, excluding Russia (*EBCC Atlas*).

Most of the vast northern breeding range is vacated in winter, the species generally becoming much more coastal. In Europe, this means that Common Gulls are then found from the southern Barents Sea and the Baltic around the whole North Sea region and, especially in cold winters, sometimes south to the Atlantic coasts of Iberia and Morocco. Smaller numbers also winter by the Black, Caspian and Mediterranean Seas and along the larger rivers of, particularly, central Europe, but only from Denmark to north France and, above all, in Britain and Ireland are Common Gulls widespread far inland. The British winter population numbers at least 430,000 (Burton *et al* 2003), perhaps 635,000 (*1981–84 Winter Atlas*), but in any event Britain and Ireland may be Europe's most important wintering area for this species (*Migration Atlas*).

Those that nest in Scotland are partial migrants, the majority of ringing recoveries coming from within Britain and Ireland, but large numbers also arrive here from the Continent, especially from Fenno-Scandia, the Baltic States and western Russia, where the majority of the European breeding population is found (*Migration Atlas*). Of only three ringing recoveries involving Wiltshire, one had been marked as a nestling at Apealen (Norway) in June 1988 (found dead at RAF Lyneham just four months later) and another as an adult female at Burgtiefe in Schleswig-Holstein (Germany) in April 1993 (seen at CWP68 nearly two years later); the third, found dead in March 1976, had been ringed as an adult in Kent in February 1969, almost seven years earlier.

In 19th century Wiltshire – as probably in other southern inland counties then – the Common Gull evidently really was the commonest gull in winter. Indeed, im Thurn (1870) recorded that, as the most frequently encountered species, it lived up to its name, flocks moving from west to east and then turning south at Marlborough. Smith (1887) noted the Common Gull as 'an indefatigable attendant on the ploughshare', that it was 'very frequently met with' in 'southern parts', and that he had 'often seen it in North Wilts passing overhead, or perched on the downs'. Its status appears not to have changed significantly during the 20th century, though other gulls have become more numerous.

In 1930, 'Apparently this species predominates among the flocks of gulls which come into the county from the Severn' (*WANHM*). In the 1940s to 1970s, counts of 100 to 300 were frequently recorded, even 600 at Cole Park in March 1956 and 1000 following plough at Monkton Deverill in 1973, as well as other references to 'several hundreds' and 'very large flocks' (*WANHM*). Peirson (1959) simply referred to 'considerable numbers', but the details published in *WANHM* generally confirmed the importance of the west of the county for this species, particularly the northwest. Buxton (1981) thought it 'common', and Palmer (1991) described it as a 'common winter visitor and passage migrant'.

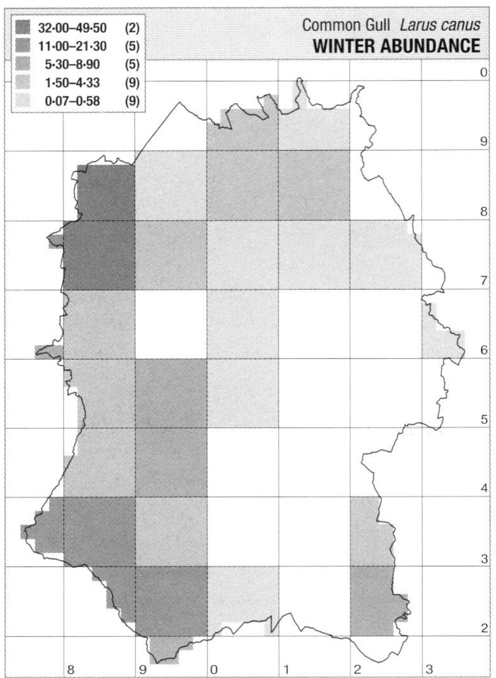

Common Gulls begin to appear in Wiltshire in early and mid July, numbers usually building up slowly through the autumn and peaking between January and March. By April most have returned to the breeding grounds, though a few stragglers, usually immatures, remain until early May. The latest specified spring date during 1974–2000 was 2–3 June 1985 (one at Boscombe Down) and the earliest specified return 21 June 1999 (adult at Swindon STW, first-summer at CWP68), but no dates were given in *Hobby* for a peak of five at CWP in June 1994 and 'A few non breeders regular at CWP May–June' in 1995.

While some of the many Common Gulls that feed on the Cotswolds (Gloucestershire/ Wiltshire) roost at CWP, most commute to spend the night on the Severn estuary – where the total can reach over 50,000 (BH Bailey) – and others may go to Chew Valley Reservoir (Somerset). The peak roost counts at CWP (table 79) appear to suggest a slow reduction in numbers there over the ten winters from 1990/91 to 1999/2000. During 1990–2000, flocks of 400 or more also occurred by day at Ludwell (1000, August 1990), Shirehill (615, January 1991), Sherston (450, January 1993), Mountain Bower (490, August 1993) and Corsham Lake (400, March 1996; 404, March 1999). All these other sites are in the west of the county where, indeed, the winter map shows Common Gulls to be most numerous. This distribution reflects the predominance of permanent pasture, though the species occurs also on winter wheat, sometimes on plough and even in open-field piggeries. Extrapolation from the winter tetrad counts indicates a total of just over 4000, a relatively small proportion of the 165,000 recorded at inland roosts in 1993 (Burton *et al* 2003).

Table 79. Common Gulls *Larus canus* in Wiltshire: peak winter roost counts at CWP 1990/91–1999/00

	90/91	91/92	92/93	93/94	94/95	95/96	96/97	97/98	98/99	99/00
Birds	200	300	200	45	200	180	65	110	100	120
Months	Feb	Jan/Feb	Jan	Jan	Feb	Feb	Feb	Feb	Mar	Mar

KJG

Lesser Black-backed Gull

Larus fuscus

Increasing passage/winter from Britain/Iceland/ north Europe, recent and spreading local breeder

The Lesser Black-backed is nowadays by far the most numerous big gull in Wiltshire, at all seasons clearly outnumbering the closely related Herring Gull. The taxonomy of the 'large white-headed gulls' of the *fuscus-cachinnans-argentatus* complex is confused and controversial, and subject to ongoing debate (*eg* Yésou 2002, see also references under Herring Gull), but, as defined in *BWP*, the Lesser Black-back's breeding range stretches from Iceland and western Iberia eastward to the Taimyr Peninsula in Siberia, and five subspecies can be distinguished.

Three of those subspecies breed in Europe: nominate *fuscus* (Fenno-Scandia and Russia, adult black above) has declined dramatically, whereas the two more westerly races – *intermedius* (Denmark, southern Norway and southwest Sweden, adult typically blackish above but variable in tone) and *graellsii* (Iceland, Great Britain, Ireland, western France and northwest Iberia, adult slate-grey above) – have both increased, the latter colonising Iberia as recently as the 1970s. Although *BWP* included the Netherlands – the country of origin of several colour-ringed Lesser Black-backs seen in Wiltshire – within the breeding range of *intermedius*, Malling Olsen & Larsson (2004) noted that those nesting in colonies near Rotterdam displayed a wide variation in mantle shade, from very pale to very dark, the majority being within the darker range of *graellsii*.

The breeding population of Lesser Black-backs in Europe, excluding Russia, has been estimated at between 212,000 and 230,000 pairs (*EBCC Atlas*). Of this total, around half – some 117,000 pairs – were nesting in Great Britain in 1998–2002, a marked increase over the 83,500 found in the mid 1980s (*Seabird 2000*). The largest colonies are in west and east Scotland, the Solway, Lancashire, west Wales, the Bristol Channel and Suffolk. Gull numbers in general have grown as a result of bird protection and the prevalence of such sources of waste food as open rubbish tips, though culling of the larger species as a reserve management practice and other forms of human intervention have caused local declines (Coulson 1991, *1988–91 Atlas*).

Although the race *graellsii* is migratory, over-wintering along the coasts of southern France, Spain, Portugal and northwest Africa, recent decades have witnessed exponentially increasing numbers staying as far north as most parts of Great Britain, especially in second-winter and older plumages. For example, a national survey found only 165 Lesser Black-backs wintering inland in England in 1953, but in repeat surveys at ten-year intervals the total counts grew to 6960 in 1963, to 15,823 in 1973, and to 36,154 in January 1983, before apparently dropping by a quarter to 27,228 in January 1993 (Burton *et al* 2003). Even allowing for the growth in numbers of observers and of sites covered, wintering Lesser Black-backs have undoubtedly increased since the 1950s, though the rates of change indicated by the totals quoted over the four ten-year periods should be treated with some caution.

Furthermore, while most juveniles still move southwest in autumn to winter along Atlantic coasts of France, Iberia and Morocco, analysis of those ringed in the Bristol Channel region now makes clear an increasing tendency for the adults and significant proportions of some other age-groups to dispense with migration and, instead, remain within Great Britain (Rock 2004b). The race *intermedius*, which likewise migrates southwest and shares the non-breeding range of *graellsii*, also occurs in Great Britain as a passage migrant and winter

Table 80. Lesser Black-backed Gulls *Larus fuscus* in Wiltshire: peak autumn (August–October) and winter (November–February) counts at CWP 1990/91–1999/00

Autumn counts are listed with those from the following winter (*eg* the autumn count for 1990 is listed in the 90/91 column)

	90/91	91/92	92/93	93/94	94/95	95/96	96/97	97/98	98/99	99/00
Autumn peak	2655	2235	1750	1450	1300	500	3000	6000	8000	900
Month	Sep	Oct	Sep	Oct	Oct	Aug	Sep	Sep	Sep	Oct
Winter peak	1750	1500	1569	909	800	700	600	1250	1350	1500
Month	Jan	Dec	Nov	Jan	Feb	Nov	Dec/Feb	Dec	Feb	Dec/Feb

visitor (*eg* Grant 1986). Contrary, however, to reports in some issues of *Hobby* (*eg* 22: 39), there have been no undoubted records of nominate *fuscus* ('Baltic Gull') in Wiltshire (see Combridge & King 1998 for discussion).

Smith (1887) noted that the Lesser Black-backed Gull came 'boldly inland' and he listed ten Wiltshire specimens, the first 'shot many years since... near Tilshead' and the earliest with a date at Bromham on 29 August 1865, whereas im Thurn (1870) had just one in his collection, shot at Rockley in March 1868, and considered it to be rarest of the three gulls seen regularly at Marlborough. Hony (1915a) made no mention of this species and the only record in *WANHM* during 1929–47 was of six at Marlborough Common on 13 September 1932; small but increasing numbers were then reported annually from 1948.

A decade later, Peirson (1959) found that Lesser Black-backs were by then 'seen every year, mostly in the west... usually in spring but also... autumn... a number of summer and winter records... numbers in winter have increased considerably near Keevil and Semington since 1954'. The species continued to become commoner in the county, so much so that Buxton (1981) was able to state that it was 'frequent... spring and autumn... quite large flocks in summer... Up to 500 at Swindon rubbish tip and smaller flocks occur in the Trowbridge, Keevil and Kingston Deverill areas. Numbers are much lower in winter but... more widespread'. Palmer (1991), for the 1980s, simply stated that it was a 'common passage migrant and winter visitor' without further qualification.

Nowadays Lesser Black-backed Gulls start to build up in Wiltshire in early July as they disperse from their breeding grounds, usually reaching a peak in early September during the main southward migration. Numbers then drop until the end of the year, when they peak again. In autumn, flocks of several hundred occur on freshly ploughed fields, but in winter the largest numbers are found feeding on refuse tips and roosting at CWP. The winter map shows this species to be most numerous then in the north of the county, and extrapolation from the sample tetrad counts indicates a total at that season of nearly 5900, a high figure when considered against the 60,800 found in Great Britain as a whole in January 1993.

The highest counts at CWP in autumn and winter during 1990–2000 (table 80) show considerable variations, but these may result as much from differences in observer effort as reflect true fluctuations. Many of the Lesser Black-backs that forage on Wiltshire farmland roost outside the county: for example, flocks can be seen over Salisbury Plain and southeast Wiltshire flying towards the Test and Hampshire Avon on winter afternoons and others in west and southwest Wiltshire heading to the Somerset reservoirs; it is also possible that some of those on the Cotswolds form part of the 15,000 roosting on the Upper Severn Estuary (Burton *et al* 2003).

The only Lesser Black-backed Gull ringed in the county during 1965–2000 was an adult caught at Coate Water on 13 September 1980, picked up 'sick or injured' at Worthing (Sussex) four days later and subsequently released there. Observations of Lesser Black-backs colour-ringed elsewhere have, however, enabled the origins and subsequent

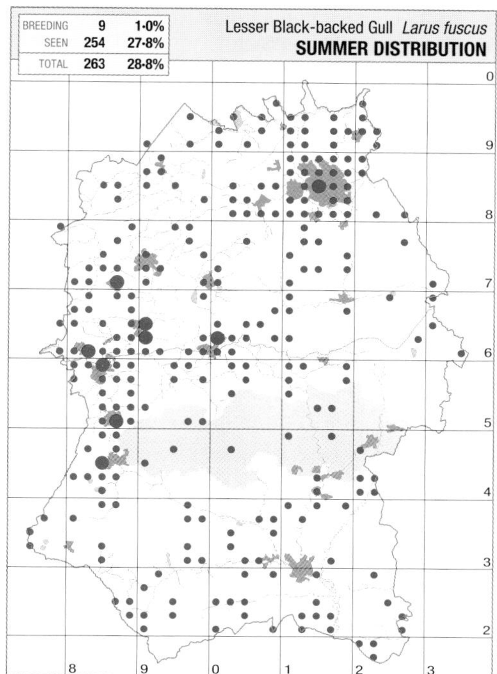

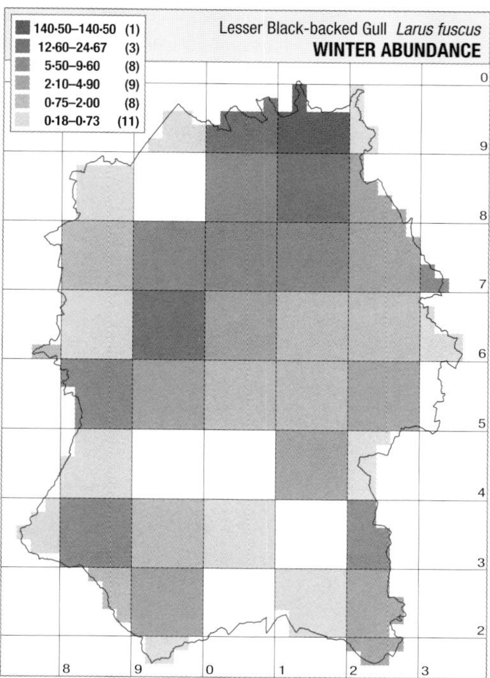

movements of quite a number of those seen in Wiltshire to be traced (Grearson 1998b, and subsequent additions in *Hobby*). From 1994 to early 1998, there were some 240 sightings of at least 156 colour-ringed individuals in the county. Of these, 99 had been marked as chicks in rooftop colonies in Bristol and eight similarly in Gloucester; seven others had hatched at Orford Ness (Suffolk) and six on Flat Holm (Glamorgan). A chick ringed on Walney Island (Cumbria) in 1981 and seen annually at CWP in 1995–98, always in late August or early September, was, at the age of 17 by the time of its last sighting, the oldest Lesser Black-back recorded in the county until another ringed in the same colony – also in 1981, but one day later – was killed when it hit electricity cables at Swindon on 29 February 2000, then in its 19th year.

Evidence of immigration from the Continent in autumn was provided by Wiltshire sightings of a total of 21 – some of them in company with individuals from Suffolk – that had been ringed as chicks in the Netherlands. In addition, a male of the south Scandinavian race *intermedius*, colour-ringed as a breeding adult in a Danish colony in June 1994, was seen at Calne on 10 October 1995. Others ringed as nesting adults came from Skomer (Pembrokeshire), Lancashire and Scotland. Many of the marked individuals recorded in Wiltshire have also been noted elsewhere, showing that there is clearly much local movement between refuse tips in the West Country and that some winter as far south as Iberia and North Africa

Wiltshire totals of Lesser Black-backs remain high from January to early March, but are much reduced by late March as most return to colonies elsewhere. In summer, since at least the 1980s, adults – usually in ones or twos, occasionally in small groups – may be seen floating by day over open country in the west of the county. Once assumed to be mainly non-breeding wanderers, flying gulls were specifically excluded from the summer tetrad instructions. Yet it is now clear that these are, and doubtless were then, part of the summer scene, for Wiltshire has its own small but increasingly significant urban gull colonies.

Table 81. Lesser Black-backed *Larus fuscus* and Herring Gulls *L. argentatus* in Wiltshire: total pairs and confirmed nests 2004 (after Rock 2003a, 2004a)

'Minimum' shows the number of confirmed nests (adults sitting or attending young) and 'Estimate' is based on gulls of breeding age in the vicinity of the colony (with adjustment for areas that could not be viewed); the ratio is of Lesser Black-backed to Herring Gull confirmed nests (Bradford-on-Avon data are from 2003; none was recorded there in 2004)

	Lesser Black-backed Gull		Herring Gull		
	Minimum	Estimate	Minimum	Estimate	Ratio
Chippenham	14	41	3	9	4·7:1
Melksham	16	33	3	6	5·3:1
Devizes	38	60	8	13	4·8:1
Trowbridge	61	125	11	23	5·5:1
Bradford-on-Avon	1	1	1	1	1·0:1
Westbury	30	60	12	24	2·5:1
Swindon	18	65	6	22	3·0:1
Totals	178	385	44	98	4·0:1

Lesser Black-backs were much slower than Herring Gulls (*qv*) to start nesting on roof tops, even in coastal towns: the first reported instance in Great Britain was in south Wales in 1945 or 1946; two colonies were known by 1960–64 and five, with a total of 61–62 pairs, by 1969–70, still mainly in south Wales but including one pair in Sussex and two small colonies in Gloucester (Cramp 1971). During 1976–94, urban breeding by Herring and Lesser Black-backed Gulls combined expanded at a rate of about 13 per cent per annum, in terms of both numbers and colonies; and a survey of nesting on buildings and other man-made structures in Great Britain in 1994 recorded 10,900 pairs of Herrings and 2500 pairs of Lesser Black-backs, resulting in estimates (allowing for those missed) of 16,900 and 3200 pairs respectively (Raven & Coulson 1997). By 1998–2002, both had increased markedly, to 20,000 pairs of Herrings and 10,800 of Lesser Black-backs, not allowing for missed colonies (*Seabird 2000*). The stronghold in the Bristol Channel region – an area edged approximately by Taunton (Somerset), Port Talbot (Neath), Hereford, Worcester, Swindon and Trowbridge – had increased and grown further; indeed, the roof-nesting colony in Gloucester had shown one of the fastest rates of increase of any colony countrywide and reached 2250 pairs of Lesser Black-backs (although no Wiltshire colonies were included in that survey) (*Seabird 2000*).

The first recorded Lesser Black-backs breeding in Wiltshire were a pair that nested on the Airsprung factory roof at Trowbridge in 1986; a pair was also seen there through the summer of 1987 without any evidence of nesting. The species then bred successfully on the same factory in 1990 and in most subsequent years; a count in 1995 revealed 86 nests. During the 1990s, territorial behaviour by adults was also reported at Melksham, Devizes, Bradford-on-Avon, Westbury, Swindon, Corsham and Wootton Bassett (*Hobby*). The summer distribution map shows breeding behaviour recorded in nine tetrads, all in the west and north; although in 1995 'territorial behaviour' was regularly noted on the island in Half Mile Pond, Longleat, one of the pair was sub-adult and there was no evidence of any attempt to nest.

Thus, except for the Trowbridge nest count in 1995, there was no information on which to base a summer population estimate for the county and, while large rooftop colonies in towns and cities as close as Bristol, Bath (Somerset) and Gloucester were well known, breeding had not even been confirmed in any other Wiltshire town. Therefore, although it meant making an exception to the policy used in this book of excluding data after the end of 2000, WOS commissioned breeding surveys of roof-nesting gulls in the county in 2003 and 2004 (Rock 2003a, 2004a). These confirmed nesting in Chippenham, Melksham,

Devizes, Bradford-on-Avon, Trowbridge and Westbury, all in the western half, as well as in Swindon, the sole site in the northeast (figure 59), thus matching the breeding behaviour recorded during the summer tetrad survey in all of these towns bar Chippenham. (Calne and Wootton Bassett were also visited, but there was no indication of nesting gulls.)

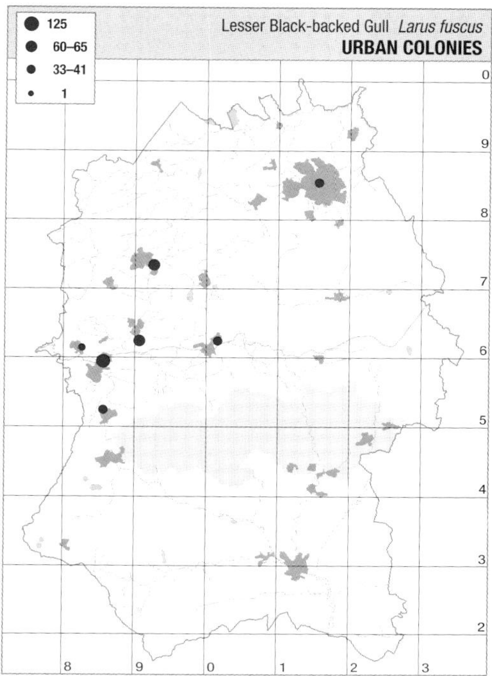

Figure 59. Lesser Black-backed Gulls *Larus fuscus* in Wiltshire: urban colonies 2003–2004 (after Rock 2003a, 2004a)

In 2004, an estimated total of 384 pairs of Lesser Black-backs in Wiltshire outnumbered Herring Gulls by a ratio of 4·0:1; differences between sites in this respect were marked, ranging from 2·5:1 in Westbury to 5·5:1 in Trowbridge (table 81, based on Rock 2005). In this connection, it must be added that Lesser Black-backs dominate all colonies in the Bristol Channel region, and it appears that this dominance is increasing; in contrast, Herring Gulls dominate the urban colonies farther west and north in Great Britain (Rock 2004b). (In 2003, Rock had found only 239 pairs in Wiltshire, but the apparent increase in 2004 is at least partly explained by the discovery then of a previously unknown site in Devizes, and the results in the first year were certainly also affected by WOS's late commission of the work.)

Trowbridge, the oldest site known to have been colonised, contained the largest number of breeding pairs in both years – still almost entirely on the Airsprung factory – but the original 1995 count of 86 nests there needs to be treated with some caution: both species sometimes build more than one nest in the same season and old nests are not always re-used in successive years (Rock 2004b). Even so, in view of the probable breeding recorded in four other towns during the summer tetrad survey, a county population in the late 1990s of at least 100 pairs, perhaps even 200, seems possible.

It is believed that the factory staff at Trowbridge made some effort to remove nesting material since 1995, which in turn may have slowed down the expansion of this colony, for Rock believed that the site was still below its potential carrying capacity in 2004. Swindon, on the other hand, even though holding the second largest population, supports surprisingly few considering the amount of suitable habitat on the industrial estates: there was no evidence of breeding within the town itself, where again there is no shortage of suitable buildings. In Worcester, by contrast, almost all breeding takes place within the city and very little in the industrial estates (Rock 2003b). During the Wiltshire survey, Rock noted two colour-ringed Lesser Black-backs from Bristol (and single Herring Gulls from there and from Bath), all originally marked as chicks, indicating that the origins of at least some of the county's breeding population are the same as many of those that winter here.

KJG

Caspian Gull

Larus cachinnans

Rare vagrant (3 records) from east Europe/central Asia

The Caspian Gull – a name coined by Jonsson (1998) – is one of the taxonomically vexing and almost wholly Eurasian *argentatus-cachinnans-fuscus* complex of 'large white-headed gulls'. The generally more southerly and typically yellow-legged taxa that form the '*cachinnans* group' have been treated as a species in their own right (*eg* Dwight 1925, *CBWP*), or placed within the Lesser Black-backed Gull or *fuscus* group (*eg* Voous 1960) – or, more usually in British literature, included in the Herring Gull or *argentatus* group (*eg* Voous 1977, Grant 1986).

Of the two members of the '*cachinnans* group' on the British List, the Taxonomic Sub-Committee of the BOURC has recently raised *michahellis* (Yellow-legged Gull, *qv*) to the species level – but, pending further study into its affinities, has retained Caspian as a subspecies of the Herring Gull (Sangster *et al* 2005). It is worth noting, however, that in comparison with both Herring and Yellow-legged, the Caspian Gull shows consistent differences in structure and plumage (*eg* Garner & Quinn 1997, Garner *et al* 1997, Jonsson 1998) as well as in genetics and in social display, this last being more reminiscent of *fuscus* (*eg* Yésou 2002). In his summary of the *argentatus-cachinnans-fuscus* complex, Yésou (2002) regarded the Caspian as a separate monotypic species, and, in anticipation of a future split, that treatment is followed here.

Formerly breeding only in central Asia – whence it migrates to winter in the region of the Black and southern Caspian Seas down to the Arabian Gulf – the Caspian Gull has in recent decades spread westwards along the river systems of eastern and central Europe to nest in European Russia, Belarus, Poland, Hungary, Germany and the Czech Republic (*eg* Yésou 2002, Malling Olsen & Larsson 2003). It is now also a regular, and increasing, non-breeding visitor to several northwest European countries, including Great Britain (*eg BB* 96: 575–578).

Wiltshire's first report of a Caspian Gull came in 1998, when a third-summer individual was seen on 16 July at CWP and again on the 20th (Prior 1999); it or another was also found there on 11 August. And in the following year, an adult was identified at Swindon STW on 12 November.

Some caution is advisable when identifying this taxon, as *cachinnans* is known occasionally to interbreed with other large gulls, including *argentatus*, *fuscus* and *michahellis* (see Yésou 2002). Such hybrids have been recorded in Great Britain: for example, an adult showing mixed characters of *cachinnans* and *michahellis* was trapped in Gloucestershire in February 1994 (Stewart 1997), and a Polish-ringed hybrid between *cachinnans* and *argentatus* was photographed in Cambridgeshire in June 2005 (*BB* 98: 529).

(See also page 727.)

PCo

Yellow-legged Gull
Larus michahellis

Scarce but increasing visitor from west/south Europe

Variously considered a subspecies of the Herring Gull (*eg* Voous 1977), of the Lesser Black-backed Gull (*eg* Voous 1960) or of the Caspian Gull (*eg CBWP*), the Yellow-legged is currently treated as a distinct species by many authorities (*eg* Jonsson 1998, Sangster *et al* 1998, Malling Olsen & Larsson 2003), now including the BOURC (Sangster *et al* 2005). It behaves as a good biological species where it meets Herring and Lesser Back-backed in western France (Yésou 1991) and appears also to differ in certain respects from Caspian (*qv* for discussion).

Yellow-legged Gulls breed from the Atlantic islands and northwest Africa eastwards across the Mediterranean to Cyprus, and on Black Sea coasts from Romania to Turkey. The nominate race *michahellis*, which is found commonly in southern Europe, spread north to nest along the Atlantic coast of France and up the Rhone valley in the 1970s (*CBWP*), so much so that by the 1990s the European population was calculated to amount to between 198,000 and 220,000 pairs (*EBCC Atlas*). In the late 1970s nominate *michahellis* also started occurring as a non-breeding visitor in parts of southern England (see *BB* 74: 349–353). Now it has nested in Great Britain – single pairs in 1997 and 1999, and three or four in 2000 (*RBBP*) – as well as in the Netherlands, and in parts of central Europe (*CBWP*).

Wiltshire's first record of *michahellis* was at Swindon rubbish tip on 29 December 1985. The next came in 1987, when there were five sightings of single individuals at Swindon rubbish tip, Peatmoor Lagoon and CWP in January, November and December. In 1988, one or two were seen from early September until the end of year at CWP, and 1989 saw the first August records. Yellow-legged Gulls became more frequent during 1990–92; and in 1993 numbers at CWP peaked at eight on 13 February, while three near Porton in January were the first for south Wiltshire. On 5 August 1995, a *michahellis* bearing an orange ring was seen at CWP and, though the inscription could not be read, the only known use of that colour at that time was in the Netherlands (Grearson 1998b) – another link between that country and CWP, similar to those demonstrated for both Lesser Black-backed and Mediterranean Gulls by both conventional and colour-ringing. The numbers recorded increased from 1995, especially in the north of the county where it is now normal for several Yellow-legged Gulls to be found in pre-roost gatherings at CWP68, Swindon rubbish

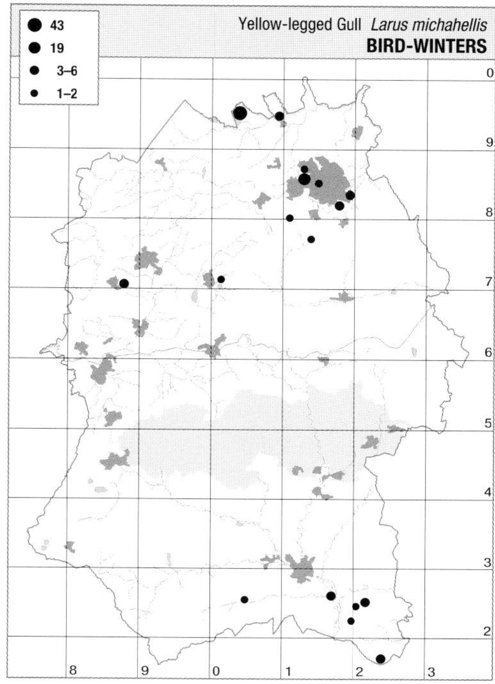

Table 82. Yellow-legged Gulls *Larus michahellis* in Wiltshire: monthly and annual totals of peak daily counts 1990–2000

	Jan	Feb	Mar	Apr	May	Jun	Jul	Aug	Sep	Oct	Nov	Dec
1990	–	–	–	–	–	–	–	–	1	1	1	3
1991	2	2	–	–	–	–	–	–	–	–	1	1
1992	3	2	–	–	–	–	–	–	–	2	3	2
1993	4	8	–	–	–	–	–	–	–	1	–	1
1994	–	1	1	–	–	–	–	1	1	2	2	5
1995	5	6	–	–	–	–	3	2	1	–	3	1
1996	1	1	–	–	–	–	2	2	4	2	3	3
1997	2	5	8	–	–	2	6	6	6	6	4	6
1998	3	1	2	1	2	1	5	5	6	1	4	6
1999	4	4	3	1	1	1	5	4	1	4	9	6
2000	5	7	1	–	–	–	10	6	2	5	1	1

Table 83. Yellow-legged Gulls *Larus michahellis* in Wiltshire: monthly and annual totals of bird-days 1990–2000

	Jan	Feb	Mar	Apr	May	Jun	Jul	Aug	Sep	Oct	Nov	Dec
1990	–	–	–	–	–	–	–	–	1	1	3	4
1991	2	2	–	–	–	–	–	–	–	–	2	1
1992	4	7	–	–	–	–	–	–	–	2	8	2
1993	7	16	–	–	–	–	–	–	–	1	–	1
1994	–	2	1	–	–	–	–	12	2	3	17	20
1995	16	7	–	–	–	–	14	9	2	–	7	2
1996	1	1	–	–	–	–	13	23	16	5	4	11
1997	5	16	23	–	–	3	30	48	37	13	7	11
1998	18	7	6	2	3	2	30	39	17	2	12	62
1999	20	24	8	1	1	1	22	11	4	18	22	36
2000	22	17	2	–	–	–	28	25	2	11	2	6

tip and Swindon STW. Occasional records elsewhere – sometimes on farmland (*eg* one in first-winter plumage following a plough at Barford near Downton on 19 October 2000) – indicate that *michahellis* may be fairly widespread. Most records involve adults, though this probably merely reflects the complexities of identifying immatures.

The peak daily counts of *michahellis* recorded in Wiltshire in each month during 1990–2000 (table 82) demonstrate their increasing regularity in late summer from 1995 onwards, as well as showing the build-up of winter numbers. These patterns are made even clearer when expressed as the numbers of bird-days involved (table 83). Turnover of individuals between the main sites in north Wiltshire – CWP, Swindon STW and Swindon rubbish tip – may mask the true figures involved in late summer and early autumn. Given that the species is likely to be overlooked away from these sites, and that immatures are rarely identified, it is probable that the true numbers may be twice as high as those suggested by the table.

KJG & PCo

Herring Gull

Larus argentatus

Scarce visitor from elsewhere in Britain/north Europe, recent and increasing local breeder

One of the bigger British species, the Herring Gull is especially vocal in the breeding season and its strident, laughing calls must be familiar to anyone who has visited a seaside resort. The taxonomy of the 'large white-headed gulls' has for many years been confused and controversial, several forms being considered either as subspecies of Herring Gulls or of Lesser Black-backs (*qv*), or as species in their own right (see P Devillers in *BWP*, Grant 1986, Sangster *et al* 1998, Yésou 2002). *Birds of Wiltshire* adopts a treatment increasingly familiar to British birdwatchers, and considers Herring, Yellow-legged and Caspian Gulls as separate species (see the texts on the last two for more detailed discussions).

In Europe, Herring Gulls breed from Iceland, the Faeroes, Ireland and western France to northern Fenno-Scandia and the White Sea; other populations are found in Siberia and northern North America. They are mainly coastal nesters, though inland breeding is not infrequent and, indeed, is spreading in Great Britain. The population of Europe, excluding Russia, has been estimated at 758,000 to 831,000 pairs (*EBCC Atlas*).

The numbers nesting in Great Britain increased during much of the 20th century, and it is thought that from the late 1940s to the early 1970s they grew by some 13 per cent annually. Then, however, the populations breeding on coasts nearly halved during the 21 years of 1967–87, from an estimated 284,000 pairs to only 144,000, and declined still further to 141,000 in 1998–2002 (*Seabird 2000*). In western England, Herring Gulls also breed inland, in relatively small numbers, within colonies of Lesser Black-backed Gulls in industrial and other urban sites in various counties, notably Gloucestershire and Somerset – a trend that has recently spread also to Wiltshire.

The winter population of Herring Gulls in Great Britain in the early 1990s was estimated at 377,000 (Burton *et al* 2003). At that season, numbers of the generally sedentary race *argenteus*, which breeds in Great Britain and other parts of westernmost Europe, are supplemented by nominate *argentatus* ('Scandinavian Herring Gulls') from Fenno-Scandia and the Baltic. Ringing returns indicate that these Scandinavian Herring Gulls occur mainly along the east coast of Great Britain and in adjacent inland counties (*Migration Atlas*). There have been winter sight records in Wiltshire of Herring Gulls resembling the Scandinavian subspecies – these probably originating from the northern parts of their range, where the differences between nominate *argentatus* and *argenteus* are most marked, whereas the Danish nesting population shows characters intermediate between the two subspecies (see Yésou 2002) – but some caution is advisable (see Chylarecki 1993) and there is as yet no firm evidence, in the form of ringed or colour-marked individuals, of the Scandinavian race in this county.

Bosworth Smith (1863) wrote of the Herring Gull that 'Flocks of this bird may not unusually be seen flying at this considerable distance from the sea'. Seven years later, however, im Thurn (1870) believed that that must have been a mistake, commenting that 'among all the Gulls, which I have seen shot near Marlborough, I have only met with one specimen of this species, which was shot at Tottenham [Park]', and he supposed that overflying gulls had been ascribed to this species without sufficient examination. Smith (1887) considered the Herring Gull to be 'a sad pilferer of its neighbour's goods' and quoted three correspondents as providing evidence of its occurrence in Wiltshire: Reverend

Table 84. Herring Gulls *Larus argentatus* in Wiltshire: peak winter counts at CWP 1990/91–1999/00

	90/91	91/92	92/93	93/94	94/95	95/96	96/97	97/98	98/99	99/00
Birds	100	164	80	42	62	31	80	71	150	400
Months	Jan	Jan	Nov	Jan	Dec	Jan	Nov	Dec	Dec	Mar

AP Morres frequently saw them 'passing overhead in the neighbourhood of Salisbury'; a Mr Baker 'often found them near Mere'; and a Mr Stratton had killed them on the downs near Market Lavington, where he regularly saw them flying north and 'conjectured they were making for Gloucester and the Severn'. Smith also recorded that he had been sent 'an immature specimen... for identification' in January 1885 – presumably the one noted by Meyrick (1906) as shot near Marlborough in that month – and that he knew of 'a stuffed specimen at Corsham Court, which was shot on the waters there'.

The next references, in 1930, simply recorded that the Herring Gull was observed 'less regularly' than the Common Gull – which was noted as 'seen most years, usually during rough weather' – in the Marlborough district (Peirson & Walford 1930); and 'Appears to be more common among [the flocks of gulls which come into the county] from the south coast than among those from the Severn' (the second bird report in *WANHM*). Then, after just two records (one of five birds) in the next annual report in *WANHM*, for 1931, there were several mentions of flocks (including one of 200 at Leigh Delamere on 31 March) in 1932 – a year in which, curiously, only one Common Gull was reported – and, in the next four years, 'greatly increased numbers', 'very common', 'great increase... well distributed in the county' and, more specifically in 1933, 'has become a nuisance in the trout streams at Longford'.

In the first three years after the 1939–45 War, gulls of any species were hardly mentioned in *WANHM*, but from 1949 there were several reports each year of Herring Gulls in ones, twos and even flocks of 40 and 80. Peirson (1959) wrote that this species was 'An uncommon visitor which comes up the valleys of both Avons particularly in rough weather', but also stated that it was 'Not uncommon on rubbish tips near Salisbury and Lacock'; he considered it to be more usually seen in winter and in 'spring particularly in March and April'. Buxton (1981) believed this gull to be 'commoner now than in the past' and 'more frequent in autumn and winter', but that 'the gull roost at the [Cotswold] Water Park seldom includes more than 40'.

Since then, Herring Gulls have continued to increase in Wiltshire and are most often found in the company of the now more numerous Lesser Black-backs, their numbers usually reaching a peak between late December and the end of February. The largest flocks are found in the Calne/Corsham area and, until it closed in 2003, at Swindon rubbish tip (maxima 700 in December 1985 and 1986). As shown by the peak counts during the ten winters 1990/91 to 1999/2000 (table 84), very variable numbers roost at CWP where the 400 on 8 March 2000 was exceptional. Counts of over 100 away from CWP during 1990–2000 were reported at Calne (110 in January 1994, 250 in April 1994, 100 in July 1995), Swindon STW (107 in December 1998, 108 in January 1999, 165 in January 2000) and Broad Chalke (250 in September 2000). The last is of particular interest, and could suggest that Herring Gulls are under-recorded in south Wiltshire. Westerly movements, sometimes reaching three figures (maximum 445 on 17 February 1998), were regularly noted at Corsham Lake during 1996–98, in January–March, May–June, August and November (*Hobby*).

The winter map demonstrates the importance of north Wiltshire for this species, and extrapolation from the tetrad counts suggests a total at that season of about 112. That is clearly too low, however, as 165 were present at Swindon STW alone in January 2000 and,

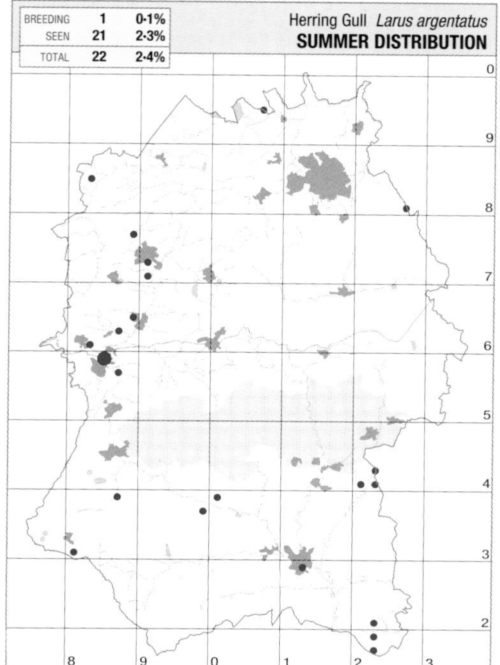

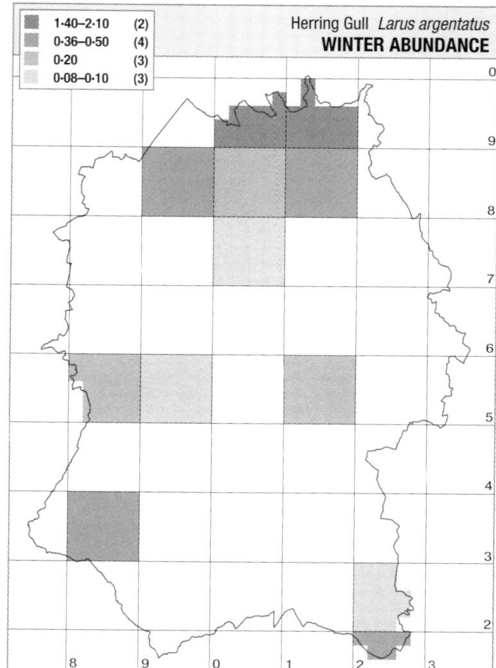

allowing for small numbers dispersed at rubbish tips and over farmland throughout the county, the true figure is probably nearer 500. This may be compared with 63,800 at inland roosts in England as a whole in 1993, a total that had increased from 42,900 ten years earlier (Burton *et al* 2003).

Before the 1939–45 War, there had been only half a dozen British records of larger gulls, all Herring Gulls in Devon and Cornwall, nesting on roofs in coastal towns, the first in 1923, but urban breeding started to develop in Great Britain during the 1940s, when 14 known colonies included only one of over 100 nests, through to the 1960s and 1970, when 55 known colonies included five of more than 100 (Cramp 1971). The subsequent development of roof-nesting by the larger gulls and its spread inland is summarised here under Lesser Black-backed (*qv*). Wiltshire's first record of breeding Herring Gulls came in 1995, when two nests were found in the by then well-established colony of Lesser Black-backed Gulls on the Airsprung factory in Trowbridge, and one pair nested there

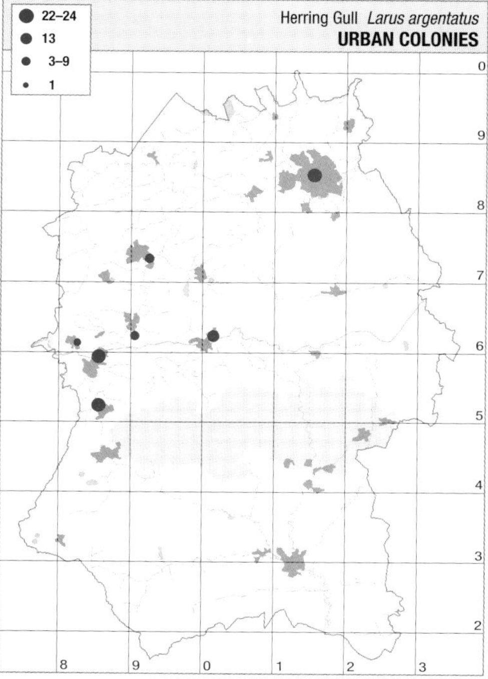

Figure 60. Herring Gulls *Larus argentatus* in Wiltshire: urban colonies 2003–2004 (after Rock 2003a, 2004a)
See also table 81 under Lesser Black-backed Gull

again in 1996. Adults, sometimes behaving territorially, were also noted during 1994–2000 at suitable sites elsewhere (*eg* in Melksham, Bradford-on-Avon and Swindon) and, though no further specific evidence of nesting was found, suspicions were sufficiently aroused for a survey of roof-nesting gulls in Wiltshire to be commissioned in 2003 and 2004.

While the summer tetrad map is able to show only the one confirmed breeding site during 1995–2000, the commissioned survey showed a much larger and more widespread population than previously realised, totalling about 97 pairs (43 confirmed nests) in 2004 (Rock 2004a): breeding was proved at Chippenham, Melksham, Devizes, Bradford-on-Avon (2003 only), Trowbridge, Westbury and Swindon (see table 81 under Lesser Black-backed Gull and figure 60 here). (Calne and Wootton Bassett were also surveyed but no breeding gulls were located.) Although this was outside the period of the Wiltshire tetrad fieldwork, and even allowing for the rapidity of the increase in inland-nesting by Herring Gulls, it seems probable that their breeding in the county was under-recorded in the late 1990s and that 25–50 pairs were already present then.

Around 12,300 roof-nesting pairs were located in England during 1998–2002 – the majority in coastal areas – which was twice the number in the mid 1990s (*Seabird 2000*). None was recorded in Wiltshire during that survey either, but the urban colonies now known to be in the county are by far the largest so far inland. It seems likely that this increasing habit in Wiltshire is fuelled by expansion from the other urban colonies nearby, particularly those in the Bristol area and, indeed, during his Wiltshire survey Rock saw single Herring Gulls that had been ringed as chicks in Bristol and Bath (Somerset), as well as two Lesser Black-backs from Bristol.

Earlier, a total of 21 Herring Gulls colour-ringed in rooftop colonies in Bristol had been found in Wiltshire, mainly at Calne or CWP, during 1994–98 (*cf* Lesser Black-backed) – mostly during post-breeding dispersal in late summer, although increasingly also in winter (Grearson 1998b). Not surprisingly, some of these 21 were also recorded in other counties, at Keynsham (Somerset), Gloucester, and Throckmorton (Worcestershire), as well as at various sites in the Bristol area; another was seen during its first winter in Plymouth (Devon), later returned to Bristol to breed, and was then observed at Calne. The oldest colour-ringed Herring Gulls recorded in the county were two marked as nestlings in Bristol in 1986 and seen at Calne nine years later, in autumn 1995. Two more from Bristol, in their fifth and sixth years, were reported in the Swindon area early in 2000 (*Hobby*). Only one Herring Gull was ringed in Wiltshire during 1965–2000.

KJG

Iceland Gull

Larus glaucoides

Vagrant (2 records), breeds Greenland, winters Iceland/northwest Europe coasts

'Iceland Gull' is something of a misnomer, for this rather elegant species nests only very rarely in that country, its main breeding range being the coastal regions of Greenland and the adjacent Canadian Arctic from Ellesmere Island south to Baffin Island and far northern Quebec; it also nested on Novaya Zemlya and probably adjacent northeast Russian coasts in the 1990s (*CBWP*). The Canadian population winters along the east coast of

North America, but many from east Greenland migrate to coastal regions of Iceland, Faeroes, Scandinavia and northern Britain and Ireland, some farther south to northern France and, more accidentally, Netherlands and other European countries. It is estimated that 'probably 100–200' normally winter in Britain and Ireland – 'although there is variation from year to year' (*Migration Atlas*) – and exceptionally up to 300 (*1981–84 Winter Atlas*). Whilst the Northern Isles and Scottish harbours provide the best chances of encountering these arctic gulls, small numbers do also reach southwest England and reservoirs in the Midlands.

Both Wiltshire records have involved immatures. The first, apparently either in its first or second winter, was identified at Erlestoke on 31 January 1973 (*WANHM*). The second, in first-winter plumage moulting to first-summer, was seen at Swindon STW during 3–9 March 1997.

(See also page 727.)

KJG

Another gull – either Iceland or Glaucous – at Wilton Water on 4 January 1973 was reported as being 'apparently in second winter plumage soft brown, mottled on white ... about the size of a Herring Gull although bill was not unduly large', a description that means it cannot have been the same individual as the largely white-plumaged Iceland Gull identified on the 31st (*WANHM*).

Eds

Glaucous Gull

Larus hyperboreus

Vagrant (7 records), breeds arctic islands, some winter down to north USA/Britain

The heavy, fierce-looking Glaucous Gull is the slightly more numerous of the two large white-winged species found in Great Britain (*cf* Iceland Gull) with a usual winter total of 200 to 500 (*1981–84 Winter Atlas*). It has a circumpolar breeding distribution, nesting on islands and cliffs of arctic and subarctic coasts. Some populations are relatively sedentary in winter, others dispersive, staying as far north as weather allows and also regularly south to the coasts of the northern USA and of the North and Irish Seas. The European population has been estimated at 17,300 to 25,900 pairs (*EBCC Atlas*), 4000 to 7000 of them in Russia and no fewer than 10,000 to 15,000 in Iceland, where the numbers have increased hugely since 1970; most of the rest are on Jan Mayen, Bear Island and Svalbard. The origins of those wintering in Britain and Ireland are not clear, but ringing recoveries from Iceland, Bear Island and Norway 'give some indication', while the origins of British Iceland Gulls 'could also suggest that some ... Glaucous Gulls ... come from eastern Greenland' (*Migration Atlas*).

In Great Britain in winter, Glaucous Gulls particularly favour Scottish islands and coasts, but, like Iceland Gulls, small numbers also occur in the Midlands and southwest England; they are also the more regular of the two on the English east coast. They are predators, scavengers and pirates, found mainly at harbours, fish quays and sewage outflows, but also inland at rubbish tips and in gull roosts on large water bodies. The majority of Wiltshire records have involved immatures between December and March:

1984	9 Feb–7 Mar	CWP area	2nd-winter
1985	30 December	Swindon rubbish tip	1st-winter
1987	9 December	Peatmoor Lagoon	2nd-winter
1990	14 January	CWP64	1st-winter
1992	1–3 January	CWP68	1st-winter
1999	27 November	Swindon STW	Adult
	18–30 December	CWP68	2nd-winter
	29 December	Swindon STW	2nd-winter (same as CWP68)

(See also page 727.)

KJG

Great Black-backed Gull

Larus marinus

Scarce migrant/winter visitor, breeds coastal north Europe south to northwest France, winters also inland in Britain

This largest of the British gulls is confined to the North Atlantic region, extending northeast in Europe to the Arctic Ocean and the Baltic, but in many areas has increased in both numbers and range during the 20th century. Nesting mainly along coastlines – in loose colonies, or often as single pairs that specialise in preying on shearwaters, petrels or Puffins, or pirating food from other seabirds – Great Black-backed Gulls breed from Greenland, Iceland, Svalbard and Novaya Zemlya south to Ireland, western Great Britain, northwest France and Fenno-Scandia; also in North America from Quebec south to New England. The numbers in Europe, excluding Russia, have been estimated at 100,000 to 110,000 pairs (Stroud *et al* 2001). In winter, most northern populations disperse southward, some reaching as far as Florida, the Azores and western Iberia.

The British population of Great Black-backed Gulls was estimated at 19,700 pairs in the late 1990s, declining to 17,400 in 1998–2002, 85 per cent of them in Scotland (*Seabird 2000*). In England, the highest numbers nest in the southwest peninsula, and the nearest to Wiltshire are in the Solent (Hampshire) and the Bristol Channel. In winter, however, they are more evenly distributed around the coast – large concentrations being recorded in eastern England (Prater 1981) – as well as occurring more widely inland (*1981–84 Winter Atlas*): a 1993 survey of roosts located 43,000, the vast majority in England and just over half inland. Ringing has shown that many Great Black-backs wintering along England's east coast come from Norway (*Migration Atlas*), but none has been ringed or recovered in Wiltshire and the origins of the small numbers seen here are unknown.

Great Black-backed Gulls have always been rather scarce in this county. Smith (1887) knew of only three specimens, one each from Wootton Bassett and Bromham in July 1873, and one from Cheverell on 27 August 1874. He also reported that the 'Rev. A. P. Morres has several times seen them flying... both in his own parish [near Salisbury] and recently at Clarendon'. Peirson (1959) noted that this species had been 'really rare during the first quarter of this century, now seen every year, usually single birds, in almost any month'; in fact, the only published observations before 1930 seem to have been 'an adult pair which haunted Swindon Sewage Farm for more than a month in Dec., 1906' and 'one on

Table 85. Great Black-backed Gulls *Larus marinus* in Wiltshire: peak winter counts at CWP 1990/91–1999/00

	90/91	91/92	92/93	93/94	94/95	95/96	96/97	97/98	98/99	99/00
CWP	8	12	4	3	14	3	3	2	8	8
Swindon STW	0	0	0	0	11	0	1	5	30	14

the Downs above Alton White Horse on April 23rd, 1910' (Hony 1915a), the latter also published as 'Milk Hill, 1910' by Peirson (1919).

In the 1930s, however, a variety of reports included a pair near Chute through the winter of 1930/31, 'two parties of seven adult birds' (no locality) in 1932 and 'often seen over Warminster' in 1933 (*WANHM*), all at a time when gulls in general were unusual in Wiltshire and apparently no Lesser Black-backs (*qv*) were being found – though it must be added that in Great Britain in those days Lesser Black-backs were largely summer-visitors or spring and autumn passage-migrants (*eg* Witherby *et al* 1938–41).

Records of Great Black-backs became more regular, if still few, from 1950. In 1956 they were 'Noted in January and February and again from September to December near Salisbury', and in 1957 'Seen regularly near rivers from January to April, in June, and from September to December by many observers', but not apparently at all in 1958 (*WANHM*), which all suggests unevenness of occurrence or reporting. Buxton (1981) noted 'since [1931] it has been recorded in most years, generally singly and more often in autumn', and Palmer (1991) considered this species to be an 'Uncommon but annual passage migrant and winter visitor'.

During 1990–2000 Great Black-backed Gulls were recorded most regularly at CWP in winter (extremes August–May), but towards the end of the period Swindon STW and Swindon rubbish tip began to attract as many, or more (table 85). The highest numbers in that period were almost always in December–January, although there were occasional summer records in the county, notably four adults and four juveniles at Westbury White Horse on 4 July 1994 and singletons at Swindon STW on 10 June 1998 and Ferndale School, Swindon, on 27 July 1999. In general, apart from those at CWP and Swindon STW and rubbish tip, the species was recorded at only 1–3 sites annually, and generally singly, but larger counts were three in flight at Hilperton, Trowbridge, in March 1990, three at Melksham in April 1990, 16 at Thorny Down Tip, Porton, in January 1993, six flying over Coate Water in March 1994, six at Standlynch in October 1994, and three at Bratton in September 1996.

Just one was recorded during the timed counts of the winter tetrad survey, clearly under-representing the average winter numbers, which are estimated to range between 10 and 25.

KJG

Kittiwake
Rissa tridactyla

Scarce migrant, breeds coastal north/west Europe, mainly pelagic in winter

This smallish gull nests on coastal cliffs of the north Pacific, North Atlantic and Arctic Oceans, and disperses out to sea in winter. Protection helped some sections of the European breeding population – estimated at 2·2 to 2·5 million pairs, even excluding Russia (*EBCC Atlas*) – to increase and spread from about 1940. In Europe, the main concentrations of Kittiwakes are on the far-northern archipelagos of Svalbard, Franz Josef Land, Novaya Zemlya, Bear Island and Jan Mayen, along the arctic coasts of Norway and northwest Russia and, farther south, in Iceland, Faeroes, Great Britain and Ireland, but there are also much smaller numbers on the coasts of southern Scandinavia, Helgoland (Germany) and north and west France, as well as tiny outposts in northwest Spain.

In Great Britain, where Kittiwakes nest on many coastal cliffs, but are especially numerous from northern Scotland south to Humberside, some 370,000 breeding pairs were estimated in 1998–2003 (*Seabird 2000*). Numbers had, however, changed considerably over the previous 35 years, increasing from 404,000 in the late 1960s to 495,000 in the mid 1980s before the recent decline – especially marked in, for example, Shetland (Heubeck 2002), but by no means confined to the Northern Isles – which has been caused primarily by declining prey stocks, particularly of sandeels (*Seabird 2000*).

Smith (1887) reported the first Kittiwake for Wiltshire as 'picked up dead on the snow in the neighbourhood of Devizes in November, 1847'; he then listed 19 other records, of which 17 were dated to year between 1863 and 1881 (including seven in 1869 alone) and, although giving no months, he noted that Kittiwakes are 'occasionally met with on our downs in summer'. There followed two in 1890, in February and July (Meyrick 1895).

Apart from a highly unlikely and hitherto unchallenged report from Orcheston in 1934 – to the effect that 'Kittiwakes pass here usually in late autumn on southward movement…when the Channel is rough they may be seen in hundreds' (*WANHM*) – no more were found until a series of seven (possibly eight) records during 1953–59 (*WANHM*). Of the six of those that were aged, three were adults and three immatures; all were dead or exhausted and in the first part of the year (probably January–March, as those found in April–May were 'long dead' or 'remains'): three (possibly four) corpses in 1957 followed a "considerable 'wreck' of Kittiwakes… in England and Wales early in the year". Three of the bodies were found by the Longleat lakes in 1953, 1955 and 1957, and the other four records came from Westbury, Tockenham, Longford and Charlton (although which of Wiltshire's four Charltons was involved is now unknown).

There was just one record in the 1960s – 'exhausted… did not revive', on Salisbury rubbish dump in January 1965 (*WANHM*) – and none at all through the 1970s. In the next decade, however, starting with CWP's first record – an immature on 17 November 1982 after an extended period of gales – Palmer (1991) was able to summarise a total of 64 individuals in five of the eight years 1982–89, represented in all months except June, July and December. Peak years were 1983 (17, including 12 at CWP on 6 February), 1988 (29, including 28 at CWP on 12 March) and 1989 (seven, including five flying west over Swindon on 6 August). The species was then recorded in eight of the 11 years 1990–2000 (table 86), always as singletons except for three together at Swindon STW in January 1998, and all but two in January–May (table 87).

Kittiwakes begin to return from the Atlantic about February (*CBWP*), and it is likely that many Wiltshire records early in the year relate to movements back to colonies. Coulson (1986) considered it likely that the majority of inland records involve storm-driven birds which are already weak or ill, adding that, 'In general, Kittiwakes do not seem able to feed adequately on inland waters'. As long ago as 1937, however, Alexander (1974) considered

Table 86. Kittiwakes *Rissa tridactyla* in Wiltshire: annual totals 1990–2000

	90	91	92	93	94	95	96	97	98	99	00
Birds	2	0	0	2	1	1	4	2	5	0	1

Table 87. Kittiwakes *Rissa tridactyla* in Wiltshire: monthly totals 1990–2000

	Jul	Aug	Sep	Oct	Nov	Dec	Jan	Feb	Mar	Apr	May	Jun
Birds	0	0	1	0	1	0	4	3	5	2	2	0

that some Kittiwakes travelled across England via the West Midland reservoirs in February and March, an idea reinforced by Hume (1976). There is also a regular passage over the Pennines in late winter (Key 1982). More relevantly at the Wiltshire level, surprising numbers – once as many as 642 in January 1993, at least 90 per cent of which were adults – have occasionally been found to fly up the Thames into Berkshire in January–April (Standley *et al* 1996), so possibly the parties of 12 and 28 at CWP in 1983 and 1988 had continued west up the river valley in this way. But others in January–March in the 1950s were clearly storm-driven, and the same may apply to the irregular records now in other months.

KJG

Ivory Gull

Pagophila eburnea

Vagrant (1 record: about 1840), breeds arctic islands, winters Arctic Ocean

Ivory Gulls nest on islands in the high Arctic of northeast Canada, Greenland, Svalbard, Franz Josef Land, Novaya Zemlya and western Siberia. Though some winter south to Newfoundland and north Iceland, most remain in arctic seas throughout the year, associating with the ice, and feeding on marine invertebrates, stranded fish, carrion, and arctic mammal faeces. A total of about 109 had been recorded in Great Britain by 2000, but only 39 of them since 1958 (*BBRC*). The pure white adults are rare so far south, and most vagrants have been in first-winter plumage, with distinctive black tips to wing- and tail-feathers and around the face.

Wiltshire's only Ivory Gull was not known to Smith (1887), but was reported to Hony (1915a) by E Cambridge Phillips as 'killed near Chippenham about 1840 and … the gem of the late Dr. Burly's collection'. Although the *BBRC* still cites 76 pre-1958 British and Irish records in its statistics, Evans (1994) 'rejected' all but 35 of those (including the Wiltshire one) on the grounds that, in his opinion, available details did not eliminate the possibility of either Iceland or Glaucous Gulls, or even albinistic individuals of other species. Ivory Gulls inland are extremely rare, but not unknown (the species has even been recorded in land-locked Switzerland: *CBWP*); and Dr Burly's 'gem' of a specimen is highly unlikely to have been mis-identified and cannot be dismissed on that basis. In the 19th and early 20th centuries good money was to be made by supplying gentlemen collectors with specimens of rare birds and eggs, which, as demand exceeded supply, inevitably led to cases of fraud (*eg* Nicholson & Ferguson-Lees 1962), but, in the absence of evidence refuting its provenance, Dr Burly's Ivory Gull is retained on the Wiltshire list.

KJG

Little Tern

Sternula albifrons

Rare migrant (40 records), breeds Britain/Europe, winters West Africa/Arabia

Little Terns are patchily distributed summer visitors to flattish shores of sand or fine shingle in Britain and Ireland, and to shingle or sand of both coasts and rivers on the European continent, as well as nesting locally in North and West Africa and in western and eastern Asia south to Australia. Closely related forms, often treated as separate species, are found in the Americas and around the Indian Ocean. The breeding population of Europe, excluding Russia, has been estimated at 20,600 to 27,800 pairs (*EBCC Atlas*), of which some 2520 pairs in Great Britain in the late 1980s had, through changing fortunes – not least, human disturbance of nesting sites – declined to about 1950 pairs by 1998–2002 (*Seabird 2000*). Western European populations winter largely along the coasts of West and probably also South Africa, while eastern European move to the shores of the Red Sea and Arabia.

Wiltshire's first Little Tern was seen at Rood Ashton on 19 April 1912 (Hony 1915a). The next seven, all singletons too, were found at Coate Water in July 1927 and July 1928; at Britford in March 1928 (still the earliest ever, although the actual date was not published); on the Salisbury Avon below Stratford sub Castle in April 1934; and at Coate again in August 1956, May 1958 (wrongly given as 'at Yellow Hill') and August 1966, the last a juvenile (all *WANHM*). The first multiple record was of three at CWP in August 1975. Through increased coverage, observations became more frequent during 1980–89: a total of 12 records (19 birds) in six of the ten years; four in April and May, the other eight in July, August and September (Palmer 1991), including the latest date for the county, at CWP on 30 September 1982.

Little Terns were seen in Wiltshire in all but two of the 11 years 1990–2000, with totals of 19 records and 27 birds (table 88). All bar one – at Shear Water on 17 August 1995 – were at CWP and all were adults, apart from a juvenile on 6 August 1996. Comparison between the nine-year and 12-year periods of 1980–88 and 1989–2000 demonstrates a clear upsurge in spring passage from 1989 onwards and also in earlier autumn records (table 89). The spring upsurge parallels a comparable increase in Sandwich Terns (*qv*), but the numbers involved are again too small for any firm conclusions – especially as half of Wiltshire's original eight records of Little Terns, back in 1912–66, were also in spring (and two of the other four in July).

Table 88. Little Terns *Sternula albifrons* in Wiltshire: annual totals of records and individuals 1990–2000

	90	91	92	93	94	95	96	97	98	99	00
Records	0	1	1	0	3	2	2	3	3	1	3
Birds	0	2	1	0	4	2	3	6	3	2	4

Table 89. Little Terns *Sternula albifrons* in Wiltshire: monthly totals of individuals 1980–2000

	Jan	Feb	Mar	Apr	May	Jun	Jul	Aug	Sep	Oct	Nov	Dec
1980–1988	0	0	0	0	0	0	0	5	6	0	0	0
1989–2000	0	0	0	7	13	0	5	10	0	0	0	0

KJG

Gull-billed Tern

Gelochelidon nilotica

Vagrant (1 record), breeds south Europe and North Sea region, winters Africa

This robust, medium-sized tern has a relatively short and thick, black bill and a less buoyant, more gull-like flight than the commoner terns. In Europe, it has a discontinuous breeding range in two main areas: very locally in Mediterranean countries from Spain to Greece and the Black Sea, and in the southern North Sea region of Denmark and north Germany; it has also nested in the past in central Europe, northwest France, the Netherlands, Poland, the Baltic States and Norway (*CBWP*), and one pair bred in Essex in 1950, possibly 1949 too (Pyman & Wainwright 1952). Elsewhere, the species nests from eastern Europe and Asia Minor across to Mongolia and southern China, as well as in Africa, Australia and the Americas, but often sporadically and always very patchily. The small European populations – estimated, excluding Russia, to total no more than 3100 to 3600 pairs (*EBCC Atlas*) – winter in Africa south to Botswana (*BWP*).

Gull-billed Terns are only rare visitors to Great Britain, though 213 were recorded during 1958–2000, over four times as many as the grand total before that period (*BBRC*). Most are seen at coastal sites, yet the species uses a wide variety of wetland habitats when breeding and is less aquatic and less marine than many other terns. It feeds mainly on terrestrial and aquatic invertebrates, rather than fish, and the only one recorded in Wiltshire – an adult at CWP68 from 27 June to 4 July 1999 (Maxfield 2000) – was seen by some observers to pick insects from the sand, or take others flying near its head while it was standing, between bouts of preening and sleeping.

KJG

Caspian Tern

Hydroprogne caspia

Vagrant (2 records), breeds Baltic, winters West Africa and Mediterranean

As its name implies, this huge, gull-like tern with a massive red or orange-red beak was first described from the Caspian Sea. Yet it has an almost cosmopolitan, if remarkably patchy, breeding range in the Baltic area (the origin of most vagrants to Great Britain) and from Black Sea countries across central Asia to Lake Baikal, south also to Arabia, Pakistan and southern China, as well as in parts of Africa, Madagascar, Australasia and North America. The species favours sheltered coasts and large, standing or slow-flowing waters. Recent declines in Europe – where, excluding Russia, only 1800 to 2300 pairs breed – have been attributed to ground predators, especially American mink and to persecution by fishermen wishing to protect their stocks (*EBCC Atlas*). Northern populations move south in autumn, and those from Baltic and Black Sea countries winter mainly in tropical West Africa, though some stay in the Mediterranean region.

Caspian Terns migrate on broad fronts, generally overland, although a minority follows North Sea and Atlantic coasts. They are fairly regular vagrants to Great Britain, with a total of 255 records to the end of the 20th century, all but 30 during 1958–99 (*BBRC*). Many are found at inland waters between July and November, which corresponds with the dispersal of the Baltic population. They often make no more than brief halts to rest, as was the case with each of Wiltshire's two. The first, in first- or second-summer plumage, was seen for just one hour at CWP68 early on 15 August 1987 before it moved on (*Hobby*). The second was an adult at the same locality on the evening of 13 June 1996, but it could not be found the next morning.

KJG

Black Tern

Chlidonias niger

Scarce migrant, breeds inland Europe, winters coastal West Africa

Black Terns nest on inland waters in Europe from Spain eastwards – though for the most part very locally anywhere west of a line from the Netherlands to Romania – across to west-central Asia and also from southern Canada to the central plains of USA and California. In contrast, they winter along coasts, chiefly those of tropical West Africa and northern South America. The European breeding population, excluding Russia, has been estimated at 41,900 to 51,100 pairs, mostly in the eastern half of the continent (*EBCC Atlas*). This is the only one of the three mainly insectivorous 'marsh terns' (genus *Chlidonias*) to occur in any numbers in Great Britain; indeed, it used to nest commonly in the marshes of eastern England in the 18th century, and still regularly until the 1850s, but has done so only occasionally since (*1875–1900 Atlas*, *CBWP*).

The Black Tern was certainly well known in Wiltshire in the 19th century. Morres (1878–85) mentioned four in the Salisbury area and Smith (1887) wrote that 'it has more frequently been met with in Wiltshire than any other of its congeners'; he listed a number of records, of which the earliest mentioned was one 'killed near Salisbury in 1840'. All dated reports were in April or May – when, of course, the black breeding plumage makes this bird much more distinctive – though both Morres and Smith referred to one 'shot at Newton Ferris in 1860 in winter dress', which suggests that the species did sometimes occur in autumn; an 'immature male' in the collection of im Thurn (1870), obtained at Ogbourne St George, may have been an autumn juvenile as most one-year-old Black Terns stay in their winter quarters.

Only five records of Black Terns (three May–June, two August) were published in *WANHM* during 1928–46, but they became almost annual thereafter, including occasional flocks of 11–20. Peirson (1959) found that the species was 'seen nearly always on spring passage but occasionally also in autumn ... most commonly from the Salisbury Avon and Coate Water ... used to be irregular but it has been seen, usually about 15 May, in most recent years'. In contrast, by tabulating the Wiltshire records of Black Terns for 1969–81, Edwards (1983b) showed that they were by then fairly frequently seen in spring (eight of the 13 years, mostly May, few others April–June), but much more regularly and over four times as numerously in autumn (all years except 1972, mostly August–September, few others July–October); in that period they were most often found at Coate Water (in 11

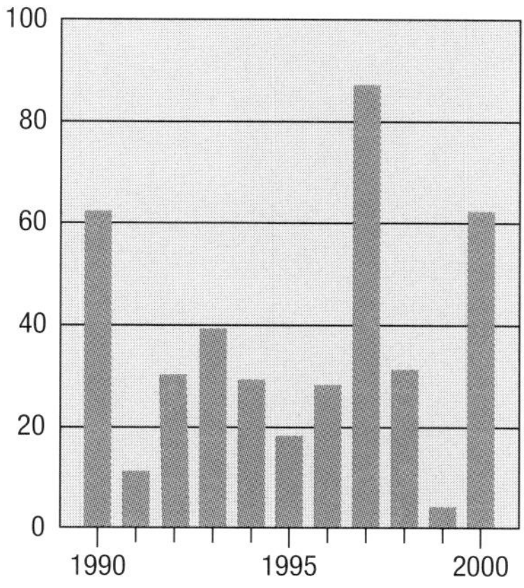

Figure 61. Black Terns *Chlidonias niger* in Wiltshire: annual totals 1990–2000

years) and CWP (in nine), but also at 11 other sites. Palmer (1991) likewise noted them as seen 'less often in spring than autumn', with 'particularly heavy' autumn passages in 1980, 1982 and 1989; he also referred to a straggler over the Bristol Avon at Melksham during 8–22 November 1984, still the county's latest date.

During 1990–2000, Black Terns were recorded annually, mostly at CWP, the development of which as a wetland area has, along with better observer coverage, led to the recording of greater numbers of this and other migrating terns. The marked differences there between years – for example, at least 70 were seen in May 1997, but just one in May 1999 (figure 61) – are thought to reflect weather conditions, the highest numbers apparently occurring during easterly winds. The shift in emphasis from spring to autumn, reported by Buxton (1981), Edwards and Palmer, has now been reversed again (table 90). Flocks are usually small, but at CWP have occasionally reached or exceeded 20 (table 91). The earliest county records have been on 22 April, in 1996 and again in 1997, both at CWP.

Table 90. Black Terns *Chlidonias niger* in Wiltshire: monthly totals 1990–2000

	Jan	Feb	Mar	Apr	May	Jun	Jul	Aug	Sep	Oct	Nov	Dec
Birds	0	0	0	18	287	6	3	48	37	2	0	0

Table 91. Black Terns *Chlidonias niger* in Wiltshire: flocks of 20 or more (all CWP) 1980–2000

Date	Flock size	Date	Flock size
3 August 1980	24	3 May 1990	51
21–22 Sep 1980	40	12 May 1993	20
19 August 1989	35	3 May 1997	64
2 May 1990	46	7 May 2000	35

KJG

White-winged Black Tern

Chlidonias leucopterus

Vagrant (3 records), breeds east Europe, winters inland tropical Africa

This smallest of the three 'marsh terns' has a discontinuous summer distribution across Eurasia from Poland and Hungary through southern Siberia to northern China. The breeding population of Europe, excluding Russia, has been estimated at only 7000 to 10,000 pairs (*EBCC Atlas*), but it seems to have been more numerous in the 19th century and to have nested farther west (*eg* Witherby *et al* 1938–41). Striking in black-and-white breeding plumage but at other times rather dull, this species favours shallow freshwater with emergent vegetation, often by lakes or flooded rivers, and feeds on both aquatic and terrestrial invertebrates. East European White-winged Black Terns, which arrive at their nesting sites in May, leave between mid August and early October to winter in sub-Saharan Africa where, in contrast to the then essentially coastal Black Terns, they stay mainly by inland water bodies. Asiatic populations also winter from the Indian subcontinent and south China down to northern Australia.

White-winged Black Terns are rare but regular vagrants to Great Britain: a total of 722 was recorded during 1958–2000 (*BBRC*). They can occur at any time between March and November, although mostly from May to September. Many are adults, but every year some juveniles appear in August–September.

Wiltshire's first was a long overlooked record of five adult White-winged Black Terns seen 'within twenty yards' at Britford on 30 April 1888 (Morres 1889, Hony 1915a). This observation was not referred to by Hartert *et al* (1912) and, perhaps for that reason, was missed by Witherby *et al* (1938–41) who noted this species as 'Rare vagrant, mostly May, also April and June, sometimes in small flocks', but did not include Wiltshire among the 17 counties listed as having records. Morres's described combination of 'white tail and shoulders of the wing' are at that season diagnostic, and he was a respected Wiltshire ornithologist who, over many years in *WANHM* (notably Morres 1878–85), had published much about the birds of the Salisbury area – among them personal sightings of ordinary Black Terns both there and in Hampshire. Smith (1887) clearly held him in high esteem, referring frequently to him and using many records of his; had these White-winged Black Terns been seen a couple of years earlier, Smith would surely have included them.

In contrast, both modern Wiltshire records have involved juveniles. One lingered with Black Terns at CWP26 for six days during 24–29 September 1982 (*Hobby*). The other was found at CWP32 on 22 August 1998 before moving, also to CWP26, for the remainder of a nine-day stay to the 30th.

KJG

Sandwich Tern

Sterna sandvicensis

Scarce on passage, breeds coasts of Britain/west Europe, winters West Africa

Sandwich Terns breed along both sides of the North Atlantic, as well as on coasts of the Caribbean, North, Baltic, Mediterranean, Black and Caspian Seas. Most of the European population – totalling around 115,500 to 135,800 pairs (*EBCC Atlas*) – winters on shorelines from Mauritania to South Africa, some also off coasts of Iberia and Arabia and in the Mediterranean and eastern Black Sea. About 10,500 pairs nest in Great Britain, a decrease of about 15 per cent since the mid 1980s, though there had been considerable increases during the 20th century, not least through protection from the 1960s onwards (*Seabird 2000*). The biggest colonies are in Northumberland and Norfolk, while the nearest to Wiltshire are around the Solent (Hampshire).

These population changes are perhaps reflected in the pattern of Wiltshire records. Here the first and only observation before the 1939–45 War involved two at Braydon Pond in August 1922; a quarter of a century passed before two more at Erlestoke Lake in April 1947, then one at Coate Water in April 1949; and, after further gaps, singletons at Walcot, Swindon, in August 1958 and Tockenham Reservoir in June 1964 (all *WANHM*). The 1970s saw a little upsurge, beginning with no fewer than eight seen and heard in flight near Wilton Water in October 1971, followed by a singleton at Langford Lakes in May 1972, three at Coate Water in June 1977, and two at Liden Lagoon in September 1978 (*WANHM*, *Hobby*). Then, more strikingly, Palmer (1991) was able to summarise 18 records in eight of the ten years 1980–89, involving a total of 41 individuals: most records (11) were at CWP and most (14) during August–September; numbers of individuals were highest in 1980 (nine) and 1984 (ten). The nine in 1980 (two at CWP, four at Coate Water, three at Langford Lakes) were all on the same day, 21 September.

Sandwich Terns are still scarce passage migrants in Wiltshire, and CWP remains the prime locality. A total of 17 records (30 birds) was seen over ten of the 11 years 1990–2000 (table 92), all in ones or twos apart from a flock of 11 flying south over Bratton on 14 September 1995. As table 93 shows, nine records were in March–May (just one in 1980–89) and only six in August–September (14 in 1980–89) as well as one each in July and October, though these numbers are all too small for conclusions to be drawn from this apparent change in seasonal pattern.

Table 92. Sandwich Terns *Sterna sandvicensis* in Wiltshire: annual totals of individuals 1990–2000

	90	91	92	93	94	95	96	97	98	99	00
Birds	1	3	2	1	1	12	2	0	4	2	2

Table 93. Sandwich Terns *Sterna sandvicensis* in Wiltshire: monthly totals of records and individuals 1990–2000

	Jan	Feb	Mar	Apr	May	Jun	Jul	Aug	Sep	Oct	Nov	Dec
Records	0	0	1	6	2	0	1	1	5	1	0	0
Birds	0	0	2	6	3	0	1	1	15	2	0	0

KJG

Common Tern

Sterna hirundo

Now breeds locally, also migrant from coasts of Britain/Europe, winters West Africa

Common Terns are the likeliest of the 'sea terns' (genus *Sterna*) to be found in land-locked Wiltshire, as they often breed by inland waterbodies and use them also as migration stopovers. Their world breeding range encompasses much of Eurasia and North America, and there are also more isolated populations in the Caribbean, on some North Atlantic islands and in West Africa. Virtually all Common Terns winter along coasts south of their summer ranges, those nesting in Great Britain then being found largely along the Gulf of Guinea from Sierra Leone to Ghana (*Migration Atlas*). Excluding Russia, some 195,000 to 227,000 pairs are estimated to breed in Europe (*EBCC Atlas*), and Great Britain held about 10,100 pairs in 1998–2002, a modest decline from around 12,000 in the mid 1980s, although numbers in general have remained broadly stable in recent decades (*Seabird 2000*).

Commenting on the status of the Common Tern in Wiltshire, Smith (1887) wrote, 'Lord Methuen tells me it has been killed at Corsham Court; I hear of another killed at Kennet in 1881, and one at Poulshot in 1861. But, indeed, I have had so many notices of its occurrence… in North and South Wilts, that it would be tedious to enumerate them… Mr. Grant [a taxidermist] alone has had the following specimens pass through his hands' and he went on to list seven records, involving eight birds, all from sites in the middle of the county; one in May and the rest between 21 August and 3 October. In his account of the Arctic Tern, however, Smith also suggested that the two species were 'doubtless often confounded' and that it was 'most probable… that several of the instances recorded above' referred to Arctics.

Peirson (1919) noted five records of the Common Tern in the Marlborough district, the last in 1888. Its status does not appear to have changed much, if at all, by the mid 20th century. Peirson (1959) described it as 'A passage migrant' but, as shown by his comment 'A few of which had been identified definitely as belonging to this species', many were not at that time being distinguished from Arctic Terns; indeed, after a confident period of identifications of Common Terns (and one party of Arctics) through the 1930s (though not every year) and then a flush of records of each in 1947, the editors of *WANHM* became more cautious and over the next 20 years, almost without exception, lumped together all reports under the heading 'Common or Arctic'.

Buxton (1981), who noted that 'Modern identification techniques have allowed far more [Common and Arctic Terns] to be correctly assigned', regarded the Common as 'a regular spring and autumn passage migrant in small numbers, mostly at Coate Water, Corsham Lake and in the [Cotswold] Water Park'. Wiltshire's first nesting was proved on an island in CWP30, where a pair raised young in 1979 and 1980 (*Hobby*). From then through to the early 1990s, the summer presence of Common Terns in the CWP area was sustained by successful breeding in the Gloucestershire part, these often wandering across the county

boundary with their young, but, though there were several nesting attempts in the Wiltshire section, the only pair successful in that period was at CWP73 in 1988.

In 1993, however, five pairs attempted to breed at CWP74 and in 1994 nine pairs nested there – but, probably because of disturbance or predation by the foxes that were regularly seen close by, only one managed to fledge young. In 1995 a raft was floated on CWP74, but not used by Common Terns until 1996, when a pair bred and raised one young. That year, too, another pair fledged two chicks on an island in CWP82. In 1997, a second raft was anchored alongside the first, and five pairs bred successfully, followed by eight in 1998 and ten in 1999, but just one in 2000. The rafts were provided by WOS – with the permission of, and much practical assistance from, Aggregate Industries Ltd – and the Common Terns now happily share them with Black-headed Gulls (*qv*). Single pairs also bred successfully at CWP83 in 1997, at CWP86 in 1998 and at Coate Water in 1999 and in 2000. This colonisation may be seen against a background of a 5 per cent decline in the number of occupied 10-km squares in England as a whole during the 1990s, but most of that decline was in the east; there was, in fact, a westward expansion during this period, notably along the upper Thames (*Seabird 2000*).

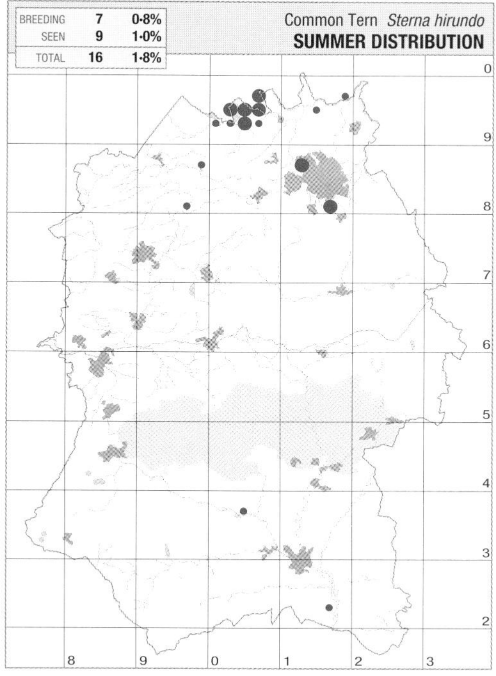

The summer tetrad map shows breeding confined to north of the county, at CWP and in the Swindon area. All the other sightings are likely to have involved passage migrants, failed breeders wandering from elsewhere and, in the north, local birds foraging away from their nesting sites. Common Terns typically arrive back in Wiltshire around 20 April, and the earliest recent date was 6 April 1993, a singleton at Braydon Pond, but ten were reported at Coate Water on 20 March 1931 (*WANHM*). At first it is difficult to differentiate between passage migrants and local breeders, but the latter start to display within days of their arrival. The noisy fish presentation by males to females is now a delightful part of spring at CWP.

Numbers at CWP increase in July as the young fledge. These can then often be found at the silt lagoon of CWP68, waiting for their parents to return with fish. It is not unusual in late summer to see as many as 20 juveniles and adults there, though colour-ringing has shown that some can be from colonies elsewhere. An adult on 10 September 1996 proved to have been ringed in 1993 at Hinksey Lake (Oxford), where it had then nested each year during 1994–96, and an adult with a dependant juvenile, both also ringed at Oxford, were seen on a number of occasions in August 1997. Several other colour-ringed Common Terns have been seen, but their origins not traced. A total of 22 Common Terns have been ringed as nestlings in Wiltshire by 2000, all on CWP rafts in 1999, but none has yet been recovered.

Large flocks of Common Terns are unusual on passage in Wiltshire, and the county's highest confirmed number was 35 at CWP68 on 7 September 1988; but a flock of around 50 Common or Arctic Terns, not confidently identified to species, was seen in flight at

Potterne on 5 May 1980. Autumn passage is normally over by the end of September, apart from occasional stragglers in the first week of October, but two exceptional winter reports came from Coate Water in 1930 (both *WANHM*, though different observers): the first, 'a bird probably of this species... for one day only in January... (a very rough day)'; and the second, nearly a year later, on 12 December, without further detail. Like other seabirds, Common Terns can be displaced inland in rough or foggy weather, and two adults flying south over Dean Hill on 21 June 1997 may well have come into that category, as a subadult Gannet was seen flying west there on the same day.

(See also page 724.)

KJG

Roseate Tern

Sterna dougallii

Vagrant (2 records), breeds coastal Britain/Ireland/ France, winters West Africa

The Roseate is the rarest of the five terns that breed regularly in Great Britain and Ireland. Close to extinction by 1900 and now endangered again, its total numbers in these islands had increased to an estimated 3500 pairs by the early 1960s (*1968–72 Atlas*, *EBCC Atlas*), but dropped sharply again to about 550 pairs 20 years later and to around 190 pairs by 1999–2000 (*Seabird 2000*). The great majority has always been in Ireland, while the British population – restricted to the Firth of Forth, northeast England, Anglesey and one or two localities in the south – fell from 691 pairs in 1969–70 to 261 in 1986 and to just 52 in 1999–2000 (*Seabird 2000*).

Apart from a handful on Madeira, the only other east Atlantic colonies are in northwest France (also declining) and the Azores (steadier at, usually, around 1000 pairs). Predation and habitat loss on the breeding grounds, and mortality through casual persecution and sport-hunting in the wintering areas, probably contributed to the serious decreases in the northwest European population in the last part of the 20th century (*EBCC Atlas*). The world breeding range is extensive, but very patchy, in the west Atlantic and Caribbean between Nova Scotia and Venezuela, around the Indian Ocean, and in the west Pacific from the Ryukyu Islands to Australia (*CBWP*); in many of those areas where trends are known, colonies have declined over recent decades – for a variety of reasons – and while some have staged recoveries, numbers remain low at most (*Seabird 2000*). Roseate Terns arrive in Great Britain and Ireland in May and leave the breeding grounds in August and September to winter off the coasts of West Africa, particularly Ghana.

These, the most marine of European terns, are never more than rare vagrants inland. It is not surprising, therefore, that only two have been recorded in Wiltshire. The first, which had been ringed as a nestling in Co Wexford (Ireland) on 30 June 1962, was found 'apparently undamaged but probably dazed' on a garden path at Seagry early in the morning on 20 August 1964 and was then released by the Bristol Avon (*WANHM*). Twenty-seven years later, an adult in summer plumage stayed at CWP29 for at least five hours on 11 May 1989 (*Hobby*), accompanying six to nine Common Terns and, at one period, joined also by a Little Gull.

KJG

Arctic Tern

Sterna paradisaea

Scarce on passage, breeds north Britain/Eurasia/ America, winters Antarctic

Arctic Terns have a circumpolar breeding distribution, north from Iceland, Ireland, Great Britain, northernmost Eurasia, northern Canada and Greenland into the high Arctic. They famously perform the longest migrations of any bird species, wintering mainly among the Antarctic pack ice. The European breeding population has been estimated at between 413,000 and 667,000 pairs, of which about 60 per cent breed in Iceland (*EBCC Atlas*). In the mid 1980s, some 76,500 pairs nested in Great Britain, almost all north of Anglesey in the west and of Northumberland in the east, though numbers subsequently declined markedly in Shetland and Orkney – primarily because of declines in sandeels, their chief prey – and by 1998–2002 the British total was down to 52,600 pairs (*Seabird 2000*).

For Wiltshire, Yarrell (1856) mentioned Devizes and Trowbridge as places visited by 'considerable numbers in the strange irruption…in 1842' detailed by Strickland in *Annals and Magazine of Natural History* for June 1842. Fourteen years later, im Thurn (1870) wrote that the Arctic Tern appeared occasionally but not as often as the Common; he also had a specimen shot in 1867 within a few hundred yards of Marlborough College grounds. Smith (1887) considered that 'Without doubt it must be a frequent visitor' and went on to list five further records, the first relating to three killed on the Kennet & Avon Canal near Devizes 'after a gale from the west' in October 1844; the others were singletons in four different years during 1867–75, the two with dates again being in September or October. Smith also thought that the Arctic Tern 'is perhaps numerically more abundant' than the Common Tern and that, because the two are often confused, some of his reports of the latter probably 'belonged to this species'.

Apart from many observations recorded as 'Common or Arctic', the only reports of Arctic Terns published over the next 80 years were 'a party of six near Berwick Bassett, at the end of September' 1932 (second-hand without further detail); and two singletons identified among Common Terns at Corsham Lake and Coate Water in April 1947, as well as an undated corpse at Foxhill near Wanborough that same year (*WANHM*). In 1956, however, at Little Somerford on 4 September, one that had been ringed as a chick at Pukhtu (Estonia) on 20 July that year 'dived at a fisherman's plug, rose sharply and struck his rod, breaking

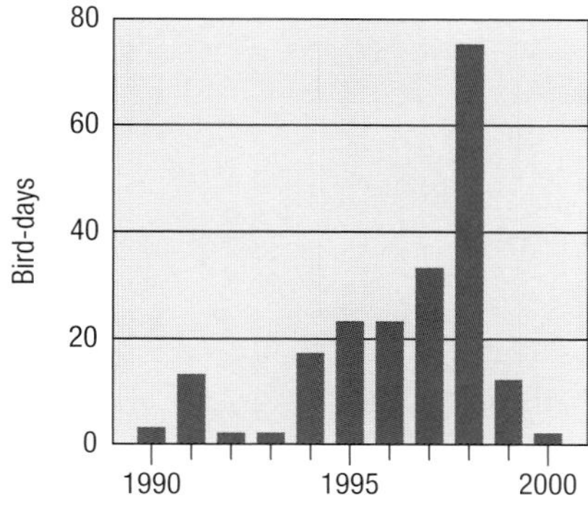

Figure 62. Arctic Terns *Sterna paradisaea* in Wiltshire: annual totals of bird-days 1990–2000

Table 94. Arctic Terns *Sterna paradisaea* in Wiltshire: monthly totals of bird-days 1990–2000

	Jan	Feb	Mar	Apr	May	Jun	Jul	Aug	Sep	Oct	Nov	Dec
Bird-days	0	0	0	47	111	2	3	32	10	0	0	0

its wing' (*WANHM*). No more specific identifications were published until 1968–70 – when there were one or two records each year – but Peirson (1959) regarded the Arctic Tern as a passage migrant. Buxton (1981) considered it regular in small numbers at Coate Water, Corsham Lake and CWP. Palmer (1991) noted that the species had been reported in every year of the 1980s, except 1981, always in April–June or August–October, most of those in spring having been in May and half of those in autumn in September; the total number of birds was only 17 in the first seven years, 1980–86, but 49 in the last three, 1987–89, an increase perhaps the result of a combination of differing weather patterns, growing numbers of observers, and improving identification techniques.

By the mid 1990s, Arctic Terns were sometimes occurring in varying numbers on successive days and it became no longer possible always to distinguish records or individuals. Although the use of 'bird-days' inevitably exaggerates actual numbers, the total for each year during 1990–2000 (figure 62) clearly shows a continuing increase, particularly during 1994–98. April and especially May now provided the peak (table 94), though numbers fluctuated widely between springs (just two bird-days in each of three years, but 75 in 1998 alone), possibly because of weather variations – which, for example, greatly influence counts of terns, as well as those of skuas and waders, migrating along the Hampshire coast (P Combridge). It may even be that the smaller totals of 1999 and 2000 were reflections of the decline then in the British population.

Arctic Tern passage through Wiltshire is now usually heaviest during the first ten days of May. The spring of 1998 produced the two largest flocks recorded in the county in modern times – 32 and 20 on 2 May – and also the earliest arrival, at CWP on 3 April. The latest in autumn, on 19 October, was back in 1988, as was the largest autumn flock, 15 on 13 August, both again at CWP. Autumn records usually involve one to three individuals, which sometimes linger for several days.

Apart from the Estonian juvenile in 1956, the only other ringing recovery in Wiltshire involved one marked as a chick at Tisnes, Tromsø (Norway), on 20 July 1992 and found dead at Orcheston five years later, on 4 September 1997.

(See also page 727.)

KJG

Guillemot

Uria aalge

Vagrant (3 old records), breeds coasts of Britain/ northwest Europe, winters at sea

Guillemots breed in dense colonies, laying their single eggs on ledges on cliffs and stacks in both the North Atlantic and the north Pacific. In the northeastern Atlantic and associated waters east to the Barents Sea and the Baltic, their colonies are found very locally along the rocky coasts of most northern and western European countries and islands from Iberia north and east to

Svalbard and Novaya Zemlya. The North Atlantic population has been estimated at 2·8–2·9 million pairs, roughly one third of that total being in Iceland. Colonies throughout the range have fluctuated in size between periodic seabird surveys, the coasts of Great Britain holding around half a million pairs of Guillemots in the mid 1980s (Lloyd *et al* 1991), but increasing to some 890,000 in 1998–2002 (*Seabird 2000*).

These auks leave their colonies during the late summer and are then exclusively marine, using both inshore and offshore waters over the continental shelf south to Portugal; the young are particularly dispersive and do not visit the nesting cliffs for at least their first two years. Inland records are few and far between and, unlike those of Little Auks (*qv*) and some other seabirds, not necessarily associated with rough weather at sea: perhaps the individual's physical state – particularly if sick or oiled – is as likely to be a key factor in any such displacement. Wiltshire has had just three Guillemots, none recent. Smith (1887) noted one 'killed' at Salisbury in December 1871, and Hony (1915a) was able to add a second for the 19th century, shot at Amesbury in 1888. The singleton in the 20th century had a kinder welcome: 'caught alive in the allotments at Warminster in May, 1916, [it] was fortunate enough to fall into the hands of captors who took it down to the sea and turned it loose a day or two afterwards' (Anon 1916).

RT

Razorbill

Alca torda

Vagrant (5 old records), breeds coasts of Britain/ northwest Europe, winters at sea

Razorbills are restricted to the North Atlantic region, breeding in loose colonies – commonly with or near Guillemots, though generally hidden in crevices – in eastern Canada, Greenland, and along north European coasts and islands from northwest France and the Baltic north to Iceland and Bear Island and the Murmansk coast of northwest Russia, but always very locally. Thus, they have a much smaller range than Guillemots and do not extend so far into the Arctic Ocean, but in winter some travel south even to the coasts of North Africa and the western Mediterranean. Iceland again has the most breeding, but British colonies were estimated to total 110,000 pairs in 1998–2002, around one fifth of the European population of 530,000 (*Seabird 2000*). Like those of other auks, Razorbill numbers have shown marked fluctuations since the 1800s and, though neither they nor their eggs are now taken for food, oil pollution and trawling nets both take their toll; British numbers have shown a modest increase since the mid 1980s.

Like Guillemots, Razorbills are exclusively marine during winter, dispersing throughout the shallower areas of the North Atlantic. Northern populations join locally bred stock in British waters, but this species is again very rare inland. Smith (1887) listed five Wiltshire records, all in the southern half of the county between December and February and, curiously, all within the space of 21 years: at Melksham in February 1862; at Netheravon on 18 January 1866; at Chitterne in late January 1871; at Salisbury 'at the close of 1871'; and near Britford on 19 February 1883. The first three were all 'shot' or 'killed', the last 'picked up' on the downs. There were no records in the 20th century.

RT

Little Auk

Alle alle

Windblown vagrant (25 records), breeds arctic coasts, winters south to North Sea

This, the most diminutive of the North Atlantic auks, is well adapted to living in harsh conditions, but food shortages and strong winds in winter sometimes result in numbers being wrecked far inland. Little Auks breed in the high Arctic, from Greenland across to Siberia's Severnaya Zemlya, probably also in the Bering Straits off Alaska, occupying nest-sites that are sometimes still covered in snow and, even there, favouring ice floes and cold currents rather than warmer waters. In arctic Europe, their colonies are confined to Jan Mayen, Bear Island, Svalbard, Franz Josef Land and Novaya Zemlya, apart from a few pairs as far south as Grímsey, off north Iceland. Estimates of numbers – understandably imprecise for a bird that nests in such remote and inhospitable areas – have varied from hundreds of thousands on each of Jan Mayen and Franz Josef Land to, in the late 1960s, 10–15 million on Svalbard alone (*CBWP*); whereas the *EBCC Atlas* suggested just 100,000 pairs in Europe, excluding Russia, nearly all on Svalbard, although it did cite a previous estimate of one million on that same archipelago.

Little Auks mostly remain in arctic waters in winter, still associating with ice floes, but some regularly reach south to Scotland during November–February, and small numbers may at times be seen anywhere in the North Sea between August and April. They feed almost entirely on planktonic crustaceans, but prolonged gales may cause the plankton to descend beyond their reach; in such conditions, many Little Auks can become weak through starvation and may then be blown inshore and sometimes far inland in 'wrecks'. Thus, although probably the least numerous in British waters, this species has mustered as many Wiltshire records as all the other auks together.

There is some confusion about the county's first Little Auks, in the Marlborough area in the 1850s and 1860s. Hony (1915a) referred to 'Two, the first about 1855', which were probably those that had been published by Hart Smith (1887) as shot on Clatford Bridge 'thirty years ago' and by im Thurn (1870) as 'on the Kennet, just opposite the "Ailesbury Arms" on the Bath road, in 1864'; the latter had previously been published in *The Field*. Perhaps because both these specimens ended in the possession of Mrs Gundry of Netley Grange, Southampton, Kennedy (1966) took it that only one bird was involved, but there seems no doubt that they were seven or more years apart. Meyrick (1895, 1906) complicated the issue by referring to one 'near Clatford about 1885' and another 'on the Kennet above Manton in 1864', but it is reasonable to assume that '1885' was an error for '1855', particularly as he also listed it first, and that the 1864 locality, unless it related to a completely different and otherwise unknown specimen, was also a mistake – which was later perpetuated by Peirson (1939).

Smith (1887) knew of only two specimens, at Gore Cross, near Lavington, on 26 October 1869 and at Wilsford Down on 17 October 1870, both reported to him by Grant, the taxidermist, while Hart Smith (1887) referred to im Thurn's 1864 record and to another, undated, at Ogbourne. With these three and the original two, the 19th century total seems likely to have been only five.

The first half of the 20th century produced three more. Hony (1912) recounted, 'Dr. Blackmore, of Salisbury tells me (May 26th) that a man brought him a Little Auk alive, from Winterbourne, "two or three months ago." Presumably this was part of the "Wreck".' Hony (1915a) added that 'Mr. Rawlence tells me that one was picked up in Grovely Wood on Dec. 11th, 1912'. Two decades later, one was 'found in Rood Ashton Wood Jan 2nd, 1930, after a fierce gale' (*WANHM*).

But then the early part of 1950 saw one of the biggest wrecks of Little Auks ever recorded in Great Britain (Sergeant 1952) and no fewer than nine were found in Wiltshire (*WANHM*) – mostly described as exhausted, injured or dead – eight of them during 11–13 February, at Avebury, Broad Chalke, Burbage, Pitton, Sutton Veny, and Wilton near Salisbury, and near both Biddestone and Britford; the ninth, more than three weeks later, was 'dead, but still warm' at West Overton on 6 March. Three of the first eight were found in urban or village 'High Streets' and two others in gardens; two of them were released on the Hampshire coast, where one, by then ringed, 'swam away strongly' but was washed up dead four or five days later.

Three years later, one was reported in an exhausted condition on a farm near Calne on 12 February 1953, and was seen there swimming in a brook the next day (*WANHM*). The only other recorded in the next 30 years – found at High Post on 6 November 1961 and released on the Salisbury Avon the following day – apparently came at a time when there was no widespread wreck but just a few Little Auks seen along the east and south coasts (*WANHM*).

The six from 1974 have all been in mid winter:

1984	10 January	Malmesbury	Seen flying south
	17 January	Coate Water	Died same day
1990	29 December	Tisbury	Released on south coast
	29 December	Shalbourne	Died in care
1991	10 January	Salisbury	Died in care
	13 January	Whitley	Died in care

The spate of four in 1990/91 occurred in a season when a national wreck in two waves in November and early December was apparently followed by a minor wreck confined to Shetland and Orkney in early January (see *BB* 84: 326–327), so these four Wiltshire records may all have been stragglers from early December.

RT

Puffin

Fratercula arctica

Windblown vagrant (16 records), breeds coasts of Britain/northwest Europe, winters at sea

Restricted to the North Atlantic region, Puffins breed on the coasts and islands of eastern Canada south to Maine (USA), of Greenland, and of northern Europe from Iceland and, in the high Arctic, Svalbard and Novaya Zemlya south to northwest France. Although sometimes nesting in crevices or among boulders, they generally excavate burrows, or take over old rabbit holes, in turf of grass and thrift, particularly on island slopes or inaccessible cliffs. Almost one half of the world total of 5·5 to 6·6 million pairs breeds in Iceland, but Great Britain supports as many as 580,000 'pairs' (apparently occupied burrows), a general increase having occurred since the mid 1980s (*Seabird 2000*).

In Great Britain, the largest colonies are in Scotland – particularly on St Kilda (Outer Hebrides), the Isle of May (Fife) and Fair Isle (Shetland) – and the Farne Islands

(Northumberland), but the Puffin's clown face, colourful bill and comical character ensure an enduring popularity that makes more 'accessible' colonies such as those at Bempton (Yorkshire) and on Skomer and Skokholm (Pembrokeshire) perhaps better known.

Puffins are highly dispersive during the winter, occurring farther offshore than other auks: even mid ocean records are not rare, the result of transatlantic movements by a proportion of juveniles (see discussion in *Migration Atlas*). Unless storm-driven inland in their first autumn, 'juveniles make their own way out to sea and stay there until they begin to visit colonies again as pre-breeders... of 4–5 years of age' (*CBWP*). Against this background, the relatively large number of Wiltshire records seems rather curious: perhaps the big Pembrokeshire colonies act as a 'local' source of young wanderers?

The first of two county specimens recorded by im Thurn (1870) 'was caught by hand by George Scott (Postman), on the banks of the River Kennet, near the village of the same name, on 25th of October, 1869'; 'in a very poor condition' and subsequently procured for the Marlborough College museum, it was presumed to have come in as a result of 'rough weather in the middle of September'. Later that same autumn, the 'second specimen [of the two noted by im Thurn] was afterwards picked up dead' near Kennet (Meyrick 1895). Morres (1878–85) recorded a juvenile brought to him in autumn 1883: 'One of the carters had caught it on a high-lying fallow in our Parish [Britford], and it had bitten his fingers so hard that he had to kill it'. Smith (1887) included all these three, adding that the first was sent to him by TA Preston, whereupon he identified it as being 'in immature plumage, and was, in fact, a bird of the year' – but he gave the year of the Britford record as 1863 instead of 1883; he also added that Grant, the taxidermist, reported another 'killed at Salisbury, December 28th, 1871', which was brought to him for preservation. Hart Smith (1887) listed the two from im Thurn and added two 'seen on a pond near the Warren by Mr. Rendle, St. Catherine's, one of which was captured November 21st, 1879', and a further specimen shot in the Forest in 1880. Hony (1915a) quoted *WANHM* to add that 'Six or seven were seen and one killed by wire' at Codford St Mary on 20 November 1893, following three days of severe northerly gales.

Buxton (1981) concluded that there were 'At least seven records for the last [19th] century and nine for this'. The above summary shows a total of exactly seven records in the 19th century – though those in November 1979 and 1883 each involved more than one bird – and only seven can now be traced for 1900–81, six of them before 1974. One caught alive near Rockley in the first week of November 1919 died a week later (Peirson 1919, Kennedy 1966). The first of two in the 1940s was picked up alive on the bank of the Kennet, at Marlborough, on the early date of 1 August 1944; and the second was a juvenile found exhausted on the downs near Ansty on 14 October 1949 (*WANHM*). A series of three in the 1950s – all juveniles picked up alive – began with one at Hartham on 20 August 1951, followed by others on Combe Bissett Down on 9 November 1953 and on Boscombe Down on 22 November 1959 (*WANHM*); the last was wrongly attributed to 1958 by Webber (1968). No more were recorded for 16 years. Since 1974:

1975	23 November	near Chippenham	Wandering amid cows, released Avon
1983	12 September	Corsham	Juvenile, grounded, released Dorset
1988	5 March	Devizes	Adult, dead on dual carriageway

The one in 1988 is noteworthy for being the county's only spring record and only reported adult.

RT

Pallas's Sandgrouse

Syrrhaptes paradoxus

Vagrant (2–3 old records) during former eruptions into Europe, breeds Asia

Although several species of sandgrouse breed in southern Europe and north Africa, only Pallas's has ever wandered to Great Britain – and, moreover, been recorded at least twice in Wiltshire, even if long ago. Now the nearest part of the normal range of this species lies inside Asia, east of the Caspian Sea, from Kazakhstan to Mongolia and northern China. It is partially migratory, northern populations moving south to varying extents depending on the snow cover, and, very infrequently, small or large numbers may erupt westward or eastward.

Pallas's Sandgrouse favour sandy and saline areas in open steppe and semi-desert. A heavy fall of snow, or the formation of a hard crust, can lead to their having difficulty in obtaining their normal diet of seeds or young shoots, a problem that may be the primary cause of their eruptive movements in autumn and winter (Dementiev & Gladkov 1951). The largest of those, however, tended to take place in May, after the worst of the weather was over, and smaller ones also in autumn, which suggests that other factors must ultimately have been involved, such as food shortage in a temporary wintering area or overpopulation after breeding (see discussion in *BWP*).

Whatever the reason, around 100 years ago these sandgrouse used very occasionally to be recorded right across Eurasia from Spain to Korea, and even Japan (Madge & McGowan 2002). In 1863, 1888–89 and 1908, spectacular eruptions resulted in widespread invasions of much of Europe, the last of which was reported by Witherby (1908) and Jourdain (1910), and analysed in some detail by von Tschusi zu Schmidhoffen (1909). But the biggest of all was that of 1888 extending into 1889, when thousands – in flocks of tens to 200 or more – spread over many parts of Great Britain, nesting even being proved in Yorkshire and Elgin (Moray) as well as in at least ten other European countries (see Witherby *et al* 1938–41, *CBWP*).

Pallas's Sandgrouse visited Salisbury Plain in the first two of those three great invasions. In 1863, a singleton was shot at Imber on 29 June: it was 'a female, and was alone, and in rapid flight from north to south' (Smith 1887). In 1888, however, 'a covey of about twenty sand grouse were seen on Salisbury Plain for several days previous to May 20, but not since they were last seen at Shrewton. On the 23rd one was found in a field at Winterbourne, which I now have; it is a female in good condition, and had been feeding on seeds. I hear that a covey was seen at Clifton on the 21st. Were they the same?' (G White, of Salisbury, writing in *The Field* of 2 June 1888, his being one of several nationwide contributions there on the great invasion of that year). Hony (1915a) referred briefly to the covey seen 'previous to' the 20th, but included no locality and did not mention the lone female shot on the 23rd: whichever 'Winterbourne' was involved then, perhaps that should be treated as a separate record.

Forty years later, there was a curious comment in *Nature* (121: 189–190) – also mentioned by Peirson & Walford (1930), Peirson (1939) and Kennedy (1966) – to the effect that the Marlborough area 'is the only place where the Icterine Warbler has been known to breed in England [now rejected (page 591)], and perhaps this is true of the Sand Grouse, which once seemed to bid fair to become a permanent resident of Martinsell, drinking from its dewponds'. This suggests that at some time a party of

Pallas's Sandgrouse settled in the Martinsell area – in which case it, too, is most likely to have been in 1888, the year of the greatest and most drawn-out invasion – but it has not proved possible to discover the source.

During 1859–1909, Pallas's Sandgrouse were also recorded in Great Britain in nine other years (Witherby *et al* 1938–41), but then came a gap of 55 years before the first of just six more acceptable British records (involving seven birds) by the end of the 20th century – in 1964, 1969 (at least three, probably others), 1975 and 1990 (*BBRC*) – mostly coinciding with a small scattering of the species on the Continent. Eruptive movements do still occur in western Asia, if infrequently, but why the movements were formerly so extensive and why the pattern has changed so much are not fully understood, although it should be added that the biggest invasions occurred in the early stages of the gradual desiccation of the Aralo-Caspian region (*cf* Tufted Duck) and that subsequently the species' western breeding limit withdrew eastwards – formerly it extended into Europe between the lower Volga and the Urals – and population numbers fluctuated markedly (Witherby *et al* 1938–41, Dementiev & Gladkov 1951, Voous 1960, Vaurie 1965, Ferguson-Lees & Sharrock 1969, *CBWP*).

RT & IJF-L

Feral Pigeon/Rock Dove

Columba livia

Common naturalised resident, descended from captive Rock Doves

Many British birdwatchers would put Feral Pigeons on an ornithological par with farmyard ducks – and a long way below even, say, Pheasants. Domestication of these pigeons' Rock Dove ancestors began centuries ago. Probably originally 'harvested' as young or eggs from sea caves and then reared for food, Rock Doves were later selectively bred for homing and racing, and for fancy varieties. They were introduced to parts of every inhabited continent, and escapes and releases built up naturalised populations almost worldwide, these being further increased by stray racers, homers and other domesticated pigeons and, more locally, by interbreeding with wild Rock Doves. Such feral populations have tended to settle in lowlands, most numerously in urban areas – where food is plentiful and where the ancestral cliff-sites are replaced by ledges on tall buildings – but also on craggy coasts and in open country, there nesting in crevices in, for example, barns and under railway bridges.

In Europe as a whole, excluding Russia, the local wild and widespread domesticated populations have together been estimated at 5·1 to 6·0 million pairs (*EBCC Atlas*), but the vast majority of this total relates to the naturalised stock with its wide range of plumages. In Great Britain, Rock Doves are probably still to be found in a more or less genetically pure state on remote islands, and perhaps some mainland seacliffs, in north and west Scotland (see discussions in *1968–72 Atlas*, *1988–91 Atlas* and *CBWP*). The same applies to the west and north coasts of Ireland and to certain east Atlantic archipelagos from the Faeroes to the Cape Verdes. Because the indigenous populations are being diluted by their generally spreading naturalised descendants, however, there are probably no true Rock Doves left anywhere else in northern and central Europe; even those in Iceland are

Feral Pigeons. Otherwise, Rock Doves are still distributed locally on islands, other rocky coasts and inland cliffs from the Mediterranean and Black Sea regions across central and southern Asia, and in the desert massifs of the Sahara and Arabia. Whether we like them or not, Feral Pigeons form an integral part of the British avifauna.

In towns, they interact with human beings because many people either enjoy seeing them and giving them bread and other scraps in public squares, or hate them because of the mess they cause wherever they roost or feed. They also compete for food with gulls and other urban scavengers. On farmland, they feed on cereals and peas and have probably – like Wood Pigeons – been encouraged by the huge spread of oilseed rape since the 1970s (Inglis *et al* 1990). Their impact on the British environment as a whole is perhaps less than that of Pheasants only because that species is more numerous through artificial breeding. Among semi-domesticated or introduced birds, their ecological significance is probably greater than those of Red-legged Partridges and even Little Owls. Perhaps most importantly in conservation terms, Feral Pigeons form a significant food supply for Peregrines and female Sparrowhawks.

The Wiltshire summer distribution map for 1995–2000 is surprisingly uneven and may reflect observers' indifference to, or even uncertainty about, what constitutes a Feral Pigeon. With white rumps and two strong black bars on the inner part of the wings, the commonest varieties can look very like Rock Doves – apart from tending to have thicker bills and ceres. Some, known as 'blue chequers', have their wing-coverts also speckled with black; many other variants range from blackish or red-brown to more or less whitish, and variously marbled or mottled, even piebald. But white dovecote pigeons do not come under this heading.

One would expect Wiltshire's greatest numbers of Feral Pigeons, and easy evidence of breeding, to be in the major urban areas. In fact, three-quarters of the breeding reports and many of the other sightings came from villages and farms. (Though observers were discouraged from recording birds of any species just flying over, it may be that some of the rural flocks of 'Feral Pigeons' involved racers passing through.) The summer map shows obvious strengths in Swindon and parts of Salisbury and nearby Wilton, and proof of breeding also in Malmesbury, Highworth, Wootton Bassett, Calne, Marlborough, Melksham, Devizes, Westbury, Warminster and Mere, but the species was only 'seen' in Pewsey and Trowbridge, and was apparently (if almost unbelievably) not recorded in Chippenham, Corsham, Bradford-on-Avon, and most of the Amesbury and Tidworth areas.

The summer abundance and winter maps show similar unevenness, with the highest densities in the northeast and southwest. Although stronger presence was recorded in winter around Chippenham, the species' apparent absence from Marlborough and Pewsey doubtless reflects the fact that neither of those two town centres fell into the randomised sample of tetrads surveyed. On the other hand, the high winter density in the next 10-km square to the north (SU17) may seem surprising because nearly all of that area, which includes half of the Marlborough Downs, is rural; there, however, 'country' flocks of Feral Pigeons can often be seen, sometimes mixing around barns or grain stores with Collared Doves, Corn Buntings, sparrows and finches (SB Edwards). Autumn and winter flocks may also feed on wheat stubbles, the largest such published in *Hobby* during the atlas period being 300 at Liddington Castle (1997) and 160 at Old Sarum (1999). Peak urban winter counts (all November–February) in *Hobby* included 310 in Swindon (1996), 40 in Wootton Bassett (1998), 40 in Chippenham (1999), 45 in Calne (1999), 130 in Marlborough (2000), 45 in Devizes (1999) and 65 in Salisbury (1999). At least in Swindon and Salisbury, Feral Pigeons are controlled as pests, which must affect their numbers.

It is almost impossible to know whether the Feral Pigeon's status in Wiltshire is changing in any way. Smith (1887) wrote, under 'Rock Dove', that it 'used to breed in

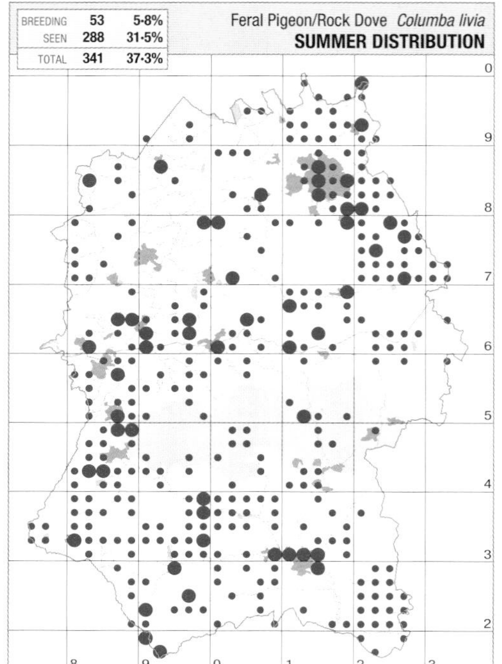

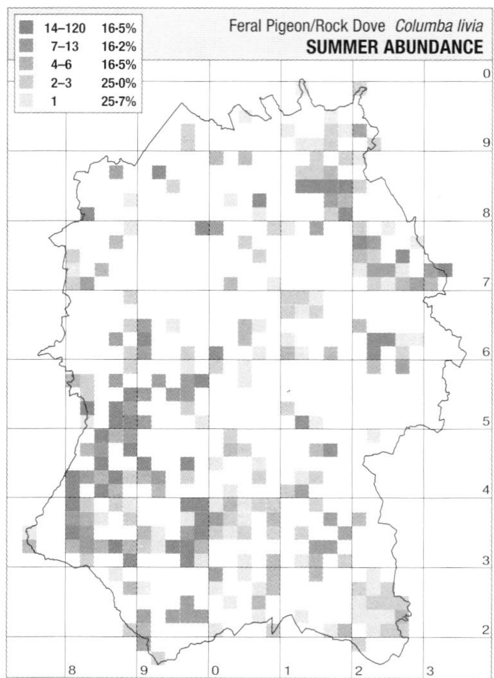

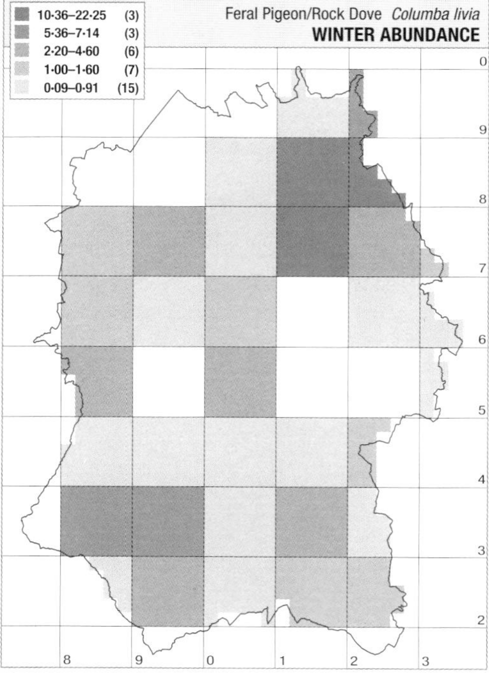

the rocks near Roundway, whence the late Mr. Withers, the skilful taxidermist of Devizes, frequently received a specimen for preservation'; and Peirson (1959) also noted that 'it is said that...some were shot near Salisbury in March 1870 (*The Zoologist* 1870, p.2101)'. So far as is known, however, the only wild Rock Doves south of Scotland were almost entirely on coastal cliffs, and were mostly extinct even there well before the end of the 19th century – by which time they were restricted to Yorkshire, one site in Cumbria, west Wales, and 'very sparingly' in Devon and Cornwall (*1875–1900 Atlas*) – whereas Feral Pigeons were a feature of, for example, not only London but 10th century Trowbridge (Bourdillon 1993) and Medieval Salisbury (Coy 1986). In the 19th century, the Roundway birds would surely have been no more than Rock Dove look-alikes. Perhaps such Feral Pigeons – as against 'the numerous varieties which inhabit our dovecots' (Smith 1887) – were more unusual in Wiltshire then.

Nationally, as indicated by the change map in the *1988–91 Atlas*, Feral Pigeons apparently spread into many 10-km squares in the 20 or so years from the early 1970s, particularly in southeast Scotland and central, east and southern England. Because the distribution in the late 1980s was very similar to that shown by the *1981–84 Winter Atlas*, Feare (1993) suggested that the increase must have been in the 1970s. It seems possible, however, that the spread was perceived rather than real, as the British ornithological literature took little or no notice of Feral Pigeons before that. After Murton & Westwood (1966) drew attention to the difficulty of defining what constituted a wild Rock Dove population, the *1968–72 Atlas* and its successors plotted both on single maps.

In the *1968–72 Atlas*, Feral Pigeons were recorded in only eight of Wiltshire's 33 core 10-km squares, and breeding in just four, but by the time of the *1981–84 Winter Atlas* they were apparently much more widespread – in 27 of the 33, and in all areas except for Salisbury Plain and parts of the northwest and southwest. Yet, while the *1988–91 Atlas* found them in a similar 27 of the core 10-km squares, and breeding in 15, its abundance map showed no real concentrations in the county apart from the Swindon area and, even there, nothing approaching the scale of the numbers in the major conurbations of Greater London, the West Midlands and the industrial north.

The summer tetrad survey of 1995–2000 recorded a further increase: Feral Pigeons were found in all 33 of the core squares, and breeding in 21, though the winter tetrad fieldwork in 1998–2000 found them in only 27 (one fewer than in the *1981–84 Winter Atlas*). In the terms of the finer summer grid, they were seen in fewer than one third of all tetrads and found breeding in less than six per cent. The count of 2333 birds in the summer survey is similar to the extrapolated estimate of 2125 for winter, as is to be expected for this resident species, and points to a likely minimum Wiltshire population of 2000 to 3000 pairs. (Analysis of data from BBS in Wiltshire suggests 1150 pairs, but this estimate is from a limited number of 1-km squares and will have under-recorded urban numbers.) With a large proportion occurring in the most urban habitats – areas that will have been little counted in atlas fieldwork because of their general unimportance for most other species – Feral Pigeons are probably under-recorded by birdwatchers and even targeted surveys. Indeed, there are no accurate data on trends from national schemes and, while the *1968–72 Atlas* suggested 100,000 or more pairs, the *1988–91 Atlas* simply noted an increase of 39 per cent in the number of occupied 10-km squares in which these birds were reported, without providing any revised estimate of numbers; *APEP* still adopted the 100,000, but noted that this was a minimum.

Nationally, the highest concentrations of Feral Pigeons are found in the major urban areas – particularly around London, in the Midlands north to Lancashire and Yorkshire, and in southern and eastern Scotland (*1988–91 Atlas*) – and although, for city dwellers, Feral Pigeons are therefore probably the most familiar of all birds, it is surprising how little is known about them. In urban conditions, where there is warmth and plenty of food, they nest almost throughout the year: a pair may raise up to six broods and the young can themselves breed at the age of six or seven months (Johnson & Johnson 1990). As they are highly gregarious and often nest in loose colonies, shortages of suitable ledges and holes may limit reproduction, though artificial food supplies are the key factor and only by removing those can overlarge urban numbers be reduced (Feare 1990, 1993). Their pest status in recent decades has seen an increase in the use of deterrents – particularly netting or spikes over favoured ledges on buildings – though it remains to be seen what effect this will have on the species' abundance and distribution, if, indeed, monitoring data for this largely unpopular bird are sufficient to assess any change.

IJF-L

Stock Dove

Columba oenas

Common and increasing resident of parkland, downland, wood edges, farmland with trees and barns, locally towns

In Gilbert White's day, in the second half of the 18th century, there was much confusion about the then three resident British pigeons and, a hundred years later, Smith (1887) wrote of the Stock Dove, 'Though by no means a rare bird, this species has been much overlooked ... and confounded with its congener [the Wood Pigeon]'. The same applies even now. This is the most unobtrusive of our common pigeons and certainly under-recorded in Wiltshire. Its gruff, repeated, two-syllable *coo-oh* is easily missed by the unwary. In winter, too, although sizeable flocks do occur, it tends to be less gregarious, and thus less obvious, than other pigeons.

Stock Doves breed from Morocco throughout much of Europe and western Asia north to southern Fenno-Scandia and central Russia, thence into western Siberia and locally in central Asia. Western and southern European populations are essentially sedentary, but those from northern and central Europe and western Asia migrate southwest and south to winter in the north Mediterranean and south Caspian regions. During the 20th century, these migratory populations seriously declined in numbers in various northern, central and east European countries (*CBWP*), while decreases of 20–50 per cent have also been noted in the mainly resident Stock Doves of Spain, France, Croatia and Bulgaria (*EBCC Atlas*).

On the other hand – despite setbacks in the 1950s and early 1960s as a result of the widespread use at that time of cyclodiene and, later, organochlorine seed-dressings – continuing increases of Stock Doves in Great Britain since the late 19th century can be correlated with the spread of arable farming (O'Connor & Mead 1984); these increases have been paralleled in the Netherlands (*CBWP*), and to a lesser extent in Ireland, Belgium and Denmark (*EBCC Atlas*). Nevertheless, although widespread in much of England and Wales as a whole, Stock Doves remain comparatively scarce in Cornwall, west Wales and northwest England, and are absent from most of the central Highlands and west and north Scotland. Even that represents a slight contraction in range – as against total numbers – since the 1970s, but still a considerable spread north and west over the past century and a half (Thom 1986, *1875–1900 Atlas*).

The archetypal habitat of this species in Great Britain is the country estate and its parkland and other open ground with scattered old trees and long established avenues. Gradually and increasingly, Stock Doves have become widespread in timbered farmland, extending to wood edges, old hedgerows and riversides, wherever large mature trees are present, but they are also found locally in old buildings in some urban areas, such as Swindon and Salisbury. In Swindon, until recently, they nested in the disused railway works.

Often as single pairs but sometimes several together, Stock Doves breed inconspicuously in holes in trees, inside barns and other buildings (sometimes in thatch) or in sheltered cavities in quarries and cliffs, less often in old nests of other birds (especially of Magpie and Wood Pigeon), squirrel dreys and rabbit holes. They take readily, too, to boxes intended for owls and Kestrels – in Wiltshire most notably on Salisbury Plain. Nests are also occasionally found under thick bushes, but one 'with eggs on the ground under a sheet of corrugated iron on Downs above West Lavington' in 1959 (*WANHM*) is noteworthy. Among other sites reported in *WANHM*, a nest in 1971 was constructed 'in the branches of a dense cypress at Hungerdown' and over the years there were several references to breeding in army tanks on SPTA, as well as, in 1966, two pairs 'with young in boxes of old water tanks' and another 'nesting in an old Daimler gun-car'. Although never referred to in *Hobby*, derelict army tanks and armoured personnel carriers are still frequently adopted by Stock Doves for nesting on SPTA (PE Castle).

In Wiltshire, in the inaugural bird report in *WANHM* for 1929, the Stock Dove was considered to be 'A common resident, which is on the increase'; the next entries, for 1933, referred to 'large numbers in the old elms at Figheldean' and 'At Clyffe Pypard it commonly nests in old pollard willows'; in 1934, it was 'Very common and resident throughout the county but reported as decreasing at Britford…and Pitton', and at Shrewton 'considerably augmented by autumn migrants'. This last point seems debatable. Although the Fenno-Scandian and central and east European populations are migratory, there is 'no known regular winter immigration' into Great Britain, even if 'continental migrants [are] occasionally drifted to eastern England' (*CBWP*); indeed, evidence for such immigration 'has been sparser' in recent years, probably because of falling numbers in Fenno-Scandia and only one of just three recoveries of foreign-ringed nestlings in England – from the Netherlands, Belgium and Finland – has been since 1979 (*Migration Atlas*). It seems more likely that autumn and winter flocks and roosts are concentrations of mainly local British stock. The only three recoveries of 249 Stock Doves ringed in Wiltshire during 1965–2000 had all moved under 10 km – though one of those, marked at Cricklade in July 1978, had strayed a total of 5 km over the border when it was shot more than three years later near Cirencester (Gloucestershire) in November 1981.

Through the 1940s, the few entries about this species in *WANHM* related to nest-sites, clutch size and late nests, including one incubating an unusual clutch of three eggs on the very late date of 17 November 1946 – that number of eggs outdone, years afterwards, by a Stock Dove sitting on no fewer than four at Corsham in March 1962 – and another nesting in the same tree as a pair of Barn Owls. (In fact, a pair now annually occupies the same barn as a pair of Barn Owls at one Wiltshire site.) In the 1950s, flock and roost sizes began to be recorded, including an estimated 200–300 near Thingley in February 1959. That same year came the interesting observation that 'Of pigeons shot near Upton Lovel [now Lovell] about 40% were Stock Doves' – regrettably, no actual numbers were published – whereas the tetrad counts from the 1995–2000 surveys showed that Stock Doves comprised just 7·8 per cent in summer and 3·3 per cent in winter of the county figures for Stock Doves and Wood Pigeons combined. In the early 1960s, the largest flocks recorded were: 'Several hundreds in Ham Hill area' in October 1961 and 'Up to 250…near High Post' in March 1962. Thereafter, apart from 'Thought to have suffered from the cold weather' in the particularly harsh winter of 1962/63 and 'Marked increase at Castle Combe' in 1964, there were no entries in *WANHM*, other than occasional laconic references to 'only a few records received'. Similarly, almost nothing was published in *Hobby* during 1974–87, apart from one or two vague comments on decreases or increases in the numbers of records submitted, but in 1988 the interest in flock size began anew and thereafter, through to 2000, the annual summaries concentrated on this aspect, though usually only a handful of observers was involved.

The highest numbers recorded in the last quarter of the 20th century were 'an exceptionally large flock of 270 at Bowood' in December 1989, 207 at Dean Hill in March 1998, and 300 at Netheravon Airfield in January 2000. Roost counts were generally smaller, mostly in the range of 30–75, but included maxima at Swindon STW of 120 in October 1998 and 150 in November and December 2000. During 1991–93, there were repeated references to a decline in numbers on SPTA, but equally frequent repetitions about the small numbers of observers submitting data on this species. The notable – if probably still inadequate – upsurge in records during the summer tetrad surveys of 1995–2000 and, particularly, during the winter counts of 1998–2000 told its own story.

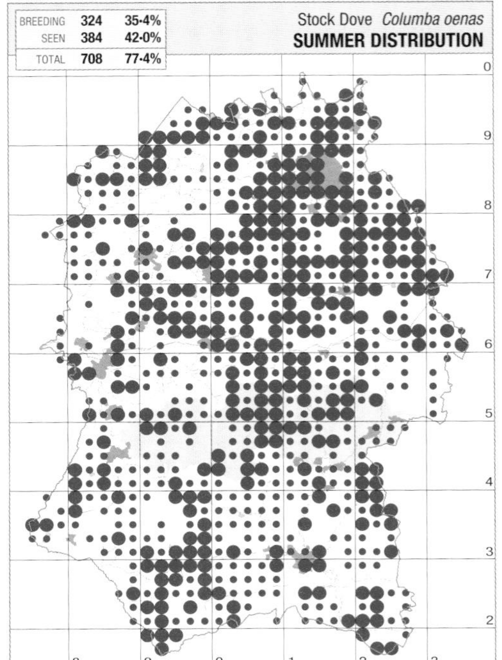

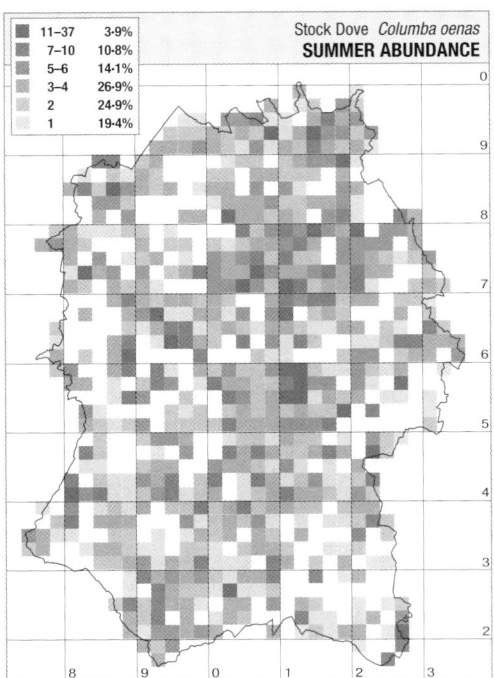

The breeding population of Europe, excluding Russia, has been estimated at 487,000 to 537,000 pairs (*EBCC Atlas*), while the *1988–91 Atlas* put the British numbers alone at 240,000 'territories'. This latter figure – approaching half the European total – may, however, be on the high side. It appears to be based on 'about double' the 'just above' 100,000 pairs in the *1968–72 Atlas*, a figure which itself was calculated from a CBC 'average of just over one pair per km^2 in 1972'. CBC/BBS data do indeed indicate a huge growth of 63 per cent in the British numbers over the last quarter of the 20th century, and the BBS an increase of 14 per cent in England during 1994–2002 (*BBWC*). Moreover, Wiltshire does lie in a region of high density (*1988–91 Atlas*). If, on that basis, an arbitrary minimum of two pairs per km^2 were converted to eight pairs per tetrad in which the species was recorded, the summer population of Wiltshire might be in the order of 5250 pairs. This figure compares favourably with a range of 3050 to 6720 pairs, calculated by applying density estimates from BBS in Wiltshire, the Cotswolds and the Chilterns. Using the ratio of timed summer to winter counts by WOS suggests that numbers in the latter season might lie between 5530 and 12,200 individuals.

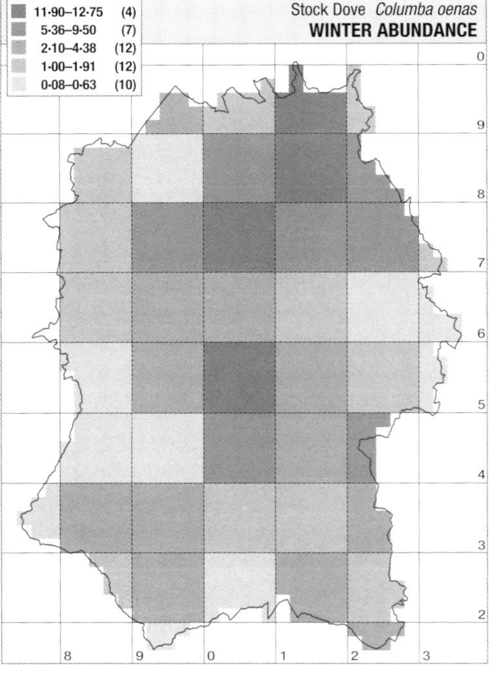

In the tetrad surveys of 1995–2000, Stock Doves were proved breeding in summer and found in winter in all of the county's 33 core 10-km squares; similarly, they had been recorded in all 33 in the *1968–72 Atlas* (breeding proved in 28) and again in the *1981–84 Winter Atlas*, and in all but one in the *1988–91 Atlas* (breeding in 29). In fact, the summer distribution map here shows some unexpected gaps – particularly in a number of adjacent tetrads north and northeast of Bradford-on-Avon, west and southwest of Braydon Pond, in the areas of Collingbourne and Great Ridge Woods, and in certain directions around Salisbury – seeming to confirm that this species is likely to have been largely overlooked by some observers and under-identified by others. Although size, shape and flight-actions are all subtly different, it is not hard to dismiss a fleetingly seen Stock Dove as a Wood Pigeon or, in some areas, as a Feral Pigeon.

IJF-L

Wood Pigeon

Columba palumbus

Widespread and common resident in arable with trees, also in towns and villages

Only 16 species of birds are estimated to have seven-figure breeding populations in Great Britain, probably just eight of which can muster two million or more 'pairs' or 'territories'. Seven of those are smaller passerines, the one larger species being the Wood Pigeon, which ranks sixth or seventh behind Wren, Chaffinch, Robin, Blackbird, Blue Tit and, possibly still, House Sparrow in that order (*APEP*). In Wiltshire, according to the tetrad counts during 1995–2000, the Wood Pigeon is the second most numerous in both summer (behind Rook) and winter (behind Starling). The summer counts produced a total of 30,854 Wood Pigeons (the highest in a single tetrad being 242) and the sample winter counts 49,726 (highest in one tetrad 2800); extrapolation from the latter figure gives a total winter figure of 99,000.

But counting birds is not straightforward and, in field conditions, those that are larger and more conspicuous are less likely to be missed, particularly if – like Wood Pigeons and, even more, Rooks – they are noisy and often visible on tree tops or in open fields. Thus, while probably neither species is really commoner in Wiltshire than several of the smaller songbirds listed above, their recorded numbers are among the most accurate (except for those of scarce birds restricted to a particular well-defined habitat, especially open water). Wood Pigeons have a characteristic display flight, and make a variety of unmistakable noises: the hoarse, rhythmic *cooo-coo coo-coo cu* is one of the most familiar country sounds; the undulating display is fairly distinctive in itself but draws attention by loud wing-claps at the top of the rise; and the thrashing around of territorial fighting in a tree just lasts longer than the clatter with which a sitting pigeon invariably leaves its nest if any danger passes too close.

Wood Pigeons are found in woodland, shelter belts, conifer plantations, tall thick hedges and other wooded places throughout the county, especially in arable farmland areas, but also increasingly in villages, towns and city parks, often in small gardens – where they will take scraps on lawns and patios and feed at bird-tables. They now often share the urban habitat with Collared Doves, to which, perhaps surprisingly, they sometimes lose position at food sources (DA Ellis in *Hobby*). They build their flimsy platform nests typically in evergreen and broadleaved trees to heights of up to 25 m, but also in hawthorn and other bushes, sometimes near or even on the ground in hedge bottoms or dense cover. Those in urban areas, where they are warmer and safer from predators, with a variety of food sources, have an extended breeding season from the end of February to early November – indeed, Wiltshire Wood Pigeons have been found incubating at Great Durnford and Clarendon as early as 23–24 January 1951 (*WANHM*) and a recently fledged juvenile was seen at Wroughton Reservoir on 10 December 1997 (*Hobby*) – but elsewhere nesting is more concentrated into the period from May to September, though eggs have been recorded in every month (Murton 1965). They usually try to rear two broods, even three, but more than two-thirds of nests fail through predation of eggs or starvation of young (whose rate of growth may depend on food supply); fledging success is highest in August because of the greater availability then of cereal crops (Murton 1958, 1965).

In Great Britain as a whole, the Wood Pigeon is represented almost everywhere, apart from some of the Northern and Western Isles of Scotland, but it is generally scarce in northwest Scotland and the central Highlands – avoiding mountains and bare uplands – where the change map in the *1988–91 Atlas* showed 50 or more 10-km squares as deserted since the *1968–72 Atlas*. The population is densest in the southern two-thirds of England and in the Welsh Borders, as well as in some smaller areas of south and north Wales, northeast England and southwest and east Scotland up to the Moray Firth (abundance map in *1988–91 Atlas*). The population in 1990 was estimated as 2·6 million pairs (*1988–91 Atlas*), and remained broadly similar – 2·5 to 3·0 million territories (*APEP*) – at the end of that decade, compared with 5·8 million birds, or 2·9 million 'pairs', in the early 1960s (Murton 1965).

On this basis, as much of Wiltshire lies within the area of denser distributions, it might be expected that the summer population of the county's 33 core 10-km squares (as a proportion of the 2308 squares in which breeding was proved in Great Britain in the *1988–91 Atlas*) would be in the range of 35,000 to 43,500 territories – or, taking Wiltshire's total area of 349,000 ha into account, equating to a county figure of 38,400 to 47,700 territories. These figures are, however, well below the 95,300 to 250,000 'pairs' obtained by applying the results of the BBS in Wiltshire, the Cotswolds and the Chilterns to the area of the county. All of those surveys are much more recent than the *Atlas*, and the much bigger contemporary estimate is compatible with the large increases nationally recorded by the BBS and CBC – of 130 per cent between 1975 and 2000, and of 17 per cent between 1990 and 2000 (*BBWC*).

The Wood Pigeon was recorded in every one of Wiltshire's 48 complete and partial 10-km squares in all three national atlases between 1968 and 1991, and in both the summer and winter tetrad surveys during 1995–2000, with evidence of nesting in all three breeding surveys except for one partial square in 1988–91 – ST73, where it certainly does normally nest. (That makes the Wood Pigeon one of only a dozen resident species that were at least 'seen' right across the board in the core squares during the five grid surveys covering 1968–2000.) Moreover, as the summer distribution map for 1995–2000 shows, it was recorded in summer in over 99 per cent (all but five) of Wiltshire's 915 tetrads, a higher proportion than that of any other species.

Though they also feed on a great variety of berries and weed and tree seeds, Wood Pigeons have always been unpopular with farmers (except as targets) and hated by gardeners (who usually have no access to such aggressive counter-measures) because of the damage they do to cereal sowings, other crops and kitchen gardens. Indeed, they are generally regarded as major agricultural pests. Populations have long been studied at a site in Cambridgeshire, the findings of which have a much wider application (*eg* Murton 1965, Murton *et al* 1974, Inglis *et al* 1990). In the 1950s and 1960s, Wood Pigeons survived the winter by feeding on clover and weed seeds (which could be affected by snow cover), but as pastures and weedy

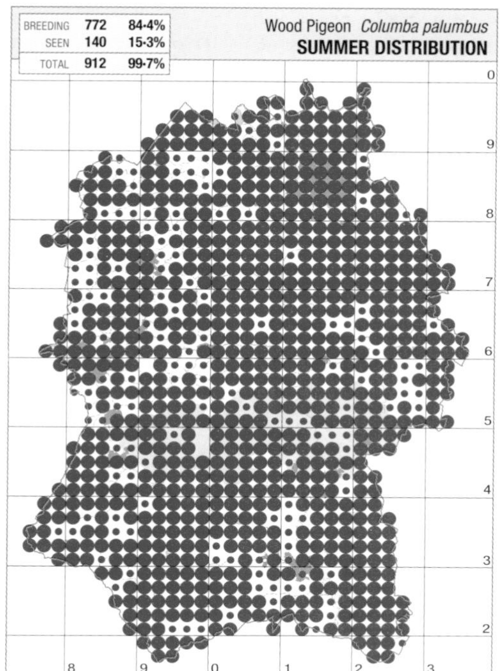

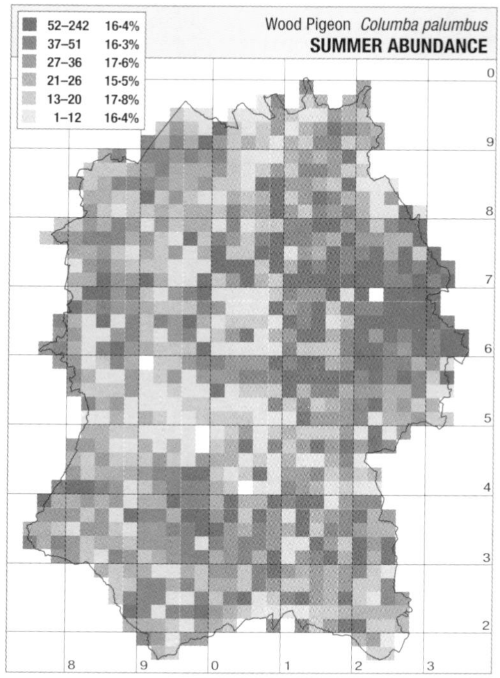

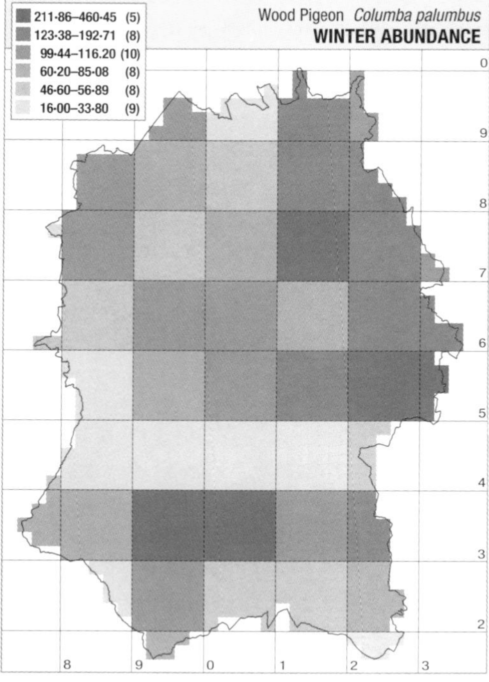

areas gave way to the increased use of herbicides on larger areas of cereals in the late 1960s and early 1970s, their numbers declined. Since the early 1970s, however, the spread of oilseed rape has more than filled the gap left by the loss of clover and has become a major winter food.

In the 1960s, when the Cambridgeshire studies of the food, ecology and behaviour of this species began – well summarised by Murton (1965) – it was concluded that the size of a Wood Pigeon population 'is primarily determined by the level of the food supply' in winter and that 'it is unlikely that enough pigeons could be killed by shooting to bring about a sustained population reduction' (Murton *et al* 1964); in other words, shooting often simply removed a surplus 'which would otherwise have eaten food before dying and in this way resources were conserved to better advantage for the survivors' (Murton *et al* 1974). With the advent of oilseed rape, however, 'those present in December survive until the following spring for there is now little evidence of overwinter mortality from starvation' and 'It appears that limiting factors are now operating during the breeding season to reduce breeding success' (Inglis *et al* 1990).

There was a marked expansion in the range of the Wood Pigeon in Britain and Ireland from the 19th century or earlier (*1875–1900 Atlas*), and in north Europe in the 20th (*BWP*): the species now breeds almost throughout the Continent, except in northernmost regions of Fenno-Scandia and Russia, and has extended northwest to establish a few pairs in the Faeroes and to nest occasionally in Iceland. But it is often much thinner on the ground than in large sections of Great Britain, so much so that the estimated population of Europe, excluding Russia, is only 8·8 to 12 million pairs (*EBCC Atlas*) – surprisingly low figures, of which the British total represents about a quarter. Outside Europe, moreover, the species has a very limited range, in the Azores (and formerly Madeira), in northwest Africa, in Turkey and parts of the Middle East including northern Oman, and thence patchily east to Turkmenistan and the northwest and central Himalayas. Almost all populations, except those of westernmost Europe and the Mediterranean area, migrate southwest in autumn to winter in the southwestern and southern parts of the range.

In Wiltshire, Smith (1887) noted that the 'Ring Dove', or 'Quisty', was 'First and foremost of its congeners...and commonly dispersed amongst us, wherever trees afford it a shelter... It is abundant throughout the county, and, except when breeding, is proverbially wild and shy. It lives with us throughout the year, and congregates in winter in large flocks... it has increased very much in numbers of late, for the hawks which used to persecute it are well-nigh exterminated by the gamekeepers, and large additions are made to its ranks every autumn by the migration of vast flocks from the Continent'. Leaving aside the interesting but unlikely idea that Wiltshire's population of Wood Pigeons might at one time have been controlled by 'hawks', this quotation raises the question of immigration from the Continent. That same idea persisted through the 1930s – though pigeons in general, and Wood Pigeons in particular, received little attention in *WANHM* at that time. Indeed, apart from the first mention, in 1932, that this was 'comparatively scarce as a breeding species', most of the other entries then were concerned with the presence or absence of immigrants. These ranged from 'great numbers of foreign birds arriving on November 10th, most of which had left a week later' in 1932, and 'a huge flock of the continental form feeding on clover near Chippenham... approximately 1,000 or more' in 1936 to 'winter migration very late' in 1933. In 1934, there were comments 'on the shortage and almost absence of autumn visitors' in the Salisbury district, but 'large flights seen on migration during November' at Lydiard Millicent.

In fact, 'Irregular autumn occurrences of Continental [Wood Pigeons] in (mainly eastern) Britain [are] believed attributable to drift movements in overcast conditions over North Sea' and the 'British population [is] basically resident, even sedentary, with reports of large-scale movements in autumn–winter often due to misinterpretation of flights to/from roosts' (*BWP*, based on Murton & Ridpath 1962). Systematic watching of the east coast in recent decades, however, 'has revealed annual movements in late autumn', though the 'numbers involved vary greatly from year to year'; these movements may concern some from Fenno-Scandia *en route* to France and Iberia, though, as there are just eight recoveries of foreign-ringed Wood Pigeons in Great Britain, evidence of regular immigration is lacking (*Migration Atlas*). In some years, however, atypical movements of British Wood Pigeons can result from local food shortages (Murton 1965) and it is likely that winter invasions of, particularly, young ones in Wiltshire originate mainly from farther north in England and Scotland. Only 96 Wood Pigeons were ringed in Wiltshire during 1965–2000, and all eleven of those recovered had moved only short distances, but two had survived for more than six years: the older had been ringed at Chisbury on 5 September 1964 and was shot at Hungerford 6 years, 10 months and 12 days later.

After the 1939–45 War, even less attention was paid to Wood Pigeons in *WANHM*. Apparently nothing whatsoever of note was reported in 21 of the 25 years between 1946 and 1970. Most of the few intervening entries involved 'two influxes of immigrants' in September 1950, after which 'Very large numbers arrived, Nov. 4, and were present to the end of the year'; 'Many reports of large winter flocks' in 1952; and flocks of 1000 and 600 in January and February 1972. More interestingly, however, in the severe winter of 1962/63, 'All observers agree that this species suffered very heavy casualties. Estimates of 50 to 90 per cent' casualties in flocks. But, by the following autumn 'Still very common, flocks of several thousand over Dellings Copse'.

The first 15 years of *Hobby* still often had no entries for Wood Pigeons, the few that there were simply involving flock sizes and aberrant leucistic plumages, but since 1991 flock sizes have really come to the fore, many involving hundreds, some thousands – up to a maximum of 4000 – though during 1995–2000 very few exceeded 1000, perhaps a reflection of the generally milder winters. On 4 December 1991, a 'Large influx of possibly continental origin [was] reported at Steeple Ashton ... flocks of 3000, 2500 and 4000 noted on three separate rape fields' but here, again, these are unlikely to have originated from abroad on present knowledge. The estimate of winter numbers at the end of the 1990s – on the basis of extrapolation from the summer calculations by the ratio between the timed tetrad counts in the summer and winter surveys – encompasses a broad range, but suggests that Wood Pigeons are likely to be Wiltshire's most numerous birds at that season, with between 481,000 and 1,260,000 individuals.

IJF-L

Sponsored by Pete Combridge

Collared Dove

Streptopelia decaocto

Colonised Wiltshire in 1962, now common resident of suburbs/farmyards

It is amazing to think that just over half a century ago there were no Collared Doves in Great Britain. Now their *coo-COO-coo* songs, with the emphasis on the middle syllable, and the males' harsh alighting calls are among the characteristic sounds of suburbs, parks, villages and the immediate vicinity of farm buildings over the whole country. Their now wide distribution is such that these distinctive calls sometimes intrude into film sets of Victorian England or the 1939–45 War – but are no less out of place there than a satellite dish or a modern car would be.

Only a hundred years ago, this southern Asiatic dove had just a slender and largely artificial foothold in southeast Europe, where it had been confined to Istanbul and parts of the southern Balkans, from Bulgaria to Albania, for 150 years or more. Originally it was indigenous to the Indian region north to Turkestan and east to Myanmar, perhaps also to parts of China, Mongolia and Korea (where, however, *BWP* stated that it had been introduced). It was certainly introduced in Japan and probably in Iran whence it 'expanded or was carried (probably both) westward to Iraq, Turkey, and the Balkans', being known in Turkey by the 16th century and in southeast Europe by the end of the 18th (Vaurie 1965).

In the late 1920s and early 1930s, Collared Doves began a dramatic and rapidly accelerating spread northwest from southeast Europe, and by the late 1940s had colonised a broad strip of eastern and central Europe as far north as the Netherlands and Denmark

(Hudson 1965). By 1959 they were resident in all continental European countries except Iberia, Finland and what was then the Soviet Union. A decade or so later they had begun to fill these gaps, were breeding in the Faeroes, and two pairs had even reached Iceland (Hudson 1972) though the species has not become established there (*CBWP*). From the 1970s they spread throughout much of the European part of the Soviet Union and also turned southwest, not only colonising parts of Spain and Portugal in 1974, but also establishing themselves in Morocco and Tunisia by 1986. In the 40 years from 1932, Collared Doves had taken over an estimated 2·5 million km² (*BWP*) and by the mid 1990s the population of Europe as a whole, excluding a few tens of thousands in Russia, was estimated – in the broadest terms – at somewhere between 4·3 and 14·4 million pairs, the upper limit of this range actually being higher than the corresponding figure for the Wood Pigeon (*EBCC Atlas*). They were now breeding even in the Canary Islands, had reached Madeira as vagrants, and had frequently been found on boats well out in the Atlantic.

The origin of the very first Collared Dove found in Great Britain, a male that held territory in Lincolnshire from May 1952 until at least 1958, was questioned at the time (editorial note after May & Fisher 1953) – with hindsight, probably wrongly – and the initial colonisation of this country is generally attributed to a pair that reared two young at Cromer (Norfolk) in 1955 (Richardson *et al* 1957). By 1957 the species had been found in ten mainly eastern counties from Kent north to Moray and west to Scilly, and by 1962 was resident in over 40 counties of Britain and Ireland (Hudson 1965). The spread continued rapidly to the mid 1960s and more slowly to the mid 1970s, but, apart from some extension into marginal habitats, there has been relatively little change in distribution in Great Britain since the early 1980s, and the majority is found in England south from Lancashire and Yorkshire (*1988–91 Atlas*); the speed of the spread here was well demonstrated by the supplementary maps at two- and three-year intervals in the *1968–72 Atlas* (page 459).

Wiltshire's first Collared Doves were found on 18 May 1962 at Marlborough, though published accounts differ slightly, suggesting either one pair (which had well-feathered young on 17 June) and an additional male (*WANHM*), or two pairs (Kennedy 1966); it was also reported that the species had been seen on a farm near Marlborough for 'most of the summer' that same year (*WANHM*). The Marlborough area became the Collared Dove's centre in the county for the following two or three years and breeding has been well established there ever since: 12 to 17 were present in autumn 1963, and there were 20+ breeding pairs around the town in 1964 (*WANHM*); Kennedy (1966) recorded that 'the population at Marlborough has increased rapidly to over 30 pairs and there have been many records from other parts of the district'.

Elsewhere in Wiltshire, the few additional records in 1963 involved three in a garden at Amesbury in January (increasing later to five), one calling at Devizes for a week in May, and one at Pitton in October (*WANHM*). There was, however, a rather wider spread from 1964 when, in addition to Marlborough, Amesbury held three pairs and the Salisbury/Coombe Bissett area 'a few more' (Hudson 1965), while there were also non-breeding reports from at least nine other localities (*WANHM*). Although most of the early breeding records came from the centre of the county, the species spread rapidly and by 1967 was generally resident throughout Wiltshire except in the extreme northwest (Webber 1968). The largest autumn or winter counts in 1965 were about 40 at Poulton, in 1966 about 70 at Amesbury, and in 1967 about 60 at Poulton Farm east of Marlborough and 50+ at Idmiston (*WANHM*). By 1972 Collared Doves were being recorded in all 33 of Wiltshire's core 10-km squares and breeding in all but one (*1968–72 Atlas*). Indeed, they were already nesting in more of the county's 10-km squares than was their highly migratory congener, the much-loved Turtle Dove (Barnes 1974) – though, occupying very different habitats and taking different foods, they played no part in the latter's subsequent drastic decline.

Thereafter, Collared Doves received hardly a mention in *Hobby* for most years to the end of the 20th century, other than references to early or late breeding or to flocks of around a hundred or more, except for a special report on a regular roost in Queen's Park, Swindon, that held at least 273 each month during November–February 1983/84 and reached a peak of 361 in January of that winter (Edwards *et al* 1985). Although this was not repeated subsequently, there had been somewhat smaller numbers at the same site in the preceding winter and, 15 years later, a rather similar roost site in ivy-covered trees on an island in Shaftesbury Lake, Swindon, was occupied by concentrations of up to 130 during 1998–2000 (SB Edwards).

Another mainly winter roost at Medbourne Farm, Liddington, from 1985 to at least 1993, produced four three-figure counts (highest 116 twice) in October or November in different years (SB Edwards). Other peak winter counts of over 100 during 1974–2000 came from Coate Water (112), Aldbourne (147), Poulshot Farm (150), Trowbridge (250) and nearby Whaddon (150), Figheldean (100), Avon Bridge (250) and Downton (120). In contrast to 1967 – when, at what was the end of the initial period of the county's colonisation, 'More records were received for this species than any other on the [Wiltshire] list' (*WANHM*) – very few record cards are nowadays submitted for what has simply become 'a common resident' (Palmer 1991).

Collared Doves were mapped as seen in all of Wiltshire's 33 core 10-km squares during the *1981–84 Winter Atlas*, and as breeding in them all during the *1988–91 Atlas*. Those remained the positions in both the summer and the winter tetrad surveys during 1995–2000. The summer distribution map also shows that Collared Doves were found in summer in more than three-quarters of Wiltshire's tetrads and were proved breeding in half. These proportions may seem surprisingly high, considering that they are mostly characteristic of suburbia and villages with sizeable gardens; they are less numerous in more densely built-up areas and largely absent from agricultural land and woods except around farmyards themselves or where chickens or gamebirds are reared, areas that provide suitable sources of food. Elsewhere in Great Britain they are conspicuously absent from uplands and moorland.

The summer maps for 1995–2000 otherwise show a fairly even distribution that serves to highlight the species' absence from the extensive open parts of Salisbury Plain, as well as its greatest abundance in the suburbs of the north and west and in the farmyards of the southwestern pastures – patterns that are rather unsatisfactorily reflected in the less complete winter map (*eg* SU22). The Collared Dove has generally succeeded less well in truly urban areas than the now ubiquitous Wood Pigeon and, though the distribution maps of both may seem to show an equally solid covering of Wiltshire's largest built-up area, Swindon, comparison of the two abundance maps will demonstrate that Collared Doves are indeed far less numerous there.

The population of Great Britain was put at about 3000 pairs in 1964 (19,000 birds by the end of the breeding season) and 15,000–25,000 pairs in 1970 (Hudson 1965, 1972), while the *1968–72 Atlas* estimated 30,000–40,000 pairs by 1972. The *1981–84 Winter Atlas* suggested at least 50,000 pairs, with a winter population of around 150,000 birds, and the *1988–91 Atlas* estimated the breeding population at 200,000 territories (or breeding pairs, without counting their progeny) in 2210 10-km squares. Although by then the expansion had slowed considerably, the numbers continued to increase – by 104 per cent between 1975 and 2000, and by 42 per cent during the 1990s alone (*BBWC*) – with the result that the population in 2000 was estimated to be 284,000 territories (*APEP*).

On the basis of the 1988–91 figure, one might expect to find well over 3000 territories in Wiltshire's 33 core and 15 incomplete 10-km squares. The 2-hour surveys suggested 3938 birds (not pairs) in summer. In most tetrads, however, especially in suburbs and large

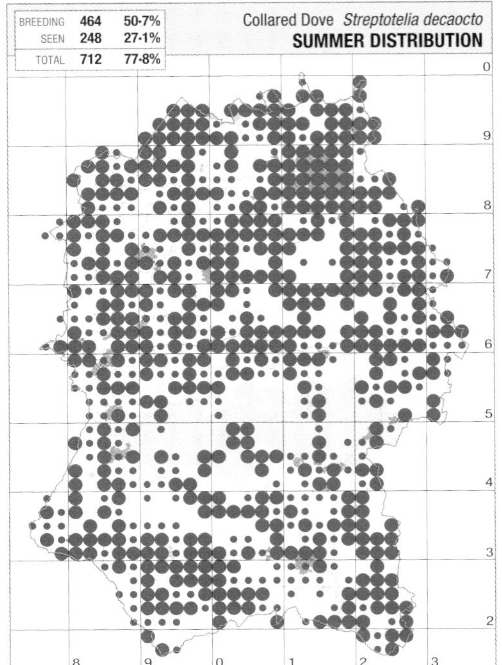

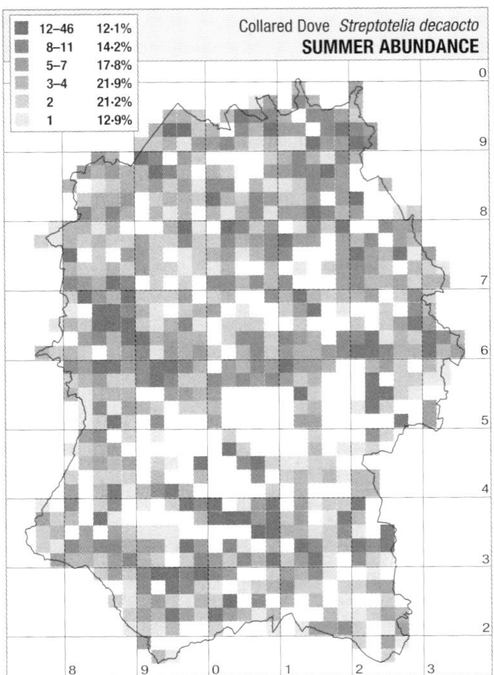

villages, 2-hour surveys cannot be expected to give complete figures even for this obvious species and counts may be biased either way. For example, in many instances, only the male will have been heard (though females sometimes call too) and his call will often represent a nesting pair; on the other hand, some observers who noted four or five birds in a small area may have failed to distinguish the collarless juveniles. Based on densities found during surveys using BBS methodology in Wiltshire and the Cotswolds, it is suggested that between 11,900 and 19,800 pairs of Collared Doves breed in this county.

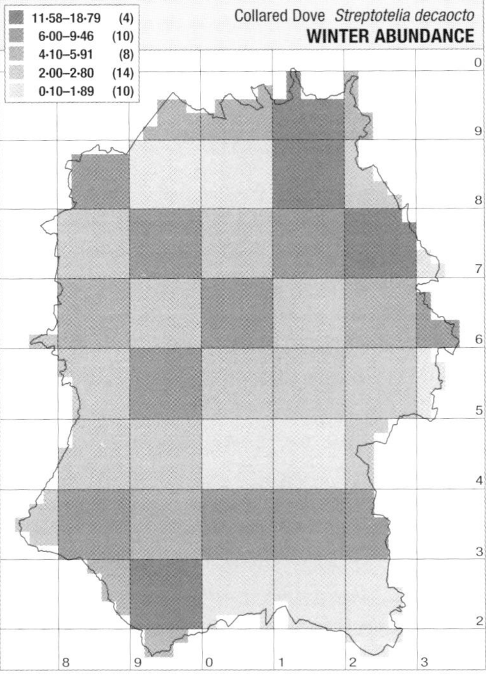

Although 'breeding adults [are] believed [to be] largely resident, as are a proportion of immatures' and 'Other immatures make pronounced dispersals, especially westwards' (*BWP*), ringing results indicated first that the British advances were by adults, 'but, since 1980, there has been no consistent pattern' (*Migration Atlas*); also that 'the mean vector of disposal has consistently been in a northwesterly or westerly direction'. Whether the advances are made by adults or immatures, the sizes of Wiltshire flocks when pairs still occupy many village and suburban territories year-round suggest that the population may be rather larger in winter than in summer.

Timed counts, however, during the winter tetrad surveys in 1998–2000 produced an extrapolation of 4326 – a number similar to that in summer – and so the total estimate for Wiltshire is just 20,000 to 33,000 individuals.

In fact, the county has provided little evidence of anything other than local changes in the breeding population since the 1970s, though nationally there has been a continuing increase, albeit confined largely to England – where the BBS results show a 28 per cent growth between 1994 and 2002. (This picture is not mirrored in marginal habitats and, as demonstrated by the *1988–91 Atlas* and *BBWC*, Wales has had only a smaller increase and Scotland even a decline over the same period.) None of the 165 Collared Doves ringed in the county during 1965–2000, mostly as nestlings, had been recovered by the end of that time; but two juveniles ringed at Twyford, south of Winchester (Hampshire), in 1979 and 1980 were found dead 14 months and three months later at Shrewton and Blunsdon respectively.

The causes of the sudden dramatic spread of the Collared Dove across Europe, most spectacularly between the 1930s and 1980s, are still not fully understood. Theories include a genetic mutation, a switch from nesting in buildings to trees, lessened predation in suburban and urban habitats, other changes in extraspecific control factors, and an increase in the number of broods possible in temperate regions – or a combination of any two or more of these factors (see *BWP*). Whatever the trigger, these doves of cultivation in dry open country in southern Asia managed to start establishing themselves in an urban niche close to human beings, relying on grain and other artificially available foods, so becoming associated with chicken runs, farmyards, flour mills, game-rearing sites and, particularly in Great Britain, eventually bird-tables.

The spread must surely have been facilitated by this species' high reproductive rate. Collared Doves have a long breeding season in northwest Europe: although mainly from the beginning of March to the end of November, eggs and young have been recorded in every month. In Wiltshire alone, one pair hatched a chick at Bromham on 11 December 1985, and nest-building has been recorded as 'early' as 2 January and as 'late' as 30 December (*Hobby*). In a single year, particularly a mild one, a pair may rear up to five broods, each of two young – though many eggs and chicks are lost to predation and disturbance, particularly in urban areas where the success rate may be as low as 26 per cent, the average pair producing only 2·5 young per year (Coombs *et al* 1981). Earlier broods can start breeding within the same year (one male successfully at four months), and it is a significant proportion of the immatures, not the adults, that have leapfrogged across a whole continent.

IJF-L

Turtle Dove

Streptopelia turtur

Now scarce, local and still decreasing summer visitor, winters Africa

The Turtle Dove is the one truly migratory British pigeon and, perhaps more surprisingly, it is the only almost exclusively seed-eating bird of any species that travels here in spring from sub-Saharan Africa to nest. (All other summer-visitors to Europe are completely or largely insectivorous, or at least feed their young entirely on invertebrates.) In Wiltshire, 'It does not come to us till the beginning of May and leaves us early in September; but during that short period it abounds in those spots which please its tastes, though it is fastidious in its choice, and is by no means universally distributed. In my own plantations on the downs it is extremely abundant...it flocks in autumn, though seldom in considerable numbers. I have, however, seen above a hundred feeding together in a stubble-field' (Smith 1887).

But that was 120 years ago. Such phrases as 'extremely abundant' and 'above a hundred feeding together' can no longer be applied to Turtle Doves in Wiltshire. Yet those words were written in the earlier stages of a prolonged period of apparently steady increase in both numbers and range across Great Britain, which had begun during the 19th century (*1875–1900 Atlas*) and was to continue for another 90 years after Smith was writing – until, indeed, about 1978/79 (Marchant *et al* 1990).

By 1900 the species was 'abundant' or 'common' in much of southern England and eastern Wales south of a line from the Wash to the Mersey, but 'uncommon' to 'rare' farther north and west respectively (*1875–1900 Atlas*). By the mid 20th century it was well established in many parts of Wales and southwest peninsular England, and had extended north into southeast Scotland. The *1968–72 Atlas* put the British population at 125,000 pairs, but by the time of the *1988–91 Atlas* the estimate had dropped to 75,000 territories, and by 2000 to only 44,000 (*APEP*). Indeed, although they had still recorded densities of 4·1 to 4·6 pairs/km^2 in Suffolk, Browne & Aebischer (2005) calculated that in Great Britain as a whole the Turtle Dove 'probably numbered only about 30,000 pairs in 2001'.

Great Britain is on the northwestern fringe of the range. This species has long bred widely in Europe, north to south Denmark, the Baltic States and north-central Russia – also extending across Asia to north-central China and Iran – and south throughout the whole Mediterranean region to northwest Africa, the Nile Valley, Turkey and Israel, as well as more locally in oases, mountain massifs and other semi-desert areas of northern Africa and Arabia. Some appear to be resident in the Sahara, but otherwise the entire Afro-Eurasian population winters in the dry savannahs of sub-Saharan Africa, from Senegal and Guinea across to Ethiopia, and in southwest Arabia. The British and other west European populations appear to migrate through Spain and Morocco to winter in parts of West Africa, but ringing recoveries are few (*Migration Atlas*).

In Europe as a whole, Turtle Doves are found mainly below 350 m, 'preferring fairly dry, sunny, sheltered lowlands' (*BWP*). Thus, the British population has always been most numerous in the drier areas of eastern and southern England, and scarcer in the wetter west and north. It is typical of bushy places, overgrown hedges, thorn copses, young plantations and woodland edges and glades – where there is access to open country and farmland edges that provide a plentiful supply of weed seeds and cereal grains. (Insects and other small invertebrates are taken only casually.)

The pattern of the decline since the 1970s is well illustrated by the 'change map' in the *1988–91 Atlas* – showing a broad band of deserted 10-km squares extending from southwest England through Wales (and Wiltshire) to, less markedly, northern England. Moreover, since the *1968–72 Atlas*, the numbers of occupied 10-km squares in Great Britain as a whole had decreased by almost a quarter and those with breeding evidence by more than one third. CBC data indicate a population drop of 73 per cent between 1975 and 2000 (*BBWC*).

The timing of the Turtle Dove's decrease in Wiltshire reflects the national picture. The definition of its status in *Hobby* changed gradually from 'widespread' in 1977 to 'scarce and markedly decreasing' in 2000 – a decline that, as in Great Britain as a whole, evidently began in the county in the late 1970s and has been continuing ever since. The *1968–72 Atlas* mapped Turtle Doves as breeding in all of Wiltshire's 33 core 10-km squares, but, while the *1988–91 Atlas* still recorded them in 30, it showed breeding as proved in only 22; and over the six years of the 1995–2000 summer tetrad survey they were seen in just

26 and evidence of breeding was found in only 14. This is no longer an easy bird to find in Wiltshire, but remains most likely to be located by its distinctive purring song, which is usually regular from early May through July. As the Bible put it, 'The time of the singing of birds is come, and the voice of the turtle is heard in our land'; unfortunately for this county, that particular sign of spring is no longer widespread.

The historical background for Wiltshire is less precise. For many years, Turtle Doves received little attention in *WANHM*. The inaugural bird report in 1929 described them simply as 'A common summer visitor'; in 1932 two observers 'considered them in smaller numbers than usual'; in 1933 the earliest record was on 2 May, 'when a regular migration passed through all day going North'; and in 1934 'General reports show this species to have arrived early and in greater numbers this year' while an 'increase after becoming scarce during the last two years at Chute' was also noted. After the 1939–45 War this was one of a number of birds for which, apparently, nobody reported anything worth publishing until 1959, when earliest and latest dates began to be quoted; on 15 May 1961 one observer counted '32 mostly paired feeding on a newly sown field near Pitton' (*WANHM*).

Arrival dates were still the main concern of the early issues of *Hobby* from 1974, and in 1976 Turtle Doves were considered to be 'widespread by second week of May'. In 1977, however, they were 'not particularly numerous' and in 1979 'Reported from most regular localities but numbers may well have been down on recent years'. The decline had begun. By 1982 they were 'Noticeably scarcer in NE quarter of county'; and 'Status unchanged' in 1984 was offset by 'Less common than usual' in 1985. After a 'slight improvement in numbers' in 1986, 1987 was a 'poor year with rather fewer records' and in 1988 the species was 'Extremely scarce, records well down even on last year's poor showing and including birds on migration only 27 sites involved'. In 1989 there was 'A slight improvement on 1988 numbers but still very uncommon and although many singing males reported there was only one confirmed breeding record'. The status line in the species reports in *Hobby* dropped from 'Summer visitor, decreasing' in 1995 to 'Scarce and seriously decreasing summer visitor' in 1996, and the qualifying adverb became 'markedly' from 1997. Although these assessments over 70 years were all subjective, they do give an idea of the scale of the decline as it affected Wiltshire.

The summer distribution map shows how patchy Turtle Dove has become in the county: in the six years, it was recorded in little more than one tenth of all the tetrads, and well under half of those provided any evidence of breeding. This species is now virtually absent from north and extreme west Wiltshire and, as emphasised by the abundance map, the highest densities are in the south and east, especially the far southeast. Moreover, the highest number of adults recorded in a single tetrad during 1995–2000 was a mere five and the total count only 124. (Compare these figures with the earlier quotations from Smith 1887 and from *WANHM* for 1961.) The breeding population thus seems unlikely to exceed 100–150 pairs – whereas 30 years earlier, on the basis of the 'estimate of 100 pairs per occupied 10-km square' in the *1968–72 Atlas* (considered at the time as 'may be conservative'), the population of Wiltshire's core squares alone could have been 3300 pairs. Only 11 Turtle Doves were ringed in the county during 1965–2000 – perhaps surprisingly, remembering how much commoner this species used to be in the first 15 years of that period – and none has been recovered.

Wiltshire's earliest (25 March 1970) and latest (21 October 1950) dates for this summer visitor are both from times when it was most plentiful – and, indeed, the observation in 1970 was considered to be 'a record of probable overwintering' (*WANHM*), though there is no evidence to indicate that and it may be significant that singletons were also recorded in Hampshire on 25 March and in Sussex on the 26th that same year (Clark & Eyre 1993, James 1996). Wiltshire's next earliest records were on 11 April, in 1932 and again

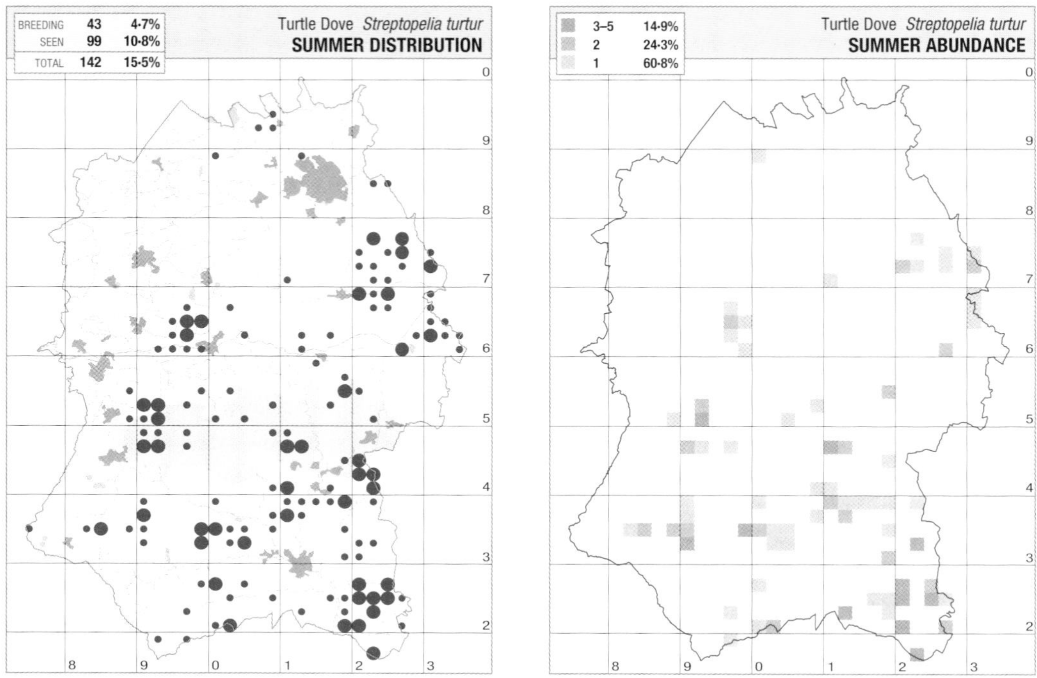

in 1991. (Note that a 'Jan' record in *WANHM* for 1969 was a misprint for 'Jun'.) Certainly most Turtle Doves leave in September and, after travelling three to four thousand kilometres each way across the Mediterranean and the Sahara, they return in the last few days of April and the first two or three weeks of May, much as noted long ago by Smith (1887) – though, using mean arrival and departure dates at six bird observatories in south and east England, Browne & Aebischer (2003, 2004, 2005) postulated that the species' average length of residence in Great Britain had decreased by 12 days during 1963–2000.

(In that connection, though casual observations from a single county can only have limited significance, it is interesting that – even leaving aside the exceptional March record of 1970 (in which year the next was not until 25 April) – the mean earliest and latest Wiltshire dates were 24 April and 23 September during 1960–70, and 27 April and 12 September during 1990–2000, suggesting that the 'length of residence' was 14 days shorter in the latter period. But the ranges of earliest and latest dates show less difference: 12 April to 2 May and 5 September to 8 October in the first period and 11 April to 5 May and 29 August to 11 October in the second.)

Browne & Aebischer argued that the shorter length of residence – coupled with evidence that 'the fruiting of various plants now occurs earlier, in response to increasing temperature' – might possibly mean 'that the peak period of Turtle Dove breeding is now out of phase with the peak in food availability', which in turn might have contributed to its decline in recent years. Browne & Aebischer's studies also showed that breeding success had 'fallen dramatically' over the same period. In the 1960s each pair of Turtle Doves laid, on average, 2·9 clutches and fledged 1·6 young (Murton 1968); the corresponding figures now are 2·1 clutches and 1·3 young, and these decreases have been related to the contraction in the breeding season (Browne & Aebischer 2004).

Several other possible factors were summarised by Browne & Aebischer (2005). Agricultural intensification, destruction of scrub, and annual cutting of hedgerows have decreased the availability of both feeding and breeding sites. As a result, Turtle Doves have become 'more dependent on (for example) spilt and stored grain and animal feed' and undertake longer foraging trips. Whereas weed seeds, particularly those of common fumitory and common chickweed, formed 95 per cent of the seeds taken by adults and 77 per cent of those identified from the faeces of nestlings in the 1960s (Murton *et al* 1964), the corresponding figures 40 years later were only 40 per cent and 31 per cent (Browne & Aebischer 2003).

But these are not just British problems. Recent widespread declines of Turtle Doves in the Low Countries and parts of Germany, and probably also in other parts of western Europe – though apparently increases farther east – have been variously attributed by a number of authors not only to 'agricultural changes on breeding grounds' but also to 'droughts in winter quarters' and 'shooting' (*CBWP*). These last two aspects were discussed by Browne & Aebischer (2005), who pointed out that Turtle Doves seemed unaffected by the first severe droughts in the Sahel in the late 1960s and actually increased during the following decade; unlike the other European summer visitors badly affected by, for example, the particularly severe drought of 1968/69 – such as Sand Martin and Common Whitethroat (*qv*) – 'the Turtle Dove is solely granivorous; it is possible that its food supply was less severely affected and it may have adapted to ... new food sources'. (It might be added that the droughts have been just as serious in the eastern parts of the sub-Saharan winter range as in the western, and yet the numbers in eastern Europe have possibly increased.)

Even though the estimates are appalling – about 100,000 shot annually on Malta (*BWP*) and up to 140,000 in Morocco (Browne & Aebischer 2005) – being hunted on migration in the Mediterranean region in particular has been a fact of life (or death) for Turtle Doves throughout the whole period of their increase, but it is sobering that the latter authors quote a paper by Boutin (2001) to the effect that the annual hunting bag for the EU alone is now thought to be 'of the order of 2–4 million'. In the mid 1990s the Turtle Dove population of the whole of Europe, excluding Russia, was estimated at only 1·9 to 2·4 million pairs (*EBCC Atlas*), to which the annual production of young has to be added. There may be rather fewer now.

IJF-L

Sponsored by Ian Gray

Ring-necked Parakeet

Psittacula krameri

Vagrant from naturalised population in southeast England, origin Africa/India

The Ring-necked Parakeet's indigenous range stretches across much of tropical Africa and Asia, but this species is also found in various other parts of the world through escapes from captivity, wanderers from free-flying flocks, or deliberate introductions. It is now self-sustaining, and thus naturalised, in several European countries, including Great Britain – where, apart from an isolated breeding record in Norfolk in 1855 (Lever 1977), it was first found in the wild in 1969 (Hudson 1974) – and very locally in Belgium, the Netherlands, western Germany, Italy and Spain, while numbers are now also well established in Israel and Egypt (*EBCC Atlas*, *CBWP*).

In Great Britain, the Ring-necked Parakeet is found mainly in suburban areas – of gardens, parks and orchards – roosting communally in tall trees. In 1983, when it was admitted to

Table 95. Ring-necked Parakeets *Psittacula krameri* in Wiltshire: totals by arrival months 1982–2000

	Jan	Feb	Mar	Apr	May	Jun	Jul	Aug	Sep	Oct	Nov	Dec
Birds	1	0	0	1	0	1	8	8	3	2	1	1

Category C of the British List, the population was put at 500–1000 (Ferguson-Lees *et al* 1984). By 1996, the estimated total at the four main roosts in Kent and Surrey was 1500 (Pithon & Dytham 1999), and by winter 2001/02 the figure at the same roosts had grown to at least 5900 (Butler 2002). Meanwhile, in 2000 the population in the six counties mainly involved in southeast England was put at about 4350 (Ogilvie *et al* 2002).

Both the *1968–72* and *1988–91 Atlases* show the distribution of this parakeet to be concentrated in southeast England, where it is now well established in the Greater London area south into Kent, Surrey and, more locally, Sussex, and west into Buckinghamshire and Berkshire (Butler 2002). The species has occurred at large in more than 50 counties of Great Britain, but the populations mapped by the *1981–84 Winter Atlas* in Essex, Greater Manchester, Merseyside and Clwyd seem to have died out. Ring-necked Parakeets are omnivores, whose 'most popular early winter food is apples on trees', but they survive even severe winter weather by regular attendance 'at birdtables and nut feeders, where they are top of the peck order' (Hawkes 1986).

Wiltshire's first record of a Ring-necked Parakeet, at Milston on 30 December 1982, was not published in *Hobby* because little attention was paid at that time to such escaped birds; and the same applied to the second, nearly seven years later, at Coate Water on 29 September 1989. That, however, marked the start of regular occurrences in the county and, from then on, all reported observations were published. Two stayed at Bratton from August to October 1990, and the species was then seen in all but two of the following ten years. By 2000 there had, in all, been 15 or more records totalling around 26 birds – although some, perhaps many, are likely to have involved the same individuals. In most cases, just one was seen on a single date, but over half the records have come from around Swindon and Salisbury, each area perhaps having roving parakeets; indeed, up to four were seen in or around Salisbury on a number of occasions from July 1999 to September 2000. Although it is unclear whether Wiltshire's Ring-necked Parakeets are wanderers from the established populations or new escapes, there is a marked peak in late summer and early autumn (table 95), possibly indicating a post-breeding dispersal. With their continued westward expansion in Berkshire, to Bray and Maidenhead by the end of 2000 (Ogilvie 2002), and a small population established in Dorset, at Studland (Butler 2002), there must be a distinct possibility that they will appear more frequently in Wiltshire.

Even so, some care in identification is essential because, through escapes from captivity, three other species of parakeets nest or have nested at large in Great Britain (Butler 2002), either as single pairs or as small groups that have failed as yet to establish self-sustaining populations, usually dying out or, in some cases, being shot. Of these, the most frequently kept in captivity is the substantially bigger and red-shouldered Alexandrine Parakeet, one of which has been recorded at large in Wiltshire, at Allington on 14 December 2000 (page 736). The position is further complicated by occasional Alexandrine × Ring-necked hybrids, which are nearer to the former in size and still have that species' red lower mandible, but an often indistinct pale orange shoulder-patch (Butler 2002).

RT

Cuckoo

Cuculus canorus

Widespread but decreasing summer visitor from Africa

As Wordsworth aptly put it, 'O Cuckoo! Shall I call thee bird, Or but a wandering voice?' The name is based on the male's well-known and easily imitated advertising-call – as much a harbinger of spring as the first Swallow – but how many people recognise a Cuckoo when they see it, not least because of its hawk-like shape in flight? Relying on sound alone, too, non-birdwatchers sometimes misidentify the disyllabic variant song of the Collared Dove – perhaps a significant cause of reports of out-of-season Cuckoos during the second half of the 20th century. Even experienced observers may overlook the far less familiar bubbling chuckle that is the female's main call, often uttered after she lays an egg.

Male and female Cuckoos are not paired as such and are probably normally promiscuous. Adult males usually call over an area of 20–50 ha but range more widely and are often only weakly territorial, especially if no females are present, thus overlapping to varying extents with other males, some of which are one-year-old nomads. Adult females, on the other hand, have more defined egg-laying territories of perhaps 10–30 ha, which they may share with one or two other sedentary or nomadic and subordinate or immature females (Wyllie 1981).

Female Cuckoos lay their eggs in other birds' nests and, when only a few hours old, the blind and naked chick throws out its hosts' eggs or young. Over 50 species have been recorded as hosts in Great Britain, but Dunnocks, Meadow Pipits and Reed Warblers together account for 80 per cent (Glue & Morgan 1972), and adding Robins and Pied Wagtails brings the combined proportion to 90 per cent (Davies 2000). For Wiltshire, Buxton (1981) remarked 'Host species noted include Meadow Pipit, Tree Pipit, Dunnock, Pied Wagtail, Robin, Reed Warbler and Reed Bunting – listed in descending order of being parasitised'. Other hosts noted in the county in the 1930s included Wren, Yellow Wagtail and Sedge Warbler (*WANHM*). (Tree Pipit and Sedge Warbler are not uncommon deviations by the female Cuckoo for Meadow Pipit and Reed Warbler.) Having such a variety of potential hosts, Cuckoos are found in many habitats, from country gardens, farmland and open woods to moorland and reed-fringed lakes.

Until the memorable studies by Chance (1922, 1940), it was often thought that a female Cuckoo laid her egg on the ground and inserted it into the nest with her bill, whereas she straddles the nest; also, more absurdly, that she could somehow match each egg's appearance to those of the host. In fact, each female tends to parasitise one particular species, probably the same as the one that raised her. Sometimes the hosts will reject her egg and desert their nest. Through such evolutionary pressures, Cuckoo eggs often bear a fair resemblance to those of the host species, though not to the sky-blue eggs of the Dunnock – showing that the latter has an unusually poor degree of discrimination (Davies & Brooke 1991). The female lays up to 25 eggs in a season, on alternate days, carefully watching the building behaviour of all the pairs of her particular host species in her territory. Occasionally she will destroy a nest with incubated eggs to make the hosts lay again.

Cuckoos breed in northwest Africa and right across much of Eurasia. In Europe – where the total population, excluding that of Russia, has been estimated at 1·4 to 1·9 million 'pairs' – their range has remained unchanged, though numbers appear to have declined in many areas since 1965, possibly through loss of habitat as a result of agricultural intensification (*EBCC Atlas*) and the variation in the numbers of caterpillars available as food in 'extreme weather conditions' (*CBWP*). Apart from small numbers in southeast Asia, Cuckoos winter almost exclusively in Africa south of the equator; the exact whereabouts then of the British-bred population is unknown, though the evidence suggests that the species overflies the Mediterranean and Sahara in a single hop, and the only relevant recovery of one ringed in Britain and Ireland came from Cameroon (*Migration Atlas*). The huge journeys involved make the fact that the adults migrate first, mostly by early August, and juveniles many weeks later, even up to mid or late September, seem all the more remarkable, particularly as this species 'Tends to migrate singly or in small groups' (*BWP*) – though separate migration by adults and young is the case with many species.

The first arrivals are usually in the second or third week of April, but Wiltshire's earliest ever was on 10 March 1938 (Witherby *et al* 1938–41); more recently, one was recorded at Yatton Keynell on 23 March 1991 and there have been at least four others in March, on the 26th in 1968, on the 28th in 1971, and on the 29th in both 1968 and 1995 (*WANHM*, *Hobby*). The main influx follows over the last ten days of April into early May. Wiltshire farming lore says, 'When the cuckoo sings on an empty bough, Keep your hay and sell your cow' (Whitlock 1976) – which is clearly advice for a late spring, since most of these old sayings have at least a basis in fact. On the other hand, there is an old West Country saying that 'When first you hear the cuckoo shout, 'tis time to plant your 'tetties out' – which could indicate that in ages past Cuckoos arrived earlier, because the second half of April, even early April, is a little late to be planting main crop potatoes (Buczacki 2002).

Few Cuckoos, apart from odd juveniles, are reported in August and, even more rarely, in the first three weeks of September, but in Wiltshire singletons were recorded on 14 October 1960 and 'in some years [up to 1930] as late as October 22nd', as well as, long ago, on the much more remarkable – but still not unprecedented – dates of 1 December 1916 and 3 December 1921 (Witherby *et al* 1938–41, *WANHM*). Only 22 Cuckoos were ringed in Wiltshire during 1965–2000, and none has been recovered. British-ringed recoveries show a southeasterly direction in autumn (northwesterly in spring) through the Low Countries, east France, west Germany and Italy to cross the Mediterranean from Algeria eastwards (*BWP*).

Cuckoos breed throughout almost all of Great Britain, and historically there has been little change in distribution but, often, local or regional fluctuations in numbers. In Wiltshire, the species was described in the 1929 bird report in *WANHM* as 'A fairly common summer visitor, local in its distribution'; and by Peirson (1959) as 'A common summer visitor'. Although Buxton (1981) later stated that 'Breeding occurs in all the 10-km. squares although sparsely on high arable land', he also noted that 'Recent reports are rather conflicting…There is little doubt that there has been a decrease during the past 20 years but this may have slowed down recently'. During the summer tetrad survey of 1995–2000, Cuckoos were recorded in every one of the 33 core and 15 part 10-km squares in Wiltshire, as they had been in both the *1968–72* and *1988–91 Atlases*. Yet, although generally regarded throughout the county literature as 'common' summer visitors, they were found in only 594 out of 915 tetrads. This 65 per cent may be compared with 84–91 per cent in Berkshire, Hampshire and Hertfordshire in the late 1980s and early 1990s (Standley *et al* 1996, Clark & Eyre 1993, Smith *et al* 1993).

Although there was 'breeding evidence' for 31 of Wiltshire's 48 core and part 10-km squares – which may not seem a high proportion in itself – it is generally difficult for anyone covering a tetrad in two hours to confirm breeding by finding a Cuckoo egg or small chick in a nest, and only slightly easier by locating, through its insistent begging calls, a larger nestling or a fledged youngster, which does not become independent for a further two to six weeks. Few reports of parasitised nests or fledged young have appeared on WOS cards since 1995, and most of the 'breeding' records were probably established by regular 'song', as defined in the methods used for the 1995–2000 fieldwork.

The '14-day song' criterion was introduced primarily for small territory-holding songbirds (page 104), but, as male Cuckoos call over an area of up to one eighth of a tetrad,

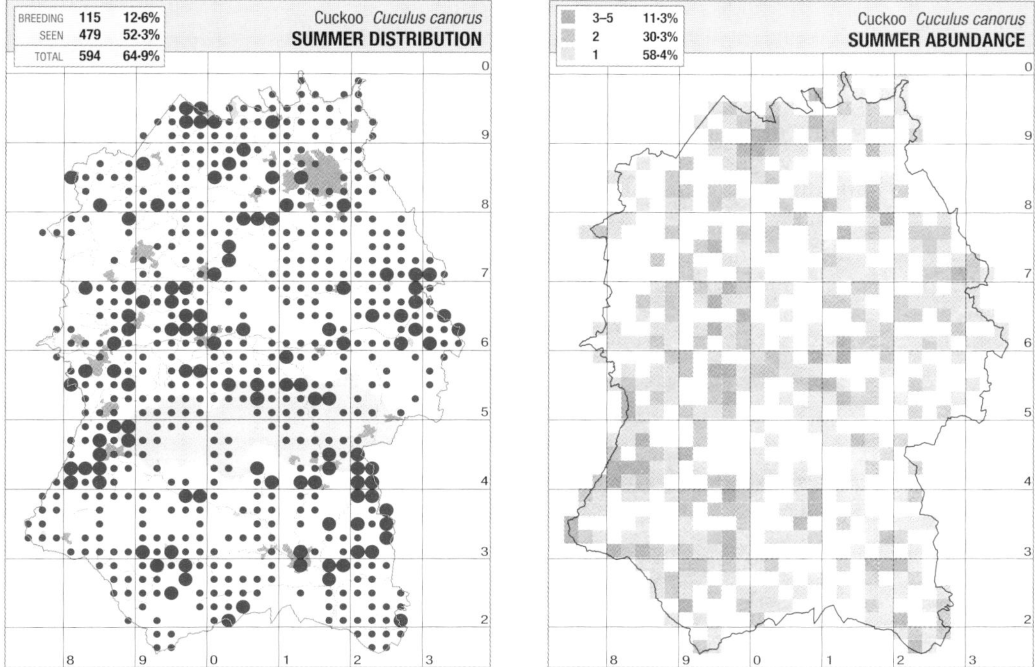

it may well be that some of the 'breeding' and other records in adjacent tetrads relate to the same individuals. Timed visits recorded 751 Cuckoos, probably mostly calling males, but, allowing for inevitable double-counting and birds mistakenly included from adjacent tetrads, an estimate of some 500 'pairs' might be possible for Wiltshire. The *1968–72 Atlas*, however, suggested a national average of five to ten 'pairs' per 10-km square (or 25 tetrads) – a figure deemed still reasonable in the *1988–91 Atlas* – and that would give a much smaller total of 185–370 for this county's 915 tetrads. Further, using such an average for Great Britain as a whole would perhaps underestimate numbers in southern England, where the highest densities are traditionally found, but, given the national decline in the 1990s and particularly during the period of the Wiltshire fieldwork, a figure of 300–400 is probably now the more likely and would represent a sizeable proportion of the 9600 to 16,000 'pairs' estimated for Britain as a whole in 2000 (*APEP*).

That may not seem unreasonable from a first glance at the maps, but these maps were compiled over a period of six years and, for a species that may call while wandering, the gaps indicate a worrying decline. Moreover, quite apart from promiscuity, calling males do not necessarily mean 'pairs', because males and females often occur in very unequal proportions (*BWP*). Tetrad fieldworkers were not asked to differentiate the sexes on the cards, but few female calls have been reported recently on Wiltshire record cards.

On a broad scale, distribution in Wiltshire appears remarkably even, with no especially marked concentrations, and no obvious correlation with particular habitats, reflecting this species' adaptability and wide choice of hosts. On the finer scale of tetrads, however, there are some notable gaps, some surprisingly large for so 'obvious' a species. In particular, both distribution and abundance seem remarkably limited on Salisbury Plain. This was also borne out by Stanbury *et al* (2000), who recorded Cuckoos in only 15 of the 141 1-km squares surveyed on SPTA in 2000 (and some of those may well have been duplicates), while the density of potential hosts there included 40 Meadow Pipits (the commonest host) per 1-km square in some areas.

The combination of all BTO monitoring schemes showed a national decline of 39 per cent during the last quarter of the 20th century, and which became more marked during the 1990s (*BBWC*). This was most notable in England, where the BBS showed a fall of 31 per cent just between 1994 and 2000. Experience in Wiltshire suggests that, whereas 1995 and 1996 were quite good years for this species, the decrease was very marked during 1997–2000. Unfortunately, it is not possible to produce maps to compare data from the first two years of the tetrad survey with the last four, but the record cards and those for *Hobby* support this widely held impression.

Clearly, numbers do fluctuate: Cuckoos had bad years in the 'pesticide era' of the 1950s and early 1960s, then recovered somewhat; and, even in the mid 19th century, comments varied from 'unusually abundant' and 'very numerous' to 'becoming more and more scarce every year' (Smith 1887). This recent, possibly serious, decline seems likely to be behind the little evidence of breeding and the low percentage of 'occupied' tetrads compared with other county atlases. What does the future hold for an insectivorous migrant that now has to face, in its African winter quarters, the use of some of the more toxic pesticides banned in Europe?

IJF-L

Barn Owl

Tyto alba

Scarce but widespread resident, increasing again after serious decline

Although Barn Owls are mainly nocturnal – and the sight of one hunting along a roadside hedge on a winter's afternoon, or glimpsed in a car's headlights, is as much as many people experience – few British birds are so widely recognised. Films, closed-circuit television at nests, publicity among examples of endangered wildlife and, not least, their attractive golden-buff and white plumage and heart-shaped faces, have all given them popular appeal.

Formerly, on the other hand, their ghostly white shapes and screeching and wheezing calls made them regarded as birds of ill omen. At one time, indeed, many considered Barn Owls to portend the death of a family member (Maton 1843); and folklore has it that the Bishop of Salisbury kept a lookout for the appearance of large white birds, assumed to be these owls: 'The appearance of two in 1885 presaged the death of Bishop Moberly and on 16 August 1911, a Miss Olivier said that she saw them while returning home, only to be told that the incumbent, Bishop Wordsworth, had just passed away' (Buczacki 2002).

Barn Owls do not necessarily nest in barns, but will do so in any large cavity in a tree or old building – such as a church tower or a ruin – sometimes even inside the loft of an occupied house or in a hole in old thatch, among rocks or in a crevice in a cliff or quarry;

they have also occasionally been found in dovecotes and old Jackdaw nests (*eg* Walpole-Bond 1938, Witherby *et al* 1938–41), and it has been known since at least the early 1950s that they will use large nestboxes in trees or barns (*eg* Campbell 1953). Countless analyses of the distinctive glossy black pellets of Barn Owls show that a wide variety of small mammals – especially mice, voles and shrews, but up to the size of brown rats and stoats – as well as some small birds and a few frogs and toads (see summaries in *BWP*) form the bulk of their prey in Great Britain. In Wiltshire there have been two records of Barn Owls feeding on roosting Starlings (NJ Lewis).

The Barn Owl is the only European representative of some 13 species worldwide of 'barn owls' and two of 'bay owls' that are classified in a separate family (Tytonidae) – distinguished from all the other owls (Strigidae) by half a dozen structural differences, the most obvious of which are their heart-shaped faces. At the same time, this Barn Owl is the most cosmopolitan of all owls, being represented by over 30 subspecies – in most of the Americas north to southern Canada, in western and central Europe, in much of Africa and Madagascar, patchily in southern Asia from parts of Turkey, the Middle East and Arabia through the Indian subcontinent to Vietnam and peninsular Malaysia, from Sumatra east through several of the Sundas, and in New Guinea and Australia, as well as on many islands of the Caribbean, Atlantic, Mediterranean, Indian Ocean and southwest Pacific.

In Europe, Barn Owls are found from all Mediterranean countries north to Ireland, Scotland, Denmark, Poland and Lithuania, but extend no farther east than westernmost Belarus and Ukraine. The European population was estimated at 120,000 to 172,000 pairs by the *EBCC Atlas* which, however, also noted a fall in numbers of one fifth or more in over half of the countries since 1940 – a decline attributed mainly to habitat loss and fragmentation, but also to pesticide poisoning, to a shortage of rodents as a result of less spilt grain being available on modern farms and farmland, and to cold winters. In the last connection, the Barn Owl is not well adapted to prolonged periods of severe weather – its plumage retains warmth poorly (Taylor 1994) – and this probably accounts for the fluctuations in numbers in northern Europe, on the edge of its otherwise largely tropical and subtropical distribution (Mikkola 1983), and the species' absence from eastern Europe and much of Asia.

The distributional gaps in the colder parts of Great Britain, well shown by the maps in both the *1968–72* and *1988–91 Atlases*, were not unexpected: few Barn Owls nest north of central Scotland or in the uplands of northern England and Wales. But there was also a marked decline in the numbers reported during the 20th century: 12,000 pairs were estimated in England and Wales in 1932 (Blaker 1933, 1934), but only 3778 pairs found in 1982–85 (Shawyer 1987). The *1988–91 Atlas* emphasised the difficulties of accurately surveying this nocturnal species, but its 'change' map showed starkly that more than 37 per cent of the squares in Great Britain in which the species had been recorded for the *1968–72 Atlas* had since become unoccupied. The population of the whole of Great Britain in 1982–85 was put at 4460 pairs (Shawyer 1987); and, while another national survey in 1995–97 calculated only 4000 pairs, it was suggested that numbers had by then stabilised (Toms *et al* 2001).

In Wiltshire, Maton (1843) noted that the Barn Owl was 'Not uncommon about Salisbury, where it is sometimes heard from the chimney-tops' and im Thurn (1870) considered it a very common species in the Marlborough district 'breeding in all the barns, Church towers, and hollow trees'. Smith (1887) described this species as 'very much diminished in numbers within the last thirty years, and it is not now the very common bird it used to be in this county…in my younger days few barns were without it'. In the Marlborough district, Meyrick (1895, 1906) stated that it was common but less so than formerly, and Peirson (1919) that it was still a common resident, though two decades later he thought it a 'resident usually seen in enclosed country, now almost uncommon' (Peirson 1939). The inaugural county bird report in *WANHM* in 1929 simply stated that it was 'a fairly common resident', and subsequent disappearances, decreases and increases – and the death of one 'found drowned in a water butt near Donhead' – were noted during 1932–34. Meanwhile, the first national survey of Barn Owls in 1932 estimated 128 pairs in each of the two Watsonian vice-counties of north and south Wiltshire (later quoted as a combined total of 255 pairs by Shawyer 1994, 1998), at densities of 8·2 pairs/100 km^2 and 6·6 pairs/100 km^2 respectively (Blaker 1933, 1934). Three years later it was shown that one pair in the county hunted over an area of 59·5 ha, equivalent to 1·7 pairs/km^2 (Ticehurst 1935).

After the 1939–45 War, the first mention of the Barn Owl in the then revived annual bird reports in *WANHM* simply involved a nest in a barn at Wylye in 1951, and the next was not until 1960 when eight localities at which the species had been seen in January–March and December were listed. Meanwhile, Peirson (1959) was less certain of population trends in the county and commented 'It may be much less common than it was a hundred years ago but estimates vary'. During the next decade the number of records in *WANHM* increased, but that probably reflected more observers rather than more owls. The first report of one killed by a car came in *WANHM* for 1965, and from 1974 onwards there were few years without records of road traffic deaths in *Hobby*, the largest number being nine in 1985. On the scale suggested by that number actually being reported, road deaths could be a significant factor for the county's Barn Owl population.

Wiltshire's own first survey of Barn Owls concentrated on winter observations between September 1977 and March 1979 (Taylor 1980). The 144 records received showed that 'North of the Kennet and Avon Canal, Barn Owls were reported regularly in only a few well-defined areas, mainly along the River Kennet. West of the Bristol Avon, sightings were few and widely dispersed. There were no sightings from a large area around Swindon. In the centre of the county records seem to be fairly evenly spaced, particularly on higher land such as Salisbury Plain. In the south the number of sightings was much higher, especially along the valleys of the Salisbury Avon and its tributaries'.

The importance of the area south of the Kennet & Avon Canal was later reflected by the Hawk & Owl Trust's national survey in 1982–85, which found only 24 pairs in north Wiltshire and just 90 pairs in the south of the county (later quoted as a combined total of 115 by Shawyer 1987, 1998), at densities of – for comparison with those of Blaker (1933, 1934) quoted above – only 1·6 pairs/100 km^2 and 4·6 pairs/100 km^2 respectively (Shawyer 1987). Nationally, 'An analysis of the breeding records revealed that 93 per cent of the population nested at an altitude of 150 m or below, usually in warm low-lying river valleys with 69 per cent of the population selecting buildings, 29 per cent tree cavities and 2 per cent rock crevices' (Shawyer 1998).

In common with earlier surveys, the summer distribution map for 1995–2000 shows that the majority of Wiltshire Barn Owls breed in the south of the county, but, in the two decades since the 1977–79 survey, the importance for these birds of Salisbury Plain and other parts of south Wiltshire has grown spectacularly. Soon after being posted to the School of Infantry in Warminster in 1983, Nigel Lewis, later aided by Alan Bush and Len Spackman, formed a Raptor Nestbox Group within the Imber Conservation Group, with the aim of putting up nestboxes for Kestrels on the Imber and Larkhill Ranges on SPTA. In 1987 Barn Owls successfully nested in a Kestrel box fixed to a tree, which suggested a need for similar tree-sited boxes for owls. As an experiment, one was placed in an adjacent tree, was used by Barn Owls in 1988, and became their permanent home for the next three years. The absence of hollow trees or suitable barns in south Wiltshire was thought to be a limiting factor to further expansion. From 1987, therefore, a network of boxes was systematically created by what had now become the Raptor and Owl Nestbox Group (see Lewis & Bush 1988–90, Lewis *et al* 1991–2001). By 2000 the Group had a total of 156 nestboxes centred on SPTA (West & Centre), and another 186 on the West Wiltshire Downs, in the valleys of the Salisbury

Avon and its tributaries, and in the Vale of Pewsey (Lewis *et al* 1991–2001). In addition, the Bulford Ornithological Group had been setting up a smaller number of owl boxes centred on SPTA (East) since 1992 (R Hayden and others) and the Wiltshire FWAG similarly on Marlborough Downs. (Although well under half of all the boxes are occupied by Barn Owls in any one year – for example, only 140 of the Raptor and Owl Nesbox Group's 342 in 2000 – and many remain empty, some are used by Stock Doves, Jackdaws and even Mandarins.) The efforts of all three groups have contributed to the expansion of the Barn Owl population in Wiltshire during 1987–2000. The total of 165 pairs in nestboxes at the end of that period (table 96) represented over 4 per cent of the British population, without taking account of any undiscovered or unreported in natural sites.

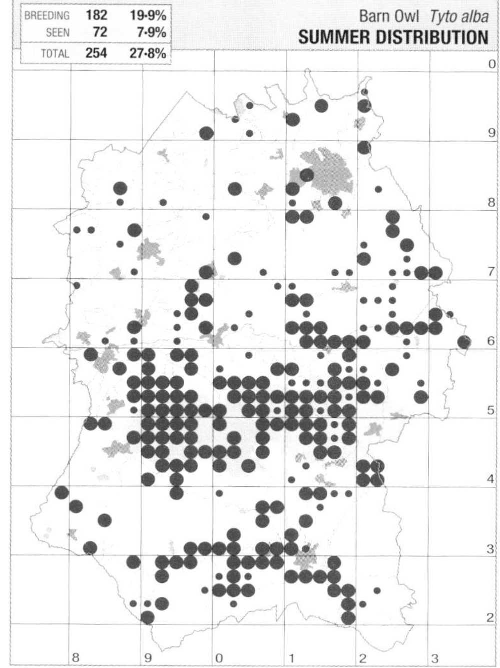

During 1995–2000, Barn Owls were recorded as breeding in 182 tetrads and 'seen' in a further 72, although the nestbox scheme showed that many tetrads – especially those on Salisbury Plain – held more than one pair. Moreover, as this is a sedentary species, it is likely that breeding also occurred in many of the 'seen' tetrads. Taking account of tetrads with more than one pair, together with under-recording in such areas as the northwest, might suggest a county population of around 300 pairs in 2000. It is believed that some 75 to 80 per cent of all known Barn Owls are nesting in boxes in the UK, leaving 20 to 25 per cent in natural sites, and that a third as many again remain undiscovered (C Shawyer): applied to Wiltshire, these figures would produce a comparable minimum estimate of some 275 pairs in 2000. A county total of 275–300 pairs then would have represented a very substantial proportion – 6·9 to 7·5 per cent – of the national total. The provision of more nestboxes elsewhere in the county would undoubtedly result in further increases in range and numbers. In particular, the total of Barn Owls recorded in north Wiltshire during 1995–2000 remained well under half that found there by the 1932 survey.

The nestbox schemes have accounted for a high proportion of the 2214 Barn Owls ringed in the county during 1965–2000. (Up to and including 1986 the total had been only 39.) The British population is 'relatively sedentary' (*Migration Atlas*), and so it is not surprising that only eight Wiltshire-ringed recoveries had moved more than 100 km; indeed, most have been within 15 km (NJ Lewis). A nestling ringed at Milton Lilbourne on 27 June 1991 and found dead at Bingley (West Yorkshire) on 15 April 1993 was, at 278 km, the most distant. Similarly, the longest inward recovery involved one found injured at West Lavington on 11 September 1996 (and later released successfully), which had been ringed as a nestling 159 km away at Avonwick (Devon) on 28 June 1995. Barn Owls usually begin breeding when one year old and live to about five, but ringing for the nestbox project in Wiltshire has found several at six or seven and three at ten years old (NJ Lewis).

The *1968–72 Atlas* mapped Barn Owls as breeding in 37 of Wiltshire's 48 core and part 10-km squares and seen in eight others, and the corresponding figures in the *1988–91 Atlas*

Table 96. Barn Owls *Tyto alba* in Wiltshire: pairs in nestboxes 1987–2000
The nestbox scheme for this species began in 1987

	87	88	89	90	91	92	93	94	95	96	97	98	99	00
SPTA (West)	1	1	2	3	2	3	7	12	10	15	21	25	28	36
SPTA (Centre)	0	0	0	0	0	1	1	2	3	5	16	10	17	30
SPTA (East)	–	–	–	–	–	4	10	10	12	9	13	15	12	25
Other South Wilts	1	5	15	12	18	17	30	25	27	27	41	37	56	74
Totals	2	6	17	15	20	25	48	49	52	56	91	87	113	165

Table 97. Barn Owls *Tyto alba* in Wiltshire: young reared in nestboxes on SPTA (Centre & West) 1987–2000

	87	88	89	90	91	92	93	94	95	96	97	98	99	00
Nesting pairs	1	1	2	3	2	4	8	14	13	20	37	35	45	66
Young reared	3	3	9	2	5	17	29	39	36	85	87	51	151	140
Average brood	3	3	4·5	0·7	2·5	4·3	3·6	2·8	2·8	4·3	2·4	1·5	3·4	2·1

were breeding only in 22 and seen in 12 others. In between, the 1977–79 survey mapped records of the species in 28 of the 33 core squares and in three of the 15 part squares (Taylor 1980) and the *1981–84 Winter Atlas* found it in 23 core squares and ten part squares. But all these surveys preceded the real growth of the nestbox scheme from the early 1990s – so it is not surprising that the summer tetrad survey of 1995–2000 found the species breeding in 29 of Wiltshire's 33 core squares and seen in the other four, as well as breeding in eight of the 15 part squares: thus, at least recorded in 41 of the 48 10-km squares represented in the county.

As pairs of Barn Owls and individual adults may hold territory throughout the year, while juveniles tend to make only limited movements in random directions from their natal areas soon after becoming independent (see also *BWP*) and as two, three or even four young are often reared by each of the nestbox pairs (table 97), it seems possible that a summer total of 275 to 300 pairs in 2000 might represent a winter total in the region of up to, say, 1000 individuals.

Not surprisingly, given the difficulties of monitoring such a nocturnal species, there are few national survey data with which to assess trends in Barn Owls. Nevertheless, marked decreases in breeding success were noted between the mid 1940s and the mid 1970s, and there was a general decline in the population during the 1950s and 1960s. Although weather, and sometimes local factors, will have contributed, this decrease was attributed largely to aldrin-dieldrin poisoning (Newton *et al* 1991, Percival 1991). This was particularly evident in eastern England, where the wood mouse – a major prey species in arable areas – will have accumulated pesticides applied as seed dressings. The withdrawal of those pesticides in the 1970s was matched by an increase in adult survival rate and breeding success nationally, although the substantial recovery in Wiltshire, particularly from the 1990s, is not typical of most other southern counties in England and is largely due to the nestbox programme on Salisbury Plain and adjacent river catchments (C Shawyer). Wiltshire is now arguably one of the most important counties for this species, and with continued help from conservation groups and support from farmers who provide permanent grassy field margins and areas of long-term set-aside, the status of the Barn Owl in the county is positive and improving.

(See also page 724.)

NJL & PEC

Sponsored by Major Nigel Lewis

Scops Owl

Otus scops

Vagrant (up to 5 records) overshooting from southern Europe, winters mainly Africa

This is the western Eurasian representative of a genus of up to 60 or more 'scops owls' or 'screech owls' spread across all continents except Australia, and including many island endemics; most are small and characterised by erectile ear tufts and monotonously repeated single or double whistles or croaks in long series. This particular species is mainly a summer visitor to northwest Africa and from Iberia east through southern and central Europe and parts of the Middle East to central Asia, in areas with warm summers and a plentiful supply of large insects. In Europe, it is found as far north as northern France, Switzerland, Austria, Slovakia and parts of Belarus, but it is common only in countries bordering the Mediterranean. The population of Europe, excluding Russia, has been estimated at 77,500 to 96,400 pairs (*EBCC Atlas*).

Most European Scops Owls are migratory, wintering south of the Sahara from West Africa to DR Congo and Kenya, there entering the range of the African Scops Owl *O. senegalensis*, a species with which it was formerly considered conspecific (*eg* Fry *et al* 1988). Some Mediterranean populations are, however, only partially migratory or even sedentary. Numbers in some countries, particularly in the north and centre of the range, have decreased during the 20th century, mainly because the use of agricultural pesticides caused not only a reduction in invertebrate prey but also the accumulation of residues in their predators (*CBWP*).

The European Scops Owl is a vagrant to Great Britain, mostly through overshooting on spring migration, and there were at least 64 records during 1805–1957 (Saunders 1899, Witherby *et al* 1938–41, *BBRC*), but only 28 during 1958–2000 (*BBRC*), despite the great increase in observers during the latter period, presumably because of the species' decline in the northernmost parts of its European breeding range. Smith (1887) knew of three Wiltshire records, the first 'killed nearly fifty years since in the south of the county' [thus about 1840], the specimen of which was 'now destroyed, having been pulled to pieces by the grandchildren of its owner'. Another, undated, in the Rawlence collection, 'was killed near Kingston Deverill', and the third was 'shot' in spring 1873 at Wilton Park near Salisbury. Hony (1915a) added that a specimen, bizarrely 'mounted on the head of a Ruff', in Devizes Museum was labelled 'Shot at Marlborough', though he gave no further information. As, however, Witherby *et al* (1938–41) admitted just one record for Wiltshire, the current grand total of British records does not include three of this county's early reports.

Much more recently, one was heard at Upton Scudamore on the night of 6/7 June 1982 and what was assumed to be the same individual was later located on MoD land at Warminster some six weeks later, on 13–14 July (*BBRC*) – when it was heard on the first night and both seen and heard the next day, but not subsequently. A chance conversation with staff at the Warminster School of Infantry had indicated that it had been present on the MoD land since early April, in which case its appearance at Upton Scudamore was presumably an isolated foray. There were no other British records that year.

RT

Snowy Owl

Bubo scandiaca

Nomadic vagrant (1 record) from north Fenno-Scandia and Russia

A circumpolar arctic owl, the Snowy occupies open treeless areas, particularly tundra, up to 1500 m. It breeds along the north European coast as far west as central Norway, but numbers fluctuate markedly between years, mainly a result of cyclic variations in rodent populations on which breeding Snowy Owls depend, although other factors, including weather, may also be involved. The numbers breeding in Europe, excluding Russia, have been estimated to vary between as few as 16 to as many as 244 pairs (*EBCC Atlas*). One pair nested on Fetlar (Shetland) during 1967–75, after which resident females remained until the early 1990s.

Snowy Owls are partially migratory and nomadic, most withdrawing from northernmost areas in winter, when 60°N is the normal southern limit. Eruptions further south, however, do occur on an irregular basis, presumably in response to food availability. In the 19th century, it was a fairly regular winter visitor to the north of Scotland but it has since become a rarity, with just 160 records in Great Britain during 1958–2000 (*BBRC*).

Wiltshire's only Snowy Owl was seen near Marlborough College on 29 January 1945 (*BB* 38: 374–376). Although LG Peirson recommended at the time that 'the record should be qualified as "probable" owing to the inexperience of the observer', he himself later included it without reservation (Peirson 1959). The published description, though clearly an honest one, lacks detail, but it was noted that the eyes appeared 'as black dots', a feature inconsistent with the yellow-eyed Snowy. Nevertheless, the record received some support from the fact that Snowy Owls were recorded in Cornwall, Devon, Somerset, Yorkshire, Morayshire and, probably, Hertfordshire in the first five months of that year, several of them similarly during the hard weather with snow in late January.

RT

In December 1922 (*WANHM* 42: 79), EH Goddard published a long extract from a letter written on 8 April that year by the Reverend FG Walker, who reported that 'at least two' Snowy Owls had been seen at Upton Lovell during the previous winter, one watched by him and several other people at 'the end of October [1921]' and at 'the end of March [1922] another' seen by his son and several others. Although Walker 'was positive' about the identification, and 'several of the villagers... remarked that they had never noticed a bird like it before', a 'retired farmer' commented 'that he had seen the bird several times in his life, which had been spent mostly in Little Langford, and recognised it at once' – a statement which strongly suggests that Barn Owls may have been involved in these observations. The record lacks descriptive detail and was clearly never accepted at the time – for example, Witherby *et al* (1938–41) did not list Wiltshire as a county where Snowy Owls had occurred – nor was it mentioned subsequently by either Peirson (1959) or Buxton (1981). It is documented here, however, for completeness. Eds

Hawk Owl

Surnia ulula

Irruptive vagrant (1 record) from northern Europe, also North America

Hawk Owls have a circumpolar distribution across northern North America and Europe, and northern and central Asia, in forested tundra and boreal taiga, shunning dense forest in preference for more sparsely wooded areas with access to clearings and other open land. In Europe, they are resident throughout much of Fenno-Scandia and eastwards through Russia north of about 55°N. The Fenno-Scandian population has been estimated at 5380 to 16,300 pairs. Following vole peaks in Lapland, Hawk Owls erupt into southern Norway, Sweden and Finland, and in exceptional years reach Denmark, central Europe and even Great Britain (Mikkola 1983, *EBCC Atlas*). Of the 11 accepted British records, seven were in the 19th century and four in the 20th – in 1903, 1959, 1966 and 1983. At least three of those in the 19th century were of the North American race *caparoch* (Witherby *et al* 1938–41, *BBRC*).

Against such a background it may seem surprising that Wiltshire can boast one of the few records of this rare wanderer, 'killed during severe weather, some thirty or more years since' – thus before 1857 – by a 'Mr. Long, then residing at Amesbury' (Smith 1887). The specimen was identified as being of the nominate European race by the renowned 19th century ornithologist Richard Bowdler Sharpe in 1876 (*eg* Saunders 1899).

RT

Little Owl

Athene noctua

Common naturalised resident introduced from Europe in 19th century

Because it is often out and about in daytime – though hunting mainly at dawn and dusk – the Little Owl is more easily seen, and thus more familiar, than most other owls. Its flat head and fierce yellow eyes set in a frowning face, combined with its compactly plump shape, give it a stern and prosperous look as it perches openly on a branch, wall, post or wire – usually very upright or, when agitated, bobbing up and down. Its flight is also characteristically bounding, or undulating like a woodpecker's. Though taking some birds, it feeds largely on voles, beetles, earwigs and earthworms, and so is generally regarded with favour, unlike many introduced species the world over. For, although it occurred in Great Britain in the Pleistocene era, as is evidenced by an English Late Ice Age fossil record (Fisher 1966), this owl is now no more than a seemingly benign alien – the result of introductions during the late 19th century (Witherby *et al* 1938–41).

The natural world range of this small and now acceptably British owl extends right across Eurasia from Portugal and Spain to China's Yellow Sea and south in the west from Denmark and Latvia to Mediterranean Africa (extending inland even beyond southern Algeria) and to the southern Arabian Peninsula; there are also outlying populations in Niger, Chad, Sudan and around the Horn of Africa (Fry *et al* 1988). Like a number of other European birds, it has also been introduced into New Zealand. The population of Europe, excluding Russia, has been estimated at 217,000 to 327,000 pairs (*EBCC Atlas*).

Saunders (1899), who noted that 'cages-full, brought from Holland, may often be seen in Leadenhall Market', reported 'many examples' of escapes or attempted introductions into England from 1758, but it was not until 1889, in Northamptonshire, and 1896, in Kent, that successful breeding areas were established (Witherby *et al* 1938–41). Little Owls occupy a wide range of mainly open lowland habitats, such as parks, cemeteries and farmland with copses, hedges, and shelter belts. Thus, they found much of southern England to their liking and, aided by further introductions, a rapid expansion followed: by the 1950s they had spread throughout England and Wales, and the first breeding in Scotland was reported in 1958 (Thom 1986).

Long before the species became established in England, Wiltshire's first Little Owl was recorded by Yarrell (1837–43), who recounted that "Mr. Rennie, in a note to a recent edition of White's Selborne, says, 'I recollect seeing in Wiltshire the remains of a specimen of the rare Sparrow Owl, *Strix passerina*, nailed up to a barn-door'". (Rennie's edition of 'White's Selborne' is dated 1833 and thus the observation clearly took place earlier than that.) Smith (1887) gave the first dated record as one killed near Chippenham in 1838, and he included two later reports from Draycot and Wardour – though all of these would have been escapes or the results of unsuccessful releases.

The first 20th century record was of one shot by a gamekeeper near Avebury in November 1907 (*MCNHS Report* for 1907: 76). No more were reported until 1910, when a pair was shot on the Hamptworth Estate in southeast Wiltshire on 8 January, but five were then 'killed… within eighteen miles of Salisbury' in late 1911 and another four 'obtained' at Totterdown during 1911–12. There were also sight records in 1913 at Milton and at Whiteparish, and in 1915 at Lydiard Millicent. Also in 1915, when three pairs were located at Downton, nesting was proved in Wiltshire for the first time; and in 1916 breeding was subsequently recorded at Collingbourne Ducis, Winterbourne Dauntsey and Lydiard Park (Hony 1915b, 1916c). The records from the southeast (at Hamptworth, Salisbury, Whiteparish and Downton) could indicate that the species spread to Wiltshire from the nearby New Forest (Hampshire), where EGB Meade Waldo liberated Little Owls in the 1880s (*eg* Kelsall & Munn 1905).

Peirson (1959) stated that 'By 1920 it was established over the whole county' and, rather oddly, cited Hony (1915b) in evidence. It seems not unlikely, however, that the reduction of persecution during the 1914–18 War, when many gamekeepers were serving with the British army, allowed the Little Owl to spread more swiftly than might otherwise have been the case. Peirson (1919) had regarded this species in the Marlborough district as 'A fairly common resident, largely on the increase'. It was also noted as still increasing in Wiltshire during 1932–34 (*WANHM*). For Great Britain as a whole, numbers were probably at a peak in the 1930s, but local decreases followed in the 1940s, perhaps as a result of the severe winters then, and again in the late 1950s, this time because of pesticide usage (*BWP*). Indeed, Kennedy (1966) stated, again for the Marlborough district, that 'there have been few records in the last two years and it may be decreasing'. These decreases have, however, been suggested as perhaps no more than a 'natural variation in the population level' (Marchant *et al* 1990).

From 1974 onwards, though local fluctuations have been reported, Wiltshire's Little Owl population appears to have remained generally stable (*Hobby*). Over the same period, too, both the *1968–72 Atlas* and the *1981–84 Winter Atlas* mapped Little Owls in 31 of the county's 33 core 10-km squares, and the *1988–91 Atlas* in 32, whereas the summer

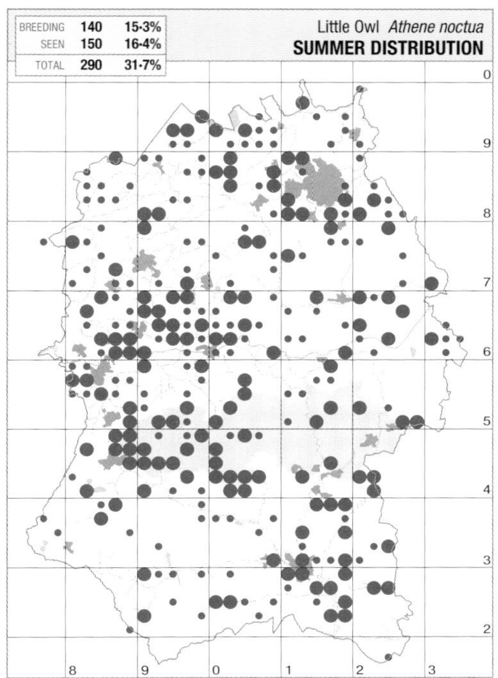

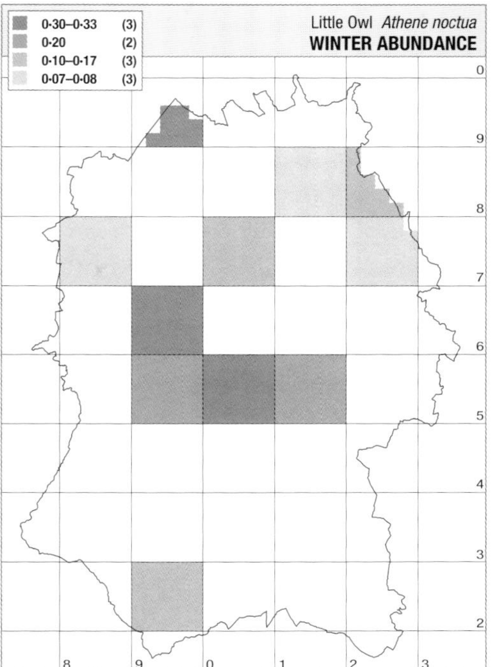

tetrad survey of 1995–2000 found them in all 33 and evidence of breeding in all but one. A formula of five to ten pairs per occupied 10-km square, as adopted by the national breeding atlases in estimating the British population, would indicate that numbers in Wiltshire's core squares alone may be in the range of 165 to 330 pairs; moreover, allowing for the county's 15 part squares, and given that this relatively unobtrusive species was recorded in 290 tetrads, it therefore seems likely that the population as a whole may total some 200 to 400 pairs, a reasonable percentage of the British total, suggested to number 5800 to 11,600 pairs (*APEP*).

British Little Owls are highly sedentary, and ringing recoveries show a mean dispersal distance of only 2 km (*Migration Atlas*). Thus, it is not surprising that the farthest recovery of the 342 ringed in Wiltshire during 1965–2000 had moved only 23 km from Castle Combe into Somerset. There are also, however, two inward recoveries of interest: one found dead near Collingbourne Ducis on 18 March 1968 had been ringed 34 km away in Berkshire on 13 June 1967; and much earlier, and more noteworthy, another found dead on the Longleat Estate on 15 March 1931 had been ringed at Branscombe (Devon) on 7 January that year, thus having moved 83 km in little more than two months.

The *EBCC Atlas* noted that the Little Owl was 'mostly declining' in northern Europe, generally in areas of intensive agriculture, such as Great Britain, and that in the Netherlands habitat destruction was another factor. The *1988–91 Atlas* demonstrated a decrease in East Anglia, the east Midlands and southwest England – the majority then being found east of a line from Dorset to Lancashire – but it also showed Wiltshire as apparently unaffected. Nationally, census data indicate fluctuating trends over the last quarter of the 20th century, partly as a result of the difficulty in censusing this species, although the BBS indicated a 32 per cent increase in England between 1994 and 2000. The *1988–91 Atlas* also mapped west Wiltshire, south from the Cotswolds to about Warminster, as amongst the areas of highest density in Great Britain. The summer distribution map for 1995–2000 continues to show records concentrated in west Wiltshire, while the winter map for 1998–2000 highlights the Vale of Pewsey; but, unsurprisingly, very few were recorded during the latter season (just 20 in all), and winter numbers are likely to be derived solely from resident breeders, perhaps some 500–1000 in total.

Despite the apparent lack of any general population change in the county during the last quarter of the 20th century, numbers have undoubtedly fallen in some areas, such as the Dean and Kennet valleys (MC Combridge, SB Edwards) – a decrease not obviously linked to habitat loss. Other factors, such as the virtual disappearance of dor beetles, cockchafers and other once common flying insects of warm summer evenings, are perhaps to blame. There is no evidence that Tawny Owls – reported to be, after Goshawks, the second most important predators of Little Owls in Europe (Mikkola 1976) – have any significant effect in Wiltshire; the distribution maps for Tawny and Little Owls suggest only limited overlap in breeding records during 1995–2000, but the problems involved in sampling these owls in a general survey preclude meaningful comparison.

Though the current status of this attractive species in Wiltshire appears secure, declines both locally and elsewhere – and the rapid slump of other, once common, avian inhabitants of agricultural land – make its fortunes worth careful monitoring.

PCo

Sponsored by the Osborne family

Tawny Owl
Strix aluco

Common and widespread resident, far more so than surveys suggest

The Tawny is the archetypal British owl, less loved perhaps than the Barn Owl, but the most frequently represented in children's books, wise-looking in pictures, and the one credited with the utterance 'to-wit-too-wooo' – which is an inaccurate combination of two of the most characteristic sounds this species produces from quite an extensive repertoire: the sharp *ke-wick* contact-call and the mellow territorial song, a far more long-drawn and quavering *hooo hu hoohoohoooooo*. This is a highly adaptable owl, inhabiting broadleaved, mixed and (less often) coniferous woodland, farmland hedgerows, parks, churchyards, large gardens and even town squares. Like other owls, it makes no nest but incubates its eggs in the debris in holes in trees or buildings, or in old nests of corvids or raptors, very occasionally in squirrels' dreys, and now increasingly in large nestboxes. When Tawny Owls have young in the nest, they can be very aggressive, as a renowned bird-photographer once found to his cost (Hosking 1970); interestingly, Mikkola (1983) suggested that this owl becomes aggressive only in more populated areas, especially 'at nests which are visited more often'.

Above all, the Tawny Owl is essentially nocturnal, which makes it impossible to census without listening for it on specific outings after dark, most profitably during January–May. Sometimes one will call briefly in woodland during the day or, less frequently, be disturbed by chance from its roosting site and fly off silently on broad rounded wings. More often, attention is drawn to a roosting Tawny Owl by the chattering of Blackbirds, Wrens, tits and finches mobbing it as a recognised threat. (This owl commonly feeds on birds, particularly in urban areas.) Because not all those who took part in the tetrad surveys during 1995–2000 were able to make special night outings, the map here for this species is far from complete and perhaps not even representative. This applies to other nocturnal birds, too, but the breeding areas of some that are scarce and local are regularly visited (*eg* Nightjar, Nightingale), while certain other owls are at least partly diurnal (Little, Short-eared, and even at times Barn Owls, which are also subject to an extensive nestbox study in Wiltshire). The common Tawny Owl is doubtless far more numerous than the map might suggest.

Almost entirely Eurasian in distribution, Tawny Owls are found in northwest Africa and across much of Europe – except Iceland, Ireland, northern and central Fenno-Scandia, and northern Russia – extending east into western Siberia, as well as through parts of the Middle East into northern Iran. After gaps in distribution, the species reappears farther south and east in Asia: along the Himalayas and east to China, Korea and Taiwan. Everywhere it is essentially sedentary, apart from the dispersal of juveniles. The population of Europe, excluding Russia, was estimated at 417,000 to 562,000 pairs by the *EBCC Atlas*, which itself commented that – while increases in either range or abundance were generally in central Europe, and decreases largely in the north and the south – the atlas census techniques used in most countries did not accurately record this owl.

Although absent from Shetland, Orkney and the Outer and some Inner Hebrides, Tawny Owls occur widely in mainland Great Britain from Cornwall to Caithness. As in the rest of their range, they are largely resident, though juveniles in Scotland and northern England disperse longer distances than those farther south; adults are extremely sedentary, the mean distance between ringing and recovery being less than 1 km (*Migration Atlas*). This pattern is reflected in Wiltshire where, although 30 of the 587 ringed during 1965–2000 were recovered, only four had moved more than 10 km. The *1988–91 Atlas* showed 10 per cent losses in occupied 10-km squares in Great Britain since the *1968–72 Atlas*, especially in parts of Scotland and southwest peninsular England, but regarded the British population as stable. CBC and BBS data also indicate remarkable stability in recent decades. There is, however, indication of a slight downturn since the 1970s, accelerating in the 1990s – the BBS alone indicated a 20 per cent decrease in England – although Tawny Owls are poorly covered by all these monitoring schemes (*BBWC*). The national population in 2000 has been estimated at 19,400 pairs (*APEP*).

Smith (1887) believed that this was the 'most plentiful of all our Wiltshire Owls' and that it had 'certainly increased … of late years' – at a time when Tawny Owls were generally decreasing in Great Britain through human persecution (*eg BWP*). But, while im Thurn (1870) also considered this one of the commonest owls in the Marlborough district, he did state that it was much persecuted. In Great Britain as a whole, the population of Tawny Owls increased during the first half of the 20th century, perhaps as a result of reduced persecution (*BWP*), but there has been little evidence of any marked long-term change in status in Wiltshire since Smith's time.

Peirson (1919) described the Tawny Owl as 'A common resident' in the Marlborough district, an assessment also used to describe its status for the county as a whole in the inaugural bird report for 1929 in *WANHM*. Other entries in *WANHM* before the 1939–45 War were concerned mainly with nest-sites – including, in 1932, one in 'an old rook's nest underneath an occupied rook's nest' and another 'in a dead beech stump in company with three pairs of rooks and a jackdaw' – and the only two references to local decreases, in 1933 and 1934, were offset by accompanying reports from other districts on how common the species was in those years. The first entry in *WANHM* after the War, in 1948, was also about nest-sites, including an adult 'sitting on two eggs at the foot of an oak' (an occasional site); and in 1949 it was simply noted that the Tawny Owl 'breeds on the gunnery ranges on Salisbury Plain'. The next mention of the species, ten years later, referred to one 'seen hunting bats near their roost at dusk at Cole Park from April to July' (not often recorded). That year, Peirson (1959) described the species as 'common' – as, later, did Buxton (1981) and Palmer (1991) – but the annual bird reports in *WANHM* varied from 'Over 35 birds... found in BTO enquiry' and 'many heard at Longleat', both in 1964, to only eight records (including one 'released after 3 days in a chimney') in 1966 and 'Fewer sight records than usual and no breeding records' in 1969. In general, a shortage of records one year prompted more to be submitted in the following one and it is no easier to analyse the entries in *Hobby*, though poor breeding success was particularly noted in some years (*eg* 1990, 1994, 1995 and perhaps 1996). The presence of Tawny Owls in all 33 of Wiltshire's core 10-km squares in both the *1968–72* and *1988–91 Atlases* is not surprising – and this was found to be the case in the summer survey of 1995–2000. But, although their distribution in the county as a whole is adequately indicated by a 10-km grid, the fact that they are under-recorded by general census techniques means that the tetrad map must be far from complete. The summer distribution map does, however, demonstrate that this species is scarcest in the north, and on SPTA (West) and SPTA (Centre), which probably reflects woodland distribution. The breeding concentration on SPTA (East) is, however, the result of a nestbox scheme there specifically targeted at this owl.

The *1988–91 Atlas* used a formula of ten pairs per occupied 10-km square to estimate a British population of 20,000 pairs. That formula would allow 330 pairs in Wiltshire's core squares, and suggest a county population in excess of 400 pairs – which is higher than the combined total during 1995–2000 of breeding evidence in 167 tetrads and 'seen' (or heard) in a further 171 (the latter including individual efforts to extend the survey into the night). But personal experience and the *1988–91 Atlas*, which shows Wiltshire as one of the areas of greatest Tawny Owl density in Great Britain, suggest that even that figure is too low. In parts of the Dean Valley, Tawny Owls outnumbered Little Owls by at least three to one in the 1990s (MC Combridge) and the species appears equally common in other parts of southeast and east Wiltshire. It may well be that Wiltshire's population is two to three times that suggested by the *Atlas* formula, and an estimate of 800 to 1200 is tentatively proposed. While no evidence of falling numbers or range contractions yet exists for this county, the effort of thorough nocturnal censusing would – periodically repeated – be well worthwhile to determine future population trends.

The winter survey results for 1998–2000 did, to a certain extent, echo the summer map – the species again being largely absent from the north – but the paucity of records (just 21) precludes any meaningful picture of distribution, let alone any estimate of numbers during that season. Although the Tawny Owl's food has been well-studied elsewhere, little analysis of its diet has been attempted in Wiltshire, but beetle elytra, common shrew, bank and field voles, brown rat, wood mouse, Chaffinch, and the ring from a Great Tit have all been found in pellets, and once four 'headless young Jays' had been brought as food for two owlets (*Hobby*).

PCo & IJF-L

Long-eared Owl

Asio otus

Rare breeder, once more numerous, and scarce winter visitor from Britain or Fenno-Scandia

The Long-eared Owl is one of Wiltshire's most elusive breeding birds. It is a well-known nocturnal hunter (Mikkola 1983), roosting by day close to a tree trunk, usually of spruce or pine, or in a dense thicket. When asleep, it may fluff up its feathers for insulation but, if danger threatens, it compresses them close to its body, erects its long ear tufts and stretches to its full height. Its tall, thin posture and cryptic coloration then create a perfect camouflage to confuse any potential enemy. It appears, however, that these ear tufts are 'more than mere head adornments for either mimicry or concealment, but rather that they somehow function as tactile organs or as a means of emotional expression' (Voous 1988).

One of the world's only six species of 'eared' owls of the genus *Asio*, the Long-eared is found in much of North America from Canada to northern Mexico, and across Europe (except the far north) and central Asia to Japan; it also nests in the Canary Islands and locally in northwest and sub-Saharan Africa. The northernmost are migratory, wintering in or beyond the south of the summer range. The breeding population of Europe, excluding Russia, has been put at 185,000 to 239,000 pairs, the largest numbers being in Germany, in other parts of central Europe and in southern Fenno-Scandia (*EBCC Atlas*).

Numbers in Great Britain were estimated at 1100 to 3600 pairs by the *1988–91 Atlas*, which also showed that there had been a reduction of nearly 25 per cent in the British breeding range since the *1968–72 Atlas*, competition with the larger Tawny Owl and shortages of habitat being suggested as possible factors. The national population was put at the same size in 2000 (*APEP*). In winter, migrants arrive from the Continent, mostly from Fenno-Scandia, but there is little evidence to suggest British-bred birds move overseas (*Migration Atlas*). None of only 18 Long-eared Owls ringed in Wiltshire during 1965–2000 has been recovered, but one found dead near Stonehenge on 26 March 1994 had been ringed as a juvenile on Lundy Island (Devon) on 30 September 1990.

The Long-eared was only a scarce breeder in southern England in the first half of the 19th century (*1875–1900 Atlas*) and a general increase in the second half is attributed to human persecution of the Tawny Owl, its main competitor, and to the maturing then of plantations, particularly of exotic trees, that provided suitable nesting habitats. Smith (1887) described the species as 'indigenous to Wiltshire, and though sparingly distributed throughout the county, breeds here annually'. He reported that Long-eared Owls had been seen or shot at Grittenham Wood, Hilmarton, Stowell, Urchfont, Wilsford, Everleigh, Lavington, Erlestoke, Chitterne and Salisbury, and found nesting at Aldbourne, Windmill Hill, Marlborough and Figheldean. He also referred to a flock of 11 at Longford Park 'congregated in a copse of yew trees…during some hard weather in winter', and to a 'sportsman' who, on 29 November 1879, 'while shooting at Grovely…disturbed a flight of Long-eared Owls – estimated at no less than twenty birds – which seemed to fly out of every tree'. In the Marlborough district, im Thurn (1870) had earlier considered this owl 'not…very uncommon', specimens being obtained 'from the various fir copses on the downs', and believed 'it to be pretty generally distributed throughout the district'.

A decline, however, then became evident at the beginning of the 20th century, coinciding with an increase in Tawny Owls, and the Long-eared was 'very scarce in many of these [southern] counties by the 1930s' (*1875–1900 Atlas*). In Wiltshire, the bird reports for 1929 and 1932–34 in *WANHM* noted nesting at Devizes, Figheldean, Warminster, Larkhill, Bulford, Pitton, Clarendon, Alderbury, Whiteparish and Redlynch. Later, Peirson (1959) wrote that 'It seems to have been not uncommon a hundred years ago but to have become scarcer towards the early part of this century. Recently its numbers seem to have increased a little but it is very local'.

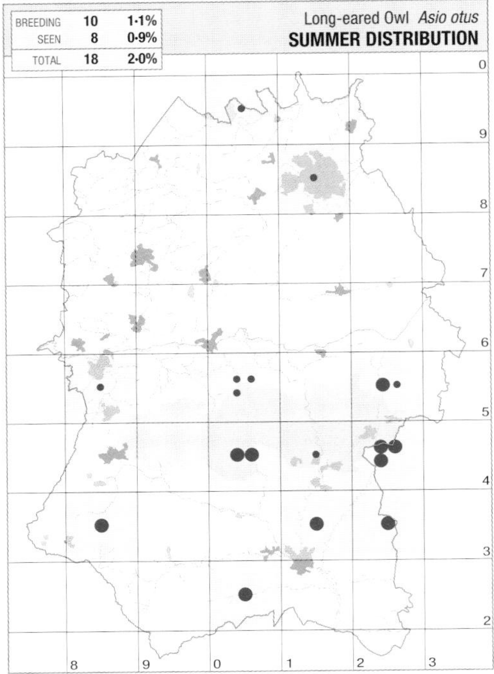

Between 1946 and the late 1960s, records in *WAHNM* were very scarce. Although observers' names were often not given, it seems likely that no more than a few were involved because the same localities – the Marlborough Downs, High Post and Clarendon – were regularly mentioned. Some nests were reported during that period, four in old Magpie nests in hawthorns, the others in pines and firs. (The latter would probably have been in old nests of Carrion Crow, possibly of Sparrowhawk or even Wood Pigeon; occasionally, too, this owl lays its eggs in a simple scrape on the ground under a bush or brambles.) In 1965, Long-eared Owls bred in five areas of the Marlborough Downs (*WANHM*). There was reluctance to name sites in the 1970s, but the species was seen then in the breeding season in several other parts of the county. It was not until 1987 that the first nest on SPTA (West) was located 'in old nest of corvid in hawthorn and three young were ringed' (*Hobby*). After that, one to three nests were reported somewhere in Wiltshire in nine of the next 13 years, the exceptions being 1989, 1994–95 and 2000. The first record on SPTA (East) came in 1993, when two pairs were found. Isolated plantations or copses surrounded by rough grassland or farmland with plentiful voles – field voles are the main prey – are the ideal habitat for this owl in Wiltshire.

In 1996 a night-time observer saw Long-eared Owls throughout the year in one area on SPTA (Centre), and in 1999 heard young there for the first time. Although he made no attempt to find the nest, the evidence indicated that it was in a 2-ha mixed wood – one of many planted in the early 1970s for military training – with three rows of conifers and three of broadleaved trees. By the late 1990s these woods had become suitable habitats for breeding Magpies and Wood Pigeons, their old nests being among those taken over by this species. A Long-eared Owl was twice seen in a large area of thick hawthorn and gorse scrub elsewhere on the same military range in the late 1990s and, in July 1999, another regular observer made tape-recordings there of the hunger calls of the young.

The summer distribution map for 1995–2000 shows breeding proved in only the south of the county, but the difficulty of locating this species makes it most unlikely that that was a complete picture. The summer tetrad survey found Long-eared Owls in ten of Wiltshire's 33 core 10-km squares, compared with eight in each of the *1968–72* and *1988–91 Atlases*, which indicates that the population was relatively stable during the last third of the 20th century. On present evidence, the current population seems likely to be in the range of ten to 25 pairs, but dedicated surveys may well reveal more. The map in the *1988–91 Atlas* suggests that, with those in Hampshire and the Isle of Wight, Wiltshire's breeding Long-eared Owls form a sparsely populated outpost of this species in central-southern Britain.

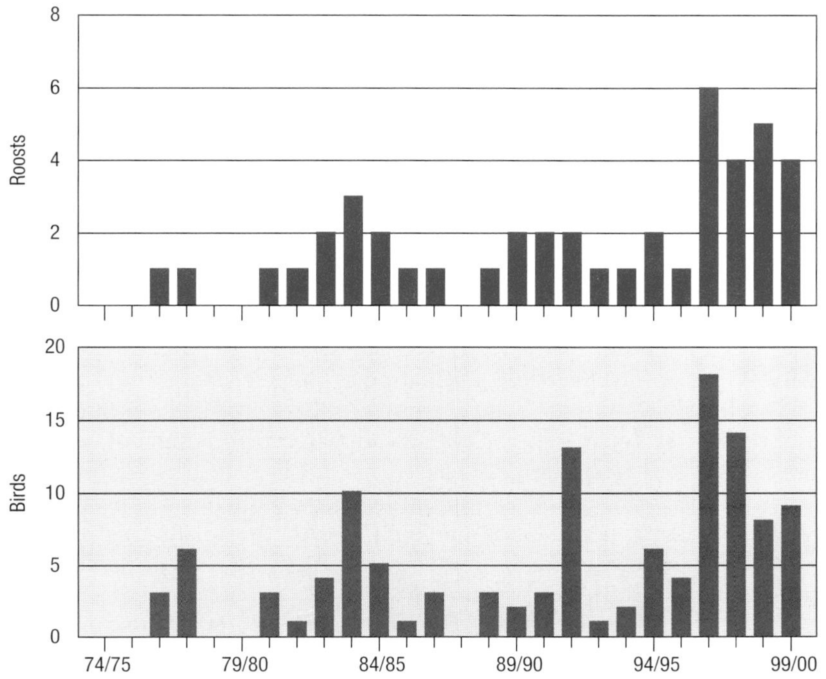

Figure 63. Long-eared Owls *Asio otus* in Wiltshire: roosts and individuals in each winter 1974/75–1999/00
Each owl total is the sum of the peak winter count at every roost, irrespective of month

The numbers of Long-eared Owls at winter roosts varied annually during 1974–2000, up to a maximum of 18 at six roosts in 1997/98, although in several winters none was recorded (figure 63). Roosts have been located across the county, mostly in scrub on downland or along watercourses, but also in evergreen trees and shrubs. The largest gathering in that 27-year period was six, at Swindon STW. As in summer, many will have been overlooked and the location of new roosts, once established ones have been abandoned, is largely hit-and-miss – so it is difficult to draw conclusions about trends. Although influxes into the county are likely to be related to cycles in vole populations elsewhere, there is no obvious correlation between the recorded numbers of Long- and Short-eared Owls in Wiltshire, which may simply reflect the difficulties in locating the present species.

More interest in the study of this owl will be necessary before its future status can be predicted but, on present evidence, it seems possible that investigation of the plantations on SPTA – many of which are surrounded by large areas of the unmanaged grassland that is the prime habitat for its main prey – may well result in the finding of more breeding pairs.

PEC & SBE

Short-eared Owl

Asio flammeus

Scarce and local winterer from north Britain/north Europe, has bred five times

One of the most widespread of all the world's owls, the Short-eared is found breeding across much of northern Eurasia and North America, in mainly southern South America, and on certain Pacific, Caribbean and Atlantic islands. Northern populations are largely migratory, and some then overwinter south to Africa north of the equator, southern India, south China, and Mexico. The breeding population of Europe, excluding Russia, has been estimated at 13,400 to 26,300 pairs, the biggest numbers in Fenno-Scandia and north Russia, but the species has declined in, or even disappeared from, much of central Europe, largely through habitat losses or changes (*EBCC Atlas*). Like other arctic predatory birds, Short-eared Owls in the north of the Continent lay larger clutches and raise more young in summers when lemming populations are high – with the result that adult owls are more numerous in the following season, but they may then have to disperse widely if the lemming populations have subsequently crashed.

This is the only British owl that nests exclusively on the ground. In summer it is found mainly in Scotland and northern England, where its chief needs for successful breeding – extensive undisturbed open areas for hunting, and plentiful small mammals for prey – are met. British Short-eared Owls rely heavily on field voles, and in poor vole years their numbers are likely to be near the lower limit in a fluctuating population of an estimated 1000 to 3500 pairs (*1988–91 Atlas*). Outside the breeding season, Short-eared Owls travel widely and British-ringed individuals have reached northern Spain and the central Mediterranean, while immigrants from Iceland, Fenno-Scandia, Germany, the Netherlands and Belgium have been recorded here (*Migration Atlas*). In winter, this species is generally more widespread in Britain, particularly in the south, where a variety of open landscapes are frequented, most notably in coastal areas; numbers may then be swollen to anything between 5000 and 50,000, depending on the severity of the weather on the Continent (*1981–84 Winter Atlas*).

Smith (1887) wrote that, in Wiltshire, this species was 'quite as numerous' as the Long-eared Owl and 'arrives in October, and leaves us again in spring'. In the Marlborough district, im Thurn (1870) had earlier considered it 'by no means common', visiting in the autumn 'when they generally frequent the turnip-fields'. The inaugural bird report for 1929 in *WANHM* described it as an 'occasional winter visitor, formerly more frequent'. Thirty years later, Peirson (1959) considered it 'A winter visitor, not uncommon to the south of Salisbury Plain and the surrounding country, less regular and scarcer elsewhere. Not many were reported between about 1900 and 1930'. Short-eared Owls were recorded in autumn and winter in each of the last three bird reports in *WANHM* before the 1939–45 War, thus in 1932–34 and 1936, mostly on Salisbury Plain but also at Tilshead, Pitton, Britford and Clearbury Down. Since the War, they have been found annually, mainly in winter, from 1946 to 2000 (*WANHM*, *Hobby*).

Until the early 1970s, Short-eared Owls were seen regularly at Totterdown (as many as 12 in January 1946) and at Fyfield on the Marlborough Downs (*WANHM*). Subsequently, those areas produced fewer records because they no longer held sufficient undisturbed long grass to provide hunting and cover for these owls. Meanwhile, in the mid 1970s, the formation of conservation groups on SPTA enabled increased, if still limited, access to Salisbury Plain's vast tracts of grassland rich in voles, and this has become a winter feeding and roosting stronghold for these owls. Other areas where they have been seen regularly, though not annually, are Oldbury Down near Beckhampton, Boscombe Down and High Post.

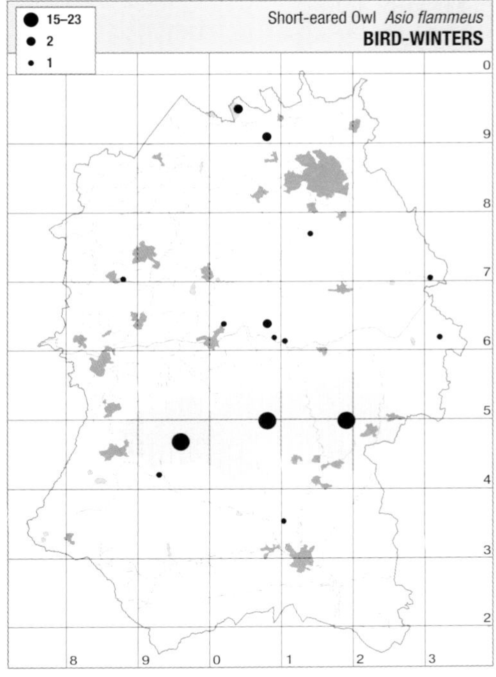

Numbers have always fluctuated from winter to winter, the inference being that they are higher after summers in which vole populations – and, therefore, owl breeding success – have been high, but more research is needed to verify this. (Vole numbers in Wiltshire may influence the local distribution in winter, and perhaps encourage roosts to develop, but it is the vole and lemming populations in the northern breeding grounds that affect how many come to the county in the first place.) Short-eared numbers were high in the winters of 1978/79, 1988/89, 1991/92, 1992/93 and 1999/2000 (figure 64). Summation of the peak counts at roosts on the three SPTA ranges suggests a maximum population of 30 individuals, but the counts were neither coordinated nor simultaneous – and, against a possible background of daily movements between roosts, the highest on each range may not even have been in the same month – so the actual total may be lower. The most recorded in a single month was 19 at seven sites in early November 1988, and the largest number seen together was 13 at Haxton in December of that year.

Because of their high mobility, and nomadic behaviour in search of feeding grounds outside the breeding season, Short-eared Owls have been recorded in winter at other, widely scattered places in the county, including river valleys in the Salisbury area and Swindon STW, and have been found as far west as Gastard near Chippenham. Wintering numbers in Wiltshire probably vary between 10 and 20 in 'normal' years, although this seems a relatively low proportion of the national total for a county with large areas of

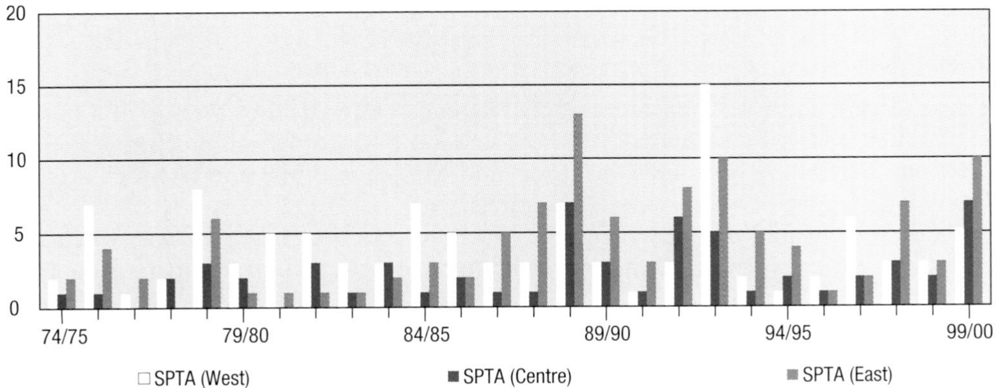

Figure 64. Short-eared Owls *Asio flammeus* in Wiltshire: peak winter counts on the three SPTA ranges 1974/75–1999/00

apparently suitable habitat. Given that much of Salisbury Plain is little visited, however, or even inaccessible, the Wiltshire winter population seems likely to be double that range in a 'good' year.

Wiltshire's first proof of breeding by Short-eared Owls came in 1964, when one of a pair near Tidworth 'circled low, making hissing sounds and diving down' on 14 June, two juveniles were flushed on the 18th, and at least six – 'adults and young' – were seen on the 26th; breeding was again reported at the same site in 1967 (*WANHM*). Another 30 years were to pass before the next records: in 1997 three Short-eared Owls were seen on Salisbury Plain during the breeding season, and in 1999 a pair reared two young on SPTA (Centre). The nest was thought to be located in unmanaged long grass in the Impact Area, and the family was watched regularly from July to mid September. This was also a good summer for breeding Barn Owls (*qv*) on Salisbury Plain and the assumption was that it was probably a peak year for voles, whereas 'a failure in the [northern] vole population' apparently caused some Short-eared Owls to breed in several areas south of their normal range (*Hobby*). Breeding was proved again in 2000, when an adult and two fledged young were seen on SPTA (East) on 7 June and an adult was watched feeding a juvenile at the same locality on the 19th. Singleton Short-eared Owls were also found elsewhere on Salisbury Plain in May, and on SPTA (Centre) a juvenile on 13 August and three owls in early September (one still defending territory) were strong evidence of a second breeding record that year.

Most winter records are on SPTA, but Short-eared Owls – presumed to be on migration – are reported more widely in spring and autumn. In the 1990s, this species typically arrived in Wiltshire in October, sometimes even in September, but in some years the first-winterers were not seen until December. Those that winter on Salisbury Plain usually stay into March or April, and records of migrants are not uncommon in May. The only Short-eared ringed in Wiltshire during 1965–2000 had been found with a damaged wing on the Plain at Bulford on 7 November 1966 and, after being taken into care, it 'flew strongly away' on being released at Neston on the 24th (*WANHM*, JC Rolls).

(See also page 724.)

PEC & SBE

Nightjar
Caprimulgus europaeus

Decreasing and now rare summer visitor, breeds Europe, winters Africa

The far-carrying churring song of the male Nightjar – uttered from the top of a bush or young conifer, or from a higher tree branch, sometimes from the ground, and audible at 200–500 m, depending on conditions, from mid May to late July and less regularly into August – is evocative of warm summer evenings.

Birds of twilight and darkness, Nightjars are rarely seen or heard by day, when their complex and intricately mottled dusky-brown plumage provides extraordinary camouflage as the female (periodically relieved by the male) incubates her two eggs, while the male crouches not far away. The nest is no more than a shallow scrape in a bare patch on the ground, and may be among bracken, long heather, small bushes or, increasingly, young plantation trees. Large-headed with big eyes and ear-holes, tiny bills but huge gapes, and silent flight – except in their wing-clapping display-flight – they are superbly adapted to catch the night-flying moths, beetles and other mainly larger insects that make up the bulk of their food.

Nightjars breed in northwest Africa and through much of Europe from the Mediterranean north to southern Fenno-Scandia; across western and central Asia to northern China and south also to Turkey, Iran and the northwest Himalayas. All populations are migratory and even the most easterly go to winter in sub-Saharan Africa, mainly down the eastern half, though there are few ringing recoveries to indicate where the British birds go. (None of the eight Nightjars ringed in Wiltshire during 1965–2000 has been recovered.) The population of Europe, excluding Russia, has been estimated at 224,000 to 264,000 pairs, the biggest numbers being in Spain and Belarus (*EBCC Atlas*), but both numbers and range have decreased since the 1950s, particularly in northwest Europe, where only Sweden has reported stability since 1970. In general, Nightjars remain common in less intensively farmed countries, indicating that habitat loss and change, and perhaps pesticide use, are the main causes of the decline.

In Great Britain, Nightjars are found from southern England to the southwest lowlands of Scotland, and erratically still farther north, but the main concentrations are now only in the southeast – in the five counties from Dorset to Kent and in parts of East Anglia. Although dry, sandy heaths with scattered trees are the most typical breeding sites, recently felled woods and young forestry plantations are also important, while other habitats include open woodland, moorland, flinty downland, sand dunes and industrial tips.

The decline in Great Britain began early in the 20th century, in some areas before the 1914–18 War, becoming general by about 1930 and very pronounced after 1950 (Stafford 1962). A population of 3000 to 6000 pairs of Nightjars was estimated by the *1968–72 Atlas*, but a national survey in 1981 located only 2100 churring males and the true population was considered to be nearer the bottom end of that range (Gribble 1983). Although the 'change' map in the *1988–91 Atlas* mapped breeding in 37 'new' 10-km squares – many probably the result of local habitat alterations – it also showed some 230 formerly occupied squares in which breeding had apparently ceased since 1968–72, and there had been a total reduction of 51 per cent in the number of squares in which the species was recorded. On the other hand, another national Nightjar survey in 1992 estimated some 3400 churring males, over 50 per cent of them in forestry plantations – those newly felled, and then up to five years after replanting, holding the highest densities (Morris *et al* 1994).

Wiltshire's first recorded Nightjar was the 'Nocturnal Goat-sucker' from Coombe in September 1796 (Maton 1843). This species was also referred to as a 'Goatsucker' by im Thurn (1870), who noted 'Nightjar' and 'Fern Owl' as local names, adding 'This remarkable bird is not common with us, though specimens have been procured from all parts' of the county. Bosworth Smith (1863) stated that, in the Marlborough district, it 'Is to be heard in most oak-plantations between the months of May and August' and, 24 years later, Smith (1887) remarked that it was 'to be met with sparingly throughout the county, wherever deep woods furnish it with shade and retirement, and even on our downs'. Subsequent authors considered it 'not uncommon generally, especially on Bedwyn Common' (Meyrick 1895, 1906); 'a fairly common summer visitor' to the Marlborough district (Peirson

1919); and 'probably not uncommon in certain localities in the [Savernake] Forest, on Clench and Bedwyn Commons and among the sarsens on the downs, but much overlooked' (Peirson & Walford 1930). The inaugural bird report for 1929 in *WANHM* described it as just a 'rather scarce summer visitor, which appears to be decreasing' in the county as a whole.

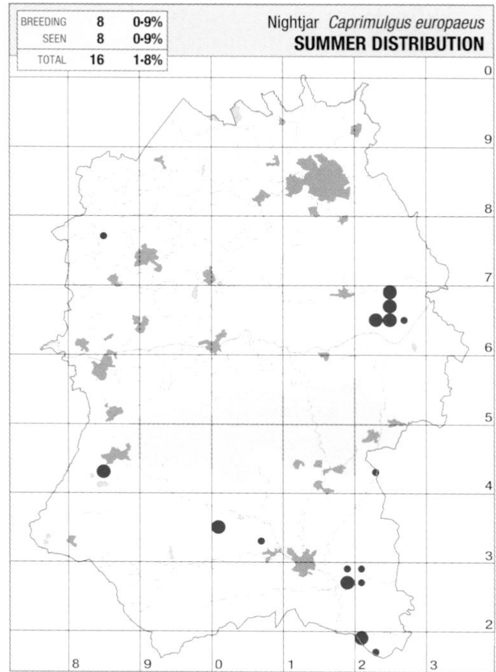

Before the 1960s, heathland in Wiltshire was found on acid soils: for example, at Spye Park; around Savernake, especially at Bedwyn Common and West Woods; in the Longleat area; and also on leached soils on chalk on, for example, Salisbury Plain and Porton Down as well as in Great Ridge and Grovely Woods; and in the southeast at Alderbury Common, Hamptworth Common, Landford Common and Pound Bottom. Between 1929 and 1955, Nightjars were reported from Lydiard Millicent, Spye Park, Clatford Bottom, West Woods, Bedwyn Common, Chisbury Wood, Clench Common, Chute, the Warminster area, Farley, Clarendon, East Grimstead, Wardour, Alderbury and Redlynch (*WANHM*). This led Peirson (1959) to state that it was 'breeding in small numbers at suitable nesting sites throughout the county', and Kennedy (1966) recorded it as a 'summer visitor to Savernake, Bedwyn Common and West Woods in small numbers'.

Some two decades later, however, Buxton (1981) commented that the Nightjar had 'decreased greatly in recent years and is now known to breed only in Bentley Wood, Grovely Wood, Longleat, Porton Down and possibly at Bulford, all sites in the northern half of the county having been vacated' – although the accompanying map did indicate presence in two 10-km squares in the north. Palmer (1991) believed Nightjars had continued to decline and were 'virtually confined to Grovely Wood, Longleat and the woodlands south and east of Salisbury'. Former sites at Southleigh and Eastleigh Woods have been unoccupied since 1985.

The *1988–91 Atlas* mapped Nightjars as breeding in eight of Wiltshire's 33 core 10-km squares and seen in two others, compared with 11 and four previously in the *1968–72 Atlas*, whereas the summer distribution map for 1995–2000 shows it in only six and four (as well as breeding in one of the 15 non-core squares). Despite this general decrease, linked largely to the decline in heathland in Wiltshire, the summer map also emphasises the continuing importance of both the Savernake area, where there has probably been an increase over the last 20 years of the 20th century, and the southeast of the county, where they were almost certainly under-recorded. Fortunes apparently varied during the 1990s (table 98) and the Wiltshire population of Nightjars probably numbered some 15–20 pairs in the latter part of that decade. High temperatures from June to August, as in 1996 and 1997, enhance breeding success, as they increase the numbers of prey insects and encourage second broods.

Breeding Nightjars in the county are now very dependent on forestry activities. Some such sites have been consistently occupied for a long time, notably Grovely Wood where Nightjars were recorded in every year during 1974–2000, except 1976, and where the highest number of churring males was seven in 1985. Other sites important in the 1990s included Alderbury and Clarendon (peak of five males in 1992 and 1996), Franchises Wood

Table 98. Nightjars *Caprimulgus europaeus* in Wiltshire: occupied sites and churring males 1990–2000

	90	91	92	93	94	95	96	97	98	99	00
Occupied sites	6	6	10	4	3	7	7	5	4	7	4
Churring males	12	13	20	8	7	17	16	10	8	9	7

(peak of three males in 1991) and Savernake (peak of six males in 1996). Woodlands close to Savernake, including Bedwyn Common, Cobham Frith and Hens Wood, became more important in the second half of the 1990s, as a result of the clear-felling of plantations, and between them probably totalled six males in both 1999 and 2000. A most unusual site was at the Westbury Trading Estate, where a churring male triggered the beam activating the intruder alarm in 1989 and was then recorded on several nights churring from the top of a security light (*Hobby*).

The earliest known arrival date in Wiltshire was 5 April in 1968 (*WANHM*), and the latest departure 2 October in 1978 (*Hobby*). Most Nightjars arrive around 12 May, however, and in the eleven years of 1990–2000 the earliest date was 3 May and the latest 'first date' was 25 May. Once males stop churring in late July and early August, the species is rarely recorded: the latest reported date during 1990–2000 was 10 September, and in three of those years none was seen after July.

The future for the species in the county is likely to reflect the national position. So long as forestry operations provide suitable habitat, Nightjars will probably continue to breed in small numbers, and sometimes at new sites. Having lost much of its heathland, however, the Wiltshire population is never likely to be nationally significant, and currently amounts to less than one per cent of the British total.

SBE

Common Swift
Apus apus

Common summer visitor, breeds Europe, winters Africa

Quite unrelated to swallows and martins, the 90 or more species of true swifts, most of them tropical, are essentially aerial – indeed, the most aerial of all birds – not only exclusively feeding and often spending the night high in the air but also (probably uniquely) copulating on the wing; moreover, the young are able to fly and feed independently as soon as they leave the nest and those of some species then have to undertake long migrations within a week or two. One such is the Common Swift, which in summer is among the most northerly and widely distributed of the whole family, breeding in northwest Africa and

almost throughout Europe – except the northernmost parts of Scotland, Fenno-Scandia and Russia – south to Turkey and Israel, and east across much of central Asia into China and south to the Himalayas. Common Swifts are strongly migratory and all but a very small proportion winter in sub-Saharan Africa.

The population of Common Swifts in Europe, excluding Russia, has been estimated at 4·0 to 4·9 million pairs and is thought to be stable overall, though 'downward fluctuations have been reported in 12 countries' (*EBCC Atlas*). In Great Britain, the *1988–91 Atlas* – which noted no evidence of any change in abundance since the *1968–72 Atlas* survey – concluded that, although total numbers had so far proved impossible to estimate reliably, there were perhaps around 80,000 pairs. Swifts were clearly a familiar sight in 19th century Wiltshire. Smith (1887) noted the use of the "provincial name…'the Screech'" and wrote that they 'frequent our downs in fine weather, where they may be met with in considerable numbers'. The 1929 bird report in *WANHM* referred to this species as 'An abundant summer visitor… increasing locally'. Peirson (1959), Buxton (1981) and Palmer (1991) all described it simply as 'common', and Buxton noted it 'a little less common in the centre of some of the larger towns than it used to be due to the modernisation of older areas and the subsequent loss of breeding sites'.

Swifts are usually among the last migrants to reach Great Britain in spring, and their screaming calls in early May bring promise of imminent summer. Wiltshire's earliest recorded arrival was a singleton at Coate Water on 4 April 1956 (*WANHM*), but the bulk of the population does not return before the last few days of April or early May, when breeding sites are then quickly investigated. At that time, however, many traditional cavities are still occupied by Starlings and will not be vacated by them before the middle of May. The two species will sometimes have prolonged aerial grappling fights over nest-sites, as indeed will Swifts with each other (Campbell & Lack 1985).

Spring and early summer gatherings can be substantial, primarily in the first month after arrival: for example, 700 to 1000 at Coate Water on 12 May 1962, 1000 at CWP on 15 May 1993, and up to 1500 feeding at CWP between 25 May and 2 June 1991 (*WANHM*, *Hobby*). Such gatherings are rarer later in the summer, and sometimes associated with poor weather, but a massive 3000 near Broad Hinton on 18 June 1970, as well as 1000 at Tan Hill 15 July 1994 and 300 at Compton Down on 22 July 1998, are worth mentioning.

The Common Swift's nesting season is inextricably linked with the weather: flying insects and airborne spiders are far more plentiful in warm and settled conditions. As soon as they leave the nest, the youngsters have to be able to feed themselves independently and then undertake the long journey to Africa a week or two later. A study of a colony of 20–25 pairs in Oxford (Lack & Lack 1951, Lack 1956) showed that in a good or even an average summer – the crucial factor being the number of hours of sunshine in the second half of June and the first half of July – there can be a high breeding success of over 90 per cent, and the young then leave the nest as strong and efficient flyers after only 5–6 weeks. In a wet summer, on the other hand, egg-laying is delayed, breeding success may be as low as 35–45 per cent and the young may not fledge for 7–8 weeks, so having less time before the journey south. Such variable fledging – involving starvation, use of fat reserves, retarded development, and even torpor – is rare among birds (Campbell & Lack 1985).

Adults – which share incubation as well as brooding and feeding the young, and lose a much higher proportion of their body weights in a poor summer – will also clump together in a semi-torpid state, clinging to vertical surfaces with two-toes-forward-and-two-back feet that are surprisingly strong on such weak legs. It is often thought that the adults fly long distances to feed, but breeding Swifts catch most of the food for themselves and their young within 10 km of the colony. Nevertheless, observations by radar and from gliders have shown that sea-breeze fronts in Hampshire have carried flocks inland as far as Berkshire and Surrey (Simpson 1967) and some Swifts may travel hundreds of kilometres to out-fly deep

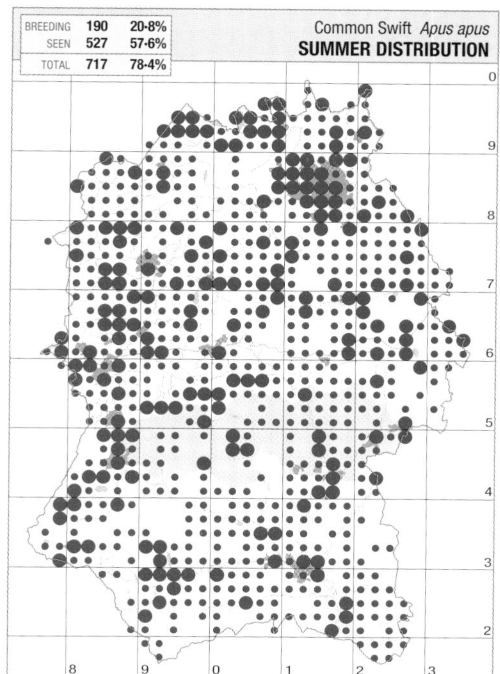

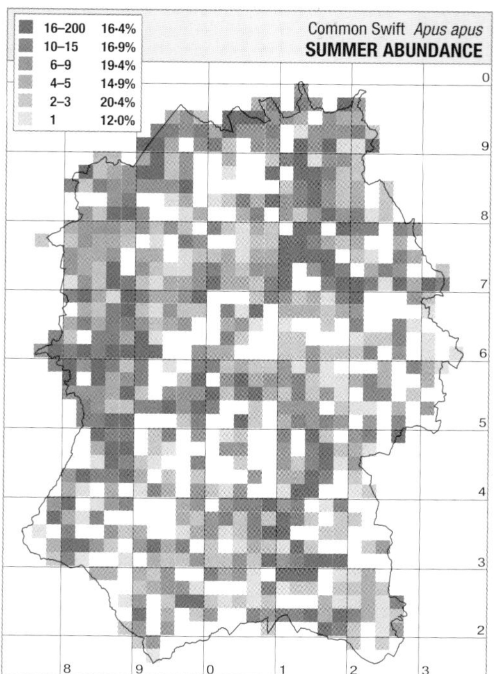

depressions in a search for food (Campbell & Lack 1985). In Wiltshire, comments about poor or late breeding were noted in several years in the 1990s, especially in 1991, 1997 and 1998, when June and July were, in all cases, cold and wet or unsettled (*Hobby*).

Swifts tend to be seen more readily in and around urban areas during the breeding season as these provide the taller buildings that they need for nesting, cavities more than 5 m from the ground being preferred (though 'traditional' sites in thatched cottages may be as low as 3 m). Most of the tetrads with breeding evidence on the summer map encompass towns, or villages with a church tower, and those simply showing 'seen' doubtless refer to overflying individuals or parties, many of which may have been foraging adults from local colonies. Timed surveys counted some 6300 Swifts in Wiltshire during the breeding season. It is difficult to be certain how many pairs this represents – particularly in view of large daily feeding movements – but it could suggest a minimum county population of around 4500–6000 pairs. This would represent a sizeable proportion of the national total, given that highest densities are found in the southeast, away from the breezier and wetter west coasts where insect food is less abundant.

Few monitoring data exist to determine national trends in the Swift population. BBS data, available only from 1994, suggest moderate declines in England as a whole and a more than 50 per cent decrease in the southwest between then and 2000, but large fluctuations between years mean that such results should be treated with caution (*BBWC*). There is little evidence in Wiltshire of any great change in numbers or distribution, and Swifts were recorded in all of the county's 33 core 10-km squares by both the *1968–72* and *1988–91 Atlases*, as well as by the summer tetrad survey of 1995–2000. Locally, demolition of old buildings in town centres may cause minor changes, but these are extremely difficult to quantify. A few local authorities, such as Salisbury District Council, have been installing nestboxes for Swifts in both new and renovated properties in large urban areas.

Adults usually begin their autumn migration a few days after the juveniles, presumably first building up their reserves after the toll taken by raising their young, and most local breeders have disappeared by early August. Stragglers are seen during September, however, and there are a few Wiltshire sightings for October: on the 4th in 1982 and 2000, on the 7th in 1986, on the 11th in 1978, and on the 24th in 1984; all involved singletons except for two together at Marlborough in 1986. The latest ever recorded in the county was at Donhead St Andrew on 2 December 1994, a month when others were seen elsewhere in England.

A total of 386 Swifts was ringed in Wiltshire during 1965–2000, and 12 had been recovered by the end of that period. Of these, only two were found more than 100 km away and just one of those abroad: an adult ringed at Longbridge Deverill on 23 June 1982 was recovered in Spain, at Grado (Oviedo), on 18 May 1984, presumably having been down to southern Africa and back twice in the interim. Another adult ringed at Longbridge Deverill on 11 June 1985 was found dead near Coventry (West Midlands) almost four weeks later, on 8 July.

GLW & IJF-L

Sponsored by Peggy Bucknall

Alpine Swift

Apus melba

Overshooting vagrant (3 records) from southern Europe, winters Africa

Alpine Swifts are summer visitors to all countries bordering the Mediterranean and Black Seas, north to Switzerland, southern Germany and the Crimea, and thence patchily east to central Asia and the Himalayas – nesting colonially in crevices and holes in coastal or mountain cliffs and in tall buildings. They winter in eastern and southern sub-Saharan Africa, Madagascar, southwest Arabia, and India and Sri Lanka, which all have resident populations as well. The numbers in Europe, excluding Russia, have been estimated at 44,600 to 62,500 pairs. Most European populations are considered stable, and during the 20th century their range extended northward in France and numbers increased in Switzerland (*EBCC Atlas*).

Alpine Swifts travel huge distances – 'an estimated 600–1000 km daily and ascend at least to limit of range of powerful binoculars' (*BWP*) – to feed on a wide variety of flying insects and airborne spiders. Thus, although generally classed as overshooting vagrants to southern counties of Great Britain in spring and early summer, it is conceivable that some are simply on feeding visits from the northern limits of their French and Swiss ranges, perhaps flying around depressions to avoid rain. Some 440 records during 1958–2000 (*BBRC*) included only two in Wiltshire; and both of them and the one older observation all involved singletons:

1927	27 October	Stapleford
1984	12–13 July	Swindon
1986	29 June	Morgan's Hill

Many British records have been brief visitors to regularly watched coastal sites, but this powerful and high-flying swift is probably often overlooked in inland southern counties.

GLW & PCo

Buxton (1981) also made mention of an Alpine Swift 'on the county boundary' at CWP in 1977, which presumably referred to one which was recorded at South Cerney Sewage Farm (Gloucestershire) on 1 June (*BBRC*); it was not noted in *Hobby* or by *BBRC* to have flown over Wiltshire. Another Alpine Swift was seen flying with Common Swifts in Old Town, Swindon, by an experienced observer on 5 May 1987, but no details were submitted to any records committee and, although it cannot therefore be included in the formal totals, it is noted here for completeness.

Eds

Kingfisher

Alcedo atthis

Scarce and local breeding resident, more widespread in autumn/winter

Familiar to all through photographs and paintings, the Kingfisher is one of Wiltshire's most colourful birds. In flight, its distinctive high-pitched call attracts attention when a flash of blue – brightest on back and tail – shoots rapidly along a river or stream, often less than a metre above the water. Sometimes one can be spotted overhead and then, in good light, the fleeting impression is one of short wings and orange-chestnut underparts.

But Kingfishers are not seen only over or near water. One of the first published references to this species in Wiltshire involved one 'found in 1867 at the top of the White Horse Hill' (im Thurn 1870); and, over 130 years later, *Hobby* for 1998 summarised reports 'of flying over fields or, in two cases, across a main road and through a petrol station remind us that Kingfishers will not uncommonly cut off corners or continue to follow routes of watercourses that disappear underground through culverts'. Moreover, aerial chases by a bonding pair – which may continue on and off for hours (*BWP*) – will take the two birds low over water or land and high in the tree-tops (*eg* Boag 1982).

The Kingfisher has a large but fragmented world breeding range, in northwest Africa, in much of Europe (as far north as central Scotland and the southern fringes of Fenno-Scandia), in a few parts of Turkey and the Middle East, in central, eastern and southern Asia, and from Sumatra east to the Solomon Islands. Most populations north of 40°N – except those of western and southern Europe and much of Japan – move south in autumn to winter in and beyond the southern parts of the breeding range. Then, for example, the species may be found along Mediterranean coasts and down the Nile valley. The breeding population of Europe has been estimated at 47,300 to 66,800 pairs, and habitat loss and pollution have been considered to constitute the main threats (*EBCC Atlas*).

Winter temperatures and rainfall also cause numbers to vary widely between years, but high mortality in cold winters is quickly offset by this species' ability to raise two broods – or even three in a good year – of up to six youngsters each. In 1962/63, the last of the really prolonged severe winters of the 20th century, Kingfishers suffered badly; indeed, they were considered to be the hardest hit of all bird species then (Dobinson & Richards 1964) and breeding numbers in Wales fell by about 85 per cent. Unfortunately, apart from 'Seemingly fewer' at Marlborough and 'None seen at Cole Park (where as many as 17 [previously] ringed in a season) until 21st Dec [1963]' (*WANHM*), the effects were not assessed in Wiltshire. Summer droughts, and now increased water abstraction from rivers, can also cause streams to become too shallow and winterbournes to dry completely.

The *1988–91 Atlas*, which estimated the British population at 3300 to 5500 pairs, showed that the range had advanced north in Scotland since the *1968–72 Atlas*, but also demonstrated evident losses of breeding areas in many parts of England and Wales, adding that 'Industrial pollution and contamination by agricultural run-off, particularly of animal waste slurries and liquor from silage clamps, may be implicated'. Population trends are not, however, entirely clear: although *WBS* data suggest a decline until the mid 1980s and a subsequent recovery – increasing by 29 per cent during the 1990s – numbers fluctuate markedly between years (*BBWC*). The British total in 2000 was estimated as 4300 to 7100 pairs (*APEP*).

Although the British population is largely resident, juveniles are known to disperse randomly from their breeding sites within days of reaching independence, and a British-ringed adult has been recovered across the Channel in Brittany (France) (*Migration Atlas*). In autumn, dispersing wanderers often reach land-locked lakes or ponds, and in Wiltshire are reported from more localities at that season (*eg Hobby* 27). Later in the year, they may move to larger waterbodies less prone to freezing, and some exploit milder conditions along the coast.

Some 16 of the 194 Kingfishers ringed in Wiltshire during 1965–2000 were recovered or retrapped away from the ringing site in that period, 11 within the county and five elsewhere in southern England, but only one of those had moved more than 99 km: ringed near Marlborough on 28 August 1968, it was caught and released nearly a year later 125 km away in Hertfordshire, on 26 July 1969. Probably rather more Kingfishers were ringed before 1965 – see references to the early 1960s above and below – but no details are readily available. It is, however, likely that a sizeable proportion of those seen in Wiltshire outside the breeding season are from elsewhere in southern England.

For breeding, Kingfishers usually require slow-moving streams, rivers or canals, or gravel pits or sand pits, with steep sand or earth banks soft enough to allow them to excavate a tunnel 50–150 cm long leading to a nest chamber, but even nests may be 'at considerable distances from water and occasionally among roots of trees or in hole of wall' (Witherby *et al* 1938–41). In this connection it is interesting to note that, in the mid 19th century, one Wiltshire nest was 'found in a very strange position, viz. in the bank of one of the clay-pits near the entrance to the [Savernake] Forest on the Salisbury road, about a mile from any running water' (Bosworth Smith 1863).

In Wiltshire, too, Maton (1843) noted that the Kingfisher was 'often seen on the banks of the rivulets about Salisbury'; Bosworth Smith (1863) that it was 'to be found, though in no great numbers, all along the Kennet' and that nests had been 'taken near Polton, and several times on the banks of the Canal near Burbage'; and im Thurn (1870) that 'It is by no means such an uncommon bird with us as it is supposed to be…I believe their nests to be common'. Smith (1887) described this species as 'not uncommon wherever there is a stream; indeed, for lack of a river or a brook, I have known it haunt the foul sluggish watercourse of a long line of water meadows, and even a stagnant pond in a cow yard'; he added that it suffered much human persecution, but despite this he did not think 'its numbers are much diminished in the county generally'.

This view was echoed by the inaugural bird report for 1929 in *WANHM*, which believed Kingfishers to be not uncommon, 'in spite of persecution'. People continued to kill them well into the mid 20th century, and the report for 1947 noted that there was 'Much persecution in the interests of fishing in the Mere District'. Peirson (1959) wrote that this species was 'resident, common on the Salisbury Avon, less common on the other rivers and streams'; and some idea of numbers on the Salisbury Avon at that time can be gained from the report for 1960 in *WANHM*: 'More than 15 at Britford over about one mile of watermeadows, where 11 birds were ringed in a day's trapping'.

Two decades later, Buxton (1981) considered that the Kingfisher was 'A relatively common resident whose population tends to fluctuate', adding that it bred 'more commonly

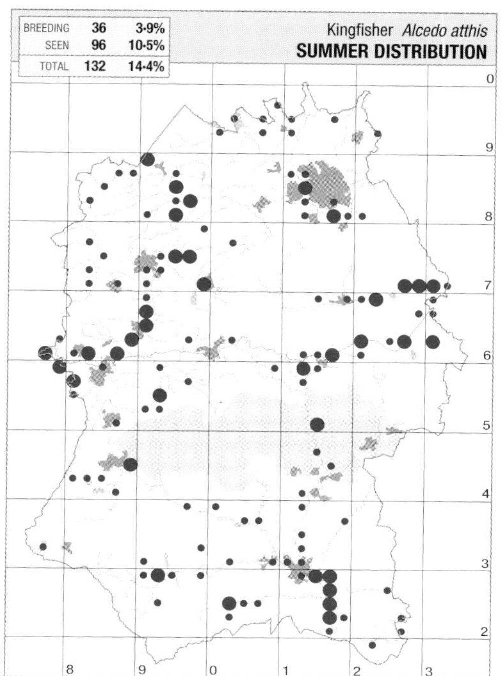

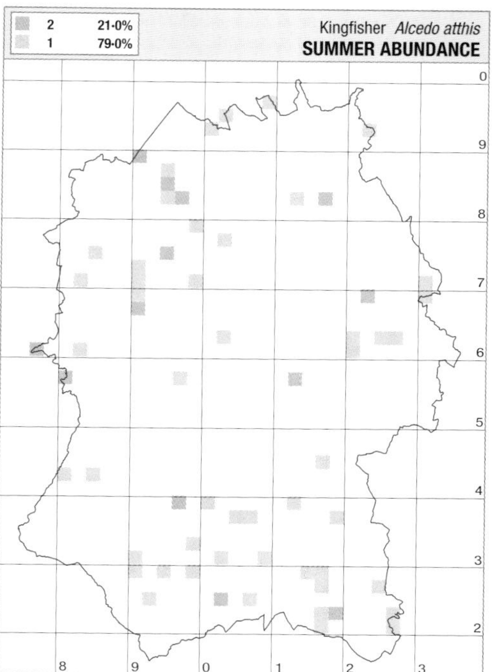

on the less polluted Salisbury Avon and its tributaries than on the Kennet, Bristol Avon, Thames, By Brook, Ray, Cole and the Kennet and Avon Canal. Most of the larger waters have occasional pairs including gravel pits in the Ashton Keynes section of the Cotswold Water Park'.

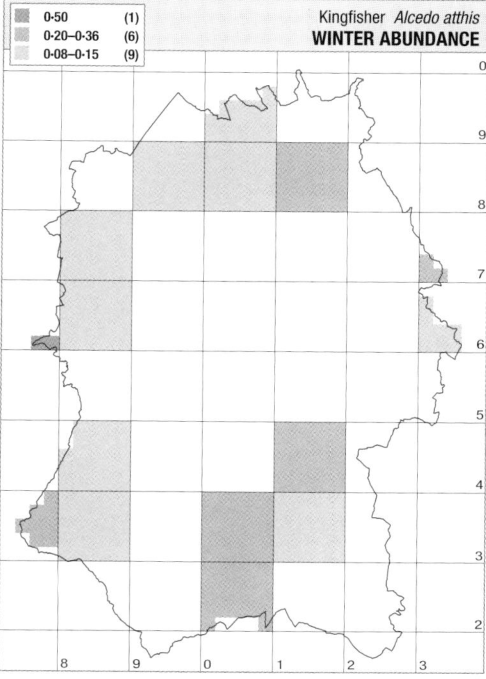

The summer distribution map for 1995–2000 shows particular concentrations of breeding around Swindon and along the Bristol Avon, the Kennet, the Kennet & Avon Canal, and the Salisbury Avon, though this may to some extent reflect better public access in those areas. It is also worth noting that a nesting male radio-tracked in Belgium had a home range 14 km in length (*EBCC Atlas*), and so caution in interpreting the map is required. Some 20 to 29 pairs were reported annually in *Hobby* during 1991–95, but there was evidence of breeding at only nine or ten sites in 1996 and no more than half a dozen during the remaining 1990s. The winter of 1995/96 was the wettest and coldest in the 1990s, which may have resulted in higher mortality, but otherwise this apparent decline is more likely to be a result of reduced reporting on standard record cards during the period of the tetrad survey or, equally, that rather more stringent rules were then being applied to the significance of summer sightings (see entries in *Hobby* 23–26).

A comparison of the numbers of Wiltshire's 33 core 10-km squares in which Kingfishers were recorded in the course of the three grid surveys of the last third of the 20th century appears to show a slightly thinning summer distribution. They were mapped in 31 core squares by the *1968–72 Atlas*, in 28 by the *1988–91 Atlas*, and in 27 by the tetrad survey of 1995–2000. If there has indeed been a slight reduction, it seems unlikely – in view of the generally milder winters through the 1990s – that higher mortality in severe weather has played any part. The national atlases used a formula of three to five pairs per occupied 10-km square to calculate the population, on which basis Wiltshire's core square numbers during the summer survey would fall into the range of 81 to 135 pairs. Breeding evidence was found in 36 tetrads, and the species seen in a further 96; a total of 75 individuals was recorded during timed surveys, though that would have represented only a proportion of the true number, particularly for this relatively unobtrusive species. From these figures, it is suggested that the county's summer population perhaps numbers 100–150 pairs.

The winter map, based on 10-km squares, certainly understates the Kingfisher's non-breeding distribution in Wiltshire and the figure of 52 extrapolated from the timed winter counts similarly underestimates the true total, which is likely to be at least 200 – perhaps as many as 400 – at that season.

PEC & SBE

Sponsored by DEF Camp in memory of KA Camp

Bee-eater

Merops apiaster

Overshooting vagrant (5 records), breeds south Europe, winters Africa

This exotically colourful species and its liquid trilling calls typify, for many Britons, the archetypal Mediterranean birdwatching experience. Apart from small populations in southern Africa, European Bee-eaters breed from northwest Africa and Iberia east into central Asia, and from Mesopotamia to the Chinese border (Fry 1984). Bee-eaters are summer visitors to Europe where, excluding Russia, a population of 91,200 to 193,000 pairs has been estimated (*EBCC Atlas*). They favour sunny, open landscapes with scattered trees, and hawk flying insects, particularly bees and wasps and, in some regions, are still persecuted by beekeepers. Gregarious year-round, Bee-eaters usually breed in colonies, digging their nesting burrows in exposed vertical banks.

European Bee-eaters winter in sub-Saharan Africa and, in spring, migrating parties on route to their breeding grounds frequently overshoot and reach northern Europe, sometimes then attempting to nest. In Great Britain, a pair tried to breed near Edinburgh in 1920 (Baxter & Rintoul 1953), and two of three pairs in Sussex in 1955 did so successfully (Barham *et al* 1956), as did another pair in Durham in 2002 (*RBBP*); nesting was also attempted in Herefordshire in 2005. Around 700 individuals were recorded in Great Britain during the latter half of the 20th century, and their numbers increased during that time: annual averages rose from around five in the 1960s to 20 in the 1980s and almost 40 in the 1990s, and occasionally there were large influxes, including over 132 in 1997 (Fraser & Rogers 2001). Most occur in southern counties and along the east coast, chiefly in spring and particularly in May, although small numbers of juveniles are seen in autumn. The five Wiltshire records have all been singletons:

1886	4 May	Bishopstrow	Male, shot
1992	31 May	Pewsey	Hawking insects from telephone wires
1994	10 November	Trowbridge	Flying northeast, calling repeatedly
1997	2 June	Westbury	Part of very large influx
1999	5 May	Swindon	In flight and calling

That all the county records bar one have been during the 1990s is in line with the national picture, and those in 1992 and 1997 were each part of a major influx. The one in 1994 is notable in that occurrences in November are unusual. The latest of all British Bee-eaters was found in Cornwall in 1963 – also on the 10th – but it stayed until it died on 3 December.

(See also page 727.)

RT

Sponsored by Marian & Earl Nuttall

Roller

Coracias garrulus

Vagrant (2 records) breeds south/east Europe, winters Africa

Predominantly blue and chestnut-brown, the startlingly coloured and rather crow-like Roller usually nests in tree-holes in open, dry and warm country from Iberia east to western China and Kashmir. During the 20th century, it disappeared from various countries of north-central Europe where it was formerly widespread, including southern Sweden, Denmark, Germany and much of Poland, the Baltic States and the Czech Republic, and it is still decreasing in other areas too, perhaps because of agricultural intensification and the consequent loss of large crickets and beetles, its favoured food items (*CBWP*). The numbers breeding in Europe, excluding Russia, are thought to lie in the range of 16,200 to 23,800 pairs, the largest populations being in Spain, the Ukraine, Romania and Bulgaria (*EBCC Atlas*). Rollers winter on the savannahs of sub-Saharan Africa, primarily in the east.

As the species has declined in Europe, so has the number of vagrants reaching Great Britain: 135 records up to and including 1957, but, despite the huge increase in dedicated observers since then, only 96 during 1958–2000 (*BBRC*). Most British vagrants occur as overshooting migrants in spring and early summer, but some also in September–October. Both Wiltshire's Rollers have been in autumn. The first was well seen by JA Lloyd, a master at Marlborough College, in Savernake on 21 October 1883 (Hart Smith 1887). The second was reported independently by two observers 'about a mile inside the Wiltshire boundary', on the border with the New Forest near Bramshaw (Hampshire), on 14 September 1947; subsequently it was located on at least three more occasions, twice in Hampshire at the end of September and then in Wiltshire again at the beginning of October (*WANHM*, Peirson 1959).

RT

Hoopoe

Upupa epops

Rare passage migrant, former irregular breeder (last confirmed 1950), winters Iberia/Africa

Despite its exotic appearance and distinctive crest – which may be held flat in a hammerhead or raised in a fan – a Hoopoe can be surprisingly difficult to see on the ground, but in flight its butterfly-like flapping on boldly patterned wings is always eye-catching. The breeding male has an unmistakable advertisement-call which gives the species both the onomatopoeic English name ('hoo-poo') and the Latin generic ('oo-poo-pah'). Hoopoes favour open country with mature trees and breed right across central and southern Eurasia, including Turkey, the Middle East and Arabia, as well as in some of the Atlantic Islands, northwest Africa, the Nile valley and much of sub-Saharan Africa. Northern populations are migratory, wintering in the southern parts of the range.

In Europe – where the breeding population, excluding that of Russia, has been estimated at 670,000 to 924,000 pairs (*EBCC Atlas*) – Hoopoes still nest as far north as the Baltic States, but numbers declined in a dozen or more other countries between the mid 19th and mid 20th centuries, probably partly as a result of persecution, and were badly affected again from the mid 1950s, first by pesticides and then probably through agricultural intensification in general. At different times over this whole 150–year period the species ceased to breed regularly in northwest continental Europe from the Low Countries to Sweden and Denmark. The bulk of the population is now found south of a line from northern France through northeast Germany, the vast majority in Spain (*EBCC Atlas*). Some European Hoopoes winter in the Mediterranean area, but most migrate to sub-Saharan Africa.

Nesting north of the main breeding range is sporadic, but has included Great Britain and, indeed, Wiltshire. The *1968–72 Atlas* knew of 'Fewer than 30 cases of confirmed breeding…for the last 140 years'; and the only proved nesting since 1977 – in which year, quite exceptionally, four pairs bred in southern England – was in Wales in 1996 (*RBBP*). Hoopoes are more familiar to British birdwatchers as scarce migrants, particularly as a result of overshooting in anticyclonic spring weather: the annual mean total of records during 1990–2000 was 111 (Fraser & Rogers 2002).

Back in the 19th century, Smith (1887) wrote, 'I have many records of its occurrence in Wiltshire', listing about 20 in all including three instances of nesting. The first two, both undated, were at Rodbourne Cheney, Swindon, where in one year four young 'the colour of woodcocks, with very large topknots' were discovered 'in a bush' and in the next 'the eggs, four in number, were destroyed by boys'; the third 19th century breeding record was in 1877, 'in the neighbourhood of Stratford sub Castle'. Morres (1878–85) gave more detail of this last event, stating that a pair and four young had been observed 'in a withy bed' on 16 June by one W Holbech, who had 'been floating down the river [the Salisbury Avon] quietly in a boat…they allowed him to approach within ten yards'.

Smith's six dated records all fell in April–June or August–September, except for one in January 1854, when a bird 'supposed to be a Hoopoe, was killed', though Smith's correspondent commented that because it 'fell into an old chimney' and had 'never been recovered, I cannot be sure of its identity'. Hony (1915a) mentioned a Hoopoe near Marlborough in December 1878 and another 'shot' near Trowbridge in April 1909, but this latter date was clearly a misprint for 1900. (Hony cited the '*Devizes Gazette*, May 3rd,

Table 99. Hoopoes *Upupa epops* in Wiltshire: monthly totals 1948–2000

	Jan	Feb	Mar	Apr	May	Jun	Jul	Aug	Sep	Oct	Nov	Dec
1948–1989	1	0	1	23	19	8	3	4	2	2	1	1
1990–2000	0	1	3	16	5	2	0	1	0	0	1	0

Table 100. Hoopoes *Upupa epops* in Wiltshire: annual totals 1990–2000

	90	91	92	93	94	95	96	97	98	99	00
Individuals	2	4	2	3	1	2	4	2	2	6	1

and *The Field*, May 26th' 1900 as his sources, and the same Hoopoe was mentioned in 1903 elsewhere in *WANHM*, vol 33 p 64, as 'found dead' at Trowbridge in April 1900, the *Devizes Gazette* of 3 May that year again being acknowledged as the source.)

The inaugural Wiltshire bird report for 1929 in *WANHM* described this as 'A very rare summer visitor. No records for its appearance since 1900 have come to hand' – but almost immediately there followed two records in 1932, at Tisbury in August and at Fonthill in September, and two more in August 1933, 'for several days' at Redlynch and found dead on Wick Down on the 22nd, which 'may have been the same'. In April 1936, there were two separate reports 'near' and 'at' Devizes, one published in the *Western Gazette* and the other sent direct to *WANHM* by a regular contributor who 'had seen this species for several days in his son's garden' and thought it 'quite likely that there was a pair there'; the possibility of breeding was 'suggested' by both him and others, but there seems to have been no attempt to follow up these observations.

No more Hoopoes were reported in Wiltshire until 1948, but from then to 1989 some 55 were documented (excluding two undated, another not certainly identified, and the breeding records below). The majority of those were in spring (table 99), although the species was recorded in every month except February; and two reports in winter (on 22 January 1955 at Patney, and for five days during 4–8 December 1982 at CWP) and two in late autumn (on 30 October 1981 at Chippenham, and on 19 November 1973 at Semington) are all noteworthy.

Breeding clearly took place at Wilsford cum Lake in both 1948 and 1950, though nothing was seen of Hoopoes in the intervening year; four young were reared on the first occasion and three on the second (Stanford 1953). It has been suggested, too, that some of the summer records in later years may also have involved breeding. For example, an instance of apparent breeding 'in the south of the county in 1955' was cited by Peirson (1959), though there is no mention of it in the bird report in *WANHM* for that year; and another near Redlynch in 1969, on the basis that one 'flew from lawn carrying food in its bill' on 8 June (*WANHM*). Again, in 1971, 'A single bird was seen on several occasions in Jun., details withheld in case breeding took place' (*WANHM*) – an event quoted both by Buxton (1981) and by Palmer (1991) as the last breeding in the county. In the absence of any conclusive evidence, however, it remains highly questionable whether Hoopoes have nested in Wiltshire since 1950.

Hoopoes were recorded annually during 1990–2000 (table 100), this time including one in February (table 99). That was at Chirton Gorse on the 15th in 1993 and, even though this species is an early migrant, it and the one shown for November – which had been seen at Ell Barrow, also on SPTA (Centre), on the 15th in 1992 – could conceivably have been the same individual overwintering.

GLW & PCo

Wryneck

Jynx torquilla

Rare passage, former breeder (last 1950), winters Mediterranean/Africa

The Wryneck – so-called because of its head movements when threatened and its ability to contort its neck grotesquely when caught and handled – belongs to a subfamily of the woodpeckers. Like them, it has two toes forward and two back as an adaptation for climbing (though usually sideways, or on an incline, rather than vertically upwards) and a sharply pointed bill (though neither that nor the head is strong enough to chip wood or withstand the effect of hammering). It, too, has a tongue that can be greatly protruded into holes in search of insects and grubs – it specialises on ants – but it is very different from the three true British woodpeckers in its relatively long, soft (not stiff) tail, and in its cryptic coloration of mottled and barred browns, greys and cream. Perched or, as is often the case, on the ground, where it proceeds with short hops and tail erect, it looks more like a slim passerine than a woodpecker.

Wrynecks breed in northwest Africa and in much of Europe (except the far north, the higher mountains, and the steppes of the extreme southeast) right across Siberia and north-central Asia to Sakhalin and northern Japan, extending south also to central China and having outposts in south-central Asia. Most populations are migratory, wintering across sub-Saharan Africa north of the equator and in southern Asia. The breeding population of the whole of Europe, excluding Russia, has been estimated at 353,000 to 423,000 pairs, but there has been a marked decline in the northwest since at least the 1960s (*EBCC Atlas*); and the decrease began much earlier than that in Great Britain – in the first part of the 19th century – with the result that Wrynecks are now virtually extinct here, except as passage migrants.

At the end of the 18th century, Wrynecks apparently nested widely in Great Britain as far north as northern England, but a hundred years later their range had contracted and the population was by then confined mainly to England south of the Humber and to parts of Wales (*1875–1900 Atlas*). By this time they were already rare in Wiltshire (Monk 1963). The national decline in numbers and range continued through the first two-thirds of the 20th century (Witherby *et al* 1938–41, Monk 1963, Peal 1968). The *1968–72 Atlas* (which included on page 461 old maps of the decrease in stages back to 1900) showed that, by then, breeding Wrynecks were restricted in England to a scattering in the southeast between Norfolk and Hampshire, but that, after occasional reports of song in Scotland from the 1950s, three pairs bred successfully in Inverness-shire in 1969 (Burton *et al* 1970) and other singing males were heard there and elsewhere in the Highlands in subsequent years.

It seemed for a time that a British Wryneck population, now fast disappearing from the south, might be saved through recolonisation of the north by migrants from Fenno-Scandia – indeed, breeding continued in Scotland through the 1970s, including at least four pairs in 1978 – but by 1988–89 there was confirmation at only one Scottish site and, though singing males were located at three others, none was now left in southeast England (*1988–91 Atlas*). That was nearly the end, and in 2000 the only suggestion of breeding involved a singing male in northern England for just two days in May (*RBBP*). The reasons behind the decline are not understood, but, as it began more than 200 years ago, recent habitat destruction and pesticide usage have clearly not been primary causes. Wrynecks are nowadays familiar to birdwatchers in Great Britain only as migrants from continental

Table 101. Wrynecks *Jynx torquilla* in Wiltshire: monthly totals 1951–2000

	Jan	Feb	Mar	Apr	May	Jun	Jul	Aug	Sep	Oct	Nov	Dec
Records	0	0	1	3	3	2	2	8	26	4	0	0

Europe, mainly along the east and south coasts in autumn: 264 migrants were recorded in 2000 alone and that was only just above the annual mean for the 1990s (Fraser & Rogers 2002).

This strange bird was already scarce in Wiltshire by the beginning of the 19th century. Seemingly the first documented report of a Wryneck in the county was by Maton (1843), who referred to one shot near Winterbourne Earls and brought to him in August 1796, adding that 'I believe *Y. Torquila* is seen in Wiltshire *very rarely*'. Bosworth Smith (1863) recorded that 'its eggs have been taken in the [Savernake] Forest'. While im Thurn (1870) considered that the species 'is by no means a common bird in this [the Marlborough] district, but a few undoubtedly come to us yearly', he rather confusingly reproduced Bosworth Smith's comment and continued 'As its nest has never been observed, it is doubtful whether it breeds here'. Hart Smith (1887) deemed it a rare visitor but recorded that eggs were taken in 1886, while Smith (1887) wrote that he had seen it only twice 'in my orchard at Yatesbury' and knew of just a few other recent records. Meyrick (1895, 1906) thought it 'An uncommon visitor, apparently arriving about the middle of April' and, while he, too, considered that reports of breeding were poorly documented, he recorded that eggs had been taken in June 1873 and that 'in 1896 a nest with six eggs was found [in Savernake], and the old bird observed on the nest'.

Evidence of the Wryneck's status in Wiltshire in the first half of the 20th century is also scant, but it appears to have been a rare breeder and scarce passage migrant. The inaugural bird report for 1929 in *WANHM* described this as an 'uncommon summer visitor', referring to 'five records for Marlborough district since 1918' and just one instance of nesting, at Devizes in 1926; it and the subsequent reports for 1930–34 and 1936 listed only seven or eight other records – all those dated being in May – as well as 'Several heard in the elms near Salisbury' in 1934. Peirson (1939) noted the Wryneck as 'a summer visitor apparently not uncommon [in the Marlborough area] in the last century but now only occasional'. After the 1939–45 War, there were no further records until 1950, when Wiltshire's last known nest was found in an apple tree at West Dean on 9 July. Since then, migrants have been reported in 27 of the 50 years of 1951–2000, involving 49 records of 51 individuals, predominantly in autumn (table 101).

Six of those 27 years came in the period 1990–2000, but only one record was in spring, at Seend on 12 March 1997. Preferred breeding habitat is open deciduous woodland with areas of bare ground or short vegetation on which to forage for ants, but migrants may be found in a wide variety of places. Not surprisingly, no Wryneck was ringed in Wiltshire during 1965–2000, but one found at Marlborough on 11 September 1989 had been ringed at Icklesham (Sussex) just six days earlier.

(See also page 727.)

IJF-L & GLW

Sponsored by Mike and Kirsty Wilmott

Green Woodpecker

Picus viridis

Widespread resident, increasing Britain as whole since 1960s

Often first located by its loud laughing call, or 'yaffle', the Green is the largest of the three British woodpeckers. It is also the most specialised, feeding mainly on the ground upon ants and their eggs and pupae which it picks up with its tongue, though it will also take beetles, flies and other insects and their larvae, including caterpillars, as well as ants as they run about on branches or vegetation. In winter, the Green Woodpecker will dig into ant nests, which it is readily able to locate under snow, and there are records of its clearing snow up to 30 cm deep and even tunnelling through 85 cm of snow (see *BWP*), but prolonged frost and ice can result in high mortality. Perhaps this is why the home ranges of some pairs include whole villages, where snow is often more quickly cleared.

Feeding observations of Green Woodpeckers were sometimes reported in *WANHM* during 1929–73. One on 31 August 1968 was 'seen to alight on a yew hedge ... and eat the flies which were abundant', also fluttering 'quite high in the air in pursuit of the insects'. Another in 1957 was 'twice seen on a lawn at Ramsbury holding a windfall apple with one foot and apparently eating it'. Also, one in January 1959 was 'feeding in a small patch of unfrozen mud' and another in 1968 'tearing out thatch from a cottage roof, presumably in search of insects'.

Gardens with extensive lawns are a favoured habitat of this woodpecker, which is otherwise found in wooded country rather than woodland, typically in parks, timbered hedgerows, copses, and heaths and commons with scattered trees. Unlike the two spotted woodpeckers, it rarely drums and its bill is comparatively weak, which means that it needs softer wood in which to excavate its nest-hole, generally drilling into trees that are externally sound but rotten in the centre. Nest-holes just 'two feet' (about 60 cm) above the ground were reported in *WANHM* for 1934 and 1951, one in 'a trunk of an old tree used as a hedge post' and the other in 'the trunk of an old apple tree'; these were exceptionally low, the normal range being 2–15 m above the ground.

Like the Kingfisher, the Green Woodpecker is known to suffer badly in prolonged ice and snow, and there were substantial losses in, especially, 1962/63 (Dobinson & Richards 1964), and also in the less protracted but for a time exceptionally cold winter of 1981/82 (*1988–91 Atlas*). Only 18 of the bird reports in *WANHM* during 1930–73 included entries for the Green Woodpecker – apparently because it was otherwise considered simply to be a common enough species – and 11 of those were consecutive annual references to the effects of, and gradual recovery from, the severe winter of 1962/63, culminating in 1973 in 'Again an increase ... the slow build up from the low numbers of 1963 still continuing'. In contrast, there were only two references to recovery from the 1946/47 winter, which was also particularly severe; and only one, in 1933, to increases after 1929.

Perhaps because it is less able to cope with severe weather, the Green Woodpecker has a more southerly distribution in Europe than either of Britain's two spotted woodpeckers – north just to southern Scandinavia and east to central Russia – and a far more limited total range, being otherwise found only from Turkey and the Caucasus to northern Iran. It is, however, replaced by two closely related species in some parts of Asia east to Japan, and by a third in northwest Africa – where Levaillant's Woodpecker was formerly regarded as conspecific – while the Iberian form, *sharpei*, may also be a distinct species. The population of Europe, excluding Russia but including Iberia, has been estimated at 450,000 to 1·4 million pairs (*EBCC Atlas*).

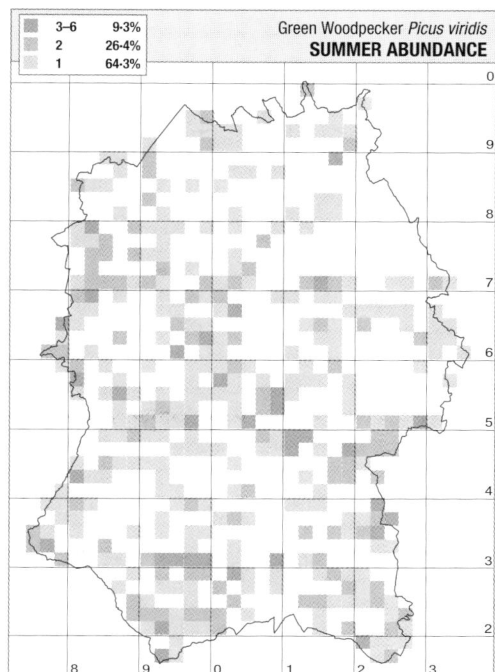

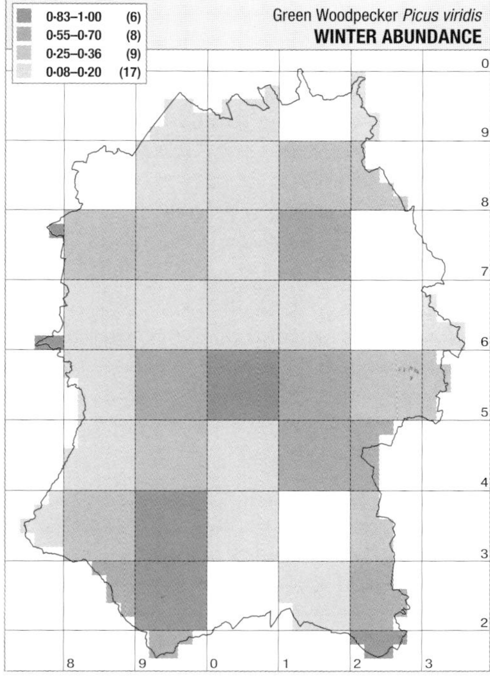

In Great Britain, despite minor declines, numbers in general have increased steadily since 1966 as recovery from the severe weather of 1962/63 began to have an effect, and there followed a long run of winters that have mostly been milder or, at worst, less protracted. The range of the species extended north in eastern Scotland between the periods of the *1968–72* and *1988–91 Atlases*; the latter, which estimated the British population at 15,000 pairs, showed that Green Woodpeckers are most numerous in southern England and south Wales. On the basis of a trend of continuing increase, as indicated by BBS, it was calculated that there were 24,200 pairs in 2000 (*APEP*).

Green Woodpeckers were evidently very common in the Marlborough area in Victorian times: 'Probably nowhere in England is the loud laugh of this handsome bird to be heard, or its perfectly circular hole to be seen, more frequently than in Savernake Forest' (Bosworth Smith 1863). While im Thurn (1870) also considered that it 'is, perhaps, commoner in Savernake Forest than in any other part of England', he may simply have been echoing Bosworth Smith, but he also noted that certain people were noosing the birds, 'wantonly destroying an immense number'. Smith (1887) described this as the commonest woodpecker in Wiltshire, and quoted the Reverend W Butt to the effect that it was far commoner at Minety than in any other district in which he had previously lived. Surveys in Savernake in spring and summer 1939 found it regularly and in apparently good numbers, favouring thorn scrub (Colquhoun 1941). Kennedy (1966) considered this a common resident in the Marlborough area in the first half of the 20th century, especially in Savernake, and the bird report for 1929 in *WANHM* noted it as 'A fairly common resident' in the county as a whole.

Peirson (1959) continued to use this same phrase, but added that 'It suffered severely in the cold of 1947 and it was some years before its numbers recovered'. Indeed, Buxton (1981) thought that the recovery from 1946/47 was hardly complete when the next prolonged severe winter of 1962/63 again reduced the population, and that even by 1978 some areas were still unoccupied. Palmer (1991) found it 'Less frequently encountered in the north-east of the County'. While Green Woodpeckers were recorded in all of Wiltshire's 33 core 10-km squares during both the *1968–72* and *1988–91 Atlases* and again in the summer tetrad survey of 1995–2000, the number in which breeding evidence was established varied – 24, 31 and 28, respectively – but that may simply have reflected differing survey methods and different observers. Certainly *Hobby* reported little significant change in status in the last quarter of the 20th century.

The summer distribution map for 1995–2000 adequately reflects the Green Woodpecker's range in Wiltshire, but under-records successful breeding. The summer abundance map indicates that, as was remarked by Palmer (1991), the species is still relatively scarce in the northeast, where it is absent from much of the higher ground of the Marlborough Downs. An RSPB breeding bird survey of SPTA in 2000 recorded just 31 Green Woodpeckers (Stanbury *et al* 2000), though the summer tetrad survey shows it to be rather more widespread there than that figure might suggest. Indeed, chalk grassland, especially with old beech trees in the vicinity, is a favoured habitat in Wiltshire. A formula of just under 10 pairs per occupied 10-km square, as used by the *1988–91 Atlas* to calculate British breeding numbers, would indicate a population of roughly 300 pairs in Wiltshire's core 10-km squares. But timed tetrad counts recorded 554 individuals in the county as a whole, suggesting that that density estimate may be too low for Wiltshire – as might be expected from the continuing national increase since the *Atlas* (*BBWC*) and this essentially southern county's high proportion of suitable habitat – while the large number of tetrads in which Green Woodpeckers were just 'seen' indicates that breeding was probably often simply not proved. Applying the densities of surveys in the Cotswolds and Chilterns to the area of Wiltshire suggest that the county total is likely to be in the range of 2100 to 2820 pairs.

None of the 52 Green Woodpeckers ringed in Wiltshire during 1965–2000 has been recovered, but this species is so sedentary that movements of more than 20 km are extremely unusual and, once again, generally associated with hard weather (*Migration Atlas*) – although immatures may move into more open habitat in autumn and winter. Green Woodpeckers were mapped in 32 of the 33 core 10-km squares by the *1981–84 Winter Atlas*, compared with just 27 by the winter survey of 1998–2000 – when, however, they were found in over one fifth of all tetrads. The highest tetrad count was six (the same as in the summer survey), but the exclusion of casual records then will have resulted in a lower percentage of occupied tetrads than in the summer; the Green Woodpecker's being less noisy outside the breeding season will also have played a part in under-recording, and extrapolation from winter counts suggested a total of just 260 at that season, less than half the number counted in summer. From the breeding estimate, however, it seems that 5000 to 7500 is a more likely figure for winter numbers.

PCo & IJF-L

Sponsored anonymously

Great Spotted Woodpecker

Dendrocopos major

Common and widespread resident, increasing Britain as whole since 1970s

This most widespread of the three British woodpeckers is often located by its commonest call, a sharp and distinctive *chik*, and in the first half of the year by its loud drumming on dead branches – by either sex, sometimes in duet – in territorial and other advertisement. As is typical of many woodpeckers, the Great Spotted can often then be seen moving in jerks up a tree trunk, its stiff tail-feathers acting as a prop, but this species is found in a greater variety of wooded habitats, and is well known to many garden observers because its adaptability has allowed it to become a frequent visitor to peanut-feeders and bird-tables.

In fact, the Great Spotted feeds mainly on insects and their larvae – by using its sticky, 4–cm long and 'harpoon'-tipped tongue to pick these from crevices in the trunks and branches of, most often, dead or dying trees, or by stripping away loose bark to expose them. But it also takes acorns, hazelnuts and, especially in winter, conifer seeds, sometimes carrying whole cones to a particular 'anvil' in order to hammer out the contents. Similarly, a male that visited a garden at Bradford-on-Avon in summer 1993 occasionally wedged peanuts in a nearby crevice and broke them up before feeding the bits to its accompanying youngsters; this individual was also seen alighting on red-hot-pokers in bloom and taking the nectar (*Hobby*). The Great Spotted will also drill holes in live trees to drink the sap and, not uncommonly, takes the eggs and young of other birds, even breaking into nestboxes to do so. Several boxes at Clanger Wood were damaged in this way in 1987 (*Hobby*).

Great Spotted Woodpeckers excavate their nest-holes in a wide variety of broadleaved and coniferous woodland, but they favour beech and oak and, in northern conifer forests, need suitable rotten trees or perhaps an adjacent birch. They are to be found from the Canaries and northwest Africa right across Eurasia to Kamchatka and Japan, south in the west to Turkey and northern Iran, and more extensively in the east through China to northern parts of southeast Asia. The population of Europe, excluding Russia, has been estimated at 3·3 to 4·5 million breeding pairs – making it by some margin the most numerous of the continent's ten woodpeckers – and numbers and range are generally considered to be stable, though increases have occurred in a few countries (*EBCC Atlas*). They are well distributed throughout the mainland, except in far northern Fenno-Scandia and Russia, and some southern parts of Russia, Ukraine and Greece – and, like other woodpeckers, they are also missing from Ireland and Iceland – but densities are thought to be highest in central Europe and this species is also very common in the taiga of Fenno-Scandia (*EBCC Atlas*).

For Great Britain, the 'change map' in the *1988–91 Atlas* showed that, mainly in Scotland and in parts of northeast England, Wales and the southwest peninsula, the number of 10-km squares recorded as occupied by Great Spotted Woodpeckers had decreased by 4 per cent since the *1968–72 Atlas*, but other CBC/BBS data indicated a rapid increase in the total population in the late 1970s and again in the late 1990s – a growth of a third during 1995 to 2000 alone (*BBWC*). At first, this increase was attributed to the additional food sources provided by the effects of Dutch elm disease (Marchant *et al* 1990), though in that case it is difficult to understand why the woodpecker numbers were sustained once the dead elms had gone. Others have suggested this species' readiness to adapt to food on bird-tables has also played a part in winter survival, but it is now admitted that the

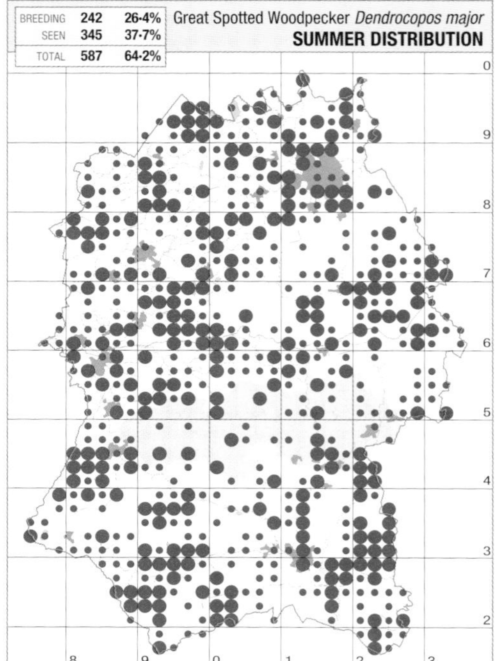

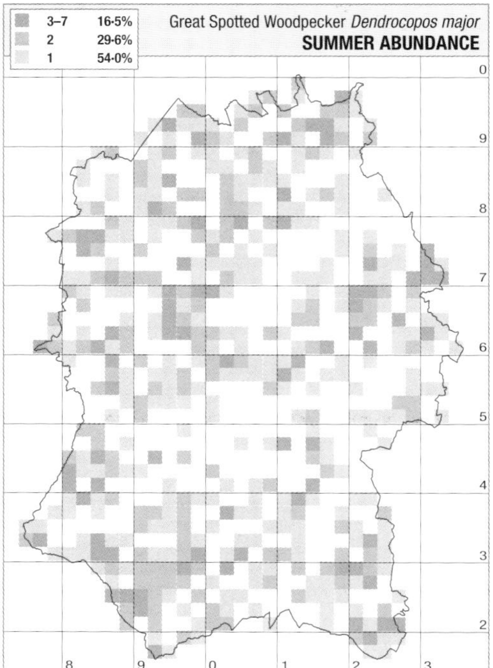

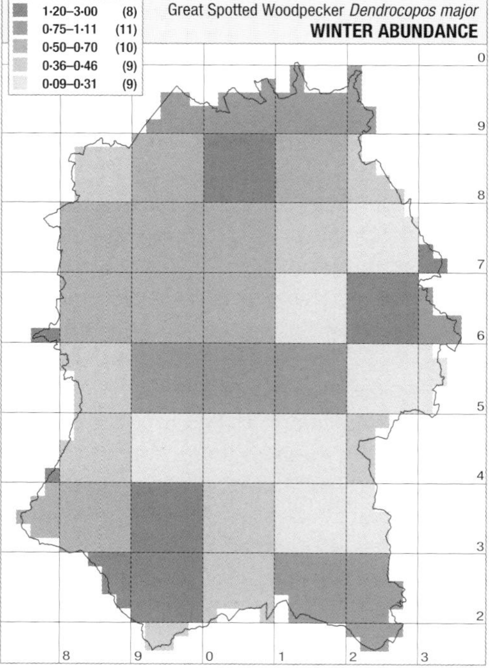

causes behind the increase during the last third of the 20th century remain obscure (*eg BBWC*). The *1988–91 Atlas* considered that some 25,000 to 30,000 pairs were breeding in Great Britain, but noted that until better survey data were available that figure should be treated with caution. Indeed, it was revised to 37,000 to 44,400 pairs in 2000, on the basis of the substantial increases nationally (*APEP*).

Whereas im Thurn (1870) believed the Great Spotted to be 'not very uncommon in the [Savernake] Forest' – indeed, he knew 'of no authentic instance of its breeding', although, on the basis of a young bird 'taken' concluded 'that its nest has been overlooked' – Smith (1887) regarded it as the rarest of the three woodpeckers in Wiltshire as a whole. It was clearly quite widely distributed, however, as he named a number of localities across the county where it had occurred. The inaugural bird report for 1929 in *WANHM* also described it as 'A rather scarce resident'. Yet, whereas Kennedy (1966) considered that it had been common in all wooded areas around Marlborough in the first half of the 20th century, counts in Savernake in 1939 found a lower density than that of the Green Woodpecker, primarily because the Great Spotted was recorded in only one month, April, during surveys from March to June (Colquhoun 1941). Twenty years later, Peirson (1959) summarised its Wiltshire status as 'not uncommon and widely distributed', but mentioned that 'Many were killed in the cold of 1947'. Large numbers were thought also to have perished in the bitter winter of 1962/63 (Buxton 1981), though 'The general opinion is that this species survived the cold weather very well in most districts ... probably due to its willingness to visit bird-tables' (*WANHM*). Buxton was able to describe the Great Spotted as common and widespread, commenting that numbers had increased rapidly after the cold winters of 1947 and 1962/63 and that there 'may have been a further increase' since 1976, which 'may have been due to ... Dutch elm disease'.

There is no evidence that distribution changed in the county over the last third of the 20th century, as this woodpecker was recorded in every one of the 48 10-km squares wholly or partly in Wiltshire by all of the three national atlases and by both the summer and the winter surveys during 1995–2000. The summer distribution map certainly shows the Great Spotted to be widely scattered across the county. Although, as in the case of the Green Woodpecker, a high proportion of tetrads appear to have produced no evidence of breeding, that is likely to have been because both species were often located only by their distinctive sounds at a distance during tetrad transects. Furthermore, the drumming of the Great Spotted – its equivalent of the song of passerines – is heard most consistently in March and April and, thus, the evidence of 'song in the same place 14 days apart' will have under-represented it during the survey period. The summer abundance map shows highest densities in Bowood and Spye Parks, in Savernake, in the generally more wooded southwest of Wiltshire and in the edges of the New Forest in the far southeast – as well as not unexpected low densities in the relatively treeless areas of Salisbury Plain and the Marlborough Downs. This is also borne out by the winter map, although the Vale of Pewsey appears to be of increased importance at that time of year.

Great Spotted Woodpeckers were found in almost 600 tetrads during the summer surveys of 1995–2000, and the counts came to a total of 814, though individuals will have been missed as this species can easily be overlooked when not calling or drumming. A 1997 survey of the Cotswold Hills ESA (Gloucestershire) – just to the northwest of Wiltshire – found average densities of 0·8 pairs/km^2 (Dodd & Meadows 2003). This is likely to be a reasonable figure for Wiltshire also, given that southern and western England were shown by the *1988–91 Atlas* to hold the greatest densities, and applied to this county as a whole, might suggest between 3140 and 4590 pairs. In less than a century, this species has easily surpassed the Green as the county's most numerous woodpecker.

Winter surveys produced an extrapolated figure of nearly 600 individuals, but actual numbers in the range of 7500 to 12,500 are more likely, given the fact that British Great Spotted Woodpeckers are essentially sedentary. Nationally, 95 per cent of all recoveries have been within 40 km of the ringing site, though the Fenno-Scandian population is migratory and some of those do reach Great Britain in winter (*Migration Atlas*). Against this background, it is not surprising that the only three recoveries from a total of 166 ringed in the county during 1965–2000 were all local; but two recoveries in Wiltshire in May 1987 and August 1984 of Great Spotteds ringed at Queen Mary Reservoir (Surrey) and Dungeness (Kent) the previous March and October, the former as an adult female and the latter as a juvenile, had moved 123 km and 193 km respectively

PCo & IJF-L

Sponsored by Philip Rabbetts

Lesser Spotted Woodpecker

Dendrocopos minor

Scarce/local resident, greatly decreasing Britain from peak in 1970s

This smallest of the three British woodpeckers is only about the size of a House Sparrow, and more the shape of a large Nuthatch. It is most easily located in spring by its slow *pee-pee-pee* song, resembling the calls of a distant Kestrel, or by its drumming – not unlike that of the Great Spotted Woodpecker, though each burst is usually marginally longer and weaker – but isolated pairs of Lesser Spotted tend to be quiet and elusive. Closely associated with broadleaved trees, and in former times particularly with decaying orchards, this species forages mainly in the highest branches and so tends to be inconspicuous. Occasionally, however, a Lesser Spotted will forage much lower, even on ground vegetation: one at Ramsbury in August 1978 was watched moving up and down the stem of a seeding hogweed (Edwards 1980).

Unlike the Great Spotted, this small woodpecker does not normally visit bird-tables. Its food is almost exclusively insects – which it gleans from twigs and leaves in summer and extracts as larvae from behind bark or in rotten wood in winter – but it does also take some seeds and, occasionally, fruit. In a special Wiltshire survey during 1957–64, which recorded Lesser Spotted Woodpeckers at 39 different sites in the county, a 'dozen records are of a pair or a single bird' seen in gardens, including one 'in the [Cathedral] Close in the heart of Salisbury'; several such visitors were watched 'at very close quarters either on clothes posts, feeding on rotten apples or, more characteristically, in trees in the garden' (Gillam 1965).

On a world scale, the Lesser Spotted Woodpecker is very local in northwest Africa and Iberia, but otherwise found widely throughout much of the rest of Europe, north to northern Fenno-Scandia, and across southern Siberia and central Asia to Kamchatka, north Japan and northeast China, also from Turkey to northern Iran. Although this is essentially a resident species, northern and eastern populations are nomadic and eruptive (*Migration Atlas*). Ringing data are generally few and none of only three marked in Wiltshire during 1965–2000 has been recovered. The breeding numbers in Europe, excluding Russia, are thought to lie in the region of 194,000 to 240,000 pairs – though national estimates of this elusive species are less certain than those of other woodpeckers (*EBCC Atlas*).

Lesser Spotted Woodpeckers were most common, and stable, in southwest England in the 19th century (*1875–1900 Atlas*), helped by the presence of decaying trees left standing in orchards disused after cider production ceased. Numbers declined when these orchards were removed after the 1939–45 War, but then increased through the 1970s as a result of the effects of Dutch elm disease, which provided these birds with abundant insect food beneath the flaking bark of the dead and dying trees. In 1979, CBC data indicated a British ratio of one Lesser Spotted to four Great Spotted Woodpeckers. The benefits of the disease were short-lived, however, and the *1988–91 Atlas* survey showed a decrease of 11 per cent in the number of occupied 10-km squares since the *1968–72 Atlas*. By 1995, the ratio in CBC data was one Lesser Spotted to 20 Great Spotted, and subsequent BBS results showed an even worse proportion of one to 30. The eventual disappearance of hedgerow trees (including elms, which BTO records show were also important for nesting) and the general reduction and fragmentation of mature broadleaved woodland have been blamed (*eg BBWC*). The *1988–91 Atlas*, citing *BWP*, put the British population at 3000 to 6000 pairs, but by the end of the millennium the estimate was only 1400 to 2900 (*APEP*).

In Wiltshire, Smith (1887) wrote that the Lesser Spotted was 'More common, at all events of late years' than the Great Spotted Woodpecker, and stated 'From the observations of various authors one would say that Wiltshire was the favourite locality of this bird'. Smith quoted Selby, Yarrell, Montagu and several local correspondents and localities to prove his point. There is, however, perhaps some confusion over the species' status in the Savernake area, because im Thurn (1870), citing Bosworth Smith's (1863) statement that it 'has been seen several times in the Forest', considered that 'As the Greater Spotted Woodpecker, the commoner species, is not mentioned, I am inclined to think a mistake has occurred'. Meyrick (1895, 1906) wrote that there was evidence of the Lesser Spotted breeding in Savernake, but that it was apparently scarcer than the Great Spotted. A survey in 1939 by Colquhoun (1941) then found small numbers of Great Spotted but no Lesser.

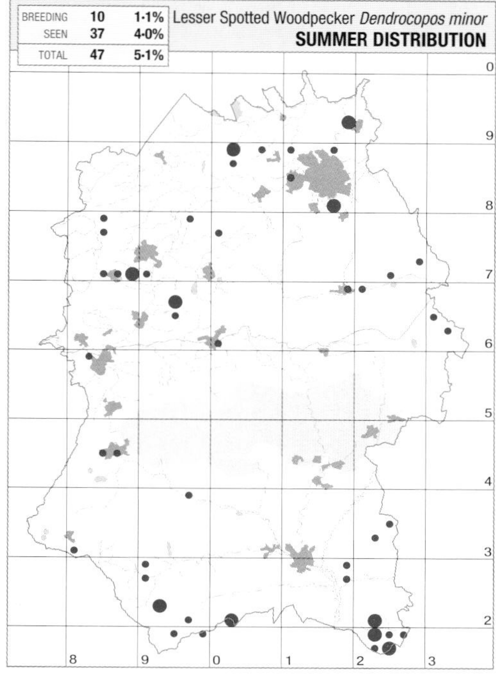

The inaugural bird report for 1929 in *WANHM* noted that, in the county as a whole, the Lesser Spotted was 'A not uncommon resident, much overlooked', whereas Peirson (1959) described it as 'An uncommon resident widely distributed' and Kennedy (1966), for the Marlborough area, as 'an uncommon resident, seen in most years' – such conflict of opinion perhaps indicating that the population had declined around the middle of the 20th century. Gillam (1965) mapped 39 sites at which the species had been recorded, though often only once, during 1957–64: 'In areas regularly watched – Coate, Clarendon and Corsham, East Knoyle and the water-meadows near Marlborough – there has been little change in the observed population ... It therefore seems likely that at Ramsbury, Spye Park, Savernake, Wardour, Cole Park and Tottenham, where records have been supplied for only one or two years ... the position may well be similar'. There were no reports, however, from 'many large wooded areas' (including Longleat and Stourhead to Fonthill and Great Ridge in the southwest), but a total of 17 isolated observations, several of them in willows, came from such river valleys as the Bristol Avon, the Kennet, the Bourne, the Wylye and the Salisbury Avon.

Buxton (1981) echoed Peirson's view of three decades earlier by stating that 'It is widely distributed but less common than the other woodpeckers'. Palmer (1991) noted that the number of sites at which the species had been seen each year during 1980–89 ranged from 16 to 28 and that an annual average of nine breeding pairs had been recorded. But the reported figures were noticeably lower in the 1990s (table 102). Interpretation of such data must, however, be cautious, because the treatment of 'possible' breeding, both by observers and by editors of *Hobby* over the years, evidently varies. Nevertheless, these numbers perhaps serve to illustrate that the species more or less held its own in the county during 1990–2000, albeit at reduced levels. It is noteworthy that Lesser Spotted Woodpeckers were reported from no fewer than 25 sites in 1998: more than one third of those were near lakes or waterways – as Gillam (1965) similarly found to be the case with

Table 102. Lesser Spotted Woodpeckers *Dendrocopos minor* in Wiltshire: numbers of sites reported in *Hobby* 1990–2000

	90	91	92	93	94	95	96	97	98	99	00
Total localities reported	14	14	14	11	17	16	12	12	25	14	12
Confirmed breeding	4	1	1	1	2	0	1	1	3	0	0
Possible breeding	5	5	6	6	9	0	1	4	4	6	3

river valleys during the 1957–64 survey – which probably serves to emphasise that this species is greatly overlooked in areas that are less frequently visited.

Lesser Spotted Woodpeckers were found in 21 of the county's 33 core 10-km squares by the *1968–72 Atlas*, but in only 14 by the *1988–91* Atlas – in which the 'change' map demonstrated that many of the deserted squares were in a swathe from Land's End to the Midlands and across to the Wash, a zone that included parts of Wiltshire. Yet now the summer distribution map for 1995–2000 shows that this species was found in 18 of the core squares, a result not anticipated from national trends. Perhaps this indicates that, as yet, a decline in range is less evident in Wiltshire than in some other parts of Great Britain. It is also clear from the summer distribution map that the Lesser Spotted is absent from sparsely wooded higher ground, and that it appears to favour damper woods at lower elevations, such as those in the extreme southeast near the border with Hampshire. Because of its usually quiet habits, however, this woodpecker is easily overlooked and thus difficult to census – indeed, none was seen during the 2-hour tetrad counts – but clearly it is still thinly and patchily distributed over the county. Its recorded presence in 47 tetrads represents, by far, the most comprehensive picture of this species' status in Wiltshire to date. It seems likely that numbers in the county are currently low and in the region of 75 pairs, though there may possibly be as many as 100.

PCo & IJF-L

Wood Lark

Lullula arborea

Rare breeder, scarce and local winter visitor, probably from New Forest

Although Wood Larks increased markedly as a breeding species over much of southern England during the last decade of the 20th century, they have maintained only a tenuous summer presence in Wiltshire and have proved more numerous, though less easy to detect, in winter.

While the Wood Lark also breeds in North Africa, Asia Minor and the Levant eastwards to Iran and southern Turkmenistan, the great majority of its range lies within Europe, from the Mediterranean north to southern Fenno-Scandia and eastwards into central Russia. It is only a summer visitor to the northern and eastern two-thirds of this area and winters chiefly in the west and south. In Europe where, excluding Russia, 1·1 to 2·2 million pairs have been estimated, populations have fluctuated widely since the mid 1960s, because of habitat loss and high mortality in cold winters, although decreases from severe weather may be only temporary (*EBCC Atlas*).

Within Great Britain, Wood Larks bred in most counties of England and Wales in the early 19th century, but numbers fell from the 1850s. A population upturn from about 1920 to 1950 was followed by another downturn until the 1990s. The *1968–72 Atlas* put the numbers at 200–450 pairs, a national survey in 1986 found 241 territories (Sitters *et al* 1996) and, from subsequent local surveys, the *1988–91 Atlas* estimated some 350 pairs, by which time the species was extinct in Wales. Since then numbers have soared, and a repeat survey in 1997 found a maximum of 1552 territories, mostly south of a line from Devon to north Norfolk (Wotton & Gillings 2000). The counties of Suffolk, Norfolk, Hampshire, Surrey and Dorset were the most important, though significant new populations were also found in Lincolnshire and Nottinghamshire. Breeding was noted as far north as Yorkshire, though again not in Wales. Wood Larks were still considered to be increasing in 2000 (*RBBP*).

In Wiltshire, im Thurn (1870, 1876) and Hart Smith (1887) considered the Wood Lark to be rare and occasional in the Marlborough area, whereas Meyrick (1895) thought it an uncommon resident there, 'though perhaps overlooked. The nest and eggs have been several times obtained in May'. For the county as a whole, Smith (1887) described this species as a 'permanent resident' and 'sparingly scattered throughout'; he knew of its 'occurrence from various localities in both North and South Wilts, proving that it is generally distributed throughout the county'. This status was largely unchanged fifty years later, the first few bird reports in *WANHM* during 1929–36 mentioning Wood Larks at Chippenham, the Marlborough district, Salisbury Plain, Pitton, Broad Chalke, Whiteparish, Downton and Redlynch, while Scott (1961) referred to a male singing at Lockeridge in April 1926. Although a 'definite increase' with 'more nesting records than usual' was noted in 1936 (*WANHM*), this lark was clearly widespread enough in the late 1920s and early 1930s to make it worthwhile for Nethersole-Thompson (1992) to hunt for their nests while he 'listened in the twilight to their glorious song on the rolling Wiltshire downs'.

The *1968–72 Atlas* found that, after 1955, 'low numbers of Rabbits following myxomatosis may have resulted in less of the close-cropped ground favoured by the species' – a factor that would have affected Wood Larks in Wiltshire. Peirson (1959) thought this a 'very local and uncommon resident' that bred regularly in the northwest and southeast, and occasionally elsewhere, whereas Buxton (1981) noted it as 'extremely rare and there have been no breeding records since 1963…never very common but bred regularly in those areas bordering the New Forest'. Other past breeding sites mentioned by Buxton included Coate Water, Bowood, Spye Park, Everleigh, Longleat, Porton Down and Grovely Wood. But whether Wood Larks were quite as uncommon as might be inferred from Peirson (1959) and Buxton (1981) is debatable, as nests and family parties were regularly found in the late 1940s and early 1950s, despite the very few observers contributing records annually to *WANHM* (*eg* just 24 names in 1946). Small flocks were sometimes also recorded, including 13 'between Corton and Great Ridge' on 3 July 1946, 20 at Brigmerston Down on 2 September 1950 and 20 at Zeals aerodrome during 21–26 January 1953 (*WANHM*).

Although Buxton (1981) stated that there had been no breeding records since 1963 – for which year the bird report noted 'One resident pair, Maiden Bradley' and 'Probably nesting on Porton' – the last record to be confirmed in that period was in 1962 (*WANHM*), before the cold winter of 1962/63. And, despite the annual presence of Wood Larks in suitable habitat from 1990, it was not until 1998 that nesting was once again proved by the discovery of a nest with eggs (Combridge & Combridge 1999). The *1968–72 Atlas* recorded Wood Larks in three of Wiltshire's 33 core 10-km squares, but the *1981–84 Winter Atlas* and the *1988–91 Atlas* each mapped them in only one of the 15 part squares and in both instances the birds were probably just in Hampshire, in the latter case on Porton Down.

The most recent national survey showed that breeding Wood Larks in England as a whole are nowadays found principally on dry heathland in the south and in young tree plantations in the north and east, as well as some in cleared woodland, and those in Devon almost exclusively on farmland; most territories were on sandy soils – 70 per cent specifically on acid sandy soils – and, despite the large increase in numbers between 1986 and 1997, the only subtle change in habitat was an increasing use of heathland (Wotton & Gillings 2000). The species used also to nest on downland, in boggy areas with raised ground, and on old industrial tips (*eg* Campbell & Ferguson-Lees 1972).

During the 1990s, most Wiltshire records in the breeding season of singing males, pairs and juveniles were in young conifer plantations, remnant heathland and rough uncultivated land along the Hampshire border – where, despite claims of breeding during 1990–93, fieldwork proved all nests to be in Hampshire. Song and display were, however, noted from a pair in north Wiltshire in 1995, a nest was found in winter wheat on the chalk in the south of the county in 1998, and a small party, perhaps indicative of local nesting, was discovered on set-aside elsewhere in August 1999. Thus, it seems likely that, while those in suitable breeding habitats along the fairly well-watched Hampshire/Wiltshire border have a good chance of being detected, pairs may be overlooked elsewhere. On this basis, the best estimate of breeding numbers in a typical year of the 1995–2000 summer tetrad survey is in the range of zero to five pairs. The claim of nine pairs in 1999 (*RBBP*) does not stand up to examination of the WOS archives (three of the breeding pairs attributed by RBBP to Wiltshire were in fact at a locality well within Hampshire's New Forest), and at best no more than two pairs bred in the county that year – though other Wood Larks nesting just over the boundary in Hampshire were occasionally seen to fly into Wiltshire. The lack of heathland and the loss of downland through conversion to arable since the 1939–45 War are undoubtedly restricting the spread of Wood Larks in Wiltshire. The population potential is demonstrated by the results of the 1997 survey, which found 294 and 105 territories in Hampshire and Dorset respectively, but only three in Wiltshire (Wotton & Gillings 2000).

British-breeding Wood Larks are thought to be partially migratory, some remaining close to their nesting grounds while others move considerable distances: for example, one ringed as a nestling in Breckland (Suffolk/Norfolk) was later found in the Netherlands (*Migration Atlas*). Recent fieldwork in Wiltshire has shown that out of the breeding season, though easy to overlook, Wood Larks occur regularly in stubbles, set-aside and winter wheat. Records in the county were mostly from near Hampshire breeding sites, suggesting that south Wiltshire may be a regular wintering area for some of the New Forest population (P Combridge). Flocks of 36 in the winter of 1998/99 (when over 60 were located in the county in total), 29 in 1999/2000 and 36 in 2000/01 (*Hobby*) are the largest recorded since Morres (1878–85) reported a group of 'about sixty ... in a wheat stubble ... not far from Trafalgar' in autumn 1868.

(See also page 725.)

GDP

Sky Lark
Alauda arvensis

Still locally common resident/passage/winter, despite serious decline in Britain

Delivered usually in flight, though sometimes from a perch or on the ground, the Sky Lark's protracted song – beloved of many poets and other writers – must be one of Britain's best known. It can be heard in Wiltshire for much of the year, most regularly from February to June and again in October.

Sky Larks breed in a variety of open country from northwest Africa and western Europe across Eurasia to Kamchatka and Japan, and have recently even nested on the Pribilof islands of Alaska (*eg* Donald 2004). (They have also been introduced into New Zealand, Australia, various islands of Hawaii, and Vancouver Island in western Canada.) The most northerly populations are migratory, some moving as far south as Arabia, Pakistan, northern India and eastern China. The European population, excluding that of Russia, has been estimated at 28 to 36 million pairs, but most countries have recorded declines linked to agricultural intensification (*EBCC Atlas*).

In Great Britain, despite heavy hunting pressure (see below), Sky Larks were widespread and common breeders at the end of the 19th century (*1875–1900 Atlas*). The *1988–91 Atlas* found them virtually throughout England, Wales and Scotland, and estimated a population of two million pairs. Regular monitoring showed a decrease throughout the 1990s, albeit at a slower rate than previously (*BBWC*), and the population in 2000 was estimated to be 1·7 million territories (*APEP*). The likely cause of this fall in numbers is thought to be the practice of sowing cereals in autumn and winter, rather than in spring, because the area of winter stubbles is thus reduced and the resulting crop is often too high for all but the earliest nesting Sky Larks in the following spring; there is also a greater preponderance of more intensively managed grasslands. The decline is clear in parts of Wiltshire but, happily, significant numbers can still be found on grassland, including much of SPTA and some areas of arable, the latter an important wintering habitat.

For many centuries, Sky Larks were slaughtered in their thousands for food, attracted to nets or guns using mirrors set in wooden blocks which were spun rapidly to catch and reflect light. For reasons unclear, these reflections proved an irresistible and ultimately fatal attraction for migrating larks, with, for example, a single mirror being capable of luring over 1000 Sky Larks to their deaths in one day (see *eg* Donald 2004 for discussion of hunting and the rise of popular protest against it). For Wiltshire, Aubrey (1656–91) related that 'We have great plenty of larkes... especially in Colern-fields and those parts adjoining to Coteswold. They take them by alluring them with a dareing-glass... and the nett is drawn over them... In the south part of Wiltshire they... catch these pretty ætheriall birds with trammolls'. Some 200 years later, both im Thurn (1870) and Smith (1887) also reported that Sky Larks were widespread, very common and caught commercially in nets. Peirson (1959) described them as 'very common in the open country', and the *1968–72 Atlas* found breeding in all of the 33 core and 15 part 10-km squares in the county, while the *1988–91 Atlas* did so in all but one.

The fine grid of the summer distribution map for 1995–2000 shows some empty tetrads, especially in the west, in the southwest and in the woodland areas of the extreme southeast, but Sky Larks are still present, and locally very common, in most open areas of the county from river valleys to land over 200 m. Evidence of breeding was established in well over half of all tetrads, and the summer abundance map shows notable concentrations on the Marlborough Downs and SPTA. Extremely high densities (an average of 65·7 birds/km^2 on grassland) were also found in the latter area by an RSPB survey (Stanbury *et al* 2000), which showed this to be the most numerous bird species there, with an estimated 14,600 territories – a figure constituting about 1·5 per cent of the British population and 16 per cent of that of southwest England. The survey also found that Sky Larks on SPTA were most concentrated on open grassland on flat ridge tops, and that scrub within the grassland had a detrimental effect on numbers. The use of the WOS timed counts to extrapolate from the RSPB estimate to the remainder of the county – much of which consists of winter cereals, set-aside and chalk downland, all highly suitable areas for breeding Sky Larks – gives a Wiltshire population of 56,100 pairs. Although other surveys that have used BBS methods

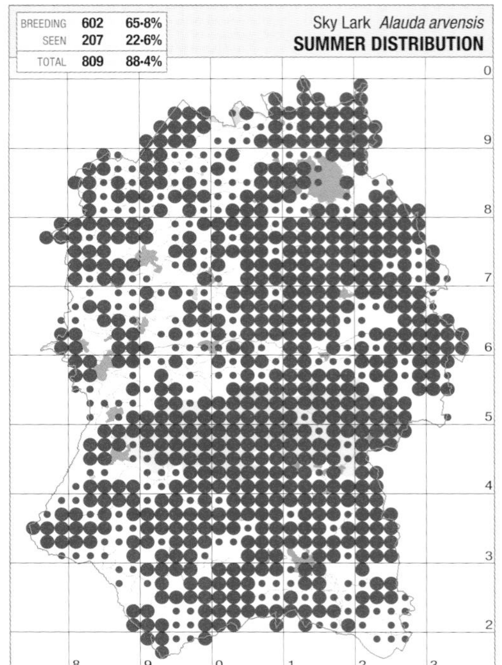

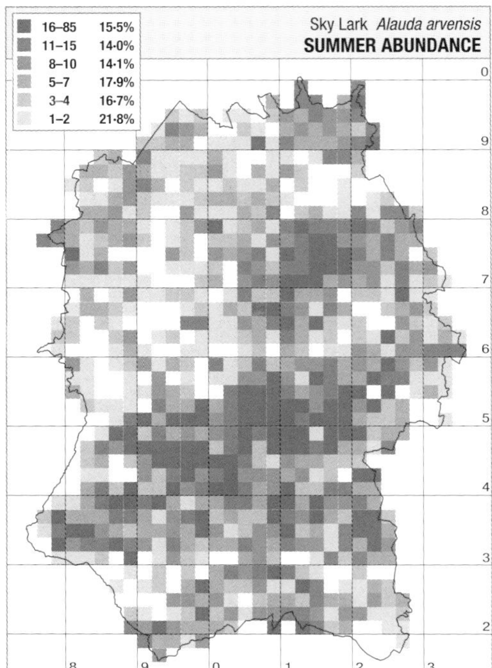

suggest smaller figures, down to 18,900, it is likely that the county total lies nearer the upper limit of the range of 18,900 to 56,100 produced by these various data.

Sky Larks appear to favour rotational set-aside, where stubbles of previous cereal crops remain unploughed and weeds are left to regenerate naturally. The optimal height of vegetation in such areas is thought to be around 20 cm, with patches of bare ground to allow the birds to forage. Indeed, the SPTA survey and research on intensively managed farmland in Switzerland have shown that Sky Larks avoid dense vegetation higher than 30–35 cm, probably because it hinders movement at ground level; in contrast, grazed fields tend to become too bare to provide sufficient cover for nesting (*eg* Evans *et al* 1995, Donald 2004, and references quoted therein).

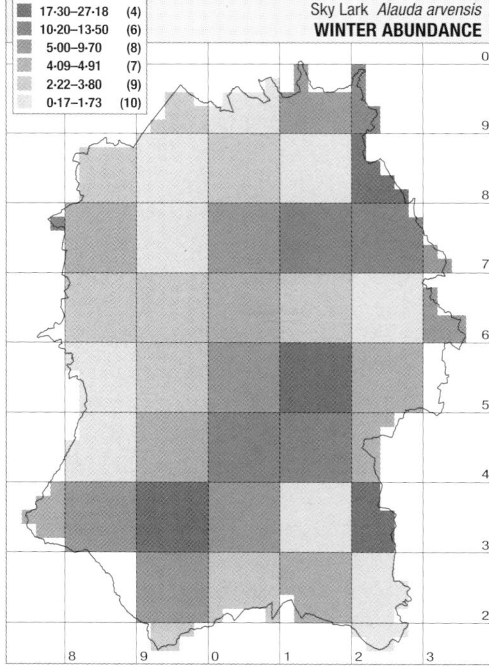

Despite the high nesting densities achieved in the most favourable kinds of set-aside, Sky Lark numbers are still decreasing in Great Britain as a whole. Creeping urbanisation and the spread of countryside leisure activities have doubtless played their part, but the changes in cropping regimes and grassland management are likely still to be the main causes. Nationally, the largest declines have occurred in arable areas of southern

England. The problems associated with herbicides and pesticides are well known, and the summer cutting or spraying of set-aside can be disastrous for nesting Sky Larks, while sprayed cereal stubbles are bereft of weed seeds in winter and, therefore, of birds. Cereal stubbles are often ploughed within a few weeks or even days of harvest, and this and the tendency towards simplified rotations of almost monocultural autumn-sown cereals also deprive Sky Larks and other farmland birds of winter food. On livestock and mixed farms, heavily fertilised grass is now cut for silage from mid May to August, and grazing, especially by sheep, has become much more intensive, so that there is simply no herbage long enough to provide nesting cover. It has been suggested that the total area of suitable set-aside is simply too small to make a difference and, therefore, that a reduction in agricultural intensity, rather than the provision of small areas of unfarmed land within an arable landscape, is the key to the species' survival (*eg* Donald 2004 and references quoted therein).

For 'most European birdwatchers today there is nothing particularly special' about Sky Lark migration (Donald 2004) and, although north and east European populations are migratory and move south and southwest, falling breeding numbers have seen the end of the once spectacular mass movements, sometimes running into hundreds of thousands – if not millions – reported by Victorian naturalists such as Henry Seebohm and Charles Dixon. Although British-bred Sky Larks appear largely resident, and analysis of ringing returns found that two-thirds of all those ringed were recovered within 10 km of the ringing site, their movements in autumn and winter tend to be longer than at other times. Apparent arrivals – though involving considerably fewer birds than those reported in the 19th century – are still noted along the east coast between mid September and early November (*Migration Atlas*), and so it is possible that some of these may reach Wiltshire, where severe winter weather certainly results in visible movements. Peirson (1959) remarked that this species was 'wiped out' near Marlborough by the cold of 1940, but that they strangely came through the even colder winter of 1946/47 unscathed. Flocks of 440, 300 and 350 were recorded in south Wiltshire in December in 1983, 1985 and 1992, though it is not known what proportions of such concentrations are migrants, or whether they involve mainly the local population. County ringing results hardly help – only 27 Sky Larks had been ringed in Wiltshire up to 2000, all as nestlings, and none has yet been recovered – but the remains of one ringed at Peakirk (Northamptonshire) in December 1975 were found in a raptor pellet (probably Kestrel) at Southdown Farm, Imber, in March 1978.

Although still widespread in winter, Sky Larks then have a more restricted distribution, avoiding upland areas to a greater extent and favouring lowland mixed and arable farming (*1981–84 Winter Atlas*). Numbers present on the rough grasslands of SPTA are much reduced from August onwards, and it is not until late February that they return there to re-establish territories (PE Castle). Therefore, the similarity between the winter and summer abundance maps is surprising, the highest densities at both seasons being associated with the Marlborough Downs and parts of SPTA. Sky Larks were recorded in all of Wiltshire's 33 core and 15 part 10-km squares by the *1981–84 Winter Atlas* and in all but one by the winter tetrad survey; even that gap was almost certainly a result of the methodology used. Some emigration and immigration may take place at this time, varying in response to weather conditions, but timed counts indicated fewer Sky Larks in winter than in summer – 5450 by extrapolation, compared with 6990 – and the winter total is calculated to fall within the range of 20,500 to 60,800 individuals.

(See also page 725.)

MVJ

Sand Martin

Riparia riparia

Scarce and local summer visitor/passage, breeds Europe, winters Africa

Among the earliest summer visitors to arrive, a few Sand Martins are often to be seen in the first half of March, and Wiltshire's earliest record of all was of three over the Wylye, near Great Wishford, on 4 March 1977 (*Hobby*). The main influx is generally in the first two weeks of April, though passage often continues well into May.

Sand Martins nest in areas of light soils, excavating tunnels in newly eroded banks of rivers, streams and lake edges – and at sites of sand or gravel extraction where, particularly if left undisturbed from one year to the next, they may form large colonies. Pairs regularly raise two broods in 'good' summers, and in July the juveniles of the first brood begin local movements that tend to be leisurely and erratic: for example, a juvenile ringed in Suffolk on 26 June 2000 was controlled (trapped and released again) at CWP on 22 July the same year. By the beginning of August, these movements 'become oriented southwards' (*CBWP*), and the main southward migration continues throughout September and well into October. The latest Wiltshire record was a singleton at CWP on 31 October 1994 (*Hobby*).

The species is widely distributed throughout the Northern Hemisphere, and nests in almost every country of Europe with the exception of Iceland. The European population, excluding that of Russia, has been estimated at 2·2 to 2·6 million pairs (*EBCC Atlas*). These are trans-Saharan migrants that winter mainly in the African Sahel, and in East Africa south to Mozambique; the British population winters almost exclusively in West Africa (*Migration Atlas*). The number of nests in Great Britain has been put at 77,500 to 250,000 (*1988–91 Atlas*). The species was known throughout the country in the late 19th century and its distribution was largely unchanged 100 years later; by then, however, its use of man-made habitats had increased and concentrations had become patchy, many areas holding only small numbers (*1875–1900 Atlas*, *1988–91 Atlas*).

Population crashes in Great Britain in 1968 and 1983 were attributed mainly to severe drought conditions in wintering areas in the African Sahel. Numbers remained very low for at least two years in each case, and the total of occupied 10-km squares fell by over 20 per cent between the *1968–72* and *1988–91 Atlases*. Long-term trends indicate that the population is now stable, but with fluctuations: WBS data suggest an all-time high during 1995–97, followed by a sharp decline (*BBWC*).

Wiltshire has recorded a slow but steady increase since 1986, but there is little historical detail of the numbers breeding in the county. Smith (1887) noted only that 'in some favoured spots, several of which exist in Wiltshire, the sandbanks these birds frequent are completely riddled with their holes'. The 1929 bird report described the Sand Martin as 'very common ... though local' (*WANHM*). Buxton (1981) stated that it 'only breeds

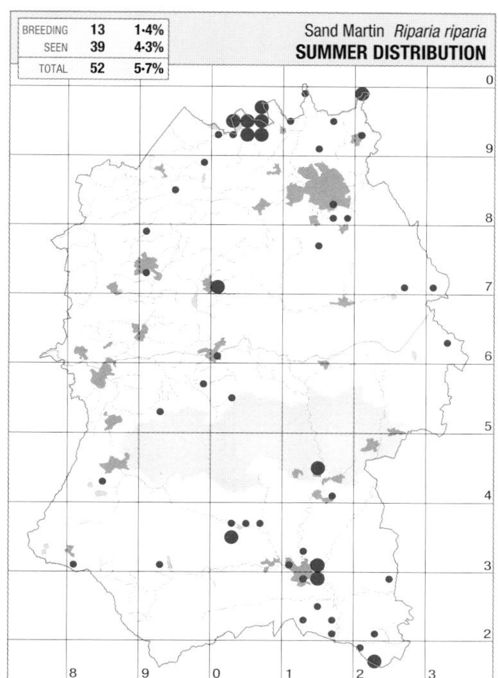

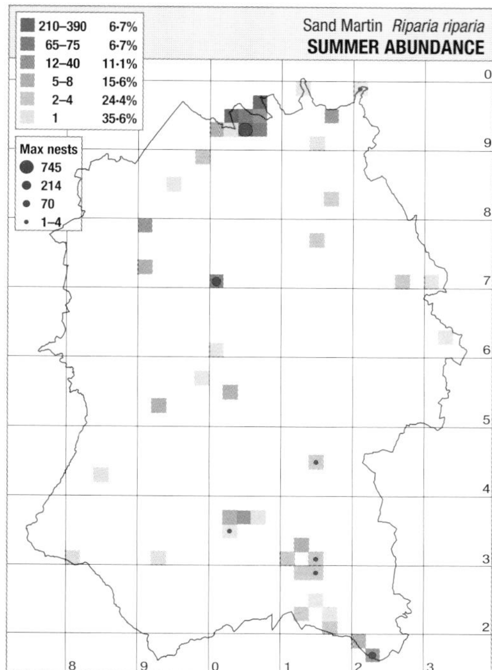

in any numbers in the north of the county', identifying CWP and Calne Sand Pits as the larger colonies. Since 1949, Sand Martins have been recorded as nesting in at least one year in sand pits at Calne, Naish Hill, Great Bedwyn, Sandridge, Dinton and Pound Bottom; in gravel pits at CWP, Christian Malford, Lacock, Langford and Britford; along rivers at Seagry, Chippenham, Lacock, Tisbury and Salisbury; and in various habitats at Coate Water, Bradford-on-Avon, Westbury, Bratton, Edington, West Grimstead and Pensworth Tip (*WANHM*, *Hobby*). But few of these sites are still used now. Most colonies were quite small until 1986, after which the huge expansion of sand and gravel excavation, especially at CWP, has provided many more potential nesting places, as well as areas of water and marsh over which the birds can feed.

The summer breeding and abundance maps show the localised nature of Sand Martin distribution in Wiltshire, and how few were recorded away from the nesting sites. Breeding was confirmed in just 13 tetrads, including the three major colonies at CWP, Calne Sand Pits, and Pound Bottom. Peak counts of nest-holes at the breeding sites used regularly during 1995–2000 were 745 at CWP, 214 at Calne, 70 at Pound Bottom – see also table 103 – and two at Salisbury (1997, 1999). Estimates based on nest-holes apparently in use during the 1998 season indicated a total breeding population of about 830 pairs (though, inevitably, this figure may have included some holes abandoned before completion) and, comparing favourably with some 1330 individuals counted during timed tetrad surveys, suggests 750–1000 pairs in the county.

Table 103. Sand Martins *Riparia riparia* in Wiltshire: total nest-holes at key sites 1990–2000

	90	91	92	93	94	95	96	97	98	99	00
CWP	87	60	491	172	482	745	–	68	410	425	350
Calne	–	185	–	130	140	140	190	90	50	35*	214
Pound Bottom	–	–	–	–	–	–	–	68	70	–	–

* based on report that 60–70 used nest-holes

The size of the Wiltshire population is linked closely to the extraction of sand and gravel. Sand Martins prefer to nest in active faces and, although some excavate their holes in stabilised stockpiles of sand and gravel, those are very much a second choice. Indeed, the productivity of a colony declines rapidly over two or three years because of the build-up of overwintering ectoparasites, so the fact that excavations cause the colonies gradually to move benefits the birds. Moreover, at CWP the next summer's sites are now planned in advance and the gravel companies leave one clean face in each working pit, making most others unsuitable for nesting before the breeding season – thus avoiding disturbance of the colonies by gravel extraction activities (G Harris). There are currently no artificial nest-sites at CWP, although some are planned for the future. At Calne Sand Pits, vertical faces due to be dug are covered with sheeting until nest excavation is complete, or faces that the birds have selected are left undisturbed for that season.

Of exactly 1400 Sand Martins ringed in the county during 1965–2000, 37 had been recovered or retrapped within Great Britain by the end of that period: eight in Wiltshire, 27 in south coast counties from Devon to Kent, one in Gwent and, more unexpectedly, a juvenile ringed at Whiteparish on 27 June 1964 that was retrapped 33 days later at Fairburn, Castleford (North Yorkshire), having travelled 305 km NNE. Two others were recovered abroad: one ringed at Calne on 24 August 1968 was found dead at Tolga (Algeria) on 29 May 1969, and another ringed at CWP on 22 July 2000 was retrapped at Madrid (Spain) just 52 days later on 12 September. Two marked abroad and found in Wiltshire were, coincidentally, both ringed at Abbeville (France) on 3 August 1981 and both recovered at Westbury, the first on 1 August 1982 and the second on 17 July 1983.

GLW & PEC

Barn Swallow

Hirundo rustica

Common and increasing summer visitor/passage, breeds Europe, winters Africa (some Spain)

The highly migratory Barn Swallow is a common summer visitor to Great Britain, where its arrival is eagerly awaited every year as one of the signs of spring. Although the first appear in the second half of March – the earliest ever in Wiltshire was recorded at Axford on 7 March 2000 – the bulk of the population does not arrive until April and, with stragglers occurring well into May, passage can extend over ten to 12 weeks. Elegant and accomplished flyers, they are diurnal migrants that keep mainly quite low over the ground, feeding as they go. In spring they usually move through the county on a broad front, concentrating over lakes and rivers during adverse weather, but in autumn they also show a marked east to west drift along the north-facing escarpments of the Marlborough Downs and SPTA, many then 'escaping' southwards down the river valleys (GL Webber).

Autumn migration is again protracted. Juveniles start to disperse in late summer, but most of the population does not begin to move south until September and the peak passage often extends from late in that month into October. In 1968 and 1973, very late broods did not fledge until 10 October (*WANHM*); in 1994, the young of a third brood in a barn at Edington did not venture from the nest until 20 October and, though the adults departed later that month, the three young continued to roost in the barn until 4

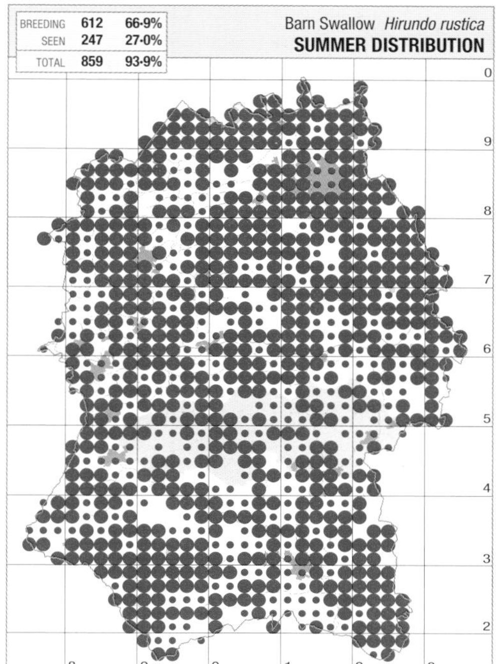

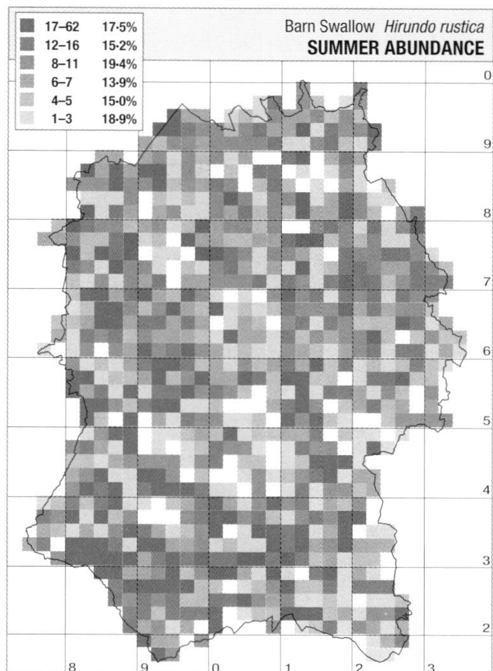

November (*Hobby*). Stragglers are regularly reported towards the end of October and in early November, and Wiltshire's latest record of all up to the end of the 20th century was a juvenile at Britford on 2 December 1957: it was found exhausted and died the following day. Autumn roosts can be substantial: at Coate Water, up to 3000 in late August and September 1962, and some 5000 on 10th and 14 August 1963 (*WANHM*). More recently, an autumn roost in maize at Lacock held 2500 in 1991, and though recorded regularly in subsequent years, it had declined steadily to just 100 by 1998; some 2000 were at CWP68 on 1 September 1990, with 1000 still present on 9th; while a count of 200 at Coate Water in September 1998 was the only other sizeable roost noted during the 1990s (*Hobby*).

Most European Barn Swallows spend the winter somewhere in sub-Saharan Africa, though small numbers do so in North Africa and southern Spain, and a few individuals may be found then in western Europe even as far north as Britain and Ireland; there are also semi-resident populations in the eastern Mediterranean. British Barn Swallows are among the farthest travellers, wintering in Namibia and South Africa (*Migration Atlas*).

Barn Swallows breed throughout the Northern Hemisphere, and it has been estimated that Europe, excluding Russia, holds somewhere between 14 and 19 million pairs (*EBCC Atlas*). Great Britain's share is in the region of 678,000 territories (*APEP*): though very widespread, they are scarce in upland areas of Scotland, the Outer Hebrides and Shetland, as well as in towns and cities in general (*1988–91 Atlas*), preferring rural areas with an abundance of insects for food and buildings such as barns and outhouses for nesting (Turner 1994).

There are few solid historical data on Barn Swallows in Wiltshire. Smith (1887) offered no detail on status, but they were apparently common and widespread in Great Britain as a whole at that time (*1875–1900 Atlas*). The 1929 bird report noted the species as 'very common' in the county, and in 1931 no fewer than 117 pairs were found breeding in Chute parish (*WANHM*). Peirson (1959) also described the Swallow as 'very common', but thought that it might have been more so in the 19th century, while Buxton

(1981) commented that 'The decrease this century has apparently accelerated in recent years'. This suggestion was echoed by Palmer (1991), who noted that 'Records indicate a very slight decline over the period [1980–89]'. Both the *1968–72* and *1988–91 Atlases* proved breeding in all of Wiltshire's core and part 10-km squares, though the latter also noted that numbers had been falling nationally since the early 1980s. Turner (1994) considered that the greatest declines had occurred in southern and eastern England, but that there had also been a trend of increasing numbers during 1988–92 (apart from a significant decline in 1991). Survey data indicate that the long-term population trend in England is one of fluctuations with a recent shallow increase, and that the fluctuations are mostly related to losses on their wintering grounds and, more recently, the amount of rain in the Sahel on spring passage (*BBWC*). Increases in the area of pastoral land in western Britain are likely to have promoted population increases there.

The distribution map demonstrates that Barn Swallows are found widely in Wiltshire, and absent only where nesting sites or food are scarce, for example in Great Ridge Wood and on parts of SPTA. The abundance map shows higher numbers along the Salisbury Avon and its tributaries, in the southwest vales and along the Bristol Avon, all areas where grasslands are grazed by cattle whose presence encourages the invertebrate food that Barn Swallows require. Breeding was proved in 612 tetrads and the tetrad survey counts recorded some 8680 individuals. The Wiltshire breeding population at the end of the 20th century is consequently suggested as lying in the region of 7500 to 10,000 pairs.

Of the total of 5882 Barn Swallows ringed in Wiltshire during 1965–2000, 36 had subsequently been recovered in Great Britain by the end of that period and five abroad, three in France (one after two months, each of the other two after 20 months) and two in South Africa (one marked as an adult and the other as a nestling, one found dead in the former Orange Free State and the other in the former Natal, each over 9500 km away in the winter after ringing). One ringed as an adult in Branchoot (Belgium) on 28 May 1965 was trapped and released at Woodford on 18 June 1966 and again in summer 1967, when the bird report commented that 'it was breeding' (*WANHM*).

GLW & SBE

Sponsored by Roche Farms Ltd

House Martin

Delichon urbicum

Common summer visitor/passage, breeds Europe, winters Africa

Familiar to many because of the mud nests they construct under house eaves – though those are often attributed to 'Swallows' by the people who live in the houses – the well-named House Martins are common summer visitors that hunt their invertebrate prey higher in the sky than do the other hirundines, often at similar levels to those at which Swifts forage. They breed almost throughout Europe (except northernmost Fenno-Scandia and Russia), south into northwest Africa, Turkey and parts of the Middle East, and east right across northern and central Asia to Japan. All winter somewhere in the tropics – where their high aerial foraging often makes them difficult to locate – but European and western Asiatic populations all migrate to sub-Saharan Africa and it appears that those from western Europe go to West Africa

(*Migration Atlas*). (None of 606 House Martins ringed in Wiltshire during 1965–2000 had been recovered outside the county by the end of that period.) The total numbers that breed in Europe, excluding Russia, have been estimated at 11 to 16 million pairs (*EBCC Atlas*).

The spring migration is mainly on a broad front and, though the earliest arrivals are often in March, the majority returns between mid April and mid May, the peak period varying widely from year to year. Wiltshire's earliest ever record is of one at Odstock on 5 March 1967 (*WANHM*), and in 1979 a pair was seen renovating a nest at Fyfield as early as 15 April (*Hobby*). The *1988–91 Atlas* estimated 250,000 to 500,000 breeding pairs in Great Britain, and national survey data show that in the long-term the population has been stable, though recent BBS results indicate fluctuations or a slight increase in the 1990s (*BBWC*), with the population in 2000 estimated at 253,000 to 505,000 pairs (*APEP*).

In Great Britain, the House Martin's range is similar to the Barn Swallow's, but it is at once far more urban, nesting even in large towns and cities where the air is reasonably clean, and also more rural, breeding on both coastal and inland cliffs. Indeed, the largest colonies are often not in urban areas but on isolated houses, farms, bridges, even disused signal boxes, wherever there is sufficient of an open area below and in front to drop away from the nest. Long ago, before solid houses and bridges were available, most nests must have been built on natural rock faces and some still regularly are, though not in Wiltshire. Clark & McNeil (1980) mapped a number of such colonies in various parts of Great Britain – mainly on coasts but also well inland in, particularly, northern England – and suggested that 'no large change in the numbers of cliff-nesting House Martins has occurred in the last 100 years, and that the present population is in the region of 800–1000 pairs'.

In Wiltshire, Smith (1887) described the House Martin as 'even more familiar' than the Barn Swallow; the 1929 bird report in *WANHM* thought it 'plentiful'; and Peirson (1959) noted it merely as 'common'. Both the *1968–72* and *1988–91 Atlases* found this species breeding in every one of Wiltshire's 33 core and 15 part 10-km squares. A WOS House Martin Survey in 1975–76, in which over 90 observers took part, recorded a minimum of 982 nests in a total of 108 localities in 1975, the more complete of the two years (Bridgman 1977), but this figure was certainly much too low. The average density of 100–200 pairs per occupied 10-km square (*ie* four to eight pairs per tetrad) postulated by the *1968–72 Atlas* (and repeated by the *1988–91 Atlas*) suggests that the Wiltshire population at that time might have been in the range of 3500 to 7000 breeding pairs. But the summer tetrad counts in 1995–2000 totalled some 8720, and the Wiltshire population therefore perhaps lies in the region of 7500 to 10,000 pairs, suggesting an increase over the period.

Although found in every 10-km square, House Martins were confirmed breeding in some 20 per cent fewer tetrads than Barn Swallows, but counts during the timed tetrad visits indicate that the population sizes of both are remarkably similar over the county as a whole. Nevertheless, assuming that Smith (1887) was correct in stating that the House Martin was the more numerous, this might be taken to suggest a change in the relative status of these two hirundines since the 19th century. The smaller number of tetrads in which House Martins were found breeding was probably simply because their being colonial means that their nests are far more concentrated; they also usually start feeding later in the morning and, away from the colonies, often much higher in the air than Barn Swallows. The distribution and abundance maps, not surprisingly, show House Martins to be absent from – or no more than seen foraging over – for example, large areas of Salisbury Plain, where buildings suitable for nesting are few. But, not far away, the abundance map also emphasises a clear breeding concentration in the vicinity of the city of Salisbury and along the valleys of the Salisbury Avon, Wylye and Nadder, presumably because suitable nest-sites and invertebrate food are plentiful in the river valleys. By comparison, very few House Martins were found at CWP. The significance of local shortages of suitable sites

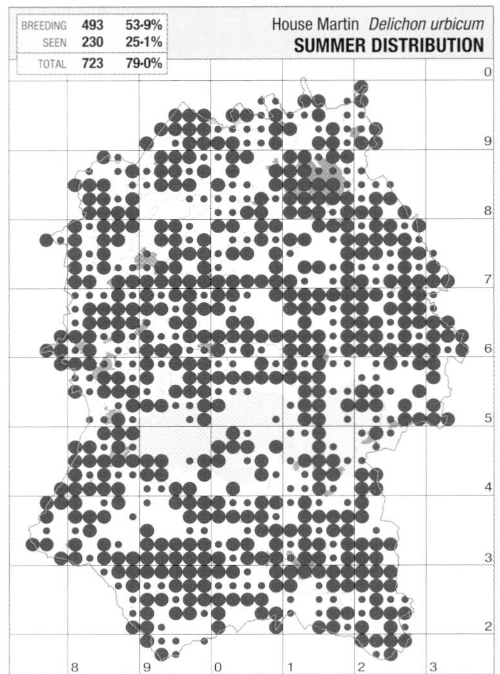

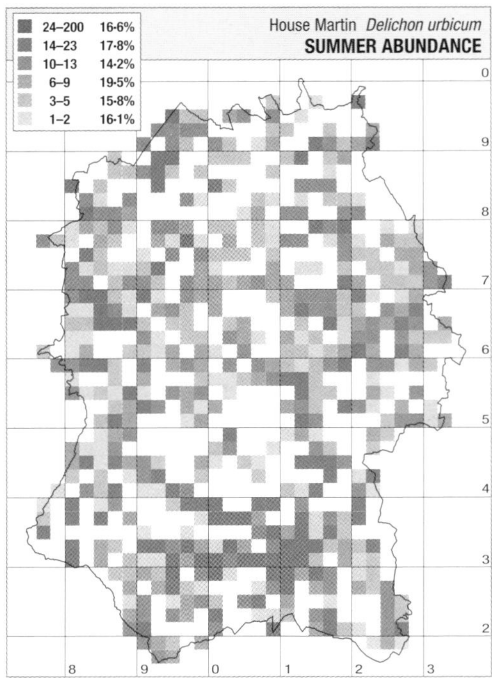

was well demonstrated by the provision of artificial nests on one house in Upavon in 1987 and 1988, which resulted in the fledging of 58 young from 14 nests in the second of those years, despite heavy predation (of 15 eggs and 12 young) by Great Spotted Woodpeckers (Crease 1989).

Because House Martins regularly have two broods, sometimes three, they are frequently still feeding young in the nest in mid September, and this is not particularly unusual even in early October; indeed, three nests at Netheravon still contained young on 12 October 1964 (*WANHM*). Thus, their autumn migration tends to be later than those of many other summer migrants, but the survival of late broods that have to set off for sub-Saharan Africa within a week or two of leaving the nest must be much reduced. Autumn movements, although by day, are on a broad front and generally at higher altitudes than those of Sand Martins and Barn Swallows, and so much less noticeable. Observations of heavy passage during the 1990s did, however, include 1000 south at Larkhill on 26 September 1992, 1500 at Standlynch on 8–9 October 1995, and 350 at Coate Water in mid September 1997 (*Hobby*). Though the majority leaves in late September and early October, stragglers continue to be seen throughout October and into November. The latest Wiltshire dates have been singletons in December, at Lower Woodford on the 2nd and 3rd in 1949 and at Upavon on the 1st in 1986 (*WANHM*, *Hobby*).

GLW & IJF-L

Sponsored by Peggy Bucknall

Richard's Pipit

Anthus richardi

Vagrant (1 record), breeds Siberia, winters southeast Asia, regular migrant Britain

Richard's Pipits are scarce but regular vagrants to Great Britain, and increasing in frequency, with a total of nearly 3000 records during 1958–2000 and an annual mean of 124 records in the 1990s through to 2000 (Fraser & Rogers 2002). Most are found from mid September to November, mainly along the east and south coasts, but the much smaller numbers in spring appear also to be growing, from an annual mean of 1·1 during 1958–88 to 6·8 during 1989–99 (Fraser & Rogers 2001).

The only Wiltshire observation was at Ebsbury Hill, Wishford, on 16 September 1986 (*Hobby*). This large, stout-billed pipit favours longish rough pasture and many are located initially in flight by their strident calls. It breeds no closer to Europe than southern Siberia and western China, and winters mostly from India eastwards to Malaysia. Some have now been found wintering in Spain and adjacent parts of North Africa (*Migration Atlas*) and the species may even be establishing a regular winter range there (Cottridge & Vinicombe 1996).

Richard's Pipit has for the past fifty years been considered conspecific with several other large spot-chested pipits of southern Asia, Africa, Australia and New Zealand, under the name *A. novaeseelandiae*, but recent authors (*eg* Alström & Mild 2003) have argued against this and the BOU has recommended that it be treated separately once more, now indeed as a monotypic species (Sangster *et al* 2005).

RT

Tawny Pipit

Anthus campestris

Vagrant (1 record), breeds south/central Eurasia, winters Africa to India

Although averaging 26 records a year in Great Britain since 1958 (Fraser *et al* 2000), the only Tawny Pipit so far found in Wiltshire was a juvenile frequenting the short grassy areas of Colerne airfield during 27–29 September 1983 (*BBRC*, *Hobby*). This large, slim pipit breeds in northwest Africa, the Levant and throughout continental Europe south of the Baltic and across to western Siberia and Mongolia; it winters in Africa, mainly just south of the Sahara, as well as from Arabia to India. The species favours arid areas, and habitat changes have resulted in a widespread decrease in some parts of Europe since the mid 1960s (*CBWP*); in the 1990s the European population was estimated at 521,000 to 765,000 pairs (*EBCC Atlas*). There was a slight increase in British records during the 1980s and early 1990s, with a mean of 36 records a year, but numbers have since fallen considerably (Fraser & Rogers 2002). The vast majority of the 1088 British records during 1958–2000 has been in south and east coast counties, most from late August to October, but a few in May and June.

RT

Tree Pipit

Anthus trivialis

Fairly common if local summer visitor, breeds Europe, winters Africa

The Tree Pipit is one of the earlier summer visitors to arrive in Wiltshire, and until late June its presence is announced by the male's characteristic song, whether from a prominent perch or during a parachuting song-flight. A well-concealed nest is constructed on the ground in any of a variety of habitats, including young conifer plantations, woodland clearings, the edges to set-aside, and downland slopes – provided that there are song posts available. Few are reported at sites away from the breeding areas, particularly in spring.

The first Tree Pipits usually appear in early April, but odd ones are sometimes noted in late March, the earliest recorded having been on SPTA (Centre) on the 18th in 2000. In autumn, their passage reaches a peak in late August and very few are recorded after the third week of September. Wiltshire's two latest records have been in October: three at Swindon STW on the 11th in 1953 and five on Milk Hill on the 22nd in 1950 (*WANHM*).

Tree Pipits breed across Eurasia from Great Britain (though virtually absent in Ireland) east to Mongolia and north almost to Norway's arctic coastline, while the southern limit extends roughly from northern Spain through Italy, the Balkans, northern Turkey and Iran to Himachal Pradesh in India, but they are missing from the arid steppes of central Asia. Except for very small numbers on a few western Mediterranean islands and in the Middle East, Tree Pipits winter in sub-Saharan Africa and the Indian subcontinent. Data from observatories and ringing recoveries indicate that British breeders migrate southwest in autumn, but their exact wintering grounds are unknown (*Migration Atlas*). None of the 39 Tree Pipits ringed in Wiltshire during 1965–2000 has been recovered, although a nestling ringed in Liphook (Hampshire) on 8 June 1985 was caught and released again in West Winterslow just five weeks later, on 13 July 1985. The European breeding population, excluding Russia, has been estimated at 15 to 19 million pairs, the majority in Germany, Fenno-Scandia and Belarus (*EBCC Atlas*). The 74,400 territories estimated in Great Britain (*APEP*) form a relatively small proportion of this total.

In Great Britain, Tree Pipits expanded their range northwards in Scotland during the 20th century, but their numbers have decreased in southern England since about 1930. This decline was noted in the *1968–72 Atlas* and was particularly marked by the time of the *1988–91 Atlas*, when Tree Pipits had disappeared from large parts of Dorset, Somerset, the Midlands and East Anglia. The *1988–91 Atlas* – which estimated some 120,000 pairs in Britain – stated that the population strongholds were in upland oak and birch woodlands of Wales, northern England and Scotland. Scottish populations were still increasing during the mid to late 1990s, but those in southern England declined substantially at the beginning of that decade (*BBWC*). The reasons for this decrease are uncertain, but habitat loss as woodland matures has been suggested, as have changes in forest management, increased grazing pressure by deer, and competition with other species (Gregory *et al* 2001).

In Wiltshire, Smith (1887) found Tree Pipits 'far from common but may be seen in most woodland districts'; in the Marlborough area, however, im Thurn (1870) and Peirson (1919) noted them as 'tolerably abundant' and 'moderately common' respectively. The 1929 bird report described them as 'rather scarce' in the county (*WANHM*), and Peirson (1959) stated that they were 'not uncommon in some areas, but scarce or absent

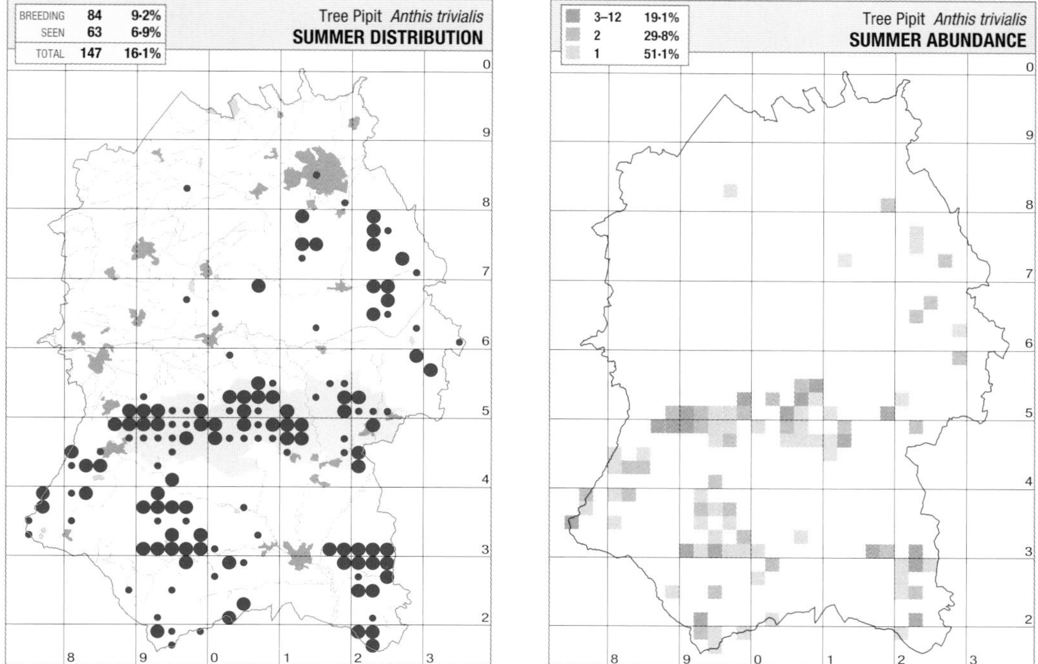

elsewhere'. Colquhoun (1941) did not mention the species in his surveys of Savernake in the late 1930s, yet Buxton (1981) – who wrote that Tree Pipits were 'widely distributed' in Wiltshire – thought that some two-thirds of the estimated 90 pairs breeding in the northeast were in the Savernake/West Woods region. (Buxton also stated that numbers breeding elsewhere in the county were unknown.) Tree Pipits were recorded in 25 of Wiltshire's 33 core 10-km squares in the *1968–72 Atlas*, in only 20 in the *1988–91 Atlas*, but in 25 again during the 1995–2000 summer survey, against the trend documented for England as a whole.

In the southeast, Tree Pipits were regular breeders at Dean Hill in the 1970s, then virtually disappeared in the 1980s, before their numbers recovered again during the 1990s (coinciding with the introduction of set-aside) and in 2000 no fewer than 14 singing males were recorded, roughly twice as many as in the 1970s; nearby, in woodlands in the Dean valley, small numbers were present in forestry clearings throughout the entire 30–year period (MC & P Combridge). In contrast, not far away at Hamptworth, the total number of pairs fell from 15–20 in the early 1980s to no more than six or seven by the late 1990s as conifer plantations matured (GD Pictor). In the north of the county, the Braydon Forest population also all but disappeared in the period between the two national atlases, and there was some contraction of range in the west of the county (*Hobby*). Numbers in strongholds such as SPTA (West) appear to have remained relatively stable.

The summer distribution map shows that Tree Pipits are now virtually confined to three areas: Savernake and parts of the Marlborough Downs in the northeast, SPTA, and the downs and woodlands of the south, while the abundance map demonstrates that concentrations are very localised away from SPTA. On SPTA alone, no fewer than 126 territories were identified and 217 estimated by an RSPB survey in 2000 (Stanbury *et al* 2000); a concentration on SPTA (West) was 'heavily associated with the plantations', a situation reflected by the abundance map. Extrapolating from the SPTA total to the remainder of the county on the basis of WOS timed counts produces a figure of 672 pairs, although that is likely to be near the upper limit of any range, and in 1995–2000 the population is estimated to have been in the region of 500 to 700 pairs.

Some breeding areas currently in use will disappear as set-aside reverts to farmland and young plantations mature, but recent woodland plantings on parts of the Marlborough Downs are likely to hold breeding Tree Pipits in the near future, as they do already along the Kennet valley.

GDP

Meadow Pipit

Anthus pratensis

Common resident, and passage/winter from Iceland/north Europe

This small, active pipit breeds from southeast Greenland to the western fringe of Siberia, and from the arctic coasts and uplands of Europe from Iceland and Fenno-Scandia south to central France, the Alps and the Ukraine, favouring open grassy areas with scattered trees and bushes. The breeding range is thus largely confined to Europe where, excluding Russia, the population has been put at 7·4 to 12 million pairs (*EBCC Atlas*).

Great Britain holds a significant proportion of that total, with numbers estimated at 1·6 million territories (*APEP*). Although widely distributed, Meadow Pipits are most abundant on the uplands of northern England, Wales and Scotland, where they are the commonest nesting passerines above 500 m (*1988–91 Atlas*). In autumn, the northern and eastern European populations move southwest and south for the winter, and Meadow Pipits are then found from Britain and Ireland, Denmark and western Germany south and southeast to the whole Mediterranean region, including northwest Africa to the Nile delta, parts of the Middle East and Turkey. While many British breeders stay in this country throughout the year, others are believed to winter mainly in Iberia. There is also a substantial passage of Meadow Pipits from Iceland and Fenno-Scandia through Britain in autumn, but as yet no evidence from ringing that any from these other countries winter in Britain (*Migration Atlas*). The 207 Meadow Pipits ringed in Wiltshire during 1965–2000, all but six as adults, have produced no recoveries.

In Wiltshire, Smith (1887) noted the Meadow Pipit as 'Very common, especially on our furze-clad downs, where it remains the whole year, though it will occasionally assemble in flocks, and haunt stubble and turnip-fields in winter' – an assessment echoed by the 1929 bird report in *WANHM*, which described it as an 'abundant resident'. Peirson (1959) stated that 'Very small numbers breed in enclosed country or more commonly the open downland', and that this was 'A common winter visitor from about late September to early April'. Buxton (1981) added little of substance, but noted that 'It breeds on sheltered downs, commonly in a few areas and less regularly on rough lowland sites'.

Most of the records published in *Hobby* concern numbers seen on passage and in winter. From mid September into October a marked south to southwest movement occurs in most years. This has been widely recorded, but chiefly from such well-watched sites as CWP, Salisbury Plain, Standlynch and Liddington Hill. In 1986, for example, 500 were estimated passing over Imber on 27 September and 1000 over Larkhill on 4 October; and in 1987, again 500 over Larkhill on 27 September, and 200 flying south over Bratton in one hour

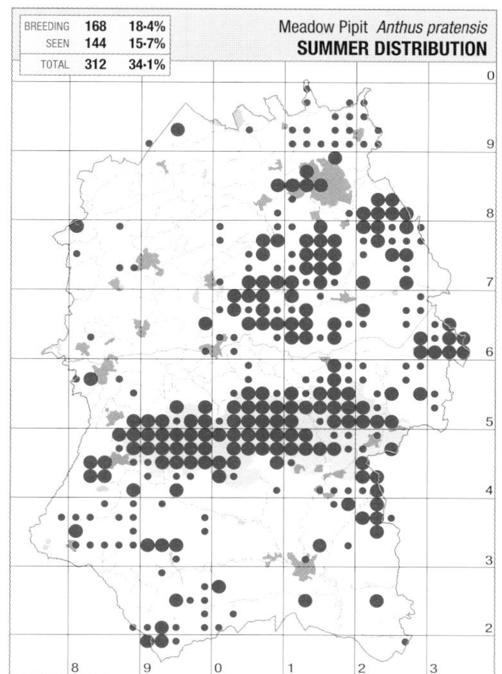

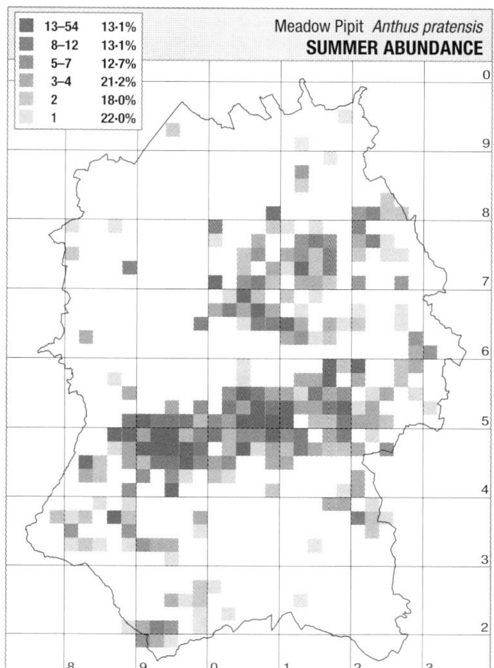

on the 30th. During 1990–2000, autumn counts of 100 or more were recorded on 18 occasions, including 500 with Sky Larks at Larkhill on 20 October 1995. In winter, it is usual for only small groups to be recorded, but larger gatherings may be seen during cold-weather movements: for example, 500 over Larkhill on 8 February 1996 and 100 at Longford on 2 February 1991. Spring passage in a north and northwesterly direction, usually from mid March to mid April, involves mainly smaller numbers.

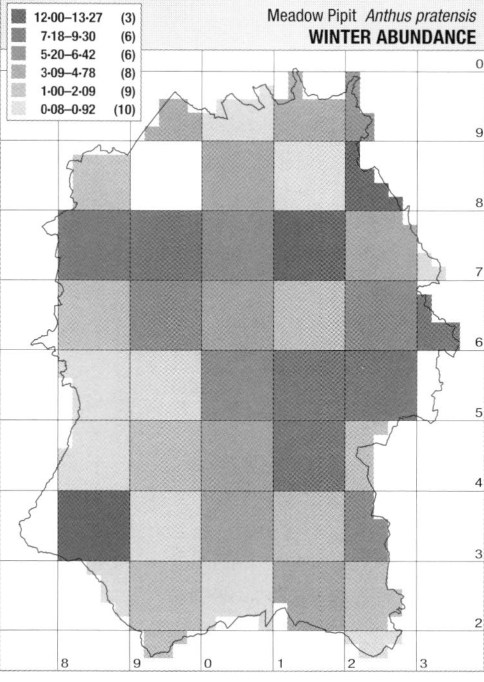

Winter habitats in Wiltshire include stubbles, water meadows and watercress beds, and the winter map shows that Meadow Pipits are widespread in the county at that season: in the 1998–2000 survey, they were found in all but one of the 33 core 10-km squares, most numerously from the Cotswolds to the Marlborough Downs and on the eastern part of SPTA. Although the *1981–84 Winter Atlas* showed a broadly similar pattern – the species was recorded then in all of the county's core and part 10-km squares – there was a slight difference in the pattern of abundance and, though that may have reflected changes in habitat in some areas, it could simply have been an artefact of the differing survey methods used. The *1981–84 Winter Atlas* estimate of one to 2·5 million Meadow Pipits in Britain and Ireland, at an average of 800 per occupied 10-km square in the areas of highest density, would suggest a Wiltshire population of around 50,000, a figure rather smaller than the range of 60,800 to 68,800 produced by a combination of WOS timed counts and other data sources.

The *1968–72 Atlas* found Meadow Pipits breeding in 19 of Wiltshire's 33 core 10-km squares and present in a further six, and the corresponding figures in the *1988–91 Atlas* were 21 and seven. The summer tetrad survey in 1995–2000 recorded evidence of breeding in no fewer than 25 of the 33 squares and presence in another four. This evidence of wider distribution is not the result that might be expected from national survey data, which recorded both a decline in numbers and a contraction in range in lowland England from the mid 1970s (*BBWC*). It has been suggested that this decline could be linked to conditions on the Iberian wintering grounds or to habitat losses in lowland England. In this connection, the summer distribution and abundance maps both demonstrate the importance of the grasslands of Salisbury Plain: an RSPB survey of SPTA in 2000 noted that the highest densities were in the core grasslands, and that the surrounding semi-improved areas held relatively few, while, in contrast to Sky Larks, grazing appeared to have a detrimental effect (Stanbury *et al* 2000). Indeed, the abundance map in the *1988–91 Atlas* shows the Plain to be the second most prominent inland breeding area, after the moorlands of the southwest peninsula, for this species in southern England. That could support the view that it is the losses of suitable habitat that has affected populations elsewhere in southern England. The Marlborough Downs – where 14 singing males had been recorded in a single tetrad in June 1993 – are also particularly important, and there is a scatter of breeding sites elsewhere in the north and south.

Stanbury *et al* (2000) estimated 8900 Meadow Pipit territories on SPTA in 2000 – the second most numerous species there after the Sky Lark – and extrapolation from these figures using the timed tetrad counts produces an estimate of 20,400–23,100 pairs for the whole county.

MVJ

Rock Pipit

Anthus petrosus

Vagrant (13 records) from rocky coasts of Britain or, more likely, Fenno-Scandia

Rock Pipits are endemic to the rocky coasts of northwest Europe, but in winter occur also along less rugged shorelines and by estuaries, where they can often be seen feeding among sea wrack. The nominate race, *petrosus,* breeds in Britain, Ireland and northwest France, and is replaced in Denmark, Fenno-Scandia and extreme northwest Russia by a more migratory subspecies, *littoralis*, that winters south to the Mediterranean. (The populations of the Faeroes and of the northern Scottish islands are usually treated as a third race, and all were considered to be subspecies of the Water Pipit until 1986: see Knox 1988.) The breeding population of Rock Pipits, entirely within Europe, has been estimated at 190,000 to one million pairs, 34,000 of them in Great Britain, where there have been indications of slight declines in recent decades (*1988–91 Atlas*).

Breeding in Great Britain primarily on western and northern coasts – those nearest to Wiltshire being in Somerset and Dorset – Rock Pipits are more widely distributed in

Table 104. Rock Pipits *Anthus petrosus* in Wiltshire: monthly totals of records 1976–2000

	Jan	Feb	Mar	Apr	May	Jun	Jul	Aug	Sep	Oct	Nov	Dec
Records	0	0	1	5	1	0	1	1	2	2	0	0

winter, then occurring along the south and southeast English coastlines (*1981–84 Winter* and *1988–91 Atlases*). They are, however, only rarely found inland, and Wiltshire's first was not identified until 1976. (Although at that time not formally recognised as distinct species, Rock and Water Pipits were recorded separately in *Hobby*.) Since then the total of records has risen to 13, all singletons seen on just one day and all bar two at CWP:

1976	26 March	Coate Water	
1977	10 October	CWP30	'probably of race *A. s. petrosus*'
1979	2 October	Liden Lagoon	'probably of the race *A. s. petrosus*'
1982	1 January	Eysey	
1988	17 October	CWP68	
1990	8 April	CWP68	
	29 September	CWP68	
1991	26 October	CWP68	
1992	13 February	CWP68	
1993	28 March	CWP74	
	3 April	CWP74	'probably of the ... race *A. s. littoralis*'
1997	20 October	CWP68	
1999	21 November	CWP68	

That at CWP on 3 April 1993 was the only one identified as being ('probably') of the Fenno-Scandian race, *littoralis*, which is known to be a passage migrant and winter visitor to both southern England (perhaps comprising the majority of the Rock Pipits in the southeast at such times) and Wales, whereas the British subspecies, *petrosus*, is believed to be largely sedentary (*Migration Atlas*). Thus, it seems very likely that all Wiltshire's records – seen only in winter or, particularly, the months of passage (table 104) – involve the former race.

(See also page 727.)

RT

Water Pipit

Anthus spinoletta

Rare passage/winter (32 records) from mountains of south-central Europe

Water Pipits nest above the tree-line in the alpine meadows of southern and central Europe, also from the Caucasus and Turkey across central Asia; some 259,000 to 351,000 pairs are estimated to breed in Europe (*EBCC Atlas*). In winter they move to lowlands, mainly south to the Mediterranean region and southern Asia, but some travel northwest to England, the Low Countries and now also southern Fenno-Scandia. Unlike the Rock Pipit – with which, until 1986, it was treated as conspecific – the Water Pipit regularly occurs inland, and is attracted to watercress beds, sewage works and lake complexes. Around 100 are thought to winter in England each year, mainly in south coast counties, East Anglia, the

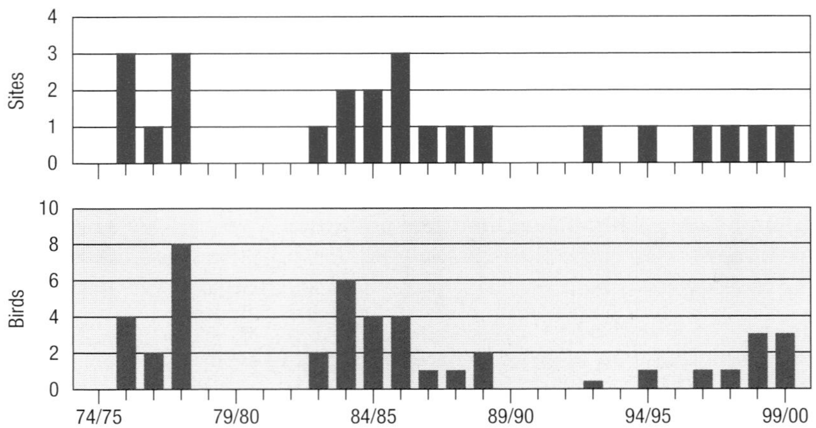

Figure 65. Water Pipits *Anthus spinoletta* in Wiltshire: totals and sites by winters 1974/75–1999/00

Midlands and the northwest, and ringing suggests that most are males (*1981–84 Winter Atlas*, *Migration Atlas*).

All Wiltshire records have been between 17 November and 16 April, chiefly in December and January but with another distinct peak in March as migrants pass through (table 105). After the first was identified at Swindon STW on 20 March 1955, singletons were seen in March at Bincknoll on 19th in 1967 and at Hill Deverill on 29th in 1972, and two at Coate Water on 7 April 1973 (*WANHM*). During 1974–2000, a further 43 individuals (28 records) were noted (figure 65), the majority at Britford, at CWP and at or near the watercress beds at Longbridge Deverill (*Hobby*). Many in spring were present for just one day, or occasionally up to five days, but some winterers apparently remained for prolonged periods between late November and March. (As numbers varied and the species was often recorded on only a handful of occasions during a prolonged stay, there was conceivably some turnover.) Up to three have been seen together on a number of occasions, but the largest count was of five at Bishopstone Cress Beds, near Salisbury, on 29 December 1983.

Table 105. Water Pipits *Anthus spinoletta* in Wiltshire: bird-months 1955–2000

	Jul	Aug	Sep	Oct	Nov	Dec	Jan	Feb	Mar	Apr	May	Jun
Bird-months	0	0	0	0	4	11	15	6	19	9	0	0

The runs of records in the mid to late 1970s and then the mid to late 1980s may have involved the same individuals returning year after year, for wintering Water Pipits are known to show a degree of fidelity to a particular site (*Migration Atlas*). The species appears to have become rarer in Wiltshire in the 1990s, and most in the latter half of that decade were at CWP, where the larger number of birdwatchers means that short-stayers are more likely to be recorded. One at CWP from 30 January 2000 was in summer plumage by the time it was last seen on 26 March.

RT

Yellow Wagtail

Motacilla flava

Local summer visitor, breeds Europe (this race mainly Britain), winters Africa

Yellow Wagtails – in summer the males of all subspecies are an eye-catchingly brilliant yellow below – breed widely from North Africa and western Europe right across Eurasia to western Alaska, and winter in Africa (mainly south of the Sahara), the Indian subcontinent and southeast Asia south to northern Australia. The systematics of this splendid wagtail are vexed, and it is sometimes treated as two or more species (see Alström & Mild 2003 for discussion).

The breeding population of Yellow Wagtails in Europe, excluding Russia, has been estimated at 3·9 to 5·3 million pairs, declines being noted in 13 countries, stability in 16, and increases in just two (*EBCC Atlas*). Six subspecies nest in Europe, but only one, *flavissima* – 'British Yellow Wagtail' – breeds regularly in Great Britain. (This race also nests along the Channel and North Sea coasts of France, Belgium and the Netherlands, on the German island of Helgoland and locally in southwest Norway.)

At the end of the 19th century, it was considered most common in southern England 'especially in the lower Severn and [Warwickshire] Avon valleys and on the east and southeast coasts' (*1875–1900 Atlas*). Smith (1950) noted a decrease in parts of southern England and south Wales but an increase in the northwest, while a similar trend was also mentioned by the *1968–72 Atlas*. By the time of the *1988–91 Atlas*, which estimated the British population at 50,000 territories, its range had contracted markedly, and it was then most numerous in central and southeast England. Breeding numbers are clearly smaller now, some 11,500 to 26,500 territories (*APEP*), as national survey data show a rapid decline since the early 1980s, with the conversion of pasture to arable and the loss of insects associated with cattle cited as possible causes (*BBWC*). British Yellow Wagtails are, like most other races of this species, long-distance migrants, and winter in West Africa from Senegal and Gambia east to Liberia, Mali and perhaps Ivory Coast (Keith *et al* 1992).

In Wiltshire, Smith (1887) reported *flavissima* as 'common', and noted that it 'flocks here every summer... frequents open plantations and arable land, and fields of sprouting wheat, as well as meadows, open downs and sheep pastures'. The 1929 bird report in *WANHM* described the Yellow Wagtail as 'fairly common'. Twenty years later, Smith (1950) was able to provide a fairly detailed summary of information from a number of local observers, in which he divided the county into two halves. In north Wiltshire, he described it as 'not uncommon around Marlborough... and the Kennet and Avon canal. Has extended its range up the Kennet of recent years. A few pairs breed near Swindon... and scattered pairs in the north-west of the county... It is however very local here, and... of rare occurrence... on the upper Bristol Avon. It is much less common in the Chippenham area than it used to be'. In south Wiltshire, he noted that it 'breeds reasonably commonly in the Avon water-meadows above and below Salisbury. Farther up the Avon its numbers diminish rapidly, and it is of very rare occurrence as a breeder above Amesbury. A few pairs breed near Limpley Stoke... but it is absent from most of Salisbury Plain, and high and dry ground generally'.

Peirson (1959) stated that it was found only in 'the lower-lying parts... and even there is far from common'. That statement was, however, considered incorrect by Webber (1968), who noted that 'In the valleys of the Bristol Avon and the Thames... breeds generally and in places quite numerously... recorded as breeding in the Devizes and Melksham areas and less commonly from other river valleys in the south'.

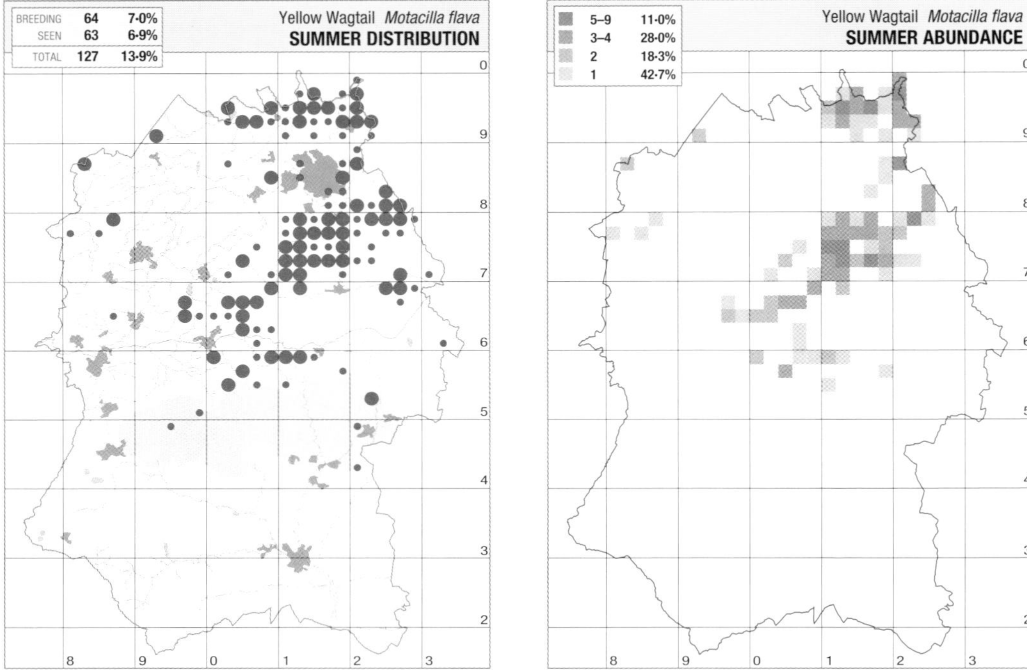

Both the *1968–72* and *1988–91 Atlases* mapped Yellow Wagtails as breeding in 12 of Wiltshire's 33 core 10-km squares, and by the time of the summer tetrad survey in 1995–2000 the number had increased to 19, but these bare figures mask changes in distribution over the three decades. The *1968–72 Atlas* recorded breeding in the valleys of both the Bristol and lower Salisbury Avons, but by the time of *1988–91 Atlas* survey it was absent from the latter. The summer map clearly shows the importance now of northeast Wiltshire, where these wagtails have increased on the Marlborough Downs, and nesting is now almost exclusively on arable land. *Hobby* has reported them in cereals, mustard, peas, linseed, oilseed rape and potatoes. Preliminary results from a survey on the Marlborough Downs in 2004 suggest, however, that almost all nests are in winter wheat, and that oilseed rape and broad beans are generally avoided (SB Edwards & J Gilroy). In the Fens of East Anglia, where potatoes are part of the usual crop rotation, Yellow Wagtails switch from winter wheat to potatoes for second broods in mid June (J Gilroy), but in Wiltshire, where the latter crop is scarce, there are few late nesting attempts.

The *1988–91 Atlas* suggested that drainage, agricultural intensification and a widespread switch from grassland to cereals were possibly to blame for losses in range. The fact, however, that Yellow Wagtails nest in cereals on the Marlborough Downs, but are absent from arable elsewhere in Wiltshire, does indicate that the reasons may be more complex. In this connection, the habitat summary quoted earlier from Smith (1887), and his stated belief that this wagtail did 'not seem so dependent on the neighbourhood of water as its congeners', are of interest. Much the same point was made by Smith (1950) who noted that, in Great Britain as a whole, this species nested not only in wet areas but also 'on heaths and moorlands in quite dry country' and in 'arable-land crops'. A recent study of breeding Yellow Wagtails on wet grassland in East Anglia found the territories to be in fields with short, sparse swards and, after prolonged winter flooding, high proportions of bare earth, but also patches of taller grass to conceal the nests (Bradbury & Bradter 2004). Thus, their disappearance as nesting birds from the Salisbury Avon and other river valleys may be connected with these areas being less affected by winter flooding at the end of the 20th century.

Buxton (1981) thought it 'doubtful that more than 150 pairs breed in the county in any one year', but, although the Yellow Wagtail has disappeared from the river valleys, its shift to arable land and the increase of 58 per cent in the number of core 10-km squares in which it was found in 1995–2000 imply a larger population. The species was recorded in 127 tetrads from the Vale of Pewsey north to the Thames valley and about 193 individuals were counted on timed visits, which suggests that – by comparison with other birds that had comparable counts – the Wiltshire population now lies in the order of 300–500 pairs.

Yellow Wagtails usually arrive in Wiltshire from early April onwards, but occasionally in March and the earliest recorded date is the 12th, at Marlborough in 1995. Spring passage is normally a steady trickle, though larger numbers are often counted at sites not used for breeding: for example, 'over 20' and 30 at Coate Water in April 1979 and 1985 respectively, although 15 at the same site in April 1997 was the only double-figure record in the 1990s (*Hobby*). Larger parties may be seen from late summer to early autumn, often feeding around the hooves of grazing cattle and horses. Roosts of up to 100 have been reported – for example at CWP in late August 1987 and between late August and late September 1991 – and still larger non-roosting counts have included 130 at Cholderton on 10 September 1994 and 200 at Collingbourne Ducis on 12 September 1999. There were October records in five of the 11 years 1990–2000, and singletons have been reported in November (at Marlborough on the 14th in 1967 and at Malmesbury on the 6th in 1969), and even in December (near Shorncote on the 13th in 1970 – though the locality itself is just in Gloucester – and at Chippenham on the 14th in 1990) (*WANHM*, *Hobby*).

Yellow Wagtails showing the characters of nominate *flava* – 'Blue-headed Wagtail', the race breeding in western and central Europe – are reported in most years. For example, during 1990–2000 there were several records in the period mid April to mid May in 1991, 1993 and 1995–96, and singletons in July 1999 and August 1990 and 1997 (*Hobby*). Smith (1887) also mentioned a specimen of *flava* 'killed at Marshfield, near Chippenham, in October 1841' (though Marshfield itself is just outside Wiltshire) and three other reports, not all certain, from Britford, Salisbury and Mere. (Smith made things potentially confusing for modern readers by calling *flava* the 'Grey-headed Wagtail', a vernacular name used nowadays for the race *thunbergi* that breeds in central and northern Fenno-Scandia east to the Kolyma in Siberia, though individuals with the characters of that subspecies have also been reported in Wiltshire: see below.) It is worth noting here that intergrades and variants complicate the field identification of vagrant Yellow Wagtail subspecies (*eg* Alström & Mild 2003); consequently, such records are generally regarded as 'showing the characters of', rather than certainly referred to any particular form.

Nesting by *flava* was reported at Manton, near Marlborough in 1907 and 1909 (Dent 1907, *MCNHR*, Peirson 1919), though both Peirson (1959) and Buxton (1981) noted these records as referring to 'variants'. Buxton also wrote that 'pairs summered at Coate Water' in the three years 1976–78, but *Hobby* noted only that examples of *flava* were present in April and May in the first two of those years, and made no mention of any records in 1978. A female thought to be *flava* was seen with a *flavissima* male at Britford on 17 July 1976.

Individuals resembling the race *beema* – 'Sykes's Wagtail', which breeds from the lower Volga to the upper Yenisei – are occasionally reported (for example, two at Coate Water in April and May 1976) but it has long been known that these occur from time to time in British breeding populations in southeast England (*eg* Milne 1959) and are more likely to be aberrants, pale variant *flava*, or intergrades between *flava* and *flavissima* (Alström & Mild 2003). There are two Wiltshire records of wagtails showing the characters of the 'Grey-headed' race *thunbergi*, one at Britford on 15 April 1936 and the other at Coate Water on 4 July 1983 (*Hobby*). The first of these was mistakenly credited to Hampshire by Witherby *et al* (1938–41) (see also *BB* 31: 94), but corrected in an addendum to the bird report for 1961 in *WANHM*, as well as by Cohen (1963).

The only return from 102 Yellow Wagtails ringed in Wiltshire during 1965–2000 was one caught at Warminster on 17 August 1975 and retrapped at Weymouth (Dorset) 18 days later. Earlier, however, one ringed at Coate Water in September 1962 was found dead near Santander (Spain) in the following April. There were also two incoming recoveries: one ringed at Radipole (Dorset) on 6 September 1973 was trapped in a roost at Lacock nearly two years later, on 7 August 1975 – having presumably been to West Africa and back twice in the meantime – and, in contrast, another ringed in Warwickshire on 7 September 1979 was found dead near Westbury only 24 days later, on 1 October.

(See also page 725.)

MVJ

Grey Wagtail

Motacilla cinerea

Common resident, perhaps also some passage/ winter from north Britain

Of the three wagtail species that breed in Wiltshire, this is the most associated with water, particularly fast-flowing streams and rivers. The lithe Grey Wagtail's preference for rippling shallows greatly influences its British range, and it is most numerous in the uplands of the north and west. The numbers breeding in Great Britain have been put at 34,400 to 41,300 pairs (*APEP*), a small fraction of the 622,000 to 898,000 pairs estimated for Europe, excluding Russia (*EBCC Atlas*).

The species breeds in the Atlantic Islands, northwest Africa and across southern Europe north to parts of Fenno-Scandia. After a vast gap in much of the eastern half of Europe east of the Carpathians, it reappears from the Urals across Asia to Kamchatka and Japan, and from Turkey and the Caucasus to Iran. Some southern and western populations are resident, others wholly or partially migratory, many wintering well south of the summer range in central Africa, Arabia, the Indian subcontinent and southeast Asia.

In Great Britain, Grey Wagtails were largely restricted to Scotland and northern England in the 1830s. Then, however, there followed a gradual expansion – perhaps aided by the spread of such artificial habitats as millstreams and canal locks – into Wales and southwest England by the end of the 19th century, although it was not until the 1950s that they started to nest regularly in eastern and southern England (*1875–1900 Atlas*).

Smith (1887) thought the Grey Wagtail 'By no means common' in Wiltshire, but 'generally, though sparingly dispersed, and to be found in most localities'; he also added that Wiltshire was 'one of the few South-Western Counties enumerated where it has been known to breed'. A little earlier, for the Marlborough district alone, im Thurn (1870) noted that this species 'Has occasionally, but very rarely, been seen during the winter months, especially near the Kennet, but only one authentic instance of their breeding with us is recorded. A nest containing young birds was found on June 16th, 1867'; 25 years later, Meyrick (1895) considered this 'A resident species, not uncommon along the river' there and that it had probably nested again in May 1893. Peirson (1919) regarded it as a common resident on the river at Marlborough and noted that there were by then 'apparently… three records of the nest in this district'.

For the county as a whole, the inaugural bird report for 1929 in *WANHM* noted that the Grey Wagtail was 'A fairly common resident, increasing its numbers and range as

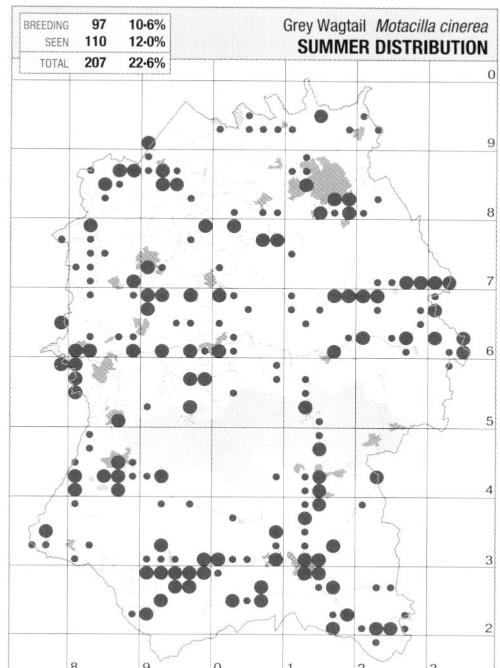

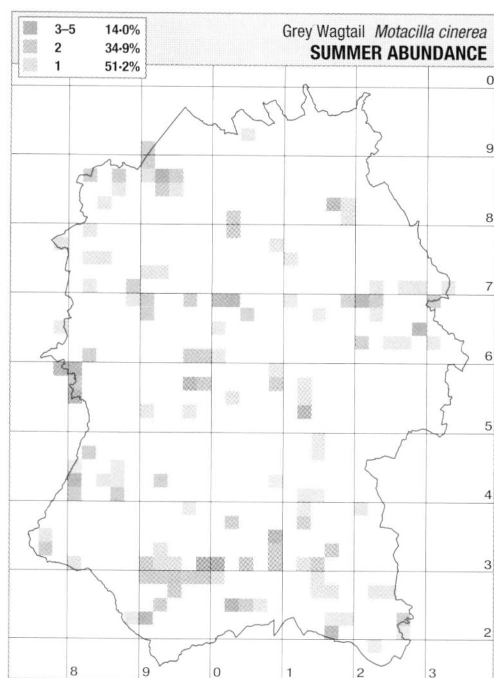

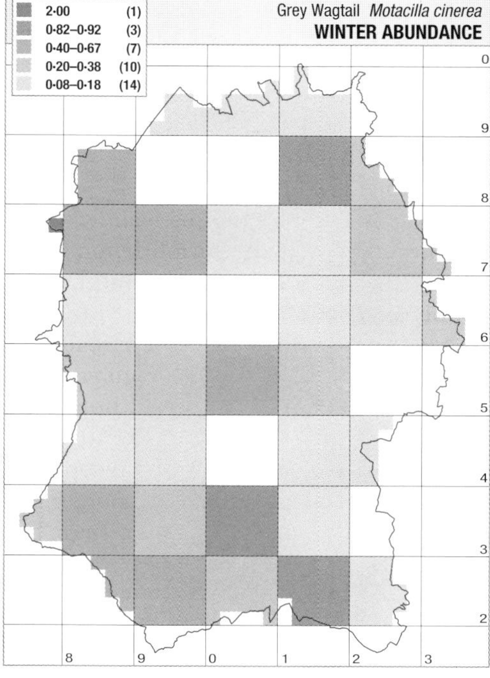

a breeding species', and 30 years later Peirson (1959) found it 'well distributed and breeding not uncommonly, particularly where bridges and weirs cross rivers or mill-streams'. Buxton (1981) echoed the 1929 view and stated 'in this century [the 20th] the number of breeding pairs increased until the severe winter of 1962/63 when there was a catastrophic decrease... but recovery was relatively rapid and numbers had risen to pre-1962 levels by 1969'; he estimated that the county's breeding population in 1978 was roughly 150 pairs. This growth in range and numbers in Wiltshire during the late 19th and early 20th centuries neatly echoes the national pattern of spread into the English midlands and south over this time.

A 1971 survey of Grey Wagtails along all the county's major rivers located 129 pairs, of which 76 were proved to have bred (Tyler & Tyler 1972); muddy, deep and slow-flowing rivers (*eg* Thames, Ray, and Cole) had few pairs in contrast to the faster-flowing streams on chalk (*eg* Wylye) and limestone (By Brook). Comparing the 1971 results with the summer map for 1995–2000 shows that, three decades later, neither the Wylye nor the By Brook was as favoured. A slight contraction in range was also indicated by *1968–72 Atlas*'s having shown breeding in 31 of Wiltshire's 33 core 10-km squares, whereas this total had fallen slightly to 26 in both the *1988–91 Atlas* and WOS summer survey.

With the species recorded as breeding in 97 tetrads and seen in a further 110, it is likely that Wiltshire's population was roughly 300 to 500 pairs at the end of the 1990s. Although direct comparison with 1971 is not possible, this might suggest that the infilling of range and numbers had continued to some extent over the intervening 25 years. This contrasts, however, with a marked decline nationally, as monitored by WBS, during the latter part of the 1970s, although there has been an increase since the end of the 1990s (*BBWC*).

Many adult and juvenile Grey Wagtails from Scotland, northern England and Wales move to southern England in winter, and some are known to move still farther south to France and Iberia. There is also evidence of passage from Fenno-Scandia and the adjacent Continent: a few of these may winter in Great Britain (*Migration Atlas*). Wiltshire usually has a significant increase in records in September and October, which doubtless reflect the movements of Grey Wagtails from upland Great Britain and, perhaps, also from abroad. It seems likely that many of those wintering in the county have not been raised locally. Some evidence of post-breeding dispersal was provided by the trapping and ringing of no fewer than 21 individuals at Calne STW on 26–27 August 2000 (*Hobby*). Although 353 Grey Wagtails were ringed in Wiltshire during 1965–2000, none has been reported subsequently. But one ringed in Gloucestershire on 5 August 1976 was recovered at Downton on 22 May 1977, and another ringed in Powys on 23 April 1990 was trapped and released at Warminster on 3 February 1991.

Grey Wagtails are more widespread in the county outside the breeding season, when they appear in and even occupy such varied habitats as farmyards, watercress beds, sewage works and the vicinity of buildings in urban areas: their presence at this time in Swindon is well illustrated by the winter map. In general, the winter map also demonstrates an expected pattern, the gaps coinciding with woodland and upland areas that lack damp habitats. Fewer of the 33 core 10-km squares were found to be occupied during the winter survey than in the *1981–84 Winter Atlas* – the total fell from 31 to 27 – but this may simply reflect the different methodologies used. Extrapolation from the timed winter counts gave a figure of 230 individuals, a number comparable to the timed summer counts, and the winter total is suggested to be 500 to 750 individuals.

PEC & IJF-L

Sponsored by Bill & Rowena Quantrill

Pied Wagtail

Motacilla alba

Common resident, passage and winter visitor,
Continental race scarce passage

Black-and-white plumage, constantly bobbing tails and bounding flight make Pied Wagtails easily recognisable. They are very adaptable, both in their choice of breeding and roosting sites and in their ability to find invertebrate food in a variety of rural and urban habitats throughout the year. They nest usually in recesses in stone walls or rock faces, in nooks formed by ivy or other climbers, in thatched roofs, even in well-vegetated banks, also on ledges inside outbuildings, in open nestboxes and in old nests of other birds. In winter, Pied

Wagtails roost communally, finding warmth and protection by gathering in large numbers on urban buildings or trees in car parks (often at supermarkets), and in a range of natural sites; roosts in rushes and reedbeds are usually abandoned when the vegetation dies down.

The Pied Wagtail is usually regarded as just one subspecies, *yarrellii*, in a complex of black-and-white wagtails represented by more than a dozen different races from southeast Greenland, Iceland and western Europe right across Eurasia to western Alaska, south to Morocco, Asia Minor, Iran, the Himalayas and the Indo-Chinese countries, and replaced by allied species in Africa and India. It nests only in Great Britain, Ireland and, with varying degrees of regularity, in adjacent coastal areas of northern France, Belgium, the Netherlands and Denmark. The nominate race, *alba* – known as the 'White Wagtail' – breeds in almost all the rest of the European range, including Iceland, and is a regular, if often overlooked, passage migrant through Britain and Ireland. Nominate *alba* is also a rare or irregular breeder in Great Britain, where it sometimes hybridises with *yarrellii* (*eg RBBP* 2002); some authors (*eg* Sangster *et al* 1998) believe that the two forms should be treated as separate species. The combined breeding population of both of them in Europe, excluding Russia, has been estimated at 8·0 to 11 million pairs (*EBCC Atlas*).

North, central and east European White Wagtails are migratory, some wintering within the range of southernmost breeders, others extending beyond, into both northern and sub-Saharan Africa; northern Asiatic and Alaskan populations similarly move down to southern Asia. Pied Wagtails are at least partial migrants and, in broad terms, some from northern parts of Great Britain winter from southern England to western France and the Atlantic coast of Spain, while those from southern England do so in Portugal and southern Spain (*Migration Atlas*). Two inward recoveries of Pied Wagtails ringed in northern England, and the three foreign recoveries of the 2305 Pied Wagtails ringed in Wiltshire during 1965–2000 – all five found in the autumn or winter after the late summer or autumn in which they were ringed – help to illustrate these distributions. Of the two inward recoveries, one ringed in Northumberland in August 1984 was found in Swindon in October and, more than 50 years earlier, one ringed in Cumbria in July 1928 had been recovered in Trowbridge the following February. Of the three foreign recoveries, one marked at Calne in October 1978 and a female at Idminston in September 1962 were recorded in France in the following January and December respectively; the third, ringed at Christian Malford in August 1966, was found dead in Portugal that November.

The *1981–84 Winter Atlas* showed Pied Wagtails to be most numerous in winter in the southern third of Great Britain and to be absent then from upland areas of northern England and Scotland. They are more widespread in summer, then being found almost anywhere, but most abundantly in Wales, northern England and eastern Scotland – a picture little changed for over a century (*1875–1900 Atlas*). British breeding numbers have been estimated at 255,000 to 330,000 territories (*APEP*). National survey data show a sharp increase during 1965–75, since when the population has remained high but fluctuating (*BBWC*).

In Wiltshire, Smith (1887) stated that 'No one can be ignorant of this very common bird' and its widespread familiarity was reflected in its local names of 'dishwasher', 'water wagtail' and 'scullery maids' (Jones & Dillon 1987). While Peirson (1959) agreed with Smith that Pied Wagtails were common, he qualified this by adding 'except in some north-west parts of the county'. Buxton (1981) noted 'It is less common on higher more exposed downland which is largely deserted in winter'. Breeding was established in all 33 of Wiltshire's core 10-km squares by the *1968–72 Atlas* and by the summer tetrad survey during 1995–2000, and in 32 by the *1988–91 Atlas*. The pattern of the summer distribution map is influenced by the availability of nest-sites, the blank tetrads indicating those where there are few, if any: these include parts of SPTA where there are no buildings and where sightings in the

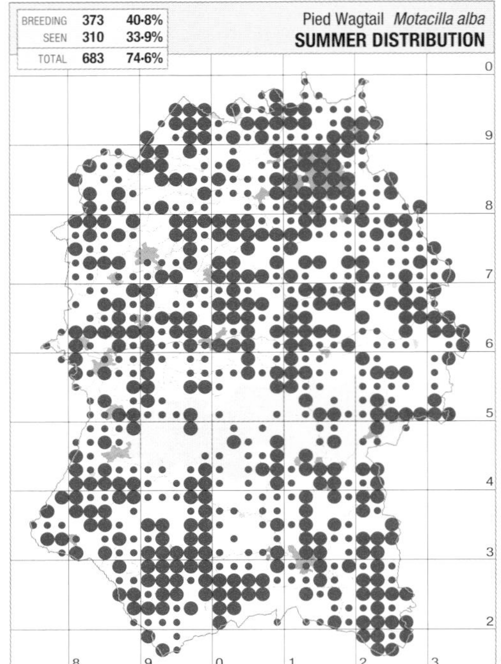

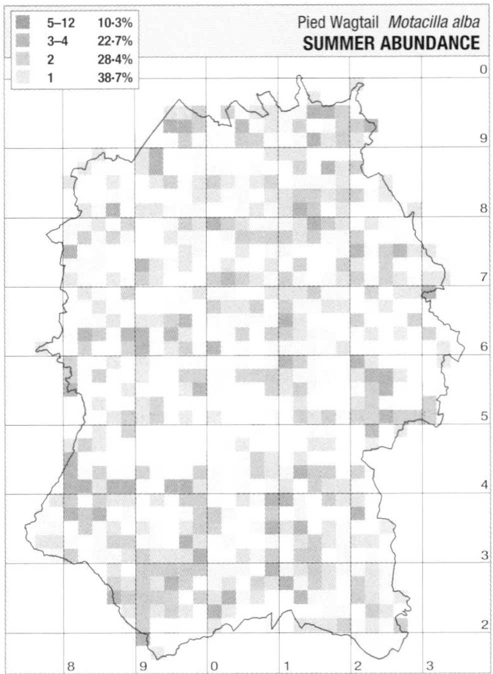

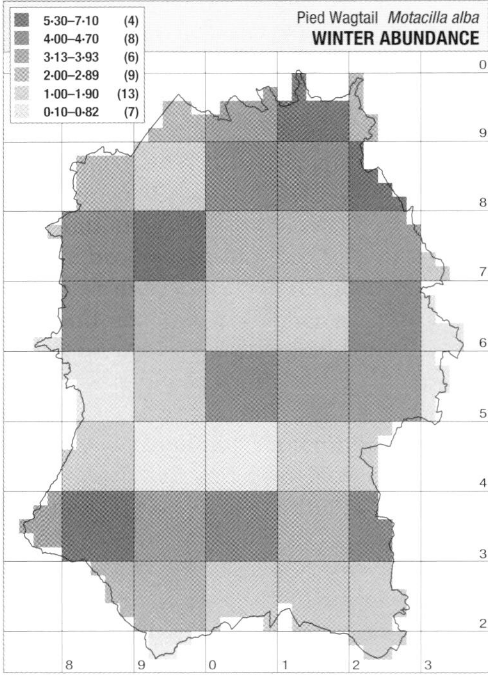

breeding season are likely to have involved adults searching for food. But a single farm building in a remote area that has a suitable nest-site, perhaps under the roof or in a hole in a wall, is likely to support a breeding pair. The summer abundance map accordingly shows a seemingly rather random distribution: although there is evidence of higher concentrations along some river valleys, where an abundance of insects associated with livestock might be expected, this is not uniform across the county, and other potentially suitable places had only low densities. The areas around Longleat and Stourhead, near Melksham and around Collingbourne Ducis all support high numbers, despite the rather different habitats in each, while the upper Nadder is one of the few parts with continuous high densities. Nearly 1500 Pied Wagtails were counted on timed visits, but extrapolation from the results of BBS surveys in Wiltshire and adjacent areas suggests the county total lies in the region of 5050–7580 pairs.

Numbers of Pied Wagtails in Wiltshire are swollen from late September as migration gets under way, and small flocks may be seen feeding in particularly favourable localities. In 1990 there was a roost of 100 at CWP in July and August, but most roosts are not

Table 106. Pied Wagtails *Motacilla alba* in Wiltshire: counts at major roosts 1990/91–1999/00

	90/91	91/92	92/93	93/94	94/95	95/96	96/97	97/98	98/99	99/00
CWP	1000	200	1000	100	200	300	250	300	600	–
Swindon town centre	400	500	–	–	–	–	–	–	200	300
Devizes	220	200	300	480	700	500	400	–	–	–
Trowbridge	–	–	300	–	–	–	–	100	–	–

occupied until October, reaching a peak in December and January, and dispersing by mid March. Urban roosts are not necessarily in the same place in successive winters, even if the previous year's site appears to have remained unchanged.

Devizes, for example, has been an established winter roost area for at least half a century. It was first mentioned in the bird report in *WANHM* in 1952, when about 70 were noted as roosting in clematis over an archway at Police HQ, but from at least October 1965 the roost was in reedmace clogging one of the Kennet & Avon Canal pounds: numbers recorded varied from 100 in October–November 1968 to 1000 in November 1969. In 1971, after the reedmace had been cleared, a smaller roost of about 100 appeared on window sills above busy Maryport Street in the centre of the town and then a similar number the following winter. In 1973, however, although the buildings had not changed, the roost moved again, this time to three plane trees in the Market Place and the roost was regular there until 1989 – though not every year as the trees were periodically pollarded and then gave no support for a winter or two. (In winter 1979/80, 37 were counted going into the illuminated Christmas tree in the Market Place.) The major part of the roost had by 1991 moved to two hornbeams in Albion Place/Sidmouth Street, an area surrounded on three sides by tall buildings, and they continued to occupy that site until 1997/98, but not so obviously or in such numbers thereafter. Until the plane trees in the Market Place were felled in 2001/02, some continued to use those, notably in 1994/95, when there were 300 in January and March but 700 on 8 February, and in 1995/96, 500 in mid December. Recorded numbers at Devizes always varied from several tens to several hundreds, but were doubtless influenced by the dates on which any counts were made (often there is no record) and perhaps also by weather conditions. Roost sizes in Devizes in the 1990s were generally smaller than in the 1970s and 1980s. Some time about the turn of the millennium the main roost moved to the Safeway's car park.

Other roosts have been located in recent years in reedbeds at Corsham and CWP, at a factory in Swindon, in St George's Mall in Salisbury, and on supermarket buildings in Trowbridge and Warminster. In the 1990s, four sites held roosts of 100 or more in at least two winters (table 106), while further three-figure roosts were counted at Salisbury in 1992/93 (200); at Marlborough (130), Chippenham (100) and Warminster (500) in 1995/96; at Swindon STW (100) in 1997/98; at Malmesbury (100) in 1998/99; and at Princess Margaret Hospital, Swindon (100+) in September 2000.

The *1981–84 Winter Atlas* found Pied Wagtails throughout Wiltshire, a distribution that the winter map for 1998–2000 shows to have remained unchanged. Numbers appear to be generally higher in the north of the county, and extrapolation from the survey data produced just over 2500, approaching twice the number recorded during summer and suggesting a winter total of 13,100 to 19,600 individuals.

White Wagtails of the nominate race *alba* occur regularly on both spring and autumn passage through Great Britain, and ringing results indicate that many of these originate from Iceland. Spring passage begins in mid March and reaches a peak in April, but autumn migration is less easily detected until separation of the races becomes easier after the post-juvenile moult has been completed. Studies in Hertfordshire in 1961 recorded passage from the end of July until mid October, with a peak in early September, and in Scilly White Wagtails are common from late August to mid September (*Migration Atlas*). Wagtails showing the characters of the nominate race are now identified annually in Wiltshire, the majority at Coate Water and CWP (though this almost certainly reflects observer coverage). During 1990–2000 they were recorded in every spring, mostly in April, but with extreme dates of 8 March and 16 May; flocks of 15 and 20 in 1993 and of 13 and 23 in 1998 were identified at CWP. Autumn migrants are almost certainly overlooked and were recorded in only four years, all between 11 September and 28 October, including 'at least six' with 80 Pied Wagtails at Collingbourne Ducis on the first of those dates in 2000 (*Hobby*).

PEC & SBE

Sponsored by the Cowen family

Waxwing

Bombycilla garrulus

Vagrant during irregular eruptions from northeast Europe into eastern Britain

Waxwings have a nearly circumpolar breeding range from northeast Europe eastward to northwest America, wintering south to central Europe and similar latitudes elsewhere. Excluding Russia, the European breeding population is estimated at between 33,000 and 89,000 pairs, the majority in Finland (*EBCC Atlas*). They rely heavily on berries in autumn and winter, so that failures in the rowan berry crops in northern Europe, coinciding with population peaks after successful breeding seasons, can prompt invasions of eastern Britain by several thousands (*eg* Cornwallis 1961, Cornwallis & Townsend 1968). These extend farther west and south in exceptional years, although relatively few ever reach Wiltshire (but see page 726). Limited ringing data show that Waxwings may disperse widely after arrival in Britain, although the precise origins of the populations involved in these irruptions are unclear (*Migration Atlas*).

In the 19th century, Waxwings were discovered in Wiltshire in 1820, 1850 ('many... killed at Potterne'), 1857, 'about 1860', and 1864/65 (Smith 1887). Two, one of which was shot, were then recorded at Downton in December 1903 (*WANHM*), another was shot at Swindon on 31 December 1913 (*BB* 7: 264), and singletons were recorded at Braydon Wood in 1913 and Marlborough in February 1914 (Peirson 1919). The only report between the 1914–18 and 1939–45 Wars came from Savernake in 1926 (number not specified), and then no more were recorded until 1946, when three appeared at Marlborough on 17 December (*WANHM*). One or two were found at each of Bulford Camp, Deptford and Marlborough in 1947, one at Woodford on the early date of 28 September 1949 and, after a hard frost, a party of about 24 feeding on fallen berries near the Trowbridge-Devizes road on 10 February 1953; then came a total of 16 records involving 21 birds in seven of the winters from 1957/58 to 1973/74, mostly in 1965/66 when there were ten records of 14 birds, the latest in Savernake on 30 April (all *WAHNM*).

In the last quarter of the 20th century, Waxwings were found in the winters of 1984/85 (two birds), 1986/87 (three), 1988/89 (five) and 1990/91 (six). Next, after a four-year gap, ten records in February and March 1996 involved a total of 18 birds, including four at Woodborough Churchyard and three each at Ramsbury and Chippenham, two of the last staying until 2 April; these formed a (very small) part of a large irruption into Great Britain during 1995/96, which reached a peak in February when 'up to 10,000' were recorded (*Birding World* 9: 467). Lastly, one was seen at Great Bedwyn on 21 November 1999. Wiltshire Waxwings have been noted feeding on berries of cotoneaster, pyracantha and spindle, as well as on crab apples and rotten larger apples.

Irruptions appear to have occurred with increasing frequency in recent decades (*Migration Atlas*), and the grand total of all the Waxwings reported in the county up to 2000 was greatly surpassed in winter 2004/05 (see page 726).

RT

Dipper

Cinclus cinclus

Local resident, some autumn dispersal, perhaps winter visitor from north Britain

Dippers are remarkable passerines, living along fast-flowing upland waterways and on slower lowland rivers broken by weirs, where they hunt their largely invertebrate prey by diving, swimming (both on and below the surface) and walking on the bottom. Their sober plumage helps them to blend into the background and often it is only their penetrating calls that draw attention to their presence. They nest by water, in such natural sites as crevices in rock faces and among tree roots, or in such man-made substitutes as ledges and cavities under bridges.

The Dipper's range stretches from northwest Africa and western Europe across central Asia to central China. The population of Europe, excluding Russia, has been estimated at 151,000 to 231,000 pairs (*EBCC Atlas*), of which Great Britain's share is 6350 to 19,100 (*APEP*). British Dippers are most numerous in Scotland, Wales, and in northern and southwest England (*1988–91 Atlas*), and, except for some altitudinal movements, are sedentary. Records outside the normal breeding range in Great Britain appear mainly to involve birds from Fenno-Scandia, but some are suspected to be from the more adjacent Continent (*Migration Atlas*). The *1988–91 Atlas* demonstrated losses in range since the *1968–72 Atlas*, but WBS data indicate a fluctuating population with no long-term trend apparent over the last 30 years – though, susceptible to acidity and other water pollution, this species warrants careful monitoring (*BBWC*).

The first three documented records of Dippers in Wiltshire were at Mere in 1876 (shot on 9 November); at Castle Combe before 1887, though undated (Smith 1887); and at Poulton in 1889 (Halliday & Randolph 1955). The species bred at Castle Combe from 1897 (*WANHM*) and at Lacock in 1913 (Jourdain 1914), and Hony (1915a) wrote that it was frequently reported in winter. Peirson (1959) stated that 'From about 1910 onwards it extended its breeding range down the west of the county and across the south to the Salisbury Avon in the south-east. A maximum was reached about 1935 or 1940. Since then… a marked regression with perhaps a minimum about 1950 and a slight increase in the last few years'. The Wiltshire bird reports for 1929–34 and 1936 in *WANHM* suggested that its range was then noticeably increasing in the river valleys around Salisbury, but there were many fewer records during the late 1940s. In 1952 the oologist Major WM

Congreve was quoted in *WANHM* as having stated that it was 'absent from an area near Salisbury where seven pairs were known up to 1950', but it was still clearly more widespread in the 1950s than in subsequent decades: for example, no fewer than five nests were located by a single observer on the Nadder in 1954. In the 1960s most reports of breeding published in *WANHM* were from the By Brook area, though occasional comments shed some light on its decline elsewhere: for example, in 1963 it was stated to have disappeared from the Ebble between Stratford Tony and Bishopstone.

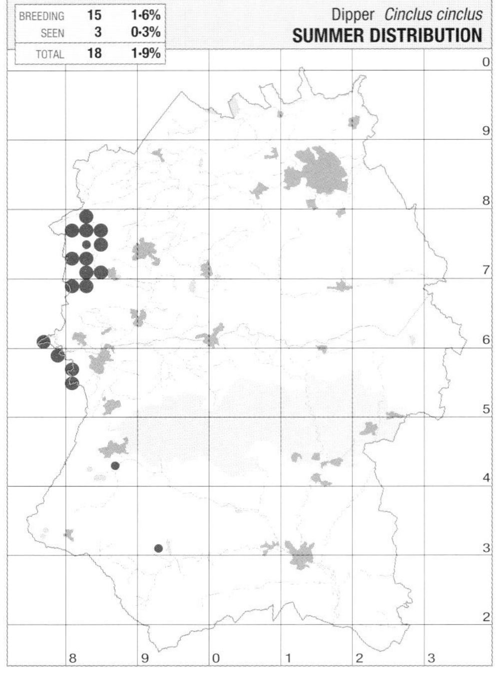

Buxton (1981), writing of the period up to 1979, noted that 'During the last ten years breeding has taken place on the By Brook (up to four pairs), Cole (one pair), Fonthill Lake (one pair), Wylye (two pairs), Ebble (one pair), Nadder (one pair), Biss Brook (one pair) and near Chippenham (one pair)'. In the 1980s – for which Palmer (1991) estimated an annual total of no more than 15 pairs – the most regular nesting sites were still along the By Brook from Box to Castle Combe and along the Wylye south of Warminster, but by then also along the Frome at Tellisford. Outside these main areas, a pair bred at Malmesbury in 1990 (*Hobby*).

Dippers remain rare residents in the county. Sightings since 1991 away from the breeding areas, most outwith the nesting season, have included singletons on the Wylye at Fisherton de la Mere in January and February 1992 (two there on 5 March), on the Nadder at Dinton Mill on 6 February that year and at Bradford-on-Avon on 4 October; on the Kennet at Ramsbury on 25 October 1993; at Amesbury on 11 March 1997; and on a small brook in Chippenham on three dates in October and November 1998. In addition, single Dippers were seen at Fonthill Lake, a former breeding site, in May and August 1997 and on two days at the end of March 2000.

Comparison between the summer distribution map for 1995–2000 and relevant 10-km squares in the national atlases demonstrates the losses of breeding range during the last three decades of the 20th century. The *1968–72 Atlas* confirmed breeding in the valleys of the Wylye, Nadder and Ebble, but the *1988–91 Atlas* only in the first of those, where five pairs were still present between Longbridge Deverill and Norton Bavant in 1993 (*Hobby*).

The summer tetrad map shows that by 1995–2000 the species was confined to the extreme west of the county, especially in the southern Cotswold catchment area of the By Brook and the Frome. A survey by the Wiltshire Wildlife Trust of the By Brook involved a questionnaire to landowners in 1997 followed by fieldwork two years later (Grinsted & Lang 2000). The survey concluded that the catchment supported 'at least 12 pairs' and that the population was 'most at risk from water pollution through fertiliser run-off and sewage effluent'. These results, and the fact that evidence of breeding was established in 15 tetrads by the WOS summer survey, suggests that the population there in 1995–2000 lay in the region of 15 to 20 pairs. Nestboxes have been erected on suitable stretches of river that lack stone structures in the By Brook catchment to encourage expansion. (It should also be noted that Dippers have occasionally bred on rivers within the Gloucestershire part of CWP, but there appear to be no records from the adjacent stretches in Wiltshire.)

The long-term trend for this species in Wiltshire is one of range extension before the 1939–45 War – no presence for the county was shown in the *1875–1900 Atlas* – followed by a decrease that matched the national decline. Dippers were mapped in just four 10-km squares in the *1968–72 Atlas*, but this figure rose to 11 in the *1988–91 Atlas*, and they were still recorded in eight during 1995–2000, suggesting a partial resurgence. The species was also found in eight 10-km squares in the *1981–84 Winter Atlas*, and in only two in the winter tetrad survey, but the methodology used may have contributed to that low result. It is likely that, based on breeding numbers, the winter total lies in the range of 30–60 individuals.

The 21 Dippers ringed in Wiltshire during 1965–2000 had produced no recoveries by the end of that period.

PEC & SBE

Sponsored anonymously

Wren

Troglodytes troglodytes

Abundant resident, some dispersal or arrivals from north Britain in hard weather

Despite its unmistakable silhouette, the Wren would often go undetected were it not for its loud, penetrating song almost throughout the year. Its diminutive size and relatively long, thin bill enable it to forage for invertebrates, mainly insects and spiders, in holes and crevices inaccessible to other species that feed in undergrowth and on the ground.

The Wren has a vast if fragmented global range that includes much of Europe, extending into North Africa and the Middle East, and large swathes of Asia and North America (where, only one of several species of wrens, it is known as the Winter Wren because it is just a winter visitor to much of the eastern United States). The population of Europe, excluding Russia, has been put at 20 to 27 million pairs (*EBCC Atlas*), of which the significant British share has been estimated at 8·0 million (*APEP*). Wrens are virtually ubiquitous in Great Britain, and national survey data show that, after a rapid increase in the 1970s, the population has fluctuated in response to the severity or otherwise of winter weather (*BBWC*).

Wrens have long been known as common and familiar birds in Wiltshire (Smith 1887, Peirson 1959), as is testified by their having no fewer than eight local names, including 'jenny-pooper' and 'scutty' (Jones & Dillon 1987). Breeding was proved in every one of the county's 33 core and 15 part 10-km squares in both the *1968–72* and *1988–91 Atlases*. The summer distribution map for 1995–2000 shows that this status has not changed, breeding evidence having been obtained in every 10-km square and in nearly nine-tenths of all the 915 tetrads, a proportion exceeded only by Wood Pigeon, Chaffinch and Blackbird. The summer abundance map indicates lower numbers on the upland chalk of Salisbury Plain and the Marlborough Downs, and the highest densities in wooded areas, especially in the southwest, and in mixed habitats, including rural gardens. Three recent RSPB surveys illustrate these differences: the survey of SPTA in 2000 recorded a low density of 4·2 birds/km^2 – a total of 957 territories – on this grassland area (Stanbury *et al*

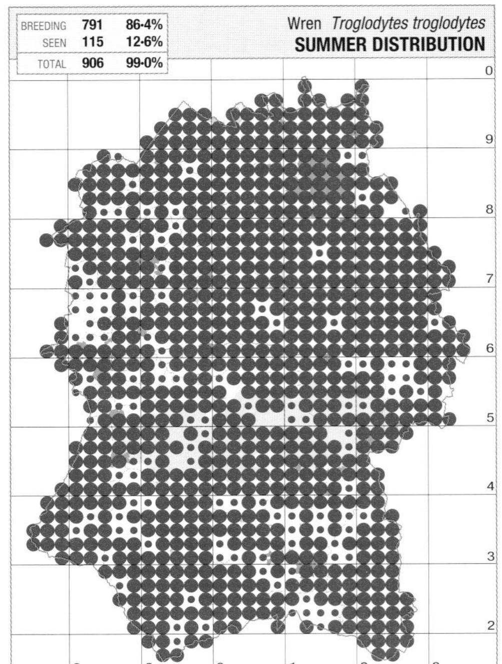

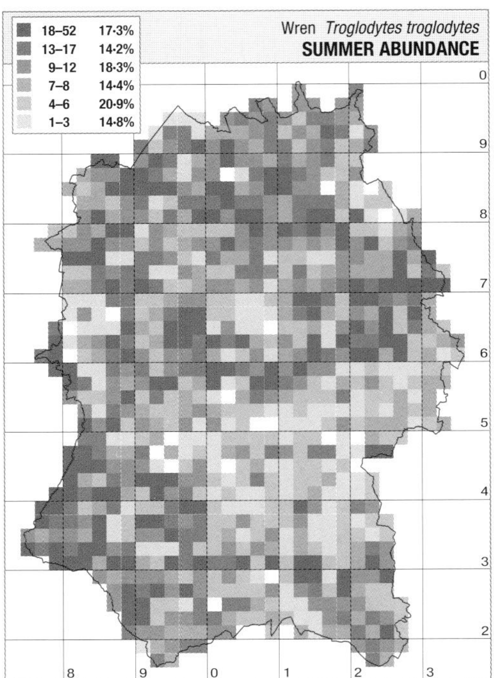

2000), whereas an earlier survey of a mainly Gloucestershire section of the Cotswolds in 1997 had found a much higher 24·2 birds/km^2 in rolling farmland with a mix of arable, grassland and broadleaved woods (Mustoe *et al* 1998); moreover, a repeat of the latter survey in 2002 showed that that density had more than doubled to 51·2 birds/km^2 (Dodd & Meadows 2003) after a series of mild winters. Based largely on these BBS surveys, the Wiltshire total is estimated as 56,500 to 94,000 pairs.

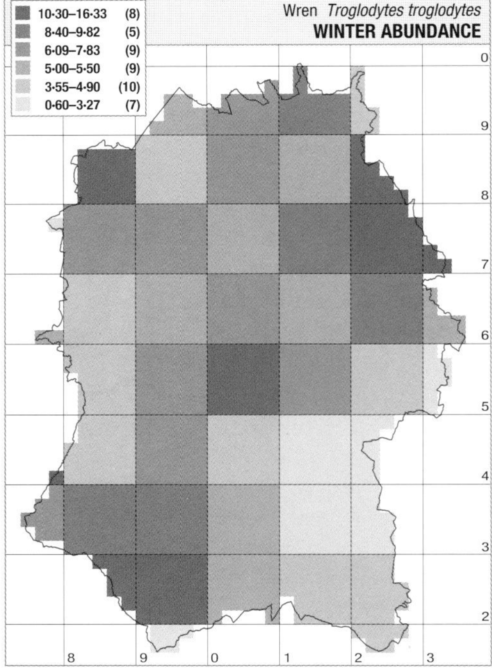

Wrens' preferred breeding habitats are broadleaved woodlands and the banks of watercourses, both with plenty of rough cover, while farmland hedgerows are a secondary habitat (Williamson 1969). Early nests are commonly built against the trunks of ivy and creeper-clad trees, in open sheds and in natural and man-made holes. Later nests are more often in thick vegetation, especially in bramble and bracken. Most are less than 2 m above the ground, but some up to about 5 m.

The small size of the territory of a pair of Wrens, and the frequency with which the male proclaims his ownership with bursts of song, make it easy to assess the numbers present in a given area. Loud alarm calls, especially when the adults are accompanied by recently fledged young, also help in the analysis. Partly because of the accuracy of the data thus accumulated from countrywide CBCs since 1962, it has been possible to calculate annual changes in national and Wiltshire populations over a long period. The striking similarity between the two sets of figures shows that local factors are relatively unimportant in determining the numbers. The overriding factor in the second half of the 20th century was poor survival in the severe winters of 1962/63, 1978/79, 1981/82, 1985/86 and 1995/96, as clearly shown by the figures for the CBCs at Sunnyhill Farm, Pewsey, during 1962–83 (Gillam 1984) and at Home Covert, Roundway, during 1981–96 (Gillam 1996).

The national CES decline of 34 per cent matched a 30 per cent decrease in the number caught in Clanger Wood in 1996 (*Hobby*). Provided, however, that the winter following a cold one was milder, numbers soon recovered – a recovery aided by the two broods of, usually, four or five (but up to eight) young that Wrens rear. This ability to make a quick recovery means that an estimate of the population's saturation point in any given area is not possible until the number of pairs has remained stable for two or three years after a severe winter. On this basis, given the cold winter at the start of the WOS tetrad survey period and the milder winters thereafter, and supported by the doubling of density recorded during BBS surveys of the Cotswolds between 1995 and 2000, it is likely that the Wiltshire total lies near the upper end of the estimated range – some 90,000 pairs. Many Wrens are individually territorial in winter, defending a feeding area with habitat preferences that are different from those in summer – though competition for winter territories may begin in July (*1988–91 Atlas*).

A small, warm-blooded animal such as the Wren has a large surface area in proportion to its size, and little capacity for storing food – so is particularly vulnerable when conditions prevent it from feeding. Although frost and very cold winds can be disastrous for Wrens, lying snow is less of a problem as there will usually be places in evergreen shrubs and dense vegetation that snow will not have penetrated and where food and shelter will be available. Communal winter roosts are also important for survival. In Wiltshire, up to 40 were counted at a roost in the thatch of a cottage at Kingston Deverill in January 1982; three or four roosted in each of 11 House Martin nests at Cholderton in 1993; and 28 entered a slot in a brick wall at Lockeridge on 8 February 1986 'during freezing conditions' (*Hobby*).

The *1981–84 Winter Atlas* and the winter tetrad survey both recorded Wrens in all of the county's 33 core and 15 part 10-km squares. The winter map shows a pattern similar to that of the summer abundance map, and the minor differences could be a result of the differing methodologies. The extrapolation of 5600 Wrens from the timed winter counts suggests a decline of 32 per cent compared with summer numbers, but this is likely to be an artefact of their greater conspicuousness during the breeding season. Based on the summer numbers, it is likely that Wiltshire's winter total is in the order of 75,000 to 150,000 individuals, perhaps more, though numbers will vary greatly in response to weather conditions.

As many as 4239 Wrens were ringed in Wiltshire during 1965–2000 – a high number that reflects the concentrated work of CES ringers – but the dozen or so recoveries have all been local. On the other hand, a nestling ringed in Sussex on 18 October 1972 was found dead at Baydon on 11 August 1973: the two places are 148 km apart. Most British Wrens are sedentary, but some do move distances of 50 km or more and, because few have been aged at the time of ringing (first-year plumage being indistinguishable from adult), it is uncertain whether these represent post-juvenile dispersal (*Migration Atlas*).

PAC & IJF-L

Sponsored by Geoff Skillen

Dunnock

Prunella modularis

Still common and widespread resident, though decreasing in Britain as a whole

Often called 'Hedge Sparrow', this slender-billed bird is not a sparrow but one of the mainly montane accentor family. With greyish head to breast and streaky-brown body, it is, as 'Dunnock' implies, dun-coloured and small. This is an innocuous ground-forager on small invertebrates and also, during August–April, seeds (Bishton 1986). Yet, in human terms, it is not the epitome of respectability that was suggested by Morris (1856): 'Unobtrusive, quiet and retiring, without being shy, humble and homely in its deportment and habits, sober and unpretending in its dress, while still neat and graceful, the dunnock exhibits a pattern which many of a higher grade might imitate, with advantage to themselves and benefit to others through an improved example'.

The last 20 words were doubtless written with his parishioners in mind, but the social and sexual lives of Dunnocks are the most complicated of any British bird. Males and females both defend often overlapping territories against their own sex. Although some are monogamously paired, females are more commonly polyandrous, especially where alpha and subordinate males share a territory, but males are also regularly polygynous. Occasionally, two or three males may share two to four females (polygynandry) (Birkhead 1981, Snow & Snow 1982, Burke *et al* 1989, especially Davies 1992). If a male feeds a neighbouring female and her young at the nest, this can be followed by 'wife-swapping' between first and second broods; sometimes, too, one male is dominant over a group and exercises a form of *droit du seigneur* (IJ Ferguson-Lees). Females are low in the hierarchy and, in hard weather, may be forced to wander away in search of food, so perhaps suffering higher mortality. All this background needs to be understood in any assessment of numbers.

The Wiltshire maps show a widespread summer distribution, with some obvious gaps in the open expanses of Salisbury Plain, but summer and winter abundance are both uneven. This is partly because the essential habitat – low dense cover – is common in some rural and suburban garden areas, woodland edges and clearings, railway cuttings and old hedgerows, but far less so in 'tidy' places, let alone farming monocultures and other large open areas. The favoured breeding sites are brambles, shrubberies, hedges, gorse, thorn bushes and tangles of nettles and dead sticks, though nests may also be built in heather, brassicas and even in the sides of strawstacks.

Whether the variations in abundance shown are really true is another matter. Dunnocks are heard more than seen. Their shrill *tseek* calls and short, high, squeaky warblings are distinctive and they sing through much of the year, but the output varies greatly with population pressure, breeding state, and weather. It is strongest on fine early mornings in January–May, when it may be regularly repeated, but tends to fall away thereafter

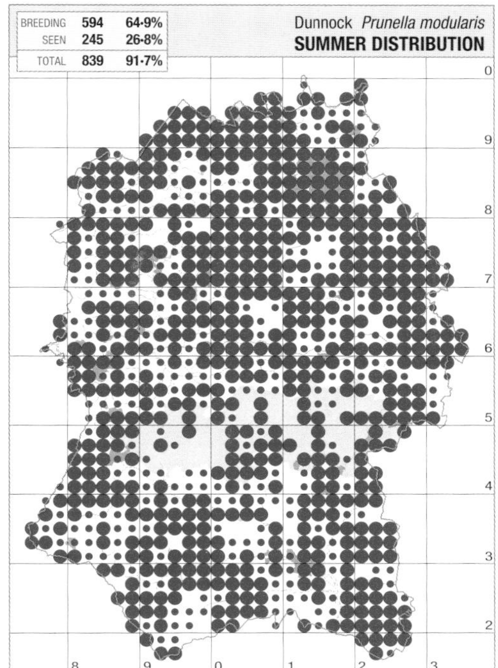

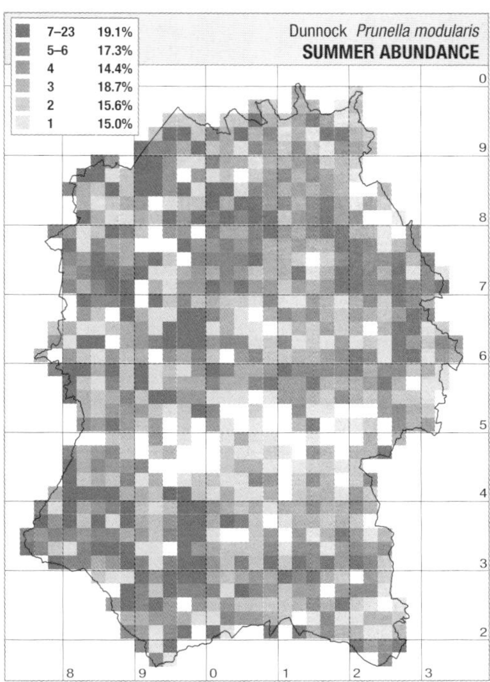

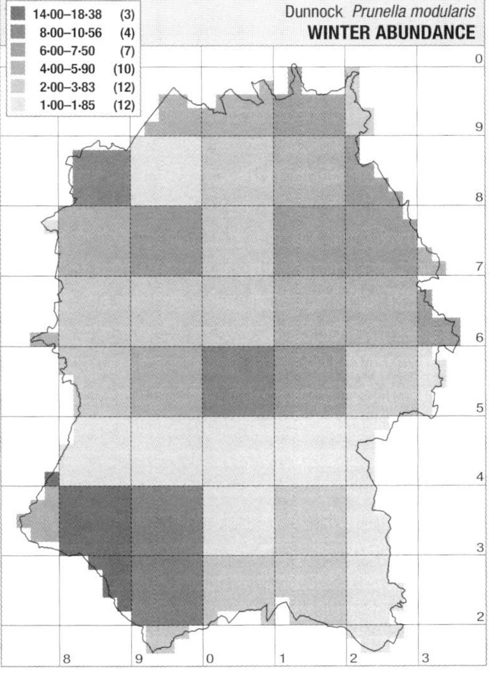

and, as an isolated phrase, is more easily missed. Subordinate males and, rarely, females also sing. A 2-hour transect close to village gardens or farmland scrub may yield 20–30 (mostly heard) in January–May but often fewer than ten later in the summer or earlier in the winter. This is an extraordinarily difficult species to assess by single transects and, not least because of its social set-up, irregularity of song and unobtrusiveness, any such casual count is bound to be very incomplete. The highest Wiltshire counts of Dunnocks must be, more than for most other birds, serious underestimates. Timed counts recorded just 3650 while data from BBS surveys suggest the county population lies between 23,500 and 49,300 'pairs'. The most recent estimate is for 2·1 million territories in Great Britain (*APEP*), which, on a proportional basis, would suggest 30,000 in Wiltshire, or an average 33 per tetrad. But that may still be too low here, for numbers are at their highest in south and east England, and the Wiltshire total perhaps lies near the upper end of the range suggested. Winter numbers recorded by WOS surveys were only marginally higher than during summer, and even the upper limit of the calculated winter total of 28,600 to 60,100 individuals is likely to be a minimum value.

All Wiltshire lists from Smith (1887) to Palmer (1991) simply stated Dunnocks to be 'common' or 'very common'. They were found in all 33 of Wiltshire's core 10-km squares in each of the three national atlases, and in both the summer and winter surveys during 1995–2000. But there was a marked national decrease from the mid 1970s to the late 1980s and, although numbers have since remained stable, that meant a decline of 46 per cent during the last quarter of the 20th century, although the reasons are unknown (*BBWC*). Yet this remains one of Great Britain's commonest birds in rural scrub and in suburban or village gardens where one hectare may hold five or more – Davies (1992) studied 60–80 in 16 ha in Cambridge University Botanic Garden. In contrast, Stanbury *et al* (2000) put the SPTA population at only 297, with a density of just one bird/km^2, but both summer maps show Salisbury Plain as a poor area for this species.

Apart from isolated populations in Asia Minor across to northern Iran, the Dunnock breeds only in Europe east to the Urals; it is no more than a winter visitor to southern parts of many Mediterranean countries and is absent from Iceland and much of Ukraine and southern Russia. The population of Europe, excluding Russia, has been put at 9·5 to 13 million 'pairs' (*EBCC Atlas*), but over much of its range the species is far less common than in England and much of Ireland, occurring chiefly in montane and coniferous scrub. The only other countries where Dunnocks are birds of gardens or lowland farmland are Belgium, the Netherlands and north Germany.

North and east European populations migrate south for the winter, some reaching Mediterranean islands and north Africa, but British Dunnocks are sedentary, most spending their whole lives within a radius of 0·1–1 km (Davies 1986). Although 3917 were ringed in Wiltshire during 1965–2000, all recoveries have been local and only one individual had moved more than 10 km. Nevertheless, small increases in mid October do indicate some movements through the county. Moreover, east coast ringing stations provide evidence of autumn movements of British-bred Dunnocks, and also noticeable immigration of birds of the Continental race in both spring and autumn – in conditions favourable to arrivals of migrants of Fenno-Scandian origin (*Migration Atlas*).

Dunnocks are one of the three commonest hosts for the Cuckoo (Glue & Morgan 1972), whose British distribution depends largely on them wherever Meadow Pipits and Reed Warblers are absent. Nests with a Cuckoo egg, or adults feeding a young Cuckoo, have been a bonus in some tetrads: two breeding category records for the price of one!

IJF-L

Sponsored by James Ferguson-Lees

Robin

Erithacus rubecula

Abundant resident/partial migrant, also winter visitor from Fenno-Scandia

The Robin is probably the most familiar and popular of all British birds. Noted in the historical record since about the year 530 (Fisher 1966) and well known in England in at least Chaucer's time (Gurney 1921), it adorns our Christmas cards and was chosen as our national bird. Although originally a broadleaved woodland species, it has become adapted to nearly all habitats except treeless moorland, downland and fens. Gardens have

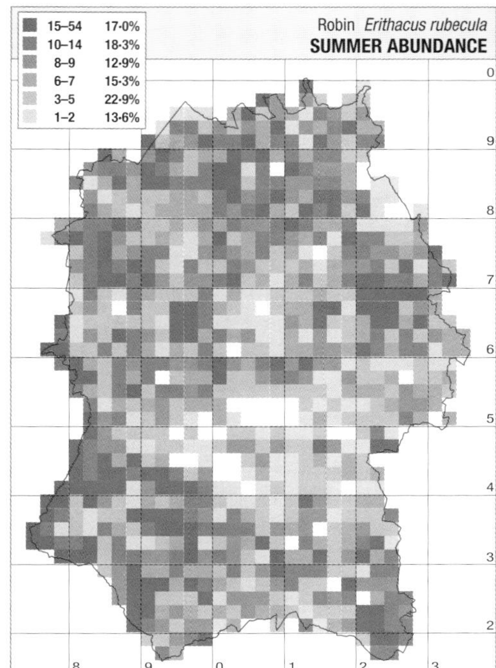

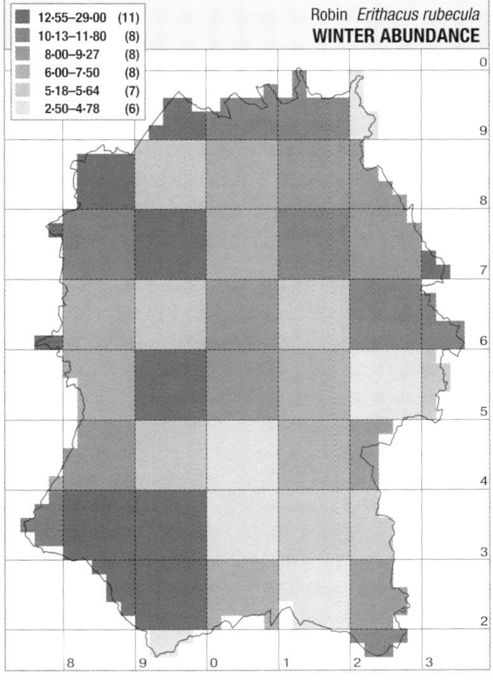

become welcome places where Robins are particularly easy to observe at winter feeding stations, taking food not only from the ground and bird-tables but also, in recent years, from hanging baskets. They are quick to exploit soil newly exposed by gardeners, though their confiding nature and choice of nest-sites near human habitation make the young prone to predation by cats.

With the exception of northernmost Fenno-Scandia and Russia, and the open lowlands north of the Black and Caspian Seas, Robins breed throughout most of Europe, also east of the Urals in western Siberia, in parts of the Caucasus and Asia Minor, in North Africa and on some Atlantic Islands, but they desert the whole northeastern half of Europe in autumn to winter in the west and around the Mediterranean. The breeding population of Europe, excluding Russia, has been estimated at 32 to 50 million pairs (*EBCC Atlas*). In Great Britain, the *1988–91 Atlas* showed Robins to be absent only from most of Shetland and some parts of Orkney and the Scottish Highlands.

The Robin was recorded as breeding in every one of Wiltshire's 33 core and 15 part 10-km squares by both the *1968–72* and *1988–91 Atlases*, and this continues to be the position in the summer distribution map for 1995–2000. The abundance map shows the highest densities to be in tetrads containing broadleaved woodland and the lowest on the open grassland of SPTA, where the species is absent from the Impact Area of SPTA (Centre).

Robins have small breeding territories, which the males strongly defend, mainly by song but also by physical attack on neighbours if the competition for space is great. Although both adults become more secretive during the breeding season, the frequency of song and, later, alarm calls in the vicinity of the nest make easy the assessment by CBC methods of the number of pairs in a given area. On farmland, the mean density of Robins can reach 33 males/km^2 and in woodland it is often twice as high (*1988–91 Atlas*). In broadleaved woodland, the optimum habitat, this is the commonest of the true singing passerines: CBC at Biss Wood indicated a density of 128 pairs/km^2 (calculated from the years 1995–2000 in Green 2000). In the mixed woodland of Home Covert, Roundway, territories are noticeably scarce in the coniferous parts but frequent enough in the broadleaved and garden areas to give a combined density of 94 pairs/km^2 (calculated from the years 1991–1996 in Gillam 1996).

Thick vegetation is important to Robins, though it is not clear exactly how they benefit (Hoeltzel 1989). They occur on farmland where there are hedgerows, especially where these form both boundaries of grassy or deep, sunken lanes. Secluded banks are the prime sites for nests, but gardens with the necessary cover and, occasionally, open-fronted nest-boxes are also acceptable. Typical nests are in banks, close to or on the ground, but in other sites – for example buildings, straw ricks and walls – they may be up to 3 m above ground.

Calculations based on BBS densities in Wiltshire and adjacent regions suggest that the county total could be as high as 116,000 territories; but these same BBS data in combination with WOS tetrad counts suggest that it may perhaps be as low as 55,400. These upper and lower limits represent an equitable proportion of the 5·5 million territories estimated for Great Britain (*APEP*, *1988–91 Atlas*).

Cold winters, such as those of 1978/79 and 1995/96, cause considerable mortality, but the population soon recovers in the following season provided that conditions allow them to produce two or, sometimes, three broods. In recent years, national survey data indicate a steady increase, particularly at CES plots, and breeding performance has shown marked improvement; the British population has risen by around 50 per cent between the mid 1980s and 2000 (*BBWC*).

In Great Britain the winter distribution is very similar to that of summer (*1981–84 Winter Atlas*). Ringing indicates that nine-tenths of all British Robins move less than 20 km, but a few are known to winter as far south as Iberia. Others from Fenno-Scandia, and to a lesser extent from the Baltic States to Belgium, also arrive along the British east coast from August to November, their numbers reaching a peak in October (*Migration Atlas*). Both the *1981–84 Winter Atlas* and the winter tetrad survey found Robins distributed throughout all 10-km squares in Wiltshire. The winter map is similar to the summer abundance map, and shows a bias towards well-wooded areas, such as Savernake. Extrapolation from winter tetrad counts gives a total of just over 7600 Robins, a number very similar to that in summer. This would suggest 65,800 to 138,000 individuals in winter, but, the species being largely resident, a total double that figure might be expected.

The large majority of the 5193 Robins ringed in Wiltshire during 1965–2000 were caught when full-grown, nestlings being represented by only a tiny percentage. Recoveries include two that had survived six years and one that had attained the great age of 8·5 years when it killed itself by flying into a window in Farnham (Surrey). Others that had moved beyond the county boundary were found dead in Gillingham (Dorset) and Tutbury (Staffordshire). Additionally, there were recoveries in Wiltshire of Robins ringed in Sussex, Cornwall and Cumbria.

Perhaps surprisingly for such a popular, confiding and familiar bird, there are few historical assessments of the status of the Robin in Wiltshire, and the accounts in relevant publications were commonly the briefest of any species. Smith (1887) had nothing to say on this subject, and the Robin received little mention in the early bird reports from 1929 in *WANHM*. Indeed. The first mention of a 'Redbreast' was not until 1932 – and that just a note of a pure white individual – while the only other records before the 1940s referred simply to unusual song, plumage and nesting sites, and the feeding of a young Cuckoo. Peirson's (1959) description as 'A very common resident though it avoids the bleak open country' was the complete entry for Robin in his review of Wiltshire birds, and Buxton (1981) was similarly unexpansive with 'A very common and widespread breeding resident, except in military training areas as for the previous species [Dunnock]'. The Robin was described as widespread and abundant in Great Britain as a whole at the end of the 19th century (*1875–1900 Atlas*) and, in the absence of evidence to the contrary, it seems likely that the current picture represents a status little changed over time.

PAC & SBE

Nightingale

Luscinia megarhynchos

Scarce summer visitor, breeds Europe, winters sub-Saharan Africa

Remarkable for its richness, variety and vigour, the Nightingale's song has inspired generations of poets and musicians (*eg* Fisher 1966). It is usually delivered from dense undergrowth – by day as well as by night – though tending to be strongest around dawn, and most regular from mid April to the end of May, and only sporadic after mid June. Eggs are laid between late April and mid June, with a peak in mid May; second broods are unknown in Great Britain.

Nightingales feed on ground invertebrates, especially beetles and ants, in the breeding season, and also on berries in late summer. They occupy varied habitats in Wiltshire, from hedgerows and pioneer scrub through coppice and young conifer plantations to mature deciduous woodlands. Sometimes high densities may be found in scrub associated with gravel pits and other wetlands. Actively managed coppice is an important habitat, though the key factor is the presence of dense undergrowth, which is typically present three to nine years after coppicing (Bayes & Henderson 1988, Fuller *et al* 1999, Fuller & Henderson 1992).

Nightingales breed in northwest Africa and in mainly southern Europe north to Britain, Germany and Poland, thence east through the Caucasus, Turkey and parts of the Middle East to Iran and western Mongolia. The population of Europe, excluding Russia, has been estimated at 3·1 to 4·7 million pairs, the largest numbers being in France, Spain and Italy (*EBCC Atlas*). All Nightingales winter in sub-Saharan Africa, from Senegal across to Kenya, and it is likely that British breeders go to the western part of that range (*Migration Atlas*). In this connection, one of the 203 Nightingales ringed in Wiltshire during 1965–2000 was a male caught near Shrewton on 8 June 1974 and found dead on 8 April 1975 in Morocco, presumably on its way north again to its breeding grounds. Another ringed at Larkhill on 13 June 1976 was retrapped there in 1982 – demonstrating site-faithfulness after six years – and a female ringed in Guernsey on 30 August 1983 may well have been a migrant from Wiltshire, as it was caught twice in Clanger Wood in May 1986, on the 17th and 25th, showing a brood-patch.

Table 107. Nightingales *Luscinia megarhynchos* in Wiltshire: numbers reported and habitat use during national surveys in 1976, 1980 and 1999

	1976	1980	1999
Mixed woodland	73	31	–
Broadleaved woodland	32	76	17
Coniferous woodland	8	48	–
Coppice	33	–	4
Scrub	24	12	16
Other	2	28	3
Totals	172	195	40

In Great Britain, the Nightingale has a southeastern distribution, most being found southeast of a line from the Humber to the Severn; there are few now in Devon and none in Cornwall (*1988–91 Atlas*). Its range has contracted markedly over recent decades, and by 28 per cent between the *1968–72* and *1988–91 Atlases*, most obviously at the northern and western limits from Lincolnshire to west Dorset. National surveys in 1976 and 1980 produced British totals of 3230 and 4770 singing males, most numerously in the extreme southeast – Suffolk, Kent and Sussex together holding 45 per cent in the latter year (Davis 1982).

Another national survey in 1999 located 4565 singing males, indicating stability in the population as a whole, but the range contraction had continued and the proportion in the core counties had increased markedly – Suffolk, Kent and Sussex by then supporting 61 per cent of the total (Wilson *et al* 2002). But analysis of the 1999 data showed that some males had been missed by the methods of all three surveys and, as a result, the true figure that year was estimated to be about 6700. Because, however, it allowed for individuals missed, this was a smaller increase than comparison with the 1980 total might suggest. This is still a very small number compared with the species' abundance in many other European countries: for example, an estimate of one million pairs was postulated for France in the 1970s (Yeatman 1976). Other surveys in Great Britain (*eg* CES) indicate that, although there had been a shallow decline in abundance between the early 1980s and mid 1990s, numbers since have at least stabilised if not increased (*BBWC*).

In Wiltshire, the 1976 national survey found 172 singing males, and noted the main habitats as mixed and broadleaved woodland (table 107); most were at altitudes of 90–120 m and only 15 were above 150 m, although about a quarter of the county falls in that category (Stevenson 1977). The 1980 survey produced 195 singing males – an increase of 23, even though approximately one quarter of suitable habitat was not checked – and, although most were still in woodland, the proportions in different types had changed markedly (table 107); the largest numbers of singing males were found in the Trowbridge and Savernake 10-km squares (Kersley 1981). By the time of the next national survey, in 1999, just 40 Nightingales were recorded in the county; declines were most marked in woodland habitats, and only in scrub habitats did this species appear to be maintaining a foothold in Wiltshire.

The decrease of 79 per cent between 1980 and 1999, to less than one per cent of the British total, was one of the largest declines in any county (Wilson *et al* 2002). Interestingly, most of the others with comparable decreases of 70 per cent or more – Avon, Hampshire, Oxfordshire, Buckinghamshire and Hertfordshire – share a border with Wiltshire. Within Wiltshire itself, many former breeding strongholds have been deserted, including Shrewton Folly, Savernake and Stanton Park Wood. On the positive side, several singing males were heard annually in the late 1990s along the Kennet Valley east of Ramsbury, where none was recorded in the 1980 survey (Kersley 1981). Nightingales also increased at CWP with the expansion of the gravel pit complex, perhaps there benefiting from the dense undergrowth that flourishes in the unmanaged areas between the lakes.

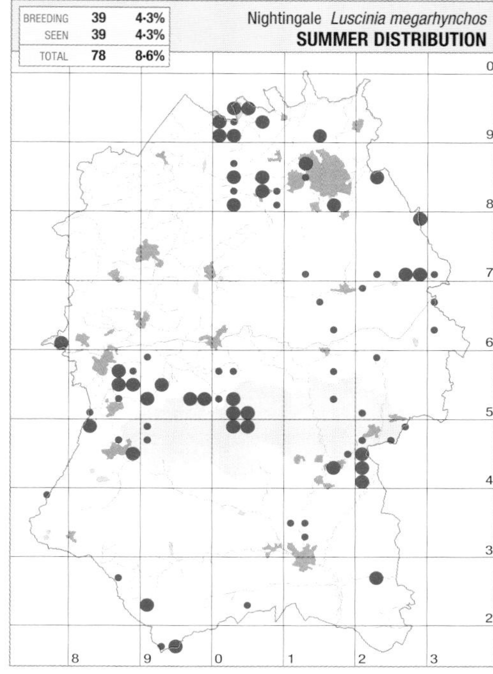

In earlier times, Smith (1887) referred to Nightingales as 'quite abundant' near Salisbury though he had 'never known them in such profusion in north Wilts'. Peirson (1919) described this species as an 'uncommon summer visitor' in the Marlborough district. Although, 20 years later, Peirson (1939) then stated that Nightingales were 'not uncommon locally in many woodlands', Colquhoun (1941) surprisingly recorded none in his 1939 study of Savernake. The highest total of singing males during three county surveys in 1953–55 – which, unfortunately, never had complete coverage – was 81 in the first year (Boyle 1956). Peirson (1959) considered the species to be 'reasonably common in the south-east and east of the county, and in the west'. The *1968–72 Atlas* noted a slight contraction in distribution between the first decade of the 20th century and the 1930s, but then a 'widespread marked decline' after a peak about 1950; it recorded Nightingales in 28 of the county's 33 core 10-km squares, but this number had dropped to 25 by the time of the *1988–91 Atlas* and to only 21 during the summer tetrad fieldwork of 1995–2000. National Nightingale surveys found them in 19 in 1980, but in just nine in 1999.

The summer map shows Nightingales to have a fragmentary distribution in Wiltshire, most now being found in a band across the middle of the county, and in the northeast. The reasons for the decline both locally and nationally are unclear, but it may be due in part to climate and habitat change, the latter including the reduction in actively managed coppiced woodland and in pioneer scrub as it matures, and increased grazing pressure from expanding deer populations (Fuller *et al* 1999). An RSPB survey of SPTA in 2000 found 16 singing Nightingales, the majority in three tight clusters – on the Bulford ranges, northeast of Warminster, and just north of Westdown Camp (Stanbury *et al* 2000). Hawthorn scrub on downland is now an important breeding habitat (PE Castle).

Wiltshire's earliest Nightingale of the year was found during 10–14 April in four years of the early 1990s, but otherwise usually during 18–25 April up to 2000; this suggestion of a trend towards a later arrival is contrary to the generally earlier reports of many other migrants. The earliest county record of all – and the earliest ever date for Great Britain at that time (Hudson 1973) – was 10 March 1961, near Farley; the next one that year was almost a month later, on 9 April (*WANHM*). After the breeding season, Nightingales are rarely seen or heard in the county. They leave mainly in August and the first half of September; passage through bird observatories on the south and west coasts reaches its peak in late August (Riddiford & Findlay 1981). The latest recorded date in Wiltshire was 4 September 1994, at Imber Clump.

SBE

Sponsored by West Wilts Ringing Group in memory of Reg Kersley

Bluethroat

Luscinia svecica

Vagrant (4 records), breeds north/central Europe, winters Mediterranean area

This small, handsome member of the thrush family favours swampy places with scrub, and is a summer visitor to various parts of continental Europe, and thence across northern and central Asia to western Alaska; it winters from the Mediterranean area, north Africa and the Middle East across to India and southeast Asia. It has been estimated that in Europe, excluding Russia, some 545,000 to 1·4 million pairs breed, mostly in the north and east (*EBCC Atlas*).

Several different races of the Bluethroat are recognised, and two occur as passage migrants in Great Britain, but only their adult males in breeding plumage are distinguishable in the field. These are nominate *svecica* of north Europe from Norway eastwards (red spot on blue gorget); and *cyanecula* of middle Europe from Belgium and east France to western Russia (white spot on blue gorget). In Great Britain, the species occurs on both spring and autumn migrations, particularly in early May to early June, and in late August to mid October; several hundred are present in some years, primarily on the east coast, most numerously in Shetland and Orkney, and to a lesser extent on southern and western coasts, particularly in autumn, but few are found inland (Fraser *et al* 2000, *Migration Atlas*). Wiltshire has just four records:

1959	25 May	Idmiston	Female in garden
1972	28 August	Swindon STW	Female trapped and ringed
	13 Sep–7 Oct	Swindon STW	Male periodically at reed edges
1993	12 May	Marlborough	Male Red-spotted in town garden

The first three were published in *WANHM*, where the male in 1972 was originally identified as of the White-spotted race *cyanecula,* but subspecific separation in September is fraught with difficulty (L Svensson) and such details as were recorded do not rule out the possibility of the Red-spotted *svecica.* (Though assumed to be the same individual and present throughout, this bird was seen on only one date between the two extremes, 30 September.) The one in 1993 stayed all afternoon, feeding on midges, and coincided with a marked national influx on the east coast (*Birding World* 6: 175).

RT

Black Redstart

Phoenicurus ochruros

Scarce passage/winter mostly from central Europe/ Mediterranean, has bred

Black Redstarts – duskier than their more widespread congener, but still red-tailed – breed from northwest Africa and Iberia through western and central Europe north to central Britain, southern Fenno-Scandia and the Baltic states, as well as discontinuously from Asia Minor and the Middle East to both central Asia and China. Most populations are migratory – wintering in North Africa, western and southern Europe, the Middle East

Table 108. Black Redstarts *Phoenicurus ochruros* in Wiltshire: monthly totals 1974–2000
Breeding pairs and their young (see text) have been excluded

	Jul	Aug	Sep	Oct	Nov	Dec	Jan	Feb	Mar	Apr	May	Jun
Birds	4	6	5	42	52	24	17	15	29	30	14	4

and southern Asia – but those of western Europe and the Mediterranean region are rather more sedentary. The numbers breeding in Europe, excluding Russia, have been estimated at 3·6 to 6·1 million pairs, and the species' range has expanded northward since the mid 19th century (*EBCC Atlas*).

Apart from isolated records in 1845 and possibly 1909, breeding was not proved in Great Britain until the 1920s and 1930s: one or two pairs nested on the Sussex coast during 1923–25, in Cornwall more regularly from 1929, and occasionally in Kent and elsewhere in the 1930s (*eg* Witherby *et al* 1938–41). Numbers then increased during the 1939–45 War as Black Redstarts began to colonise bombed buildings in London, Dover and other towns in the southeast (*1968–72 Atlas*). The still small British population – which the *1988–91 Atlas* estimated at 80–120 pairs/territories and mapped as breeding west to Dorset and Gwynedd and north to Yorkshire – still has a stronghold in London and the Home Counties, but other concentrations in East Anglia and the West Midlands, though numbers have declined to some 25 to 73 pairs at the end of the 1990s (*APEP*). Many now nest in derelict industrial sites, gasworks, power stations, railway sheds and housing under construction, neither particularly favouring the coastal cliffs adopted by the early colonists nor exploiting other habitats they use on the Continent, such as town houses, farm buildings and mountains. Black Redstarts are more familiar in Great Britain as regular passage migrants, both in spring – when ringing has shown that at least some central European breeders are involved – and in autumn when they are thought to originate from the western Continent (*Migration Atlas*).

In Wiltshire, Smith (1887) reported just two Black Redstarts: one, undated, killed at Amesbury; and the other shot at Enford Farm in April 1881. Hony (1915a) was able to add three sight records: a 'fine adult male…near Marlborough in the spring of 1881'; a 'young male' at Downton on 13 March 1910; and 'a particularly striking bird' seen by the Vicar of Britford 'on the old Shaftesbury Road' on 6 November 1912 (*WANHM* 38: 107). The next published records were one each at Swallowcliffe from 31 October to 4 November 1927 and at Salisbury in November 1929; a female near West Grimstead in November 1932; a male at Ford, near Salisbury, in 1932 – which 'has been seen for the last two years' – and two (sex not given) there in February–March 1934 (all *WANHM*).

Greater ornithological coverage in the years after the 1939–45 War doubtless contributed to the increase in observations. During 1946–73, *WANHM* documented no fewer than 38 records, mostly in spring (nine in March–April), late autumn and early winter (21 in October–December). During 1974–2000, Black Redstarts were found annually and in all months, ranging from a minimum of three records in three years to at least 17 in two. Most were seen on passage – particularly in October–November and March–April (table 108) – and most appeared singly; four at Greenland Camp on 13 November 1982 and three at Colerne Airfield on 20 September 1975 were the highest numbers reported together (*Hobby*). The only Black Redstart ringed in the county was one at Salisbury on 9 March 1996.

The *1981–84 Winter Atlas* showed that Black Redstarts seek warmer areas at that season, favouring west and south coasts from Lancashire and north Wales round to Kent; the species was mapped during those three winters in 11 of Wiltshire's 33 core 10-km squares, mostly in the south. In contrast – although there were four November–February records (five birds) in the county in 1998/99 and three in 1999/2000 (*Hobby*) – none was found during the 2-hour tetrad counts of the winter survey, and the Wiltshire total in winter probably numbers fewer than ten. Several extended winter stays have been noted, the longest at Chippenham from 7 November 1995 to 2 March 1996.

There have been just four successful breeding records in Wiltshire. A pair reared two broods in a garage at Bulford in 1975 and again in 1976; the female returned alone in 1977 and laid an unfertilised clutch of eggs. Also in 1976, a female was seen with three juveniles (not two as published in *Hobby*) at Netheravon. In 1979, a pair reared two broods at Swindon's former GWR works; a male held territory at this site in 1980–82 and presumably different individuals again in 1987 and, close by, in 1999, but no further nests were found.

GLW & PCo

Common Redstart

Phoenicurus phoenicurus

Scarce and decreasing summer visitor, breeds Europe, winters Africa

The Common Redstart's brief but, once learnt, distinctive song is a rare and localised sound in Wiltshire. This small species of thrush, or chat, is more widely familiar in the county as a passage migrant, when its flashing red tail catches the eye as it flits along fence lines or woodland and scrub edges.

Common Redstarts breed from northwest Africa and western Europe east to Lake Baikal, and from Asia Minor and the Caucasus to Iran. Most winter in sub-Saharan Africa north of the equator and in parts of Arabia, but a minority stays north of the Sahara around the western Mediterranean. The few winter recoveries of British breeders have been in southern Iberia and North and West Africa (*Migration Atlas*). During 1965–2000, 117 Redstarts were ringed in Wiltshire, but none has been recovered. A male ringed on 7 May 1990 at Weybourne (Norfolk) was found dead at Chippenham on 23 April 1994.

The breeding population of Europe, excluding Russia, has been estimated at 1·9 to 3·4 million pairs, although declines were reported from 23 countries during 1970–90 (*EBCC Atlas*). Numbers in Great Britain fluctuated at various times during the 20th century: 'There was a marked decline in much of England before 1940, but a good recovery by 1967–68' (*1968–72 Atlas*). National survey data then showed another sharp decline into the early 1970s, attributed to drought in the African Sahel zone, but the numbers subsequently increased in a trend that continued to the end of the 20th century (*BBWC*).

The *1988–91 Atlas* postulated a British population of 90,000 pairs, an estimate that it noted was at odds with the figure of 330,000 territories that had been calculated from mean CBC densities, and suggested that numbers lay towards the lower end of the two extremes. It also pointed out that, although the population had increased within the main parts of its British range, it had decreased or disappeared from the periphery, with the result that Redstarts were by then less widespread than in 1968–72. Based on BBS trends, the British population in 2000 was calculated to number 101,000 pairs (*APEP*). This species is most numerous in upland areas of Scotland, Wales and northern and southwest England, the nearest stronghold to Wiltshire being in Hampshire's New Forest. It breeds in wooded areas of all types, including mature Scots pine in Scotland, except young conifer plantations.

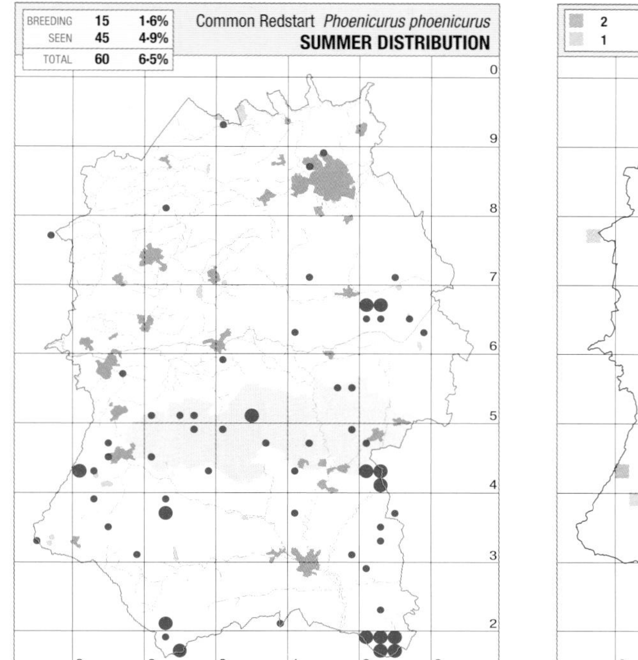

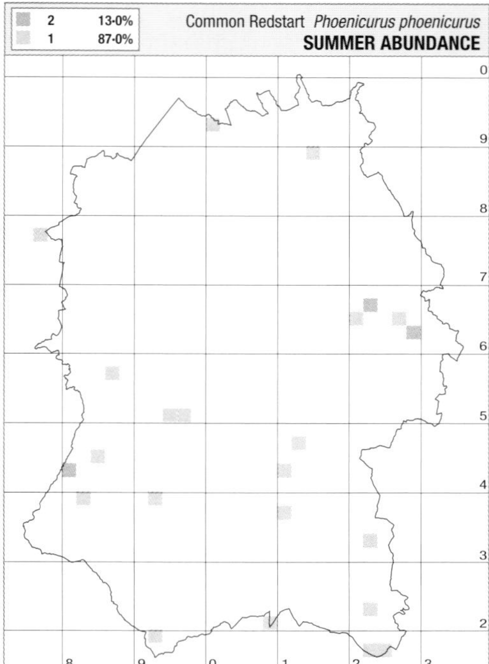

In Wiltshire, as in much of southern England, Common Redstarts are found chiefly in mature, open deciduous woodland with limited undergrowth and abundant holes for nesting. Sunny glades and woodland edges are particularly favoured. The optimum breeding habitat in the county seems to be in the extensive old oak and beech woodlands in the west at Longleat, in the northeast in Savernake, and in the extreme southeast. The summer map shows these three areas; most of the scattering of 'seen' records elsewhere will have referred only to individuals on spring passage. In 2000, however, singing males were also recorded at eleven sites on SPTA, mainly within old beech plantations, particularly around Imber village (Stanbury *et al* 2000). This may indicate that isolated males were overlooked in other areas of the county during the summer survey (which found just 26 Redstarts), but even allowing for this it seems unlikely that numbers currently exceed 20 to 50 territorial males.

The Common Redstart seems always to have been local in Wiltshire, and the increase in the national population in the 1990s was not reflected in the county. A century earlier, Smith (1887) wrote that 'From my own observation I should say it is now much more scarce than it was a few years back; certainly its numbers in the localities where I have annually watched it are much decreased'. The 1929 bird report noted it as 'scarce…much decreased in numbers' (*WANHM*), but in 1939 Colquhoun (1941) found no fewer than 41 singing males in Savernake and estimated the total population there at 80 birds. A survey of Redstarts in Wiltshire during 1949–51 (Rice 1952) suggested that, although the number of pairs reported actually increased over those three years – 11, 12 and 20 pairs respectively – the results pointed to a fluctuating population, as might be expected for a species near the edge of its range; and he attributed the apparent increase in part to the varying numbers of observers involved in the enquiry. He also commented that the population was probably larger, as four apparently suitable areas (Clarendon, Fonthill, Grovely and Great Ridge) had been inadequately covered. (In this connection, it is worth noting that the 1947 bird report in *WANHM* noted 'Several nests found in the Clarendon district'.) Loss and fragmentation of Redstart habitat in other parts of the south, however – for example, in Bentley Wood in the years following the 1939–45 War – no doubt had a negative influence on the county breeding population at that time.

Peirson (1959) wrote that the species was 'local and uncommon. Apparently... much less common and widespread than it was a hundred years ago'. Buxton (1981) also described it as 'An uncommon summer visitor'. During 1975–83, only one to five pairs were reported in any year (*Hobby*). In 1984, however, when again this was a species whose numbers were believed to have been seriously affected by drought in the African Sahel, at least 31 or 32 pairs were recorded – including just nine or ten in sample surveys on the Longleat Estate where the total population was considered likely to be in the range of 15 to 25 pairs (Ferguson-Lees 1984). This was followed by further county peaks of 31 pairs in 1988 and 26 in 1991, but, whereas the *1968–72 Atlas* proved breeding in 14 of Wiltshire's 33 core 10-km squares, the *1988–91 Atlas* did so in only 11 and that figure more than halved to just five 10-km squares during the 1995–2000 survey. The summer distribution map shows just how fragmented the population has become in the county, and the abundance map demonstrates the large declines in such former key areas as Longleat and Savernake.

One Wiltshire stronghold remains the extreme southeast bordering the New Forest, though even there 14 pairs in 1987 in the Hamptworth area had fallen to perhaps only two or three pairs by 1995–96 (GD Pictor). For Hampshire's New Forest itself, Clark & Eyre (1993) estimated a more than doubling in numbers of Redstarts from the mid 1970s into the early 1990s, but much of the old deciduous woodland in adjacent southeast Wiltshire was felled and replanted with conifers during the 1970s and 1980s.

Small numbers of migrant Common Redstarts are recorded in Wiltshire in both spring and autumn, but the species is then often skulking and shy and doubtless many are overlooked. Certain sites may seem particularly favoured at this time (*eg* Bratton and Little Hinton), but this undoubtedly reflects observer coverage. Spring arrival reaches a peak from mid to late April, and the autumn passage extends from late July through to October, particularly from mid August to early September. Earliest and latest dates are 10 March 1996 and 16 November 1980.

GDP

Sponsored by Roy Fussell

Whinchat

Saxicola rubetra

Locally common summer visitor, scarce passage, breeds Europe, winters Africa

Brief and cheerful, the Whinchat's song is less frequently heard nowadays in lowland Britain after a drastic decline in breeding numbers from about the 1940s (*eg 1875–1900*, *1968–72* and *1988–91 Atlases*). The BBS index suggests that this trend may have continued through the 1990s, albeit with considerable fluctuations (*BBWC*). A decrease has been also evident elsewhere in western and central Europe, and more recently in Fenno-Scandia, but breeding densities remain high in eastern Europe (Bastian & Bastian 1994).

Nesting Whinchats occur in a variety of open country, preferring tall vegetation, such as bracken, hogweed and coarse grasses, a liking once reflected in Great Britain by the local name 'Grass-chat' (Saunders 1899). In the 19th century this chat bred throughout

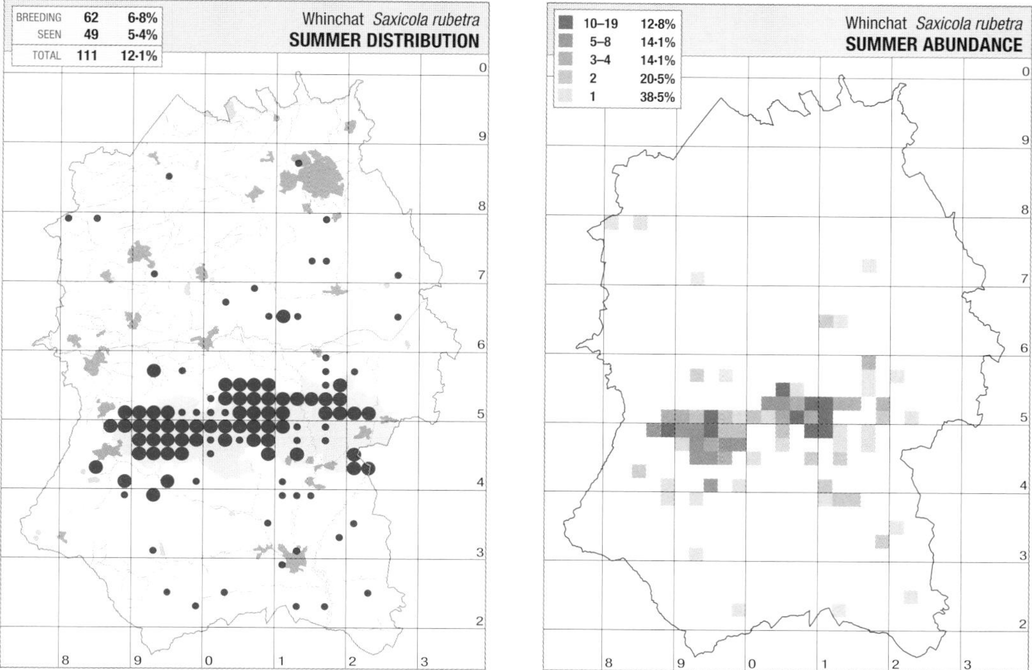

the British mainland, and was particularly common on, for example, certain southeastern downlands (*1875–1900 Atlas*), but by the time of the *1988–91 Atlas* it was mostly confined to the west and north. The loss of rough grassland, meadows and heaths to cultivation and overgrazing has been blamed (*1988–91 Atlas*), and so it is not surprising that, in Wiltshire, the ungrazed and uncultivated grassland of SPTA is a haven that holds the most significant population remaining in lowland England.

Smith (1887) noted that George Montagu had described Whinchats as 'plentiful' in Wiltshire, and further implied that they had decreased during the 19th century, qualifying his statement that they 'may often be seen on our downs' by adding 'not now numerous'. Little information is available for the first half of the 20th century, but in 1931 they were considered 'very plentiful... near Bulford' (*WANHM*). Both Peirson (1959) and Buxton (1981) believed that they had been commoner in the 19th century, but neither speculated on the beginning of the decline – although there is no evidence to suggest that it differed from elsewhere in Great Britain.

The *1968–72 Atlas* found Whinchats breeding in 11 of Wiltshire's 33 core 10-km squares, the *1988–91 Atlas* in seven, and the 1995–2000 survey in 11 again, but with a difference. The summer distribution and abundance maps both demonstrate that nesting is now virtually confined to SPTA. Breeding on the Marlborough Downs and in south Wiltshire, evident in the *1968–72 Atlas*, has ceased and the scatter of small 'seen' dots on the distribution map refers to migrants.

Buxton (1981), who noted that the 'majority of breeding records are for the Imber, Everleigh and Larkhill military training areas', put the county breeding population at no more than 50 pairs. The formation of MoD Conservation Groups in 1981 allowed the natural history of SPTA to be more fully investigated, and a survey in 1987 found 111 pairs or singing males: 65 on Imber, 36 on Larkhill, and at least 10 in the Haxton/Everleigh area of the Bulford Ranges (*Hobby*). But even that failed to reveal the true importance of the area, as an RSPB survey in 2000 located no fewer than 401 territories and estimated the total SPTA breeding population at a previously unsuspected level of 586 pairs (Stanbury *et al* 2000). This survey also found that nesting Whinchats occurred mostly within the unimproved grassland areas of the artillery ranges and were concentrated in the valleys, where densities reached ten pairs/km². If the numbers recorded during WOS timed counts away from SPTA be included, the Wiltshire population in 2000 comprised 747 territories; and the application of alternative correction factors for pairs and detectability to Stanbury's estimate of individuals suggests a still higher county total of 1120 pairs – roughly two and a half to, possibly, as much as eight per cent of the 14,000 to 28,000 pairs estimated for the whole of Great Britain (*1988–91 Atlas*).

Whinchats winter almost exclusively in two main areas of sub-Saharan Africa: from southern Mauritania and Liberia east to Cameroon and north Gabon, and from northeast Zaire and southern Sudan south to Malawi and northern Zambia (Keith *et al* 1992). The British population is suggested to winter in western Africa (*Migration Atlas*). The first arrivals in Wiltshire are usually in April, the bulk arriving late in that month and in the first week of May, but a handful of March records has included singletons on the 13th (1913, no locality; Witherby *et al* 1938–41) and 24th (1991, Imber), pairs on the 19th (1974, Rushall) and 25th (1983, Heytesbury), and three on the 27th (1997, West Down Farm). Although the onset of autumn passage is sometimes detectable in July, it occurs largely during August and September and is most obvious when small parties appear on bushes, hedgerows and fencelines in non-breeding areas. Such parties typically number fewer than ten, but larger groups (for example, 20 at Haxton Down, 19 September 1998) are occasionally recorded. Odd stragglers are usually encountered in Wiltshire in October (records in all but one of the 11 years 1990–2000). There have also been four reports in November – singletons on the 6th (1976, Purton), 9th (1978, Wylye) and 28th (1971, Fyfield Down), and three on the 19th (1974, Rushall) – and two singletons in December, on the 3rd (1994, Everleigh) and 18th (also 1994, Imber).

Of the 134 Whinchats ringed in Wiltshire during 1965–2000, only one – ringed at Imber village on 21 August 1982 – has subsequently been reported: it was found 16 days later on board a ship off Hendaye, Pyrénées-Atlantiques (France), and was afterwards released on shore. One ringed near Tregaron (Cardiganshire) on 21 June 1979 was retrapped and released again nearly three years later at Imber village on 1 August 1982.

Whinchats breed from northern Spain to the Ural Mountains, and beyond on to the west Siberian plain. Over 75 per cent of the summer range lies within Europe where, even excluding Russia, total numbers have been estimated at 2·4 to 3·0 million pairs (*EBCC Atlas*). Nevertheless, in terms of southern England, Wiltshire holds an important and largely isolated population which deserves regular monitoring and conservation.

(See also page 725.)

PCo

Stonechat

Saxicola torquatus

Local resident, widespread passage/winter, including some from north Britain

Often bold, and noisy for their size, Stonechats have a vast but fragmented summer range that includes western, southern and northeastern

Europe, much of Asia south to the Himalayas, Turkey and southwestern Arabia, North and sub-Saharan Africa, and Madagascar. The population of Europe, excluding Russia, has been estimated at 1·1 to 2·1 million pairs and, whereas large declines have been noted in several countries – attributed to agricultural intensification and changes in farming practices during the 20th century – the species' range has extended to coastal southwest Norway since 1974 and Finland since 1992 (*EBCC Atlas*, *CBWP*). Rather curiously, the Norwegian colonists appear to have originated from northern Britain rather than continental Europe, while those in Finland are of the race *maurus* – the 'Siberian Stonechat' – spilling westwards from European Russia (see also below) (Urquhart 2002).

Severe frost and snow can have a serious effect on populations of Stonechats in at least the subsequent breeding season (*eg 1968-72 Atlas*) and this sensitivity to cold weather is reflected in their British distribution – confined mostly to the milder west from north Scotland down to Cornwall and Hampshire, apart from some heaths and coasts of the southeast (*1981–84 Winter Atlas*, *1988–91 Atlas*). The *1988–91 Atlas* revealed a marked contraction in range since the *1968–72 Atlas* but, more recently, BBS data for 1994–2000 have shown a substantial overall increase, though numbers have fluctuated (*BBWC*).

Smith (1887) had little concrete to say about Stonechats in Wiltshire, but classed them as 'tolerably numerous'. Nationally at that time, they were considered 'widespread and stable throughout the 19th century' (*1875–1900 Atlas*). The next assessment of status was not attempted until the 1929 bird report in *WANHM*, which described this species as 'A rather scarce resident… in water-meadows in hard weather' – doubtless referring to the consequences of that year's 'very severe frost of February [which] caused heavy mortality among many of our birds' – whereas the 1930 report, after a mild winter, found it a 'Locally common' breeder in south Wiltshire, but almost exclusively a winter visitor and passage migrant in the north of the county. Stonechat fortunes seem to have improved during the 1930s, and 'a remarkable increase in South Wilts' was recorded in 1933, but this trend did not last and in 1951 they were 'still absent from their old haunts around Salisbury' (*WANHM*).

The 'still absent' clearly related to the effects of the series of bitterly cold winters during the 1940s, and it is likely that the 'Dig for Victory' campaign during the 1939–45 War, when large areas of downland and rough pasture were ploughed to produce food, had also taken its toll. No evidence of nesting was reported in *WANHM* in 1953–54, 1957–59, 1962–68 or 1970–71, but thereafter an increase was noted (Buxton 1981). Bridgman (1982), who analysed the county records for 1971–80, found Imber to be the most important breeding area. In the last year of that decade, *Hobby* noted 13 pairs on Imber, one on Everleigh/Haxton, and an unspecified number on Porton 'where breeding probably took place'. The reported total of breeding pairs fell to four in 1982, again following severe winter weather, and numbers did not apparently reach the level of 1980 again until 1991, when 16 pairs were recorded (*Hobby*).

Whereas the *1988–91 Atlas* mapped Stonechats as breeding in just six of Wiltshire's 33 core 10-km squares – though that was twice the number in the *1968–72 Atlas* – the summer tetrad survey of 1995–2000, less than a decade later, found breeding evidence in no fewer than 18 core squares – three times as many again – and in six of the 15 part squares. These figures show a marked expansion in the range of Stonechats in the county during the 1990s, after a series of milder winters and an increase in areas of rough ground in the form of set-aside. More breeding pairs were also being reported in *Hobby* (figure 66): seven pairs in 1990 rose to 32 in 1995 but, perhaps as a result of the severe weather early in 1996, dropped to 26 in each of the next two years. But these figures are only a fraction of the true total.

Although confirming the expansion in range and numbers during the latter part of the 20th century, the casual breeding records reported in *Hobby* greatly understate Wiltshire's

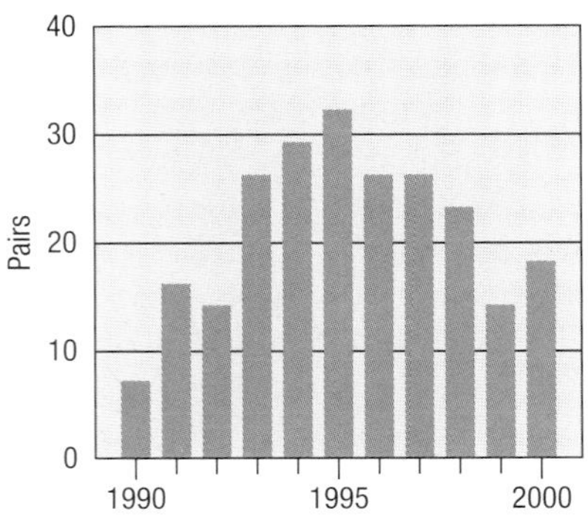

Figure 66. Stonechats *Saxicola torquatus* in Wiltshire: breeding pairs recorded in *Hobby* 1990–2000

Stonechat population, particularly as the tetrad survey results were not necessarily included there. In 2000, an RSPB survey identified 197 territories and estimated no fewer than 223 pairs on SPTA alone (Stanbury *et al* 2000). The summer map for 1995–2000 does, however, confirm the major significance of Salisbury Plain, where rough ground in valley bottoms provides scattered bushes for nesting, and tall herbs – notably wild parsnip (SB Edwards) – for song-posts and look-outs. The map also shows a scatter of breeding records elsewhere, including the West Wiltshire Downs and the southeast of the county, near the species' strongholds on the heathlands of the New Forest (Hampshire). A combination of the RSPB data for SPTA in 2000 and the timed summer counts for 1995–2000 indicates that the Wiltshire population is now in the region of 353 to 498 pairs – perhaps as much as six per cent of the 8500 to 21,500 pairs estimated for Great Britain by the *1988–91 Atlas*.

British Stonechats are partial migrants, some remaining on territory to face the northern winter and others dispersing as far south as southwest Europe and North Africa. Continental breeders possibly also occur on passage or in winter (*Migration Atlas*). It therefore seems likely that some Stonechats recorded in Wiltshire outside the breeding season may originate from elsewhere in Great Britain and perhaps from the Continent. The numbers recorded in October certainly indicate that there is some passage through the county. The Marlborough Downs are often favoured during migration: small parties have been noted at several sites there, especially in autumn, these disappearing within a day or two (SB Edwards). As, however, none of the 27 Stonechats ringed in the county has been recovered, and there are no inward ringing returns, the origins of migrants and winterers remains unknown.

Winter numbers, which are likely to be influenced by the previous season's breeding success as well as by the severity of the weather, tend to remain high through November and into December, but then decrease in January. The largest reported January total, 52 in 1995, was followed by a record 67 in October that year (*Hobby*). Falling numbers in February and March may indicate dispersal back to breeding areas elsewhere, though passage is sometimes again evident in March (*Hobby*).

The *1981–84 Winter Atlas* mapped Stonechats in 22 of the county's 33 core 10-km squares and, as in summer, the bulk was on Salisbury Plain. Similarly, for example, 15 of the 19 recorded in January 1992 were on Larkhill, Imber and Haxton Ranges (*Hobby*). Elsewhere in Wiltshire, river and streamside habitats are used, especially in hard weather (Peirson 1959), and, when kale fields were more widespread in the 1970s, they too were an important wintering habitat, often shared with Tree Sparrows and Reed Buntings (P Combridge). From the late 1990s set-aside has been utilised in the southeast (P Combridge). The same locations may frequently be used in a series of consecutive winters, raising the possibility

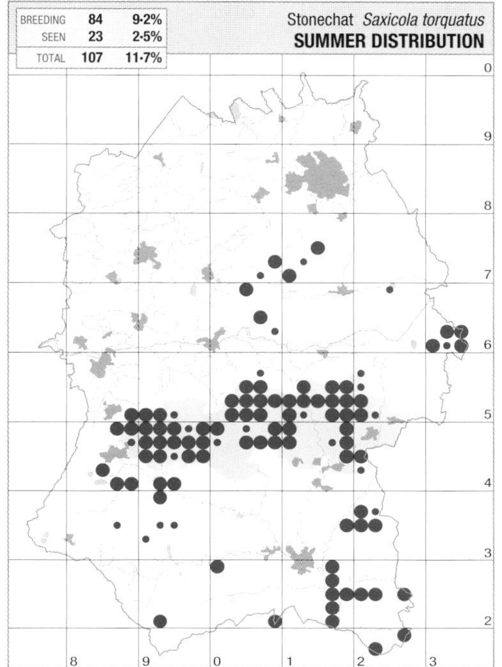

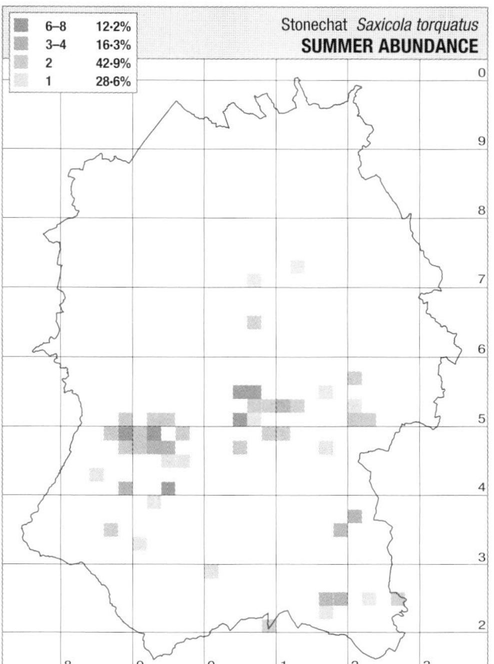

that the same individuals are involved, and it is curious how often winter sites involve roadsides and bridleways. Many winter records relate to pairs, and these often occupy territories throughout that season (*1981–84 Winter Atlas*).

The winter map for 1998–2000 shows that Stonechats were present in 17 of the 33 core 10-km squares, and in five of the 15 part squares, a combined total very similar to that in summer. Extrapolation from the survey figures indicates that some 160–170 individuals were seen, compared with a total summer count of 125 – which might suggest that, in Wiltshire, Stonechats are more numerous in winter by about a third. This result is, however, likely to be misleading because, although they may be slightly more widespread in winter and on passage, the high densities breeding on SPTA (not fully represented by the 1995–2000 tetrad survey) indicate that their numbers are probably greater in summer (SB Edwards); the winter total is probably between 650 and 1000 individuals.

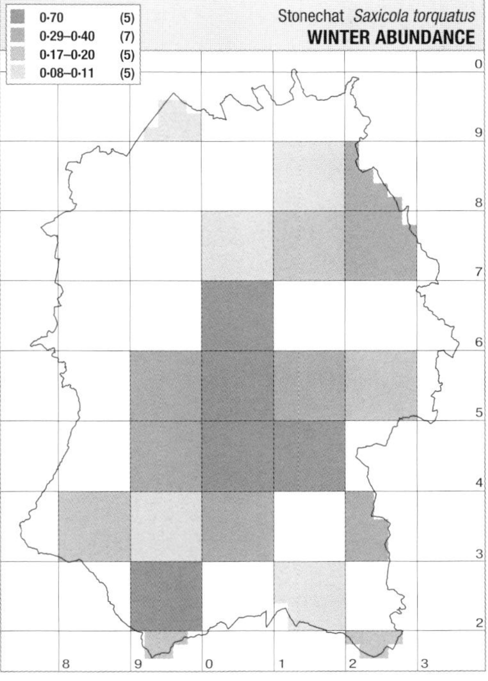

A female of the eastern race *maurus* ('Siberian Stonechat'), sometimes regarded as a distinct species – which normally winters from the Middle East across southern Asia – stayed at Chirton Gorse, Larkhill, from 21 November 1987 to 7 February 1988 (*BBRC*).

In summer, Siberian Stonechats inhabit a wider altitudinal range than do western European races and are found from north European Russia across northern Asia to the Sea of Okhotsk and north Japan; as noted above, they have also bred sporadically in Finland since 1992, and a male was paired with a female of the continental race *rubicola* on Helgoland (Germany) in 1997 (Urquhart 2002).

(See also page 727.)

PCo

Sponsored by Norma J Braine in memory of Winnie Doble

Wheatear

Oenanthe oenanthe

Scarce but regular migrant from Britain/Iceland/ Greenland to Africa, now rare nester

Its arrival keenly awaited every year as one of the first signs of spring, this handsome chat – once a familiar breeding bird described by Smith (1887) as 'generally dispersed over the Wiltshire downs' – is now almost exclusively a spring and autumn passage migrant through the county.

The Wheatear is one of the world's great colonists and over the centuries has acquired an almost circumpolar summer range. Although it has decreased in southern England and parts of Ireland, France and the Low Countries, it breeds commonly in much of Europe (and northwest Africa) and across central and northern Asia, whence it slowly extended across Siberia to the Anadyr peninsula and, via the Bering Strait, into Alaska and northwest Canada, while at the same time spreading northwest through the Faeroes, Iceland and mainly coastal Greenland into northeast Canada. All populations retire, via their routes of ancestral colonisation, to winter in sub-Saharan Africa, where they occur in a broad swathe from Mauritania and Senegal to Ethiopia, Kenya and Tanzania. Those that breed in Britain and Ireland are believed to winter in West Africa (*Migration Atlas*). In Europe, Wheatears are found from the Mediterranean and Black Seas north to the arctic coasts of Fenno-Scandia and Russia. Even without Russia, the European population has been estimated at 2·6 to 3·8 million pairs (*EBCC Atlas*).

As elsewhere in southern England, the fortunes of Wiltshire's breeding Wheatears have clearly fluctuated in response to changes in land use. At one time this was one of the few inland counties in which the species was considered common, doing best on open and well-grazed sheepwalk but declining as this was lost to the plough (*1875–1900 Atlas*). It was undoubtedly widespread during the 19th century – 'few inhabitants of Wiltshire can be ignorant of its handsome active figure' (Smith 1887) – and this state of affairs appears to have continued into the 20th. In 1929, indeed, the Wheatear was still 'fairly common' on the downs; in 1930, conditions south of Salisbury were described as 'very favourable to its increase'; and in 1931 several observers remarked on its abundance, while 13–16 pairs nested around Chute alone that year (*WANHM*). Between the 1914–18 and 1939–45 Wars, arable land was reverting to grass and being abandoned at the height of the farming depression in the late 19th and early 20th centuries, thus creating much suitable Wheatear habitat.

This was a brief respite, however, for agricultural intensification during and after the 1939–45 War resulted in much further habitat loss – 'Ploughing of the southern downlands, especially in Wiltshire, Hampshire and Sussex, led to the virtual extinction of the species there' (*1875–1900 Atlas*) – and confining the 'remaining pairs to higher and steeper downs' (Buxton 1981); it was remarked in the 1948 bird report that, though 'A few pairs' nested at Pitton, they were not in 'comparable numbers to the years before the ploughing-up campaign' (*WANHM*). Numbers received a further setback when the population of rabbits – providers of nest-sites and short turf – was greatly reduced by the arrival of myxomatosis in 1954.

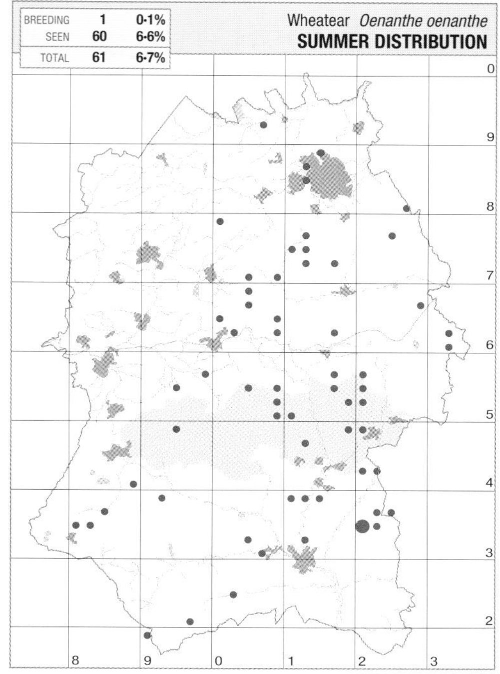

The national breeding atlases illustrated the last stages of the Wheatear's decline in Wiltshire: the *1968–72 Atlas* showed breeding in six of the county's 33 core 10-km squares and presence in another 12, whereas the corresponding figures in the *1988–91 Atlas* were just three and seven. During the last quarter of the 20th century breeding was proved in only seven years (1976, 1978, 1988–91 and 2000) – with a maximum of three pairs in 1990 – at Wylye and Porton Downs, Yarnbury Castle, Larkhill and, in 1978, a disused factory site in Swindon (*Hobby*). The isolated breeding site on the summer distribution map for 1995–2000 relates to a pair on Porton Down in 2000 (the first proved nesting for nine years), while the scatter of 'seen' records involved just spring migrants. The *1988–91 Atlas* put the British population at 55,000 pairs and noted that numbers had fallen throughout the lowlands, with the result that the species was by then confined mostly to ground over 300 m in the north and west. The BBS has shown large fluctuations nationally since 1994, but no clear trend in abundance (*BBWC*).

Wiltshire's earliest spring record was on 5 February 1994 at Parsonage Down NNR; others in February were noted on the 17th (1965), 25th (1989) and 27th (1994, two sites). More typically, the first arrivals appear in March, often during the second week, and migration continues throughout April and May into early June. The highest spring count during 1974–2000 – 86 on SPTA (Centre) on 29 March 1987 – included some showing the characters of the 'Greenland Wheatear', the slightly larger and more richly coloured subspecies, *leucorhoa*, which breeds from Iceland to northeast Canada. This race has been sparingly, but not annually, identified in spring in Wiltshire, and Peirson (1959) also reported it in October, but field identification of subspecies has its problems and the exact status of *leucorhoa* as a migrant passing through the county is uncertain. Just 11 double-figure counts of Wheatears on spring passage during 1990–2000 included five of 20 or more: 22 at Imber on the early date of 20 March 1993, 20 at Larkhill on 28 March 1998, and no fewer than three records in April 2000 – 30 at Upavon Down on the 6th, 23 on SPTA (East) on the 20th and 38 there on the 27th.

Wheatears return through Wiltshire from July to October, most in August and September. The largest recent autumn concentrations have all been on Salisbury Plain in August: 30 on the 9th (1987, Porton Down), 30 on the 10th (1986, Larkhill), and 27 on the 20th (1988, Larkhill). No autumn gatherings exceeding ten were published during 1990–

2000. There have been 13 November records, all since 1959 and all involving singletons between the 1st and the 25th, on which date the latest of all was seen in Swindon in 1995.

None of the six Wheatears ringed in Wiltshire has been recovered, but one ringed in the New Forest (Hampshire) on 12 June 1981 was found dead between West Dean and East Grimstead just over six weeks later, on 26 July.

(See also page 725.)

PCo

Ring Ouzel

Turdus torquatus

Scarce passage, has possibly nested, breeds Britain/ Fenno-Scandia, winters Spain/north Africa

Longer-winged than the familiar Blackbird, adult Ring Ouzels have a white or whitish crescent across the chest – and a distinctive rattling chatter which is usually the first indication of one on passage. Scarce but regular migrants through Wiltshire, they nest on western and northern moorlands from Devon to Caithness, mostly above the 250 m contour. The *1988–91 Atlas* put the British population at 5500 to 11,000 pairs, but showed that the number of occupied 10-km squares had fallen by just over a quarter since the *1968–72 Atlas*. Moreover, a further fall of 58 per cent was estimated between 1988–91 and 1999 – when corrections for differences in survey effort were incorporated and the estimate revised to 6160 to 7550 pairs – prompting conservation concern (Wotton *et al* 2002b, Gregory *et al* 2002), though the reasons for this sharp decline are not yet understood (*BBWC*).

British Ring Ouzels are part of a northern to arctic European population, otherwise found only in Ireland – where, too, there has been a serious decrease – and Fenno-Scandia, mainly Norway and Sweden, although breeding has also been recorded in Brittany, Belgium, Denmark and the Faeroes. Other races breed in mountain areas from northeast Spain through southern and central Europe, Turkey and the Caucasus to northern Iran and Turkmenistan. The *EBCC Atlas* put the population of Europe, excluding Russia, at 247,000 to 355,000 pairs and noted that, though numbers were stable or decreasing in most of the breeding range, local increases had been reported.

Most Ring Ouzels are short-distance or merely altitudinal migrants, wintering patchily in northwest Africa, southern Europe and the Middle East, but the northern populations move the farthest. British Ring Ouzels migrate from late August into October, and it is thought likely that the small peak in numbers evident at bird observatories in late September represents the main departure of these. They travel down to winter in southern France, Spain and northwest Africa (*Migration Atlas*). Individuals occasionally overwinter in southern England, but the origins of these are unknown.

Fenno-Scandian populations do not start leaving their nesting grounds until the last part of September, and it is suggested that the substantial passage from mid October until early November recorded at British bird observatories, most obviously along the east coast, is part of their migration (*Migration Atlas*). This thrush has also long been known to halt regularly in southern England while on migration; indeed, it was noted in Gilbert White's *Selborne*.

The Ring Ouzel was frequently seen on migration in 19th century Wiltshire. Smith (1887) was able to report 'numerous records of its occurrence' and quoted one correspondent who

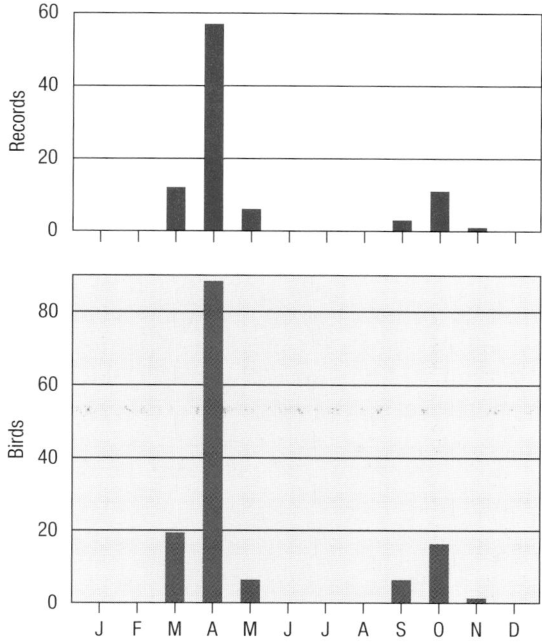

Figure 67. Ring Ouzels *Turdus torquatus* in Wiltshire: monthly totals of records and individuals 1974–2000
One record in spring was not dated

had 'often seen... flocks of five or six'. Smith also mentioned a report of breeding at Mere in 1858, when one bird, later identified as a Ring Ouzel, was 'shot' and its nest and two eggs 'secured'. It is difficult to know what to make of this claim a century and a half later, but Hony (1915a) – who likewise noted that this species was seen 'often on migration' – dismissed further claims of nesting in 1887 and 1901 as having involved partial albino Blackbirds. Yet Ring Ouzels frequently bred on the western edge of the Cotswolds in Gloucestershire until around 1885, although many were shot there by collectors and few remained by the turn of the century (*1875–1900 Atlas*).

The 1929 bird report described this species as an 'uncommon' passage migrant 'usually in April or October', but in the decade before the 1939–45 War just five records were published, all in April, in 1929, 1932 and 1934 (*WANHM*). No more were reported until 1951, but, from then to 1973 inclusive, 26 records involved 43 individuals. Of those 26, all but one were dated, most having been in March (eight), April (six), September (three) and October (three); the remainder were in February (one at Burderop Down on the 28th in 1965), July (one at Shalbourne on the 26th in 1963), August (two) and November (one at Clarendon on the 24th in 1952). The largest recorded flock in this period was seven at Barbury Castle on 31 March 1963 (*WANHM*).

The next 27 years, up to and including 2000, saw a notable increase in Wiltshire records, though numbers varied and 1982, 1984 and 1985 were complete blanks. During this period, 76 records in spring between 22 March and 12 May involved 113 birds, and 15 records in autumn involved 23 (figure 67). Of those sexed during 1974–99, significantly more males (64) than females (25) were reported. (Spring 2000 has been excluded because of uncertainty about the number of individuals.) But it must be added that 'Many [Ring Ouzels] are indeterminate, difficult – sometimes impossible – to sex' (Svensson 1992) and some of the 'males' in Wiltshire, particularly if seen only briefly, may have been well-marked females.

A 14–year study of migrant Ring Ouzels at a site on the South Downs in Sussex (Leverton 1993) similarly found an excess of males in spring and that numbers varied greatly from year to year; arrivals in both spring and autumn were usually associated with anticyclones giving light easterly winds and haze or coastal fog. Steep slopes and coombes of grazed chalk grassland with patchy gorse and scrub were the favoured habitat. The turf was totally unimproved, herb-rich and grazed, and had a high invertebrate population. Generally staying for several days in both seasons, even in ideal weather, the Ring Ouzels were seen taking surface items from the shortest turf in spring and fed almost entirely on berries in autumn.

The vast majority of Wiltshire records during 1974–2000 involved singletons, and the largest groups in spring were five at Giants Grave, Oare, in April 1987 and five again at Liddington Hill in April 1994; the largest in autumn was four at Dean Hill in October 1997. The longest recorded stay by a Ring Ouzel in Wiltshire was six days, at Liddington Hill during 23–28 April 1998. Liddington Hill, Fyfield Down and Imber have been the most favoured places, though that is probably a result of observer bias. Regular coverage of suitable sites during migration periods, as has been the case in the Liddington Castle area since 1993, would no doubt significantly increase the number of records. Only one was ringed in Wiltshire during 1965–2000.

SBE

Sponsored by West Wilts Ringing Group in memory of Tony Rowe

Blackbird
Turdus merula

Common resident, partial migrant, also winterer from north Britain/Europe

The Blackbird is among Great Britain's most familiar birds, and its rich, languid, fluted song, audible over long distances, is regarded by many as one of the country's best. Wiltshire Blackbirds sing usually from February to July, exceptionally as early as December. They feed mainly on the ground, taking insects and earthworms, but also in bushes and trees on fruit, especially berries, from late summer to early winter. Blackbirds are found in a great variety of habitats, including dense woodland, farmland, parks, heaths, moors, some wetlands, and suburban and inner city sites. In urban gardens they are so bold and obvious for much of the year – and so noisy when they have young in the nest and cats are about – that their almost total inconspicuousness while moulting in the late summer seems to leave a hole.

Normally nesting in hedges and bushes from ground level to 4 m, but some in trees up to 12 m, Blackbirds will also use a wide variety of other sites, especially in and on walls and buildings. Though ground nests under cover are not exceptional, one such with eggs was found in cow parsley at Marden in 1990 (*Hobby*). The substantial open structure is generally built of dry grasses, moss, roots, paper and other materials, cemented inside with a mud cup and an inner lining of fine grasses, but a wide variety of available materials may be used and one in a Warminster scrapyard in 1982 was composed entirely of wire (*Hobby*). Two or three broods are regular, and up to five have been recorded.

The Blackbird has a huge range in the Old World, in various Atlantic islands (from the Canaries and Azores north to the Faeroes and, irregularly, Iceland), from North Africa throughout Europe (except for northern Fenno-Scandia and northern and much

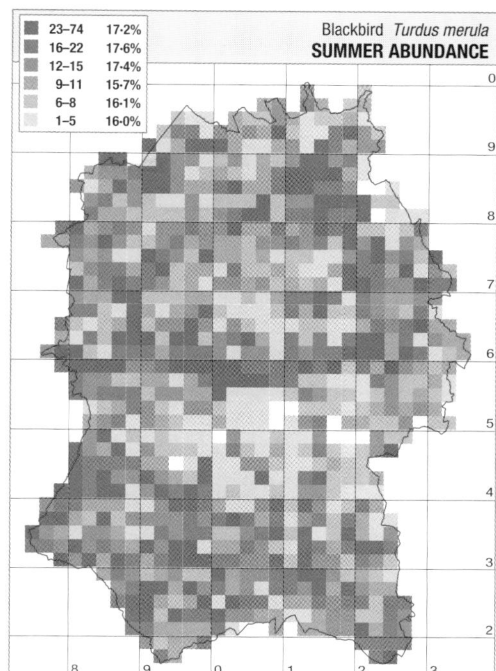

of southern Russia), and from Asia Minor and the Middle East discontinuously across southern Asia, mainly in uplands, to eastern China and south to Sri Lanka; it has also been introduced into New Zealand and southern Australia. The breeding population of Europe, excluding Russia, has been put at 38 to 55 million pairs; and it is noteworthy how, since the mid 19th century, most European towns have been colonised, a process still continuing in the northeast (*EBCC Atlas*).

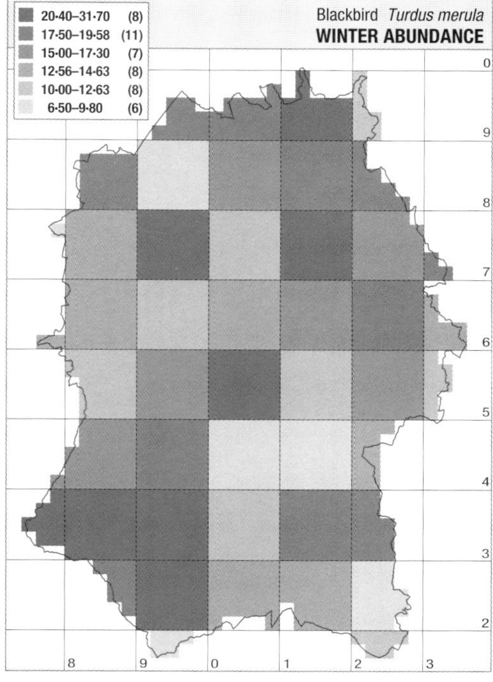

Particularly since it ventured from its favoured woodland habitats into gardens and towns 100–150 years ago, the Blackbird has become one of Great Britain's most widespread breeding species. It is, however, thinner on the ground in the Scottish Highlands and islands and, to lesser extents, parts of southwest Scotland, northwest England and upland Wales, as shown by the abundance map in the *1988–91 Atlas*, which estimated some 4·4 million territories and showed little change in distribution since the *1968–72 Atlas*.

In Wiltshire, the Blackbird was well known to Smith (1887), who noted 'its penchant for soft garden fruits in the summer… but it changes its residence with the season: as soon as wet weather sets in, the blackbirds may be found in the turnip-fields, where they find slugs and snails in abundance; and in hard weather the hedgerows and thick bushes are its resort'. There are, however, few quantitative data and still fewer assessments of status. Mention of Blackbirds in early *WANHM* reports was confined largely to unusual nest-sites, early breeding, and aberrant plumage. Both Peirson (1959) and Buxton (1981) described them simply as 'very common' residents, an assessment confirmed by the *1968–72* and *1988–91 Atlases*, which proved breeding in all of Wiltshire's 33 core and 15 part 10-km squares.

The summer distribution map for 1995–2000 shows Blackbirds virtually throughout the county. They were recorded as breeding in a higher proportion of tetrads (93 per cent) than any other species, and the number of tetrads in which they were seen was exceeded only by Wood Pigeon and Chaffinch. On the other hand, the summer abundance map shows their comparative scarcity on the grasslands of Salisbury Plain and in some other open areas, such as parts of the Marlborough Downs. Breeding densities are very variable, and can be as high as 250 pairs/km² in suburbia (Batten 1973b) and as low as 26 pairs/km² in farmland (*1988–91 Atlas*). On the densities calculated from BBS surveys in Wiltshire and adjacent regions, the county's breeding population probably lies within the range of 65,100 to 112,000 pairs, but perhaps nearer the upper limit.

National survey data show that Blackbirds underwent a shallow long-term decline in numbers of almost one third between the mid 1970s and mid 1990s, but more recent figures suggest a recovery (*BBWC*) – a pattern identical to the better-known decrease of Song Thrushes in all but the magnitude of the drop. The Blackbird decline may have been partly related to the colder winters from the mid 1970s to mid 1980s (Marchant *et al* 1990), but also to changes in farming practices. The conversion of permanent grassland to arable crops resulted in farmers' need to enlarge field units by removing hedges – which drastically reduces the availability of food for this and other farmland species – but declines in woodland numbers, too, point to additional factors being involved (*BBWC*). The population in 2000 was estimated to number 4·6 million territories (*APEP*).

British Blackbirds are virtually all sedentary, though a small proportion moves to Ireland and France. On the other hand, those that nest in many parts of northern and eastern Europe migrate to winter in the south and west, mostly within the boundaries of the breeding range; as a result, large numbers – mainly from Fenno-Scandia, Germany and the Low Countries – move into Great Britain in autumn and, though many may stay here for the winter, others appear to be passage migrants on their way to southwest Europe (*Migration Atlas*). This influx is regularly noted in Wiltshire every autumn, often in association with arrivals of Redwings and Fieldfares, and it is not then unusual to hear their calls as they pass overhead at night. The winter population of Britain and Ireland has been put at over 14 million and 'could well exceed 20 million individuals' (*1981–84 Winter Atlas*).

Some Wiltshire ringing results reflect the sedentary nature of most British Blackbirds, as well as the northern origins of the winter influxes and the southerly and westerly directions of hard-weather movements. No fewer than 339 of the 7327 Blackbirds ringed in the county during 1965–2000 had been recovered by the end of that period, but 316 of those had moved less than 10 km. Only eight had travelled more than 100 km within Great Britain – to various counties west to Cornwall, Devon and Pembrokeshire and north to West Yorkshire and Dumfries & Galloway – but five others were recovered abroad: two in Germany and one each in France, Sweden and Finland.

The French recovery – of a female ringed as a nestling at Porton on 5 June 1962 and found dead at Blainville (Manche) on 25 February 1963 – had thus been raised in southern England and moved across the Channel in what was one of the two most prolonged severe winters since the 1939–45 War. The Finnish one, having been ringed at Corsham on 10 February 1980 and recovered on 6 April 1981, was presumably a winter visitor to Britain that had returned to its country of origin. In the reverse direction, one ringed in Sweden on 4 November 1989 was recovered at Edington on 8 December 1989, and a first-year male ringed at Beervelde in West Vlaaderen (Belgium) on 27 September 1992 was found dead at Tisbury on 25 March 1993.

The Blackbird's attraction to soft fruits can sometimes make ringing easy in summer: for example, 90 were caught in five hours at Bromham Fruit Farm on 29 July 1995. Ringing has also demonstrated site-fidelity: one ringed at Larkhill on 8 July 1983 was retrapped there on 4 March 1987, and another caught at Clanger Wood on 15 May 1994 was still at the same place almost exactly five years later, on 16 May 1999.

Blackbirds were found in all but one per cent of tetrads covered in the winter survey during 1998–2000; only Chaffinches were recorded in more. The winter map roughly mirrors the summer abundance map, and any differences apparent may be due to the latter's coarser scale. Extrapolation from tetrad data gives a winter total of just over 14,400, and a combination of the summer estimate and the ratio of summer-to-winter timed counts suggests that the figure at that season is likely to lie between 101,000 and 174,000 individuals.

SBE

Sponsored by the Appleford family in memory of Bert Appleford

---

Fieldfare

Turdus pilaris

Common winter/passage, breeds Fenno-Scandia, winters west/south Europe

This large and handsome thrush – possessed of loud and very distinctive *chack-chack-chack* calls – is familiar to Wiltshire birdwatchers only as a winter visitor from late autumn through to early spring, though it has nested elsewhere in southern England. Fieldfares breed regularly from eastern France, the Low Countries and Fenno-Scandia across Eurasia to eastern Siberia, but have also nested as far west as Greenland and as far south as Greece. The breeding population of Europe, excluding Russia, has been estimated at 5·2 to 7·4 million pairs (*EBCC Atlas*).

In Great Britain, Fieldfares were first discovered nesting in Orkney in 1967, and in the next seven years small numbers did so from Shetland southward as far as the English Midlands (*1968–72 Atlas*). Although the *1988–91 Atlas* found none in Shetland or Orkney, continued breeding in the northern half of Britain – though involving fewer than 25 pairs – suggested a link with Fenno-Scandia. On the other hand, a pair that successfully fledged young in Berkshire in 1988 (Standley *et al* 1996) and another pair in Kent in 1991 (*1988–91 Atlas*) could point to a connection with the then rapidly increasing Belgian population. During 1992–2000 the maximum number of reported British pairs varied between zero and ten (*RBBP*).

Fieldfares winter mainly in western, central and southern Europe, from Turkey to the Nile delta, and in northwest Iran, and are irregular farther south of those areas. (But large numbers have sometimes arrived in, for example, northwest Africa during severe winters.) They were familiar visitors to 19th century Wiltshire and 'many a day's sport and much disappointment too do these wary birds afford to the schoolboy gunner' (Smith 1887). Seven local names indicate how well-known Fieldfares have long been in the county; one of them, 'felt' (field), being used in many other parts of England (Jones & Dillon 1987). The status of the species was clearly unchanged four decades later, when the 1929 bird report in *WANHM* described it as 'not uncommon'. Peirson (1959) added that it was 'usually more numerous than the Redwing... common at the end of winter on the northward migration but in the middle of winter... less common and many birds seem to have moved away south'.

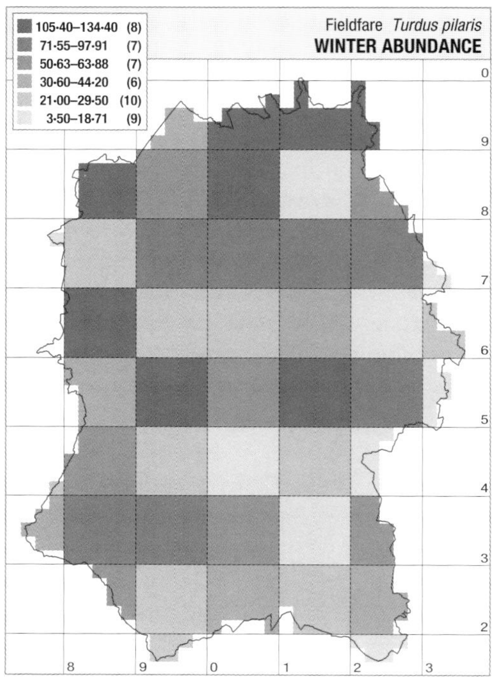

Buxton (1981) improved on this with 'Whilst the weather remains mild the high ground is occupied by large flocks. Cold weather soon moves those flocks down into more enclosed areas where hawthorn berries are more available. If hard weather continues for more than a few days numbers dwindle rapidly as the birds move on'. The *1981–84 Winter Atlas* recorded Fieldfares in every one of Wiltshire's 48 core and part 10-km squares, and showed that the majority of these had counts of over 500.The winter map for 1998–2000 shows that Fieldfares were again found throughout the county, most numerously in the north, centre and southwest. Areas of lower density were in large urban areas (*eg* Swindon) and heavily wooded areas (*eg* Savernake), but the species' apparent sparseness on parts of Salisbury Plain could have been influenced by the periods when the counts were made: as Buxton pointed out, the numbers on the higher areas tend to be in the early and late parts of the winter.

Extrapolation from the sample tetrad counts produced a figure of roughly 50,000 – twice as many as Redwings (*qv*), which made the Fieldfare the fourth most numerous winter species in Wiltshire, after Wood Pigeon, Starling and Rook – and the county population is estimated to lie between 125,000 and 175,000. This represents a remarkably high proportion of the total of roughly 680,000 Fieldfares thought to winter in Great Britain in the 1980s (*1981–84 Winter Atlas*).

Flocks usually arrive in central and southern England during October (*1981–84 Winter Atlas*). Found anywhere, though scarcest in the highlands and islands of Scotland, they all originate from Fenno-Scandia (*Migration Atlas*), where the timing of departure depends on the abundance of the rowan berries there: the heavier the crop, the later Fieldfares migrate. Wiltshire's earliest ever record was on 7 August 1958, and during 1974–2000 the first dates were in August (three years), September (five), October (18) and November (one), though widespread arrivals never took place before October and usually in the second half of that month.

Only 183 Fieldfares were ringed in Wiltshire during 1965–2000, but these generated two overseas recoveries, both in France: one ringed in Chippenham on 12 December 1981 was shot 220 km away only 15 days later, on 27 December; the other ringed at Corsham on 22 February 1986 was shot in Charente-Maritime on 1 January 1987. There have also been two recoveries in the county of foreign-ringed Fieldfares, one from Sweden in 1952 (no details available) and the other ringed on 19 October 1982 in Norway and recovered at Lyneham on 18 February 1985. These four results fall into the general British pattern of arrivals from Fenno-Scandia and then onward migration by some at least to the adjacent Continent later in the winter (though the one ringed at Corsham had presumably returned north for the intervening breeding season). Movements within and out of Great Britain vary from year to year, depending on the availability of berries and other wild fruit crops, and of invertebrates in open fields; fallen apples in orchards are also a favourite food.

Fieldfares form large roosts, usually in hedges or woodland, occasionally on open stubble, grassland or other open ground (Simms 1978). Roosts have been found at Cricklade, Water Eaton Copse, Somerford Common, Sells Green, Erlestoke and Grovely Wood. An estimated 8000 roosted at Somerford Common on 9 March 1984. A total of 25 other four-figure counts were recorded in *Hobby* during 1990–2000, the largest being 4000 at Chute and 3500 at Hackpen and Everleigh in November–December 1990, 3000 at Water Dean Bottom on Larkhill and 2500 at Parsonage Down in spring 1996, 3000 at Imber in November that same year, and 3000 each at Larkhill and Imber during a large influx in November 1998.

Before they leave in spring, Fieldfare flocks become increasingly restless. Wiltshire's latest records were on 23 May in both 1970 and 1988. The latest dates during 1974–2000 were in April in 13 years – the earliest being on the 17th – and in May in the other 14.

SBE

Sponsored by Eleanor Osborne

Song Thrush
Turdus philomelos

Fairly common if declining resident, partial migrant, winterer from Europe

Having a breeding season that can last from March to July or even into August, this thrush may be heard declaring its territory over a long period. Its song is powerful, audible at distances of up to a kilometre, and highly distinctive, with a repertoire of any of a hundred phrases repeated two to four times. Originally a species of forest with a rich shrub layer, the Song Thrush has adapted to living in residential areas with gardens, but is surprisingly inconspicuous. In winter, it is subordinate to its more numerous cousin, the Blackbird, which drives it off when both are in competition for food. It has, however, the advantage of being able to smash the shells of larger snail species and so obtain a rich source of protein in dry or frozen conditions when earthworms, its preferred food, are unavailable.

Apart from outposts in central and eastern Spain, the Song Thrush breeds from northern Iberia east to Lake Baikal in Siberia, and from Italy and the Balkans north to Ireland, Britain and Fenno-Scandia, as well as in Turkey, the Caucasus and Iran; it has also been introduced to Australia and New Zealand. Numbers in Europe have been estimated at 14 to 18 million pairs (*EBCC Atlas*), and Great Britain's share at 1·0 million territories (*APEP*).

British Song Thrushes are mainly sedentary, but the northern populations are more migratory than the southern (*Migration Atlas*). Of those that do move away from their breeding areas, most remain within Great Britain or cross to Ireland, but a few migrate to western France or Iberia. There is also a significant passage of Fenno-Scandian Song Thrushes through Britain in autumn, although the numbers involved and their ultimate destinations remain unknown. Many from the Low Countries winter in Britain, but they form a small part of the total, predominately British, population at that season.

A nestling ringed on 1 June 1961 at Porton was shot in France on 2 January 1962 and there were also winter recoveries of Wiltshire-ringed Song Thrushes in Devon and Cornwall in 1963, all perhaps indicating southerly cold-weather movements. One ringed in Corsham on 10

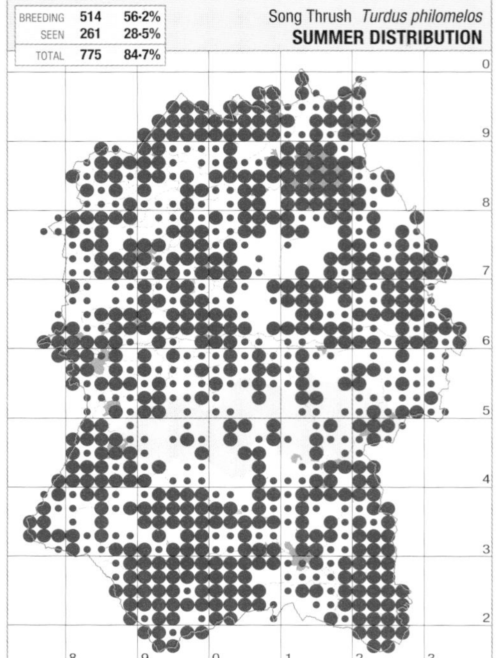

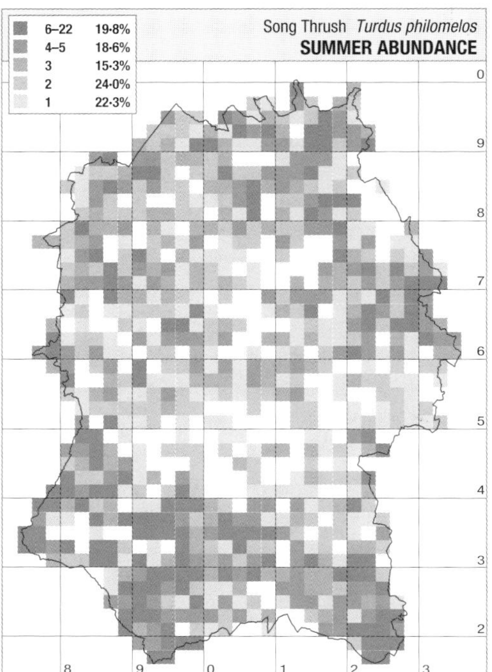

February 1986 and found dead in Burnham Market (Norfolk) on 29 April 1987 was possibly a Continental immigrant returning northeast. The number of Song Thrushes ringed in Wiltshire during 1965–2000 was 1912, but, whereas the highest combined total of fledged birds and chicks in any one year was 139 in 1983, numbers showed a general decline during the 1990s, with an all-time low of just ten in 1998. This pattern does not, however – as will be seen below – accord with that of the Song Thrush's population changes in the county.

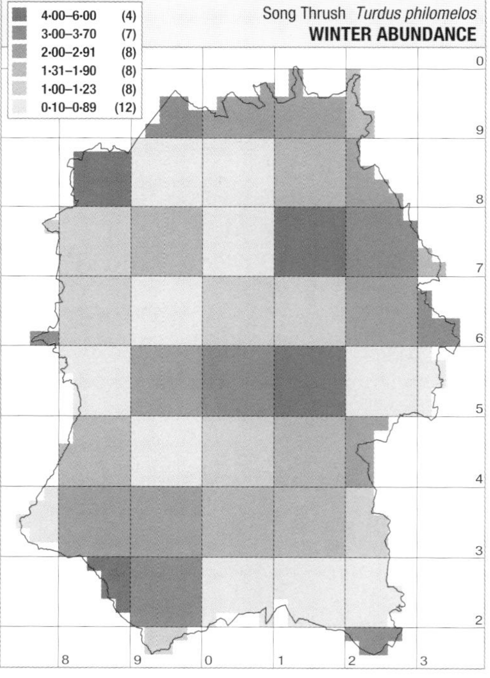

Historically in Wiltshire, Smith (1887) noted the Song Thrush as a 'favourite songster known to all', and described how numbers increased 'periodically' with arrivals from elsewhere, while at other times they seemed 'almost to have deserted us'. Peirson (1959) – who reported many killed by the cold of early 1947 – and Buxton (1981) both described this species as common, the latter adding that it was 'much less numerous than the Blackbird'. The *1988–91 Atlas* showed Song Thrushes to be distributed virtually throughout Great Britain, but to be most numerous in the southeast, while much of Wiltshire formed part of a large area of relatively low density compared with the rest of southern England. Nevertheless, this species was recorded as breeding in all of the county's 33 core 10-km squares by both the *1968–72* and *1988–91 Atlases*, and also by the summer tetrad survey of 1995–2000.

A national decline in Song Thrushes occurred from about the 1940s, attributed to cold weather, particularly in 1947/48 (*1875–1900 Atlas*). Although there followed a slow recovery, the harsh winter of 1962/63 was estimated to have killed about 40 per cent of the British population. Song Thrush pairs on a CBC plot of 100 ha at Sunnyhill Farm near Pewsey (Gillam 1984) then numbered only three, but the total increased annually to a maximum of 16 in 1968; that number was halved in 1971, then fluctuated between four and eleven pairs until 1976 when it crashed to two; by 1980 only one pair remained, and there was none in 1982 and 1983. This typified a drastic national decline that reached its lowest figure in 1992. In Great Britain as a whole, the crash in the mid 1970s was attributed at the time to prolonged droughts in the summers of 1975–76, when food for juveniles was very scarce. The British population more than halved between the mid 1970s and early 1990s (*BBWC*). Agricultural intensification, woodland drainage and depletion of the shrub layer were all implicated; but, while the falling survival of first-year birds is known to have driven the decline, the primary cause remains unknown. There was, however, an increase of around 20 per cent between 1997 and 2002 nationally, and a local recovery from about 1992 was reflected by increases on the CBC sites at both Ravensroost and Biss Woods, though there was no change at Home Covert, Roundway (Gillam 1996).

The Wiltshire summer maps show evidence of breeding by Song Thrushes in over half of all tetrads, and presence in nearly a further third. Most of the blank tetrads on the distribution map are either on SPTA or where there are large areas of arable land or grazed downland, mainly on high ground. Only 94 territories were estimated on SPTA by Stanbury *et al* (2000), a density of 0·4 birds/km², compared with an average of 15 territories/km² at Home Covert (Gillam 1996). Swindon, the largest urban area in the county, occupies the 10-km square with the highest number of 'proved breeding' tetrads. There Song Thrushes probably nest mainly in gardens, where adults carrying food are more easily seen than in the wider countryside. It is likely – as, of course, for many other species – that a proportion of the tetrads where Song Thrushes were noted as only present, as in ST95, would have proved to hold breeding pairs if additional observations had been possible. The abundance map indicates that much of Wiltshire is not prime Song Thrush habitat, but a number of surveys using BBS methodology in the county and surrounding regions suggest a breeding population of 10,100 to 21,200 pairs.

Both the *1981–84 Winter Atlas* and the WOS winter survey recorded Song Thrushes throughout the county at that season, the winter map roughly agreeing with the summer abundance map. Except in autumn, Song Thrushes tend to be rather solitary and – unlike Fieldfares and Redwings – to feed in cover rather than in the open; so it is not surprising that the winter survey during 1998–2000 produced an extrapolated total of just 1600, compared with 50,000 Fieldfares and 24,100 Redwings. This figure is, however, less than two-thirds of the summer count, whereas the *1981–84 Winter Atlas* suggested that winter numbers of Song Thrushes in Great Britain differed little from those of the breeding population. On that basis it may not be unreasonable to conclude that the numbers in Wiltshire during winter may be of the order of 25,000–50,000 individuals.

The Song Thrush has prompted conservation concerns because of its marked decline since the mid 1970s. It may not, however, be too optimistic to predict that the slight upturn in its fortunes at the end of the 1990s could be the beginning of a stabilisation in the population, albeit at a much lower level than in the early 1970s.

PAC & SBE

Sponsored by Ian & Gill Cardy

Redwing

Turdus iliacus

Common winter/passage, breeds Iceland/north Europe, winters southwest, may have bred once

When perched these small and rather restless thrushes are easily identified by their bold white supercilia and chestnut-red flanks, and in flight the chestnut-red wing-linings that give them their English name catch the eye if the light is right. Although often associated with Fieldfares, Redwings prefer smaller and less rough fields and, when feeding singly or in small groups, are easily overlooked. They forage for earthworms on pasture, particularly on moist ground, and in stubble and root fields; they also feed on tree fruits in open woods and hedgerows, and in hard weather move into urban areas to eat berries on shrubs.

Redwings breed right across northern Eurasia from Iceland to eastern Siberia. The breeding population of Europe, excluding Russia, has been estimated at 5·0 to 6·5 million pairs, of which the largest numbers are in Fenno-Scandia (*EBCC Atlas*). The Redwings of northern Europe, including Iceland, are migratory and winter from Ireland, Britain and adjacent continental countries as far east as Denmark and Germany and southward in the west to North Africa, as well as in other Mediterranean countries eastward to the Black Sea region, Asia Minor, the Levant and the southern Caspian.

Although mainly winter visitors to Great Britain, Redwings were first recorded nesting in Scotland in 1925 and then sporadically until 1967, in which year seven pairs were located; in 1968 no fewer than 20 pairs were found in Wester Ross alone and by 1972 some 300 pairs were breeding in Scotland (*1968–72 Atlas*). Two decades later, the population was only 40–80 pairs in any one year (*1988–91 Atlas*), and during 1992–2000 the highest numbers reported varied between nine and 38 (*RBBP*). Redwings have now also nested in a few English counties, notably in Kent where this was proved at least five times during 1975–91 (Taylor 1981). A pair that nested on Fair Isle in 1935 was thought to be of the slightly larger and darker subspecies *coburni*, which is native to Iceland and the Faeroes, but most British breeders are believed to be of the nominate race, which is found over the whole of the rest of the range.

Redwings were familiar winter visitors to Wiltshire in the 19th century and arrived 'a few weeks before' the Fieldfares (Smith 1887). The 1929 bird report described this species as 'A fairly common winter visitor' (*WANHM*), to which Peirson (1959) added 'common at the beginning and end of winter but less common in the middle … when many birds seem to move away further south and west. In severe winters those that do not are mostly killed by the cold. This was very noticeable in 1916–17, 1929 and 1947'. The severe winter of 1962/63, when many moved westwards to the milder climate of Ireland (*1981–84 Winter Atlas*), can be added to that list.

The extremes of Wiltshire's arrival and departure dates have been 3 September in 1931 and 1934 (*WANHM*) and 21 May in 1978 (*Hobby*), and the earliest arrivals were in September in 14 of the autumns of 1974–2000 and in the first 13 days of October in the remainder. The latest departure dates were during 5–27 April in all but two of those 27 years.

Of 1143 Redwings ringed in Wiltshire during 1965–2000, nine were later recovered abroad – in France (two), Italy, Belgium, Denmark, Sweden, Poland, Finland and Russia – and singletons ringed in Belgium and Estonia have also been found in the county. Those recovered in summer in Poland, Finland and Russia give an indication of the breeding areas of at least some of the Redwings wintering in Wiltshire. National ringing data show that most winterers in Great Britain are from Fenno-Scandia and north Russia, and even from across the Urals; there have also been a few late-autumn recoveries of the Icelandic *coburni* in Scotland (*Migration Atlas*), and some trapped in a roost of 3000 at Bratton in December 1983 showed characters of this race.

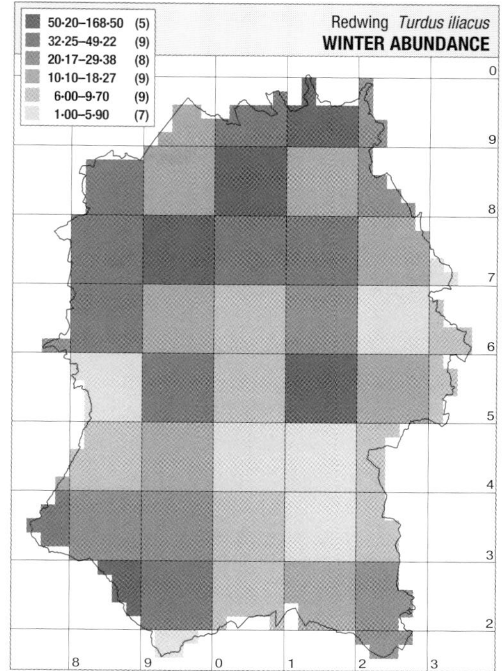

Redwings are nomadic in winter and move widely in response to weather conditions and availability of food. Those that winter in Great Britain in one year may be in southeast Europe in a subsequent winter (*1981–84 Winter Atlas*), but one ringed at Longbridge Deverill on 15 February 1984 and recovered close by at Hill Deverill on 19 January 1985 indicated wintering in the same area in successive years.

Some 650,000 Redwings wintered in Great Britain in the 1980s (*APEP*), and the *1981–84 Winter Atlas* recorded them in all of Wiltshire's 10-km squares, with counts in excess of 396 in the majority. The WOS winter survey in 1998–2000 likewise found them in every 10-km square, and in over three-fifths of all the tetrads surveyed. The winter map has some subtle differences from that of the Fieldfare, and in general shows lower densities in urban and wooded areas. The low density on the open grasslands of SPTA may be related to the methodology used or to availability of food; but Redwings tend to avoid high ground and favour damp pastures in the clay vales. Extrapolation from the winter survey data indicates a figure of some 24,100 Redwings in Wiltshire, about half that of Fieldfares, and the actual total is estimated to be in the range of 60,400 to 181,000 individuals. Clearly, though, numbers wintering vary with the breeding success in the previous summer, the availability of food both here and elsewhere, and the severity of the weather.

Before leaving in spring, flocks of Redwings can frequently be heard uttering a musical chorus and there are several county records of full song in March and April. Although breeding has not previously been considered to have taken place in Wiltshire, Jefferies (1879) described three or four pairs of Redwings and shot one to 'make quite sure', adding that 'Afterwards I found a nest, and had the pleasure of seeing the young birds come to maturity and fly'. Unfortunately, he gave few details, but the evidence points to its having been in the Coate Water area during 1868–77. This was not mentioned by Smith (1887), Hony (1915a), Peirson (1959) or Buxton (1981) in their reviews of Wiltshire's birds, but, as none of them formally dismissed it either, it seems likely that the published report may have been overlooked, probably because of the lack of specific reference to Wiltshire. There appears to be no good reason to reject this observation and, although no other British records of nesting records are known before the 1920s and 1930s, the now regular (if fluctuating) population in Scotland and the odd instances of breeding in English counties in the last three decades of the 20th century make it seem less unlikely.

SBE

Mistle Thrush

Turdus viscivorus

Common resident and perhaps partial migrant

Mistle Thrushes are easy to locate when, on high exposed perches, from December through to early summer, they utter their distinctive fluty songs – not unlike the Blackbird's, but louder and faster, with shorter pauses and a strangely desolate quality – even in strong winds and heavy rain, a habit that gave rise to their long-used colloquial name of 'Storm Cock' (Smith 1887). Their no less distinctive, dry, rattling calls can be heard at any time. They feed mainly on beetles, earthworms and other invertebrates and, from autumn onwards, on a wide variety of berries – especially yew, holly and hawthorn. Although they do also take the white berries of mistletoe in Great Britain, it is their liking of the red berries of another species of mistletoe in Mediterranean countries that appears to have given them their name (Hardy 1969). They nest early, laying their first clutches by mid March or even late February.

The Mistle Thrush breeds from northwest Africa through much of Europe east into Siberia, and also from Turkey patchily eastwards through northern Iran to central Asia and the northwest Himalayas; northern and east European and most Asiatic populations are migratory, wintering in and just beyond the south of the range. Historically, the species was associated chiefly with the middle-altitude montane forests of continental Europe, but during the past 200 years spread along the Atlantic and North Sea coasts of northwest Europe, colonising most of Ireland during 1807–50 and also gradually northern Britain, the Netherlands and Denmark in the late 19th and early 20th centuries (*BWP*, *1988–91 Atlas*). The breeding population of Europe, excluding Russia, has been estimated at 2·2 to 3·1 million pairs, and the species is now absent only from Iceland, from treeless regions of Fenno-Scandia, from both arid and wet lowlands of Spain and Italy, and from the great open plains that stretch from eastern Hungary through Romania into the Ukraine and southern Russia.

In Great Britain, Mistle Thrushes are widespread, though largely absent from the Scottish islands, most frequent in southeast England and, as in for example the East Anglian fens, least numerous where trees are few (*1988–91 Atlas*). Before 1800, they were rare north of a line from the Gower peninsula to the Wash and uncommon even in the south (*1988–91 Atlas*) – where, however, they were perhaps commoner in the southwest (*1875–1900 Atlas*). The reasons for their subsequent increase in range and numbers remain unclear. Their preferred habitats are woodland edges and open grassland with scattered mature trees and hedgerows, and they have spread from woodlands into cultivated land, parks, large gardens and even city centres, but despite this expansion into new habitats and a great widening of their range their population density has remained relatively low; they also defend larger territories than do other thrush species in the same habitats (Simms 1978).

In Wiltshire, Smith (1887) found the Mistle Thrush 'common everywhere' and 'for the greater part of the year ... a lonely bird ... often ... seen amidst the clumps of trees in the open spaces of a park'. Peirson (1959) described it as 'A very common resident, in summer and autumn it forms small flocks, particularly on the downland. Many were killed by the cold of 1947 but the numbers recovered quickly'. Buxton (1981) added little, but stated that it was 'much less numerous than either Blackbird or Song Thrush' and that its late summer flocks 'rarely exceed 100 individuals'.

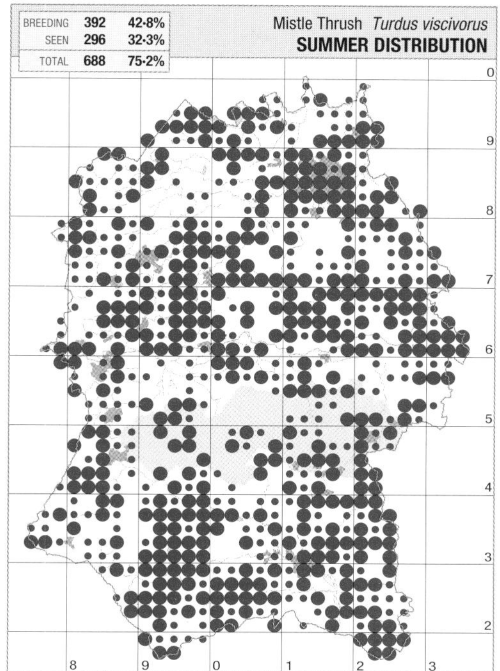

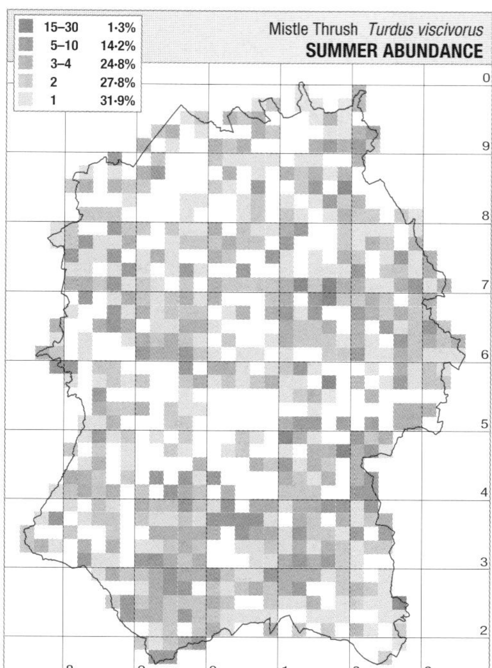

National trends show a period of relative stability in numbers during the late 1960s and early 1970s, followed by a downturn in the mid to late 1970s – falling by a third between then and the mid 1990s (*BBWC*). Similar trends have been noted for Blackbird, Song Thrush and Sky Lark, which suggests that the same environmental factors may have applied. The decline was especially notable on farmland, but recent data suggest that numbers have now stabilised (*BBWC*). Despite this fall, only a two per cent reduction in range was noted between the *1968–72* and *1988–91 Atlases*, and Mistle Thrushes were mapped as breeding in all the county's 33 core 10-km squares by the first of those and in all but two by the second.

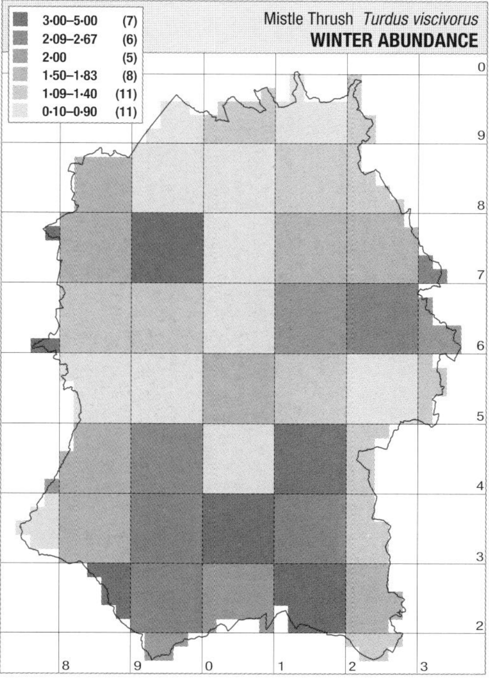

The summer survey of 1995–2000 again showed Mistle Thrushes breeding in all the core squares. Indeed, it recorded the species in three-quarters of all tetrads, and found evidence of breeding in just over two-fifths. The summer distribution map demonstrates absence or scarcity in parts of Salisbury Plain and on the higher ground of the Marlborough Downs – areas with few trees – but other gaps are more difficult to explain. It also shows that, whilst more than half of the occupied tetrads held only one or two birds, between three and ten were counted in two-fifths and 15 to 30 in a few, probably including some post-breeding flocks concentrated on the Marlborough Downs, edges of Salisbury Plain, West Wiltshire Downs, Vale of Wardour and Cranborne Chase.

This species is clearly less numerous in Wiltshire than the Song Thrush, and a figure of 2980 to 6770 pairs, produced from local BBS surveys, suggests numbers are around a quarter of those of its congener. This total appears to be an equitable proportion of the 205,000 pairs of Mistle Thrushes estimated for Great Britain as a whole in 2000 (*APEP*), given the size of the county.

Post-breeding flocks of Mistle Thrushes form from late summer. In Wiltshire during 1990–2000 – apart from a 'Highly unusual spring count of 60 at Coate Water…with Fieldfare flock' on 5 April 1998 (*Hobby*) – double-figure concentrations were noted only between mid June and mid November, mostly in July and August. Indeed, the latter month saw the largest count of the period, an exceptional 250 on set-aside at Cholderton on 27 August 1994. Only five other flocks exceeded 50 during this 11–year period, the largest having been 68 at Durrington on 2 August 2000. In southern England at least, the flocks break up in late autumn when many adults remain close to the fruit-bearing trees or shrubs that they defend from November to February (Snow & Snow 1984).

The *1981–84 Winter Atlas* mapped Mistle Thrushes throughout Wiltshire, as did the winter survey of 1998–2000 – which found them in well over half of all surveyed tetrads, but at higher densities in the south and the northeast. No winter tetrad counts were higher than five, which reflects the dispersal of the post-breeding flocks; indeed, most counts were between one and three and, as in summer, the density was slightly higher on the chalk downs. The *1981–84 Winter Atlas* also considered that numbers in Great Britain at that season were 'appreciably smaller than the breeding population'– and the winter survey counts in 1998–2000 totalled just 1390, compared with 1760 in summer – but ringing results suggest that most British Mistle Thrushes are highly sedentary (*Migration Atlas*). On that basis, the winter population is estimated to be of the order of 7500 to 15,000 individuals.

National ringing data show little indication of any appreciable emigration in winter, although there are a few recoveries in France, Belgium and Ireland, and evidence that small numbers of Continental immigrants arrive in Great Britain in autumn (*Migration Atlas*). A total of 281 Mistle Thrushes ringed in Wiltshire during 1965–2000 generated only six recoveries, none of which had moved more than 9 km. Nor had either of the two inward recoveries travelled much farther, having moved just 21 and 29 km from neighbouring counties: one ringed near Bath (Somerset) on 30 April 1978 and found dead near Warminster on 28 April 1981, and the other caught at Winchester (Hampshire) on 26 May 1963 and recovered at Newton Tony on 28 July the same year.

SBE

Sponsored by Peggy Bucknall

The curiously patterned juvenile Mistle Thrushes, with their buff spots and streaks and slightly scaly darker markings on heads and backs, can be pitfalls for the unwary in summer and have more than once been misidentified as White's Thrushes (*eg* BW Tucker in Witherby *et al* 1938–41), which are rare autumn vagrants to Britain and Europe. That seems likely to have been the identity of the supposed White's Thrush caught in fruit nets in a garden at Upton Lovell in July 1934 and published in the bird report for that year in *WANHM* with the introductory and doubtless cautionary comment by the then editor, CMR Pitman, 'I feel obliged to include…'.

Eds

Cetti's Warbler

Cettia cetti

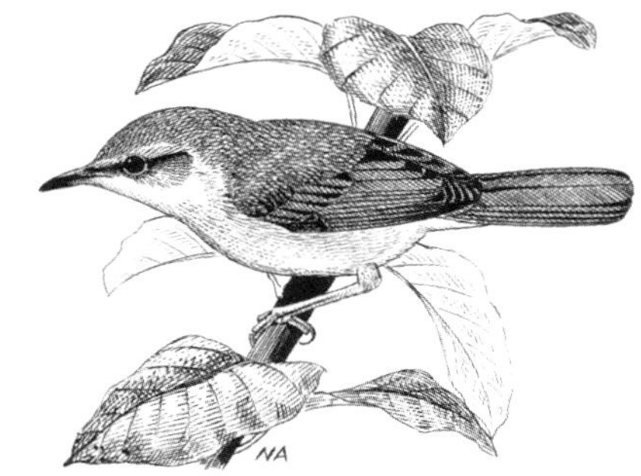

Very local resident since 1987, colonised Britain from France in early 1970s

The startlingly loud and far-carrying song of the male Cetti's Warbler – which can be heard at virtually any time of the year – is usually the only way of locating this shy and skulking bird, which is Europe's one representative of a largely Asiatic and Indonesian genus of 'bush-warblers'. The historical breeding range of this particular species extends from North Africa, Iberia and the Mediterranean countries through Asia Minor east to Afghanistan; it is also a summer visitor to the Caucasus, the shores of the Caspian and the lowest stretches of the Ural River.

In the 19th century, Cetti's Warblers were found no closer to England than Provence, but a gradual northward expansion through western France became obvious from the 1920s and, although this species is very vulnerable to severe weather and its advance was significantly checked from time to time by hard winters, it had reached the Channel coast by 1961. Great Britain's first appeared in Hampshire that same March – three old specimens from Sussex during 1904–16 had been among the 'Hastings Rarities' later rejected as fraudulent (Nicholson & Ferguson-Lees 1962) – and breeding was confirmed in Kent 11 years later (*1968–72 Atlas*).

Singing males increased dramatically in England over the next decade, from two in 1972 to about 300 by 1983, but the population then dropped by roughly a third in a series of cold winters in the 1980s (*1988–91 Atlas*). Its numbers subsequently recovered, however, and went on to reach a record total of 678 'pairs' by 2000. ('Pairs' is no more than a convenient term, as males can be monogamous or polygamous, or unmated.) By this time east and southeast counties were no longer the stronghold, as the species was being found north to a line from southern Wales to the Wash and more than half of the total was in the milder southwestern counties, especially Devon, Dorset, Somerset and Hampshire (*RBBP*). The breeding population of Europe as a whole, but excluding Russia, has been estimated at 431,000 to 1·3 million 'pairs' (*EBCC Atlas*).

Cetti's Warblers are generally regarded as residents, yet are clearly capable of dispersing to find new breeding areas. Individuals from the Continent still cross to England in autumn. Evidence about the movements of the British population is limited, but, once established as breeders, adults become mainly sedentary and it is mostly juveniles, especially the females, which disperse in random directions (*Migration Atlas*).

The first Wiltshire records were both of singing males in October at Coate Water, on the 30th in 1980 and on the 3rd in 1981; in 1985 an adult was ringed at Steeple Langford on 12 August and a singing male was located at Britford on 13 October. Breeding was first proved at Petersfinger in 1987 and 1989; a pair at Standlynch Meadows during 1987–89 was possibly also nesting. Fieldwork for the *1988–91 Atlas* confirmed breeding in one 10-km square and presence in three more; since 1990 Cetti's Warblers have been regular on the Salisbury Avon between Downton and Salisbury, and breeding was proved there in 1992, 1996 and 1998 (*Hobby*). The nesting of this skulking species is difficult to confirm, but the regular presence of singing males in established territories makes it highly likely that it is now annual.

In the east of the county, Cetti's Warblers were first recorded on the Kennet in 1991 and at Chilton Foliat in 1992, followed by an increase to four singing males between the latter site and Ramsbury in 1993. Three males were singing in the Kennet valley in 1994, but none was recorded in 1995–96 or 1998 and only one in 1997; one of two in 1999 was farther west, at Axford, and the other at Littlecote, where an adult was seen carrying food to two young in June. Elsewhere in the county, singing males were recorded at Sharcott in 1990, at CWP in 1997–98, and at Corsham Lake in 1998.

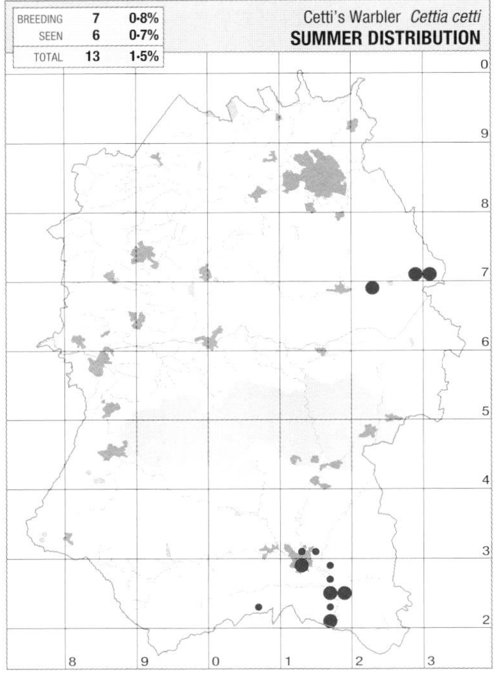

The summer map shows the limited nature of the distribution of Cetti's Warblers in Wiltshire, and suggests that they have spread up the Salisbury Avon from Dorset and Hampshire, and along the Kennet from Berkshire. In 2000, five singing males were found along the Kennet and ten on the lower Salisbury Avon, and allowing for a few unrecorded on private land it seems likely that the current population is in the range of 15–20 territories. The irregularity of singing males at CWP is noteworthy: perhaps this site is too remote from the sources of colonisation and, in Wiltshire, rivers rather than lakes are the preferred habitat, probably because they remain ice-free in winter. In southern Great Britain as a whole, Cetti's Warblers breed in tangled, dense scrub along wetland margins, and forage on the shaded open mud beneath. Most of these sites are adjacent to reedbeds, which are not themselves much occupied until winter. It thus appears that there is scope for the population to expand in the county, especially if milder winters continue, although suitable habitat is limited in comparison with what is available in the main British strongholds.

No Cetti's Warblers were located during the winter survey, but this was certainly no more than an artefact of the method employed. Given that breeding adults are largely sedentary (*Migration Atlas*), the population at that season must surely be in excess of 30 individuals, perhaps as many as 60 – though most or all could be lost in prolonged icy weather.

Although Cetti's Warbler is such a recent addition to Wiltshire's avifauna, no fewer than 34 had been ringed in the county by the end of 2000. Two of those were recorded subsequently: a juvenile ringed at Downton on 7 August 1994 and then trapped and released at Hungerford (Berkshire) on 29 October the same year showed typical juvenile dispersal, whereas a male ringed at Standlynch Farm on 25 May 1998 and retrapped there more than a year later, on 19 June 1999, emphasises that territorial adults are more strictly sedentary.

(See also page 725.)

SBE

Grasshopper Warbler

Locustella naevia

Local and decreasing summer visitor, breeds Europe, winters Africa

Male Grasshopper Warblers utter their monotonous, high-pitched, 'mechanical' songs, reminiscent of the noise of a fishing reel, in the contrasting Wiltshire habitats of downland scrub and river valley. This 'reeling' may be heard by day or night – but, unless the bird is unmated, chiefly in the early morning and late evening. Without this sound (which older human ears cannot always hear), they would easily be overlooked, as the species tends to skulk in low and tangled vegetation, but, once its surprisingly ventriloquial reeling has been pinpointed, the singing male can often be seen singing on a low exposed perch.

Fortunately, this species has a longer period of regular song than most other migratory British warblers because it normally raises two broods, and sometimes three, particularly in southern England (Walpole-Bond 1938) but even as far north as Cumbria in favourable warm summers (Callion *et al* 1990). They arrive in April, the earliest ever Wiltshire date being 5 April 1999, and reeling usually continues into early August, after which few Grasshopper Warblers are found, the latest county record being on 5 October 1996 at Chirton Gorse.

Grasshopper Warblers breed across Eurasia from northernmost Spain, France, the north Balkans and the Caucasus north to Ireland, Britain and southern Fenno-Scandia, and thence eastwards across Russia to Siberia and Mongolia. The population of Europe, excluding Russia, has been estimated at 279,000 to 427,000 pairs: both range and numbers increased during the mid 20th century, but, while subsequent trends are unclear, there is some evidence that the species has been significantly affected, not only by habitat change and destruction in its breeding areas, but also by drought in its sub-Saharan winter quarters (*EBCC Atlas*). The European population appears to winter mainly in West Africa, though the limits are not well known: British-ringed individuals have been recovered in Algeria (February) and Senegal (January), and two ringed in Senegal in the northern winter have subsequently been recovered in Great Britain (Urban *et al* 1997) – but the one in Algeria in February may well have been on its way north again. (None of the 51 Grasshopper Warblers ringed in Wiltshire during 1965–2000, most as adults, has been recovered.)

In Great Britain, Grasshopper Warblers breed in young conifer plantations, rough grassland, downland scrub and damp and boggy areas which provide suitable sites for their nests; these are usually on or near the ground in the sides of tussocks of dry grasses, rushes or sedges, hidden by overhanging stems and entered by a run. The *1988–91 Atlas*, which estimated the population at 10,500 pairs, showed them to be widely scattered across the country, but noted an alarming thinning in range since the *1968–72 Atlas*. A rapid decline between the mid 1960s and mid 1980s has prompted conservation concerns, but is difficult to quantify; since then, the small numbers involved have made analysis difficult, but national schemes suggest fluctuations with no net change since the mid 1990s (*BBWC*).

In Wiltshire, 200 years ago, the Grasshopper Warbler was described as plentiful on Malmesbury Common (Montagu 1802). Nearly a century later, when it was known as the 'mowing machine bird' because of its reeling song, Smith (1887) had 'many notes of its occurrence in all parts of the county, but sparingly, for it is not so common as either

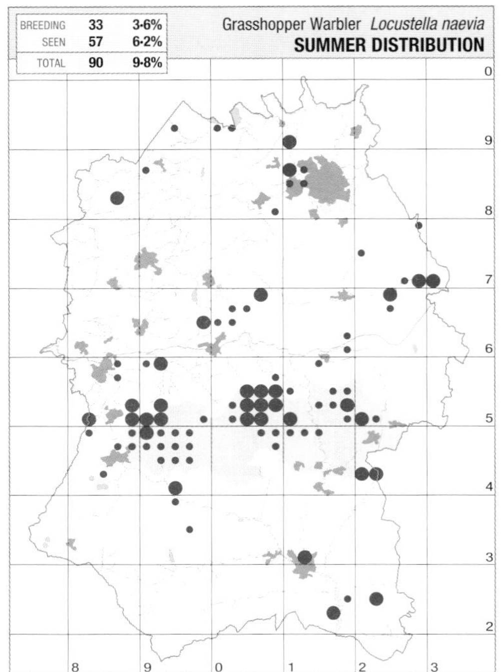

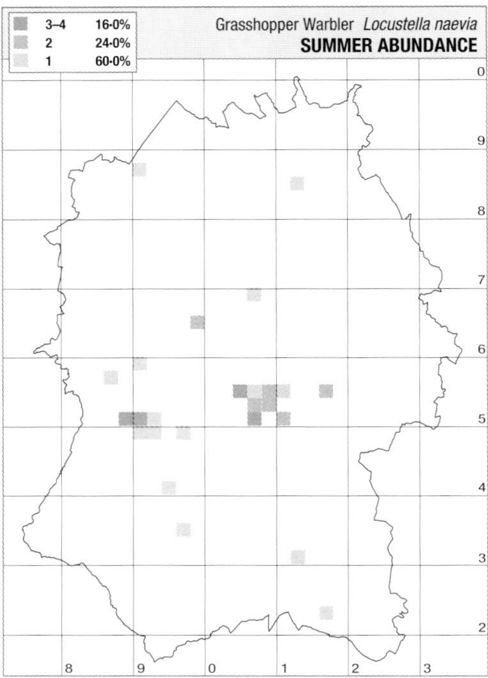

of its congeners' – by which he meant Reed and Sedge Warblers, at that time placed in the same genus – but added that many nests were taken in the vicinity of Marlborough in 1866, where 'unusually large' numbers were also recorded in 1881.

The 1929 bird report in *WANHM* regarded Grasshopper Warblers as 'uncommon…nesting regularly in a few suitable localities', but in 1936 they were 'Seen and heard in surprising numbers, breeding in many localities and varied situations in the neighbourhood of Salisbury'. Peirson (1959) described this species as 'A regular but uncommon summer visitor to river valleys and young plantations…also reported as a passage migrant'. Breeding was proved or probable in 16 of the county's 33 core 10-km squares in the *1968–72 Atlas*, in 15 in the *1988–91 Atlas*, and in 16 again in the 1995–2000 summer tetrad survey. These figures, however, mask the fact that gaps appeared outside the core squares, so that overall the Wiltshire range has thinned.

The distribution map shows that Wiltshire's Grasshopper Warblers are, nowadays, concentrated particularly on Salisbury Plain. Other favoured sites are certain river valleys, notably of the Kennet (from Chilton Foliat to Ramsbury) and of the Ray (at Swindon). The nests of this species are one of the hardest of any British passerine to find, so evidence of breeding was based largely on the presence of reeling males at the same sites on dates at least 14 days apart. Some of these may have been unmated, of course, just as many of those heard singing on only one occasion may actually have been paired and nesting. Salisbury Plain is, however, a long-established breeding area and it seems likely that most of the records from there, at least, related to pairs.

The abundance map further emphasises the importance of Salisbury Plain, where Grasshopper Warblers breed in grassland with such scrub as hawthorn, gorse and brambles. Stanbury *et al* (2000) likewise found scrub – not necessarily at high densities – to be an important part of this species' habitat there. But distribution is variable in Wiltshire because of the transient nature of some habitats. For example, the development of rank grassland at west Swindon and the maturing of young conifer plantations at

Table 109. Grasshopper Warblers *Locustella naevia* in Wiltshire: singing males reported 1990–2000
The count from the RSPB survey of SPTA (Stanbury *et al* 2000) has been excluded to make the other data comparable

	90	91	92	93	94	95	96	97	98	99	00
Singing males	49	38	45	33	35	34	30	27	22	26	22
Sites	33	26	36	14	20	22	25	19	16	18	18

Grovely and Savernake make these sites no longer suitable. Perhaps surprisingly, the overgrown margins of the lakes at CWP rarely attract this species.

In 1989, 54 reeling Grasshopper Warblers were recorded at 43 sites (*Hobby*), but subsequent published totals (table 109) suggest that numbers of both halved during the 1990s. It is now clear, however, that these casual records greatly underestimate numbers on Salisbury Plain. In 2000, an RSPB survey (Stanbury *et al* 2000) identified 85 Grasshopper Warbler territories on SPTA (44 West, 34 Centre, seven East) and, from that sample, estimated a total of 264 territories there, or roughly 2·5 per cent of the British population. It is thus clear that numbers in Wiltshire were considerably higher than records in *Hobby* suggest, but the difference between the annual figures and the much larger estimate produced by the 'distance sampling' analysis used by Stanbury *et al* is considerable and surprising for a species that is relatively well recorded even by casual observations (SB Edwards); it is conceivable that difficulties of judging the distance from the observer to any singing birds may have resulted in overestimation of the total, and Wiltshire's population, including birds away from SPTA, is here put conservatively at 150–275 pairs.

Like those of all migratory species, the Grasshopper Warbler's future in Wiltshire depends not only the availability of suitable habitat in the county but also on factors on its wintering grounds. Yet, given the opportunity, with a laying season that extends from late April to early August, two or three broods, an average brood size of nearly five young and a fledging success rate of 65 per cent (Glue 1990), this species could make a rapid recovery.

(See also page 725.)

SBE

Savi's Warbler
Locustella luscinioides

Vagrant (1 record) from southeast Britain/ west-central Europe, winters Africa

Savi's Warblers are summer visitors to extensive reedbeds from the Mediterranean to the southern Baltic and east into western Asia; though the exact limits are unclear, they winter in sub-Saharan Africa from Senegal to Eritrea. Their distribution is inevitably fragmented by the availability of their habitat, and the breeding population of the whole of Europe, excluding Russia, has been estimated at only 152,000 to 221,000 pairs (*EBCC Atlas*).

Small numbers of Savi's Warblers used to breed in the fens of East Anglia in the 19th century, but drainage is thought to have led to their extinction (*1875–1900 Atlas*). Nesting was not proved again in Great Britain until 1960, this time in Kent, where by 1965 no fewer than 12 males held territories; breeding occurred subsequently in several other southern and eastern counties, and the species even began to spread farther inland (*1968–72 Atlas*). Two decades later there were still 10–17 singing males at a total of 13 localities (*1988–91 Atlas*), but the peak was over.

On the adjacent Continent the moderate increase that had begun in the 1960s was reversed in at least Belgium and the Netherlands from the 1980s (*CBWP*). Correspondingly, the annual numbers of British records of vagrant Savi's Warblers declined from a peak of 38 in 1980 to an average of only nine through the mid 1990s (Fraser *et al* 2000); and in 2000 just one pair bred (*RBBP*). In 1999, the declining status of this warbler, even as a vagrant, had led to its being re-admitted to the list of species considered by the BBRC.

Wiltshire's only Savi's Warbler – a male singing at Coate Water from 6 May 1965 to at least the 20th – had the distinction of becoming the first ever to be ringed in Great Britain when it was trapped on the 10th (*WANHM*, *BBRC*).

GLW & IJF-L

Aquatic Warbler

Acrocephalus paludicola

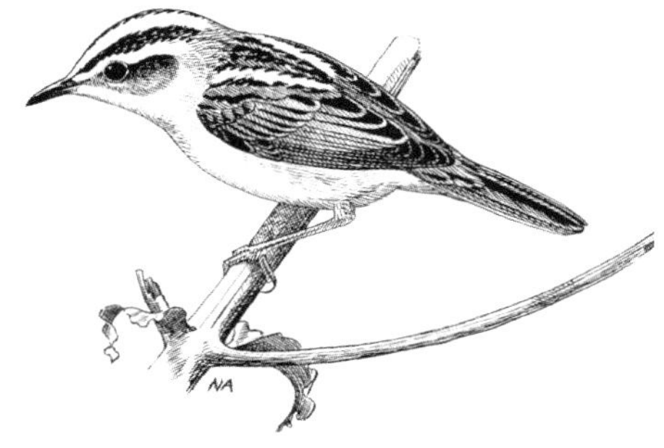

Westward vagrant (3 records), breeds east-central Europe, winters Africa

Aquatic Warblers are summer visitors to low sedge marshland in a narrow and increasingly fragmented strip from eastern Germany, Poland and Hungary through Belarus and across to the Ob in western Asiatic Russia. Their numbers are decreasing and estimates of the population of Europe, excluding Russia, have been put as low as 2850 to 7860 pairs (*EBCC Atlas*). They have a markedly westerly to southwesterly autumn migration that takes some along both sides of the English Channel and down through western France on route to winter quarters in West Africa and other areas south of the Sahara. Thus, they are annual but rare autumn migrants along coastal counties of south England and southwest Wales, almost entirely between early August and early October, but seldom found far inland.

The first of Wiltshire's three Aquatic Warblers was trapped and ringed at Coate Water on 2 September 1958; the other two were both seen at Swindon STW, on 1 September 1970 and on the relatively late dates of 30 September and 1 October 1972 (*WANHM*, *BBRC*). There was an annual average of ten records in Great Britain from 1958 through the 1960s, but this rose to 40 in the 1970s, dropped to 23 in the 1980s and climbed again to 42 in the 1990s (Fraser *et al* 2000, Fraser & Rogers 2001); fewer than ten have been found in some autumns, more than 50 in others and once, in 1976, over 100 (see Fraser & Rogers 2002). These very variable numbers of records of this inconspicuous species on passage are probably influenced not only by weather patterns, but also by the amount of mist-netting in coastal reedbeds.

GLW & SBE

Sedge Warbler

Acrocephalus schoenobaenus

Common summer visitor, breeds much of Europe, winters Africa

Scarce or absent from the strong summer heat of the Mediterranean region, breeding Sedge Warblers favour cooler and wetter conditions from Ireland and western France to western Siberia, and from parts of the Balkans and Asia Minor north even into arctic Fenno-Scandia and Russia. They winter throughout much of sub-Saharan Africa, from Senegal to Ethiopia and south to South Africa. All recoveries of Sedge Warblers ringed in Britain and Ireland have, however, so far been confined to West Africa, especially Senegal but also Mali and four other countries just to the south of those two (*Migration Atlas*).

Sedge Warblers were considered widespread and common in Great Britain during the 19th century (Saunders 1899, *1875–1900 Atlas*). Thus, it is not surprising that Smith (1887) described this species as 'by far the commonest of the genus' in Wiltshire. The inaugural bird report for 1929 in *WANHM* considered it 'A fairly common summer visitor'. There was apparently little change in the British status until the late 1960s, since when there have been marked fluctuations, including four troughs in population size, all linked to survival rates on the African wintering grounds (*BBWC*). In years of drought, the vital habitat provided by extensive floodplains around the Senegal and Niger Rivers is missing, and Sedge Warbler mortality is then high there. After a particularly severe drought in 1983/84, fewer than five per cent of adults returned to the breeding sites in England (Peach *et al* 1991) and 1984–85 marked an obvious low in numbers through the last third of the 20th century.

Elsewhere in Europe, excluding Russia, between 2·1 and 2·7 million pairs have been estimated; numbers are thought to have decreased in France, the Low Countries and Germany but increased in Austria, Finland, Norway and the Ukraine (*EBCC Atlas*). These reported trends may, however, simply be the result of short-term population fluctuations in response to conditions in sub-Saharan Africa during the northern winter.

Sedge Warblers sometimes nest up to 500 m from water, in dry scrub, young conifers and arable crops, but more typically in wetland habitats throughout Great Britain, where their population strongholds lie mainly, but not exclusively, in the east (*1988–91 Atlas*). Singing males are occasionally found away from water in Wiltshire, and reports were published from up to three such sites in five of the years during the 1990s (*Hobby*); in 2000, an RSPB survey of SPTA found two singing in dry grassland and a third in umbellifers (Stanbury *et al* 2000).

The *1968–72 Atlas* recorded Sedge Warblers breeding in 25 of Wiltshire's 33 core 10-km squares, and the *1988–91 Atlas* in 28. The summer distribution map shows evidence of nesting in 25 core squares, so the county population appears to have remained roughly stable during the last third of the 20th century. The same map also shows an unsurprising concentration along rivers, streams, lakes, ponds and canals, where they nest mostly in a variety of rank waterside vegetation. The summer abundance map indicates that the greatest concentrations are found at CWP and along the Thames, Ray, Kennet, Kennet & Avon Canal, Wylye and both the Salisbury and Bristol Avons – though, oddly, the Nadder appears deserted.

Some 297,000 Sedge Warbler territories were estimated in Great Britain in 2000 (*APEP*), but Wiltshire's share is very small. The totals of singing males reported to *Hobby* during 1990–2000 varied from 70 in 1997 to 120 in 1999, and timed counts during the summer tetrad survey in 1995–2000 produced a total of 585 birds. No BBS survey data on

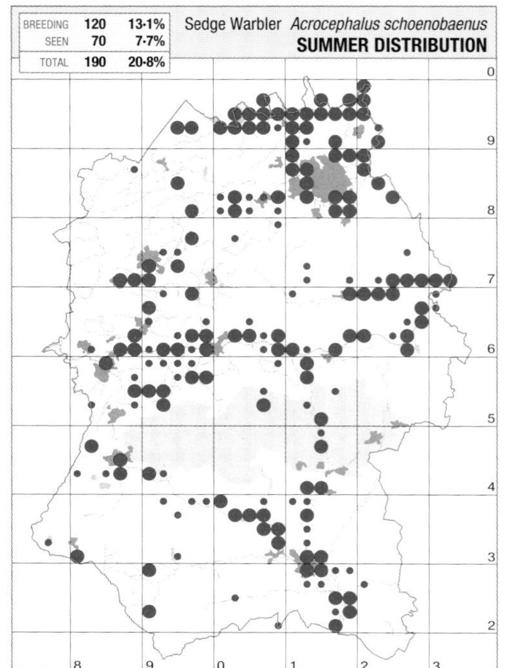

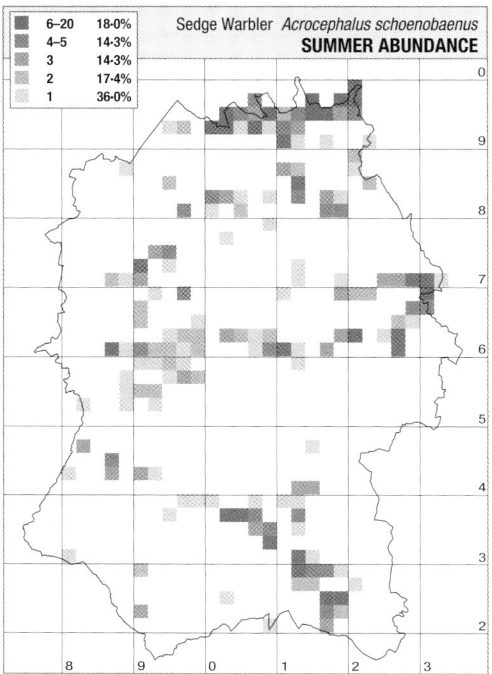

this species are available, but, using the ratios of summer timed counts to the final estimates for other warblers – the latter are generally between four- and eight-fold larger – the Wiltshire population of Sedge Warblers seems likely to be in the range of 2340 to 4680 pairs.

Most Sedge Warblers return to Wiltshire from mid April, though records earlier in that month are not unusual and there have been three in March: on the 20th at Ford and on the 23rd at Clarendon, both in 1957 (*WANHM*), and on the 30th at Petersfinger in 1989 (*Hobby*). In autumn, migration begins in July and continues throughout August and into September. The latest of at least six October reports was on the 23rd at Salisbury in 1952 (*WANHM*). Migrants are sometimes encountered in dry habitats, such as set-aside, field margins and hedgerows (P Combridge).

No fewer than 1141 Sedge Warblers were ringed in Wiltshire during 1965–2000. Ten had been recovered or retrapped elsewhere in Great Britain by the end of that period – all in southern England – and three in continental Europe: ringed at Coate Water in September 1967 and recovered on Helgoland (Germany) in May 1968; ringed near Corsham on 28 August 1970 and retrapped in Seine-Maritime (France) eight days later; and ringed at Corsham Lake on 5 August 1979 and found dead 27 days later in Pyrénées-Atlantiques (France). Half a dozen Wiltshire recoveries or retraps of individuals ringed elsewhere included three from Sussex and two from Kent, as well as one ringed in Northumberland on 31 July 1971 and found dead at Swindon just 17 days later.

PCo

Marsh Warbler

Acrocephalus palustris

Former rare breeder, now overshooting vagrant from east Britain/Europe, winters Africa

Marsh Warblers are summer visitors to Europe, breeding from northern and eastern France north to southern Fenno-Scandia, south to northern Italy, the Balkans and the Caucasus, and extending east into western Asiatic Russia and northwest Iraq. The population of Europe, excluding Russia, has been estimated at 1·5 to 1·9 million pairs (*EBCC Atlas*). The species winters mainly in southeastern Africa. West European Marsh Warblers migrate southeast in autumn, passing through the Middle East and, after an apparent stopover in northeast Africa, continue down to the region of Zambia southwards to the former Cape Province in South Africa (Dowsett-Lemaire & Dowsett 1987). Thus, they return northwest in spring, which means that most of the 50–100 still recorded in Great Britain each year are the result of overshooting in May–June. The number of autumn migrants – mainly on the east coast north to Shetland during September to early November – has, however, been growing since the late 1980s (Fraser e*t al* 1999, Fraser & Rogers 2002), which may have some connection with recent increases in Sweden and Finland.

In spring, variable numbers of lone singing males settle down to hold territories in Great Britain and some pairs still breed. The *1988–91 Atlas* put the national population at fewer than 12 pairs, compared with the 60–80 pairs indicated by the *1968–72* Atlas and a peak in the early part of the 20th century of, conceivably, over 180 pairs (Kelsey *et al* 1989). But proof of breeding is far more difficult than simply finding singing males (which may often be unmated) and, taking the latter as evidence of possible nesting, the maximum annual British total during the 1990s was 58 and the average 34, all mainly in southeastern, eastern and central England; by 2000, 14 of the 21 localities and 20–24 of the maximum of 31 singing males or pairs were in Kent and Suffolk (*RBBP*).

Although Wiltshire lies inside a triangle of one-time established breeding areas from Herefordshire and Worcestershire down to Gloucestershire and Somerset, and eastward through Oxfordshire, Dorset and Hampshire to Sussex and Kent (see Kelsey *et al* 1989), Marsh Warblers have never been well known here. They were evidently breeding in nearly every county around Wiltshire towards the end of the 19th century (*1875–1900 Atlas*), but the species was not even mentioned by Smith (1887). Hall (1900) reported the first breeding – his son having 'had the good luck to find a nest of the Marsh-Warbler… on June 18th of the present year… on one of the tributaries of the river Wylye, near the village of Stapleford… ' – and Hony (1915a) also included this record.

Marsh Warblers then appeared to establish a tentative hold in the county from 1913 to the early 1930s. In the Kennet valley, Peirson (1919) described it as 'A rare summer visitor: the nest was first recorded in 1913: since then in 1914, 1916, 1918, 1919'. Kennedy (1966) added 'then in most years up to 1922', and breeding may have continued after that as Peirson & Walford (1930) described this as 'a summer visitor which possibly nests every year in the [Marlborough] district but is overlooked'. It is worth noting that that particular period coincided with several records of breeding in nearby Berkshire, in 1909, 1918 and 1920–23 (Standley *et al* 1996).

Two nests found 'close to Calne' on 27 May 1916 – 'in the near neighbourhood of many nests' of Reed Warblers – were identified as those of Marsh Warblers, even though the observer added a note of caution as he had had no previous experience of this species, but 'nest, eggs, birds and their song, and locality of nests, seemed to be distinctive' (Gilbert

1916); the Marsh Warbler nests were 'in a dense dry thicket of scrub willow, bramble, coarse grass, etc', which is far less likely for Reed Warblers, and, as nests and song were different, there seems no reason to doubt the record; 27 May is indeed early, but not impossibly so, for nests of this latest-arriving of all summer visitors, whose first eggs are sometimes laid in the last few days of that month (Campbell & Ferguson-Lees 1972).

Breeding was next proved in the parish of Chirton in 1922, when 'Mr. G.W. Godman… found the Marsh Warblers on June 10th… and watched them for some hours… took the nest and five eggs on June 22nd… found… a second nest… with three young on 26th July… This nest was built… in meadowsweet' (Goddard 1922a). The inaugural bird report for 1929 in *WANHM* noted that the species nested near Rowde that year and also stated that it 'Usually nests near Warminster', on the authority of two separate observers, one of whom then reported a 'colony of several pairs' there in 1930 but only a single bird in 1931 (after which neither observer apparently contributed any further records to the bird report). A singleton was identified near Alderbury on 11 May 1934, where it was 'believed to be nesting' (*WANHM*), but this was quite an early date for this late migrant to have arrived – 'there are probably no reliable reports earlier than the second week of May' (*Migration Atlas*) – and it certainly could not have had a nest by then.

Records were infrequent during the next three decades. (Localities were often suppressed at the time in *WANHM* for security, but that is no longer necessary and, where known, they are now included.) Nesting was recorded in 1946 in the Kennet valley near Ramsbury, where 'The young flew on July 20' (Cooke 1946); and a male was reported singing at Mere on 10 September 1948 (*WANHM*), a very late date for song. A male was watched singing by the Kennet & Avon Canal near Devizes on 8 June 1954, and a pair was seen at the same locality five days later (NW Orr). Song was also recorded at Britford on 25 May 1955, and by the Salisbury Avon at Downton on 1 June 1957 (*WANHM*, WOS files). An adult was trapped and ringed on 26 July 1961 at Coate Water, and a male was singing there two years later, on 20th and 23 June 1963; in 1963, too, one was seen near Porton on 15 June and 20 July (all *WANHM*, Webber 1968).

Breeding was established at Coate Water in 1977 (one ringed 7 July, 'Subsequently adult feeding newly fledged young') and 1980 ('2 adults feeding young… and male in song on 27 July, two seen again on 3 August') (WOS files); the pair was also present in 1978 and 1979 (Buxton 1981). A singing male was located at another site in 1978 (Buxton 1981) and an adult was ringed elsewhere in 1984 (*Hobby* 11: 42), though unfortunately neither of these localities can now be traced. Meanwhile, in 1983, 'two adults with newly fledged young' were seen near Ashton Keynes (WOS files). Singing males were found near Salisbury on the early date of 12 May in 1984 and at CWP on 27 June 1987 – a period in which the one-time 100+ population in Worcestershire crashed from 31 territory-holding males to just four (Kelsey *et al* 1989). Thereafter, records in Wiltshire have been few and far between: just lone singing males by the Bristol Avon at Chippenham on 19 June 1993, and by the Kennet at Stitchcombe during 13–15 June 2000 (*Hobby*). Marsh Warblers are great mimics of other birds and the male in 2000 imitated at least 18 different species (see *Hobby*).

The decline in England, which contrasts with increases in continental Europe, particularly during the latter part of the 20th century, is thought to have arisen largely through isolation (*EBCC Atlas*). Kelsey *et al* (1989) discussed such other possible factors as decreasing breeding success, as well as loss of habitat and climatic change (both of which 'may have been important earlier' in reducing the population size), but concluded that by the 1980s the Worcestershire population had reached too small a size to withstand "emigration losses and other factors [such as adverse weather] operating on an isolated 'island' population".

IJF-L & GLW

Reed Warbler

Acrocephalus scirpaceus

Common and increasing summer visitor, breeds Europe, winters Africa

Often parasitised by Cuckoos, breeding Reed Warblers are found in Wiltshire wherever there are suitable reedbeds, even quite narrow strips flanking rivers, and sometimes in other tall riparian vegetation. Singing males have also been recorded in hedgerows, chalkland scrub and rape fields (*eg Hobby* 19, 20, P Combridge).

These Reed Warblers belong to the nominate race, which breeds from northwest Africa across Europe to southern Finland, Russia and western Anatolia; they are confined largely to the lowlands by their essential association with reedbeds. The race *fuscus* – now sometimes treated as a distinct species, 'Caspian Reed Warbler' (*eg* Sangster *et al* 1998) – has a fragmented breeding range from central Turkey and the Caucasus east to China and south to the Levant, Egypt and Arabia (Pearson *et al* 2002). Another taxon, *avicenniae*, in the coastal mangroves of the Red Sea and Gulf of Aden, may also belong to this species or species-group (*eg* Dickinson 2003).

During the 20th century, particularly from the 1940s, Reed Warblers extended their range northwards into Norway, Sweden and Finland, and the population of Europe as a whole, excluding Russia, was put at 2·7 to 3·7 million pairs in the 1990s (*EBCC Atlas*). The *1988–91 Atlas* showed that their British range had also spread north and west since the *1968–72 Atlas* survey, but that most were still in the southern third of England and that the estimate of 40,000 to 80,000 pairs had changed little, even though CBC results suggested an increase. More recently, national survey data have indicated a shallow decline since 1983, but a partial recovery from the early 1990s (*BBWC*) and, on this basis, the British total has been revised upward to between 60,800 and 122,000 pairs (*APEP*). The *1875–1900 Atlas* noted that by the end of the 19th century Reed Warblers bred in much of Wales, and in England from Cornwall (where this species was only an occasional nester) to Lancashire and Yorkshire, but that, though there had been indications of a northward expansion earlier in that century, the difficulties of field identification in those days made any trends uncertain. There was some evidence of losses in range from boundary areas by the 1930s, but overall there was little apparent change between 1900 and the time of the *1968–72 Atlas* (*1875–1900 Atlas*).

In Wiltshire, the 1929 bird report considered the Reed Warbler a 'not uncommon summer visitor' (*WANHM*), and no increases in either population or range were noted by Peirson (1959), Buxton (1981) or Palmer (1991). Whereas, however, the *1968–72 Atlas* found this species breeding in 12 of the county's 33 core 10-km squares, the *1988–91 Atlas* did so in 16 and the 1995–2000 tetrad survey in no fewer than 18. Thus, it appears that its range in the county did expand during the last third of the 20th century. Breeding Reed Warblers need beds or strips of *Phragmites* reeds, whether large or small, and the tetrad abundance map shows the greatest concentrations of both are to be found in the Thames valley (especially at CWP), at Coate Water and along the lower Salisbury Avon, the Bristol Avon, the Kennet, and the Kennet & Avon Canal. Smith (1887) considered this species 'not nearly so common' as the Sedge Warbler in 19th century Wiltshire, and the timed summer visits of 1995–2000 – which recorded 275 Reed and 585 Sedge – show that this is still the case.

The Wiltshire population of Reed Warblers during 1995–2000 is estimated to have been in the region of 1100 to 2200 singing males. (Although there are no specific survey data in this case, that figure is based on the ratio of timed counts to population estimates for other

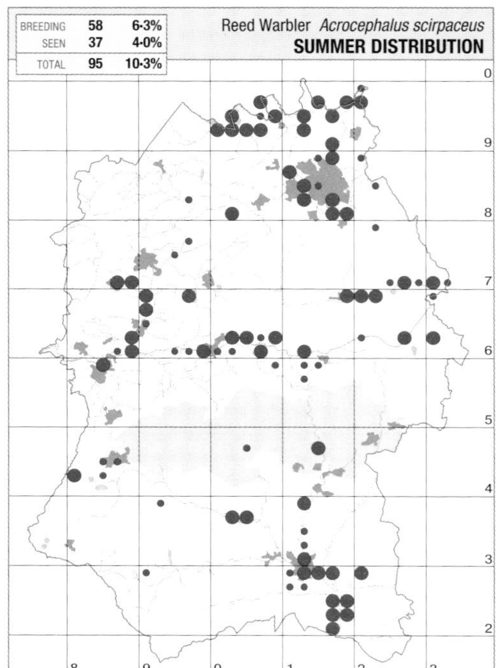

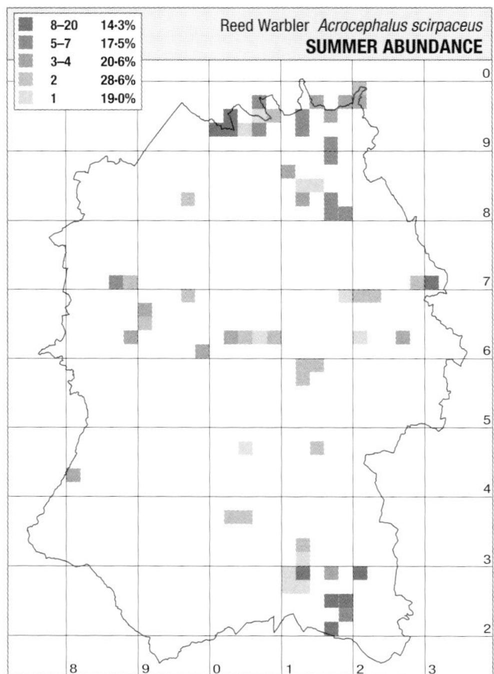

warblers.) This is rather more than might be expected from the information published in *Hobby*, where the highest number of singing males in any one year of 1990–2000 was 114, but a survey at Coate Water in 1990 (Winter 1991) found no fewer than 42 pairs, a much larger figure than the casual annual totals might suggest. During 1990–2000, five or more singing males were recorded in at least one year at CWP (21 in 1999), Stanton Fitzwarren Lake, Peatmoor Lagoon, Swindon STW (20 in 1998), Coate Water, by the Kennet at Mildenhall, Littlecote (13 in 1999), Crofton, Horton, Lacock gravel pits, Corsham Lake, Whaddon near Trowbridge, and Clarendon Lake, as well as along the Salisbury Avon (14 in 1998) (*Hobby*).

Reed Warblers winter in sub-Saharan Africa from Senegal east to the Red Sea and south to at least Zambia. Ringing recoveries indicate that the British population goes to West Africa, but exactly where is uncertain (*Migration Atlas*). Of 2320 Reed Warblers ringed in Wiltshire during 1965–2000, the 39 recovered outside the county have included nine overseas, in France (four), Portugal (two) and Spain, Morocco and Senegal (one each). The last had been ringed at Downton on 28 June 1992 and was retrapped and released at Djoudi on 22 March 1996, suggesting that it would shortly have left for its fourth return journey. One ringed at Corsham Lake in 1978 was retrapped later the same year at Tring (Hertfordshire) and then again at Corsham seven years later in 1985. There have also been 18 inward ringing returns from elsewhere in Great Britain and one from abroad: the last had been ringed in the province of West Vlaanderen (Belgium) in June 1987 and was retrapped at Downton four years later in June 1991.

In Wiltshire, the first spring arrivals appear in April – the earliest record of all was at Bishops Cannings on 3 April 1958 (*WANHM*) – but most come in May. Departure from the breeding areas begins in July and continues throughout August; there are annual observations in September and the species was even recorded in October in 13 of the 27 years 1974–2000, though only one of those was in the 1990s. The county's latest record was at Corsham Lake on 23 October 1985 (*Hobby*).

PCo

Icterine Warbler

Hippolais icterina

Vagrant (1 record), breeds adjacent Europe/Fenno-Scandia, winters Africa

Summer visitors from sub-Saharan Africa, Icterine Warblers breed widely in Europe and western Asia from eastern France and Fenno-Scandia across to the Black and Caspian Seas, and to the River Ob in Asiatic Russia. Common enough in adjacent continental countries – with maximum population estimates (pairs) of 10,000 in Belgium, 55,000 in the Netherlands, 400,000 in Germany, 225,000 in Denmark and 300,000 in Norway (*CBWP*) – Icterine Warblers are regular migrants to Great Britain, both through overshooting in spring (May–June) and through westward drifting in autumn (mainly August to mid October), with an annual average during 1990–2000 of 129 (Fraser & Rogers 2002). Most arrive along the east and south coasts, and to a lesser extent down the west side, but quite a few have appeared in inland counties (including most of Wiltshire's neighbours) over the last 35 years. The only valid record for Wiltshire, however, was a male singing at Salisbury on 11 July 1944 (*BB* 38: 115).

Curiously, Wiltshire also had a long accepted record of a nest with three eggs at Mildenhall, near Marlborough, in May 1907, neither identified nor published until 1926 (*MCNHS*). These are preserved in the Marlborough College Museum and, though the eggs are certainly those of a *Hippolais* warbler, they cannot now be confirmed to specific level. Further, as the incubating adult was seen only as it was flushed by a 14–year-old schoolboy on 3 May and again on the 5th – dates much too early for this long-distance migrant to be breeding – it is now concluded 'that some mistake, misplacement or other confusion occurred during the 19 years that the nest and eggs lay in limbo' before identification (see interesting discussion by Andrew 1997).

RT

Sponsored by Marlborough College Natural History Society

Melodious Warbler

Hippolais polyglotta

Vagrant (1 record) from southwest Europe, winters West Africa

Melodious Warblers breed in northwest Africa and western Europe, where, until the mid 1950s, they were confined to Iberia, south and west France, Italy and parts of former Yugoslavia (now Croatia and Slovenia). Their range has, however, extended northward since then, and they now nest regularly in southern Belgium, Luxembourg, extreme western Germany and the western fringes of Switzerland; they have also done so in the Netherlands. The European population is estimated at 1·3 to 2·8 million pairs and, apart from habitat availability, the only factor limiting further spread is thought to be interspecific competition with the closely related Icterine Warbler, which replaces it as a breeding species in north and east Europe (*EBCC Atlas*).

In Great Britain, although a few now occur in spring, the vast majority are reported in autumn, chiefly from August to mid October. The annual average during 1990–2000 was 29, although numbers appeared to decline towards the end of this period (Fraser & Rogers 2002). Most are found on the south coast, particularly between the Isles of Scilly and Dorset.

The only Melodious Warbler so far recorded in Wiltshire was watched for 20 minutes at Swindon STW on 25 September 1966 (*WANHM*).

RT

Blackcap

Sylvia atricapilla

Common summer and scarce winter visitor, winters west Europe/North Africa

On their arrival in late March and early April, male Blackcaps soon start uttering the series of rich and powerful notes that make up their short song. The females are less conspicuous because their small 'skullcap', similarly extending only to the tops of the eyes, is red-brown instead of black. The increasing numbers of Blackcaps now wintering in Great Britain, and particularly their visits then to garden bird-tables, have made this otherwise inconspicuous species better known to the casual observer.

Blackcaps breed from the Atlantic Islands and northwest Africa across Europe – where they are widespread and absent only from Iceland, central and northern Fenno-Scandia, and far northern and lowland southern Russia – into western Siberia, as well as through northern Turkey and the Caucasus to Iran. Some winter – in increasing numbers – in Britain and Ireland, and in west and central France, while others do so in the Mediterranean region, and in sub-Saharan Africa from Senegal to Nigeria in the west and Sudan to Malawi in the east. Ringing recoveries have shown that the vast majority of British breeders migrates to southern Iberia and northwest Africa, and that those that winter in Great Britain originate mostly from west-central Europe (*Migration Atlas*).

Some 19 to 26 million pairs have been estimated to breed in Europe, excluding Russia (*EBCC Atlas*). The *1988–91 Atlas* demonstrated that Blackcaps had extended their range northwards in Great Britain since the *1968–72 Atlas* – though the strongholds still remained largely in southern England – and put the breeding population at 580,000 territories. National survey data show that the long-term trend is one of rapid increase in all habitats, doubling in number between the mid 1970s and 2000, although the reasons are unknown (*BBWC*), and the total in 2000 was estimated at 916,000 territories (*APEP*).

In Wiltshire, Smith (1887) commented that Blackcaps were 'known to most observers' and that he saw them 'frequently in many parts of the county'. The 1929 bird report in *WANHM* considered the species 'fairly common', Peirson (1959) classed it as 'common', and both the *1968–72* and *1988–91 Atlases* and the summer survey 1995–2000 mapped it in all of Wiltshire's 33 core 10-km squares. Although Blackcaps are primarily woodland birds, their territories must include patches of thick scrub, in which they build their neat nests suspended by 'basket handles'. They also breed in large gardens where at least a few tall trees are present.

During the summer survey, as the distribution map shows, Blackcaps were recorded in 88 per cent of all tetrads, and breeding was confirmed in almost 60 per cent. They

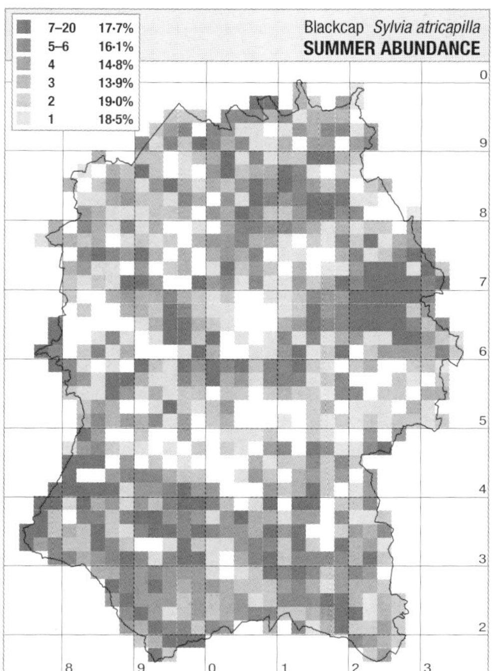

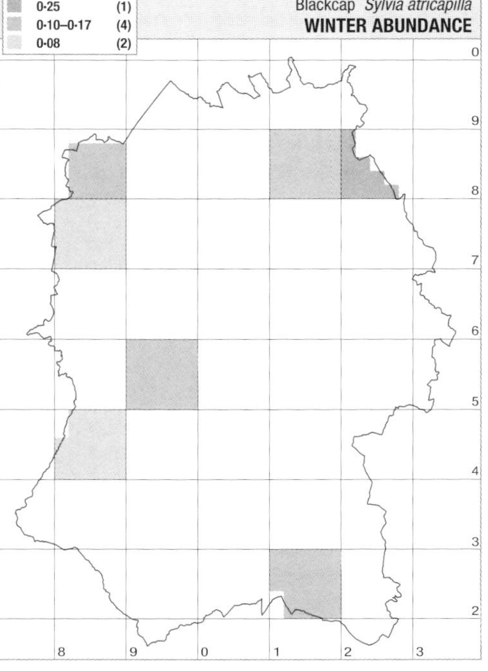

probably occurred in most tetrads that had suitable habitats. Both summer maps show gaps in distribution in the northeast and centre – treeless areas of the Marlborough Downs and Salisbury Plain – and, rather more curiously, between the By Brook and the Bristol Avon. The highest densities on the summer abundance map are in the Swindon and Savernake areas of the north and in the southwest and south. CBC results in the 1980s and 1990s show that the population remained stable in three Wiltshire woods, but that at Biss Wood there was an increase from nil in 1987 to eight pairs in 1998. Data from a number of BBS surveys in Wiltshire and surrounding counties point to a summer population within the range of 16,100 to 37,800 pairs.

The earliest reference to a wintering Blackcap in the county was of one seen in mid winter in 1891 (Smith 1891a), but there were then no further records until the middle of the 20th century, when 15 of a total of 256 individuals reported in Britain and Ireland during the winters of 1945–54 were in Wiltshire (Stafford 1956). Of 16 sightings published in *WANHM* during 1946–69, the majority came from the areas of Swindon, Chippenham, Marlborough and Salisbury, where birdwatchers were most numerous (Rice 1970).

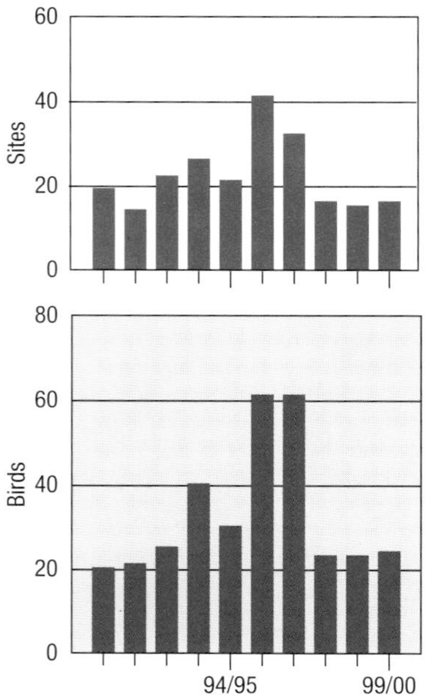

Figure 68. Blackcaps *Sylvia atricapilla* in Wiltshire: reported winter maxima 1990/91–1999/00

A comprehensive analysis by Bridgman (1980) – of all records of Blackcaps submitted to WANHS and WOS in the ten winters from 1969/70 (when none was recorded) and 1970/71 (when there was one report of two) through to 1978/79 (when 23 reports involved no fewer than 40) – showed that there had been a massive leap in the number of observations between the successive winters of 1975/76 (three reports, four birds) and 1976/77 (26 reports, 42 birds). He demonstrated, by analysing the annual numbers of contributors of records to the bird reports in *WANHM* and then *Hobby*, and of Blackcaps reported, as percentages of the ten-year totals of each, that this increase was genuine and not the result of observer bias. Of a grand total of 166 Blackcaps reported in the county over that period, 81 were males and 85 females; and 103 were in January–February, compared with only 32 in November–December and 31 in March. The reports over the whole period came from 38 named urban areas, villages and farms throughout the county; and 84 per cent of those in which the habitat was noted involved gardens. Bridgman also summarised 36 reports where the food taken by the Blackcaps had been noted: apart from a variety of berries, (bits of) apples and, in one case, larvae/flies on broccoli – all of which were previously recorded foods of this and other insectivorous species in winter – these included small rosehips, coconut, peanut fragments/nuts, breadcrumbs, cheese, oatmeal, and suet/fat.

By 1979 the spring and autumn migration dates were being obscured by wintering Blackcaps. The *1981–84 Winter Atlas* mapped this species in no fewer than 25 of Wiltshire's 33 core 10-km squares. The rather poor showing on the winter map for 1998–2000, of just seven out of all the 48 whole and part 10-km squares, was surely a result of the methodology used, in that few 2-hour tetrad counts necessarily included gardens. Most wintering Blackcaps are reported from regularly watched gardens, where they are then often seen at feeding stations and where, contrary to Bridgman's earlier findings, males outnumber females (though this may partly be because the female's red-brown cap is less distinctive).

Since 1988 the numbers of birds and sites have been tabulated annually in *Hobby* (figure 68). The totals reported there showed little change during the 1990s – the highest figures again invariably in the second half of each winter – with the notable exceptions of over 60 individuals in each of the colder winters of 1995/96 and 1996/97; the weather then may have caused the arrival of more Blackcaps from farther east, or may simply have forced more to seek supplementary food from bird-tables. Thus, the map certainly understates the situation. These casual observations are of course just a small part of the true Wiltshire wintering population, which extrapolation from timed counts suggests may lie in the region of 114 to 269 individuals. The *1981–84 Winter Atlas* noted that numbers wintering were increasing during the second half of the 20th century, and estimated a combined total of some 3,000 for Britain and Ireland, though it seems likely that this figure is now too low.

Wiltshire ringers caught a total of 4263 Blackcaps during 1965–2000, of which 23 had been recovered by the end of that period. One ringed at Swindon on 4 August 1964 and another at Longbridge Deverill on 8 July 1986 were respectively shot and found dead in France on 5 October 1964 and 20 October 1986. A third ringed at Beanacre on 19 July 1967 was recovered in Spain on 1 October that year. Two have been reported in Algeria: the first, ringed at Great Wood on 30 April 1987, was shot on 25 March 1990; the second, ringed at Cowleaze Wood on 30 April 1988, was 'taken captive' on 30 December 1989 at Mechtras Tizi-Ouzoo. A winterer ringed at Westbury in January 1990 was found dead in Kilkenny (Ireland) in March 1991. In addition, one ringed in the Netherlands in September 1992 was found dead at Laverstock, near Salisbury, the following month. Thus, most were showing movement south or west in autumn or winter, except the first of the two in Algeria, which may have been on its way north again.

PAC & PCo

Garden Warbler

Sylvia borin

Common summer visitor and passage migrant, breeds Europe, winters Africa

This brownish and rather nondescript warbler is not found in gardens, unless they are very large and overgrown, but inhabits luxuriant broadleaved or mixed woodland with a dense understorey – thus overlapping with the Blackcap – and also thick bushes and scrub, including young conifer plantations, well away from trees. It does not often show itself but sings as it skulks inside the vegetation. The song is a mellow warbling, more sustained than the typically richer notes of the Blackcap, but the two may be confused.

The Garden Warbler's breeding range extends from central Iberia, France, northern Italy and Greece north to Great Britain (few in Ireland) and northern Fenno-Scandia, and from there east to the Yenisei in Siberia, also in northern Turkey and the Caucasus to Iran. The population of Europe, excluding Russia, has been put at 10 to 13 million pairs (*EBCC Atlas*). In Great Britain, where 190,000 territories have been estimated (*APEP*), Garden Warblers are most numerous south of a line from the Mersey to the Humber and, though extending north to south-central Scotland, they are largely absent from the Highlands and islands (*1988–91 Atlas*).

Garden Warblers usually arrive in Great Britain later than Blackcaps, most frequently in May. During 1990–2000 the earliest arrival date in the county varied between 4 April and the 24th, but the county's earliest record of all was on 31 March 1956. They usually depart in August or September – though the latest Wiltshire date was 2 October in both 1965 and 1982 – to spend the winter in sub-Saharan Africa from Senegal east to Kenya and south to Angola and South Africa. The limited national ringing data suggest that

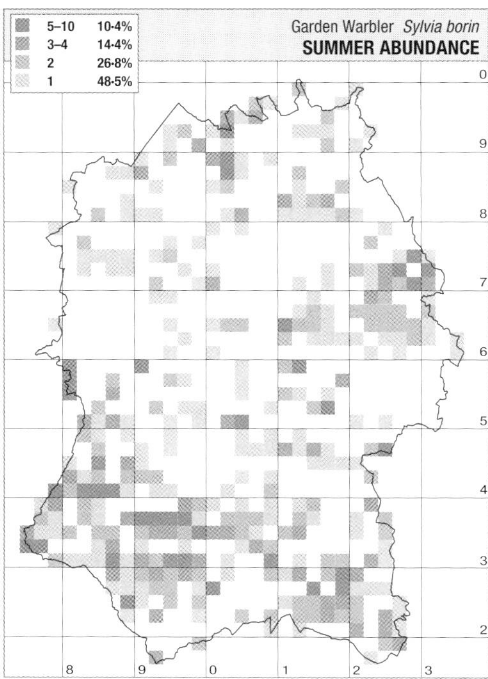

Ghana in West Africa is important as a wintering area for Garden Warblers migrating from, though not necessarily breeding in, Great Britain (*Migration Atlas*).

Just five of the 840 Garden Warblers ringed in Wiltshire during 1965–2000 had generated recoveries elsewhere by the end of that period, all within England, but three of those were juveniles retrapped in Sussex and Surrey later in the same autumn, suggesting an initial easterly migration route before crossing the Channel (*cf* Chiffchaff). Additionally, an adult ringed at Froxfield on 14 June 1962 was captured in Morocco on 15 May 1965. Garden Warblers at Clanger Wood seemed particularly site-faithful and long-lived. Several were retrapped there up to five years after ringing, and two ringed as adults on 8 June 1980 and 30 May 1983 were each caught again seven years later, on 12 July 1987 and 10 June 1990 respectively, by which time the first must have been at least eight years old (possibly even a month or two more) and the second not much younger – both having been to sub-Saharan Africa and back at least eight times. The national longevity record for this species is eight years, one month and four days (Clark *et al* 2001). (Unfortunately, the habitat at Clanger Wood became increasingly less suitable as a CES during the 1990s, or further instances of long-lived Garden Warblers might have come to light.)

In Wiltshire, Montagu (1802) found the Garden Warbler 'not uncommon' and Smith (1887) noted that it was 'at least as equally common' as the Blackcap, which he saw 'frequently'. The 1929 bird report in *WANHM* gave its status as 'not uncommon'. Three decades later, Peirson (1959) wrote 'It is now almost uncommon, certainly less common than the Blackcap, though between about 1920 and 1940…the two species were considered equally common', and Buxton (1981) reported it as 'widely distributed throughout the county but much less common than the Blackcap'.

Garden Warblers suffered a marked decline in the mid 1970s, apparently linked to drought in the sub-Saharan Sahel zone which they cross on migration (*1988–91 Atlas*), but national survey data show that, despite such fluctuations, the British population has remained stable over the longer term (*BBWC*). The *1968–72 Atlas* recorded this species in all of Wiltshire's 33 core 10-km squares and breeding in 21, and the corresponding figures in the *1988–91 Atlas* were 32 and 29. The summer survey during 1995–2000 found it in all the core squares and evidence of breeding in, again, 29. The total recorded during the timed visits was 762, but a combination of surveys using BBS methods suggest that the county's breeding population probably lies in the region of 3320 to 4850 pairs.

The distribution and abundance maps show a rather patchy pattern. Garden Warblers are scarce in areas where there is little suitable habitat, such as SPTA and the Marlborough Downs, and most numerous where there is broadleaved woodland or scrub. They are clearly commonest in the north (especially around Swindon), south of the Marlborough Downs in the West Woods–Savernake area, and in the south and southwest, being particularly numerous on the West Wiltshire Downs and in the Vale of Wardour.

PAC & PCo

Sponsored by Jo Heigham in memory of Phyllis Heigham

Barred Warbler
Sylvia nisoria

Vagrant (1 record) from central/east Europe, winters Africa

Barred Warblers are summer visitors to Eurasia, breeding in a broad band from southernmost Fenno-Scandia, eastern Germany and north Italy across to Mongolia – but hardly abundant as the numbers in Europe, excluding Russia, have been estimated at only 164,000–645,000 pairs (*EBCC Atlas*). The entire Eurasian population migrates through the Middle East to winter in East Africa from Sudan to Tanzania, which means that those that nest in central Europe fly southeast in autumn and northwest in spring.

Surprisingly few overshoot to Great Britain in spring, but through reverse migration some 80 to 230 are recorded each year from July to November, especially in the Northern Isles and down the east coast south to Norfolk (Fraser *et al* 2000), the great majority of them juveniles. Inland records are rare and the only Barred Warbler ever found in Wiltshire was a juvenile at Coate Water on 6 September 1980 (*Hobby*).

GLW & SBE

Lesser Whitethroat
Sylvia curruca

Locally common summer visitor, breeds Europe, winters Africa

Hearing the loud, repetitive, rattling song – audible at 150–200 m, though often preceded by a short, soft warble that carries hardly any distance – is the usual way of locating Lesser Whitethroats. Generally difficult to see, because this is a skulking species, the male usually sings and moves deep inside tall thick hedges, particularly hawthorn, or quite frequently from the dense canopies of larger trees within the hedges. Although song may be heard from late April to early July, many males tend to sing for only short periods once mated – and the male of an isolated pair may then cease completely. Harsh *tac-tac* alarm calls, subdued and infrequent at first, become louder and rapidly repeated when the young are large or have recently left the nest, which is usually constructed among dead twigs right inside hawthorn, blackthorn or brambles, sometimes in elder, box, small conifers or other evergreens (Campbell & Ferguson-Lees 1972).

Lesser Whitethroats are summer visitors to much of Europe, as well as parts of Turkey and the Middle East, through to east-central Siberia, Mongolia and western China in a complex of races, some of the eastern and southeastern of which may be distinct species (see Shirihai *et al* 2001). In Europe – where the population, excluding that of Russia, has been estimated at 2·0 to 2·6 million pairs (*EBCC Atlas*) – the Lesser Whitethroat is absent as a breeding species from northernmost Fenno-Scandia and Russia, from Iceland, Ireland (has nested) and much of west and southwest France (gradually spreading westwards), and from Spain (only a vagrant) and almost all of Italy.

This is a more easterly species than the Common Whitethroat and its winter quarters are mainly in northeast sub-Saharan Africa but some as far west as Chad, Niger, Mali and even Senegal (Urban *et al* 1997). Most return to Europe round the eastern end of the Mediterranean, though there are indications that some British breeders may cross the Mediterranean from Italy or Greece on their way back in autumn (which may account for winterers now being found farther west in Africa). Nevertheless, arrivals and departures in Great Britain are concentrated on eastern and, especially, southeastern coasts (*Migration Atlas*). In this connection, it is interesting that a Lesser Whitethroat retrapped and released at Edington on 11 May 1994 had been ringed in Israel on 18 March that year, and was the first Israeli-ringed bird of any species to be recovered in Great Britain. Another, ringed at Bromham on 1 September 1987, was 'found alive' over 2400 km away in Greece just 46 days later. In all, 912 Lesser Whitethroats were ringed in Wiltshire during 1965–2000.

Thus, with migrations that are northwesterly in spring and southeasterly in autumn, it is not surprising that the Lesser Whitethroat, here on the edge of its range, has a predominantly southeasterly breeding distribution in Great Britain. It is scarce north of a line from the Solway to the Firth of Forth, and is also uncommon or absent from many areas farther south, in uplands of northern England and, particularly, mid Wales and much of the southwest peninsula.

The *1968–72 Atlas* suggested 25,000 to 50,000 pairs of Lesser Whitethroats in Great Britain, but by the time of the *1988–91 Atlas* the estimate had risen to 80,000 territories. Over that 20–year period, CBC densities on farmland increased from 0·65 pairs/km^2 to about 1 pair/km^2 and the breeding range expanded, especially in south Wales, Anglesey, and parts of northern England and southeast Scotland. But numbers of this species fluctuate and the CBC showed significant changes between consecutive years: for example, decreases of 22 per cent between 1986 and 1987, and 43 per cent between 1996 and 1997; but also increases of 30 per cent between 1987 and 1988, and 50 per cent between 1998 and 1999. National survey data now show, however, a rapid decline from the late 1980s to 2000 (*BBWC*), sufficient to trigger conservation concerns, and the population was estimated to have fallen to 64,000 pairs by the end of the century (*APEP*). Suitable farmland has decreased as hedges have been grubbed out and those that remain have been degraded by mechanical trimming (O'Connor & Shrubb 1986); and, in Wiltshire, housing and industrial development on greenfield sites, particularly in the northeast of the county, has also reduced suitable breeding habitat.

Smith (1887) considered that the Lesser Whitethroat was 'Quite as common in Wiltshire, if not more so' than the Common Whitethroat – a situation that was apparently not

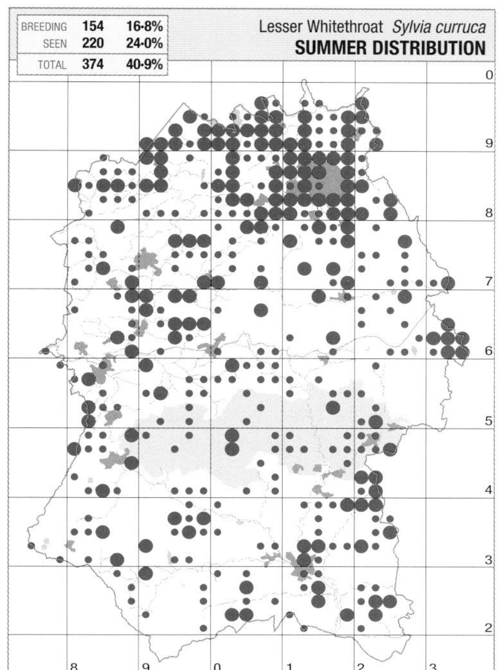

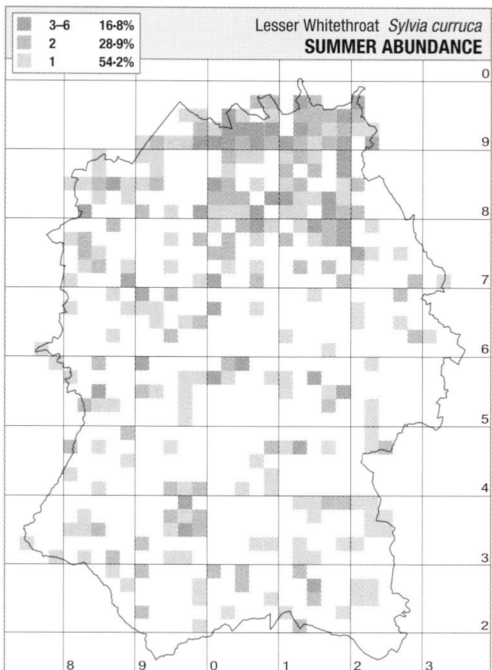

general in England at the time (*1875–1900 Atlas*) – whereas Peirson (1919), referring to the Marlborough district, indicated that it was the less numerous. The 1929 bird report in *WANHM* stated that the Lesser was 'A fairly common summer visitor', but Peirson (1959), now writing of the county as a whole, believed it was 'uncommon'. Buxton (1981) again assessed it as 'fairly common', though that, even at the county level, 'numbers fluctuate widely from year to year'.

The *1968–72 Atlas* mapped Lesser Whitethroats in 31 of Wiltshire's 33 core 10-km squares (breeding in 21), and the *1988–91 Atlas* in 32 (breeding in 26), whereas the summer tetrad survey during 1995–2000 found them in all 33 (and breeding in 30). In contrast to the decline in numbers nationally, these totals suggest at least stability in the county, if not an increase, over the last few decades of the 20th century. The maps show the greatest concentrations and highest abundance in lowland north Wiltshire, especially in the Swindon area. Thick hedges are more plentiful there, and the patchy nature of the distribution elsewhere in the county may be explained by the species' general avoidance of higher ground, open farmland and woodland (*1988–91 Atlas*). BBS surveys in 38 1-km squares in Wiltshire suggest a county population of 2990 pairs, but since Lesser Whitethroats were recorded only in small numbers by BBS surveys on SPTA, the Cotswolds and the Chilterns – precluding any alternative estimates – it is difficult to know how much confidence to place in this figure

Most Lesser Whitethroats usually arrive in late April or early May – the males normally about a week before the females (*1968–72 Atlas*) – but Wiltshire's earliest recorded date was 3 April in both 1957 (*WANHM*) and 1977 (*Hobby*). Many leave again in August and early September, and stragglers have usually gone by the end of that month, but the county's latest migrant date was trapped and ringed at Edington on 30 October 1988 and a few winter records in southern England and Wales included one in a Swindon garden on 28 December 1999 (*Hobby*).

SBE

Common Whitethroat

Sylvia communis

Common summer visitor and passage migrant, breeds Europe, winters Africa

The Common Whitethroat is probably the most conspicuous of all Wiltshire's warblers, partly because of its erratic, dancing display-flight and distinctively scratchy song, and partly because it inhabits more open country than many of the other species. But, while the singing male displays his white throat and white outertail-feathers, the female tends to remain out of sight, skulking in dense vegetation near the nest-site. The pair's territory is small, often centred round a few square metres of low bushes, thick hedge-bottoms, or long grass with patches of bramble and nettles that are enough to harbour a reliable supply of insect prey.

Common Whitethroats are found almost throughout Europe in summer, but are absent from most of southern Iberia and from the northern and higher regions of Fenno-Scandia and Russia. The population, excluding that of Russia, has been estimated at 6·7 to 8·9 million pairs (*EBCC Atlas*). They breed also in northwest Africa, Turkey and Israel, and across central Asia east to Lake Baikal and south to Iran. All winter in sub-Saharan Africa, in the Sahel zone from Senegal east to Somalia, southward in the east to South Africa; the small numbers of ringing recoveries indicate that those that breed in northwest Europe, including Great Britain, winter in the westernmost part of this range (*Migration Atlas*).

Over the last third of the 20th century, conditions in African wintering areas perhaps had a greater influence on the fortunes of the Common Whitethroats than on those of any other summer visitor to Great Britain. The first dramatic crash in its numbers came in 1969, when CBC data showed that 77 per cent of the previous year's breeding stock had failed to return after the 1968/69 winter of severe drought in the Sahel zone on the southern edge of the Sahara (Winstanley *et al* 1974). The Sahel is important as winter quarters and as a pre-migration fattening area for a number of species, particularly those that, like the Common Whitethroat, depend on the berries of the saltbush in the weeks before making the return crossing of the Sahara. Berthold (1973, 1974) calculated a decline of 50–100 per cent in the Common Whitethroat populations of parts of western and central Europe after 1968. This and subsequent crashes are considered to be the result of a series of such droughts in the West African section of the Sahel, and British numbers reached an all-time low in 1974. A partial recovery was halted again in 1983–84, when further crashes saw numbers fall to just 20 per cent of pre-1968 levels, and yet another setback was apparent in 1991. The underlying trend suggests, however, that the British population made a slow but steady increase during the last two decades of the 20th century, reaching an estimated 931,000 pairs in 2000 (*APEP*), though numbers are perhaps still only a quarter of those of the mid 1960s (*BBWC*).

The second year of fieldwork for the *1968–72 Atlas* coincided with the first dramatic crash. Coverage of substantial areas of England had been completed in the first year, but comparatively little in Wales and, particularly, Scotland and Ireland – where it was thought that, otherwise, there might well have been fewer 10-km squares left blank on the 1968–72 map. The *1988–91 Atlas* was preceded by the third decline and the distribution and change maps in that show further losses, particularly a retreat from areas of high ground where the habitats are less favourable for Common Whitethroats. Even without a comparable abundance map for 1968–72, it seems clear that altitude has been a significant factor in the process of gradual re-establishment. The *1988–91 Atlas*, which estimated a British population of 660,000 territories, showed many of the highest densities were in the eastern half of England and that, in the western half, such concentrations were confined largely to coastal counties – though pockets were apparent inland in the Severn Vale, on the Somerset Moors and Levels, and in central Wiltshire.

In Wiltshire a hundred years earlier, Smith (1887) had remarked that this was 'the commonest of all our little summer warblers, and may be seen in every shady lane or thick hedge, almost in every bramble and bed of nettles'. Despite this familiarity, or perhaps because of it – since the *1875–1900 Atlas* noted that Common Whitethroats were often considered to be the commonest of all summer migrants throughout Britain and Ireland in the 19th century – this species featured little in other publications for the next 80 years. It was not mentioned in the 1929 bird report in *WANHM* and in only four subsequent years (mostly referring to the finding of nests) until a 1951 observation of 'A party of 30–40, with some Lesser Whitethroats, in hedges at Pitton, April 29'. Peirson (1959) noted this simply as 'A very common summer visitor'. Although there continued to be few references to it during the 1960s, the effects of the first population crash were evident in the 1969 bird report in *WANHM*: 'This species extremely rare throughout the county and only 3 breeding records received', while the following year 'very few were seen compared with pre-1969 figures'. After 1975 the numbers rose slowly but steadily and, in 1979, there was "A large increase in breeding pairs, most traditional sites now re-occupied but not to original pre-'crash' densities at all of them" (*Hobby*).

A CBC survey on 100 ha at Sunnyhill Farm, near Pewsey, during 1962–83 reflected the rise and fall in the national figures: after a peak of 19–21 pairs in 1966–68, the number fell to seven pairs in 1969, increased to ten in 1970, declined to three by 1973, and then none in 1974, after which the population remained at 3–6 pairs over the remaining nine years of the study (Gillam 1984). Another CBC site at Pinkflower Gorse, near Kingston Deverill, in 6·5 ha of downland gorse and hawthorn scrub – an optimum habitat for Common Whitethroats – showed a recovery from a low of eight pairs in 1974 to an annual average of 14 pairs during 1981–91; after the 1991 crash, the average dropped again to 9·5 during 1992–95, but had risen again to 14 by 1998 (JD Pollard). This species' need for only a small area of suitable breeding habitat has enabled it to recolonise most parts of the county.

Although the Common Whitethroat was recorded as breeding throughout Wiltshire by the *1968–72* and *1988–91 Atlases*, the maps in both obscured the marked changes that were occurring at those times. The summer tetrad survey of 1995–2000 also found it throughout the county, and both the distribution and abundance maps show it to have been most numerous on the Marlborough Downs and parts of Salisbury Plain, in the far northeast and in a central band towards the southwest. An RSPB breeding bird survey of SPTA in 2000 estimated 4000 territories, about 0·6 per cent of the national population; densities there were found to increase with the amount of scrub available, resulting in concentrations around Warminster ranges and Imber, and between Upavon and Everleigh (Stanbury *et al* 2000). Distribution is more fragmented in the southeast of the county and along the southwestern edge, but those areas are among the most extensively wooded. From the summer tetrad counts and the densities found by a number of BBS surveys, the population as a whole is likely to be in the region of 23,300 to 38,600 pairs.

Although as many as 1831 Common Whitethroats were ringed in Wiltshire during 1965–2000, these had generated only two recoveries by the end of that period. One ringed at Chisenbury on 12 August 1987 was retrapped and released, while breeding, at Binstead (Hampshire) on 10 June 1990, and another ringed near Salisbury on 20 July 1963 was shot in Spain on 2 October that year, at Salas (Oviedo). In addition, two from Wales have been recovered in Wiltshire: one ringed on the island of Skokholm (Pembrokeshire) on 12 May 1958 was found dead at Corsham in May 1960, and another ringed in Caernarvon on 4 June 1967 was found dead near Trowbridge on 29 August that year.

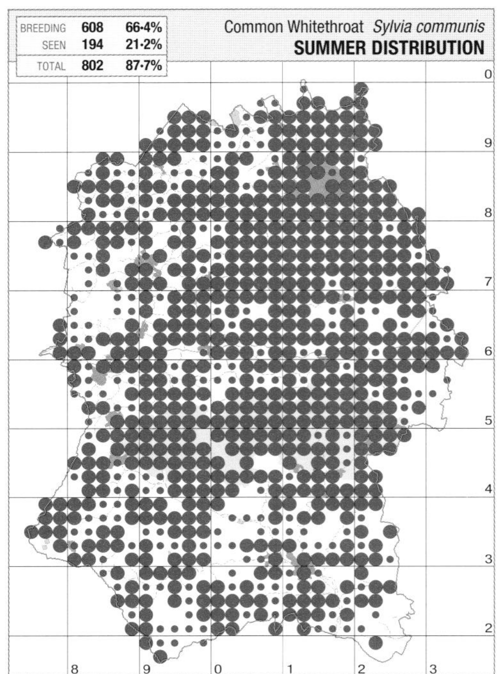

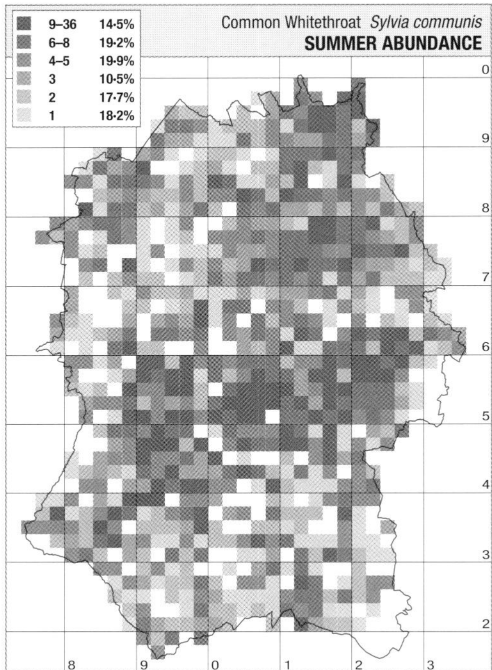

In spring, Common Whitethroats do not usually arrive in any numbers in Great Britain before the third week of April, though occasionally odd ones do appear in late March and early April. Wiltshire's earliest known date was 31 March 1958 (*WANHM*), but in the 11 years of 1990–2000 the first recorded arrivals were all during 10–24 April. When a significant influx does occur, however (usually including some that are simply passing through), Common Whitethroats can still be seen, or rather heard, 'in every shady lane or thick hedge' – to use Smith's words of more than a century ago – as their scratchy songs are often then audible through an open car window. This species mostly leaves in August, and few remain after mid September. During 1990–2000 the last record varied between 15 September and 9 October, but the county's latest was a singleton at Manton on 24 November 1976.

IJF-L & SBE

Dartford Warbler

Sylvia undata

Now only irregular visitor, occasional breeder when English numbers high

Characteristic of southern heathland with gorse, the Dartford is – apart from the newly colonising Cetti's – Great Britain's only essentially resident warbler. Dark above and pinkish below, with a long white-edged tail often cocked, it tends to skulk and is easiest to see on windless days in spring when males utter their scratchy songs from the top of a gorse bush. Dartford Warblers have a small world range, being confined to southern England, the Channel Islands, western and southern France, Iberia, peninsular Italy, the larger west Mediterranean islands, and coastal North Africa. The total breeding population, excluding North Africa, has been estimated at 2·0 to 3·6 million pairs (*EBCC Atlas*), of which Great Britain's share is not large and, at these higher latitudes, this species is badly affected by snow and ice in hard winters.

Formerly much more widespread in England – from Cornwall round to Suffolk and north inland to Oxfordshire and even Shropshire – Dartford Warblers suffered a steep decline in the late 19th century, probably as a result of habitat loss (Gibbons & Wotton 1996). Severe winters in 1961/62 and, particularly, 1962/63 saw a crash to just 11 pairs by the mid 1960s, after which there was a steady if fluctuating recovery. The *1968–72 Atlas* estimated 'about 560 pairs' in 1974, and by the time of the *1988–91 Atlas* that figure had grown 'probably up to 950'. Very significant increases then took place following continued mild winters and a survey in 1994 estimated some 1800 to 1890 territories (Gibbons & Wotton 1996) – three-quarters of which were in Hampshire and Dorset, and most of the remainder in Surrey and Devon. In Somerset, too, Dartford Warblers were found breeding on the Quantocks in 1991, on the Mendips in 1993 and on Exmoor in 1995; by 1996–98 the totals on those upland heaths had risen to 30–45 occupied territories. Nationally, although the population apparently fell back to below 1000 'pairs' in 1996–98, after the cold winter of 1995/96, numbers had almost doubled again by 1999–2000 (*RBBP*).

In Wiltshire, the Dartford Warbler was probably common towards the end of the 19th century, when gorse was managed for fuel (*1875–1900 Atlas*). Smith (1887) gave no indication of its numbers, but wrote that 'This pretty little warbler frequents the downs and commons abounding in furze'; he also quoted it as being seen regularly on the downs near Mere, 'three [killed] in one morning in the neighbourhood of Chippenham', and 'several … shot annually at Amesbury'. Cold winters in 1880/81 and 1886/87 are thought to have caused large national decreases, and the particularly severe winter of 1916/17 reduced the population to its lowest level since ornithological records began (*1875–1900 Atlas*); it probably also marked the end of the Dartford Warbler's regular occurrence in Wiltshire in all but isolated pockets.

Consequently, the 1929 bird report in *WANHM* described these warblers as 'rare and local residents, increasing in numbers in the autumn', but referred to just three records, presumably of breeding pairs, in 'North Wilts' in 1927 and in 'South Wilts' in 1928–29. It is evident from the bird reports for 1930–34 and 1936 that the species was still a regular breeder in small but increasing numbers near the 'borders of Hants'. Few hard data were published, but in 1934 there was a nest 'with four eggs on May 13th; another on May 17th; three nests with young on May 19th; more young and another with four eggs on May 23rd'. Breeding was considered likely in gorse at Shute End on 13 May 1938 (CMR Pitman diaries), though the entry is laconic and unfortunately contains no clue to how this conclusion was reached.

After a gap in the published record until 1946, it was stated that there was 'Still no sign of recovery following winter 1944–45 … One pair in their old haunts on October 25th, after an absence of many years'. There were no records in the following year, after the prolonged severe winter of 1946/47 'killed the only surviving pair known'. A male was seen on 27 December 1948, a pair bred in 1949 and no fewer than four pairs in 1950, and one to two pairs or lone males were noted in 1952–53 and 1955–57, though no records were published in 1951 or 1954 (*WANHM*). Peirson (1959) stated that 'Severe winters, fires and collectors have almost wiped it out but it has just managed to survive in the county'.

It is likely that the cold winters of the early 1960s, combined with the adverse effects of suitable habitat lost to agriculture, were responsible for the near-extinction of the Dartford

Warbler in Wiltshire. The period 1958–73 produced just two records: a female ringed at Ford on 21 April 1962 and a first-year male seen near Broad Chalke on 21 September 1973 (*WANHM*). Buxton (1981) referred to one or two pairs along the county boundary with Hampshire, 'but it is doubtful if they have bred since 1976' and 'very occasionally individuals are seen in autumn and winter at sites outside the breeding areas'. None of this statement is, however, confirmed by *Hobby*, in which no records were published during 1974–87.

The most recent chapter in the occurrence of the Dartford Warbler in Wiltshire began with a male seen at the northern fringe of the New Forest (Hampshire), on the Wiltshire side of the county boundary, on 20 February 1988 and again during 27–31 December, and for five or six years the species maintained a tenuous foothold in the southeast. None was reported in 1989, but in 1990 a pair was present at that same site all year, observations including the male in song, the female carrying food and two juveniles in August, although it is not known if the nest was inside the county boundary. There was only one record in 1991 – a female on 1 February on the Hampshire border – and none at all in 1992. In 1993, however, a pair bred and a second male was seen on SPTA: a male was found on 21 February, two males were singing on 1 May, and a female was noted carrying food on 6 June. Four remained at this site until at least 5 December, and a male was still there on 8 January 1994. None was seen during the following breeding season, but two males and two females were recorded in November 1994 and one male stayed until 5 February 1995. A first-year bird found at Whiteparish on 13 August 1994 had probably dispersed from nearby breeding areas in Hampshire.

There were no records in 1996 or 1997, presumably a consequence of the cold winters in the early parts of both years, since when records have again become less regular. One in a forest clearing at Hens Wood during 17–20 November 1998 was all the more remarkable for its being so far north in the county. In 1999, an immature was found on SPTA on 30 August, and a male and female at the same site on 21 November. What may have been the same male and female were seen there on 19 March 2000, and later the same year singletons, the second aged as a first-year, were recorded at Fifield Bavant on 29–30 October and at Whiteparish on 4–10 November (*Hobby*).

Dartford Warblers feed predominantly in gorse because it is richer in invertebrates than heather (Bibby 1979a). Although they suffer so badly in severe winters, when numbers can drop by as much as 80 per cent, recolonisation eventually takes place after such losses as a result of autumn dispersals from elsewhere (*1988–91 Atlas*). Unfortunately, Wiltshire now has few large areas of gorse, and even they are fragmented, the most extensive being on the leached tops of the chalk, especially on SPTA (Gillam 1993), and any populations would be vulnerable because of the small size and isolation of those areas. The 1993 and 1994 events represent only opportunistic breeding that might be expected to become more frequent if the trend to warmer winters continues and the strongholds in adjacent counties remain – but habitat losses make it unlikely that these will result in genuine recolonisation on any large scale. Gibbons *et al* (1996) included this rare and localised breeder as one of the only two passerines in their table of 'UK breeding species that have undergone the greatest population declines since 1800' – and that in spite of its having 'increased four-fold in the last decade'.

(See page 727.)

SBE

Yellow-browed Warbler

Phylloscopus inornatus

Vagrant (7 records), breeds across Asia, migrant Britain/Europe, winters south Asia

Although nesting no nearer than the Urals in northeast European Russia, Yellow-browed Warblers are annual migrants in considerable numbers to western and central Europe. In Asia they are among the commonest of all warblers, both in their summer range across much of Siberia north to the tree line and in their winter quarters from Nepal to southern China south to peninsular Malaysia. So perhaps it is not surprising that they are the most numerous of all Asiatic passerine vagrants to Great Britain. Nearly 7600 were recorded in the country as a whole during 1968–2000, mainly between mid September and early November, with an annual average of 320 during 1980–2000 (Fraser & Rogers 2002). The vast majority occurs from Shetland to Scilly along the east and south coasts, and only a few of these tiny warblers – little bigger than Goldcrests – are ever found inland. Nevertheless, seven have been recorded in Wiltshire (*WANHM*, *Hobby*):

1972	19 October	Trowbridge
1986	4 October	Melksham
	17 October	Hankerton
	3–4 November	Lydiard Park
1987	6 October	The Lawn, Swindon
	8 November	CWP68
1988	24–29 September	Coate Water

Many observers saw the one in 1988 as it fed and called in waterside willows. Those in 1986 and 1988 occurred during two of the three years with the highest numbers ever recorded in Great Britain, 498 and 739 respectively (Fraser & Rogers 2002).

(See page 727.)

SBE

Wood Warbler

Phylloscopus sibilatrix

Local summer visitor, decreasing, breeds Europe, winters Africa

Wood Warblers are summer visitors to much of Eurasia, from Ireland and France east to the Mongolian Altai, and the whole population winters in equatorial Africa from Sierra Leone to Lake Victoria. West European breeders have a clockwise annual migration route, travelling southeast in autumn over the central and eastern Mediterranean and then over the Sahara – one of the few migrants to make such a direct crossing – and then returning in spring up the west side of Africa before apparently taking a more westerly route across the western Mediterranean (*Migration Atlas*). Their arrival back in Great Britain is always rather mysterious, too: few are seen at coastal sites and it is thought that most must fly direct to their breeding areas (but see final paragraph).

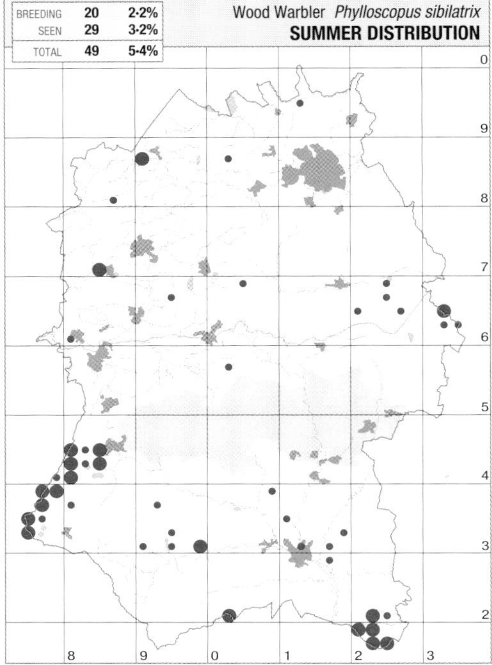

The numbers in Europe, excluding Russia, have been estimated at 6·2 to 7·0 million pairs and, in general, this figure has remained stable despite large local fluctuations (*EBCC Atlas*). In Great Britain, Wood Warblers are commonest in upland woods of sessile oak in Devon, Wales and parts of Scotland, occurring also in local concentrations elsewhere, for example in the New Forest (Hampshire) (*1988–91 Atlas*). A national survey in 1984–85 estimated some 17,200 singing males in Great Britain (Bibby 1989), but BBS data have indicated a marked decline since 1994, that total perhaps halving in number by 2000 (*BBWC*). As the summer map for 1995–2000 shows, Wiltshire's small and declining population is now confined mainly to two areas in the southwest and southeast.

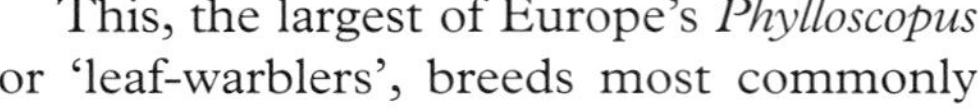

This, the largest of Europe's *Phylloscopus* or 'leaf-warblers', breeds most commonly in mature broadleaved woodland with more or less closed canopy and little or no understorey. The domed nest is built on the ground where the forest floor has sparse vegetation and is normally concealed by dead leaves and bracken, grass, bluebells or other low herbage. In Wiltshire, the favoured woodlands are mostly dominated by beech or oak, but also include birch, ash and some conifers.

The male has two quite different songs – an acceleration of notes ending in a shivering trill and, separately or in conjunction, a mournful and gradually slowing series of *pwee* notes – which are both distinctive, far-carrying and not easily missed. Although song diminishes in June when the young hatch, unmated males can still be heard well into July. Thus, it is likely that the summer maps accurately reflect the distribution of the species during 1995–2000. It must be noted, however, that there is often an excess of male Wood Warblers, particularly in fringe areas, and, because the tetrad survey accepted regular song more than 14 days apart as evidence of nesting, the maps may well overstate the breeding distribution and abundance.

In the southwest, old broadleaved woodlands, now broken up by conifer plantations, extend for 20 km along the border of Wiltshire and Somerset from west of Mere to south of Warminster. Wood Warblers are traditionally most regular in the vicinity of Alfred's Tower, in the woods west and north of Maiden Bradley and in parts of the Longleat estate eastward to Southleigh. In 1996, there were ten singing males within 1 km of Alfred's Tower (some on the Somerset side in tetrads shared by the two counties) and at least four west of Maiden Bradley. At Longleat, however, where 17 singing males had been found in sample surveys in 1984 (three in the Somerset parts of shared tetrads) and a total of 20–25 occupied territories estimated (Ferguson-Lees 1984), tetrad counts in 1995 yielded only nine; by 2000, the species had disappeared from Heaven's Gate, King's Bottom and Black Dog Woods, each of which formerly held three or more males. The total of territories in southwestern tetrads is likely to have been more than 40 in the 1980s, but was reduced to perhaps less than a third of that number by 2000. (The national survey in 1984–85 recorded only 42 territories in all of Wiltshire, but full coverage was not achieved and the 17 singing males at Longleat was apparently used as the figure for the whole southwest.)

Wiltshire's other main concentration of Wood Warblers is in the old oak woodlands of the southeast between Redlynch and the boundary with the New Forest. This area held more than 20 territories in several years in the 1980s (the national survey noted 23 in 1984–85) and 18 singing males in 1995. Then, despite a loss of habitat through the clear-felling of sections of broadleaved trees in some woodlands, the southeast had its 'best showing…for several years' in 2000, with 14 singing males reported at Langley Wood NNR alone on 9 May, though only four others elsewhere that spring (*Hobby*).

A third traditional area of regular occurrence is the oak and beech of Savernake, where Peirson (1919) thought Wood Warblers 'fairly common' and the 1946 bird report described them as 'Common' (*WANHM*) – though, oddly, Colquhoun (1941) did not record this species in a general survey of the forest in 1939. Numbers have clearly declined in Savernake since the 1940s, as Kennedy (1966) wrote that it was 'extremely local and not common'. This decline apparently began earlier than in the south, perhaps because of the site's greater isolation from other breeding populations. The most singing males reported in *Hobby* during 1980–94 (the 15 years before the summer tetrad survey) varied from zero (in 1983, 1986 and 1990) to five in 1991 and perhaps six in 1994. At the end of the 20th century no Wood Warblers stayed for any length of time in the forest and nesting may not have been annual.

The Wood Warbler was first recorded in Wiltshire at 'end April…1790', at Easton Grey, by George Montagu (1796) who, 'attracted by a note of a bird I had never before noticed…presently discovered it in an oak tree' and promptly 'shot it'. Less than 100 years later Smith (1887) knew it as an annual visitor 'not so numerous' as either the Willow Warbler or the Chiffchaff: 'I have occasionally met with its nest near Devizes, as well as... Yatesbury. Mr. Morres says that it is not common...near Salisbury; but that it has been recognised at Mere and Stourton, and near Warminster'. The 1929 bird report stated that it was 'not uncommon', listed seven localities in the southwest, southeast and northeast, and noted that at Fovant it was 'Scarce this year' (*WANHM*). Peirson (1959) presented a similar picture, as he thought this warbler 'locally not uncommon in beechwoods on the chalk, scarce or absent elsewhere', but he added that 'Its numbers seem to be diminishing'. At that time, however, it was 'well distributed' in the woods around Maiden Bradley during 1954–64 (JCC Oliver) and 'plentiful' in various parts of Longleat in 1957 (G Bright).

The *1968–72 Atlas* found Wood Warblers in 12 of the county's 33 core 10-km squares but breeding was proved in only two, while the corresponding figures in the *1988–91 Atlas* were 15 and eight, and in the 1995–2000 tetrad survey 17 and six (though the criteria for proof of breeding were not the same throughout). While numbers of Wood Warblers appeared to have fallen significantly in Wiltshire in the late 20th century, their pattern of distribution within the county remained roughly the same. Clearly, this small and fragmented population – of perhaps no more than 20–30 territories by 2000 – is a tiny proportion of British numbers, and very vulnerable to changes in its broadleaved woodland habitats.

Wood Warblers are seldom noted on migration through the county, being easily overlooked when not singing, but regular coverage at Coate Water produced a number of passage records during 1990–2000 – in spring in seven of the 11 years, the earliest on 16 April in both 1992 and 1996, and a few in autumn in eight of them, all between 22 July and 7 September (*Hobby*). The earliest and latest recorded dates for the county as a whole are 24 March 1948 and 17 September 1952 (*WANHM*). Only nine Wood Warblers were ringed in Wiltshire during 1965–2000, all but two as nestlings, and none has been recovered.

GDP

Chiffchaff

Phylloscopus collybita

Common in summer, scarce in winter, winters west and south Europe/Africa

An early March Chiffchaff singing 'even in the bleakest and most boisterous weather' (Smith 1887) is a welcome sign of spring – but it may not nowadays be a newly arrived migrant. Wintering by this species was recorded in Great Britain as far back as the 19th century, and the numbers doing so have increased greatly since the 1940s. A British total of about 1000 was estimated in the *1981–84 Winter Atlas*, but figures from southwest England show that the total is now significantly higher, though the relative scarcity of winter recoveries of Chiffchaffs ringed in Great Britain suggests that most are not of British origin (*Migration Atlas*). As an example of the numbers now in the southwest, no fewer than 120 were recorded at a single site in St Austell (Cornwall) early in 2000 (*Birds in Cornwall* 2000: 116).

For Wiltshire, Peirson (1959) knew of just a single winter record – one seen at Trowbridge on five dates from 29 January to 31 March 1955 (*WANHM*) – but two decades later Buxton (1981) was able to report Chiffchaffs wintering in 'very small numbers, seldom more than one or two together', and the *1981–84 Winter Atlas* mapped this species in 15 of Wiltshire's 33 core 10-km squares. They were found in just 11 core 10-km squares in the course of winter tetrad fieldwork during 1998–2000, but that apparent decrease is likely to be an artefact of the sample survey methods used then. Indeed, though numbers remained small, the 1990s saw a slight but steady increase in the totals of wintering Chiffchaffs recorded in Wiltshire, from up to 18 late in 1992 and 17 late in 1995 to 22 in January and February 1999 and 23 in January 2000 (*Hobby*). Most were found in such damp habitats as sewage farms, ponds and streamsides, CWP and Swindon STW being the most favoured localities, though that may simply reflect greater observer coverage. Wintering Chiffchaffs can be very unobtrusive and many must go undetected: the winter survey extrapolated count of 47 is, roughly, one per cent of the summer numbers in the county, and suggests a total in that season of 202–464 individuals.

The presence of wintering Chiffchaffs makes the dates of early and late migrants uncertain, but the earliest immigrants in spring undoubtedly appear in the first half of March, and arrivals continue throughout April. Autumn departures begin later in August than those of Willow Warblers, and passage is strongest in September. Chiffchaffs are, however, still widespread in October, even if only in small numbers, and at least some of those seen in November may still be migrants rather than winterers. Song has been recorded in Wiltshire up to 27 November and from 29 January (*Hobby*).

Breeding wherever there is broadleaved or mixed woodland with smaller trees or prominent lower canopy suitable as song-posts and tangled undergrowth for nest-sites, Chiffchaffs have now nested as far north as Orkney, though most of Great Britain's estimated 749,000 territories (*APEP*) are found in the southern third of the country, and the highest densities in the southwest (*1988–91 Atlas*). Analysis of some 40 years of national survey data showed a fluctuating population, but no discernable long-term trends (*BBWC*): there was a crash in the late 1960s and early 1970s – like those of certain other summer visitors, such as Sedge Warblers and Common Whitethroats (*qv*) – but, after a decade of stability, numbers recovered strongly in the late 1980s and have since continued to grow slowly; over-winter survival is most likely to be a critical factor in this recovery.

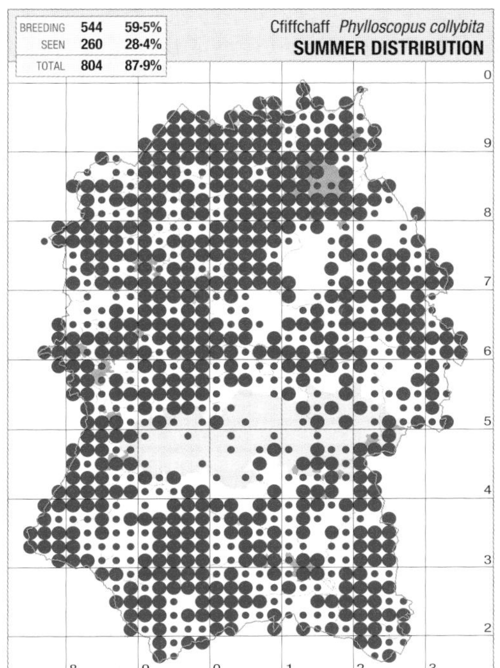

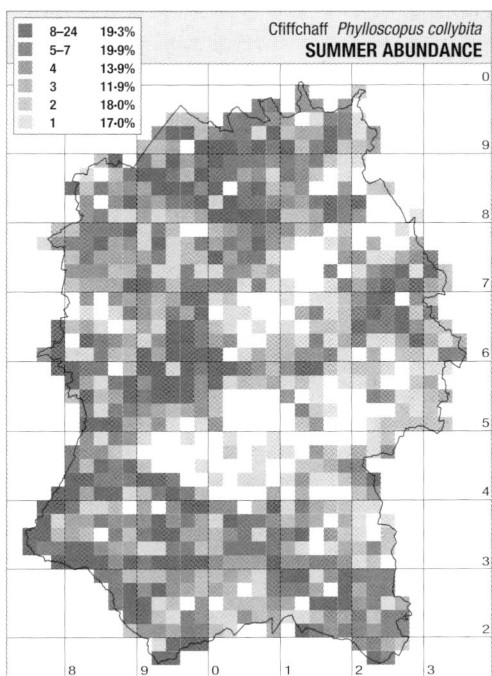

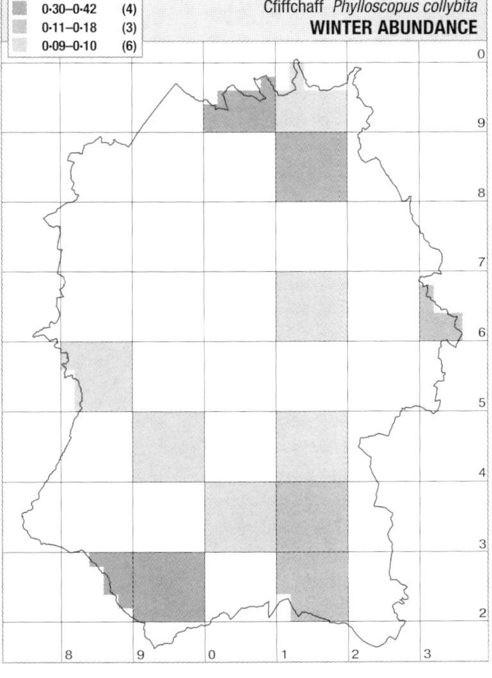

All of Wiltshire's 33 core 10-km squares were occupied by Chiffchaffs during the *1968–72* and *1988–91 Atlases* and, again, in the summer tetrad survey of 1995–2000. There is thus no evidence of any local range changes during the last third of the 20th century. Though fluctuations in numbers have been detected in Wiltshire (*eg Hobby* 12, 19), in general the population appears to have remained stable. The summer timed counts during 1995–2000 recorded just over 3500 individuals; applying the results of BBS surveys in Wiltshire suggest that the county population during the period fell in the range of 12,200 to 28,000 territories. The distribution and abundance maps show the Chiffchaff to be widespread and common, favouring wooded areas and the clay vales of the northwest quarter of the county in particular, though it is absent from large sections of SPTA and the Marlborough Downs, where there is a very low proportion of broadleaved woodland. A survey of SPTA in 2000 estimated a total of just 87 territories of Chiffchaff compared with 619 of Willow Warbler (Stanbury *et al* 2000).

It seems likely that the status of this species has changed little over time. Smith (1887) noted that 'it is much more familiar than its congeners… and does not leave us till

October, being one of the last to depart as it was one of the first to arrive here'. With only slight variations on this theme, the 1929 bird report in *WANHM* considered the Chiffchaff to be 'An abundant summer visitor', and Peirson (1959) 'A common summer visitor, also a passage migrant'.

Chiffchaffs breed from western Europe east across Eurasia to the Kolyma in Siberia. (The Iberian, Canary Island and Mountain Chiffchaffs have at one time or another all been treated as races of *P. collybita*, but are currently considered to be three distinct species: *eg* Sangster *et al* 2002.) The breeding population of Europe, excluding Russia, has been estimated at 15 to 21 million pairs (*EBCC Atlas*). Wiltshire's breeding Chiffchaffs are of the nominate race *collybita* (which nests from Great Britain, Ireland and western France east to Poland, and from the Mediterranean north to Denmark and perhaps southern Sweden), but individuals showing the characters of *abietinus* (the race breeding north and east of *collybita*) and *tristis* (breeding in Siberia) have also been reported, mainly in winter (*eg Hobby* 16, 23, 25).

The various forms of Chiffchaff overwinter in western and southern Europe, North Africa, the Middle East, the northern Indian subcontinent and sub-Saharan Africa from Senegal to Ethiopia, Somalia, Kenya and Tanzania. Ringing data show that Senegal is a major wintering area for British Chiffchaffs (*Migration Atlas*). Indeed, of the 6874 Chiffchaffs ringed in Wiltshire during 1965–2000, three were later retrapped and released again in Senegal (November 1987, March 1990, November 1991) and one in Morocco (December 1979). Others were reported in Spain (four) and the Republic of Ireland, and 13 elsewhere in Great Britain. In the last category, two autumn returns in Sussex and Kent in the year of ringing could suggest that Wiltshire's Chiffchaffs take an easterly route before crossing the Channel and then heading southwest through Iberia into Africa (see also Garden Warbler). In the period before 1965, one ringed at Swindon on 4 April 1958 was 'shot or killed' in the province of Cádiz (Spain) on 14 October that same year (*WANHM*). There were also 13 inward returns, but only one had been ringed abroad, in Seine-Maritime (France) in September 1984, and that was retrapped in Great Wood in May 1987.

Some ten records of Chiffchaffs showing the characteristics of *tristis* or *abietinus* have been listed in *Hobby* since 1974 – all bar two (at CWP and Salisbury) in the Swindon area, particularly at Swindon STW – and seven of them since 1990. The first, of the race *abietinus*, was trapped at Coate Water on 14 May 1976. One of four Chiffchaffs at Swindon STW on 5 December 1998 was considered to be *tristis* and was heard to give a call thought to be characteristic of that form. Although the occurrence of either is not unlikely, it should be noted that certainty in subspecific identification is complicated by intergrades and variation in plumage and voice, and sure identification of pale individuals in Britain has recently been questioned (Dean & Svensson 2005).

PCo

Willow Warbler

Phylloscopus trochilus

Common summer visitor, breeds Eurasia, winters Africa

Breeding Willow Warblers avoid the enclosed canopies of mature woodland, but prosper in a wide range of bushy habitats that includes open woodland, copses, scrub and young conifer plantations. In summer, they are found patchily in northern Spain and otherwise from Ireland, Britain and central France east across temperate and boreal Europe and Siberia in a narrowing band almost to the Bering Sea. Missing from most Mediterranean and Black Sea countries, they and their gentle songs that distinctively fade away at the end are among the commonest summer sights and sounds of northernmost Fenno-Scandia and Russia. Although local declines have been noted, the population for Europe as a whole appears to have remained stable and, excluding Russia, has been estimated at 35 to 46 million pairs (*EBCC Atlas*).

Distributed widely from the English Channel coast to the Outer Hebrides and Orkney, Willow Warblers are Great Britain's most numerous summer visitor, with an estimated 2·3 million territories (*1988–91 Atlas*). National survey data show that the long-term trend is one of moderate decline and, after 20 years of relative stability, the CBC recorded a rapid decrease between the mid 1980s and the mid 1990s, when numbers more than halved – a drop largely confined to southern Britain (*BBWC*). Subsequent CBC and BBS results suggested that numbers may have stabilised, but another decline appears to have started in 1998, and the national population in 2000 was estimated as 2·0 million pairs (*APEP*). Nevertheless, Willow Warblers were found breeding in all of Wiltshire's 33 core 10-km squares during the summer tetrad survey of 1995–2000, as well as in both the *1968–72* and *1988–91 Atlases*.

Classic long-distance migrants, all Willow Warblers – even those from eastern Siberia – withdraw deep into sub-Saharan Africa for the winter and are then found from southwest South Africa north to Ethiopia and southern Senegal. British breeders appear to winter mainly in the Gulf of Guinea region of West Africa, especially in the Ivory Coast and Ghana (*Migration Atlas*). Most Willow Warblers returning to Wiltshire do so during April, but March arrivals are not unusual and were noted annually during 1990–2000 (*Hobby*). The county's earliest recorded dates, both in March 1959, were on the 5th at Box and on the 9th at Little Langford (*WANHM*). Autumn passage is strongest during August; much smaller numbers occur in September, and early October stragglers are not particularly unusual, even if much less than annual, having been recorded in nine autumns in the 27 year-period 1974–2000, the latest at Westbury on the 12th in 1985. On passage, this and other warblers can sometimes be found foraging for invertebrates on such plants as wild parsnip in set-aside.

Of 5511 Willow Warblers ringed in Wiltshire during 1965–2000, five had been recovered elsewhere in Great Britain by the end of that period, and two in the Basque country of northern Spain: the first of the latter, ringed at Froxfield on 6 August 1965, was killed at Basauri (Vizcaya) on 23 October that year and the second, ringed near Upavon on 3 July 1969, was killed in Lerida on 28 March 1970. Apart from 12 inward recoveries of Willow Warblers ringed elsewhere in Great Britain, one ringed at Gibraltar on 19 September 1981 was found sick, and released, at CWP on 2 May 1982. Two Wiltshire recoveries of individuals from Co Down (Northern Ireland) – one ringed at Ballycreen on 20 July 1997 and found dead at Broad Chalke at the end of the same month, the other ringed at Copeland Bird Observatory on 29 July 2000 and taken by a cat at Oaksey 15 days later – demonstrate that Irish Willow Warblers, like the British population, begin migration on a southeasterly heading (*Migration Atlas*).

Most of the above had rather short lives, but, in contrast, five retraps at the same Wiltshire places where they were ringed showed greater longevity and – interestingly for summer migrants that will have been back to sub-Saharan Africa each winter – strong side-fidelity: one such at Larkhill was caught again five years later, and four ringed at Clanger Wood were retrapped there after five years in two cases and after six years in the other two.

Smith (1887) described this species as 'by far the most abundant of the genus' in Wiltshire, an assessment later echoed by the 1929 bird report in *WANHM* ('very abundant')

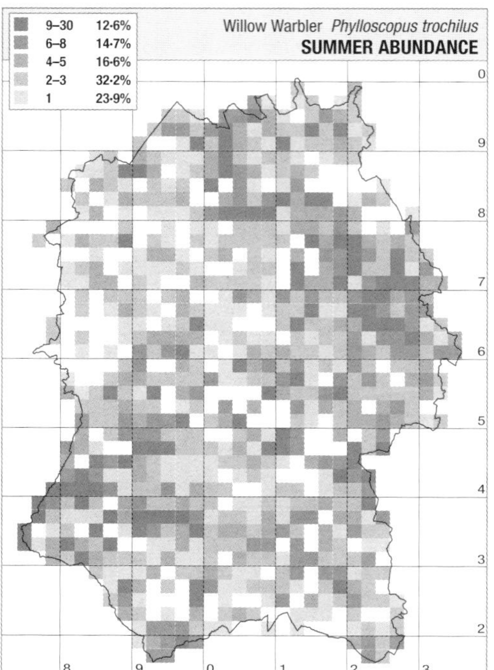

and in 1959 by Peirson ('probably the commonest of the warblers'). Although the summer distribution map still shows Willow Warblers to be widespread across the county, including open areas with scrub on Salisbury Plain and the Marlborough Downs where the closely related Chiffchaff is absent, these descriptions do not fit today. Compared with the Chiffchaff, it bred in fewer tetrads (468 against 544) and had a marginally smaller population as indicated by the total summer tetrad counts (3223 against 3536). The distribution map clearly indicates that densities are highest in the central east and in the southwest, as well as – though more patchily – across Salisbury Plain where, using BBS methodology, Stanbury *et al* (2000) estimated 619 pairs on SPTA in 2000. Extrapolation from this figure, on the basis of the WOS timed tetrad counts in 1995–2000, indicates a total of about 6520 pairs in the county as a whole, but applying densities found during a BBS survey of the Cotswold ESA (Gloucestershire) would suggest as many as 23,200. Given that the abundance map shows SPTA densities to be broadly similar to those across Wiltshire, it is likely that the actual population is nearer the lower of these two calculations.

Great Britain's breeding Willow Warblers are of the nominate race, but the subspecies *acredula*, which summers from Norway, most of Sweden and much of eastern Europe east to the Yenisei, occurs as a spring and autumn passage migrant along the east coast and in the Northern Isles, while 'brown-and-white' individuals resembling *acredula* actually breed in northern Britain (Williamson 1967). This subspecies has been reported twice in Wiltshire, on 15 April on each occasion, though with a gap of 35 years – the first found dead under telephone wires at Pitton in 1949 (*WANHM*) and the second trapped at Longbridge Deverill in 1984 (*Hobby*) – but the size, structure and wing-formula of each of the two races is identical (Svensson 1992) and so the occurrence in the county of the northern form cannot be regarded as proved.

PCo

Goldcrest

Regulus regulus

Common resident, also passage and winter from north Fenno-Scandia

The Goldcrest and its close relative, the Firecrest, are the only European 'kinglets', a distinctive group of five tiny species found mainly in the temperate and boreal zones of the Northern Hemisphere. (By some authorities the kinglets are treated as atypical warblers, by others placed in a family of their own.) Often high in the foliage, Goldcrests have an insignificant and high-pitched song and calls that make locating them easier, but these are inaudible to some people, perhaps particularly those of advancing years – which may account for the species' apparent absence from certain tetrads on the maps for Wiltshire. The Goldcrest's main song period is from late February to mid July (*eg* Witherby *et al* 1938–41), but they also sing irregularly in August–October and exceptionally even in January, as was noted at both Swindon and Coate Water in 1997, on the 23rd and 29th respectively.

Goldcrests are closely associated with coniferous woodland – particularly of Norway spruce, Douglas and silver firs, and other introduced species – but occur also in gardens, parks, cemeteries and broadleaved woodland where at least a few conifers are present. They feed more in conifers than Firecrests do, and the two species are ecologically separated by their habitat and food differences. The Goldcrest almost exclusively eats insects and their larvae, spiders, small snails and other invertebrates, but seeds, especially those of spruce and pine, form roughly one per cent of its diet. It often forages with roving tit flocks or in small groups of its own species.

These tiny birds breed on certain Atlantic islands, extensively from northern Iberia, Ireland and Britain across Eurasia to Lake Baikal in Siberia, from Turkey and the Caucasus to Iran, in central and eastern China, and in Sakhalin and Japan. In Europe – where they extend north to all but the far north of Fenno-Scandia and Russia – the breeding population, excluding that of Russia, has been put at 9·5 to 12 million pairs (*EBCC Atlas*). Of this total, some 560,000 territories have been estimated for Great Britain where, although distributed throughout, the species is most numerous in Scotland, Wales, and northern, western and southern England, reflecting its preference for coniferous habitats (*1988–91 Atlas*). National survey data suggest no long-term population trends, but show that numbers are affected by severe winter weather: for example, the increase in the CBC index up to the mid 1970s was thought to reflect the species' recovery from the mortality suffered in the prolonged winter freezes of the early 1960s, particularly that of 1962/63 (*BBWC*). After a decline from the mid 1970s, the recent trend is one of stability or shallow increase, particularly in the series of mainly mild winters since the mid 1990s, and the population was estimated to have increased to 773,000 territories by 2000 (*APEP*).

British Goldcrests appear to be partial migrants. Two-thirds of ringing recoveries have moved less than 20 km, but there is some evidence that the populations of northern Britain travel farther than those in the south; the extents of any such movements are, however, confused by autumn arrivals from the Continent of passage migrants and winterers, some of which are known to have originated from as far away as western Russia (*Migration Atlas*). As many as 1280 Goldcrests were ringed in the county during 1965–2000, but none of those has been recovered. On the other hand, one ringed on the Isle of May (Fife) on 28 September 1983 was retrapped at Bromham on 11 March 1984, and another ringed at St Margaret's (Kent) on 26 October 1985 was found dead at Dilton Marsh only two weeks later, on 9 November.

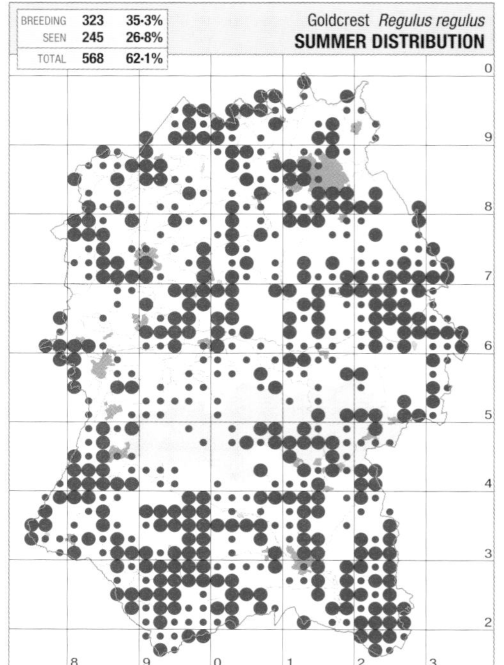

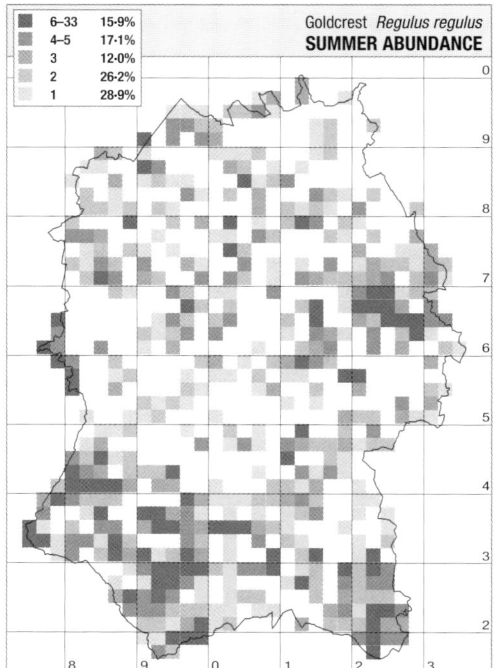

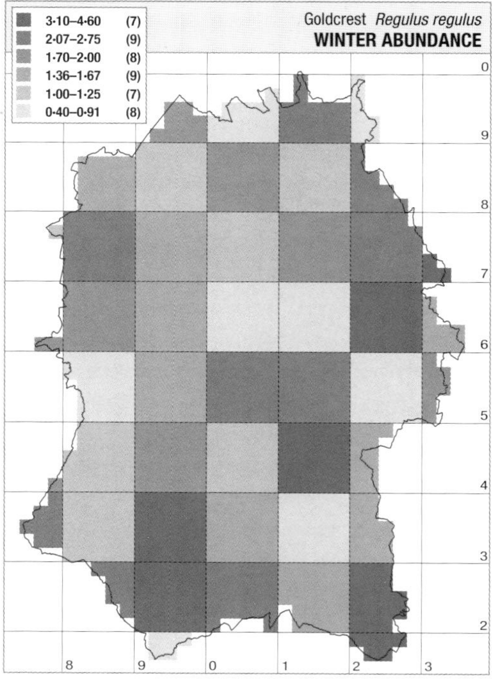

In Wiltshire, Smith (1887) stated that the Goldcrest 'abounds in the county', but later writers described how it was affected by cold winters: 'In 1916–17 ... it almost disappeared and after 1947 it took some four years to recover' (Peirson 1959); 'Suffered from effects of severe winter, 1928–1929' (*WANHM*); '1962–1963 almost exterminated it ... a marked decrease in 1979 following severe weather in the early months of that year' (Buxton 1981). Both the *1968–72* and *1988–91 Atlases* proved breeding in 29 of Wiltshire's 33 core 10-km squares, whereas the summer tetrad survey of 1995–2000 did so in 31 – a slight increase that perhaps again reflected the run of generally mild winters during the 1990s.

The summer distribution and abundance maps both show the greatest concentrations to be in the Savernake area of the northeast and in the wooded parts of the west and the southeast, a not unexpected distribution in view of the Goldcrest's habitat preferences. The *1988–91 Atlas* showed northeast and southeast Wiltshire to be among the regions of its highest abundance in Great Britain as a whole. Thus, even allowing for areas with low numbers – such as most of SPTA, where only 2·1 pairs per tetrad were estimated (Stanbury *et al* 2000) – the present county population seems likely to lie between 15,500 and 22,200 pairs, this being based on the densities recorded in the Cotswolds ESA (Mustoe *et al* 1998), but there will of course always be fluctuations in response to the severity of the preceding winter.

Both the *1981–84 Winter Atlas* and the winter survey of 1998–2000 found Goldcrests in all 33 core 10-km squares. At that season, many British Goldcrests remain on or near their breeding territories (*1981–84 Winter Atlas*) and the winter map shows that the highest densities are found in much the same areas as in summer, notably the southwest, the far southeast, and around Savernake. Unlike summer, however, seemingly high concentrations were also mapped for the eastern part of Salisbury Plain, which may have been a consequence of the 10-km scale used for winter, but these were associated with woodland on the MoD range between Bulford and Tidworth that is dominated by Scots pine. The figure of 1644 extrapolated from the winter counts is very close to the summer total of 1680, indicating a winter population of 15,900 to 22,600 individuals. That might suggest some emigration – much higher figures would be expected if based on the numbers of breeding pairs and their young – but it is difficult to know how much confidence to place in estimates for such an unobtrusive species.

SBE & IJF-L

Sponsored by Shirley & Danny Tuffin in memory of their son Steven

---

Firecrest
Regulus ignicapilla

Scarce (probably overlooked) winter/passage and very local breeder

The Firecrest has been described as 'marginally bulkier and seemingly larger-headed' than the Goldcrest (*CBWP*), but any heavier appearance surely results from its brighter upperparts and 'fierce' (rather than 'surprised') face-pattern, with bold black-edged white supercilia. Its mean weight and wing-length are fractionally less and, apart from a marginally longer bill, its other measurements also average smaller (*BWP*). Thus, the Firecrest is arguably our smallest breeding bird.

Until the 1960s, Firecrests were little more than scarce migrants along the south coast of England and north to East Anglia, as well as regular winterers in even smaller numbers from Dorset to the Isles of Scilly (*BOU* 1971). In Hampshire's New Forest, three singing males were located in 1961, fledged young were seen in 1962, and a nest was found in 1965 – by which time Firecrests were established in up to five areas there (Adams 1966). No fewer than 27 singing males were recorded in the New Forest in 1969, while others appeared in Hertfordshire in 1968 and Dorset in 1970. A wider colonisation became clear by 1971, and the following year 43 singing males were found in six counties (Batten 1971, 1973a). By 1975, singing males had been recorded west to Monmouthshire and north to North Yorkshire (*1968–72 Atlas*). By 1983, the national total was 175 in 75 localities (*RBBP*) and the *1988–91 Atlas* recorded summer presence in 99 10-km squares of England and Wales, largely in central-southern England, though with breeding evidence in 48 northward to Lancashire and the Wash. The RBBP reports in the mid to late 1990s might suggest a decline then, because the annual listed number of possible/ probable breeding pairs apparently fell to only 50–60, but that figure rose again to about

100 in each of 1999 and 2000 (including a singing male in Scotland in April 2000) and, regrettably, these reports are never complete.

Wiltshire's first Firecrest was 'shot... with a catapult' in Savernake Forest on 10 October 1881 (Hony 1915a). Apart from an observation of 'a pair believed to be this species' in 1934 (*WANHM*), no more were noted until 1943 when one was seen near Bulford Camp in March (Peirson 1959); this was followed by two at Shear Water on 21 November 1948 and singles at Oare on 16 December 1954 and Fonthill on 16 March 1958 (*WANHM*). From 1966, however, the species was recorded almost annually, mostly in or between autumn and spring, apart from the tantalising observation of a 'male feeding an apparent juvenile at Chase Woods' on 8 May 1976 (*Hobby*). Unfortunately, this is an almost impossibly early date for a fledged juvenile, and a male Firecrest's courtship-feeding of a female Goldcrest is more likely.

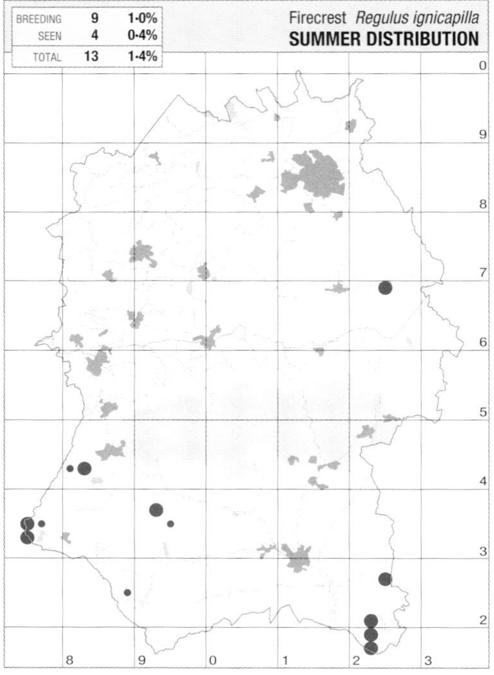

Since the early 1980s, this species has gradually colonised certain parts of Wiltshire. In January and early February of 1980 itself, at least four Firecrests – possibly up to ten – were found wintering at Shear Water, and on 18 July 1983 came Wiltshire's first proof of breeding when two adults were seen feeding four young near there (*Hobby*). The very next year, as many as seven winter records in January–April and October–December provided the wrapping for two significant summer records in April–June 1984: a male singing in an avenue of holm oaks next to two gardens with a mix of broadleaved trees and yews in Swindon, where a female was seen gathering nest material in late April; and two singing males found in Hens Wood, near Marlborough. From then on, Hens Wood became the first of three well-established Wiltshire areas for this species: one or two singing males or pairs being found in all but three of the 17 years 1984–2000, generally favouring Norway spruce.

The second main area is Longleat, where in May 1986 at least two singing males in mixed, and partly exotic, woodland near the track to Heaven's Gate were the first evidence of a regular population of one to four singing males or pairs found there in all but one of the 15 years 1986–2000, breeding being proved in two of those years by observations of family parties, and in another by seeing adults repeatedly visiting a nest high in a cypress; in 1995, at least four males were singing, two regularly, and at least six, possibly ten, birds were present in total (IJ Ferguson-Lees). Heaven's Gate is little more than 2 km west of the original Longleat breeding site near Shear Water, and not far away from its entrance track, on the other side of the road, lies the southwest corner of Center Parcs – where holiday chalets, open lawns, ponds and broadleaved trees set in an extensive area of Douglas fir, larch, Sitka spruce and Corsican pine provide a mixed habitat which, after several years of construction, was opened as a holiday centre in 1994. That year Firecrests were noted in that southwest corner, but, unfortunately, only two surveys of Center Parcs were made by WOS members during 1995–2000, producing at least one singing male in 1995 (IJ Ferguson-Lees, JD Pollard) and seven in

Table 110. Firecrests *Regulus ignicapilla* in Wiltshire: totals of sites, confirmed breeding and other singing males, and totals by regions 1983–2000

Not all these records were published in *Hobby*, some coming from additional data supplied later by NP Adams, IJ Ferguson-Lees, and Collins (2005). Many males were almost certainly unmated, but in some years (*eg* 1995) the number of individuals seen clearly exceeded the number of singing males. Females have, however, been excluded as far as possible from these totals

Year	Total sites	Confirmed breeders	Other singing males	Total territories	Regional totals: confirmed breeders/singing males: Northwest	Northeast	Southwest	Southeast
1983	1	1	–	1	–	–	1	–
1984	2	–	3	3	–	3	–	–
1985	1	–	2	2	–	2	–	–
1986	1	–	2	2	–	–	2	–
1987	3	–	6	6	–	2	4	–
1988	2	1	4	5	–	3	2	–
1989	2	–	3	3	1	2	–	–
1990	2	1	4	5	–	–	2	3
1991	1	–	3	3	–	1	2	–
1992	2	1	1	2	–	–	1	1
1993	2	1	7	8	–	2	6	–
1994	3	–	7	7	–	2	4	1
1995	3	1	5	6	–	1	5	–
1996	4	–	8	8	–	2	5	1
1997	3	–	4	4	–	1	3	–
1998	7	–	17	17	–	1	14	2
1999	3	–	12	12	–	2	10	–
2000	3	1	10	11	–	1	9	1

1998 (NP Adams); subsequently, however, additional records were obtained from Collins (2005) for 1997 (one), 1999 (six) and 2000 (five). Singing Firecrests were also recorded in some years in four other sites in wooded areas south to Alfred's Tower, but fuller searches of suitable semi-open habitat on the Longleat estate might well produce more.

In the southeast of the county, one to three singing males or pairs were present in six years: records came from three localities and included a nest in a yew. Thus, the species is becoming established in Wiltshire, if still only very locally (table 110). The summer distribution map shows presence in thirteen tetrads, eight in the southwest, four in the southeast and one in the northeast. It must be added that many singing male Firecrests apparently remain unmated, so regular song over long periods probably indicates no more than a territory held. Only one individual was found during winter tetrad work, but four others were recorded in the county during those two winters (*Hobby*).

It might be thought that these tiny birds were overlooked until the great increase in birdwatchers over the last three decades or so, but the Firecrest has been extending its European range for the past 100 years, especially from the 1930s through to the 1970s. Apart, however, from northwest Africa, various Mediterranean islands and, locally, Asia Minor, it is still confined to continental Europe west of the former USSR, north to Denmark and Lithuania, but always very patchily and with an estimated breeding population of 3·2 to 4·6 million pairs (*EBCC Atlas*). In the northeastern quarter of that range it is a summer visitor that migrates southwest in autumn and northeast in spring. This migration used to account for the small regular passage along the south coast, and probably still does. It is unknown if 'British breeders are purely summer visitors and whether they leave the country in winter' (*Migration Atlas*), but it does seem possible that some do stay in southern England, perhaps favouring waterside woodland.

In this connection, it is interesting that breeding was first proved in Wiltshire close to Shear Water where at least four had been found wintering three years earlier, and the only Firecrest recorded during the WOS winter survey was about 1 km from where a male sang throughout the following summer. Only 11 Firecrests have been ringed in the county and none recovered. The patchy distribution, not only in Wiltshire and Great Britain but also in its continental range, is a mystery. Although Firecrests are associated with conifers – perhaps especially spruce, larch and cypress – they are more catholic in habitat than Goldcrests and nest in a variety of broadleaved trees, often in ivy, and usually in mixed woodland. Although they do not generally arrive on their breeding grounds until well into April (rarely March), weeks after most Goldcrests have established territories, there seems to be no question of serious competition. Firecrests have a wider range of arthropod foods and feed more in broadleaved trees almost down to ground level. Clearly they are overlooked, especially by those unfamiliar with the differences in songs, although this is not enough to account for the localised distribution. Interestingly, almost all their regular summer haunts in Wiltshire are on higher woodland or wooded ridges, but this is not necessarily the case elsewhere.

The New Forest remains one of the English strongholds, and there must be more Firecrests where this extends into southeast Wiltshire. The *1988–91 Atlas* put the national total at 80–250 singing males. No more than 17 singing males have been recorded in Wiltshire in a single summer, and the Wiltshire total probably lies between ten and 20 territories in recent years, but locating this tiniest of British birds will continue to provide a rewarding challenge.

(See also page 725.)

IJF-L

Sponsored by Mike Randall in memory of Joan Turner

Spotted Flycatcher

Muscicapa striata

Widespread but declining summer visitor, breeds Eurasia, winters Africa

Frequent aerobatic forays for insects from a fence or twig often give away the presence of this flycatcher, which occurs in summer from northwest Africa throughout much of Europe north to Fenno-Scandia, and thence east to beyond Lake Baikal and the western highlands of central Asia, as well as through Turkey to Iran. It is a long-distance migrant, and the entire Eurasian population winters in sub-Saharan Africa, the majority in woods and forest edges south of the equator. Spotted Flycatchers ringed in Great Britain have been recovered in both western and southern Africa (*Migration Atlas*).

Of 535 Spotted Flycatchers ringed in Wiltshire during 1965–2000, two had been found abroad by the end of that period, both in the year of ringing: an adult ringed at Pewsham, Chippenham, on 24 July 1966 was reported as 'alive and probably healthy' near Madrid (Spain) on 11 September; and a nestling marked at Longbridge Deverill on 21 June 1987 was recovered in Nigeria on 7 October. Additionally, of nine other recoveries within Great Britain that involved Wiltshire, most were local or had made only short-distance movements, but an adult ringed at Spurn (Humberside) on 24 May 1989 was retrapped at Edington a year later, on 18 May 1990, perhaps still on its way north.

Spotted Flycatchers are found somewhat patchily throughout Great Britain, apart from a scattering of gaps most noticeably in the Scottish Highlands and outer island groups. The species' distribution patterns were similar in both the *1968–72* and *1988–91 Atlases*, but, whereas the latter estimated some 120,000 Spotted Flycatcher territories in Great Britain – a decrease of nearly 7 per cent since 1968–72 – national surveys have now demonstrated a large, consistent and long-term decline in numbers by 2000 to barely one fifth of the level of the mid 1960s (*BBWC*), representing a national total of just 58,800 territories at the end of the 1990s (*APEP*). This is thought most likely to have been driven by a decrease in the survival rate during the first year of life (although the reasons for that are unclear), but deteriorating woodland habitats in Great Britain and, more probably, conditions on migration or in winter quarters may also be involved (*BBWC*); cooler summers, which affect insect numbers, perhaps play a part (*EBCC Atlas*). In Europe as a whole – where the population, excluding that of Russia, has been estimated at 7·1 to 8·8 million pairs – large declines in numbers have similarly been reported in a number of countries since the 1960s (*EBCC Atlas*).

Usually arriving singly in their territories, Spotted Flycatchers are among the latest summer migrants to return to Great Britain. During 1974–2000, Wiltshire's earliest date of all was 3 April 1981 and the latest 'first record' in any year was 14 May 1975, but May provided the first date in 13 of the 27 years (*Hobby*) and the main influx is always in that month. Even then, breeding may be strongly influenced by weather conditions: more pairs will nest early if temperatures are warmer, and clutch sizes are higher when there is more sunshine (O'Connor & Morgan 1982); given an early start, many Spotted Flycatchers are double-brooded in southern Britain (Summers-Smith 1952).

Favoured breeding habitats in Great Britain include woodland edges and glades, copses, and parks and gardens, where this flycatcher's food consists mainly of flying insects, particularly large flies but also moths and butterflies. Peacock, small tortoiseshell, painted lady and meadow brown butterflies have all been recorded as its prey in Wiltshire, some individuals apparently showing preferences for particular species (Edwards 1983c). When the air temperature is too cold for insects to be on the wing, Spotted Flycatchers take insects from tree foliage (Davies 1977) and, if cool, wet conditions continue for about a week, broods will often starve (*1988–91 Atlas*).

Spotted Flycatchers build their nests in a variety of crevices, holes and ledges, and also use open-fronted nestboxes and old nests of other species, especially those of thrushes and Barn Swallows (Summers-Smith 1952). In Wiltshire, one pair took over an old and slightly damaged House Martin nest at Atworth in 1985, and another a hollowed coconut nailed to a tree near Durrington in 1984 (*Hobby*).

Smith (1887) described the Spotted Flycatcher as 'very common' in Wiltshire and 'most regular in its arrival in the middle of May'. Peirson (1919) considered it a 'common summer visitor, sometimes very common' in the Marlborough district and, 40 years later – then referring to the county as a whole – the same author mentioned 'collections of some 30 or 40' in late August 1951 and 1952 'which seemed to be pre-migration assemblies' (Peirson 1959).

The *1968–72 Atlas* mapped this species as breeding in all of the county's 33 core and 15 part 10-km squares, and Buxton (1981) still found it 'widespread' and 'common in some localities', with numbers fluctuating 'considerably from year to year', though it had 'probably decreased in the last ten years'. The *1988–91 Atlas* also recorded it in all of the core and part 10-km squares, but with no evidence of breeding in four of the squares, and the summer distribution map for 1995–2000 shows that, despite the declines, nesting still occurred in all but one of the county's 48 10-km squares.

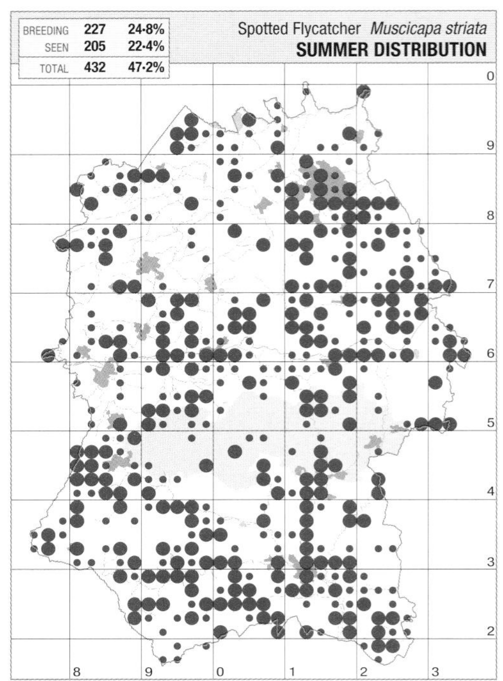

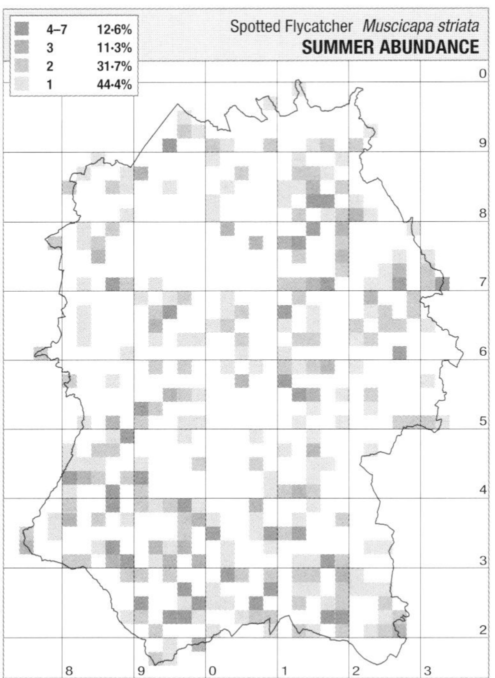

The abundance map shows most to have been in the southwest, the northeast, and the valley of the Salisbury Avon, but distribution was patchy even in those areas. An annual survey at Center Parcs, Longleat, recorded eight territories in 1997–99, but from a half-survey in 2000 extrapolated a total of 12 that year (Collins 2005).

Spotted Flycatchers were reported from an average of only 63 sites in Wiltshire each summer during 1990–2000 (*Hobby*), breeding being confirmed in fewer than half of those. In contrast, results from the BBS in Wiltshire suggest that the county's breeding population may number as many as 2050 pairs. Although fieldwork for that survey was undertaken in just 38 1-km squares – and estimates for some other species based on counts in those few squares have proved notably high or low – the BBS figure compares favourably with the counted total of 601 during the timed tetrad surveys in 1995–2000. (Most timed counts have proved to show around one third to one quarter of the actual population estimates for other species.) A range of 1500 to 3000 pairs is therefore suggested for Spotted Flycatchers in Wiltshire, even though that would represent a high proportion – 1·5 to 2·5 per cent – of the British breeding population estimated by the *1988–91 Atlas*.

After breeding, Spotted Flycatchers begin to leave in late July, but mainly through August and into September, sometimes in small parties. During 1974–2000, the latest autumn records published in *Hobby* were in September in 14 years (earliest 15 September 1979) and in October in 13 years (last 26 October 1990), though 27 October 1962 (*WANHM*) remains Wiltshire's latest record of all. Double-figure counts in autumn have decreased significantly since 1990, and only 14 such counts were recorded during 1990–2000 (eight of those before 1993), the highest being 36 at Boyton on 19 August 1992 (*Hobby*). Favoured autumn migration sites across the county are associated with open water and an abundance of food, including The Lawn (Swindon), Coate Water, Corsham Park, Lackham, Fonthill Lake and Britford.

SBE

Sponsored by Peggy Bucknall

Red-breasted Flycatcher
Ficedula parva

Vagrant (1 record), breeds central-east Europe/ Siberia, winters south Asia

This smallest and most agile of the European flycatchers – of which only the adult male has a red breast – is a summer visitor to much of Europe eastward from southern Fenno-Scandia, eastern Germany, Austria and the Balkans to western Siberia. It is replaced in eastern Eurasia by a closely related (and recently separated) species, the Taiga Flycatcher.

The numbers of Red-breasted Flycatchers breeding in Europe, excluding Russia, have been put at 316,000 to 380,000 pairs (*EBCC Atlas*), but the population as a whole migrates southeast to winter in southern Asia. Even so, a few occur every year as autumn vagrants to Great Britain, typically through reverse migration in anticylonic weather. Nearly 3000 were recorded during 1968–2000 at an annual average of 69 (Fraser & Rogers 2002). The vast majority are juveniles seen along the east and south coasts, but a few adults also overshoot on return migration between mid April and early June.

Wiltshire's only record, a male watched at Calne by four observers on 13 May 1944 (*BB* 38: 173) came into the latter category. That year a male was also recorded at Portsmouth (Hampshire) on 1 May (*BB* 38: 174) and the first breeding was proved in Sweden, perhaps indicating what was at the time an exceptional westward movement.

RT

Pied Flycatcher
Ficedula hypoleuca

Rare breeder, scarce but regular passage, breeds Europe, winters Africa

The handsome Pied Flycatcher is a summer visitor with a strong westerly and northerly bias in its British distribution (*1988–91 Atlas*), and is a prize find in Wiltshire. It also breeds locally in Spain and France and more numerously from central Europe north to northern Fenno-Scandia and thence east to the Yenisei in western Siberia; it winters in western and central Africa. Not all of those seen in Great Britain are necessarily British nesters, as ringing recoveries show that some from Fenno-Scandia, northern Germany and Russia occur on autumn passage (*Migration Atlas*). The population of Europe, excluding Russia, has been estimated at 4·7 to 6·1 million 'pairs' (*EBCC Atlas*), though it should be added that males are often polygamous.

The westerly distribution of Pied Flycatchers in Great Britain is related to local climate and available habitat (Campbell 1954–55, Yapp 1962), coinciding mainly with areas where the annual rainfall is over 1000 mm and the dominant trees are sessile oaks with sparse ground cover. Thus, they are found mainly in wooded upland valleys and hillsides from southwest England to Scotland, but most densely and widely in Wales. They will also nest in belts of riverside trees and in large gardens and orchards. Probably the most important factor limiting their numbers and range within suitable habitats is the availability of nest-sites – usually holes in trees, most typically old woodpecker holes, and sometimes holes in walls and buildings, but nowadays perhaps most commonly nestboxes. The most recent estimate put the British population at 35,000 to 40,000 pairs (*1988–91 Atlas*), significantly higher than the 20,000 pairs calculated by the *1968–72 Atlas*.

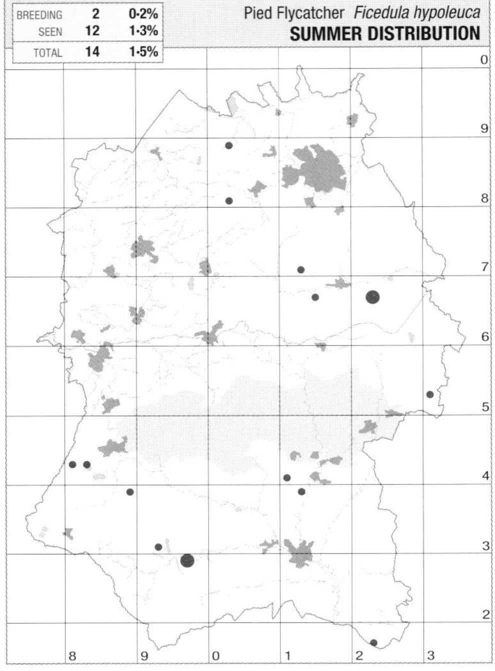

In the 19th century, Smith (1887) listed a number of Wiltshire records, mostly of specimens shot in spring, of which the first one dated was at Ford in 1837; Pied Flycatchers appear to have been regular migrants through Wiltshire then – 'obtained near Warminster... every year' – but with no suggestion of nesting, though 'a pair' was seen near Salisbury in 1860. Peirson (1919) regarded this species in the Marlborough district as 'a scarce bird of passage usually seen early in May' and four decades later he noted that in the county as a whole it was 'A passage migrant... regularly seen usually in spring but occasionally also in late summer' (Peirson 1959).

The 1929 bird report in *WANHM* considered the Pied Flycatcher to be no more than 'an uncommon passage migrant' in Wiltshire, but just two years later, in 1931, came the county's first 'Satisfactory evidence of the breeding of this species in the garden at Standon House, near Chute'; 'both cock and hen at the nest' were seen, though the outcome was not recorded. In 1934 a pair at Purton from 10 May 'were joined by six hen birds five days later when they all disappeared' (*WANHM*). About this time Pied Flycatchers began a general expansion in Great Britain: they had been restricted largely to north Wales and Cumbria until the last few decades of the 19th century, but spread slowly thereafter and during 1940–1952 colonised five new counties (*1875–1900* and *1968–72 Atlases*).

Buxton (1981) noted that Pied Flycatchers were 'regularly reported in both spring and autumn' and 'pairs had been seen in apparently suitable breeding habitat', but there was no further record of nesting until 1986, when a pair raised two young in a tree hole east of Heaven's Gate, Longleat. On five other occasions in the late 1980s males were found singing in suitable habitats, once with a female present, but there was no further proof until a series of breeding records in the 1990s: in natural tree holes east of Heaven's Gate, Longleat, in 1990 and 1993, and in a nestbox at Haredene Wood, near Tisbury, in 1995, 1996 and 1997. In the 1990s, also, males were seen singing in suitable habitats in 1990 itself (Clanger Wood), in 1991, 1992 and 1999–2000 (all Savernake), in 1995 (Fonthill Lake, Shear Water, and two males disputing a natural hole for just one morning in High Wood, Longleat), in 1997 (Ravensroost Wood) and in 1998 (Heaven's Gate). The summer map shows records in 14 tetrads 1995–2000, but breeding evidence in only two.

Pied Flycatchers arrive in Great Britain generally from mid April to late May – the males reaching the breeding areas about a week ahead of the females – and in autumn depart between mid August and mid September. In Wiltshire they are found more commonly in spring than in autumn: of 247 records during 1974–2000, just over two-thirds (167) were in spring, no fewer than 23 in 1985 alone. Of those 167, more than three-quarters (129) were males, but this may be because their singing and their bold black-and-white plumage makes them more conspicuous. The lower numbers seen in autumn probably reflect the species' generally quiet habits at that season, but there may also be a seasonal difference in migration routes. Wiltshire's earliest and latest dates are 30 March 1989 and 6 October 1983.

During 1965–2000, ten Pied Flycatchers were ringed in Wiltshire: one of these, a male caught at Bratton on 10 April 1985, was retrapped and released at a nestbox at Llanfair Talhaiarn (Denbighshire) just two months later. The county has also had two incoming recoveries only eight to 11 weeks after being ringed as nestlings in Wales: one marked on 5 June 1993 was recovered near Tollard Royal, on the county border with Dorset, on 18 August and, the following year, another ringed on 15 June 1994 was found dead at Whiteparish on 15 August.

Although the BBS showed a sharp decline nationally during 1994–2000 (*BBWC*), Pied Flycatchers appear to have become more widespread in the county in recent decades, being found in just two core 10-km squares in the *1968–72 Atlas*, but in eight (breeding in two) in the *1988–91 Atlas* and in ten (again breeding in two) during the tetrad survey of 1995–2000. Although nesting in Wiltshire is sporadic, it might become more frequent if suitable boxes were erected in areas such as Savernake Forest and Longleat.

(See also page 725.)

SBE

Bearded Tit

Panurus biarmicus

Vagrant (12 records: 25+ birds) from within Britain or adjacent Continent

Bearded Tits – which are not true titmice, but the only British representatives of the large, mainly tropical family of babblers (Timaliidae) – breed in more than 20 countries of Europe from Spain, Italy and Greece north to southern Fenno-Scandia and southernmost Russia, and from Turkey and the Caspian Sea to northeast China. But everywhere their distribution is exceedingly patchy because extensive reedbeds are the essential habitat. The population of Europe, excluding Russia, has been estimated at 196,000 to 306,000 pairs (*EBCC Atlas*).

Early in the 19th century Bearded Tits were resident in most east and south coast counties from Lincolnshire round to Devon, but drainage, persecution by collectors, and their own inability to survive heavy snowfalls or coatings of ice on the reeds had reduced them to parts of East Anglia by the 1930s. The unusually prolonged snow and ice of the harsh winters of 1939/40 and 1946/47 then cut the British population to no more than four pairs in Suffolk and a single male in Norfolk. But a considerable expansion began in the 1960s – swelled by irruptions from the adjacent Continent, particularly the Netherlands – and, despite a setback in the severe winter of 1962/63, numbers had increased to at least 590 pairs in 11 counties by 1974 (*1988–91 Atlas*). A peak of 665 pairs was estimated in 1977, after which several cold, but less prolonged, winters were responsible for a decline, and a dedicated survey in 1992 showed just 339–408 pairs (Campbell *et al* 1996). By 2000, however, the population was substantially higher again, at 483–520 pairs (*RBBP*), no doubt aided by milder weather throughout all but one of the winters in the 1990s.

Wiltshire's first record involved a female at Corsham Lake during 16–23 October 1965 (*WANHM*). That was followed, five years later, by the first of several observations at the same site in three successive autumns: at least two calling on 17 October 1970 (JC Rolls); calls heard on 28 November 1971, and a female trapped on 11 December probably remained until the 28th; and another female on 30 September 1972 (*WANHM*). Also in 1972, at Swindon STW, a pair was seen on 6 October, a male on the 7th, and two males and four females on the 8th; almost six weeks later what may have been a different pair was found there on 18 November 1972 (*WANHM*). (The last record was incorrectly dated '1978' in Buxton 1981.) Then a single male was trapped and ringed at Lacock gravel pit on 27 October 1973 (*WANHM*). From 1974:

1975	5 January	Corsham Lake	Two calling
	19–31 March	Corsham Lake	Pair
1976	9 October	Lacock gravel pit	Pair
1978	13–15 October	Corsham Lake	Two males, one female
1982	16 October	Coate Water	Pair

Thus, most of Wiltshire's Bearded Tits have been recorded after the completion of their autumn moult, when some may disperse widely (*Migration Atlas*). Small parties are formed from mid September onwards, and eruptive movements occur from late in that month until mid November. British Bearded Tits move west, particularly in October, and it is likely that most Wiltshire records involved individuals from East Anglia, north Kent or the Solent area, which have then returned to their breeding sites in the following spring. No fewer than five were ringed in the county during 1965–2000, and one of those, an immature male at Corsham on 15 October 1978, was retrapped at Winchelsea (Sussex) just over a month later, on 30 November.

Although Bearded Tits have not become established in Wiltshire, small numbers now breed regularly in several neighbouring counties: in 2000, for example, 16–18 pairs in Hampshire, 12 pairs in Dorset, and six pairs in Somerset (*RBBP*). The species has also nested in Berkshire. Bearded Tits readily spread to new areas in autumn after a successful breeding season when their numbers are high and so, against a background of generally mild winters, the planned creation of an extensive area of reeds in one of the many gravel pits at CWP may well be rewarded.

(See also page 727.)

RT

Long-tailed Tit

Aegithalos caudatus

Common resident, population stable after series of mild winters

Tiny, restless and acrobatic, Long-tailed Tits inhabit scrub, hedgerows and treetops, where they attract attention by their persistent calls. Undulating from tree to tree, often one after another in series, with narrow tails longer than rounded bodies, they might be said to resemble fluffy flying teaspoons. Although feeding largely on invertebrates throughout the year, some populations have now learnt to take nuts and fat from garden feeders, which may have contributed to the steady increase in their numbers. In autumn and winter they are highly gregarious, and forage in roving flocks, often with other tits, Nuthatches, Treecreepers, Goldcrests and woodpeckers, sometimes on their own in family parties or groups of up to several dozens: for example, 70 at CWP on 28 January 1996 (*Hobby*).

Unlike the other five species of tits that breed in Wiltshire – which are classified in a separate family – the Long-tailed does not build a nest in a hole, a process requiring little time or skill compared with those it needs to construct its domed oval masterpiece of moss and cobwebs, often covered with grey lichens, and lined with as many as 2000 or more feathers. It is not surprising that building can take three weeks and, as this often begins in March before the leaves are out, the chosen site has to take advantage of as much protective coverage as available. Some nests are high in conifers, others quite low in brambles or other shrubs with thorns or prickles, such as gorse and blackthorn.

Long-tailed Tits are found right across Eurasia from Iberia to China and Japan and, in Europe, from the Mediterranean north to Fenno-Scandia. They are common enough throughout their European range where, excluding Russia, the population has been put at 2·6 to 4·3 million pairs (*EBCC Atlas*). The 210,000 territories estimated by the *1988–91 Atlas* in Great Britain alone, the vast majority in the south, had risen to 261,000 by 2000 (*APEP*).

For Wiltshire, Smith (1887) stated that this species was 'common in all woods, and may be found in hedgerows, but rarely visits our gardens', while the 1929 *WANHM* bird report, Peirson (1959) and Buxton (1981) all noted it as common but adversely affected by severe winter weather. The *1968–72* and *1988–91 Atlases* each found Long-tailed Tits in all of Wiltshire's 33 core 10-km squares, and proved breeding in 31. The summer survey of 1995–2000 established nesting in every core square except ST94, where the species was just seen in only five tetrads. The blank areas in that square, and in those to the north and east of it, lie on SPTA, where there is little suitable habitat for Long-tailed Tits and access is difficult. Their density depends largely on the availability of hedgerows and woodlands. Thus, the summer abundance map draws attention to Savernake and the county's wooded southwest as favoured areas, but only a patchy distribution in the northwest and obvious gaps in open downland.

The summer tetrad counts totalled fewer than 1800 adults, whereas local surveys using BBS methods suggest an estimate of 10,900 to 19,700 pairs in Wiltshire. On that basis the extrapolated winter count of 3900 Long-tailed Tits might indicate a total of some 37,200 to 67,000 at that season − the winter map shows the species throughout the county − though apparent greater numbers are likely to reflect the higher chance of encountering the larger and often conspicuous flocks that may be formed then.

Long-tailed Tits are less affected by changes in farming practices than many other small birds, and the planting of new hedgerows and management of an increasing number of woodlands for biodiversity bodes well for them in Wiltshire. Although severe winters invariably cause particularly high mortality for this tiny-bodied species – resulting in a serious reduction in the number of pairs breeding in the following spring – the county's CBC results since 1971 demonstrate that numbers have always recovered within one or two years. Figures from four Wiltshire woodlands in the 1980s and 1990s show small annual fluctuations with no obvious trends except at Green Lane Wood, where the number of pairs doubled between 1991 and 1998 (B Gillam). At Pinkflower Gorse, a 6·5 ha area of downland scrub with hawthorn and gorse dominant and suitable nest-sites

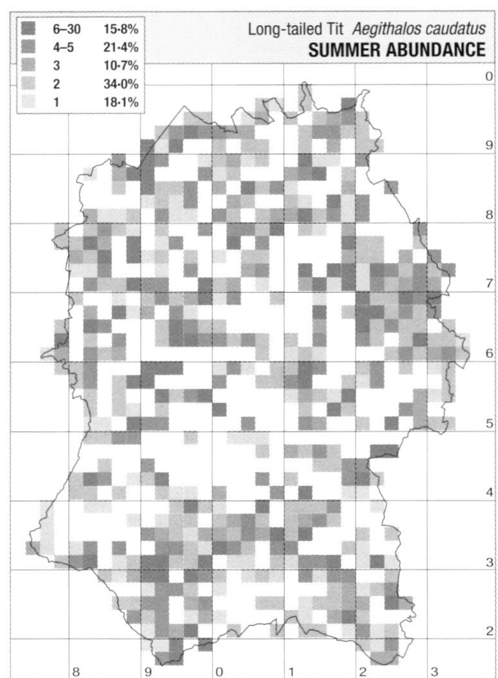

apparently plentiful, Long-tailed Tits were proved breeding in only three years during 1981–96 but then in both 1997 and 1998 (JD Pollard). These examples of local increases reflect the national trend of large changes in abundance over short periods – primarily the results of hard winters – with a high peak in the early 1970s, generally low numbers through the 1980s, but large and relatively stable numbers since the early 1990s (*BBWC*). The unusual cooperative breeding system of Long-tailed Tits is unique among British birds. Failed breeders seek out relatives and help them to feed their young, the additional care resulting in substantially higher chances of survival for members of the helped brood (Hatchwell *et al* 2004).

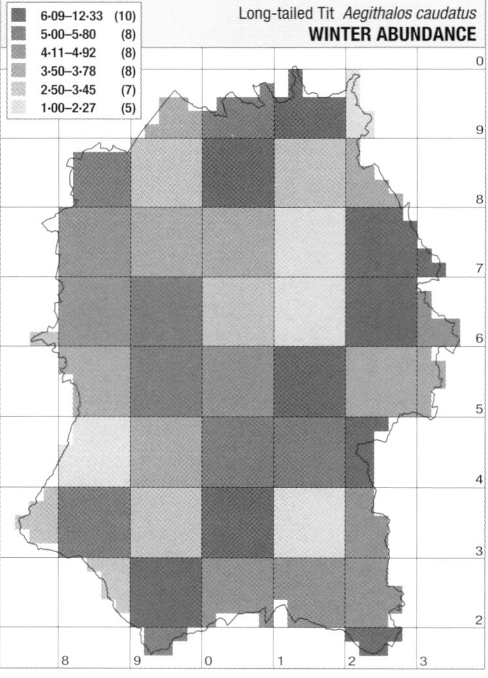

Only 15 of the 3146 Long-tailed Tits ringed in Wiltshire during 1965–2000 have been recovered, and all within 99 km. This is not surprising as the population as a whole is generally sedentary; indeed, 95 per cent of all British recoveries have been within 60 km (*Migration Atlas*). But ringing in Clanger Wood has produced three instances of notable longevity for such a small and vulnerable species: all three were first caught as juveniles and then retrapped in the same wood six, seven and eight calendar years later. In increasing age order, the dates of the first were 19 June 1983 to 3 September 1989; of the second, 16 July 1983 to 28 April 1990; and of the third, 1 July 1982 to 1 April 1990, by which time it must have been approaching eight years old – the national longevity record is 8 years and 25 days (Toms & Clark 1998).

SBE & IJF-L

Sponsored by Hans Bromley in memory of Iris Bromley

Blue Tit

Cyanistes caeruleus

Abundant resident in broadleaved or mixed woodland, often in gardens

Jaunty and colourful, Blue Tits are the commonest and most widespread of the tit family and familiar to many as regular visitors to garden feeders. They breed in an extraordinary variety of natural and man-made holes from those in trees (even behind loose bark) and old walls to pipes, letter boxes, street lamps and, of course, nestboxes; one pair used an old House Martin's nest at Ebbesbourne Wake in 1996, and another an electrical control cabinet at Swindon STW in 2000 (*Hobby*). While found in a wide variety of rural and urban habitats – extending farther into towns and cities than do Great Tits – they typically inhabit broadleaved woodland, especially of oak, though rarely conifer plantations.

Blue Tits are to be seen from the Canary Islands and North Africa through much of Europe north into southern Fenno-Scandia and north-central Russia, but elsewhere only from the Caucasus and Turkey east to Iran and the far side of the Caspian Sea. (Recent research suggests that the forms breeding in the Canaries and North Africa are better treated as a separate species, the 'North African Blue Tit', *eg* Salzburger *et al* 2002.) Throughout this range it is largely sedentary, though irregular eruptive movements of central and northern populations do occur: British breeders are usually separated as a distinct subspecies, *obscurus*, and irruptions into Great Britain involving the nominate continental race have occasionally been recorded, though, perhaps as a result of milder winters and garden feeding, such movements are now rare (*Migration Atlas*). Without giving any detail, Buxton (1981) noted that individuals of nominate *caeruleus* had 'been trapped in winter' in Wiltshire, and he may have been referring to 1967, when 'quite a number of long winged birds' mist-netted during an apparent influx at Swindon in December were considered 'of continental origin' (*WANHM*). As, however, *obscurus* from eastern England 'tend towards nominate *caeruleus*' (*BWP*) and Svensson (1992) did not find *obscurus* well differentiated enough from nominate *caeruleus* to recognise it, it may be more prudent to regard the occurrence of continental Blue Tits in Wiltshire in 1967 as unproved. On the other hand, the last massive irruption of Blue, Great and Coal Tits from the Continent into Great Britain – in autumn 1957 (Cramp *et al* 1960) – certainly did involve Wiltshire: records of all three species, but especially Blue Tits, in numbers ranging from a 'great many' and 'remarkable' to 'exceptional', were reported in various parts of the county from September 1957 through to April 1958 (*WANHM*).

In Europe – where, excluding Russia, an estimated 16 to 21 million pairs breed – the population as a whole appears to have been stable during the 20th century, except

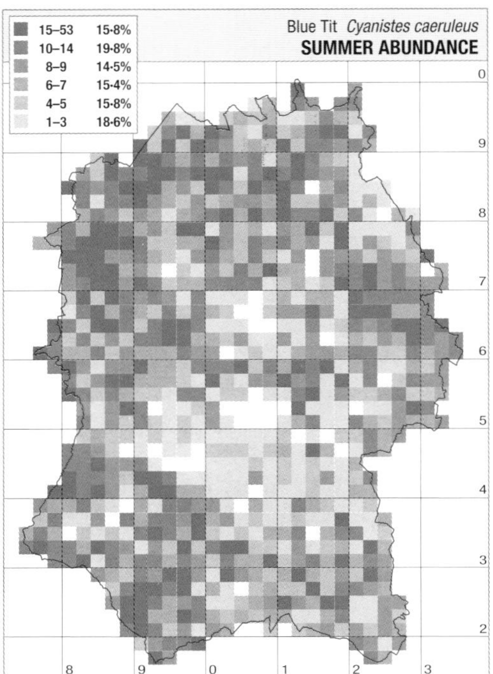

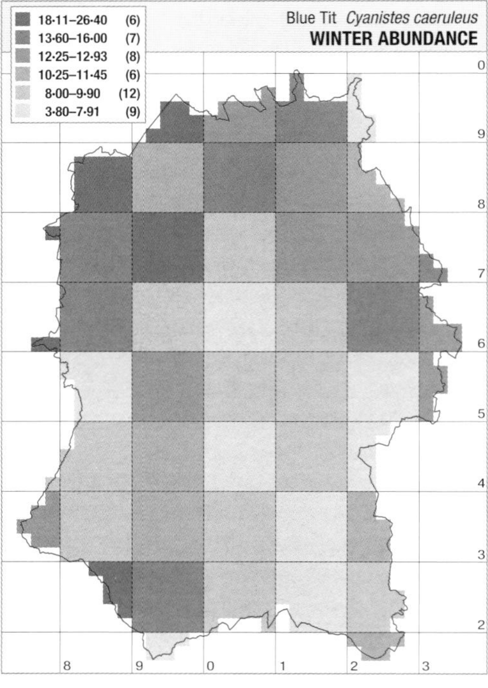

in Fenno-Scandia where this species has spread northwards and increased significantly (*EBCC Atlas*). Blue Tits are found almost everywhere in Great Britain, and are particularly common south of a line from the Mersey to the Tees, but are at low densities in, or even absent from, much of the Highlands and southern uplands of Scotland down into the Cheviots and northern Pennines (*1988–91 Atlas*). Little change in distribution was noted between the *1968–72* and *1988–91 Atlases*, and the latter estimated 3·3 million territories in Great Britain. National survey data show a shallow increase in abundance since the 1960s, with numbers at an all-time high in the late 1990s (*BBWC*).

The Blue Tit was considered the commonest of its family over much of its British range in the 19th century (*1875–1900 Atlas*). It was clearly numerous in Wiltshire then – Smith (1887) stated that 'It is so constantly before our eyes that I need say no more about its habits' – and Peirson (1959), Buxton (1981) and Palmer (1991) all agreed it to be a common resident in the 20th century. Both the *1968–72* and *1988–91 Atlases*, as well as the *1981–84 Winter Atlas*, mapped Blue Tits in every one of the county's 33 core and 15 part 10-km squares, and breeding was proved in every square in 1988–91. The summer distribution map for 1995–2000 confirms that they are to be found almost everywhere in Wiltshire, though the greater detail of the tetrads shows them to have been absent from parts of Salisbury Plain and from open downland lacking trees for nesting and feeding. The abundance maps show them to have been particularly numerous in the north and southwest of the county at both seasons. They were, however, perhaps rather scarcer than might have been expected in the far southeast, particularly so in winter when, apart from the upper reaches of the Nadder, the lower density in the southern half of the county as a whole is particularly marked.

Blue Tit densities, calculated by BBS methods, are highly variable locally across the region – ranging from just 5·2 pairs/tetrad on SPTA (Stanbury *et al* 2000) to 122 pairs/tetrad in the Cotswolds (Mustoe *et al* 1998); Wiltshire's total summer population is thought to lie in the region of 39,300 to 106,000 pairs. The winter counts suggest numbers are some 25 per cent higher at that season than in summer, though this may reflect the greater likelihood of detecting actively foraging parties then; the county's winter total is calculated to lie somewhere between 81,900 and 220,000 individuals.

As many as 28,927 Blue Tits were ringed in Wiltshire during 1965–2000 – the highest figure for any species and nearly twice as many as that for Greenfinches, the second highest – but only six of the 266 recovered by the end of that period, all within Great Britain, were more than 99 km from where they had been caught, demonstrating the sedentary nature of the British population of this species. One, however – a juvenile ringed at Kington Langley on 24 September 1966 and retrapped in Suffolk on 19 November 1967 – had moved a distance of 256 km.

In summer Blue Tits feed themselves and their young chiefly on small invertebrates, particularly on the geometrid moth caterpillars that are at their highest densities in oak woodland. They are normally single-brooded, but one female may lay anything up to 13–16 eggs in a nest. In towns, however – where they are attracted by year-round supplies of food, but where caterpillars are scarcer – clutches are generally smaller and the proportions of young reared smaller still (*1988–91 Atlas*). At other times of year they eat a great variety of seeds and fruits, and their readiness to come to garden feeders helps them to survive hard weather. It is sometimes assumed that the Blue Tits at any bird-table are always the same ones, but ringing has shown that different individuals will do regular rounds of known food sources and that as many as 200 may visit a favoured site in the course of a single day (*1981–84 Winter Atlas*). They are adventurous foragers, exploring every possible food source and pecking at paper bags, putty and milk bottle tops – the last a widespread practice in the 1940s and 1950s.

Blue Tits are always ready to exploit new opportunities. One returned several times to strip the fluorescent yellow-green covering from a tennis ball at Pewsey, presumably to line its nest; another more daring individual was seen to steal material for the same purpose from an occupied Carrion Crow's nest at Swindon STW (*Hobby*).

PCo & PAC

Sponsored by Laura Mynott

Great Tit

Parus major

Common resident of open broadleaved or mixed woodland, parks and gardens

Great Tits are familiar throughout western Europe and, because of their readiness to use nestboxes, are among the most studied passerines in the world (*eg* Gosler 1993). They have a vast distribution, from northwest Africa and Iberia across most of continental Eurasia, in a wide range of zones from the subarctic to the tropical and, though typically lowland birds, from sea level to the treeline in mountains. In Europe, they are among the most ubiquitous of all birds, from northern Fenno-Scandia and Russia south to Mediterranean coasts and islands, and their population, excluding that of Russia, has been estimated at 37 to 52 million breeding pairs; numbers are thought to be generally stable, but significant increases have been recorded in some countries, such as the Netherlands, Estonia and Ukraine (*EBCC Atlas*). In Great Britain, there has been a general increase since the 1960s, particularly from the 1990s, which the BBS suggests is continuing (*BBWC*). One of the commonest of British resident birds, Great Tits are most abundant in the southern two-thirds of England and absent only from parts of Scotland. They were found in almost every 10-km square for the *1968–72* and *1988–91 Atlases*, a well as for the *1981–84 Winter Atlas*. The *1988–91 Atlas* estimated the British breeding population at 1·6 million territories, a figure that was revised to 2·0 million in 2000 on the basis of increases shown by the BBS (*APEP*).

Great Tits were clearly common and widespread in 19th century Wiltshire, and Smith (1887) described them as 'found in every wooded district'. They received little mention, however, in the county bird reports in *WANHM* from 1929, and 'more in evidence this year' in 1934 and 'some decrease since the severe weather' in 1947 were the only comments on their status up to 1950. In the latter half of the 20th century, Peirson (1959) noted that they were 'common … even very common', a statement with which both Buxton (1981) and Palmer (1991) agreed. The *1968–72* and *1988–91* Atlases, as well as the *1981–84 Winter Atlas,* showed them in all of Wiltshire's 33 core and 15 part 10-km squares.

The summer survey of 1995–2000 did the same, and found this species to be marginally more widespread than the Blue Tit, though it was recorded as breeding in five per cent fewer tetrads. The abundance maps show the Great Tit to be commonest in north and southwest Wiltshire, a pattern similar to that of the Blue Tit, but also, unlike its smaller relative, having areas of greater density throughout much of the centre of the county, both in summer and winter; there were comparatively few of either species in the far southeast.

Using densities from BBS surveys in Wiltshire and adjacent regions suggests a county total summer population of some 26,600 to 50,500 pairs of Great Tits, around half that of Blue Tits. The timed tetrad surveys in winter indicated numbers 40 per cent higher than in summer, and a range of 61,400 to 117,000 individuals is estimated. The likelihood of finding Great Tits at that season may be increased by the lack of cover in broadleaved trees, but a higher midwinter total would be expected before colder weather in January and February resulted in greater mortality, particularly among inexperienced youngsters, and it is likely that the winter figure therefore lies nearer the upper end of that range.

The total number of Great Tits ringed in Wiltshire during 1965–2000 was 14,241. This species is largely sedentary in Great Britain (*Migration Atlas*) and so it is no surprise that, of the 109 so far recovered, only six had moved more than 99 km – the farthest-travelled being a juvenile ringed on 28 December 1992 in a Trowbridge garden and

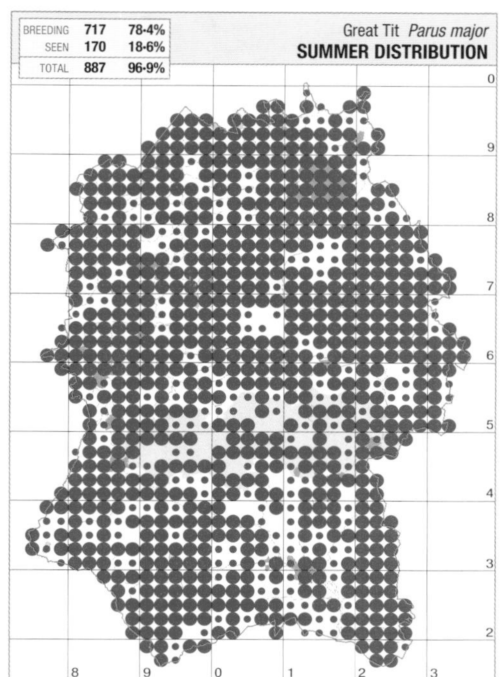

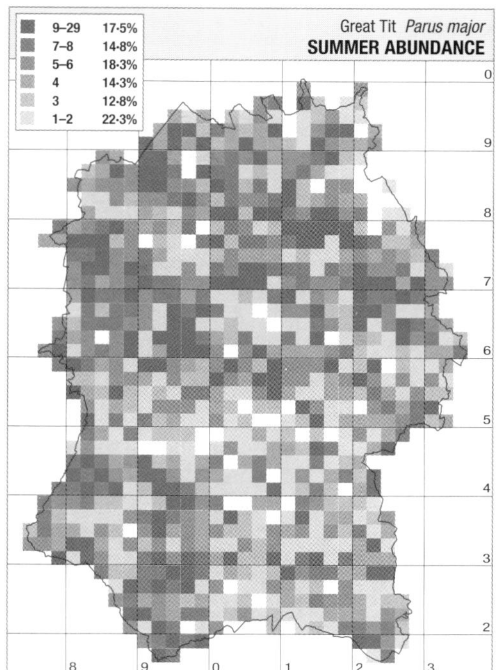

retrapped 251 km away on 30 January 1994 at Thornham Magna (Suffolk). One ringed at Beanacre on 20 August 1994 was retrapped there more than five years later, on 22 January 2000. In contrast, Continental Great Tits are more mobile and at times whole populations may make eruptive movements: in the autumn of 1957 many were involved in the massive irruption of tits into Great Britain (Cramp *et al* 1960), which was widely reported in Wiltshire (*WANHM*, see also Blue Tit).

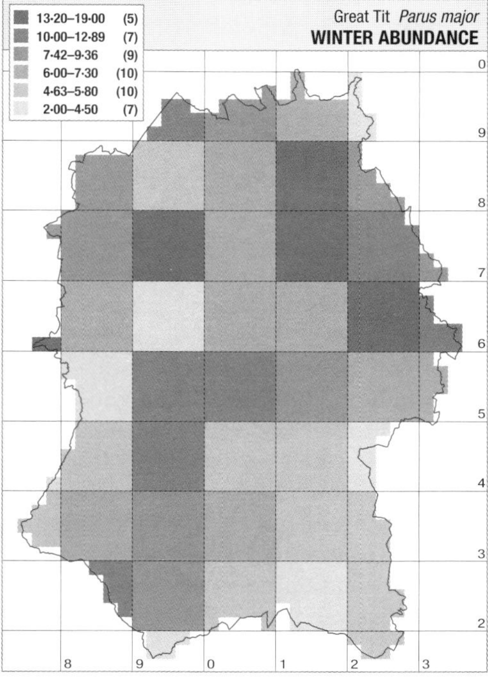

Like other tits, the Great Tit feeds primarily on invertebrates in summer and on seeds at other times of year (and urban individuals on almost anything provided on bird-tables). Its bill is strong enough to hammer open hazelnuts, acorns and sweet chestnuts, and beechmast is an important part of its diet. Among less usual food items recorded in Wiltshire in *WANHM* and *Hobby* were a bumblebee and a maybug, and a family party was seen to drink nectar from a red-hot poker at Bradford-on-Avon. Less common nesting sites included a letter box in Broad Chalke, a metal pipe on the ground at Swindon STW, and a hole just 20 cm above the ground in a wall in Imber.

PAC & SBE

Coal Tit

Periparus ater

Common resident, especially in conifers, some moving into gardens in winter

Marginally the smallest of Wiltshire's tit species, the Coal Tit is a restless and particularly acrobatic little bird with a narrow bill adapted to picking out small insects and spiders, and extracting spruce seeds, in its preferred habitat of large conifers. It is closely, though not exclusively, associated with coniferous woods and forest, especially of spruce, throughout a vast range that stretches from northwest Africa, Iberia and Ireland right across Eurasia to Kamchatka and Japan, and south to the eastern Himalayas. But it also inhabits younger plantations, mixed woods, and parks and gardens with some coniferous trees, and has locally managed the transition to pure broadleaved woodland. In winter it is familiar at garden feeders, where it generally seems to be low in the pecking order.

Coal Tits nest usually in or near the ground, often in a mouse hole or a cavity among tree roots, an adaptation to finding nest-sites in coniferous forest where natural holes are much scarcer than in broadleaved, but they will readily take to nestboxes several metres up in coniferous woods. Even more than Marsh and Willow Tits, too, they have a well-developed habit of storing food – of any sort, but particularly conifer seeds when the cones open – in crevices and holes, another adaptation that helps them to survive winters in often hostile forest.

The breeding population of Europe, excluding Russia, has been put at 12 to 17 million pairs (*EBCC Atlas*). This total includes an estimated 610,000 in Great Britain, where Coal Tits are absent only from some Scottish islands and the fens of eastern England; and where they are most numerous in forested parts of Wales and Scotland and in localised pockets in England, such as the New Forest (Hampshire) and the Forest of Dean (Gloucestershire) (*1988–91 Atlas*). By 2000, the national figure had been revised slightly downward to 604,000 (*APEP*).

Although Coal Tits are eruptive at times of high population in some parts of the range, and short-distance migrants in, for example, eastern Europe, the British population is largely sedentary and has almost identical summer and winter distributions (*cf 1968–72* and *1988–91 Atlases*, *1981–84 Winter Atlas*). In this connection, seven of the nine recoveries from the 916 Coal Tits ringed in Wiltshire during 1965–2000 were reported within a distance of 9 km, though one ringed in Westbury on 19 November 1983 was found dead as far away as Whitchurch (Hampshire) on 9 April 1984 – for this species, an exceptional movement of 58 km. At times of high population on the Continent, irruptions into Great Britain do occur occasionally, these roughly coinciding with the dispersal of juveniles in late summer and autumn (*Migration Atlas*). National survey data show that the British population has fluctuated but remained broadly stable over the long-term – though there have been regional differences and numbers have increased rapidly on farmland (*BBWC*).

In Wiltshire, Smith (1887) described Coal Tits as 'Not so common' as Great and Blue. The 1929 bird report in *WANHM* assessed them as 'fairly common … more or less confined to fir-woods', whereas the 1931 report stated, interestingly, that 'In most parts of the county this species is found less commonly than' the Marsh Tit. Peirson (1959) noted that it was 'not uncommon where there are conifers' and Buxton (1981) considered it 'a common resident in conifer woodland but less frequent elsewhere'. The Coal Tit's range appears to have changed little in Wiltshire in recent decades: it was recorded in all

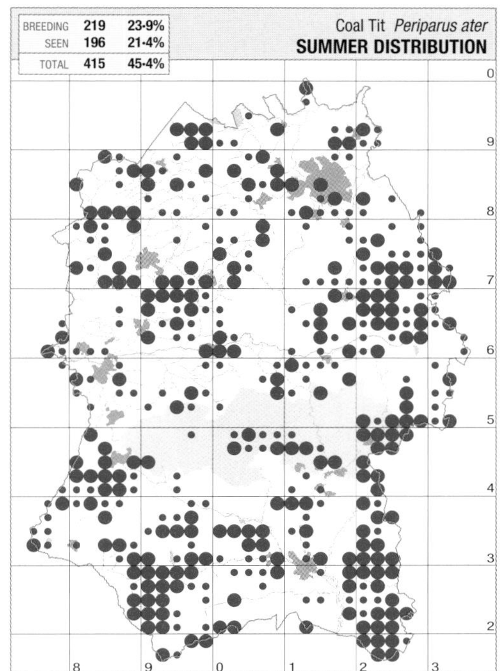

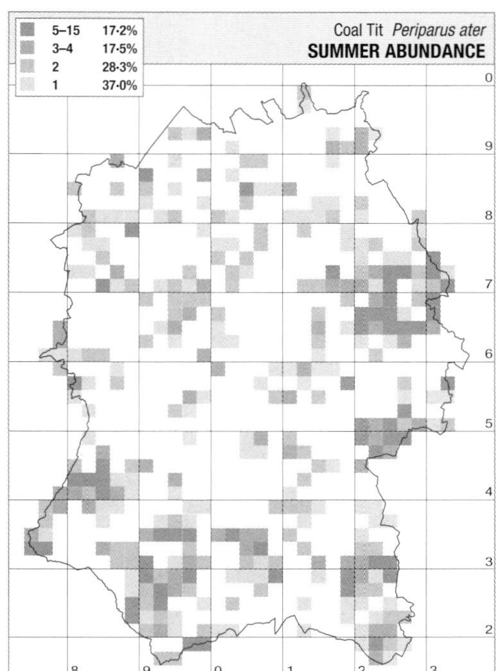

of Wiltshire's 33 core 10-km squares in three of the five grid surveys during 1968–2000, though in only 32 in the *1968–72 Atlas* and 31 in the 1998–2000 winter tetrad survey.

The summer distribution map shows Coal Tits in nearly half of all tetrads, and also, not surprisingly, their absence from open land. Both summer and winter abundance maps show a bias towards the south and east, and a preference towards areas rich in conifers such as Savernake Forest, the south of SPTA (East) and Bentley Wood – a county distribution not dissimilar to that of the Goldcrest apart from, perhaps surprisingly, a marked concentration in the Tidworth area, which is not evident on the Goldcrest map. Coal Tits are ordinarily encountered at low density, usually in ones or twos, but Hens Wood has produced counts of 50 and 60 – even 72 on 9 February 1990.

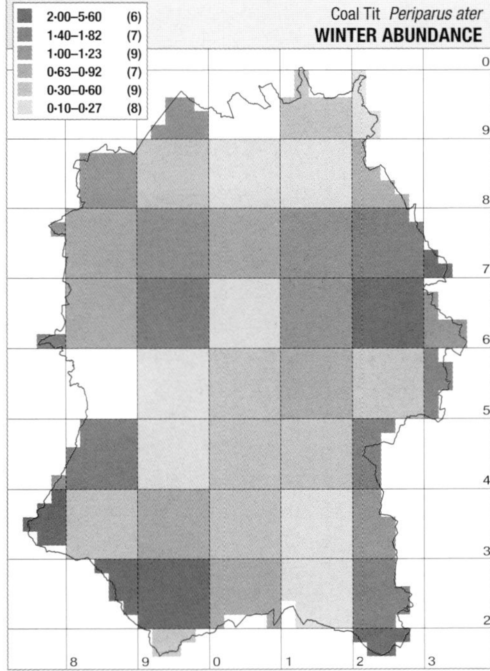

Coal Tits are less numerous in Wiltshire than in many other parts of Great Britain (*1988–91 Atlas*), but the county could hold in the region of 6050 to 9730 pairs, or around one per cent of the British breeding population. The figure of 825 extrapolated from the timed winter surveys is comparable with the summer count of 957, suggesting numbers in the range of 7180 to 11,500 individuals; but both Blue and Great Tits (*qv*) were higher in winter by 25 and 40 per cent respectively; thus, it seems likely that Coal Tits were under-recorded at that season and an estimate of 12,000 to 20,000 is suggested.

PEC & SBE

Sponsored by Gilbert Green (Biss Wood)

Willow Tit

Poecile montanus

Scarce local resident, following large decrease since 1970s

Unrecognised as such in Great Britain until 1897 – when a series of skins previously thought to be Marsh Tits were re-examined – the Willow Tit is sedentary, as it is throughout much of its vast Eurasian range. Moreover, the British population is an endemic race, named *kleinschmidti* from the type specimen collected in 1900. (For further details of an interesting story, see, for example, Simson 1966, Alexander 1974.) An eruptive northern subspecies, *borealis*, also occurs as a rare vagrant in the north and east of the country (*eg* Witherby *et al* 1938–41, Limbert 1984). Elsewhere, the Willow Tit's distinctive nasal call can be heard from central France to Kamchatka and Japan. In Europe, the range extends from northern Fenno-Scandia south to mountain areas in Italy and the Balkans and, excluding Russia, the breeding population has been estimated at 4·4 to 6·1 million pairs – which makes it a rather commoner and more widespread bird than the Marsh Tit.

In Great Britain, the reverse is true, even though Willow Tits are found in many areas north to southern Scotland, if most densely in south Wales, in the Midlands north to south Yorkshire, and in East Anglia and southeast England (*1988–91 Atlas*). The *1968–72 Atlas* calculated the British population at 50,000–100,000 pairs, but two decades later the *1988–91 Atlas* estimated only 25,000 territories, less than half its figure for Marsh Tits. National survey data show that a rapid decline in numbers of Willow Tits from at least the mid 1970s, although now less severe, has continued to the present time – prompting a revised estimate of just 8500 pairs in 2000 (*APEP*); the causes of the decline are unknown, but may involve reductions in dead wood and the shrub layer, as well as increased woodland drainage (*BBWC*).

Wiltshire's first Willow Tit was identified at Little Bedwyn (Alexander 1910), though unfortunately the date was not published. On the basis of that one record, Hony (1915a) included the species in his list of the county's birds, but had no evidence that it had ever nested. The 1929 bird report commented that this was 'A rare resident, overlooked; no records since 1920', but then 'several' were seen at Sheepless Hill in November and December 1931, one at Pepperbox Hill in April 1933 and 'several' again at East Grimstead in February 1934 (all *WANHM*). By the mid 20th century, Peirson (1959) knew the Willow Tit as 'resident now reported every year… scanty records suggest it is local and uncommon'. Webber (1968) was able to add that it had been 'Increasingly recorded since 1957 and has been proved to breed in many new areas'. Buxton (1981) noted this as 'An uncommon resident… more frequently reported from high ground than the Marsh Tit… breeds in the north-east around Swindon and westwards to Malmesbury and on high ground near Marlborough; also in central areas, along the eastern border with Hampshire, south and west of Salisbury and in the extreme south-west around Semley'.

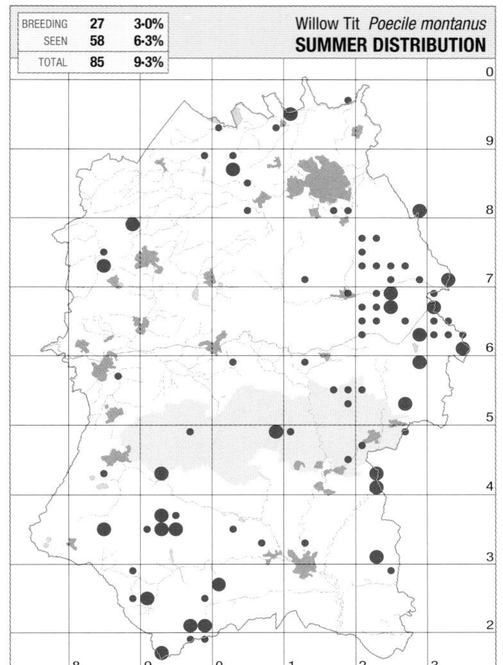

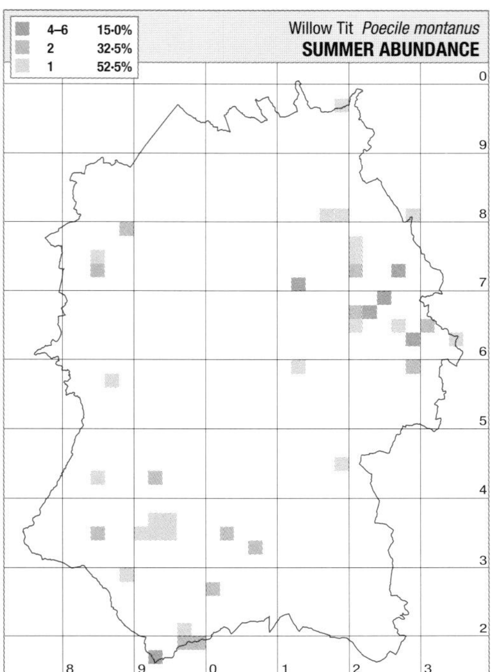

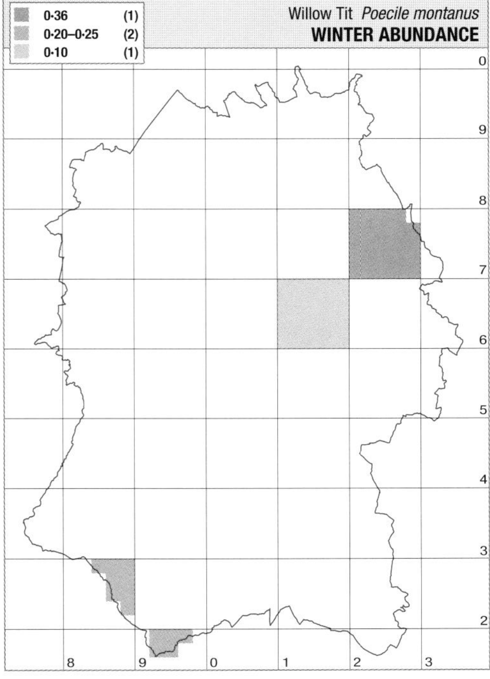

Unlike most other tits, the Willow Tit invariably excavates its own nest chamber in rotten wood. (Marsh Tits will sometimes oust a pair from a finished nest, or even do some partial enlarging of existing holes themselves.) A key habitat requirement, therefore, is the presence of small rotten boughs or stumps soft enough for the female to dig out the nest; the male may also dig out smaller trial holes. The reference above to Semley relates to a study of some 30 occupied nests and many old or incomplete holes examined in southwest Wiltshire during 1963–78 (Major 1979). These were in nine different species of trees and shrubs, including hazel, alder, holly, birch, willow, elder and crab apple (possibly in that order of frequency), as well as sometimes in fence posts of ash and other 'inferior' timber; the excavated sites were always in limbs of small diameter – 'three inches or less being not unusual' – and only one old nest chamber survived in a suitable state to be used, by a pair of Blue Tits, in a subsequent year.

Both the *1968–72* and *1988–91 Atlases*, as well as the *1981–84 Winter Atlas*, found Willow Tits in 23 of Wiltshire's 33 core 10-km squares, and the summer tetrad survey in 1995–2000 did the same. Thus, atlas fieldwork provides no evidence for any general decline in the county, but the summer tetrad survey did show them to be absent by then from SU22, where they nested regularly but uncommonly in Bentley Wood and on Dean Hill in the 1970s and early 1980s (P Combridge). It is perhaps relevant, too, that only three of the 74 Willow Tits ringed in Wiltshire during 1965–2000 (none recovered) were in the last decade of this period (but see page 725).

The summer breeding and abundance maps show Willow Tits to be scarcer and less widely distributed in Wiltshire than Marsh Tits, with distinct southwest and northeast biases, a feature also brought out by the winter map. All three maps demonstrate a preference for woodlands, both large and small, on such higher ground as Hens Wood and Great Ridge Wood, especially where there is a hazel understorey. This species also appears to tolerate conifers more than the Marsh Tit does. (Indeed, its montane populations in southern Europe inhabit mainly coniferous forest.) The ratios of numbers recorded during the timed summer surveys suggest that Willow Tits are only about one seventh as likely as Marsh Tits to be located, but they can be very quiet and inconspicuous except when excavating nests or feeding young, as is borne out by their having been recorded in only two of the 33 core 10-km squares during the winter counts.

The results of using BBS methods in 38 Wiltshire 1-km squares suggested a county population of 2900 pairs, but no contemporary data are available from other regions for comparison. The *1968–72 Atlas* applied a formula of 40–80 pairs per 10-km square to estimate the British breeding population, on which basis Wiltshire's 33 core 10-km square might hold between 920 and 1840 pairs – but even the bottom of this range figure is surely too high for a county where densities are lower than in other parts of Great Britain (*1988–91 Atlas*). Wiltshire estimates for other tit species are, very roughly, some tenfold larger than their respective timed summer counts; thus, the total of just 76 Willow Tits during the summer tetrad survey of 1995–2000 might indicate a county population of some 500 to 1000 pairs, but this would still represent a disproportionately large percentage of the national total, and so a more conservative range of 250 to 750 pairs is suggested. Very few were recorded during the winter survey of 1998–2000, but the total at that season may number between 500 and 1500 individuals.

(See also page 725.)

PCo & IJF-L

Marsh Tit

Poecile palustris

Uncommon and decreasing resident

Restless and – but for its song and calls – unobtrusive, the Marsh Tit is not associated with marshes, but rather with open broadleaved woodland (perhaps especially of oak, ash, birch and alder, often with a good understorey) and also wooded country gardens, parkland copses and riverside belts. It avoids conifers and towns, being seldom seen even at bird-tables in winter, and prefers larger woods to small, damp to dry, and is often found near ponds and streams in areas with old and decaying trees, thus overlapping with the Willow Tit.

Marsh Tits have a peculiar world distribution, with a gap of some 2000 km separating their European and Asiatic ranges. In Europe, they are found from northern Spain, Italy and

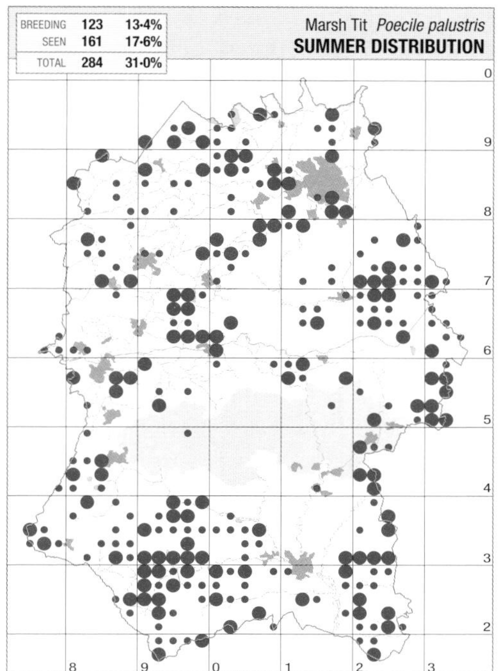

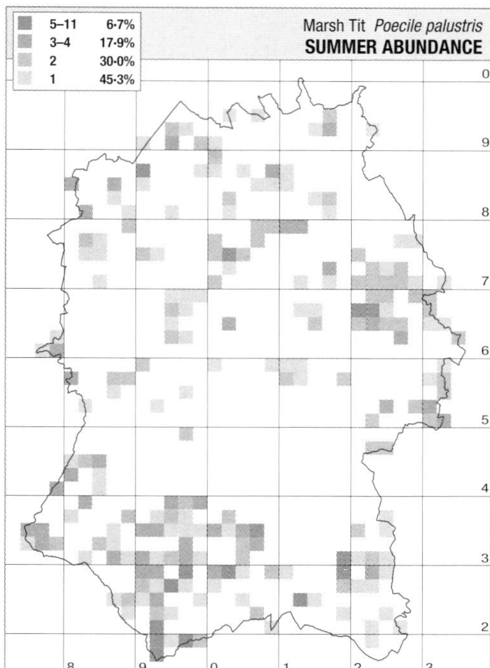

the Balkans north to Britain and southern Scandinavia east into central Russia and south to the Caucasus. (But they are only in the southeast of Scotland and, like Willow Tits, missing from Ireland.) The farthest west they occur in Asia, apart from northern Turkey, is in the Russian Altai, whence they extend through southern Siberia to Sakhalin and northern Japan, south to northern and western China. The population of Europe, excluding Russia, has been estimated at 2·9 to 4·4 million breeding pairs, but declines have been noted in several countries (*EBCC Atlas*).

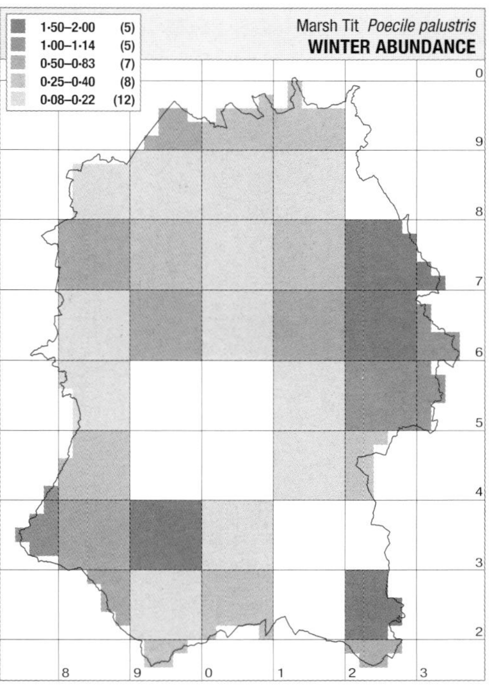

The *1988–91 Atlas* put British breeding numbers of Marsh Tits at 60,000 pairs, and its maps showed that they were recorded in 17 per cent fewer 10-km squares than by the *1968–72 Atlas*, which had suggested a population of 70,000 to 140,000 pairs. The range contractions were most obvious in southeast Scotland and northern and eastern England, but there had been losses elsewhere and most of the highest densities were then, albeit patchily, in southern Wales and south of a line from there across England to the Wash. National survey data also show a long-term and rapid decrease in numbers by around two-thirds since the late 1960s, prompting a revision of the population estimate to just 52,800 pairs in 2000 (*APEP*): this decline appears to be driven by low annual survival rates, perhaps the result of increased isolation of woodland and the loss or reduction of both understorey and dead wood (*BBWC*).

British Marsh Tits are largely sedentary (*Migration Atlas*) and belong to the small, dark race *dresseri*, which occurs also in northwestern France. It was not understood until the end of the 19th century that the very similar Willow Tit (*qv*) was also a British bird and thus the history of both these species before the 20th century is obscured. What Smith (1887) said of the 'Marsh Titmouse' in Wiltshire needs to be considered as covering both species, and his description of its habitat – 'wherever there is moist ground, and alders and willows flourish' – could apply equally to the Willow Tit. Smith thought that the Coal Tit was commoner than the 'Marsh Titmouse' or, in other words, than both the black-capped species combined.

The first attempt to define the status of the Marsh Tit in Wiltshire was published in the 1929 bird report in *WANHM*, which stated that it was 'In greater numbers than the Long-tailed and Coal Tits in most parts of the county', and in the 1931 report it was found to be 'the commonest of the tits' at Lydiard Millicent (*WANHM*). Both these comments were at odds with Peirson's (1959) statement, 30 years later, that it was a 'resident that used to be considered scarce but now is only uncommon'. Yet Buxton (1981) thought it 'common ... most frequent in low-lying woodland and rather scarce on high ground' and Palmer (1991) noted it simply as 'common'.

The *1968–72 Atlas* mapped Marsh Tits in 32 of Wiltshire's 33 core 10-km squares and the *1988–91 Atlas* in 31, as did the *1981–84 Winter Atlas*, which can be used as a comparison because this species is so sedentary. Like the *1968–72 Atlas*, the summer tetrad survey of 1995–2000 found them in all but one of the core squares, and thus the range appears to have remained unchanged in Wiltshire throughout the last third of the 20th century. The fine detail of the summer distribution map illustrates a large gap in central Wiltshire, where woods are sparse or lacking, and the summer abundance map highlights the southwest and, to a lesser extent, the Savernake area as strongholds.

The *1968–72 Atlas* used a 'conservative' estimate of 50–100 pairs per 10-km square to calculate breeding numbers, which would have indicated a Wiltshire population in the region of 2300 to 4700 pairs. Applying densities from recent surveys in the Cotswold Hills ESA similarly suggests a current total of 2640 to 4860 pairs in the county – though, in view of recent decreases, the true figure is perhaps likely to lie nearer the lower end of that range. The winter survey estimated almost 370 Marsh Tits, compared with summer counts of 480, though this may simply reflect their less obtrusive nature when not singing; on the basis of the breeding numbers, the winter population is very roughly estimated as 5000 to 8000 individuals.

A total of 592 Marsh Tits was ringed in Wiltshire during 1965–2000, but – not surprisingly for such a sedentary species – there had been no recoveries away from the ringing sites by the end of that period. Worthy of note, however, was a juvenile ringed in Clanger Wood, Trowbridge, on 24 June 1984 and retrapped in the same place there more than ten years later, on 14 August 1994: this was only seven days short of the national longevity record for the Marsh Tit (Toms & Clark 1998) and it was still alive and well when released.

PCo & PEC

Nuthatch

Sitta europaea

Common and increasing resident

Widespread across Wiltshire in old broadleaved woodland and parkland, the perky and often noisy Nuthatch has become an increasingly familiar visitor to garden peanut-feeders. Its usual nest-sites are holes in mature trees – often old knot-holes or woodpecker borings – and it is unique among British birds in reducing the entrance to an exact size with mud, and also in lining the cavity with nothing but flakes of larch, pine or birch bark, sometimes dead leaves of oak or beech. The birds then regularly cover the eggs with some of these flakes when the nest is unattended – as was noted in the 1930 bird report in *WANHM*, which also recorded a nest in a hole in a Wiltshire sand pit that year. Nestboxes are regularly adopted and more occasional sites are cavities or cracks in buildings and old walls, even Sand Martin holes, old Magpie nests, and sides of haystacks (Witherby *et al* 1938–41), but always with mud used somewhere in the construction: a nestbox needs little alteration to the hole, but mud is still plastered round the edges of the lid, while one ragged cleft in an apple tree and two cavities in stacks in Sussex had been reinforced by 2–5 kg of mud (Walpole-Bond 1938).

Nuthatches are found right across the Northern Hemisphere in the Old World, from Morocco and Iberia east to Kamchatka and Japan, and south into Turkey, Iran, the Indian subcontinent and southeast Asia. But in Europe they are missing from most of Scotland, much of Fenno-Scandia and northernmost Russia, and – like a number of other mainly sedentary woodland birds, such as Tawny Owls, all the woodpeckers, and Marsh and Willow Tits – they never reached Ireland after the Ice Age before rising sea levels cut it off. The breeding population of Europe, excluding Russia, has been estimated at 6·5 to 8·1 million pairs (*EBCC Atlas*).

Within Great Britain, as elsewhere in its range, the Nuthatch prefers open broadleaved or mixed woodland, especially where oak, beech or sweet chestnut dominate. After an apparent southward contraction in the 19th century, it has, since about 1940, expanded in both numbers and range, and spread northwards again quite rapidly (*1968–72 Atlas*). The *1988–91 Atlas* showed a continued northward expansion, with increases in Cumbria and Northumberland very evident, and breeding first confirmed in Scotland in 1989 – though nest-building was reported there as long ago as 1927 (Baxter & Rintoul 1953). The abundance map in the *1988–91 Atlas* shows the Nuthatch's strongholds to be the woodlands of southern England and south and central Wales. The estimated number of pairs in Great Britain was around 20,000 in the early 1970s (*1968–72 Atlas*), but a much higher 130,000 two decades later (*1988–91 Atlas*). National survey data show that numbers increased rapidly from the mid 1970s, and were continuing to do so, despite fluctuations, through the 1990s (*BBWC*).

Although the *1875–1900 Atlas* gave the impression that Nuthatches had been rare in Wiltshire at that time, they were certainly common in some parts. Smith (1887) noted that the species was 'to be found…all the year round…wherever woods abound…Lord Arundel says it is…numerous at Wardour…I should say it occurs sparingly throughout the county'. In the Marlborough district, it had been a common resident in areas of old trees in the late 19th century (Kennedy 1966); and Peirson (1919) referred to it as 'a fairly common resident, especially in the Forest [Savernake]'. It seems likely that in the late 19th and early 20th centuries, as now, Nuthatches were well represented in broadleaved woodland in the northeast, southwest and adjacent to the New Forest (Hampshire) – including,

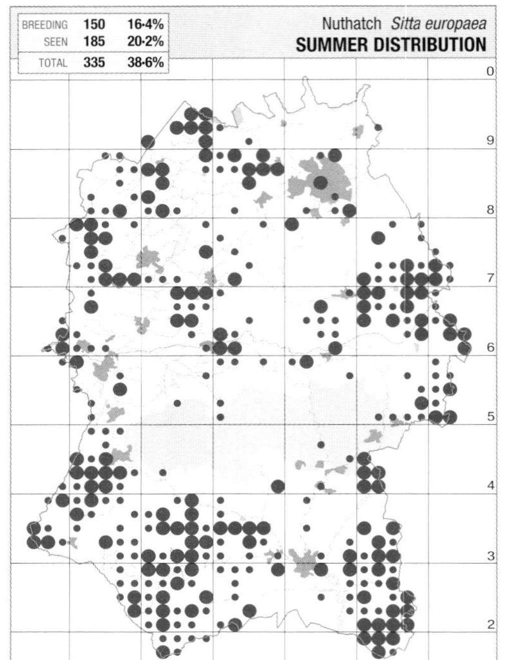

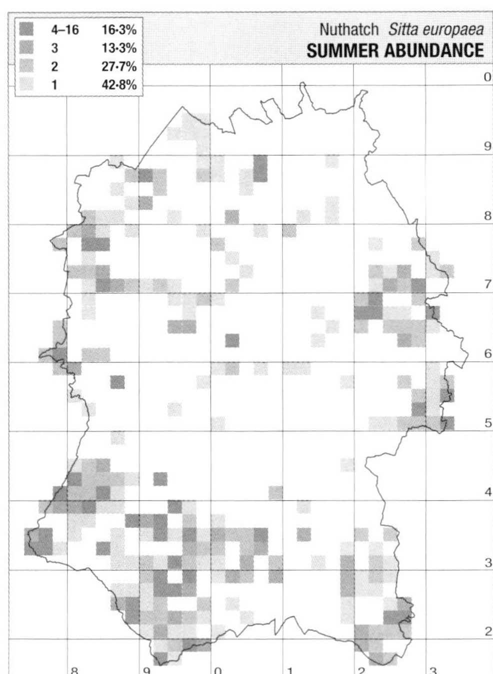

for example, Bentley Wood, which was then oak woodland and not cleared for conifer planting until the mid 20th century (Baskerville *et al* 2005).

For the county as a whole, the 1929 bird report in *WANHM* considered the Nuthatch simply to be 'common'. Another 30 years later, Peirson (1959) stated that it was 'not uncommon where there are old trees but decreasing in number as these are felled. It seems to be commoner in the south of the county than the north'. Buxton (1981) believed that 'It is much less common than formerly and is steadily becoming rarer in the north'. Records in *Hobby* for the mid to late 1970s reflect Buxton's view, though over the next two decades the species was noted in several new, or at least previously unrecorded, locations. The *1968–72 Atlas* mapped Nuthatches in 31 of Wiltshire's 33 core 10-km squares, the *1981–84 Winter Atlas* in 30, and the *1988–91 Atlas* in 31. The summer survey of 1995–2000 found them in 32, so it appears that their range remained unchanged in Wiltshire in the latter part of the 20th century.

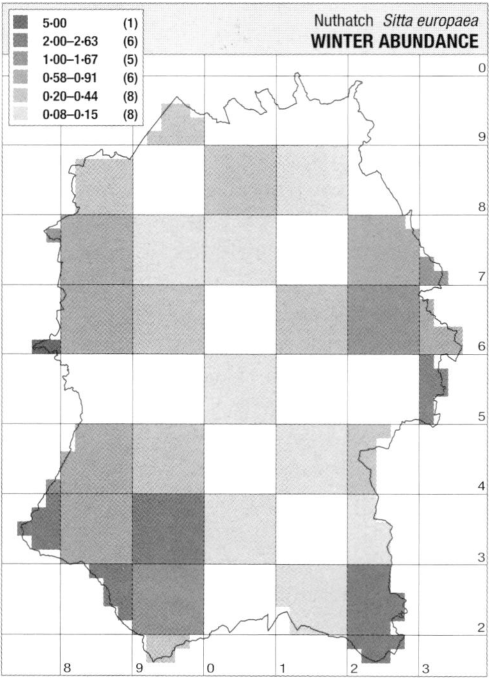

The summer distribution map shows Nuthatches to be absent from the extreme northeast of Wiltshire and scarce on Salisbury Plain, where suitable habitat is sparse or lacking. The summer abundance map demonstrates that they are most numerous in the Marlborough area and in the southwest and the southeast of the county towards the Somerset, Dorset and Hampshire borders. There are also notable concentrations in the west at Conkwell and in the By Brook area, and in established parklands, for example at Spye, Bowood and Corsham.

This map more closely matches the distribution of broadleaved woodland in Wiltshire than do those of almost any other species. Although densities of Nuthatches are generally lower in this region than in other parts of southern England (*1988–91 Atlas*), a survey of the Longleat estate in 1984 calculated 85 pairs in the broadleaved woodlands, parkland, village gardens and timbered hedgerows which made up a total area of some 750 ha, or 7·5 km² (Ferguson-Lees 1984). At the time this was over twice as many as had been expected from the then CBC woodland and farmland averages, but this is now clearly equalled or even exceeded in several southern areas of the county, where it could approach or even match the 25 pairs/km² indicated by CBC surveys in optimum habitat in the New Forest (Clark & Eyre 1993). Based on BBS in Wiltshire and the adjoining Cotswold Hills ESA, the county breeding population may currently lie in the range of 2300 to 3030 pairs, at best some two to three per cent of the 140,000 pairs estimated for Great Britain at the end of the 1990s (*APEP*).

The British population of Nuthatches is generally sedentary (*Migration Atlas*), so it is not surprising that the few recoveries from the total of 187 Nuthatches ringed in Wiltshire during 1965–2000 have all involved little or no movement. The only inward recovery involved one found dead at Littlecote in February 1986, and even that had been ringed a mere 6 km away at Hungerford (Berkshire) in May 1985. Nevertheless, an adult ringed at Corsham on 3 January 1971 and retrapped at the same location on 7 March 1976 represented a good record of both site-fidelity and, at the age of at least almost six, longevity – although the British record for this species is nearly twice as long (Clark *et al* 2002).

Against this background, it is not surprising that the winter map shows the distribution to be little changed from that of summer. Timed winter counts suggested that numbers were only around two-thirds of those in summer, but that is likely to have reflected differences in detection rates – Nuthatches are generally rather silent in November and December – and the winter total for Wiltshire is estimated to be 5000 to 8000 individuals.

GDP

Sponsored by Maureen Woolfall

Treecreeper

Certhia familiaris

Common but overlooked resident of woodland and wooded gardens

Arboreal and unobtrusive, almost mouse-like as it climbs up a trunk, the Treecreeper is best detected by its high-pitched calls and song. This species occurs widely in temperate and boreal woodland from parts of western Europe right across north-central Eurasia to Sakhalin and Japan, south to northeast China and the northern Himalayas, Iran and Turkey. In

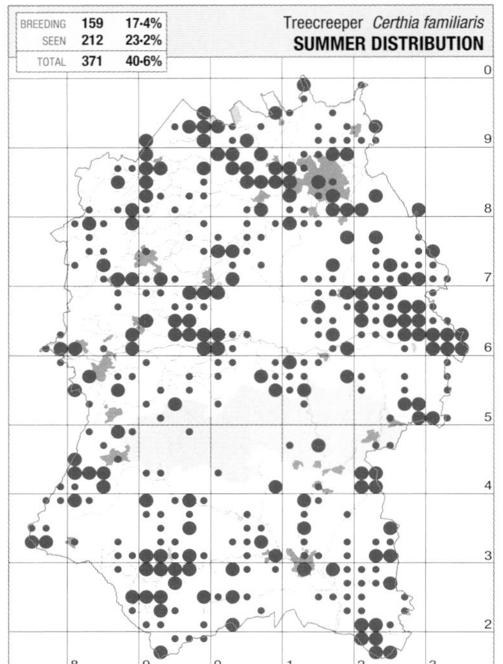

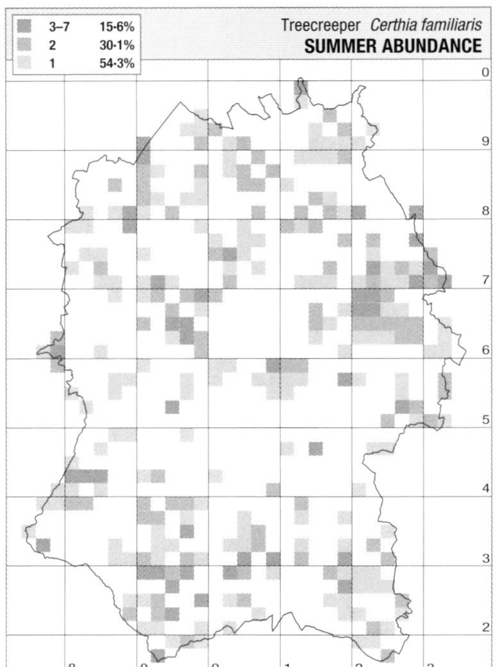

Europe itself, it is absent from much of Iberia, France, Italy and the Low Countries – where it is largely replaced by the very similar Short-toed Treecreeper. (Although the two overlap in central and southeast Europe, the present species tends there to be restricted to upland conifers.) The European population of the Treecreeper is thought to be more or less stable and, excluding that of Russia, has been put at 2·7 to 3·6 million pairs (*EBCC Atlas*).

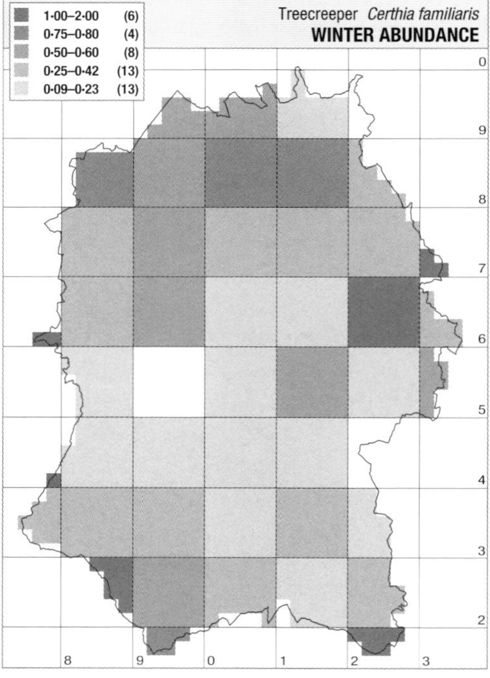

Treecreepers breed in most of mainland Britain and are absent only from some of the outermost Scottish islands. The national population, estimated at about 204,000 territories (*APEP*), has been roughly stable since the end of the 1970s, though a peak in the early 1970s had been followed by a steady decline for several years (*BBWC*) and, for Wiltshire at least, the severe winter of 1978/79 was a disaster for this species (see below). Treecreepers are found not only in mature woodland – preferring, in Britain, broadleaved to mixed or coniferous – but also in copses, shelter belts, parks, timbered hedgerows, and pollarded streamside willows. Its more catholic range of habitats probably explains why this species was recorded in 10 per cent more Wiltshire tetrads than the much noisier and more conspicuous Nuthatch.

In Wiltshire, the Treecreeper was 'very common' in the 19th century (Smith 1887), and 'A common resident' in the Marlborough area in the early 20th (Peirson 1919). This status was echoed for the county as a whole by the inaugural bird report for 1929 in *WANHM*, but Peirson (1959) considered it to be 'scarce or uncommon except in the south-east of the county where it is common. Many were reported killed by the severe cold of 1929 and 1947'. Buxton (1981) wrote that Treecreepers were 'widespread but nowhere common', adding that they were 'almost exterminated in the north of the county by the cold weather in early 1979 ... a rapid recovery has been made with numbers nearly normal in 1980'.

The *1968–72 Atlas* mapped Treecreepers in all of Wiltshire's 33 core 10-km squares, and the *1988–91 Atlas* in 31, whereas each recorded breeding in only 26. The summer tetrad survey in 1995–2000 again found them in all 33 core squares and, indeed, with breeding evidence in 32. They were also mapped in all 33 by the *1981–84 Winter Atlas* and in 32 by the WOS winter survey in 1998–2000. On the other hand, the finer detail of the summer distribution map shows Treecreepers recorded in only two-fifths of all tetrads; and breeding evidence in under half of those. This map demonstrates a distribution pattern similar to that of the Nuthatch, though the Treecreeper is more widespread in north Wiltshire (especially in the northeast Swindon/Minety/Cricklade area) and scarcer in the south (*cf* Peirson 1959).

It must be added that British Treecreepers are largely sedentary (*Migration Atlas*), which suggests that most if not all of the 'seen only' records may have involved breeding birds. In this connection, only two of 523 Treecreepers ringed in Wiltshire during 1965–2000 had been recovered by the end of that period – curiously, both marked in 1985 and both found not far away in 1987 – one ringed at Coate Water was recovered at the same site and the other, originally at Westbury, had in the two years moved only 3 km to Dilton Marsh.

The population of such an unobtrusive species is hard to estimate. On the limited number of 1-km squares in Wiltshire for which data are available, BBS methods suggest a county total of 1230 pairs, though it is difficult to know what confidence to place in that figure. By comparison with other species, the summer counts of 493 during the timed tetrad surveys of 1995–2000 indicate a much higher population, which is therefore roughly estimated as 1000 to 4000 pairs – perhaps as many as two per cent of the British breeding population. Although the extrapolation from the timed winter samples was only 332, this is, given the sedentary nature of this species, likely to reflect the difficulties of survey at that time, rather than a genuine decrease and the county total at that time is broadly estimated to be between 3000 and 10,000 individuals.

The summer and winter abundance maps show a strong correlation, once again reflecting the sedentary nature of Treecreepers. As already mentioned, their numbers are badly hit by severe winters – such as those of 1928/29, 1946/47, 1962/63 and 1978/79 – especially when freezing rain or frost glazes tree trunks and branches. Survival is also reduced by wet winters (Peach *et al* 1995). But numbers seem to recover quickly in a series of milder winters following successful breeding seasons. The excavation by this species of roosting hollows in the soft bark of wellingtonias – first recorded nationally in the 1920s (Savage 1923) – has been reported in Wiltshire for many years, but observations of a Treecreeper making six visits to a garden peanut holder in Marlborough on 19 April 1996, and of another feeding on nuts in Bradford-on-Avon on 8 January 1998 and again on the 18th (*Hobby*) are also of note, this food source not being mentioned in *BWP*.

GDP

Sponsored by Moira Robertson

Golden Oriole

Oriolus oriolus

Overshooting spring vagrant (28+ records), may have nested in past, breeds Eurasia (few also Britain), winters Africa

Quite a number of Golden Orioles – the males strikingly yellow and black – arrive in Great Britain every spring and summer, most commonly in coastal areas from Scilly along to Norfolk, but odd ones are seen now in up to 30 or 40 counties. A few stay to nest, chiefly in East Anglia, where in each year of 1990–2000 some 20–42 pairs or singing males were found and 5–16 pairs proved to breed (*RBBP*). The main annual influx is in May and June – the result of overshooting on return passage to Europe from winter quarters in sub-Saharan Africa – but a few migrants usually turn up through to October. Excluding those at known breeding sites, the average annual total of records in Great Britain increased from 48 in the late 1960s and 1970s to 84 in the 1980s and 129 in the 1990s (Fraser & Rogers 2001). But they have always been rare in this country: for example, the last few decades of the 19th century produced acceptable breeding records from just five counties (*1875–1900 Atlas*).

In contrast, Golden Orioles are quite common throughout continental Europe from the Mediterranean north to southern Fenno-Scandia, and the breeding population, excluding Russia, has been estimated at 1·2 to 2·1 million pairs (*EBCC Atlas*). The species also extends across Asia to Mongolia and the eastern Himalayas, but the eastern populations winter in southern Asia.

For Wiltshire, Smith (1887) gave the first county record as two males 'taken' near Tidworth 'very many years ago'; his first dated occurrence was the 'capture' of a male at Tisbury on 1 May 1862; and a male 'shot in an orchard near Mere in 1870' may or may not have been the same as the male seen on 'the western borders of the county' on 9 May that year. Smith also recorded a pair seen at Dinton in spring 1877, and added that the species 'had been reported to have bred on Teffont Common'. Though that seems to have been third-hand information at best, Golden Orioles were proved to have nested in nine (mainly southern) English counties in the middle of the 19th century, and suspected to have done so in a further three – see *1875–1900 Atlas* (though the list there does not include Wiltshire) – while 'there may have been a small, regular population in N Devonshire and Dorset' at the same time. That publication also noted breeding records, regarded as acceptable by contemporary naturalists, in five counties during 1875–1900; these were not listed; but the possible Wiltshire instance (though not dated) probably also fell in that period.

Hony (1915a) recorded that Golden Orioles had been seen at Great Ridge Wood 'more than once', and also a pair at Lacock Abbey in May 1913, while *WANHM* added another pair at Lydiard Park in April 1916. After a gap of ten years, singles were seen between Barford St Martin and Compton Chamberlayne in 1925 or 1926, at Luckington in April 1928, in the Dean valley near Salisbury on 29 September 1930 (another but unconfirmed report that year must be discounted), and singing near Downton in 1936 (all *WANHM*), at Stock Close in 1937 (Kennedy 1966) and a female at Whaddon near Salisbury on 1 May 1938 (CMR Pitman diaries). After the 1939–45 War, excluding unconfirmed reports in 1948 and 1963, there were records of singletons in four years before 1974: at Stock Close on 11 April 1953 and again on the 20th, and another at Axford in June that year; at Totterdown in April 1957 and at Farley on 1 June; at Upper Upham Farm for ten days in April–May 1963; and at Marlborough College during 5–7 May 1970 (*WANHM*, Kennedy 1966).

Buxton (1981) wrote of 'some slight evidence to suggest it may have bred in recent years', but there is no published evidence to substantiate this. From 1974:

1981	Late May	Pewsey Manor	Pair
1992	16 May	CWP Swillbrook	Male flew across from Glos
	16 May	Gare Hill	Male singing
1998	24 May	near Chippenham	Male singing
2000	7 June	Dinton	Male
	10 June	Figheldean	Snatches of song
	29 July	Avebury	Male
	3 August	Wroughton	Male

The first of the two in 1992 was seen to fly into Wiltshire from CWP46 (Gloucestershire). It and the other were part of the second largest influx ever recorded in Great Britain, in fine anticyclonic weather that caused various other European birds to overshoot; the total number of Golden Orioles reported that year was 183 (Fraser *et al* 2000). One other report published in *Hobby* – involving a male behaving in an uncharacteristic manner on the surprisingly early date of 4 April 1977 – is not now considered acceptable.

RT

Red-backed Shrike

Lanius collurio

Former breeder until 1970s, now vagrant from Continent, winters Africa

Less that a century before WOS was formed, Smith (1887) wrote that the Red-backed Shrike was 'very well known' in Wiltshire – so much so that 'I have not kept any accurate record of a species I used to consider common' – but added that it had 'become more scarce than it was: certainly I have not seen it for several years past'. Indeed, he was able to cite only six county records for the 1870s and 1880s. There was no other assessment of status until the 1929 bird report in *WANHM* described this species as 'rather scarce', noting also that it was 'Slightly increasing in S. Wilts' but 'Slightly decreasing in N. Wilts'; the subsequent bird reports for 1930–34 and 1936 (the only others published before the 1939–45 War) indicated that it was still widely if thinly distributed, but decreasing.

The trend of decreasing numbers continued after the 1939–45 War, though there were clearly fluctuations: 23 pairs were located at Redlynch in 1950, where just two had been found in 1949. Webber (1960) reported on an enquiry undertaken in Wiltshire during 1956–59 that was 'commenced after it appeared that the Red-backed Shrike was decreasing in some of its haunts'. He noted just one pair in the Swindon-Marlborough area (compared with at least ten pairs in 1940–50), while a maximum of about 15 pairs on Salisbury Plain and its escarpment in 1958 represented 'a very considerable decrease in the last ten years'. Webber considered that these shrikes were 'holding their own' in the extreme southern fringe of the county adjoining the New Forest, but concluded that they had 'definitely decreased during the last ten years, at least in Wilts' and suggested that a restriction of range was taking place near the Red-backed Shrike's western limits in Great Britain. Wiltshire's earliest arrival and latest departure dates for this summer visitor – 4 May 1946 and 21 September 1950

– were, not surprisingly, recorded during this period when the species was still regular and reporting was becoming more thorough.

Numbers of Red-backed Shrikes in the county fell dramatically after 1960: just one was recorded in 1962 (at Bulford in June) and none at all during 1963–65, but then three males and a female were found at Winterslow in May 1966, in which year a pair also bred at Bulford (one juvenile noted) and individuals were seen in two other areas. Single pairs were recorded during 1967–70, successfully breeding in the first of those years, near Lavington, and again in the last, when the only detail provided by the observer was 'in the north of the county'. The final recorded nesting was in 1977, on the edge of a large housing estate in Swindon, but the eggs disappeared and, though the male returned in 1978, no female joined him. The only other records during the 1970s involved lone males in May 1971 and June 1973, and a female in August 1977 (*WANHM*, *Hobby*), also a male at 'Picket Hill' (now known as Pecked Hill) in August 1972 (letter to Ruth Barnes from Eileen H Ingram). Unsurprisingly, none was ringed in the county during 1965–2000, but one found dead on 29 July 1959 at Aldbourne had been marked as a nestling on 14 June that year almost 70 km away near Lyndhurst (Hampshire).

The decline and virtual disappearance of Red-backed Shrikes in Wiltshire over the hundred or so years from the third quarter of the 19th century was but a symptom of a much wider problem that gradually affected England and Wales. These shrikes are summer visitors to much of Europe from northern Iberia and the Mediterranean region north to southern Fenno-Scandia and north-central Russia, also extending east into western Siberia and through Turkey and Israel into northwest Iran. Breeding numbers in Europe, excluding Russia, were estimated at 2·6 to 3·7 million pairs in the mid 1990s, but the species was and is declining in many countries, particularly in the northwest of the range (*EBCC Atlas*). The entire world population winters in eastern and southern Africa, mainly from Zambia southwards, those from western Europe travelling through the eastern Mediterranean in autumn and returning by a still more easterly course through the Arabian peninsula in spring – a phenomenon known as loop migration.

In Great Britain, Red-backed Shrikes used to nest as far north as Cumbria and south Yorkshire in the mid 19th century, but had started to withdraw down both sides of England, as well as from Cornwall, early in the 20th. By 1950 few still bred in Wales and most of the rest were south of a line from the Gower peninsula to the Wash; ten years later the British population was put at only 250 pairs, entirely southeast of a line from the Severn Estuary to the Wash. By 1971, the year after Wiltshire's penultimate nest, only 81 pairs were known, all in a band from Hampshire to East Anglia (Bibby 1973). Numbers continued to dwindle, but in 1977, when some 50 pairs remained in England – including that unexpected nesting in Swindon – three pairs bred in Scotland. Apart from 'probable breeding' in 1932 and 1970, this was the first confirmed record in that country (Thom 1986) and the species has continued to appear there, and sometimes nest, in most summers since (not necessarily in the same places) – rather like Wrynecks which, following a similar decline in England and Wales, colonised Scotland in 1969. It has been suggested that these northern colonisations are from Norway, because of some increase in numbers and expansion in the ranges of both species there in recent decades (*Migration Atlas*).

Many possible reasons have been put forward as contributing to this decline in Great Britain, which has been followed in, especially, Belgium, the Netherlands, Sweden and Finland. They have ranged from skin- and egg-collecting in the first place, to pesticides, the availability of fewer beetles and other large insects as prey, habitat destruction, and climatic change. But none of these makes sense on its own: for example, areas of the downland scrub, heathland, old hedgerows and shrubby railway cuttings that used to form the main habitats in of Red-backed Shrikes in England still remain. On the other hand, it is often suggested that migratory species on the edges of their ranges are more at risk from subtle combinations of factors. It has even been suggested that these loop migrants' more easterly spring routes may have resulted in dwindling numbers travelling as far west as before, but Red-backed Shrikes still occur on passage, chiefly along the east and south coasts. The annual average of migrants recorded in Great Britain during 1986–2000 was 232, most in May and June (Fraser & Rogers 2002). In the two decades from 1980, however, only eight singletons were found in Wiltshire:

1980	31 August	near Biddestone	Male
1983	25 July	Westbury	Female
1989	28 May	SPTA (West)	Male
1995	24 May	Bowerchalke	Female
1996	3 June	Swindon	Female
1999	10 June	near Downton	Male
	18 Jul–1 Aug	SPTA (West)	Male
2000	11 June	SPTA (East)	Male

Curiously, particularly good years for migrant Red-backed Shrikes in Great Britain were 1988 and 1992 (when there was none in Wiltshire), whereas 1999 (when there were two in the county) was by far the poorest year since 1986.

(See also page 727.)

IJF-L & GLW

Sponsored by Richard Baatsen

Lesser Grey Shrike

Lanius minor

Vagrant (1 record) from south Europe/southwest Asia, winters southern Africa

Wiltshire's only Lesser Grey Shrike was an adult at Castle Eaton, in a dairy-farming area of fields interspersed with thick hedgerows of hawthorn and bramble, on 26–27 June 1965 (*WANHM*, *BBRC*). This species is a rare vagrant to Great Britain as a whole, but at least one is found somewhere in the country in most years – there were four others in 1965 – and the total during 1958–2000 was 126. The numbers of reported occurrences were, however, declining over that period, which may well reflect the serious decreases that have been, and still are, taking place across its western and central European range.

Towards the end of the 19th century Lesser Grey Shrikes were widely distributed in Europe north to north-central France, Germany, Poland and parts of the Baltic States (Witherby *et al* 1938–41), but significant declines then began in the north and west. Despite local resurgences in the 1930s and 1960s – during the second of which small populations were even established in southwest France and northeast Spain – this species became extinct, so far as is known, in most of France and the whole of Switzerland, Germany, the Czech Republic, Poland and the Baltic States, and has now all but disappeared even from northeast Spain and southern France, as well as from much of Italy, Austria, Slovakia and Belarus; it is probably common now only in the eastern Balkans, southern Russia, the Caucasus and southwest Asia from Turkey to Afghanistan (based on *CBWP* and Internet data).

The population of Europe, excluding Russia, was put at 66,000 to 107,000 pairs in the mid 1990s (*EBCC Atlas*), but seems likely to be rather lower now. This species winters entirely in southern Africa, and is a loop migrant, following routes farther east in spring than in autumn. Vagrancy north to Great Britain, Denmark and southern Sweden has been a result of overshooting in spring (mainly mid May and June) and of reverse migration in autumn (mid August to mid November), but seems destined to become much rarer.

RT

Great Grey Shrike

Lanius excubitor

Scarce winter visitor from Fenno-Scandia, also resident France/central Europe

A very few Great Grey Shrikes – strikingly grey, white and black, with longish tails which they may raise or spread as they perch conspicuously – are now seen in Wiltshire in most winters. They are highly territorial then, as in the breeding season, and, if a Great Grey finds a good hunting area with plenty of lookout posts and some suitable cover, it is likely to return in successive years. The county's earliest recorded date during 1974–2000 (but see dates and footnote on page 728) was 11 October 1986, at Hackpen, and the latest 21 April 1975, at Imber, but most of those seen in Great Britain in October and April are on passage, moving to or from winter territories that may be several square kilometres in extent. Once settled in a territory, a Great Grey will cache prey by wedging it in the fork of a bush or impaling it on a thorn or wire barb, and Sky Lark, Blue Tit, Wren and Goldfinch have all been found in such 'larders' in Wiltshire.

This species breeds right across the north-temperate and subarctic regions of both North America and Eurasia. In Europe, where most populations are decreasing, it nests from central France north to Fenno-Scandia and thence eastwards through central Europe and north and central Russia; it is replaced to the south by the rather similar Southern Grey Shrike (*qv*) – until recently regarded as conspecific – in northern Africa, Iberia and southern France, and from Caspian Russia and parts of the Middle East across south-central Asia.

Migrants from Fenno-Scandia, Great Grey Shrikes have long been known as scarce but regular winter visitors to Great Britain (*eg* Saunders 1899), though the suggestion by Witherby *et al* (1938–41) that they were more regular in the east was not borne out by the results of the *1981–84 Winter Atlas*, which found them to be evenly distributed throughout the country and in numbers that fluctuated between winters. Fraser & Ryan (1995), analysing British records from 1986 to 1992, considered that Great Greys could be classified in three separate categories: winter residents (long-staying or site-faithful individuals), winter wanderers (recorded during December–March but remaining for ten or fewer days), and autumn or spring migrants. They concluded that 'an upper maximum for the number of Great Grey Shrikes recorded in [any] winter' might be 75, about 35 of those holding territories and around 40 being 'wanderers'. Migrant records averaged 40 in autumn and 15 in spring, but there was no way of knowing how many in different places related to the same individual, so it is not possible to combine these figures into a total. Indeed, looking at dates without overlap, Fraser & Ryan found that there was 'no hard evidence that there are ever more that about 15 Great Grey Shrikes in Britain at any one time' – though they assumed that this merely indicated how difficult the species is to record. Despite a high of as many as 234 records in 1998, annual totals declined during 1986–2000: just 56 Great Grey Shrikes were reported in Great Britain in 1997 and the annual mean during 1990–99 was only 126 (Fraser *et al* 2000, Fraser & Rogers 2002). Long-term changes in numbers of British winterers appear to reflect breeding population trends in Finland and Sweden (*Migration Atlas*).

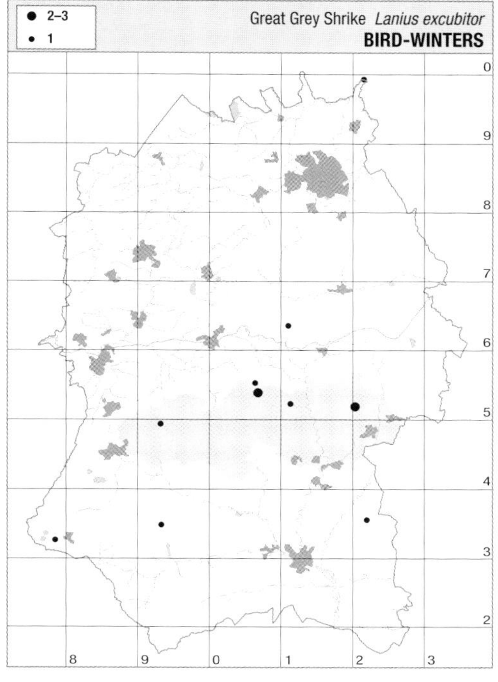

Buxton (1981) noted that the Great Grey Shrike occurred in Wiltshire in 'most winters', on Salisbury Plain, in 'the Marlborough area and in the New Forest areas of the county'. The bird-years map for 1995–2000 shows the continued importance of Salisbury Plain, but the virtual absence of records elsewhere indicates that a range contraction has occurred. Although numbers wintering have not apparently declined since Buxton's time (figure 69), this is probably because of past under-recording on SPTA, where, until recently, public access was far more limited.

Much earlier, Smith (1887) had stated that Great Greys had 'been noticed in this county quite as often as in any other', and quoted Montagu as having secured his only two specimens in Wiltshire, both in November; he further cited Yarrell and Stanley as authorities for the occurrence of this species in this county, and listed 16 records during 1837–76, all but one killed. Morres (1878) described an unlikely breeding report from Fisherton, Salisbury, in 1839, though nesting in Great Britain was as unknown in the 19th century – *eg* Saunders 1899 – as it is today. Hony (1915a) added two more records, of which only one, in January 1912, was dated, and a further 14 were reported in *WANHM* between 1922 and 1936, in November–February, May, and June–September.

Those in June–August were noted as unusual at the time and – although some were probably erroneous (*eg* three together in July 1933), and identification of others questionable (*eg*, as more fully reported in *BB* 29: 120, one seen from a moving train near Ludgershall on 30 July 1936) – another at Pepperbox Hill in June 1932 was watched independently by two observers familiar with the species, and is thus less easily dismissed. In this connection, it is worth noting here that Witherby *et al* (1938–41) referred to the species'

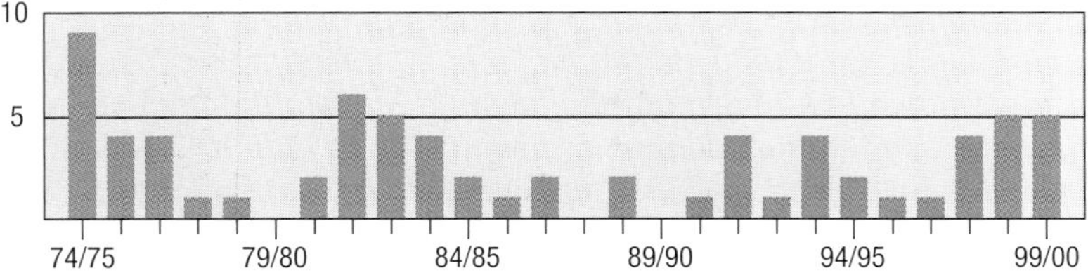

Figure 69. Great Grey Shrikes *Lanius excubitor* in Wiltshire: individuals by winters 1974/75–1999/00

Table 111. Great Grey Shrikes *Lanius excubitor* in Wiltshire: monthly totals 1974/75–1999/2000

	Oct	Nov	Dec	Jan	Feb	Mar	Apr
Birds	12	15	18	18	16	16	10

occurrence 'occasionally in June and July' in Great Britain, and that summer records in neighbouring counties have included one 'killed' in Berkshire on 10 July 1940 (Standley *et al* 1996) and, more recently, one seen in Dorset on 16 June 1974 (Green 2004). During 1946–73 there were 30 Wiltshire records, all during October–April except for singletons on 31 (*sic*, presumably 30th) September 1972 and 2 May 1957 (*WANHM*).

Great Grey Shrikes were reported in all but three of the 26 winters from 1974/75 to 1999/2000 (figure 69), all as singletons – as would be expected, since individuals generally defend their territories fiercely – apart from two together after heavy snow at Wilton, near Salisbury, on 10 January 1982. Of the total of 71 during this period, most were in the southern half of the county and, given this species' liking for heathland and other open country with scattered bushes or trees, it is no surprise that just under half were on Salisbury Plain. Those recorded within the military ranges of SPTA stayed for an average of 25 days apiece, ten remained for at least one month, and the longest period was 113 days (8 November 1980 to 28 February 1981), at Larkhill. Although half the records on Salisbury Plain involved only one date, care is needed in assessing the status of individuals in such relatively inaccessible sites; it is likely that some of those simply reflected the difficulty of finding and relocating single birds in large landscapes. In contrast, those away from Salisbury Plain averaged a mere eight days, just three remained for 30 or more days, and about 80 per cent stayed for only one or two days – figures that are probably a fair reflection of the more transient nature of Great Grey Shrikes in general farmland habitats, particularly bearing in mind how much easier it is for observers to visit such sites.

Apart from Larkhill and Imber Ranges, the Great Bedwyn/Burbage area provides the best chance of finding this species on a bright winter's day (see table 111 for the months involved).

RT

Sponsored by Rob Turner

Southern Grey Shrike

Lanius meridionalis

Vagrant (1 record) from Caspian area, also breeds south France/Iberia/Africa

The Southern Grey Shrike is a rare vagrant to Great Britain, with just 16 accepted records during 1958–2000 (*BBRC*). The seventh of these, and the first inland, was a road casualty taken into care at Wanborough on 23 September 1993 and released as a 'grey shrike' the next day near Swindon STW; it was then properly identified only when it was found again on 24 October, still at Swindon STW where it remained until the 28th (Pleass 1994). It was in first-winter plumage and was watched at close range feeding on earthworms.

Until that very same year, this species was generally considered to be a race of the more familiar Great Grey Shrike, but its separate treatment was proposed by Isenmann & Bouchet (1993) and later accepted by the Taxonomic Subcommittee of the BOURC (1996). The Wiltshire record was of the easternmost subspecies, *pallidirostris* – known as the 'Steppe Grey Shrike' and notably paler than western forms – which breeds from the lower Volga east to Mongolia and south to northeast Iran and northern Afghanistan. It winters in southwest Asia, Arabia and northeast Africa, and is thus the only long-distance migrant population of the Southern Grey Shrike, which is otherwise more or less sedentary in the Canary Islands, Iberia and southern France, in northern Africa south to the Sahel, in the Middle East and Arabia, and in the Indian subcontinent. Over much of this range, it is a bird of low scrub, steppe and even desert. It is reputedly a confiding species, and it was only when observers found the vagrant at Swindon STW to be very approachable that suspicions were raised that it might not be a 'normal' Great Grey Shrike.

RT

Woodchat Shrike

Lanius senator

Vagrant (7 records), breeds North Africa/south Europe/Levant, winters Africa

Wintering in sub-Saharan Africa north of the equator and breeding in northwest Africa, the Middle East and much of southern Europe, the Woodchat Shrike reaches Great Britain chiefly by overshooting on spring migration (late April to June), but smaller numbers of (mainly) juveniles occur through reverse migration in autumn (August to early October). The annual average in Great Britain of both combined during 1958–99 was 15 (Fraser & Rogers 2001), but four years in the late 1980s and 1990s produced the highest ever totals of 25–36. This was despite decreases in the European population – particularly in the more northern parts of its range (*eg* France, Germany, Poland) – which, excluding Russia, has been estimated at 496,000 to 985,000 pairs (*EBCC Atlas*).

Hony (1915a) noted the first Wiltshire record at Salisbury in 1872, and others at Savernake on 6 June 1884 and Aldbourne on 13 June 1906. Smith (1887) evidently did not know of either of the first two of these, but we have no reason to question their authenticity, unlike an observation at Wishford on 31 May 1898 which, though published in *The Field*, was doubted at the time by the editor and has been variously included or excluded by county recorders and authors ever since. In the circumstances, it seems best to omit it from the county total. More than 60 years were to pass before another was seen, a juvenile at Fyfield Down on 5 September 1969 (*BBRC*). From 1974:

1974	17 July	Great Bradford Wood	Adult
1990	23 August	Ogbourne St George	Adult
2000	8–9 September	Middle Woodford	Juvenile

(See also page 727.)

RT

Jay

Garrulus glandarius

Common resident of both broadleaved and coniferous woodland

Often revealed by their harsh calls, Jays are found from northwest Africa and Iberia right across Eurasia to Japan, and from Iran and the Himalayas to China and south into southeast Asia. They breed almost throughout Europe, apart from Iceland, the far north of Fenno-Scandia and Russia, and much of the lower surrounds of the Caspian Sea. The population of Europe, excluding Russia, has been estimated at 5·1 to 9·4 million pairs (*EBCC Atlas*). Although largely sedentary in the west and south of this range (including Britain and Ireland), they are very variably eruptive in the north and east.

A particularly large irruption into Great Britain during late September and October 1983 was attributed to 'a severe failure of the acorn crop both in Britain and on the Continent' (John & Roskell 1985). The movement was noted mainly in East Anglia and in counties bordering the English Channel, but in Wiltshire that October 40–50 were seen flying southwest at Devizes on the 4th, some 40 west at Berwick St James on the 5th, and a total of about 200 also west at Salisbury on the 6th – 160 of these last in just half an hour from 08:15. In the following spring, a larger than usual movement for that time of year was noted in the county in February and March 1984, and it was thought that this perhaps involved 'birds returning to Europe after the autumn influx of 1983' (*Hobby*). More than 30 years earlier, the bird report for 1950, having noted influxes in the preceding September and December at East Grimstead, suggested that 'A big flock seen flying E. near Clarendon, Apr. 9, may have belonged to the continental race' (*WANHM*). Although some larger movements – such as that of 1983 – clearly provide good evidence of influxes from the Continent, it must be added that no foreign-ringed Jay has ever been recovered in Britain or Ireland (*Migration Atlas*).

In Great Britain, though absent from the Fens, the Pennines, parts of mainland Scotland and all of its islands, Jays are otherwise familiar inhabitants of woods, parks and gardens, and are especially common in southeast England from Hampshire to Kent. In the early 1990s, the British population was put at 160,000 territories (*1988–91 Atlas*). Although no long-term trend is discernable from national surveys, there was a shallow decline in numbers in the species' preferred woodland habitat during the 1990s, after an earlier fall on farmland CBC plots (*BBWC*), but the population in 2000 was estimated to be unchanged (*APEP*).

Jays were apparently scarcer in the 19th century, Yarrell (1871–84) describing them as 'still well known in most wooded districts of England though far less numerous than formerly'. Apart from suffering the general persecution meted out to most members of the crow family, Jays were also shot for their blue wing-coverts, which were used to make fishing flies (Saunders 1899). Numbers certainly increased in the 20th century, as a result of lessened persecution during the 1914–18 and 1939–45 Wars and the increased habitat provided by conifer afforestation (*1875–1900 Atlas*).

In Wiltshire, Smith (1887) noted that the Jay was 'much persecuted by gamekeepers', but thought that it was still to be found 'in almost all woods and plantations throughout the county'. Nearly 40 years later, the 1929 bird report considered it a 'very common resident', but then local changes became evident throughout the 1930s and 1940s, 'decreases' and 'considerable increases' being regularly reported (*WANHM*). Peirson (1959) stated that

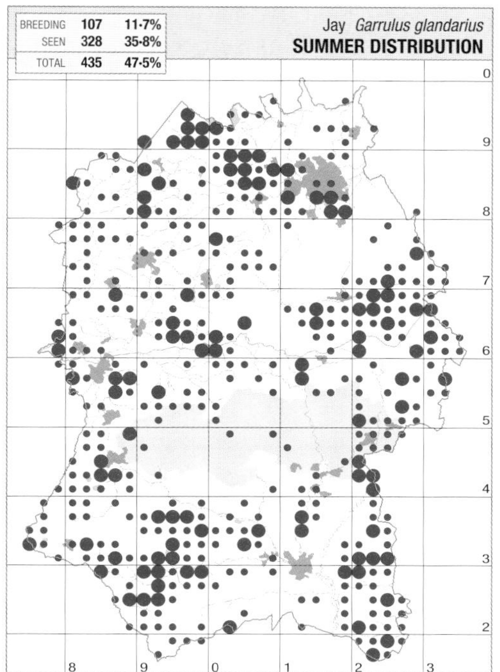

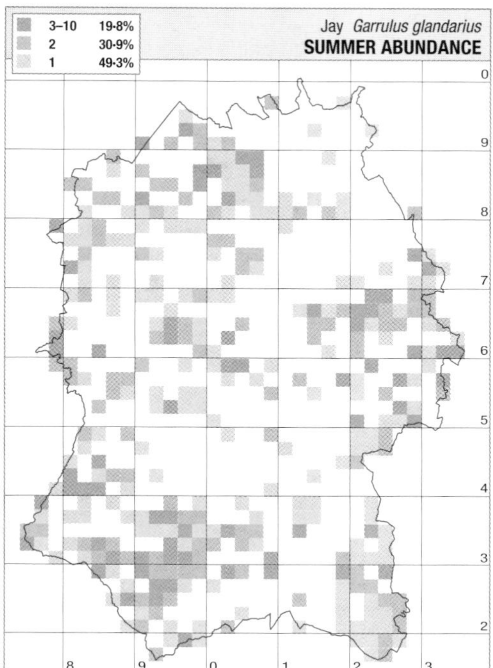

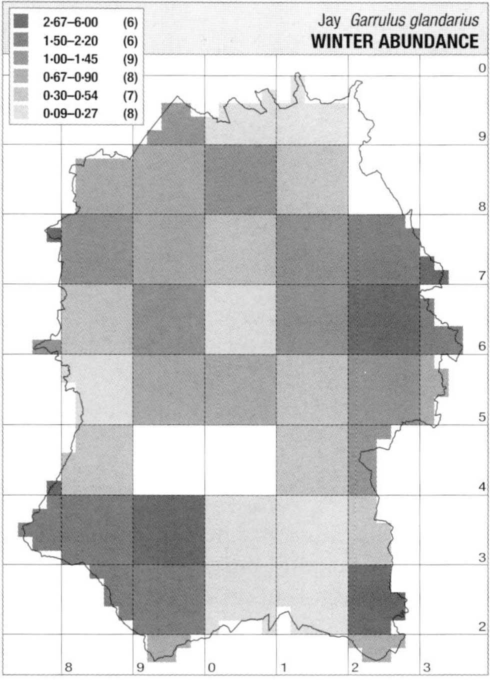

Jays were 'common in wooded country' and that 'numbers seem to be increasing'. The *1968–72* and *1988–91* breeding atlases and the *1981–84 Winter Atlas* recorded them in all Wiltshire's 33 core and 15 part 10-km squares. *Hobby* noted an increase in localities in the mid 1990s, from 41 sites in 1994 and 46 in 1995 to 68 in 1996. This increase was sustained in 1997 (63 sites), 1998 (60) and 1999 (78), though not in 2000 (54), but may have reflected varying observer interest rather than any real population trend.

British Jays are highly sedentary – the median distance of ringing recoveries is less than 1 km (*Migration Atlas*). Against this background, it is not surprising that the only four Jays ringed outside Wiltshire and recovered in the county, mostly shot, had originated in Surrey, Berkshire, Somerset and, a little more distantly, Staffordshire. Similarly, of 99 Jays ringed in Wiltshire during 1965–2000, all but three of them adults, the six recoveries in that period showed little evidence of significant movement and only two of them were outside the county: one marked at Sells Green on 15 November 1986 was shot at Bucklebury Common (Berkshire) on 22 June 1992, and another ringed at Savernake on 25 March 1984 was likewise shot at Bucklers Hard

(Hampshire) on 31 January 1986. The greatest distances between the points of ringing and recovery of all the above were 108 km from Surrey and 153 km from Staffordshire.

The summer distribution map shows Jays to be widely distributed except in such areas as the Marlborough Downs and SPTA – where trees are scarce or absent – and also northeast of Swindon. Both the summer and the winter abundance maps underline this species' preference for woodland. The *1968–72 Atlas* calculated breeding numbers by using a figure of 50 pairs per occupied 10-km square, the equivalent of two pairs per occupied tetrad. On that basis, Wiltshire's breeding population would have amounted to some 870 pairs, but, even allowing for the fact that densities are lower in this county than in certain other parts of southern England (*1988–91 Atlas*), that figure is certainly not high enough now. As many as 664 Jays were counted during the WOS timed tetrad surveys and, using the densities obtained by BBS methods in the Cotswold Hills ESA (Gloucestershire), that figure suggests a Wiltshire total of 2770 pairs. An estimate of 2500 to 3000 pairs would represent just under two per cent of the British population.

The winter map shows distribution at that season to match that of summer closely. Numbers are thought to be stable year-round. Whilst extrapolation from the winter counts gave an estimate of some 796 Jays, a 20 per cent increase over the summer counts, seasonal differences have to allow for the rearing of young and any subsequent mortality and dispersal. A calculated winter figure of 4970 probably represents a minimum, and perhaps the total then may even be as high 7500.

MVJ

Magpie

Pica pica

Common and increasing resident of open woodland and gardens

Handsome but often vilified, Magpies are adaptable and successful birds that are found across much of Eurasia south to Iran, the Himalayas and southern China, as well as in North Africa and Asia Minor, locally in southern Saudi-Arabia, and in western North America south to central California. Their success probably reflects the ability of a generalist feeder to adapt to a changing environment. The breeding population of Europe, excluding Russia, has been put at 7·7 to 12 million pairs, and numbers have increased in most countries since 1965 (*EBCC Atlas*).

The *1988–91 Atlas* showed Magpies to be common and widespread in much of Great Britain – though absent from large areas of Scotland and almost all its islands – and estimated the population at some 590,000 territories. National surveys demonstrate a steady increase in numbers from the early 1970s to the late 1980s, since when the general status of this species has stabilised (*BBWC*), and a review of British bird populations for 2000 left the estimate unchanged from that of 1988–91 (*APEP*). In Great Britain as a whole, the advent of game preservation resulted in Magpies being extensively shot and poisoned from the late 18th century onwards, and some 19th century writers considered their extinction a possibility in parts of the country (*1875–1900 Atlas*). Because Magpies are less secretive than Jays, and their bulky domed nests are often very visible, their destruction is easier.

In 19th century Wiltshire, Smith (1887) noted that they were 'now generally detested' and 'ruthlessly destroyed', and 'common in some few wooded districts' but 'rarely... met with on our downs'. In *WANHM*, the inaugural bird report for 1929 described them as 'Plentiful locally'; but five years later one at Alderbury on 22 January 1934 was the 'first reported near Salisbury for a number of years'; that same year, on 24 April, 'a flock of about 50 were seen on Salisbury Plain' – although, as no nests were found, 'it appears the birds were on migration or local movement'. The 1947 bird report commented, 'Still increasing in numbers and now becoming a menace. Until 1939... scarce in the Pitton district... Now it is possible to see a score or more in almost any walk... Undoubtedly commoner about Marlborough... and Clarendon'. Peirson (1959) stated that they were 'uncommon in the early years of this century', but were 'now common again', as numbers had 'increased noticeably during both World Wars and are still increasing where game is not preserved'. Two decades later, Buxton (1981) thought that the species was still increasing and noted that it was moving 'into the suburbs of the larger towns' and by 1984 it was judged to be 'Increasing alarmingly in some areas' (*Hobby*).

The *1968–72* and *1988–91 Atlases* mapped Magpies as breeding in all of Wiltshire's 33 core and 15 part 10-km squares, while the *1981–84 Winter Atlas*, which also found them throughout, showed that they were generally more abundant in the north and west of the county. The summer survey in 1995–2000 recorded them in nearly all of Wiltshire's 915 tetrads and showed breeding evidence in just over half. Gaps in distribution reflect a shortage of suitable habitat with trees or tall hedgerows in such areas as Salisbury Plain, and perhaps also the effects of persistent persecution – which is almost certainly responsible for the lower densities in certain parts of the county in both the summer and the winter abundance maps. Comparison of these low density areas with the Pheasant maps indicates that game preservation still influences distribution on a local scale: high densities of Pheasants in the northernmost tetrads of SU03, and where ST91 meets ST92, coincide with conspicuous 'gaps' in the Magpie maps, while the greatest densities are evident around such wooded habitats as Savernake and parts of the southwest, and particularly in and around the urban areas of Swindon and the central west.

Based on densities found during BBS surveys in this and adjacent counties, the Wiltshire population is calculated at 9200 to 17,100 pairs, though perhaps nearer the lower end of that range. This represents some two per cent of the British figure estimated by the *1988–91 Atlas*, perhaps a higher proportion than expected given that that atlas showed much of Wiltshire to represent a hole of low density in southern England. Counts in the summer survey (3990) and those extrapolated in the winter one (4500) were broadly similar – the winter total estimated at 17,400 to 32,400 individuals – and the maps themselves even more so, as might be expected for what is an essentially resident species (*Migration Atlas*). Its very sedentary nature is illustrated at the county level by the few recoveries of the 112 ringed in Wiltshire during 1965–2000 (mostly as adults) being mainly local. One shot at Upper Inglesham on 15 June 1992 had, however, been ringed as a nestling no less than 140 km away, at Clifton (Nottinghamshire) on 12 May 1990 – only the fifth movement of over 100 km recorded by ringing schemes nationally.

Despite the earlier suggestion that a group of 50 on Salisbury Plain in April 1934 involved 'migration or local movement', concentrations of Magpies are not infrequent in autumn through to at least early spring: for example, 84 at a Swindon rubbish tip on 3 February 1988. There was also a well-established winter roost at Bratton during at least 1983–90 that remained fairly constant, with annual maxima mostly exceeding 50, and up to 65 were recorded there in January–February and November–December 1990. In 1991, however, *Hobby* stated that there were 'possibly fewer records than usual', adding that the use of Larsen traps 'may be having a significant effect... in some areas' and going on to record

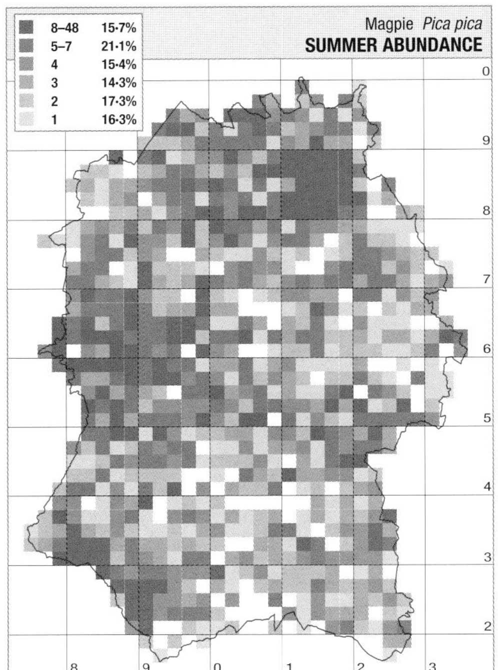

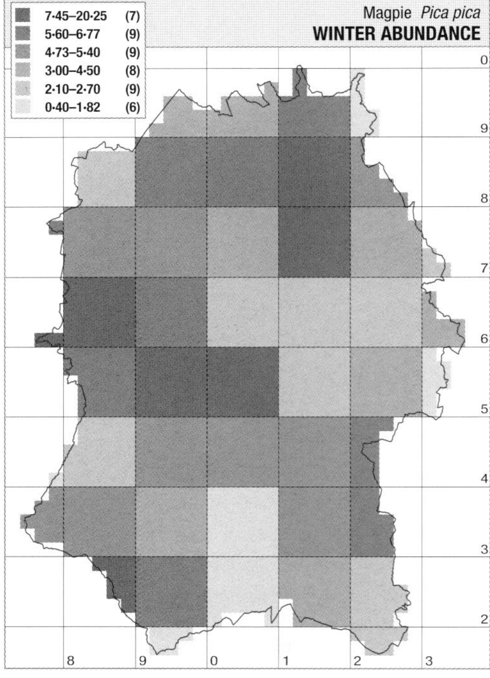

that known numbers taken in such traps in just three places in one small area of west Wiltshire during the breeding season were 52 at Steeple Ashton, 46 at West Ashton and 38 at Erlestoke. Certainly, only four flocks reported during 1991–2000 exceeded 30, the two largest being 44 at CWP on 3 June 1993, and 46 at SPTA (Centre) on 14 February 1998.

Although the *EBCC Atlas* stated that Magpies had never been shown to have a directly adverse effect on the breeding success of any bird species, a Wiltshire study on SPTA (East) to test the effects of predation by five species of mammals and four of corvids on Grey Partridges (Tapper *et al* 1996) found that where 'predation control [had] significantly reduced the abundance of foxes, carrion crows and magpies during the critical partridge nesting period ... Breeding stocks [of partridges] in years following predation control [control of all nine predators] were 36% larger than stocks in years that did not follow predation control – excluding the effects of year and site. After 3 years this had produced a 2·6–fold difference in breeding density'. At the same time, two other studies (Gooch *et al* 1991, Thompson *et al* 1998) found no link between the national increases of Magpies and the declines of many small songbirds in either gardens or farmland, and in this connection, a joint statement in 2000 by the Game Conservancy Trust and the RSPB concluded that 'It is unfortunate that magpies are a smokescreen distracting attention from the effects of intensive farming...No amount of predator control will reverse the decline of species such as the corn bunting and skylark' (Potts & Avery 2000).

MVJ

Nutcracker

Nucifraga caryocatactes

Vagrant (3 records) in 1968 irruption from northeast Russia/Siberia, also resident Europe

Often tame and confiding, Nutcrackers are rare vagrants to Great Britain. In autumn 1968, however, eruptive movements – like those made by Waxwings and Crossbills at times of high population and food shortage – coincided with 'an exceptional area of high pressure' and the premature onset of cold weather over north Russia and central Europe; as a result, at least 315 Nutcrackers (roughly five times the total of all previous British records) were seen in, particularly, East Anglia and Kent but also in more than 25 other counties west to Cornwall and Carmarthenshire and north to Lancashire and Yorkshire, as well as stragglers in Scilly and Shetland, between early August and late October (Hollyer 1970). Even these numbers paled in comparison with 800 in Belgium, 650 records (over 1300 birds) in West Germany, 6000 records in the Netherlands, and a total of 4400 birds flying past a single site in Sweden in one August day (Hollyer 1970). Not surprisingly, Wiltshire's only records occurred during that period:

1968	21 September	Warminster–Shaftesbury roadside	One
	21 Oct–end Jan **1969**	Rushmore Park, Tollard Royal	One at least
	November	Coombe Bissett	Two

All three of these were listed by Hollyer (1970) in his report on the Nutcracker invasion, but he mentioned just one for Coombe Bissett, whereas the county bird report for 1968 (*WANHM*) clearly stated that 'Two were present in the Coombe Bissett area during Nov.'; the latter also referred only to the September record as accepted by the BBRC, so it must be made clear that the numbers that year quickly became so large that BBRC temporarily removed this species from its list and left assessment to county level. For Rushmore Park, which lies largely within Wiltshire though a small section straddles the Dorset border, Hollyer referred to a singleton from 21 October to 15 January, whereas *WANHM* stated 'First seen on the Rushmore estate, Tollard Royal, 21st Oct. and at least one still present at the end of Jan. 1969' – which implies that more than one may have been involved – but that summary apparently came second-hand via the observer who saw just one on 15 January.

Nutcrackers have a wide normal distribution in alpine France, Switzerland and the mountains of central Europe and the Balkans and in mountains or boreal forest from Poland, the Baltic States and southern Fenno-Scandia across European Russia and northern Asia to Kamchatka and Japan, south also to the Himalayas and parts of China. The race breeding in most of Europe east to central Russia is nominate *caryocatactes*, sometimes called the 'Thick-billed Nutcracker' and, like most of the Asiatic subspecies, largely sedentary, whereas westward and southward eruptions of the more migratory 'Slender-billed' race, *macrorhynchos*, of east European Russia and northern Asia are triggered by a combination of high population numbers and the failure of the seed crops of pine and spruce. Following particularly massive invasions, sporadic breeding has occurred outside the normal range (*eg* in Denmark) and the 1968 irruption resulted in temporary or more permanent colonisation of new areas as far west as the Netherlands and the Belgian Ardennes (later spreading to the French side).

RT

Chough

Pyrrhocorax pyrrhocorax

Former vagrant (5 records in 19th century), perhaps from English south coast

Nowadays, Choughs in Great Britain are almost confined to southwest Scotland (especially Islay, Colonsay and Jura) and the coasts and adjacent mountains of Wales – perhaps no more than 250 pairs in all – but there are stronger populations in the Isle of Man and, particularly, on the north, west and south coasts of Ireland. Formerly, they were quite common here and there along the coastal cliffs of England from Cornwall to Kent, as well as in Yorkshire and east Scotland. Isolated populations became increasingly fragmented, and the *1968–72 Atlas* noted the coincidence between declining numbers and the long series of harsh winters during the 1800s, noting also that the severe winter of 1962/63 saw 'a marked diminution in SW Scotland'. All English Choughs died out in the 19th century, many before 1850, except those in Devon (nested until 1910) and Cornwall, where 20th century breeding was last confirmed in 1947. (A brood may also have hatched in 1957, but the adults soon lost interest and it is suggested that any young perished.) The last pair persisted in Cornwall until 1967, when one was found dead; its mate survived until 1973 (Penhallurick 1978).

In 2001, however, a small influx of Choughs took place in far southwest England, and a territorial pair was later discovered on the Lizard peninsula; this pair hatched four chicks in 2002, of which three fledged (Carter *et al* 2003), and successfully raised a brood in each subsequent year until at least 2005; some of the group moved to other parts of the far southwest (*Birds in Cornwall* 2004). Maritime Choughs also breed in Brittany (France), but otherwise the European population, estimated at 12,300 to 17,400 pairs (*EBCC Atlas*), is restricted to mountainous parts of Iberia and other southern countries and Mediterranean islands through to Greece and Crete, as well as the Caucasus. Elsewhere, the species is found in northwest Africa, Ethiopia, and in Asia Minor and the Middle East through central Asiatic mountains to north China and the Himalayas.

Choughs everywhere are largely sedentary. Thus, it may appear surprising that Smith (1887) was able to list no fewer than five Wiltshire records, all but one confirmed by specimens, though mostly dated no more precisely than 'many years ago'. One was killed at Yatesbury in August 1832 and others 'on Salisbury Plain', at Battlesbury Camp near Warminster, at Lake and, finally but still 'many years since', on the downs near Tidworth where two had been seen 'for many days previous'. Of this Tidworth record, Smith went on to say, prophetically, 'This I fear is likely to be the last specimen of this truly graceful bird wandering to our county'. It seems reasonable to assume that these individuals had come from the south coast – despite their sedentary nature, post-breeding flocks may range more widely in search of feeding and roosting sites, and there are many records of movements of up to 45 km from the natal sites (*Migration Atlas*) – but it should also be mentioned that at least in Sussex as early as the 1870s Choughs were often kept as pets, sometimes free-flying (Walpole-Bond 1938).

RT

Jackdaw

Corvus monedula

Common and increasing resident in open or wooded country and towns

Jackdaws are the smallest of Wiltshire's four black crows and often closely associated with man, nesting in holes and crevices in used and disused buildings, as well as in such natural sites as tree holes. They are ground feeders, joining Rooks and Starlings in their search for invertebrates, preferably on grazed grassland; they also visit arable, particularly after it has just been ploughed and again when spilt grain is available after harvest. In more recent times they have taken advantage of human cast-offs by scavenging for scraps thrown away in car parks and town streets and looting rubbish tips; and they are also readily attracted to food scraps and bird-tables, even in small urban gardens.

Jackdaws are found from northwest Africa eastwards across much of Eurasia to Mongolia and Kashmir. In Europe, they are absent only from Iceland, northern and inland Fenno-Scandia and northernmost Russia; and the breeding population, excluding that of Russia, has been estimated at 4·0 to 8·1 million pairs (*EBCC Atlas*). Most are resident, but those of north-central and eastern Russia, and to a lesser extent of Fenno-Scandia, move WSW in autumn; others in the colder regions merely concentrate near human habitation in winter or, in west Norway, keep to coastal regions; some from the Continent reach the British east and south coasts in autumn (*CBWP*).

Western European Jackdaws are less migratory than those from Fenno-Scandia and northeast Europe (*Migration Atlas*). In Great Britain, indeed, they are largely sedentary. This is demonstrated on a local scale by Wiltshire's ringing results. Only 354 Jackdaws were ringed in Wiltshire during 1965–2000, the majority as nestlings – indeed, the highest number of adults ringed in any one year was seven – and the 17 recoveries have all been within southern England: only two had moved more than 9 km, and neither of those more than 99 km.

The *1988–91 Atlas*, which estimated 390,000 breeding territories in Great Britain, showed the species to be very widespread – except in Scotland, where it is absent from large parts of the northwest mainland and some offshore island groups – and to be at high densities in some parts of east Scotland and northeast England, but most abundant southwest of a line from the base of the Wirral peninsula (Cheshire) to Beachy Head (Sussex).

This small crow was clearly common in Wiltshire even in the 19th century: Smith (1887) found it to be as 'well-known' as the Rook, with which it was 'invariably' feeding. In the Marlborough area, it was a 'plentiful resident' in the early 20th century (Peirson 1919), and common and widespread, particularly at Savernake, into the 1960s (Kennedy 1966); the population did not appear to have changed by 2000 (B Gillam). For Wiltshire as a whole,

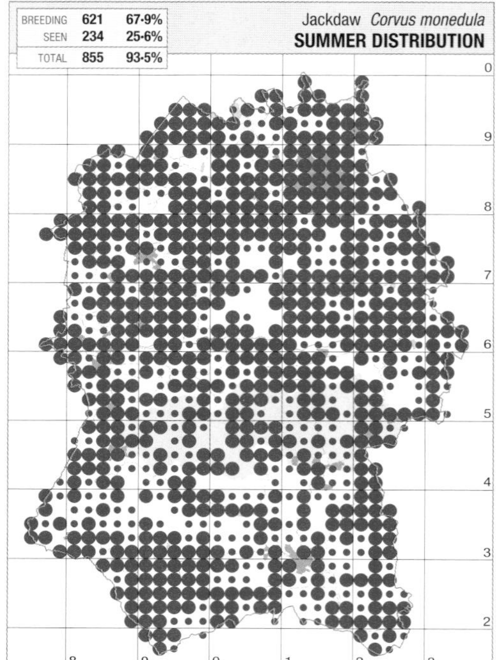

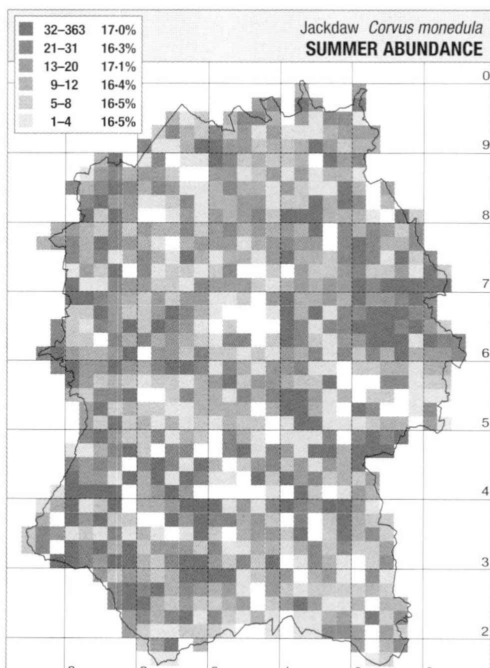

the 1929 bird report in *WANHM* described Jackdaws as 'very abundant' and, 30 years later, Peirson (1959) considered them 'very common', a view echoed by Buxton (1981) who did, however, note a decrease 'in some of the larger towns'. The *1968–72* and *1988–91 Atlases* and the 1995–2000 tetrad survey mapped them as breeding in all of Wiltshire's 48 core and part 10-km squares, and the *1981–84 Winter Atlas* and the winter survey of 1998–2000 also found them in all. Jackdaws frequently gather in large roosts with Rooks, particularly in winter, and, though these tend to be under-reported, more recent examples included 2000 at CWP on 10 January 1998, 1200 at Aldbourne on 25 January 1998, and 1200 at Weather Hill on 8 December 2000 (*Hobby*).

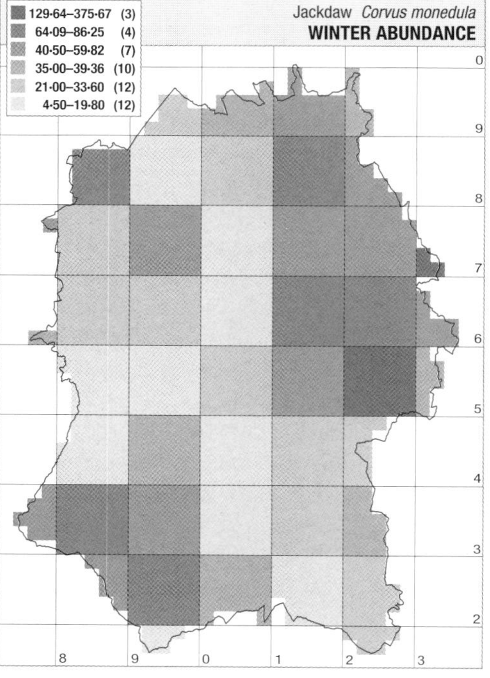

The summer distribution map shows breeding evidence to be more extensive nowadays in the northern half of Wiltshire than in the south. This is perhaps because small farms are more numerous there; these have a number of outbuildings that provide suitable nest-sites for Jackdaws and also have a much higher percentage of grazed pasture, their favoured feeding ground. The south of the county has large areas of arable cultivation, which these birds find unsuitable for much of the year. Although their requirements are not commonly available on most of Salisbury Plain, breeding was confirmed in roughly half of the tetrads within SPTA. Nest-sites there include the remains of old buildings in, for example, Imber village and Greenlands Camp, old beech and ash trees that cannot be safely felled because of the shrapnel embedded in them, and, in recent years, larger nestboxes erected for owls and Kestrels (*qv*).

Although tetrads with high densities of Jackdaws were evenly scattered almost throughout the county, only the areas southwest of Avebury and south of Shrewton forming conspicuous gaps, the summer abundance map reveals concentrations associated with woodlands, both at Savernake and in the southwest. The winter map similarly shows the northeast and southwest to be particularly important at that season. The Jackdaw's ubiquity in Wiltshire is reflected by its presence in over 90 per cent of tetrads in both the summer and the winter timed surveys – at those seasons respectively the tenth and ninth most widespread species.

More rapidly in wooded country than other habitats, Jackdaw numbers have increased in Great Britain since the 1960s, particularly during the 1980s, and this trend continued through the 1990s (*BBWC*), so much so that by 2000 the British population was estimated to number 503,000 territories (*APEP*). Improved breeding performance, which probably reflects the species' generalist feeding habits, has been cited as the likely cause of this success. Results from regional BBS studies in and around Wiltshire suggest that the county as a whole holds between 20,600 and 49,400 pairs, or just under one per cent of the British total; based on the ratio of summer to winter counts during WOS surveys, the winter numbers are estimated at 76,900 to 185,000 individuals.

PAC & PCo

Sponsored by Pete Combridge

Rook

Corvus frugilegus

Common resident, colonies in trees often by villages, roads or rivers

Rooks are highly gregarious and among Great Britain's most familiar farmland birds. Often feeding with Carrion Crows, Jackdaws, Starlings, Wood Pigeons and Stock Doves, they probe deeper into the soil than their companions and thereby avoid competition. They are omnivorous, their diet varying with the season. In the breeding season, grassland invertebrates are their main target, these including the destructive wireworm larvae that can cause serious damage to the roots of young grass and cereal crops. In winter, when invertebrates become scarce, they turn more to seeds and the remains of root crops, and will scavenge on rubbish tips and locally even visit garden bird-tables for peanuts and scraps.

Rooks breed across Eurasia from western and central Europe through southern Siberia, Asia Minor and northern Iran to central and northeast China and the lower reaches of the Amur and Ussuri rivers; they have also been introduced to New Zealand. While more northerly populations, particularly in eastern Europe and across Asia, migrate to winter in the southern parts of the range and beyond, Rooks are largely sedentary in Great Britain, seldom moving more than 50 km (*Migration Atlas*). Thus, it is not surprising that all of the 15 recoveries by 2000 of Wiltshire-ringed Rooks were within the county. Moreover, none of the eight ringed elsewhere and recovered in Wiltshire had moved more than 99 km. (Only 54 Rooks were ringed in Wiltshire in the 28 years of 1965–92, but in the next eight years special efforts were made to reach nestlings and, as a result, the grand total ringed had climbed to 659 by 2000.)

In Europe, where Rook numbers fluctuated during the 20th century as a result of agricultural changes, chemical poisoning and persecution, they have now stabilised and are increasing in the west (*EBCC Atlas*). The population of Europe, excluding Russia, has been estimated at 3·3 to 3·9 million pairs, of which 1·0 to 1·3 million pairs – roughly a third – are in Great Britain (*APEP*), where their need for well-grown trees in which to nest eliminates them only from the barer uplands of Scotland, Wales and northern England (*1988–91 Atlas*). Rooks are also absent from large urban conurbations – notably in the London area, where eight 10-km squares showed no proof of breeding in the *1968–72 Atlas*, a figure that had risen to 16 in the *1988–91 Atlas*. They are most abundant in coastal areas of northeast and southern Scotland, in northeast England and in a swath from Oxfordshire to Devon. The 1996 national Rook survey indicated a population increase of approximately 40 per cent since 1975, a growth associated with improvements in nesting success, which possibly reflects this crow's adaptability to agricultural change (*BBWC*). The abolition of straw and stubble burning in 1993 may have been beneficial to Rooks by providing an easily available supply of food in late summer and, in general, the BBS shows a continuing increase since 1994.

The mainly agricultural county of Wiltshire has suitable trees in which Rooks can nest in every 10-km square and thus a correspondingly large and widespread population. In the 19th century, Smith (1887) called this a 'most familiar bird' and noted that, thanks to his personal protection, numbers had increased around his house in Yatesbury to the point where he could count over 200 nests annually. More than 40 years later, the 1929 bird report in *WANHM* described Rooks as 'very abundant'. In the 1940s, censuses were carried out near Mere in the southwest (Cawkell 1948, 1949, 1950) and Patney in the centre of the county (Cross 1949, 1950). Comparison with figures from the same localities in a national survey in 1975 showed a 50 per cent reduction in the number of nests, but while, in both areas, about 30 per cent of the rookeries had become extinct in the quarter-century interval, a roughly similar number of new ones had been established (Gillam 1976). By 1995–2000, the total nests in Wiltshire had increased by just over 41 per cent – from 25,848 to 36,553 – since the 1975 survey.

In 1975, 47 per cent of those Wiltshire rookeries in which the tree species was identified were in English elm, the most numerous tree in the county at that time; beech came second with nearly 36 per cent; otherwise only ash, oak, Scots pine, sycamore and horse chestnut, in that order, totalled more than a hundred nests apiece (Gillam 1976). Slow-growing native trees – beech, oak, ash and Scots pine – produce more densely structured crowns and are therefore favoured as choices for nest-sites over the quick-growing non-native species (such as sycamore and horse chestnut). Although willows grow rapidly into tall trees, their crowns are weak and any Rooks that colonise them do so for only a few years before abandoning them in favour of other sites. In 1975, a small number of Wiltshire nests were built in 14 other trees and shrubs, including hornbeam, elder and larch.

By 1980, when a sample repeat survey was made of nine 10-km squares in the county, most elms had been killed by Dutch elm disease. As a result, while the total of nests in those squares had increased by 7 per cent, the number of rookeries had decreased by 26 per cent (Gillam 1981). Some elms were still strong enough to support nests and Rooks remained faithful to them for a few more years, but in the 1980 survey an additional four species of non-native trees (walnut, holm oak, blue cedar and Monterey pine) and three of native shrubs

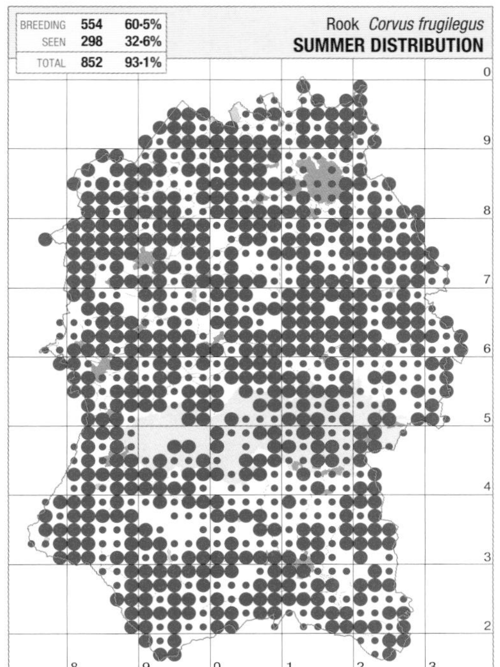

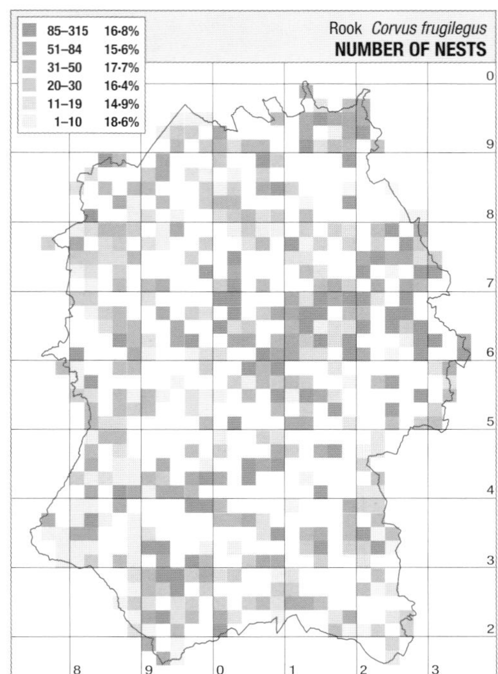

(hawthorn, elder and field maple) not used in 1975 were found to hold rookeries. On chalk, beech is the commonest large tree and there it was always the most frequently used. Following Dutch elm disease, some of the beech rookeries increased and supported many more nests. The large rookeries at Cherry Lodge Farm, Shrewton – now Parsonage Down NNR – began to grow in the early 1950s after felling of the beech trees in the village that had held the local rookeries. The total numbers of nests there, in three separate colonies in belts of beech, fluctuated between 157 and 354 during 1981–2000 (figure 70). Wiltshire's highest nests above ground level have been on the arms of electricity pylons. Having the ability to adapt to changing circumstances, this crow will surely never lack places to breed.

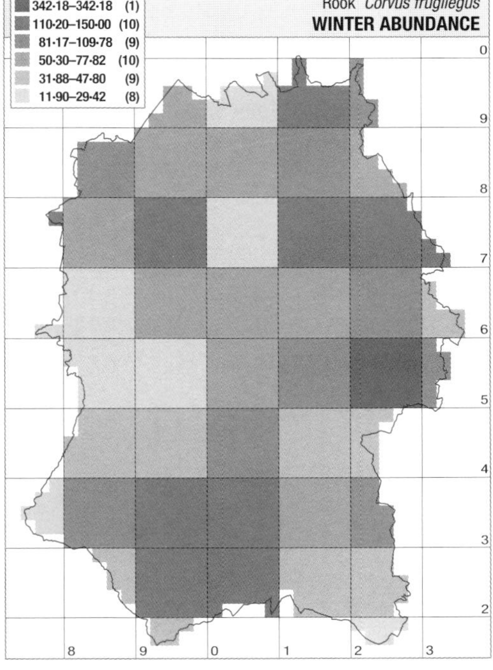

Rooks nested in every one of Wiltshire's 33 core 10-km squares during both the *1968–72* and *1988–91 Atlases*. The summer distribution map for 1995–2000 shows presence in all of the county's core and part 10-km squares, and evidence of breeding in three-fifths of all tetrads. The most notable gaps in distribution are on SPTA (West), where trees are sparse, and on the high chalk of the West Wiltshire Downs. It should be noted that the summer abundance map is based purely on

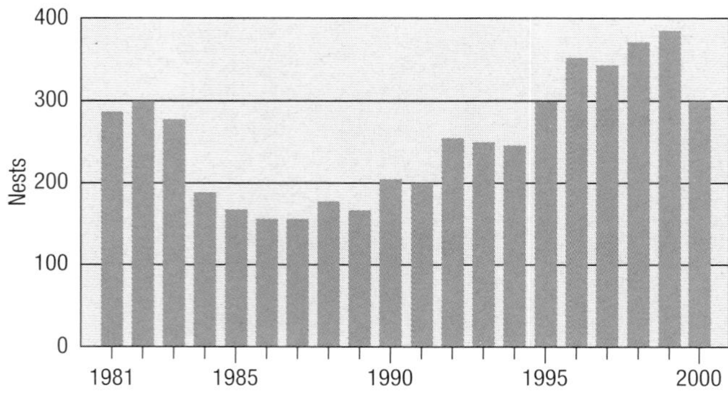

Figure 70. Rooks *Corvus frugilegus* in Wiltshire: nests at Parsonage Down NNR 1981–2000

the numbers of nests in specific counts of rookeries, mostly in April, not on 2-hour visits through the summer as for other species. This in part explains the patchy nature of the map, some tetrads containing high densities adjoining one or more with no records; this in turn reflects not only the availability of suitable sites but also the nature of colonial breeding, with nests aggregated in high densities at fewer places. (Had the conventional timed visits been used, a far higher number of tetrads would have registered counts as Rooks fed away from the rookeries.) Higher densities appear to be concentrated in more open habitats, including some downland sites, where a combination of pastoral areas (with grassland for feeding) and stands of suitable trees occur.

As a result of the intensive nature of the tetrad fieldwork, it is thought that the vast majority of rookeries in Wiltshire were found, and so the count of 36,553 nests is believed to be reasonably complete and accurate. That would represent about three per cent of the British population, demonstrating the county's continued importance to this species. In this connection, however, Rooks will visit colonies and even build at least partial nests when one year old, but do not usually breed until they are two (*BWP*); other nests will be constructed and abandoned. On SPTA (East) a detailed study by the Bulford Ornithological Group of three rookeries in 1999 and four in 2000 confirmed that the number of nests does not necessarily equal the number of breeding pairs. One rookery with 31 nests included 11 with nestlings, two with eggs and 18 empty (R Hayden). Were this ratio of active to total nests applied throughout Wiltshire, the county figure would be only a little over 15,000, although it is worth adding that marked variations in productivity were also shown by the Bulford study: in 1999, 74 nests were found to contain 137 nestlings at an average of 1·9; in 2000, on the other hand, 118 nests held only 114 nestlings at an average of 0·97; shooting and natural losses during fledging were judged to reduce productivity further (R Hayden). (Densities obtained during local BBS studies in the region suggest a county breeding total of between 11,900 and 24,100 pairs.)

The winter survey estimated some 72,700 Rooks – the third most numerous species at that season, exceeded only by Wood Pigeons and Starlings – and they were found in every one of Wiltshire's 33 core 10-km squares, as they had been in the *1981–84 Winter Atlas*. Even though this is an easily counted species that gathers in conspicuous flocks, some will have been missed, and yet others duplicated as a result of movements between fields; Rooks at this season are quite mobile, and may feed up to 20 km from their night-time roosts. The winter population is estimated to lie between 41,800 and 84,700 individuals. There are considerable similarities in the winter maps for Rooks and Jackdaws, as might be expected given their similar choices of habitat at that season and the fact that they often feed together.

PAC & PCo

Carrion Crow

Corvus corone

Common and increasing resident, spreading more into urban areas

Carrion Crows are generalists, which appears to be the secret of their success. Although typically feeding on grain in winter and small mammals and insects in summer, they are opportunistic and catholic in their diet and adapt well to human activities by, for example, exploiting rubbish tips and animal road casualties. In recent years in Wiltshire they have been recorded taking freshwater mussels, dead fish and young wildfowl, as well as plucking bread off the surface of a lake in flight, and robbing a Short-eared Owl of its prey (*Hobby*).

In Europe, Carrion Crows of the nominate race *corone* are found mainly in south and east Scotland, Wales and England, and from Iberia east to the Elbe in Germany, the Czech Republic, and Austria. They are common throughout this range, but no population estimates are currently available for Europe as a whole, as most datasets for the *EBCC Atlas* did not distinguish between the national totals for this species and the recently separated Hooded Crow (*qv*), with which it hybridises in a narrow contact zone. A second population of Carrion Crows, *orientalis*, is found in Asia from Iran to China, Japan and Kamchatka, though there is now evidence that that form and nominate *corone* are less closely related to each other than the latter is to the Hooded Crow (Knox *et al* 2002).

Carrion Crows have long been persecuted and still are, though the impact of this has lessened since the late 20th century as gamekeeping activities have been reduced. In Great Britain, indeed, the CBC index for the Carrion Crow has shown a sustained increase – by about 95 per cent during 1968–99 – associated with improved nesting success and earlier egg-laying, the latter perhaps a result of generally milder winters and earlier springs (*BBWC*). At the time of the *1988–91 Atlas* the British population was estimated at about 790,000 territories, a figure that must surely now be too low.

Smith (1887) had little specific to say about Carrion Crows in Wiltshire, but did note that, despite human persecution, they were still common. The next assessment of their status remained essentially the same, when the 1929 bird report in *WANHM* described them as 'Very common and well distributed'. Three decades later, Peirson (1959) wrote that they were 'common or even very common and still increasing in numbers'. Buxton (1981) added that 'Numbers appear to increase in winter when large flocks are noted in some areas'. Both the *1968–72* and *1988–91 Atlases*, and the *1981–84 Winter Atlas*, mapped them in all the 33 core and 15 part 10-km squares in the county.

The summer distribution map for 1995–2000 shows that, although evident in every part of Wiltshire, breeding was densest in the west and north. That impression is confirmed by the summer abundance map, which demonstrates that Carrion Crows are less common, in the southeastern third of Wiltshire, being much less numerous in the woodlands bordering the New Forest (Hampshire) and on parts of Salisbury Plain and the high chalk of Cranborne Chase. The greater densities around Salisbury and Swindon underline this species' exploitation of the surplus food associated with urban areas. While food supply or nesting sites may be mainly responsible for the otherwise relative scarcity of Carrion Crows in the east, many gamekeepers still wage war on them, which may be another factor in certain parts. But individuals forage over considerable areas and, although about 300 were shot on the Longleat estate during February–March 1984 – many of them in the

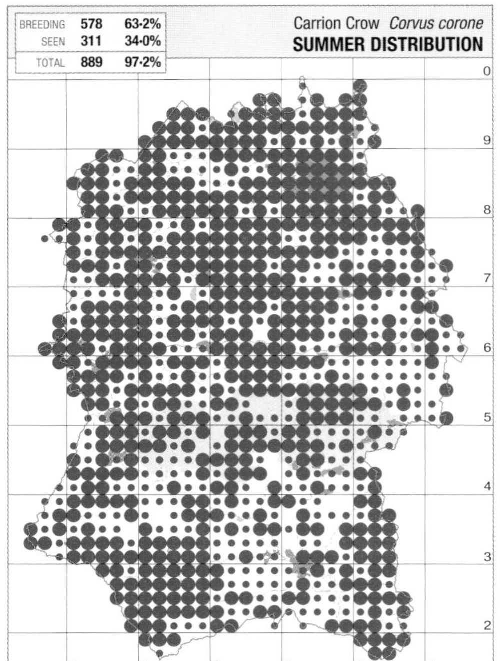

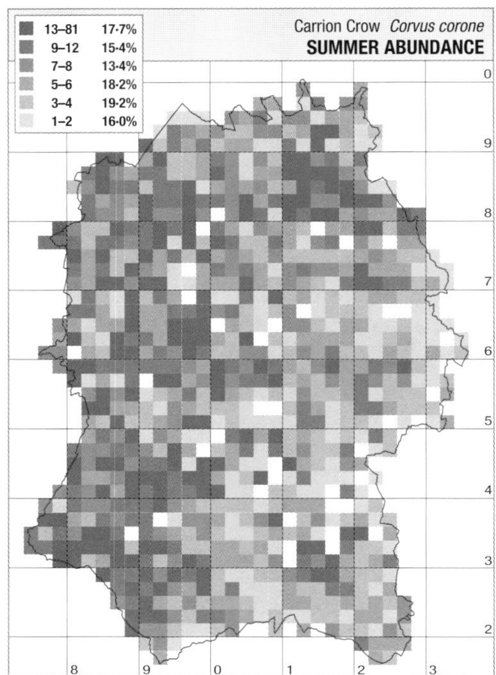

lion, tiger and wolf enclosures of the Safari Park, which provided relatively undisturbed roosting areas with plenty of pickings – the estimated population of 150+ pairs on the whole estate of 3707 ha was still higher than the predicted 130+ pairs based on the national CBC figures for woodland and farmland at that time (Ferguson-Lees 1984). The results of surveys in Wiltshire and adjacent counties using BBS methods, if extrapolated to Wiltshire as a whole, suggest that the county breeding total lies between 11,300 and 25,100 pairs.

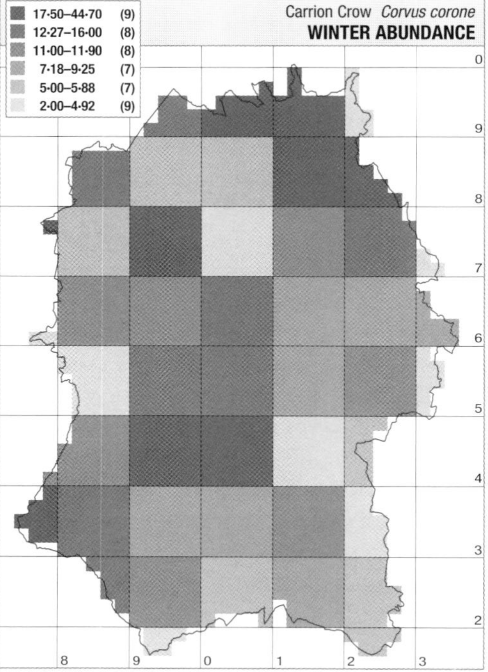

Although Carrion Crows will forage over wide areas, the British population is essentially sedentary, and few ringing recoveries have shown movements of over 20 km (*Migration Atlas*). One such, however, involving Wiltshire, was ringed at Pitsea Marsh (Essex) on 16 May 1981 and found at Swindon – a distance of 158 km – on 30 June 1981. The only six recoveries of just 75 Carrion Crows ringed in the county during 1965–2000 were all very local.

Like other corvids, though less typically than Rooks and Jackdaws, Carrion Crows will sometimes congregate in large flocks, particularly in winter. High numbers at that season in the 1990s included 146 feeding on a muddy shoreline at Coate Water on 1 December

1998 (when the lake was partially drained) and 329 at Swindon STW on 24 January 1999. The latter site – including its adjacent tip – is responsible for most of the larger counts, and 100 or more were recorded there in every year from 1997 to 2000. The only other locality with a three-figure winter count during the 1990s was the landfill site at Pound Bottom, where 100 had congregated on 3 December 1996. Large gatherings of Carrion Crows can also be seen in spring and summer at the same rich food sources: for example, 200 at Swindon STW and adjacent rubbish tip on 16 May 2000, and 100 at the landfill site at Pound Bottom on 24 June 1998 (*Hobby*).

During the winter survey of 1998–2000, the species was found in nearly every tetrad, and the winter map roughly confirms the summer pattern – fewer in the east, more in the north and west – while counts at that season give a Wiltshire total of about 10,100 individuals. This species' sedentary nature suggests that winter numbers in Wiltshire are likely to consist largely of local birds, and the county population at the time, based on the ratio of summer to winter counts during WOS surveys, is estimated to number 27,600 to 61,500.

SBE

Hooded Crow

Corvus cornix

Formerly common winter visitor from Fenno-Scandia, decreased during 20th century, last recorded 1983

Although treated as a race of the Carrion Crow for most of the 20th century (*eg* Witherby *et al* 1938–41, *BWP*), the Hooded Crow had previously been considered a separate species (*eg* Saunders 1899, Dresser 1902). Now, on the basis of differences in plumage, vocalisations and a limited gene flow, these two crows are once again regarded as specifically distinct for the purpose of the British List (Knox *et al* 2002).

Hooded Crows breed in Ireland, the Isle of Man and northwest Scotland, in the Faeroe Islands and Fenno-Scandia, in eastern Europe eastward from parts of Denmark and Germany south to the Balkans, and in the north Mediterranean eastward from southern France, Corsica, Sardinia and Italy, as well as in Egypt, the Middle East, Asia Minor, central Asia and western Siberia. The remainder of the British and west European 'crow' range is filled by Carrion Crows, fairly sharply divided from the Hooded by a narrow but stable zone of hybrids that produce fertile and variably plumaged offspring. Thus, the British and Irish populations of Hooded Crows form an isolated group separated from the nearest others by more than 300 km of the North Sea or by a much wider area of land occupied by Carrion Crows. Data on the numbers of Hooded Crows in Europe as a whole are incomplete, but the British population – in Scotland (mainly north and west of a line from Shetland to Kintyre and Arran), the Isle of Man and one small area on the west coast of Wales – has been estimated at 160,000 territories, and hybrids account for an additional 20,000 (*1988–91 Atlas*).

Hooded Crows from Fenno-Scandia formerly wintered regularly in England, but nowadays rarely do so, as greater numbers remain farther north in the milder winters (*Migration Atlas*). These north European immigrants were once well known enough in Wiltshire to have acquired the local name of 'Beckhampton Grey Crows' (Jones & Dillon

1987). The first reference to this species in Wiltshire seems to have been made by John Aubrey (1656–91) who wrote 'On Salisbury plaines are gray crows, as at Royston'.

In the 19th century, Smith (1887) reported that the Hooded Crow appeared only 'occasionally' in the county, though he also wrote that it was 'frequent enough to render it familiar to most people' and that he had himself 'seen it on the Marlborough Downs'. Smith also knew of 'many notices ... from various parts of the county, more especially in the neighbourhood of Salisbury, where it frequents water meadows in the winter ... but its visits are, I fear, yearly becoming more and more rare'.

In view of Smith's comment, it is perhaps surprising that Peirson (1919) should still have described the Hooded Crow as 'A fairly common winter visitor' in the Marlborough District which 'may often be seen near sheepfolds in lambing time'. Even more surprisingly, he also noted that it 'has nested in Wiltshire', but gave no further details to make it possible to judge whether this was a regular or an isolated event. (The same bald statement was retained by Peirson 1926, but dropped by Peirson & Walford 1930.) Breeding in Wiltshire was not mentioned in the *1875–1900 Atlas* (shown only as of occasional occurrence no farther south than Yorkshire); and Witherby *et al* (1938–41) wrote simply 'Has bred occasionally [in England], mostly eastern counties, and seldom inland'. The inaugural bird report in *WANHM* for 1929 also noted the Hooded Crow as a 'Fairly common winter visitor in N Wilts; less often seen in S Wilts', but neither it nor the six other reports published before the 1939–45 War (covering the years 1929–34 and 1936) really supported that status, documenting a grand total of just 18 records involving 22 individuals.

After the War, there were records of Hooded Crows in 11 of the 14 years of 1946–59 (and in 13 of those 15 winters) – though no more than five in any one – but during the next decade they were seen in only three years, the last in 1964 (*WANHM*). Among these were the last reports of regular wintering in Wiltshire, by two that frequented Broome Manor Sewage Farm, Swindon, during 1958–60 and just one also in 1961; the extreme dates were 6 November and 9 March. In the 1970s, singletons were seen near East Knoyle on 6 April 1972; at West Ashton on 14 December 1977; and in the vicinity of Dunstable, near Salisbury, from 24 February to 31 March 1979 (*WANHM*, *Hobby*). After that, the only Hooded Crow reported in Wiltshire was seen flying northwest over Swindon with about 175 Carrion Crows on 18 November 1983.

Any future records need careful observation. Hybrid Hooded × Carrion Crows from the contact zone in north Europe, which show varying amounts of grey, could conceivably occur in Wiltshire.

SBE

Raven

Corvus corax

Former resident to late 1880s, recolonising from southwest since 1993

For many birdwatchers, the Raven's resonant voice and aerial prowess epitomise Great Britain's remaining wild places; yet this handsome and powerful crow was once a familiar sight in and around Medieval towns and villages, where it was often protected and welcomed as a useful scavenger of discarded food. As town hygiene improved, however, it gradually lost this urban niche and, from about the middle of the 17th century, human persecution – often encouraged and rewarded by bounty payments – became an increasing factor as the Raven's reputation changed to that of a killer of livestock and game (Ratcliffe 1997). There is, nevertheless, some evidence that nesting in urban situations persisted into the early 1800s: for example, Baxter & Rintoul (1953), on the authority of pioneer ornithologist William Macgillivray, stated that a pair 'built on the rocks of Arthur's Seat' in Edinburgh in 1837. Where tolerated, Ravens still live closely with man: in the absence of suitable breeding cliffs on Alaska's north coast, they are thought to owe their year-round presence to human settlements, where they nest on, for example, buildings and other man-made structures at the Prudhoe Bay oil field (Johnson & Herter 1989).

Despite the loss of its beneficial image and sometimes protected status, there is testimony that Ravens used to breed in all but four British counties at the beginning of the 19th century, a situation that was, sadly, not to last. The rise in popularity of rearing gamebirds for sport, which was fuelled by the invention of the breech-loading shotgun in the 1850s, led to increasingly severe persecution by gamekeepers, and Ravens were also ruthlessly trapped, shot and poisoned by livestock farmers. Egg- and skin-collecting and the taking of chicks for pets added to the pressure, and by 1900 these magnificent crows were extinct in much of lowland Britain; their nesting was then mostly confined to wild rocky uplands and sea-cliffs in the north and west. Persecution then gradually slackened during the 20th century, especially in the decades following the 1939–45 War, and allowed surplus individuals to form pairs and spread back into adjacent areas. For example, there was an increase in numbers and range in Somerset during the 20th century, and Gloucestershire was recolonised from 1952 (*1875–1900 Atlas*, Ratcliffe 1997). British breeding numbers in the second half of the 20th century were considered to be in the region of 5000 pairs by the *1968–72 Atlas*, and 7000 pairs by the *1988–91 Atlas*, though the latter also noted that there had been losses in range between the two surveys – most noticeably in Northumberland, Galloway and the Scottish borders – as a result of afforestation, improved sheep husbandry, and conversion of grassland to arable. Other distributional gaps in northern Britain were linked to continued harassment by gamekeepers on grouse moors, but recent increases in the Welsh Marches and parts of lowland England have helped to offset these declines. BBS results show population growth in Scotland and England, and stability in Wales, during 1994–2002, but other BTO data indicate poorer breeding performances, including long-term declines in brood sizes and greater losses at the egg stage (*BBWC*, Ratcliffe 1997).

Given its close association with human settlements in Great Britain during the Middle Ages, it is not surprising that in Wiltshire, a county with renowned and well-investigated prehistoric monuments, the Raven figures in the archaeological record as far back as 3300 BC (see page 70). Ravens are birds of augury, myth and fable, with a literary history stretching back to the Old Testament, and were famously important in the belief systems of, for example, the Norsemen, Inuit ('Eskimos') and many indigenous North American tribes (see summaries in Heinrich 1990 and Ratcliffe 1997). Thus, it may well be that, in addition to any benefits they brought to Wiltshire's early inhabitants by scavenging discarded food, their association with such sites as Stonehenge held some cultural importance. In this connection, it should not be forgotten that such significance persists to this day, as is borne witness by the keeping of six Ravens at the Tower of London – a custom begun in the reign of Charles II, allegedly after a soothsayer's warning that a great disaster would otherwise befall the country (Heinrich 1990).

Smith (1887) wrote that in Wiltshire these large crows had been 'persecuted, shot down, trapped, and despoiled of their young', and on the basis of 'careful enquiry in every part of the county' he listed 25 'localities which, earlier or later, Ravens have been known to

Table 112. Ravens *Corvus corax* in Wiltshire: territorial pairs 1993–2000

	93	94	95	96	97	98	99	00
Confirmed breeding	0	1	1	2	1	1	1	5
Probable/possible	2	1	1	2	5	9	10	12
Total territorial pairs	2	2	2	4	6	10	11	17

occupy, and some few occupy still'. Of these, two were just over the county boundary in Hampshire, one of which, at South Tidworth, became part of Wiltshire as a result of boundary changes in 1992. Smith reported that, at the time he was writing, only South Tidworth and Wilton Park near Salisbury were certainly occupied, though Ravens were present in several other areas. (According to Kelsall & Munn 1905, South Tidworth was abandoned in 1888, when one of the pair disappeared, 'probably having been shot'.) Ratcliffe (1997) erroneously quoted Smith to the effect that nesting occurred also at Compton Park in 1887 – but what Smith reported was the owner's 'regret' that none had taken place that year. Hudson (1910) added another nesting site of about 'thirty-five or forty years ago' and Peirson (1919), writing of the Marlborough district, added a further two, the last in 1885.

Although persecution played the key role in the demise of the Raven in Wiltshire during the last decades of the 19th century, reduced food availability indirectly brought about by economic factors may also have contributed. Ravens are omnivorous, but sheep carrion (including afterbirths at lambing time) forms an important part of their diet (*1968–72 Atlas* and *1981–84 Winter Atlas*). From the 1870s, however, cheap wool imports from Australia led to many fewer sheep being farmed in lowland Britain, a downward trend that continued until about 1947 (*1875–1900 Atlas*).

Whether or not Smith's 1887 breeding records were indeed the last of the 19th century is unknown; Hony (1915a) simply listed the Raven as having nested, without further comment. Wiltshire's inaugural county bird report, for 1929, in *WANHM* summarised its early 20th century status as 'Not uncommon as a breeding species many years ago, now only a very occasional visitor', but reported also that three had been seen that year at Lydiard Millicent on 10 October. No more were detailed in *WANHM* until a singleton at Totterdown in 1947, and then records totalling 14 birds (three of which were shot) occurred in eight of the 12 years 1948–59. Next, there were sightings involving at most ten individuals – and probably as few as eight – in just seven years during 1960–91 (1962, 1966–67, 1974 and 1982–84). Analyses of the whole period 1946–91 shows that Ravens were mostly seen between October and March, the exceptions beings singletons in May and September 1949, June 1957 and August 1984 (*WANHM*, *Hobby*).

A change in status was apparent from 1992 when, after seven blank years, there were three records, including one of a pair seen 'in sub-display flight' during November and December. It may also be relevant that 1992 saw the resumption of regular inland nesting in Dorset (Green 2004). In 1993 two pairs were established in Wiltshire and breeding was considered 'probable', though this was not confirmed until 1994 when one of the two pairs certainly nested. The totals of confirmed and probable or possible nesting pairs continued to increase, particularly rapidly towards the end of the decade (table 112). The summer map for 1995–2000 shows a predominantly westerly distribution, from the Cotswolds to southwest Wiltshire, as well as breeding evidence in the general area of Savernake and the Marlborough Downs, and presence in the extreme southeast. The Ravens that gave rise to the records in the southeast were known to have ranged more widely than the map suggests, northwards to at least the Dean valley and southwards across the county boundary deep into Hampshire (P Combridge). In North America, non-territorial

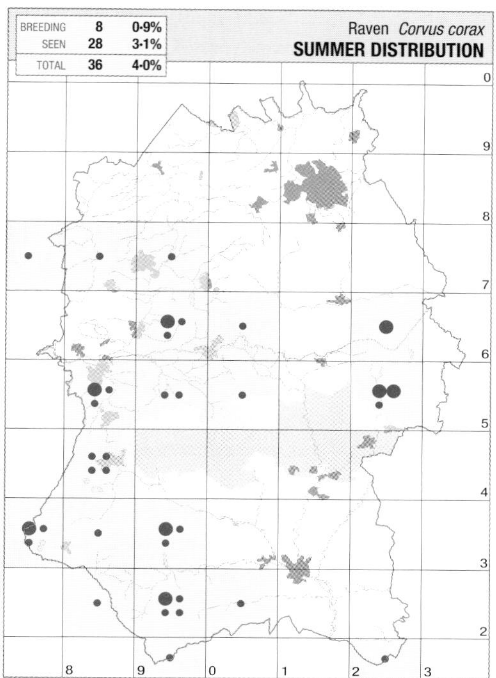

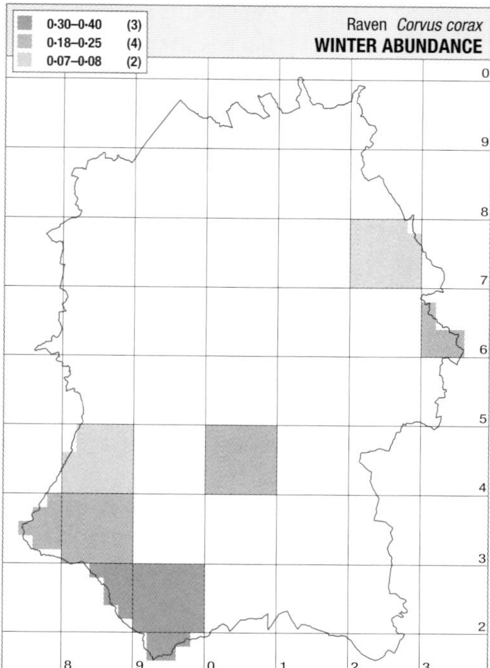

individuals or pairs have been reported as covering an area of up to 1800 km² in search of food (*BWP*), and flying up to 50 km from roost to food sources (*Migration Atlas*). Thus, it is feasible that the breeding map overstates the extent of the Raven's summer distribution in Wiltshire at the end of the 20th century – but, in contrast, the winter map certainly understates it. Although capable of occasional long-distance movements (for example, a nestling ringed in Northern Ireland in 1987 was recovered in East Anglia the following January), British Ravens are relatively sedentary (*Migration Atlas*) and territorial pairs stay in the vicinity of breeding sites throughout the year (*1981–84 Winter Atlas*).

Comparison between the winter and summer maps suggests, therefore, that the sampling methodology used in the winter survey of 1998–2000 failed to reflect the species' presence properly at that season. No Ravens have been ringed in Wiltshire, nor are there any inward recoveries, but the marked westerly bias shown by both maps is not unexpected and supports the notion of recolonisation from the expanding populations in the Welsh Marches and southwest England. Land use and food availability may also play a part in this distribution, and it will be interesting to see if these two factors do indeed prove important in limiting future occupation of other areas. Ravens in Wiltshire are mainly tree nesters, though they have also used quarries, disused buildings and other man-made structures.

Although the combined total of breeding and non-breeding pairs reported in 2000 was 17, the fact that non-breeders are known to range widely in search of food suggests the possibility of some double-counting, and so the summer population may in fact have been slightly fewer than that figure – perhaps eight to 12 pairs – whereas winter numbers could lie in the region of 30 to 75 individuals. Most recent reports of Ravens in Wiltshire have been of singletons, pairs or family parties, but 18 were seen leaving a presumed roost in south Wiltshire on 22 October 2000.

The Raven is not only the world's largest passerine, but also one of the most widely distributed of all landbirds, occurring as a breeding species across the Northern

Hemisphere from the Arctic south through much of the Americas and Eurasia as far as Nicaragua, the Canaries, North Africa, Israel, Iraq, Pakistan, northern China and the Kuriles. Indeed, it is so widespread that the 'concept of habitat is hardly applicable', although in general terms Ravens require nest-sites inaccessible to ground predators but near enough to open areas for 'long-range food-gathering, often involving high flights'; and they avoid enclosed habitats and intensively farmed or grazed lands (*CBWP*). In Europe, though absent from many lowland areas, they are found from north Norway and Iceland south to the Mediterranean, and achieve their greatest breeding densities along the cliffs of Shetland and in the mountains of Wales. After nearly a century of steady decline resulting from persecution, the early 1950s saw a largely natural recolonisation, even though aided by re-introduction programmes in Belgium, the Netherlands, Germany and the Czech Republic. The most recent estimate of European breeding numbers, excluding those of Russia, put the population at 203,000 to 257,000 pairs (*EBBC Atlas*), of which no fewer than 60,000–90,000 were in Spain and 20,000–50,000 in Norway (*CBWP*).

All birds are fascinating but – to paraphrase George Orwell's *Animal Farm* – some birds are more fascinating than others. The Raven possesses an aura and undoubted presence matched by few other species and its recolonisation of this county should be welcomed – or, it is to be hoped, at least tolerated – for it poses no threat to human interests and can only enhance the appeal of Wiltshire's countryside.

(See also page 725.)

PCo

Sponsored by Chris Ward in memory of John Pollard

Common Starling

Sturnus vulgaris

Seriously decreasing resident, common winter visitor from north Europe

The ubiquitous Starling is probably as well known as the Robin to the general public – though not so well loved. At a distance the adult may look all black, or in winter buff-spotted, but in spring or summer sunshine its metallic sheen produces a vivid assortment of bronze-greens and blue- and reddish-purples (and, because birds can see ultra-violet light, these iridescent colours will appear much brighter to them than they do to human eyes). This species feeds mainly on the ground and, especially during the breeding season, prefers grasslands, including garden lawns, where it finds insect larvae, worms, spiders and other soil invertebrates. At other times of year, it is omnivorous, adding fruit, cereals, berries and seeds to its diet, and becomes a frequent visitor to bird-tables and nut-holders. It also feeds at sewage farms and among domesticated animals, particularly pigs.

Starlings are now almost cosmopolitan, having been introduced into North America, southern Africa, Australia and New Zealand. They breed in the Azores, have recently colonised the Canary Islands (*CBWP*), and are otherwise widespread across most of Europe – though missing from much of Iceland, Iberia, the Mediterranean fringe and north Russia – into western Asia as far as the region of Lake Baikal and south to Tien Shan, as well as in Turkey, northern Iraq, Iran and Pakistan. In general, the populations of north and east Europe are migratory (as are those in Siberia and central Asia), while those of the west and south, north to southern Scandinavia and the Ukraine, are only partially migratory or resident. In winter, European Starlings become numerous south of the breeding range, reaching northernmost Africa and Arabia. British Starlings are largely sedentary, but in winter are joined by many from the Low Countries and Fenno-Scandia east as far as the Urals (*Migration Atlas*).

In Europe, the breeding range expanded and the numbers increased during the 19th century and the first half of the 20th, since when, especially from the 1970s, most populations have been decreasing. Declines in Finland and adjacent countries have been linked to loss of habitat, particularly that of dairy farms; and corresponding decreases on the wintering grounds are evident in Britain, France and Spain (*EBCC Atlas*). The *1988–91 Atlas* showed Starlings to be widespread in Great Britain except in parts of the Scottish Highlands, where their range had contracted since the *1968–72 Atlas*; the highest densities were in England and southern Scotland, and especially associated with urban areas. British breeding numbers have continued to fall steadily, especially since the early 1980s, and BBS results suggest that this decline is still going on in England and Wales – triggering conservation concerns – although it has stabilised in Scotland. Breeding success generally improved during the period, but it is possible that subsequent survival rates have been affected by the losses in the species' preferred feeding habitat of permanent pasture (*BBWC*). The population of Starlings in Great Britain in 2000 was estimated at 737,000 territories (*APEP*), a marked decrease from the 1·1 million territories at the time of the *1988–91 Atlas*, while that for Europe as a whole (apart from Russia), which was put at 35 to 49 million pairs in the mid 1990s (*EBCC Atlas*), is likely also to be much too high now.

Starlings were common in 19th century Wiltshire. Smith (1887) described them as 'one of our most constant companions' and noted that 'on the Lavington Downs, at New Copse…these birds flock in thousands and tens of thousands'. He knew also of a 'favoured haunt…in the parish of Nettleton, near Chippenham', where 'one thousand were killed a few years since' in 'a piece of wanton cruelty', and of further large roosts near Grittleton and Odstock. The species' status in the county apparently changed little during the first three-quarters of the 20th century, the inaugural 1929 bird report in *WANHM* noting it as 'very abundant' and Peirson (1959) describing it as 'very common…numbers are greatly increased in winter'. Both the *1968–72* and *1988–91 Atlases* confirmed breeding in all of Wiltshire's 33 core 10-km squares; the *1981–84 Winter Atlas* also found Starlings in all the core squares, but showed them to be generally commoner in the north and central areas of the county.

The summer distribution map for 1995–2000 still shows evidence of breeding in every 10-km square in Wiltshire, and in nearly three-quarters of all tetrads. Starlings nest in holes of almost any description – high or low, and in walls, trees, rocks, even a metal pipe or a discarded oil drum – but spaces under house roofs are most frequently chosen. This species is clearly more widespread in the north of the county, partly at least because of the greater availability of nest-sites there. In Swindon, for example, Starlings breed chiefly in areas of Victorian and Edwardian housing, which still have holes available under the eaves, whereas they (and House Sparrows) are excluded by the plastic fascia boards on more modern houses. There are also more urban areas in north and west Wiltshire than in the south and east, where Victorian terraces are relatively scarce. (The availability of permanent pasture for feeding may also be important and, again, there is more grassland in the north and west.)

The summer abundance map certainly demonstrates some correlation with towns and villages, especially in the Swindon area, and shows that this species is only patchily distributed on Salisbury Plain and the downs. Large post-breeding flocks used to be a summer feature of SPTA grasslands, but these declined during the 1990s. Based on a number of local

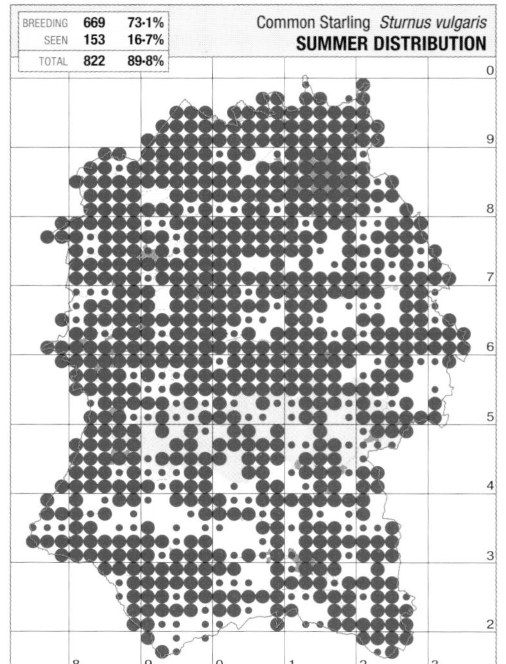

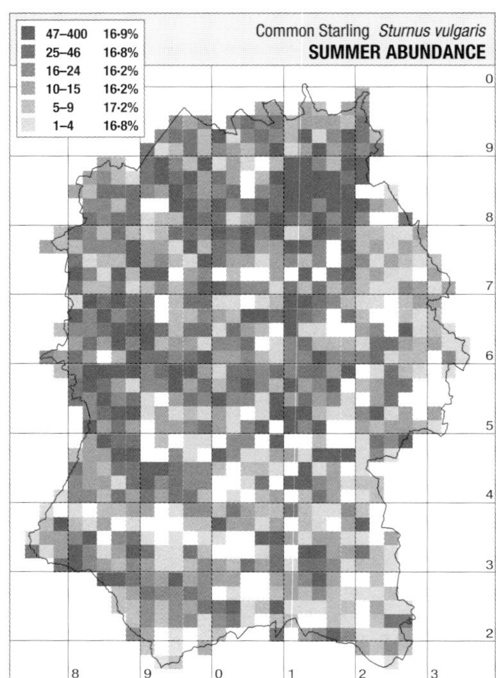

surveys using BBS methods, Wiltshire's nesting population of Starlings is estimated at 18,300 to 52,400 pairs.

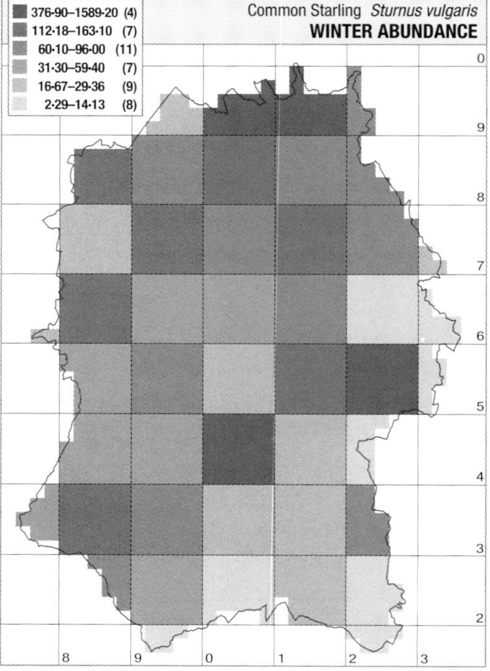

Recently fledged juveniles can be found in flocks by early June, and the roosts they occupy then are abandoned in early autumn, when larger congregations are formed and later augmented by immigrants from the Continent. Ringing returns from Belgium, the Netherlands, Germany, Sweden, Poland and Russia of Starlings ringed in Wiltshire in winter illustrate their subsequent eastward movements. Similarly, there have been inward recoveries in winter of Starlings ringed in Belgium, the Netherlands and Lithuania. Although as many as 5414, mainly adults, were marked in the county during 1965–2000, the annual totals fell towards the end of that period and, for example, just 40 were ringed in 2000. This may be partly because Starlings are fewer and perhaps partly because enthusiasm for targeting autumn roosts has fallen.

The Wiltshire bird reports in *WANHM* from 1929 and then in *Hobby* from 1974 reveal something about the decline of Starling roosts in the county over recent decades (although they may well also indicate fluctuating observer interest). The reports for 1946–59 in

WANHM gave the locations and approximate sizes of roosts, those at Clench Common near Marlborough, at High Post near Salisbury and at Corsham each holding estimated numbers of half a million to two million Starlings – though such figures can only have been broad approximations – and creating winter spectacles that naturalists travelled some distances to experience. During 1960–67, additional roosts were listed in *WANHM* but, gradually, the largest estimated numbers became only 120,000. The annual reports over the next 17 years did not mention Starling roosts at all, and then in 1985 an estimate of 75,000 at Druid's Lodge, near Amesbury, was the largest. In 1991 came the first reports of small numbers roosting in hedges and young conifers, a habit that has continued. No recorded roosts in the early 1990s exceeded 9000, but during 1996–2000 there were two reports of 10,000 (both at CWP, in November 1996 and November 2000) and four of 15,000 (at Swindon in February 1997, at CWP in November 1998, near Bratton in February–March 1999, and at Trowbridge in January–February 2000). More roosts have always been noted in the northern half of the county than in the southern, but it is not known if this, at least in part, reflects observer coverage.

The winter map for 1998–2000 shows that, as in summer, the southeast is less favoured, but otherwise suggests a rather different distribution, including seemingly less reliance on major towns. Differing areas of high density at this season are likely to reflect availability of grasslands and locally also of pig farms, as well as the presence or absence of winter roosts in the general vicinity. The timed counts during the winter survey produced a total of 112,281 – a larger figure than that for any other species – and underlines the considerable effect of the influxes of winter visitors. Based on the summer estimates and the ratio of winter to summer counts during WOS surveys, the total is estimated to lie between 140,000 and 402,000 individuals, figures second only to those of Wood Pigeons.

PEC & PAC

Rose-coloured Starling

Sturnus roseus

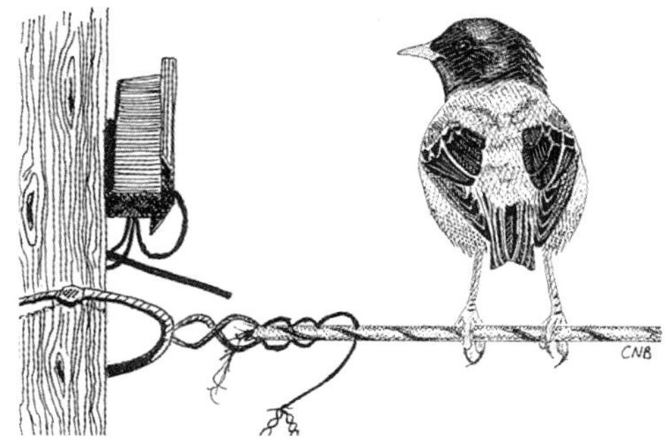

Vagrant (7 records) during eruptions from southeast Europe, winters India

Rose-coloured Starlings are highly dispersive migrants that summer on steppes and open foothills from southeast Europe to southern Siberia, Kazakhstan and northern Afghanistan, and winter in India. The western limits of their range fluctuate as a result of variable eruptive movements in spring, often involving considerable flocks that may nest and then disappear without returning the following year. Thus, breeding is generally regarded as erratic in Turkey and less than annual in the eastern Balkans, though the species has nested as far west as Hungary and Italy, and as far south as Israel.

Breeding is now considered to be annual in Bulgaria, however, and it is believed that one colony there – recently holding 1100 to 1800 Rose-coloured Starlings – may even have been occupied since 1960 (Nyagolov *et al* 2003). On the other hand, westward invasions have become more frequent in recent years, large numbers appearing in Romania, too: over 28,000 passed through one site on just one day on 28 June 2002 (Gantlett 2002), and 14,000 pairs nested in that country that year and 16,000–18,000 pairs again in 2003 (Szabo-Szeley 2003).

Some reach Great Britain in most years, and over 450 were recorded during 1958–2000 (*BBRC*). Smith (1887) listed four Wiltshire records of the 'Rose-coloured Pastor', as it was then known: one killed by a shepherd on Salisbury Plain, near Wilton, at the 'end of July or beginning of August' in 1853; one shot in the parish of Bremhill in 1868; one of two which were seen 'for some days near Box... was shot under Kingsdown' (no date); and one shot 'on the western borders of the county... about two miles from Road Hill' (now Rode, which itself lies just inside Somerset) on 29 July 1869. No mention was made of the ages of these, but the national pattern shows two distinct waves: adults and first-years widely from May to August and juveniles concentrated more in the southwest from September to October (Cottridge & Vinicombe 1996). The Wiltshire dates suggest that all four were probably adults. It is also likely that the far less conspicuous juveniles would have been more easily overlooked. There were no further records for almost a century, but all three subsequent sightings up to 2000 also involved adults: at Kingston Deverill on 16 March 1963; at Brinkworth during 22–28 July 1963; and at Bishopstone (probably near Salisbury) on 23 July 1972.

RT

House Sparrow

Passer domesticus

Common resident, trends in Wiltshire uncertain but large decrease nationally from 1970s

One of the world's most widespread landbirds, the House Sparrow is now found naturally right across Eurasia – except in the most inhospitable strip along the arctic edge of the two continents – as far as the Sea of Okhotsk and western Mongolia, and south into northern Africa, Arabia, the Indian subcontinent and Myanmar. Only in the 19th century, however, did this species start spreading east from the Urals across Asiatic Russia and it did not reach the Pacific coast until 1929 (*CBWP*). House Sparrows have also become established, mostly with human assistance, in various parts of North and South America, sub-Saharan Africa, Australia and New Zealand, as well as on many oceanic islands. In Europe this species is ubiquitous, except in Italy where *italiae*, the 'Italian Sparrow' – a stabilised hybrid with the Spanish Sparrow replaces it. The breeding population of Europe, excluding Russia, has been estimated at 50 to 63 million pairs (*EBCC Atlas*).

In Great Britain as a whole, the distribution map in the *1988–91 Atlas* showed House Sparrows to be widespread except in parts of mainland Scotland – where more than a hundred 10-km squares had been deserted since the time of the *1968–72 Atlas* – and the abundance map that they were most numerous down the eastern side of England but with comparable high densities more patchily in some central and western parts. A general population decline of 15 per cent was suggested in the *1988–91 Atlas*, while the CBC/BBS, which was inadequate for monitoring House Sparrows before the mid 1970s, demonstrated a rapid national decrease of around two-thirds from that time to the end of the century; that involved near-extinction in some urban areas of Great Britain. This has been thought to be an effect of increased winter mortality – perhaps linked to changes in both rural and urban habitats – and suggested possible causes have included the reduction in spilt grain on farmland and the use of toxic additives in unleaded petrol (*BBWC*).

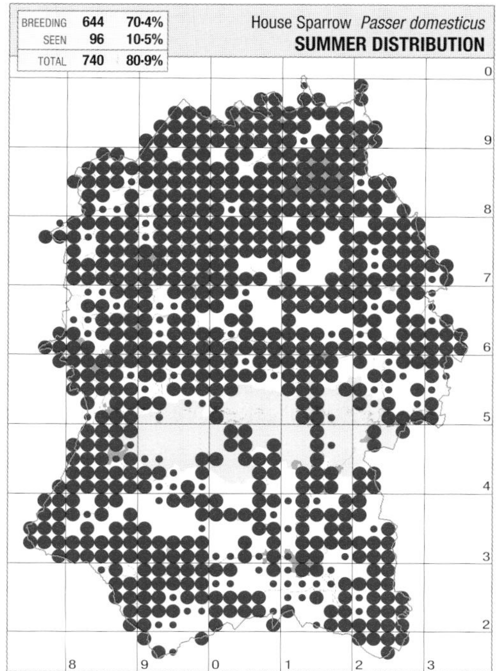

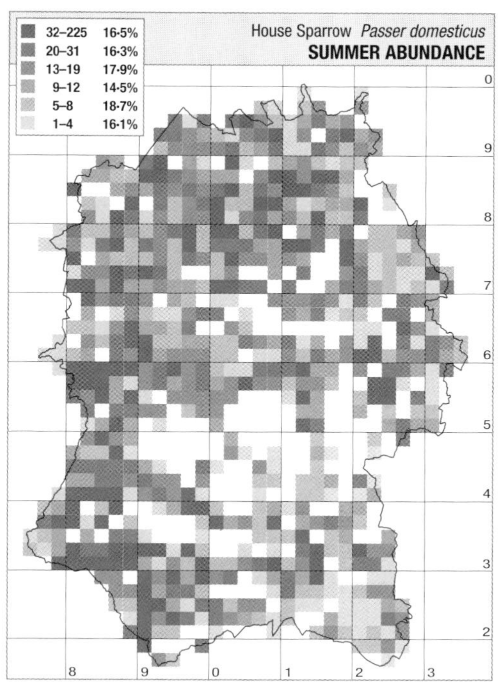

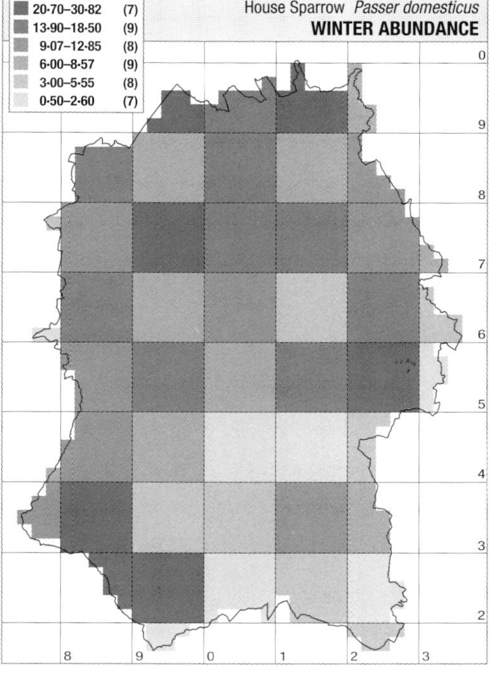

Historically, House Sparrows are known to have increased during the 19th century, an increase linked to both the spread of urbanisation and agricultural changes (*1875–1900 Atlas*). By then they were very common in Wiltshire and, in the 19th century, were described by Smith (1887) as 'well known to everybody'. But they were regarded as pests for causing damage to crops and, in the 18th and 19th centuries, local 'Sparrow Clubs' were established with the sole purpose of eradicating these birds. For many years, large numbers were killed. Smith (1887) recorded an old churchwarden's book for his parish of Yatesbury 'dating from above 100 years ago', which detailed 'every year from 20 to 90 dozen old Sparrows at 4 [old] pence the dozen, and from 10 to 70 dozen young birds at 2 [old] pence the dozen'. As similar examples from Britford parish, 'headage' payments of £2 7s 3d were made for '141 dozen, and 9 sparrows' in 1827 and subsequently a total of £12 5s 3d for 8892 during 1828–35 (Morres 1878–85, part IV: 156). The minutes of the Edington, Tilshead and Coulston Sparrow Club for 1909–11 also make for illuminating, if grisly, reading: on 17 November 1909 'It was resolved that the heads of sparrows, green linnets [Greenfinches] and starlings be paid for as follows: sparrow at…3d per dozen, the other two…at 2d per dozen'; the chairman of the Sparrow Club stated that it was 'only by united action in as large an area as possible that an effective check [against House Sparrows] could possibly be made', and there was also reference to the 'good results' obtained at Bratton, where a certain Frank Wheeler had accounted for '13 doz & 6' in December 1909 (SB Edwards).

Despite this history of persecution, there was no apparent change in the abundance of House Sparrows in Wiltshire over the first two-thirds of the 20th century. The only reference to numbers in the bird reports in *WANHM* during 1929–60 concerned 'A large flock, nearly all males', near Wilsford in April 1956. Peirson (1959) described this species as a 'very common resident'; and both the *1968–72* and *1988–91 Atlases* mapped it as breeding in all of Wiltshire's 33 core and 15 part 10-km squares, while the *1981–84 Winter Atlas* also showed it throughout the county.

The WOS summer and winter surveys show this broad distribution to be unchanged at the turn of the millennium. The finer detail of the summer distribution map for 1995–2000 demonstrates that House Sparrows were breeding in more than two-thirds of all tetrads, but that they were absent from much of Salisbury Plain – though using the valleys that dissect it – and from parts of the downs where buildings are lacking, while both the summer and winter abundance maps demonstrate that the numbers were thinner in the southeast of the county. The House Sparrow remains numerous, however, in much of the north of Wiltshire and in the far west in ST83, 84, 85 and 92: many towns and villages in ST84 and 85 provide suitable breeding sites, though the species' success in the other two squares, which both have extensive tracts of downland and fewer buildings, is less understandable.

An absence of good census data means a lack of firm evidence of a decline in Wiltshire during the last quarter of the 20th century, and individual observers' opinions on population trends have often been conflicting (*Hobby*). Surveys within the county and in adjacent regions using BBS methods give varying densities, and applying these to Wiltshire as a whole suggests that the population lay between 17,900 and as many as 49,500 pairs at the end of the 1990s, less than one per cent of the 13·2 million individuals estimated to be present in Great Britain during 1994–2000 (Robinson *et al* 2005). The ratio of summer to winter counts during the WOS timed surveys suggests that the winter total in the county was in the region of 23,900 to 66,200 individuals. In recent years, large concentrations have included roosts of 300 at Swindon STW in January–March and October 1997 and again in January and October–December 1998, and of 250 in December 2000, as well as a post-breeding flock of 200 at Whaddon, near Salisbury, on 15 August 2000.

Odd pairs of House Sparrows will occasionally nest in any month, and there have been at least three records of breeding activity in Wiltshire in December: in 1934, a pair was recorded building a nest at Whiteparish on the 23rd; in 1950, one was noted carrying nest material on the 19th (no locality published); and, in 1990, a male was seen feeding nestlings at Westbury on Christmas Day (*WANHM*, *Hobby*).

A total of 1506 House Sparrows was ringed in Wiltshire during 1965–2000, though for many of those years this species was excluded from the national ringing scheme because of its abundance. It was reinstated when the national population was clearly declining, but still only small numbers were caught. The 76 recoveries from that total have been almost all within the county, an unsurprising result for a bird that is known to be largely sedentary in Great Britain (*Migration Atlas*).

MVJ

Sponsored by Doreen Ellis

Tree Sparrow

Passer montanus

Local resident, increasing after long-term decline

Tree Sparrow numbers have long fluctuated in irregular cycles. In Great Britain, they were generally high from the 1880s to the 1930s, decreased to a low in the 1940s and, after starting to rise again from 1957, had increased six-fold by 1964–65; fluctuations through the 1970s were generally at high levels, but another decline began about 1979 and quickly accelerated, until by 1990 the population had fallen back to the 1955 level (Summers-Smith 1988, 1998). In Britain and Ireland combined, numbers dropped from an estimated peak of 900,000 pairs in 1965 to only 292,000 pairs by 1985 (Summers-Smith 1989), and to fewer than 120,000 territories by 1991, of which the British proportion was 110,000 (*1988–91 Atlas*). By the end of the 20th century, the range had contracted, most markedly in western Britain and southernmost England.

Other national surveys similarly confirm that the British population crashed between the late 1970s and the mid 1980s, and that the declines, though less severe, continued until the mid 1990s, so that the numbers by the end of the millennium stood at just 3 per cent of the levels of only 25 years earlier (*BBWC*). For 2000, the best estimate available for Great Britain was 68,000 territories, although the actual population was considered to be smaller than that (*APEP*). Consequently, the Tree Sparrow was one of a group of farmland species afforded high conservation priority.

Although similar trends have been noted in the Netherlands, Germany and Switzerland, Tree Sparrows have expanded their ranges elsewhere, especially in Fenno-Scandia, and the population of Europe, excluding Russia, has been estimated at 14 to 17 million pairs (*EBCC Atlas*). In Ireland, the species had become extinct in the 1950s, but after recolonising in the 1960s had been found breeding in no fewer than 21 counties by the 1990s (Summer-Smith 1998).

In 19th century Wiltshire, Smith (1887) described the Tree Sparrow as 'local, nowhere ... by any means common' and 'somewhat capricious in its choice of abode'. He even hesitated to include it in his list of county nesters, apparently because of a lack of personal knowledge, though he admitted that it was 'doubtless often overlooked'. More recently, the county pattern has generally reflected national fluctuations. The inaugural 1929 bird report in *WANHM* described this species as no more than a 'scarce resident', and the 1934 report considered it to be 'generally distributed but not common'. Peirson (1959) found it 'A resident widely distributed over the county and apparently scarce but perhaps only uncommon and overlooked'.

The *1968–72 Atlas* mapped Tree Sparrows as breeding in 28 of Wiltshire's 33 core 10-km squares and at least seen in four of the other five. Buxton (1981) was still able to describe them as widespread, if more numerous in the north of the county, including large flocks in winter (and the *1981–84 Winter Atlas* mapped them in 30 of the 33 core squares), but by the time of the *1988–91 Atlas* they were seen in only 24, while the number with breeding evidence had dropped from 28 to 19. Moreover, the summer survey of 1995–2000 found them in only 21 of the core squares and breeding in just 14. By 2000, the species could be regarded only as very local in Wiltshire, still commoner in the north and absent from large areas, especially in the south. The breeding population was widely dispersed but centralised on a few major winter food sites. In the summer survey of 1995–2000 Tree Sparrows were found breeding in only 38 tetrads, although seen in a further 38, and even this combined

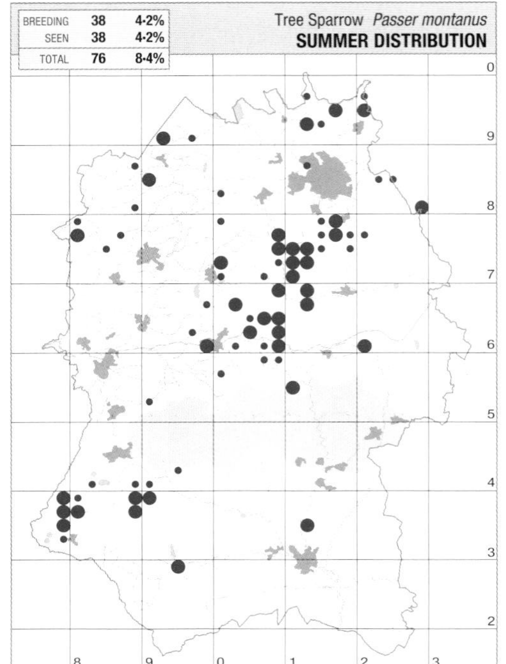

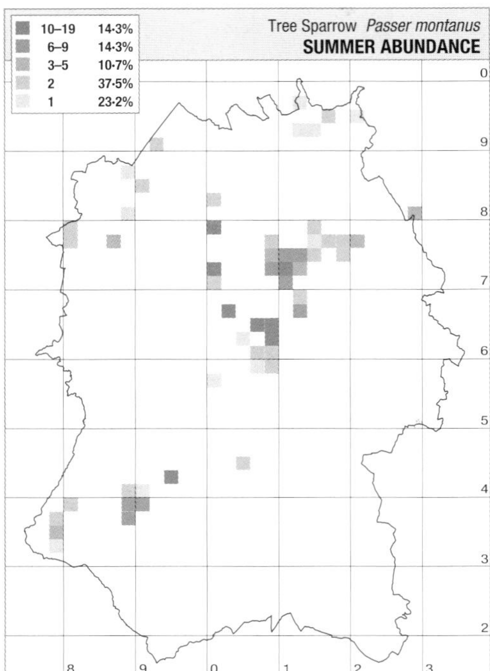

total represented just 25 of the 48 core and part 10-km squares. The winter survey of 1998–2000 found them in only five core and two part 10-km squares, but timed visits to random tetrads under-recorded such scarce species in general.

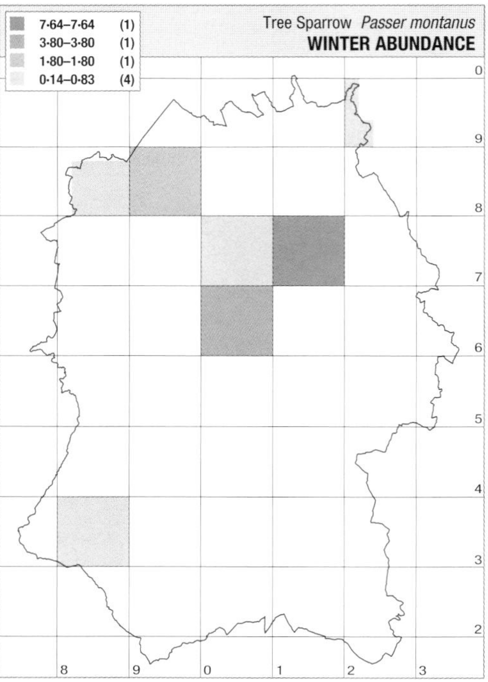

The Tree Sparrow is an urban or even city-centre bird over parts of its vast range across Eurasia – extending from southern Fenno-Scandia, Ireland and Iberia east to Sakhalin, Japan and the Greater Sundas, although missing from the far north and most of the Middle East and the Indian subcontinent – and it has been introduced into North America, the Philippines, eastern Indonesia and Australia.

In Wiltshire, as in much of Great Britain, its main habitat is open arable land with scattered broadleaved trees in tall hedgerows, where it nests mainly in tree holes. Tree Sparrows generally nest colonially, commonly in such sites as mature trees in old hedgerows or at the edges of copses, old orchards, pollarded willows along slow-flowing streams, and barns and other farm buildings within easy reach of a plentiful supply of arable weed seeds. Apart from an isolated population adjacent to the West Wiltshire Downs, the summer map shows that most of this county's Tree Sparrows are now found on the Marlborough Downs and in the adjacent vales to the north and south. Although this species is still spread widely throughout England, and in pockets in Scotland and eastern Wales, the areas of highest density are in the centre and east of England; as a result, the concentrations in northern Wiltshire form the most southwesterly outpost for a bird that, except in Kent, is otherwise very thinly distributed to the south of a line from the Severn Estuary to the mouth of the Thames (*1988–91 Atlas*).

In autumn 1999, WOS set up the Wiltshire Tree Sparrow Recovery Project, which aims to safeguard the county's remaining populations by providing nestboxes and year-round feeding stations. At the four sites supported in 2000, as many as 58 nests were recorded and winter flocks totalled some 260 individuals. The best site – centred on farm buildings used for housing cattle and on a maize silage clamp – also had a single post-breeding flock of about 200. The scheme was extended in autumn 2000 to a further ten sites, at which there were at least 52 Tree Sparrows. The summer tetrad counts during 1995–2000 totalled 235, and extrapolation from the winter counts of 1998–2000 produced an estimate of 376. Given this species' general scarcity in the county away from the project sites, these figures are probably a fair reflection of the true numbers at the end of the 1990s. They suggest a total population then of some 60–75 breeding pairs and around 400 individuals in winter. The Wiltshire Tree Sparrow project has continued since 2000 and not only have large increases in breeding numbers been sustained, but also one winter flock is believed to be the largest in Great Britain (see page 725). Pheasant feeders form a major food supply. Apart from boxes, Wiltshire nests have been found in holes in ash, oak and willow trees, in old farm buildings, and in the base of a disused Carrion Crow nest; some are also built in the open in thorn bushes (inviting confusion with the sometimes similarly sited, but generally untidier, nests of House Sparrows).

None of the 662 Tree Sparrows ringed in Wiltshire during 1965–2000 was recovered outside the county in that period, but three ringed in Lincolnshire, Warwickshire and Hampshire in August 1972 and in September and December 1976 were recovered at Coombe Bissett, Sutton Veny and Aldbourne respectively after three, 17 and four months, indicating movement into Wiltshire – although these were at a time of higher population levels than in the last quarter of the 20th century. As part of the Biodiversity Action Plan for this species, no fewer than 115 Tree Sparrows, including 24 nestlings, were ringed in 2000. A colour-ring scheme has also been started, with a view to improving knowledge of individuals.

This usually sedentary species makes eruptive movements 'including apparent arrivals on the east coast of England… these movements appear to be more akin to a dispersal than to a directed migration, and are of only limited extent' (*Migration Atlas*). They may result in new colonisations and local disappearances, and appear to have coincided in the past with increases and declines in England and elsewhere (Summers-Smith 1989). But, in view of the success of the WOS project in providing nesting sites and year-round food supplies, it seems more likely that the huge drop in the British population in the late 20th century resulted from a combination of loss of nesting habitat (through the rooting out of high thick hedges with mature trees and the destruction of old farm buildings) and the switch from spring to autumn sowing (reducing the availability of weed seeds in winter).

(See also page 725.)

PEC

Chaffinch

Fringilla coelebs

Abundant resident, also common winter visitor from Fenno-Scandia

With its cheerful 'bowler's run-up' song, not to mention its *chink* and other distinctive calls, the Chaffinch is surely one of Wiltshire's most familiar birds. In the wider sphere, it breeds virtually throughout Europe (except Iceland, and northernmost Norway, Finland and Russia) east into central Siberia and south through Asia Minor and parts of the Middle East into northern Iran. Elsewhere – in North Africa, and on various Atlantic islands – two other groups of subspecies differ so distinctly in the head-patterns and back-colours of the males that they are 'perhaps better considered' separate species (*BWP*, *CBWP*, but see also Collinson 2001). European Chaffinches have also been introduced to New Zealand and South Africa.

In Europe, where the breeding population, excluding that of Russia, has been estimated at 80 to 96 million pairs (*EBCC Atlas*), Chaffinches are found in all types of forest, but usually in the more open areas and on the edges, as well as in small woods, farmland, parks, gardens and orchards. With such a wide range of habitats and a very varied diet, they are among this continent's commonest birds. Nearly all Chaffinches in north and east Europe migrate to southern and southwestern parts of the species' breeding range for the winter, and those in Siberia go still farther south.

Smith (1887) reported this finch to be 'As common as the Sparrow, and as well known to everybody' in 19th century Wiltshire. The *1875–1900 Atlas*, which showed it as abundant and widespread throughout most of Great Britain during the latter part of that century, also stated that Chaffinches were able to profit from the growth of arable farming through much of the 18th and 19th centuries, since weed seeds and spilt grain are important food resources for them. Because of their predilection for seeds, Chaffinches are vulnerable to agricultural chemicals, particularly seed-dressings based on organo-chlorines – which are considered to have been instrumental in a decline in this and a number of other species nearly everywhere in Great Britain around 1960 (Newton 1972). National survey data have, however, subsequently shown rapid rises in numbers since the early 1970s, which have stabilised since 1990; in general, Chaffinches have been less affected by agricultural intensification than some other species, because they do not depend to the same extent on open-field habitats, and this slowing of their population increase is associated with a reduction in their annual survival, which is perhaps density-dependent (*BBWC*).

An analysis of ringing data by Newton (1972) showed that British Chaffinches were essentially sedentary: 90 per cent moved no more than 5 km from their birthplace and the rest no more than 50 km, the more distant mostly in their first year. The *Migration Atlas*, which examined a much larger set of recoveries, confirmed Newton's findings, adding that the median distance moved by those ringed during May–July was, at any season, less than 1 km. (It should be added, however, that Chaffinches ringed in the breeding season in northern Britain were found to have a tendency to move farther than those ringed in the south, especially in autumn.) Thus, it is not surprising that, of 4926 Chaffinches ringed in Wiltshire during 1965–2000 – the great majority as adults – 32 of the 35 recoveries within Great Britain had moved no more than 9 km. But the population is roughly doubled in winter by the arrival of many others from Fenno-Scandia and northwest Russia (*Migration Atlas*). Midwinter numbers in Britain and Ireland have been estimated at some 30 million (*1981–84 Winter Atlas*).

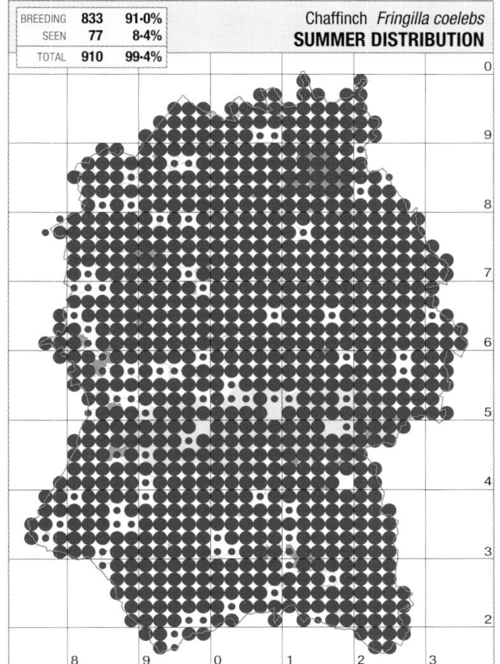

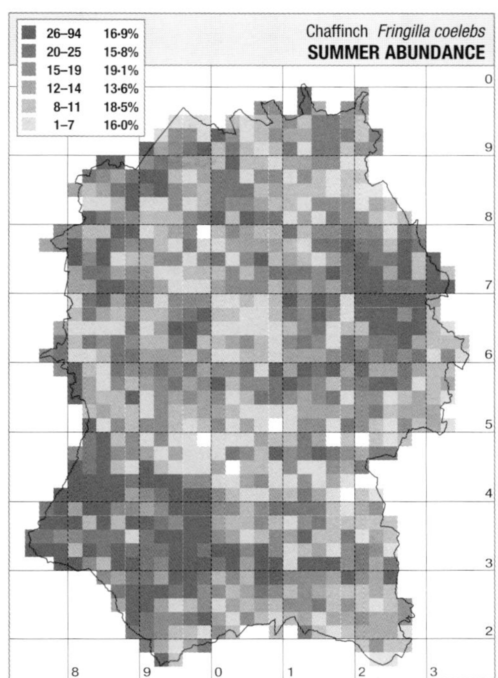

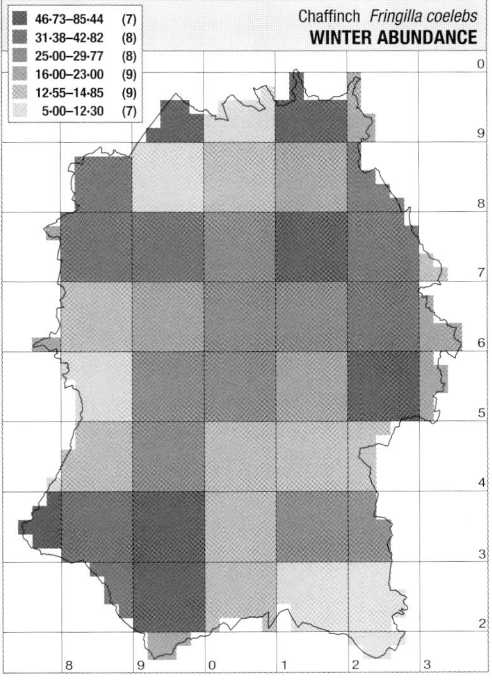

The resident population breeds almost throughout Great Britain, being absent only from the Scottish islands, though the species is scarce in upland areas and anywhere that trees are few (*1988–91 Atlas*). In winter, the largest numbers of Chaffinches are found in southern England, Wales and, perhaps more unexpectedly, much of eastern and southern Scotland (*1981–84 Winter Atlas*). Some evidence of the sources of Wiltshire's winter visitors was provided by the recoveries in Sweden (caught by a cat) and in Norway (found dead), both in August 1985, of two Chaffinches that had been ringed at Bratton and Westbury in March and November 1983 respectively; and, still farther east, a female retrapped and released at Lyokki (Finland) in May 1990 had first been ringed at Westbury in February 1987. Another female ringed near Mandal (Norway) in April 1992 was found dead at Broad Hinton in January 1994. Three more Chaffinches ringed in winter in Wiltshire have been recovered on autumn or spring passage in Belgium (two) and Germany; and there have also been winter recoveries here of three marked in autumn, in Belgium (one) and the Netherlands (two). Most records published in *Hobby* concern winter flock sizes, and these vary from year to year, partly depending on the supply of beechmast, which is a favourite food at that season. Some of the largest flocks have included 750 at Wilton in December 1980, 400 at Hannington in October 2000 and, in January 1985, a massive 2880 in Savernake and 1000 at Warminster. Sites where winter flocks are reported regularly include Ashton Keynes, Little Hinton, Barbury Castle, Hackpen, Savernake Forest, Pewsey Downs, Roundway Hill, Larkhill, Imber, and Longbridge Deverill. Doubtless some of these flocks – which tend to dwindle in size towards the spring – involve Fenno-Scandian immigrants, but one of 150 at Whaddon, near Salisbury, on 18 August 2000 was too early for that and clearly local.

The *1968–72* and *1988–91 Atlases*, and the *1981–84 Winter* Atlas, all mapped Chaffinches in every 10-km square of Wiltshire. The summer distribution map for 1995–2000 confirms this, and its much greater detail shows them to be absent only from four tetrads on Salisbury Plain and from one part-tetrad in the northeast corner. Only Wood Pigeon (recorded in 912 tetrads) was more widespread, and only Blackbird was found breeding in more tetrads (847) in the county than Chaffinch. The summer and winter abundance maps both indicate that, as might be expected, this species is commonest in such well-wooded areas as Savernake and the southwest, and scarcest in open and sparsely wooded habitats. Applying the densities found during local surveys using BBS methodology, Wiltshire's breeding population currently lies in the region of 78,100 to 160,000 pairs, perhaps as much as roughly three per cent of the British population of 5·6 million territories (*APEP*). Winter numbers, calculated from the ratio of timed winter to summer counts, are probably between 182,000 and 374,000 individuals.

MVJ

Brambling

Fringilla montifringilla

Winter visitor, in very variable numbers, from Fenno-Scandia

This colourful and unmistakable finch breeds mainly in birch woods and open conifer forests right across boreal and subarctic Eurasia from Fenno-Scandia to Kamchatka, and is most numerous near the limits of tree growth, whether at high latitudes or at high altitudes (Newton 1972). The numbers of Bramblings breeding in Europe, excluding Russia, have been estimated at 4·0 to 5·8 million pairs (*EBCC Atlas*). In autumn, all populations move south of the breeding range and, in Europe, winter widely from southern Sweden west to Britain and Ireland, south to Iberia and the north Mediterranean, and southeast to Turkey and the Caucasus, extending also to northwest Africa and Israel. In Great Britain, where odd pairs do nest rarely – just one singing male was found in Scotland in 2000, for example (*RBBP*) – they are widespread if patchily distributed winter visitors. Numbers vary greatly, perhaps as few in total as 50,000 or as many as two million in different winters (*1981–84 Winter Atlas*).

In winter – often in company with Chaffinches, their closest relatives – these finches particularly favour beech woodland, where they feed on beechmast, and will also regularly forage in weedy stubbles; they take a variety of other seeds, such as alder and flax, even spruce and rowan, and opportunistically turn to garden feeders, particularly later on when the beechmast may be depleted. Therefore, it is no surprise that the winter map for 1998–

2000 shows them to be more numerous in areas with beech woodland, especially in the southwest, nor that *Hobby* has often recorded Bramblings visiting garden feeding stations. But numbers are essentially very variable, corresponding with variations in the beechmast crop both here and on the Continent, and with the severity of the winter weather.

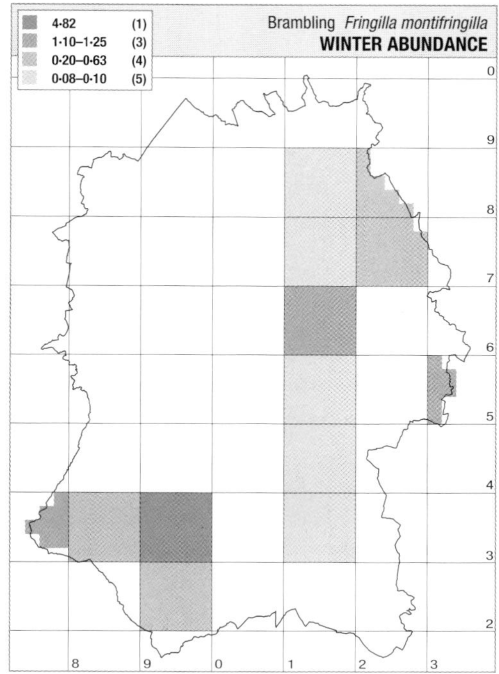

The *1981–84 Winter Atlas* mapped Bramblings in all but six of Wiltshire's 48 core and part 10-km squares. The fact that the winter tetrad survey of 1998–2000 found them in only 13 of the 48 core was likely to be a consequence of the survey methods, but those last two winters happened also to be 'poor' for Bramblings. The 27 winters from 1973/74 to 1999/00 included nine in which the numbers were generally low in Wiltshire (1974/75, three consecutively in 1976/77–1979/80, two consecutively in 1982/83–1983/84, 1996/97 and, unfortunately for the WOS winter survey, two consecutively in 1998/99–1999/2000); but also 11 in which they were generally high (1973/74, 1975/76, two consecutively in 1980/81–1981/82, three consecutively in 1984/85–1986/87 and again in 1993/94–1995/96, and 1997/98). (Numbers could be described as moderate in the remaining seven winters.) Extrapolation from the winter survey counts confirmed that numbers were low then and amounted to little over 200 individuals; numbers in good years might be expected to reach, and perhaps even exceed, 5000.

In 19th century Wiltshire, Smith (1887) reported that the Brambling (which he preferred to call the 'Mountain Finch') occurred 'so frequently as to be by no means uncommon', though its visits to the county were 'most irregular… several consecutive winters often elapse without… a single individual'. He listed a number of localities where the species had occurred, including his own garden in Yatesbury where he shot one 'out of a small flock… occupying some larch trees'. He quoted a *MCNHS Report* about 'vast numbers' in the Marlborough area in early February 1873, 'when thirty-five were secured at a single shot'. Earlier, Morres (1878–85) had reported that in 1868 'these birds visited our neighbourhood [the Salisbury area] in vast numbers, one might say, in thousands. Forty were killed by a man, at one shot'. Further, that a bird-catcher 'caught six or seven dozen in a day at Pentridge [in fact, just inside Dorset] and could have caught, he tells me, as many more as he liked, but not being good songsters, he did not care for them'.

Many other local writers, including Peirson (1959), have remarked on the irregular nature of the Brambling's arrival dates and the numbers involved. No flocks 'amounting to thousands' have been noted since the 19th century; indeed, just 18 of 100 or more were recorded during 1929–73 (*WANHM*) and only 35 during 1974–2000 (*Hobby*). In the latter period, the most frequently mentioned wintering sites were Ravensroost Wood, Aldbourne, Wick Down on the Marlborough Downs, Hens Wood, Savernake, Bowood, Great Ridge Wood and Porton; the largest concentrations were 300 at Lydiard Millicent on 1 February 1976 and 400 in Savernake on 2 November 1997; but only four of the 35 flocks of 100 or more were in November–December, compared with 20 in January–February and 11 in March–April. Thus, the bigger numbers are usually in the second half of the winter through into early spring, but it is more usual to find ones and twos, perhaps up to 30 or 50. Bramblings may occur in Wiltshire at any time from October to April inclusive, the county's earliest and latest dates in the 20th century being 2 October 1966 and 11 May 1988.

A total of 136 Bramblings was ringed in the county during 1965–2000 – including 44 in one Chippenham garden during January–February 1982. One of these, and another ringed before the 1939–45 War, both males, were recovered in Belgium one and two winters later: the more recent, marked at Edington on 7 February 1986, was trapped and released again at Wolfsdonk (Brabant) on 12 February 1987; the earlier one, ringed at Netheravon on 20 February 1938, was simply 'captured' at Mol (Antwerp) on 2 November 1939. Two more, ringed in Hampshire and Somerset in 1957 and 1987, were recovered in Wiltshire later in the same winters.

MVJ

Serin

Serinus serinus

Overshooting summer vagrant (1 record), breeds Europe north to Channel coast and irregularly south England

A male singing by the Wylye south of Codford St Mary on 4 May 1998 (Ferguson-Lees 2000) is the only Wiltshire record of this small finch. Breeding in continental Europe – where some 10–13 million pairs are estimated (*EBCC Atlas*) – as well as in northwest Africa and Asia Minor, Serins are resident in Mediterranean countries and lowland France, but only summer visitors north and east from central Europe. The absence of previous Wiltshire records is perhaps surprising, because this species began to spread slowly from southern Europe around the 1840s and reached southernmost Fenno-Scandia and the Baltic States about 100 years later.

Serins have occurred annually in English south coast counties from the late 1960s, when pairs also bred in Dorset and Sussex, and five to nine pairs were recorded every year from the late 1970s through much of the 1980s – some nesting, most regularly in Devon – while singing males reached as far north as Shropshire and East Anglia (*RBBP*). The 1990s saw much less evidence of breeding, but many more casual records – at an annual average of 68 individuals – in line with the increase on the Continent; most were in southern and southeast England, and the majority occurred as overshooting spring migrants (Fraser *et al* 2000, Fraser & Rogers 2002).

IJF-L

Greenfinch

Carduelis chloris

Common resident, especially at urban edges, more widespread in winter

The Greenfinch must rank as one of Wiltshire's commoner garden birds – the male easily recognised by its green and yellow plumage and by its distinctive trills and nasal *tsweee* in spring – and it is a frequent visitor to hanging nut baskets and bird-tables in winter.

Greenfinches occur naturally from the Canaries, Madeira and northwest Africa almost throughout Europe (except for much of the far north) and east into central Asia; they have also been introduced into the Azores, New Zealand, southeast Australia and Argentina. In Europe, though originally a species of bushy areas and forest edge, the Greenfinch has since 1950 become increasingly common in towns and villages, and has also spread northwards; the breeding population of Europe, excluding that of Russia, has been put at 12 to 15 million pairs and is thought to be stable (*EBCC Atlas*). It is estimated that there are some 695,000 territories in Great Britain (*APEP*), where it is widely distributed, though absent from treeless areas of central Wales and north and west Scotland (*1988–91 Atlas*); national abundance has varied little since the 1960s, but data from CBC and BBS indicate an increase from the mid 1980s (*BBWC*).

In Wiltshire, Smith (1887) described Greenfinches as 'extremely common throughout'. No assessment of status was given in early bird reports in *WANHM*, either before or after the 1939–45 War, but Peirson (1919) considered this species to be 'An abundant resident' in the Marlborough district, and some 40 years later thought it 'A very common resident' in the county as a whole, often seen in winter in 'considerable flocks' (Peirson 1959). Both the *1968–72* and *1988–91 Atlases*, and the *1981–84 Winter Atlas*, confirmed these assessments, all mapping Greenfinches in every one of the county's 33 core and 15 part 10-km squares.

The fine detail of the summer distribution map for 1995–2000, however, shows them to be absent from most of Salisbury Plain and other areas of higher ground, and the abundance map demonstrates that they are otherwise only patchily common, but areas of high density include some of the conurbations, such as Swindon, Malmesbury and Chippenham, as well as along much of the Cotswolds to the west of the last two towns. The results of surveys in adjacent counties using BBS methods suggest that the Wiltshire population lies between 24,600 and 50,500 pairs. This would constitute as much as seven per cent of the British total, a remarkably high proportion of the national figure given the size of Wiltshire and the apparent relative scarcity of the species in the county as shown by the *1988–91 Atlas*.

Extrapolation from the winter survey counts in 1998–2000, and the ratio of winter to summer counts, suggest a total of 37,500 to 77,100 individuals at that season. The winter map broadly matches that of summer in indicating that Greenfinches are less common in the south of the county, but shows apparent contradictions, too: seemingly fewer in certain towns – notably Swindon and Malmesbury – and higher numbers in some downland areas, around Marlborough and the north of Salisbury Plain.

Large flocks outwith the breeding season have included 'hundreds … in the stubbles during October and November' 1933 in the Figheldean area; and estimates of 300 at Burcombe on 2 February 1962 and 300 in Oakhill Water Meadows during September–October 1964; of up to 1200 at Chippenham in January 1982 (in the course of which

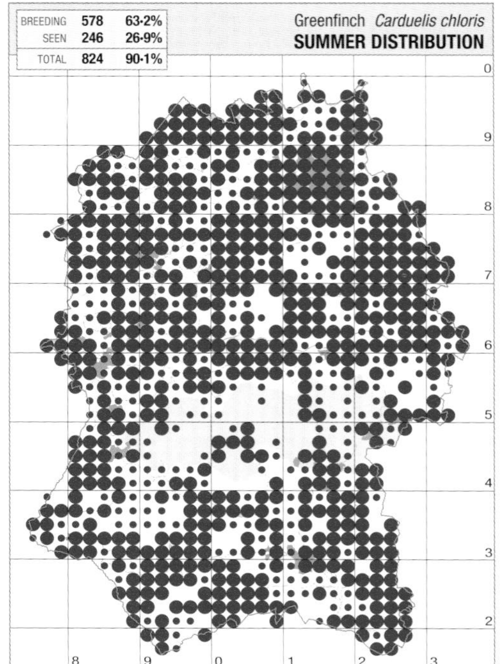

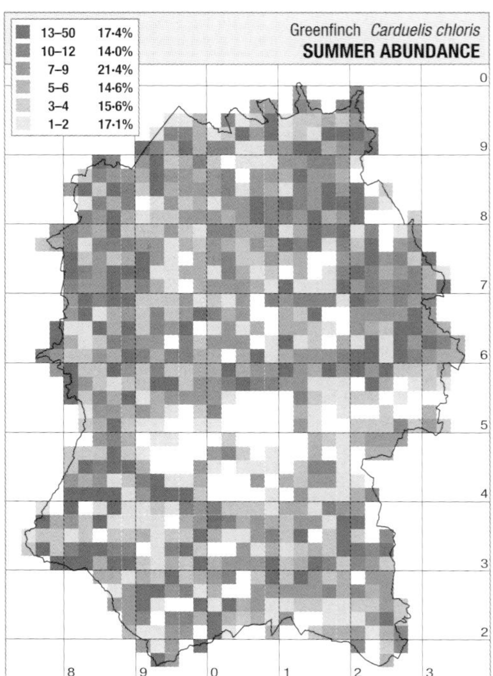

month 1034 were ringed there: see below) and 400 at Wick Down on the Marlborough Downs in January 1987; of 1000 at Barbury Castle on 16 October 1992, 500 at Tan Hill on 1 October 1994, 900 at Stanton St Bernard on 4 February 1996 and 450 at Hannington on 16 November 2000 (*WANHM*, *Hobby*). Communal roosts sometimes reach three figures, too: for example, 200 at Everleigh in January 1984, 175 at Longleat in February 1984 and 150 at Swindon STW on 13 January 1997.

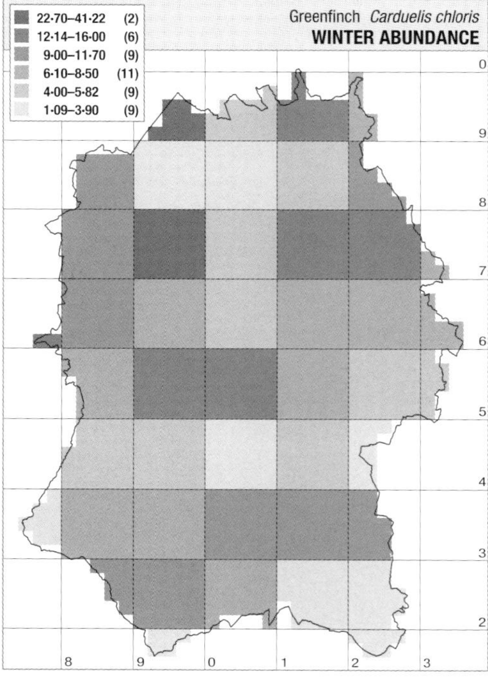

A total of 15,576 Greenfinches was ringed in Wiltshire during 1965–2000 – the county's second highest figure for any species (but still little more than half of that for Blue Tits). Although most British Greenfinches make no significant seasonal movements and few ringing recoveries exceed 20 km (*Migration Atlas*), the many exceptions to this rule tend to show southwesterly directions in autumn, and northeasterly in spring. During the winters of 1980/81 and 1981/82, an intensive ringing programme at Chippenham 'processed' over 2000 Greenfinches. Analysis of the results also took account of six winter recoveries (found dead or injured) or controls (retrapped and released) in a broad 'Chippenham area' (west to Bristol and north Somerset) of others ringed elsewhere in spring or summer at that time. The analysis showed clearly that many Greenfinches that breed in East Anglia, west to Oxfordshire, do move southwest to winter in north Wiltshire and adjacent counties farther west, and return northeast in spring (Kersley & Marsh 1983). There was, indeed, a particular concentration of Chippenham returns from Epping Forest and the Chelmsford area (Essex). Of 41 recoveries and controls in one or other of the two subsequent springs or summers, 25 showed clear movements. Except for three in Bristol, Pembrokeshire and Kent, the other 22 had come from, or were moving back to, a variety of sites lying between two diverging lines, one northeast to the Wash (Norfolk/Lincolnshire) and the other east-northeast to the Blackwater Estuary (Essex). One ringed at Westbury on 14 February 1982 was retrapped at Ongar (Essex) 21 days later. It is worth adding that, of the 41 recoveries in this analysis, ten were retrapped elsewhere, five were road casualties, 12 were simply 'found dead' without a cause being specified, and no fewer than 14 (34 per cent) were killed by cats.

Subsequent ringing returns have confirmed East Anglia as a regular source of a number of the county's winter Greenfinches. There have been still more recoveries of Wiltshire-ringed individuals from there and from counties in the intervening corridor, such as Cambridgeshire, Northamptonshire, Hertfordshire and Buckinghamshire, and recoveries in Wiltshire of others ringed in Norfolk, Essex, Hertfordshire and Oxfordshire. One individual marked at Bromham on 23 December 1984 was shot near Beccles (Suffolk) on 29 June 1985.

At the same time, other counties with outward or inward recoveries of Wiltshire Greenfinches, apart from the exceptions already mentioned, now include Warwickshire and Leicestershire to the north of the corridor and East Sussex, Surrey, Hampshire, Dorset and Devon to the south. The last of these presumably indicates that some East Anglian Greenfinches move on through to the southwest peninsula. In this connection, too, an adult male found dead at Dauntsey on 16 August 1996 had been ringed on Jersey (Channel Islands) on 24 February that year and is the only recovery in Wiltshire from across the Channel. But the British total of outward or inward Greenfinch recoveries involving France or the Channel Islands was as high as 143 by the end of 2000.

MVJ

Sponsored by Professor John Lawton

Goldfinch
Carduelis carduelis

Common resident, especially at urban edges, more widespread in winter

Brightly coloured Goldfinches and their liquid, trisyllabic, twittering calls have long gladdened the hearts of country folk. They tend to be associated in people's minds with seeding thistle heads, but they live largely on seeds of many different herbs and trees throughout the year and have constantly to move from one species to another as the seeds start to ripen. Among the food plants noted in *Hobby* have been burdock, dandelion, evening primrose, flax, knapweed, lavender, mugwort, pyracantha, ragwort, rudbeckia and teasel, but the list could be almost endless. In winter they turn mainly to alder and pine seeds, but readily take to nyjer and sunflower seeds in garden feeders. They are particularly agile in climbing plants and make much use of their feet to hold down stalks as they stretch for the seed-heads.

These little finches are found from the Atlantic Islands and North Africa throughout most of Europe (except much of Fenno-Scandia and northern Russia) east in Asia as far as Lake Baikal and western Mongolia, and from Asia Minor and parts of the Middle East to the western Himalayas; their undeniable attractiveness has also seen them introduced into Bermuda, Argentina, southern Australia and New Zealand. In Europe, apart from some range expansion north and south, the population is believed to have remained stable since 1975 and, excluding Russia, has been estimated at 7·2 to 9·8 million pairs (*EBCC Atlas*).

In Great Britain, Goldfinches expanded northwards in Scotland between the periods of the *1968–72* and *1988–91 Atlas* surveys, though they are still most numerous in England and Wales. Some 80 per cent of British breeders migrate to winter in Belgium, France and Spain (Newton 1972), but it has been suggested that there are no fixed wintering areas and this species simply stops where it finds conditions appropriate (*Migration Atlas*). A sharp fall in population from the mid 1970s to the mid 1980s has been followed by a significant rise, accompanied by greater use of gardens in winter (*BBWC*). The earlier decrease may have been linked to lower annual survival rates, perhaps caused by agricultural intensification and hunting pressure on the Continent.

In Wiltshire, Smith (1887) noted that, during his 'early days', the Goldfinch was 'quite common throughout the county, though never so abundant as to beget too great familiarity', but went on to add that 'it is diminishing rapidly... within my own memory not nearly so abundant as when I was young'. For this decline he blamed loss of habitat, 'as every year... waste lands and commons taken into cultivation, and thistle beds done away with'. The *1875–1900 Atlas* cited this colourful finch's enormous popularity as a cage-bird – huge numbers were trapped for sale – as another cause of decline; it was not until the end of the 19th century and beginning of the 20th that the population began to recover, as persecution by birdcatchers lessened following a series of bird protection acts, and as land fell out of cultivation during the agricultural depression. The 1929 bird report in *WANHM* found the species 'common' and commented that it had 'increased considerably during the last few years'. Peirson (1959) noted 'large and irregular fluctuations both in its numbers and in its distribution' and that many 'were killed in the cold of 1947'. (The winter of 1946/47 was one of the two most severe and prolonged since the 1939–45 War.) The *1968–72* and *1988–91 Atlases* and the *1981–84 Winter Atlas* all recorded Goldfinches in every one of the county's 33 core and 15 part 10-km squares.

The summer distribution map for 1995–2000 shows evidence of breeding in just under half of all tetrads and includes notable areas of continuous breeding distribution around Swindon and Tisbury in particular, perhaps also along much of the western part of the Kennet & Avon Canal. The summer abundance map reveals them to be more numerous in the southwest – especially in the Warminster to Longleat area, and the Vale of Wardour – and in the northeast. Goldfinches penetrate villages and towns, breeding in large gardens and parks, but are often absent from intensively farmed land, as well as from the Cotswolds around the By Brook and from parts of Salisbury Plain where breeding habitat is scarce. Breeding densities from local surveys, using BBS methods in this and adjacent counties, produces an estimate of 18,100 to 27,100 pairs in Wiltshire as a whole. That represents about 9–14 per cent of the British population, which was estimated at 199,000 territories in 2000 (*APEP*), and suggests that, as in the case of the Greenfinch, Wiltshire is a particularly important area for this species – although the *1988–91 Atlas* mapped several areas of the county as having relatively low densities of Goldfinches.

The winter map for 1998–2000 demonstrates a distinct southerly bias at that season, when flocks frequent such open areas as Salisbury Plain and Cranborne Chase, and extrapolation from the 2-hour winter counts, and the ratio of summer to winter counts during WOS surveys, suggests a total then in the region of 30,000 to 44,900 individuals. Reports of Goldfinches

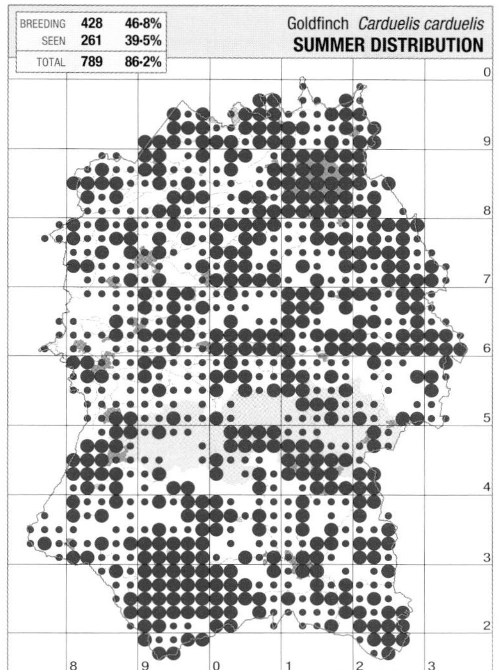

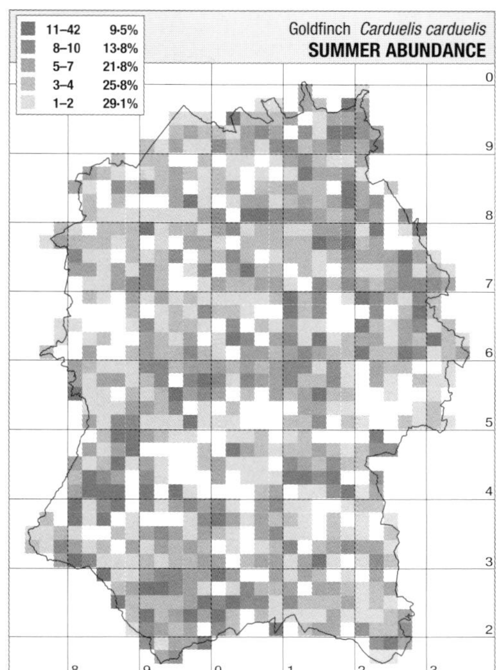

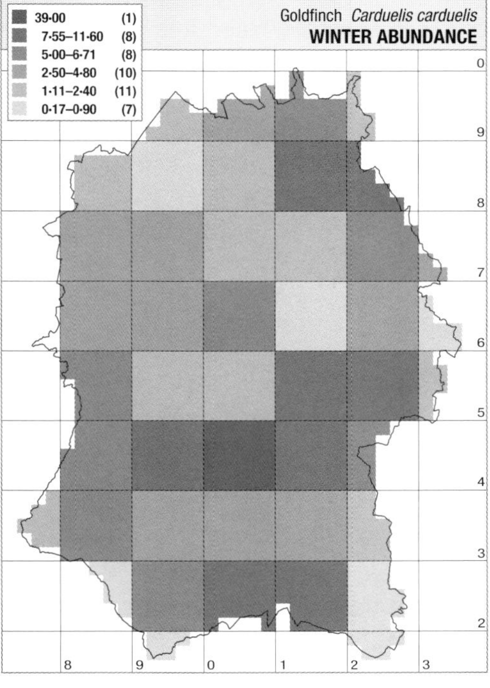

in *WANHM* and *Hobby* have always been concerned mainly with the apparent success or otherwise of the breeding season and with flock sizes. Flocking has been recorded from late June – though three-figure counts are scarce before September – through to December and again from February, or even January, through to March or early April. More recent examples of large flocks in those periods include 300 at Hens Wood in March 1993, 200 at Figheldean at the beginning of December 1993, 300 at SPTA (Centre) in October 1994, 300 at Parsonage Down in September 1995, 200 at Trowbridge in September 1996, and 200 again at Parsonage Down in September 1999.

The high proportion of larger counts in September and October may indicate movements through the county of Goldfinches from northern Britain en route to wintering grounds in France and Iberia; and a 'noticeable passage' at Bratton on 12 October 1991 coincided with an influx of Sky Larks and Meadow Pipits. But many British Goldfinches remain in Great Britain during the winter – small parties sometimes associating with Siskins and Lesser Redpolls in alders and conifers – and there is little evidence of immigration from the Continent (*Migration Atlas*). Only 12 of the 1108 Goldfinches ringed in Wiltshire during 1965–2000 had been recovered by the end of that period: five of those were in southern England, four in France and two in Spain, but a juvenile ringed at East Tytherton on 14 August 1983 and recovered at Sidi Kacem (Morocco) on 29 December that year had travelled a distance of 1139 km. Particularly interesting, too, was a much earlier record of a nestling ringed in Marlborough on 3 July 1930 and recovered 472 km away at Kinsale (Co. Cork) on 26 February 1931 – still one of only two recoveries of British-ringed Goldfinches in the Republic of Ireland.

Midwinter flocks in late December and January are generally smaller, such as 100 near Shrewton on 28 December 1982, 100 at Chirton Gorse on 2 January 1983, and 50 at SPTA (Centre) and Clarendon Lake in January 1985. Then, as is the case with other finches, larger flocks in the late winter and early spring provide some evidence of vernal passage. For example, 35 at Hens Wood in February 1988 rose to 90 in March and 120 on 4 April, and a flock of 120 reported there on 20 March 1994 increased to 500 on 27 March before reducing again to 225 on 16 April.

MVJ

Sponsored by Clive Power

Siskin
Carduelis spinus

Common winter visitor from north Britain/Europe, now breeds very locally

A compact and lively little finch, the Siskin breeds in the northern half of Europe and in southern mountains from the Pyrenees through to Asia Minor and northern Iran, as well as discontinuously across Asia to Sakhalin and north Japan. It nests in conifers, perhaps most commonly in spruce, but in southeast Wiltshire in larches and silver and Douglas firs (P Combridge). The population of Europe, excluding Russia, has been put at 2·2 to 3·7 million pairs, the majority in Fenno-Scandia (*EBCC Atlas*). Those in north Scotland and northern and eastern Europe move south and southwest for the winter, many reaching southern England.

In the 19th century, Siskins breeding in Great Britain were confined largely to Scotland's native pine forests, though there had been records in north Wales and Surrey (*1875–1900 Atlas*). Some local declines in numbers are thought likely to have taken place in the late 19th and early 20th centuries, as a result of the felling of conifer woodlands and the activities of birdcatchers (*1968–72 Atlas*), but breeding was regular in northern England by the 1930s. A spread of new conifer plantations led to a major increase in Scotland, Wales and parts of England from about 1950 (*BWP*), and by the time of the *1968–72 Atlas* the British breeding population was thought to be in the range of 20,000 to 40,000 pairs. This increase continued, and the *1988–91 Atlas* estimated 300,000 pairs, still mostly in Scotland, Wales and northern England. BBS data indicate that numbers have fluctuated, but that there has been no significant change in population size since 1994 (*BBWC*), and the total in 2000 was estimated as 357,000 pairs (*APEP*).

In Wiltshire, Smith (1887) noted that the Siskin was 'Better known…as a cage bird', but described it as a winter visitor 'by no means rare…appearing…almost every year…sometimes in great numbers'. He also quoted the Reverend AP Morres as believing

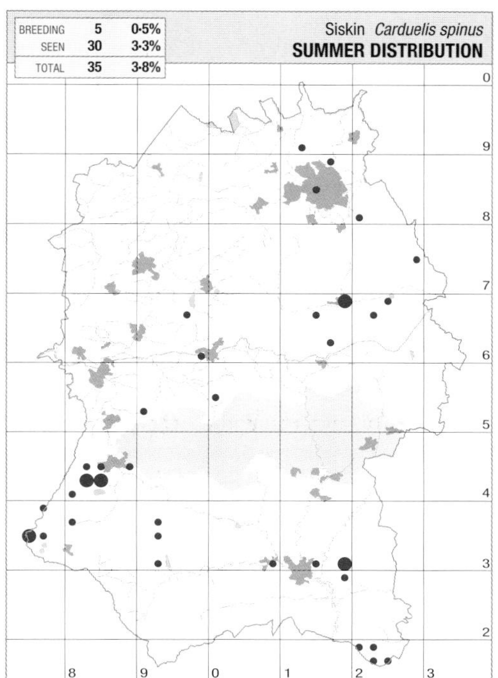

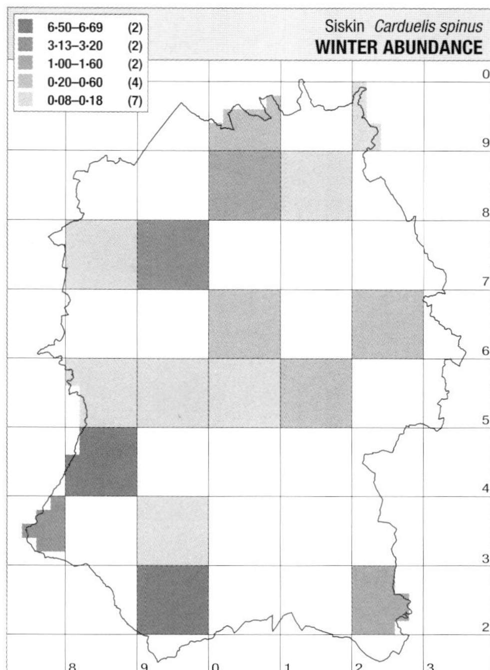

that Siskins occasionally bred here, because a birdcatcher in his Britford parish had trapped a party of seven that included 'five evidently young' in July 1871; Morres also believed that they had nested in the neighbouring parish of Nunton. But Witherby *et al* (1938–41) considered that breeding 'exceptionally in Berkshire, Surrey, Sussex, Kent and other southern counties' was 'in most cases in abnormal sites and probably due to escaped caged birds'.

The 1929 Wiltshire bird report thought Siskins to be merely 'occasional and irregular' visitors, but in 1936 they were 'Very common as a winter visitor in South Wilts' (*WANHM*). Peirson (1959), although describing them as winter visitors, quoted Morres's reference to the family of seven in July 1871 (but incorrectly ascribed it to Broad Chalke) and also 'a party of young birds considered to have been Siskins' at East Grimstead on 21 August 1950, commenting that this species 'might one day be proved to breed'. Although the *1968–72 Atlas* did not find any evidence of nesting in Wiltshire, a change in status was soon under way and Buxton (1981) felt able to state that 'There have been a few records suggesting that breeding may have taken place but this has not yet been confirmed'. He also commented that 'During the past fifteen years there has been a marked increase in the numbers wintering', and the *1981–84 Winter Atlas* found them in all but seven of the county's 33 core and 15 part 10-km squares.

In 1984, one was seen in Franchises Wood as late as 16 May; and a pair visited a garden at Redlynch all summer, juveniles later being seen there. Further records followed in southeast Wiltshire woodlands in May and June of both 1985 and 1986, and in 1987 a female was watched collecting nesting material at Franchises Wood. That same year, a male was singing on 16 May in the northeast of the county, at Hens Wood. Juveniles were seen at Shear Water in June 1988 and breeding took place in the Shear Water–Center Parcs–Heaven's Gate area of Longleat in every subsequent year through to the end of the millennium. At Center Parcs alone – where the establishment of the forest holiday centre in 1994 has provided ideal 'edge' habitats for this species in both summer and winter – 34 territories were reported in 1997, 18 in 1998, and 12 each in 1999 and 2000 (Collins 2005), though it is not clear how strict were the criteria applied in the first of those years. Elsewhere in the county, there have been observations in the breeding season since the late 1980s in several woodlands between Salisbury and the Hampshire border, and at Stourhead, Alfred's Tower, West Woods and Great Ridge Wood. Although breeding has been proved only in a few of these areas, it is likely to be more widespread than the summer map suggests, as this finch builds one of the most difficult of all passerine nests to find (*eg* Campbell & Ferguson-Lees 1972).

In connection with the earlier comment by Witherby *et al* (1938–41), it is interesting to note that an adult male Siskin caught at Shear Water on 14 April 1988 was found to be wearing an avicultural ring (BC44017) and, being trapped again on the 25th, was thought to be breeding as it was the only one of 84 Siskins (and 93 Lesser Redpolls) to be retrapped in that February–May period; two female Siskins with brood patches and a total of four juveniles were also caught there in May (Creighton 1989). Others of the 83 ringed at Shear Water earlier in that period were clearly winter visitors. First, one ringed on 6 April was retrapped and released near Selby (North Yorkshire) on 14 May, when it was probably in its breeding territory. Secondly, a female ringed on 13 March 1988 was twice retrapped at a site in Limburg (the Netherlands) in October and December of that same year. Thirdly, and most spectacular of all the recoveries of the Siskins caught at Shear Water in spring 1988, an adult male ringed on 6 April was found in captivity in Algeria on 29 March 1989, then released and subsequently retrapped at Flackwell Heath (Buckinghamshire) in February 1990 (BTO data). During 1965–2000, including those at Shear Water, a total of 267 Siskins was ringed in Wiltshire, of which five others were recovered within Great Britain: two each in Scotland (Borders and Grampian regions) and Surrey, and one in Oxfordshire. In addition, one ringed at Oisterwijk (Netherlands) on 8 October 1993 was recovered at Alderbury on 26 February 1996. Thus, Wiltshire ringing recoveries reflect both the influx of Fenno-Scandian breeders during winter – known to reach England via the Low Countries – and the departure of some local breeders to Iberia and adjacent North Africa (*Migration Atlas*).

The *1988–91 Atlas* recorded Siskins in ten of Wiltshire's 33 core 10-km squares, but with breeding proved in only one. The summer tetrad map for 1995–2000 shows breeding evidence in four 10-km squares (three of them core) and emphasises the localised nature of their distribution in the county. Siskins are largely dependent for food on the seeds of conifers in the breeding season and thus populations fluctuate in relation to the cone crop (*BWP*). With all these factors in mind, it seems unlikely that the county's population amounted to more than 20–50 pairs in any year of the summer survey. Siskins continue to be more commonly encountered in Wiltshire as passage and winter visitors, often feeding with Lesser Redpolls in waterside alders, although they also frequent other food sources such as birch, larch and, increasingly, peanut-feeders in gardens (especially in February and March). Passage is normally at its greatest in March and October, but is variable from year to year. For example, unprecedented numbers were recorded in September 1997, when records from 22 sites included 200 at Ravensroost Wood on 7th, 138 at Franchises Wood on 18th and 180 at Hens Wood on 24th. Most of the 84 Siskins ringed at Shear Water in spring 1988 were trapped in the first two-thirds of March – many of them already heavier than the mean lean weight for this species – indicating that that was the time of peak passage, over a month earlier than that of the Lesser Redpolls (Creighton 1989).

Wintering totals likewise vary annually, though the largest flocks occur mainly in the second half of winter (January to March), rather than in the first half – a pattern also noted by Peirson (1959), who wrote that higher numbers were found more often 'after Christmas than before it'. In autumn through to spring, records are widespread across Wiltshire, the biggest concentrations being most regularly reported from Shear Water northwest through the Longleat plantations and in Hens Wood. In the former area, concentrations of over 200 were recorded nine times during 1974–2000, the highest total being 500 in four flocks on

20 March 1994. At Hens Wood, however, that number has been equalled on at least four occasions, including a county record of 650 on 7 March 1993. Extrapolation from the 2-hour counts of the 1998–2000 survey, on the basis of the ratio of timed counts to estimates for other finch species, suggests a county total in the region of 3170 to 5820, a relatively large proportion of the estimate that 'In some years, certainly, well over 150,000 Siskins must be wintering in Great Britain and Ireland' (*1981–84 Winter Atlas*). The winter survey map, though recording this species in fewer 10-km squares than the *1981–84 Winter Atlas* did, nevertheless shows its distribution to be widespread if patchy.

(See also page 725.)

GDP

Sponsored by the Gaca family

Linnet

Carduelis cannabina

Seriously decreasing resident, also passage migrant and winter visitor

Linnets are now of high conservation concern in Great Britain. National survey data show a rapid decline during the last part of the 20th century, evident especially from the mid 1970s to the mid 1980s, and – although, more recently, the population as a whole has been largely stable (*BBWC*), with the estimate of 535,000 territories in 2000 (*APEP*) little different from the 520,000 of the *1988–91 Atlas* – CES and BBS data indicate further decreases in England during the 1990s. Poor breeding performance has been suggested as a cause, possibly as a result of deterioration in hedgerow quality, and a decline of rough grassland with thorn bushes, thus limiting areas of suitable extensive cover for this frequently social nester. The *1988–91 Atlas* showed them to be widely distributed – except in large areas of northwest and central Scotland where the range had contracted since the *1968–72 Atlas* – and the highest densities were mainly in east coastal counties from Kent to Aberdeenshire, and to a lesser extent more patchily in essentially seaside squares in the west and south.

Otherwise, Linnets breed in the Canary Islands and Madeira, and from Iberia and much of the Mediterranean region north to southern Fenno-Scandia and north-central Russia, thence east into west Siberia, central Asia, Iran and Afghanistan. The breeding population of Europe, excluding Russia, has been estimated at 7·1 to 9·1 million pairs (*EBCC Atlas*). Fenno-Scandian and east European populations are essentially migratory, wintering in the south of the species' range. Even British Linnets are partial migrants and, while some are known to remain within Great Britain in winter, others migrate to western France, Spain and Morocco (*Migration Atlas*).

In this connection, two Wiltshire-ringed Linnets have been reported from France and three from Spain. Both French recoveries were shot in the province of Gironde in October of the year of ringing, the first having been marked as a nestling at Porton in May 1961 (*WANHM*, *BB* 56: 538), and the second as a juvenile female at Winterbourne, near Salisbury, in August 1966. The first Spanish recovery had been ringed near Salisbury on 14 April 1962 and was found dead in the Basque province of Vizcaya a year and six days later. The other two, like those in France, survived only until October of the year

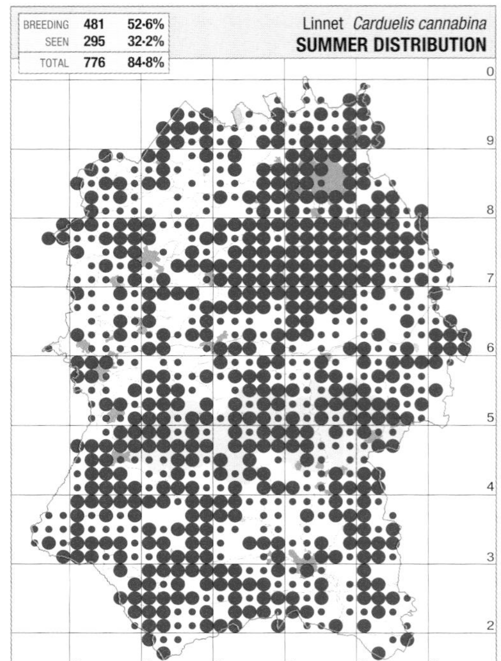

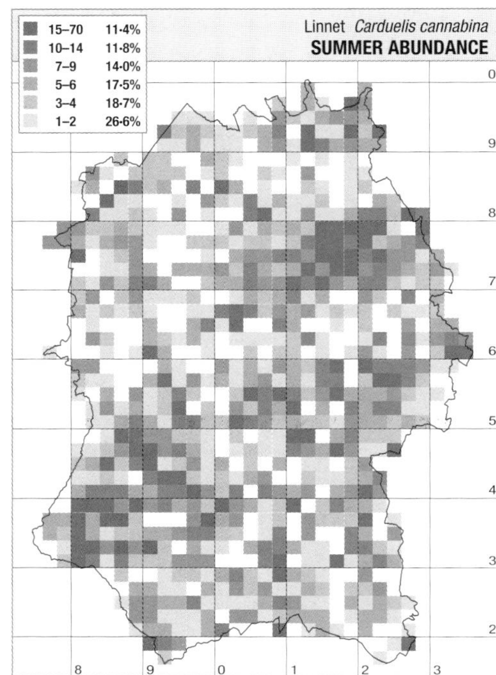

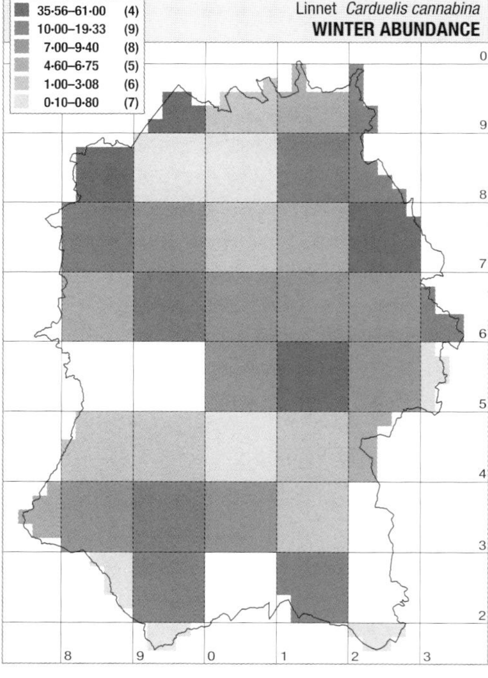

of ringing: the first, a juvenile, marked at Winterbourne in August 1965 was shot in the province of Ciudad Real; and the second, of unknown age, ringed at East Tytherton in July 1985 was found dead at Hontoria del Pinar (Burgos). In addition, one French-ringed Linnet has been recovered in Wiltshire – a juvenile marked at Cap Breton (Landes) on 13 November 1976 and found dead at Shrewton on 28 May 1980. Another Linnet trapped and released at Longbridge Deverill on 15 December 1974 had been ringed at Ryhope (Co Durham) six months earlier, on 6 June. A total of 905 Linnets was ringed in Wiltshire during 1965–2000 and, apart from those in France and Spain, only four others had been recovered by the end of that period, all in Great Britain: one, rather interestingly, involved the ring put on a Linnet at Longbridge Deverill on 3 January 1977 being found in an owl pellet at Stevenage (Hertfordshire) on 12 March 1978. It is perhaps significant that nearly all these ringing recoveries were in a period when Linnets were much commoner than they are now.

In 19th century Wiltshire, Smith (1887) regarded Linnets as 'Extremely numerous throughout... particularly on our downs, where they congregate in autumn in large flocks', but added that they were 'diminishing in numbers' because 'waste places and commons, where thistles and weeds luxuriated' were at that time (as in much of the 20th century) being 'brought into cultivation'. Linnets were also very popular cage-birds in the 19th century and depredations by birdcatchers are known to have wiped out populations close to some urban areas (*1875–1900 Atlas*); following a ban on the cage-bird trade in wild-caught finches in Great Britain, numbers are known to have recovered during the first part of the 20th century (*1968–72 Atlas*). Peirson (1919) described Linnets as very plentiful residents of the Marlborough district, especially on the downs, and 20 years later there was no apparent change (Peirson 1939). In 1952, no fewer than 47 nests with eggs or young were found in an area 'of approximately one acre' in the vicinity of Packway Mess, Larkhill (*WANHM*). For Wiltshire as a whole, Peirson (1959) noted that this species bred 'commonly or very commonly… except in the low-lying western parts of the county'. Describing it as 'resident', he also noted that 'most… breeding birds' moved away in autumn and did not return until 'any time between late February and mid-April', whereas Buxton (1981) reported that Linnets 'returned in strength normally in late March'.

Both the *1968–72* and *1988–91 Atlases*, like the summer distribution map for 1995–2000, recorded Linnets breeding in all of Wiltshire's 33 core and 15 part 10-km squares. The summer abundance map shows them to be generally commonest in the northeast and southwest; and that the highest densities were on the Marlborough Downs, and the north and west of Salisbury Plain. Breeding was recorded in just over half of all tetrads and, based on densities found during surveys in both this county and adjacent regions, the Wiltshire population is estimated to lie between 27,100 and 37,200 pairs.

Post-breeding flocks, which do not unusually reach 50–90 individuals in July, exceeded 100 on 12 occasions in August during 1990–2000, the highest number being 300 at Sherrington Down on 13th in 2000. Particularly large (probably migrant) flocks in autumn 1992 included 700 on SPTA (Centre) on 26 September and 800 at Barbury Castle on 16 October. Some 35 years earlier, however, flocks of as many as 1000 were being recorded, at Walcot on 4 August 1957 and at Roundway Down on 12 October that year (*WANHM*).

The *1981–84 Winter Atlas* mapped Linnets throughout the county, but more numerous in the south and east. The winter map for 1998–2000 does not reflect that earlier pattern, showing them to be generally commoner in the north then, though winter abundance is no doubt influenced by availability of food. Extrapolation from the survey data suggests a Wiltshire population of between 64,700 and 88,800 individuals – making Linnet, after Chaffinch, the most numerous of the finches at that season. During 1990–2000, the biggest winter flocks were in 1992 (600 at Liddington Castle on 17 November, 500 at Tan Hill on 5 December, and 500 at Rushall Down on 17 December) and in 2000 (550 at Fyfield on 27 December). Some 300 at Bratton Vedette Post on 16 April 1992 was the largest spring flock of recent years.

(See also page 725.)

MVJ

Sponsored by Brenda Hillier in memory of Roy Hillier

Twite

Carduelis flavirostris

Winter vagrant (11+ records) from coasts, breeds north Britain/Eurasia

Though declining, especially in Scotland in the 20th century, Twites breed quite commonly on open moorland and upland pastures in much of northern Great Britain south to the Pennines and north Wales, and less numerously in Ireland. Elsewhere, they nest in northern Fenno-Scandia (almost exclusively in Norway) and, quite separately, in Turkey and the Caucasus, as well as discontinuously from northern Kazakhstan and northern Iran to Mongolia and the eastern Himalayas.

Scottish Twites tend to be rather sedentary, wintering in the coastal lowlands there, but many from the Pennines and other English uplands move to the saltmarshes of the east coast, particularly around the Wash, and it is likely that migrants from Norway join them (*Migration Atlas*); midwinter numbers in Britain and Ireland have been estimated at 100,000 to 150,000 (*1981–84 Winter Atlas*). The autumn movement is at a peak from September to November, some reaching the Severn Estuary and the south coast, and the return begins in late January, few remaining by mid March. In general, Wiltshire's records fit this pattern.

Smith (1887) was satisfied that Twites were occasional, and possibly annual, in Wiltshire in autumn and winter, but this may have been a rather optimistic view, as he was citing mainly birdcatchers' reports from Odstock and 'Wittsbury Down' in August and September; and, while he considered that they were also 'not infrequently met with on Mere Downs', his only listed observation involved 'a pair' in autumn 1870. Over six decades later, in 1934, one was 'seen on the Downs near Cranborne Chase during March and another on May 6th' (*WANHM*). There were then no more until three records in the early 1970s: two males on downland near Ashmore on 20 October 1971; one in a large finch flock at Swindon STW on 9 December 1972; and a party of seven at Rushall Down on 8 April 1973 (*WANHM*). From 1974:

1983	22 February	Shear Water	Three
1989	18 October	Codford	Two in mixed finch flock
1990	7 November	Shear Water	One with other finches at pool
1994	13 November	SPTA (West)	Flock of 14 flying west calling
1997	2 February	SPTA (East)	One in mixed finch flock
2000	2–5 January	Wick Down, Marlborough	Two with other finches

Note that four of the records involved mixed finch flocks. Those in 1989 were with Linnets and Goldfinches, and those in 1990 at a small pool with Lesser Redpolls, Siskins and Crossbills.

RT

Common Redpoll

Carduelis flammea

Rare vagrant from Fenno-Scandia (4+ records), but perhaps overlooked

Until recently regarded as conspecific with the rather similar Lesser Redpoll (*qv*), the Common Redpoll is now treated as specifically distinct (*eg* Sangster *et al* 2002). This finch has an extensive circumpolar breeding distribution, but in Europe nests only in Fenno-Scandia – where the population is thought to lie in the region of 1 to 2 million pairs (*EBCC Atlas*) – and north Russia. Although the majority of Common Redpolls in Fenno-Scandia tends to migrate between south and east in autumn to winter in southeast Europe, in most years some move between south and west; variable numbers then reach Great Britain, where they were formerly known by the vernacular name 'Mealy Redpoll'. This is an eruptive species and in some autumns many thousands appear in west-central Europe, but the last major influx into Great Britain occurred as long ago as 1910 (*Migration Atlas*).

There are just four Wiltshire records of Common Redpolls, but this may simply reflect a combination of identification problems – darker individuals are confusingly similar in plumage to Lesser Redpolls, while their calls are doubtfully separable by the human ear – and a lack of interest by at least some observers when Common and Lesser Redpolls were regarded as conspecific. The county's first was trapped and ringed at Purton on 6 March 1974. The other three were all sight records of singletons: at Picket Wood on 20 February 1982; at Coate Water on 7 February 1997; and at Oare on 12 February 1999 (*Hobby*).

In addition, there are a number of uncertain reports: small parties ('seven' and 'several') in January 1934; groups of two and 'about 12' in January and February 1934 (regarded at the time as 'doubtful'); and singletons in December 1957 and October 1959 (*WANHM*). More recently, one considered 'possibly' *flammea* was seen at CWP on 22 February 1987 (*Hobby*). Despite the difficulties of field identification, the interest generated by the treatment of the Common Redpoll as a distinct species will probably lead to a better definition of its Wiltshire status.

(See also page 727.)

SBE

Lesser Redpoll

Carduelis cabaret

Local and decreasing breeder, scarce winter visitor from north England

Until very recently treated as a subspecies of the Common Redpoll (*eg* Sangster *et al* 2002), the Lesser Redpoll is endemic to Europe. It is found only in Britain and Ireland, in countries bordering the North Sea from northeast France to the southern fringes of Norway and Sweden, and in mountain areas of central Europe (*eg* Knox *et al* 2001). Until the 1880s, indeed, Lesser Redpolls were found mainly in Ireland, northern Britain and the Alps,

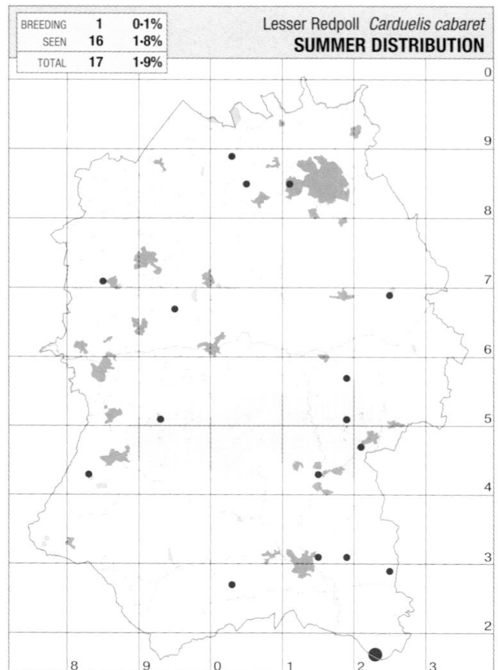

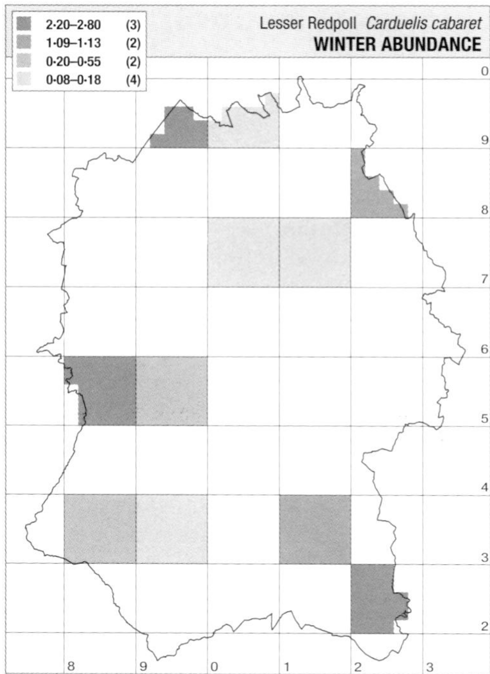

mostly at higher altitudes. By 1910 they had spread into lowland Britain, only for numbers and range to contract and then expand again – this time into the Netherlands, Germany and Denmark in the 1950s, France in the 1960s, and Belgium and southern Sweden in the 1970s. The central European population also spread, from the 1950s into the former Czechoslovakia and central Germany (there eventually linking with the expanding North Sea population) and in the early 1970s into the French Jura.

This remarkable range extension of the Lesser Redpoll in the 20th century has been attributed to increased afforestation. The most recent estimate of the European population put breeding numbers at some 300,000 pairs, 80 per cent of them in Britain and Ireland (*EBCC Atlas*), while the *1988–91 Atlas* estimated some 160,000 pairs in Great Britain alone. But the latter also showed quite a range contraction, since the *1968–72 Atlas*, in eastern Scotland and northeast and central England; in 1988–91, the areas of highest density were in much of the rest of Scotland and in Wales and north and southeast England. National survey data indicate a large increase from the late 1960s to mid 1970s, followed by an even larger decrease to the mid 1990s, so much so that the estimate for 2000 had slumped to just 25,300 pairs (*APEP*). Although there has been apparent stability in the late 1990s, declines may still be continuing in England (*BBWC*).

In Wiltshire, Smith (1887) stated that Lesser Redpolls were 'seldom seen here but in winter', though 'Mr. Elgar Sloper had a female in his collection that was killed at Rowde on its nest in May, 1850', while eggs were taken at Castle Combe in 1866 and near Marlborough in 1878. Smith also mentioned summer reports from Mere and of occasional nesting at Warminster, but commented that, as no specimens were available, these should be treated with caution. Hony (1915a) noted three early 20th century breeding records and quoted a Dr Hinton as claiming to have taken eggs near Warminster as a child 'about 1885'. Single nests were found at Clarendon in 1934 and 1948, and two at Porton in 1936 (*WANHM*), and were presumably the basis for Peirson's (1959) assertion that 'It has very occasionally nested in the county'. Buxton (1981) stated that 'It has bred irregularly at several locations', but mentioned only Somerford Common as a site where it was 'resident regularly', and the *1968–72 Atlas* confirmed breeding in just two of Wiltshire's 33 core 10-km squares.

In the 1970s and 1980s, large numbers of Lesser Redpolls were widely recorded in winter, particularly in the Shear Water/Longleat area in the southwest, at Hens Wood in the northeast and at Hamptworth Common and Langley and Franchises Woods in the southeast, but, although some stayed well into April and even early May, even singing, few remained through the summer and records of confirmed or even probable breeding were even fewer (*Hobby*). By the end of the 1980s winter flocks were smaller and the *1988–91 Atlas* was unable to show breeding in any of the 48 core and part 10-km squares in Wiltshire. The summer distribution map for 1995–2000 shows confirmed breeding only in the extreme south of the county, near the border with Hampshire's New Forest, and the records in most, if not all, of the remaining tetrads probably referred to late migrants. A single territory was reported in Center Parcs in spring or summer 1997 (Collins 2005), but no evidence of nesting given. An isolated observation of six at Hens Wood on 22 June 1998 was, however, thought possibly to indicate local nesting (*Hobby*). The Wiltshire breeding population was clearly insignificant during the summer tetrad survey, perhaps amounting to no more than zero to ten pairs in any of those years.

In autumn, British Lesser Redpolls depart their upland breeding areas, particularly in Scotland and Wales, and then become more widespread in England (*1981–84 Winter Atlas*). They are therefore much more familiar in Wiltshire as migrants and winter visitors. Passage can be quite extended – in spring from March to early May, and in autumn from September to November – and late and early wintering flocks further confuse the picture. National ringing data suggest that British Redpolls arrive at potential wintering sites in southern and central England during October and that, in years when food is short, many cross the Channel to the Low Countries and France, beginning to return in early April (*Migration Atlas*). The only three ringing results that involve the county fit this general pattern. Of 142 Redpolls ringed in Wiltshire during 1965–2000, no fewer than 93 were caught at Shear Water during February–April 1988, the great majority in April and the highest proportions of heavy individuals – indicating fat stored for migration – in the latter two-thirds of that month (Creighton 1989). One of them, ringed on 6 April, was retrapped near Selby (North Yorkshire) on 14 May that year; and another, caught on 13 April, had been ringed at North Baddesley (Hampshire) on 5 November 1982; last, a Redpoll found dead near Salisbury on 2 March 1974 had been ringed in Cheshire on 7 July 1973.

In winter, Redpolls are greatly attracted to alder, the cones of which are a major food source for them at that season, and it is likely that, to some extent, the winter map reflects the distribution of this tree in Wiltshire. When Redpolls were more widespread in the 1970s and 1980s, flocks of 100 or more were recorded at Shear Water (150 in November 1983), in Hens Wood (100 in March 1978 and May 1989, 120 in April 1993), and in Franchises Wood (100 in December 1985) (*Hobby*). The *1981–84 Winter Atlas* reflected this wider pattern, mapping them in 27 of the 33 core 10-km squares and particularly in the southwest. In 1990–2000, although the species was still widespread in Wiltshire in winter, its numbers were generally lower and only two flocks exceeded 50, both in May 1998 – 60 (feeding in larch) at Clarendon on the 3rd and 90 at Hens Wood on the 5th – these dates suggesting that they were on passage (*Hobby*).

The mobile nature of wintering Redpoll flocks and the transient presence of migrants in spring and autumn make it difficult to estimate non-breeding numbers in Wiltshire. Extrapolation from the roughly 200 recorded during the timed winter surveys, on the basis of the ratio of counts to estimates for other finch species, suggests a county total in the region of 1100 to 2100 individuals, although there is much variation between winters and in migrant flocks. Such numbers are only a tiny proportion of the 350,000 to

850,000 estimated for Britain and Ireland (*1981–84 Winter Atlas*) – although, in view of the population decline in the 1980s and early 1990s, by more than 80 per cent, those figures are now presumably far too high.

(See also page 725.)

GDP

Crossbill

Loxia curvirostra

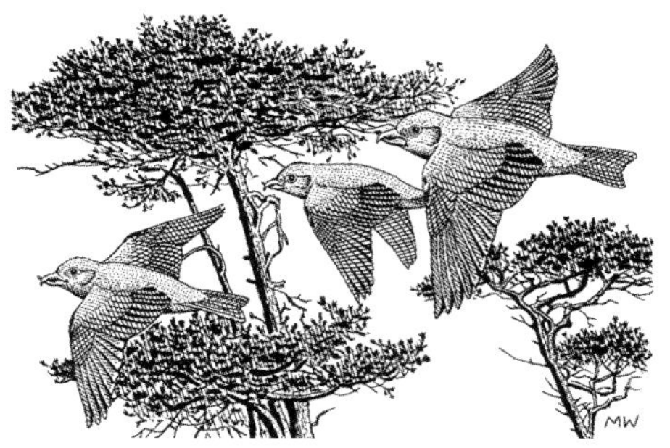

Local and irregular breeder in years after irruptions from Fenno-Scandia

Lively and noisy with its distinctive *jip jip jip* calls, the Crossbill is one of a small group of finches peculiarly adapted to exploit the seeds of coniferous trees. Thus, its numbers and presence in Wiltshire are dependent on the success or failure of the cone crop, not only locally but, more especially, elsewhere. In 1990, for example – following a particularly large irruption into Great Britain that apparently even involved some from northern Russia (*Migration Atlas*) – there were records at 11 Wiltshire localities, including up to 220 in September on the Longleat estate in the mixed coniferous triangle up to 1·5 km west and north of Shear Water (particularly in the Corsican pine, Sitka spruce and Douglas fir of what has since become Center Parcs); but in 1995, a year without the influence of an invasion, the only report was of three in Ravensroost Wood on 15 March (*Hobby*). Irregular, but not infrequent, irruptions into Great Britain have been recorded since the 13th century, and are the result of a combination of high population levels and widespread failure of the spruce crop in the vast boreal forests of northern Europe (Newton 1970, 1972).

Writing of the Crossbill in Wiltshire, Smith (1887) had 'many notices of its occurrence in almost all parts of the county', with dated records in 1838, 1866, 1868, 1870 and 'about 1873'. Hony (1915a) added four more records, in 1889, 1904, 1909 and 'a flock of twenty…in Savernake Forest in March, 1910'. Peirson (1959) stated that 'It is seen nearly every year in the extreme south-east…known to have bred successfully in 1950 and 1953 and in the 1930s'. Webber (1968) noted only that the species 'Probably breeds most years at Stourhead', and Buxton (1981) added that it 'recently was seen carrying nesting material…in the southwest'. In the last quarter of the 20th century two large influxes, in 1990 and 1997, and eight smaller ones, were represented in Wiltshire (*Hobby*) and were often noticeable from mid June onwards. During larger irruptions, Crossbills have sometimes been seen using food sources and habitats not usually associated with the species, for example beechmast and deciduous trees in farmland hedgerows (P Combridge).

The breeding of Crossbills in England has been regular since 1910 (Witherby *et al* 1938–41), and its increased frequency during the 20th century has been attributed to a greater availability of suitable conifer plantations since the 1914–18 War (*1875–1900 Atlas*). Nesting was first noted in Wiltshire at Redlynch in 1932 and again in 1936, when 'several nests with young' were found in April, but not proved again until 1950 (*WANHM*). Despite Peirson's (1959) claim of breeding in 1953, the bird report for that year in *WANHM* refers merely to young birds in June and August, and as 1953 was the first of a series of eight irruption years up to 1972 (*1968–72 Atlas*), it seems more likely that they were not raised locally.

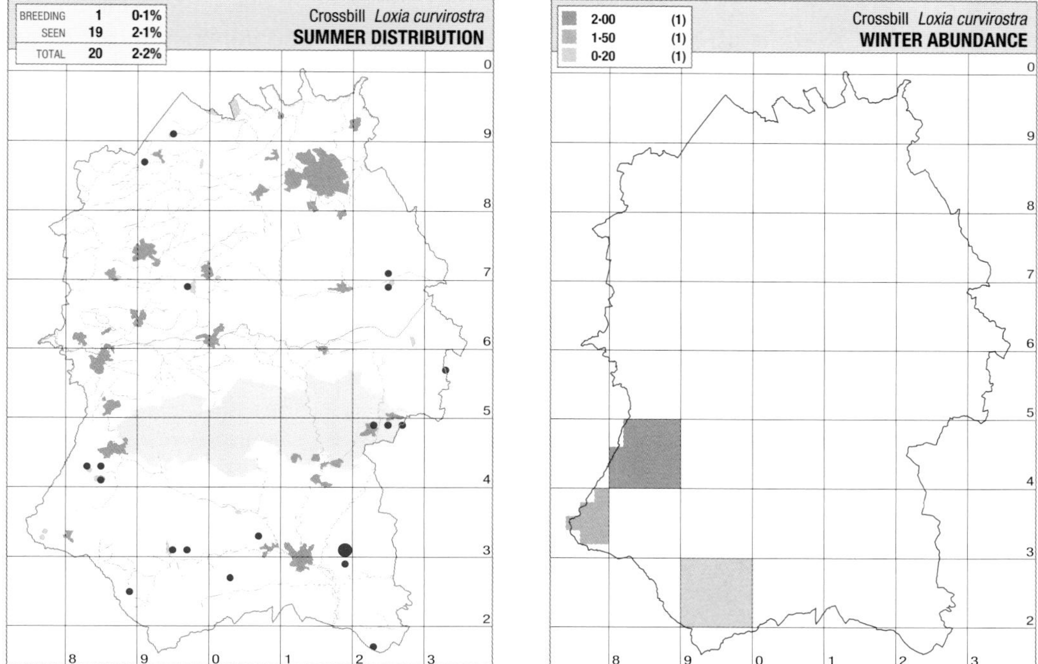

In central-southern England, Crossbills nest mostly from February through to April, and fare best in areas of mixed conifers, especially those with stands of Scots and Corsican pines. They rarely use Corsican pine for nesting, because of its open and loose structure, but its small cones, which retain seed for much of the year and which they can easily open, are an important and reliable food source (P Toye & P Combridge). The *1968–72* and *1988–91 Atlas* surveys respectively mapped presence in four and five of the county's 33 core 10-km squares, and the *1981–84 Winter Atlas* – which, as Crossbills can nest from January onwards, is perhaps as good a guide to breeding – also showed them in five. The summer survey in 1995–2000 recorded the species in ten of the core squares, but proved breeding in only one.

Because of the erratic distribution and numbers of this finch from year to year, and a lack of good census data, the *1988–91 Atlas* did not attempt an estimate of the breeding population of Great Britain; it postulated that fewer than 1000 individuals may be present between irruption years, but also noted that in Northumberland in November and December 1990 – following the irruption in the summer of that year – up to 40,000 were estimated in Kielder Forest alone. It is similarly difficult to suggest a figure for Wiltshire, but, from personal experience elsewhere in southern England, it seems possible that breeding may not be annual and that, even in better years (which do not necessarily coincide with high numbers of birds), nests are usually relatively few; an estimate of zero to 50 pairs is thus suggested. Despite the problems associated with censusing Crossbills, the *EBCC Atlas* put the European breeding population, excluding Russia, in the region of 1·0 to 1·6 million pairs.

Since 1975, breeding has been suspected or claimed from several widespread localities in Wiltshire. Most of these reports have, however, involved juveniles, which are an unreliable guide as they can migrate for considerable distances soon after fledging. Thus, not even a 'pair with 2 or 3 juveniles newly fledged' at Shear Water on 7 April 1981 (*Hobby*) is proof of nesting there; but it and observations of a female carrying nesting material into a spruce in that area of Longleat in February 1977 (*Hobby*) and again in 1982 (JD Pollard) are useful evidence of nesting in an area where breeding was undoubtedly occurring in at least some years from the mid 1970s to the late 1980s (IJ Ferguson-Lees) – though it must be added that Crossbills do occasionally build platforms without completing the nests. In 1983 Crossbills were regularly seen in the area of Shear Water, including singing males in February, alarm calls in March, and three juveniles seen during June and July (*Hobby*). No nests were located, but it was the strong impression of all concerned that breeding was regular by a small population that was also increased at intervals in invasion years. The same applies to the area of Longleat now known as Center Parcs, where Crossbills could be seen throughout the year in the late 1980s – even in the first quarter, when song was noted on several occasions (IJ Ferguson-Lees) – and where single pairs or territories were located in 1997 and 1998, three pairs in 1999 and two in 2000 (Collins 2005).

Data from continental Europe have provided evidence that some erupting Crossbills return to their home range in a later year (*eg* Newton 1972). Unfortunately no recoveries have involved Wiltshire, and during 1965–2000 the only Crossbill ringed in the county was a full-grown individual at Shear Water on 11 May 1988. The one confirmed breeding during the summer tetrad survey came in spring 2000, when two young were raised in a nest in a Douglas fir in south Wiltshire (*Hobby*), and it may be significant that nesting was widespread in the New Forest (Hampshire) in that year (P Toye). The summer map shows a wide scatter of records, and the winter map again pinpoints the southwest, where the extensive conifer plantations on the Longleat estate, particularly between Center Parcs and Shear Water, remain an important area, as possibly does Stourhead to Alfred's Tower. The erratic and nomadic nature of Crossbills makes their distribution difficult to define, and both maps would have looked very different had either the summer or winter surveys coincided with an irruption similar in size to that of 1990. In large irruption years the number of Crossbills in Wiltshire may reach a peak of 500–1000, but the turnover is probably high and the total using the county's woods over an autumn-winter then is likely to be considerably greater.

Wiltshire's Crossbills are of the nominate race, which fills much of the species' range, from western Europe right across Asia to the Sea of Okhotsk, but some 18 other subspecies are found elsewhere in Europe and Asia, in northwest Africa, and in North and Central America. There are also three more species of crossbills, of which two – the Parrot Crossbill and the Scottish Crossbill – are now known to breed in Scotland (Knox 1990a, b, Summers 2002, Summers *et al* 2002); this is a rather confusing situation as the Crossbill also nests there, sometimes even in the same woods, and their taxonomy remains a matter of some debate. Throughout its range, the Crossbill inspires interest and study – not least the important monograph by Nethersole-Thompson (1975) – yet much still remains to be learned about it, and in Wiltshire a more precise definition of breeding status is undoubtedly required.

(See also page 725.)

PCo & IJF-L

Bullfinch

Pyrrhula pyrrhula

Moderately common resident of woods and scrub, visiting gardens in winter

Despite the male's bright plumage and the flashing white rumps of both sexes, Bullfinches are unobtrusive and easily overlooked in

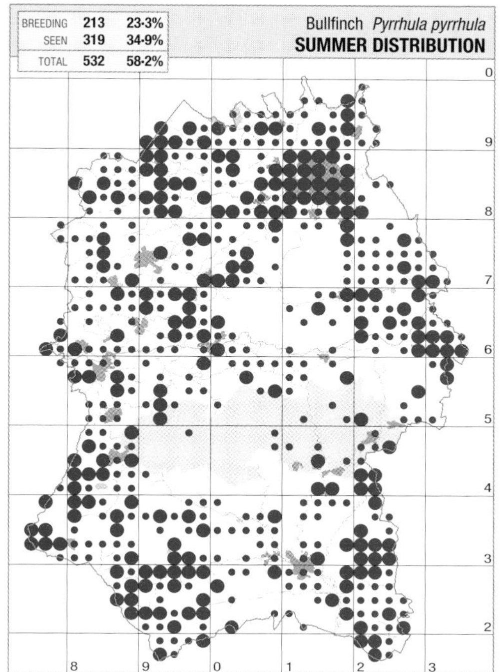

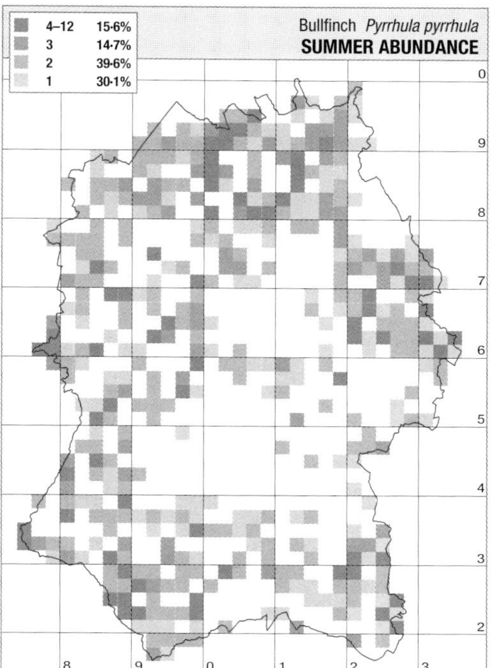

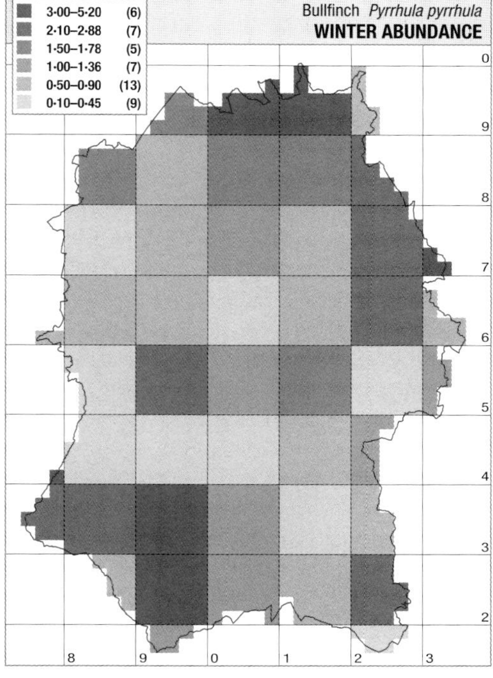

wooded habitats, where their soft calls and the male's surprisingly quiet song – inaudible at more than a few metres – are easily missed. These attractive finches are to be found from the birch zone of Fenno-Scandia south to the uplands of Mediterranean countries, and from Spain's Cantabrian mountains and Ireland east throughout much of continental Europe, apart from the plains of the Balkans, Ukraine and southern Russia; in the Caucasus they reach as high as 2500 m or more, extending from there into northern parts of Turkey and Iran. Farther east, they breed across much of northern Asia from the Urals through Siberia and northern Mongolia to Kamchatka and Japan.

Both the *1968–72* and the *1988–91 Atlases* mapped Bullfinches throughout Wiltshire, recording them in all 33 core and 15 part 10-km squares, and the *1981–84 Winter Atlas* produced the same results. Likewise, the summer distribution and abundance maps for 1995–2000 show this species in every 10-km square, but the finer detail of the tetrads demonstrates that the highest concentrations are in areas of extensive mature woodland. Bullfinches are found in relatively discrete areas around the periphery of the county, associated with woodlands in the Cotswolds, Braydon Forest and Bowood, at

Savernake, from Longleat down to Stourhead and the Vale of Wardour, and from Bentley Wood to the New Forest, as well as in parkland around Swindon. They also breed well away from trees in bushy areas and overgrown hedges, but are largely scarce or absent from open downland, such as the Marlborough Downs, Salisbury Plain and Cranborne Chase, where wooded and bushy habitats suitable for nesting and shelter are sparse or lacking.

This pattern fits well with the view of Peirson (1959) that Bullfinches were 'not uncommon except in the bleak open country', and agrees with their being assessed as 'common' by both Buxton (1981) and Palmer (1991). Much earlier, Smith (1887) had stated that they were 'sparingly distributed throughout the county', and the 1929 bird report in *WANHM* considered that the Bullfinch was 'A fairly common resident, but decreasing'. Thus, although there is no evidence that their distribution in Wiltshire has changed since the 19th century, we have the implication that their numbers have grown. This apparent increase may be real for, during the 19th century, Bullfinches were heavily persecuted by gardeners and fruit growers, and widely trapped as popular and often expensive cage-birds (*1875–1900 Atlas*). Because of the coarser scale used, the winter map less dramatically depicts the scarcity of these finches in more open habitats, but again shows its strongholds in woodlands around the periphery of the county.

Bullfinches are found throughout mainland Great Britain; their total population has been very differently estimated at 600,000 breeding pairs (*1968–72 Atlas*), some 190,000 territories (*1988–91 Atlas*) and just 158,000 in 2000 (*APEP*). These snapshots in time, however, mask large variations: they had increased dramatically during the 1950s and were considered economically significant pests at fruit farms (*eg* Newton 1972), but that problem has largely disappeared as a result of the species' decline since the 1970s. Initially the decrease was rapid, but – though continuing, especially in southern Britain – it has been less severe since the early 1980s (*BBWC*). The reasons remain obscure, but, as it has been most marked in farmland habitats, agricultural intensification may be implicated; other recent theories have suggested Grey Squirrels both as nest predators (Vanhinsbergh *et al* 2003) and as direct competitors for such foods as buds and seeds (Hewson *et al* 2004), though these mammals seem unlikely to have much effect in more open agricultural areas. The difficulties of estimating the numbers of breeding Bullfinches are well known (*eg 1988–91 Atlas*), but, on the basis of surveys using BBS methods, it seems likely that there are in the region of 6500 to 10,400 pairs in Wiltshire. Timed counts during the winter survey recorded roughly 1200 individuals, but extrapolation using the ratio of winter to summer counts suggests that the total is more likely to number 10,400 to 16,600 individuals. In Europe, excluding Russia, the population has been estimated at 2·8 to 3·9 million pairs and other countries appear to have had few changes apart from small regional increases and decreases (*EBCC Atlas*).

Although most Bullfinch populations are at least partially migratory – the winter distribution in Europe then extends down to include much of the continental south – the endemic British and Irish race *pileata* is largely sedentary, as is well shown by ringing data. As many as 93 per cent of 185 British Bullfinches recovered during 1910–60 were found less than 5 km from the ringing site (*BWP*), a trend confirmed by more recent analysis for the *Migration Atlas*, which showed that, regardless of season, the median distance between ringing and recovery was less than 1 km. At the local level, just 27 of no fewer than 2016 Bullfinches ringed in Wiltshire during 1965–2000 had been recovered by the end of that period and only two of those had moved more than 10 km. Thus, although it has been suggested in *Hobby* that there is evidence of autumn influxes in some years and winter movements in others, it is probable that these were the results of relatively local dispersal and that very few Bullfinches in the county originate from farther afield.

PCo

Sponsored by Anna Grayson

Hawfinch

Coccothraustes coccothraustes

Scarce local resident, easily overlooked, possibly some movement within Britain

Widespread as a breeding species from North Africa and Iberia north to southern Fenno-Scandia and thence across Eurasia to Kamchatka and the islands of Japan, this large but often elusive finch is equipped with a particularly powerful head and bill that enable it to feed on fruit stones too hard for other finches to exploit (Mountfort 1957). Associated primarily with broadleaved woodland, Hawfinches occur also in mixed woods and well-wooded cemeteries, parks and gardens; although rarely breeding in conifers in the west of their range (*CBWP*), they have nested in yew in Wiltshire (P Combridge). The population of Europe, excluding Russia, has been estimated at 1·1 to 1·4 million pairs (*EBCC Atlas*), and that of Great Britain at a mere 3000–6500 pairs (*1988–91 Atlas*).

In Great Britain, Hawfinches are present in the historical record from 1666 (Fisher 1966), although breeding was not proved until early in the 19th century (*eg 1875–1900 Atlas*). An undoubted extension in range in the latter half of the 19th and early 20th centuries resulted in nesting records from almost every English county and parts of Scotland and Wales (*eg* Saunders 1899, Witherby *et al* 1938–41). Much more recently, the *1988–91 Atlas* 'change' map showed losses in range since the *1968–72 Atlas* – a trend counter to that in much of Europe (*EBCC Atlas*) – the suggested cause being a reduction in broadleaved woodland, though the British population has fluctuated, apparently erratically, through the 20th century (*1968–72 Atlas*).

For Wiltshire, Smith (1887) noted a wide scatter of Hawfinch records, including reports of regular breeding at Savernake Forest, Erlestoke and Grittleton, occasional breeding 'in the district round Warminster', and a family party at West Dean. Kennedy (1966) listed the species as nesting in considerable numbers in Savernake about 1860, still common there but decreasing by 1870, and not seen for several years early in the 20th century. Presumably basing their accounts on Smith, both Peirson (1959) and Buxton (1981) considered Hawfinches to be scarce residents that had been commoner in the 19th century. To judge from statements in *WANHM*, however, they were at least locally common between the 1914–18 and 1939–45 Wars. In 1929 they were noted as a 'not uncommon resident', especially in the Devizes and Trowbridge areas, and in 1930 as regular in the Marlborough district and increasing around Devizes and Trowbridge. 'Over 20' were present 'on several occasions' at Longford Park early in 1932, and in 1933 they were described as 'undoubtedly well established' in the county, with 'large numbers seen during Autumn at Longford'.

The summer distribution map indicates the Hawfinch's current limited distribution in Wiltshire: in the northeast, in the Marlborough district; in the southwest, close to the Somerset border; and, in the southeast, in the vicinity of Salisbury. The lack of tetrad records from the Devizes and Trowbridge areas indicates that its range has contracted since the 1930s. No firm data exist to be sure when this contraction took place, but the 1947 bird report quoted the oologist Major WM Congreve as believing Hawfinches to be 'scarcer than formerly', suggesting that the decline may have taken place around the time of the 1939–45 War (*WANHM*). Ancient woodlands such as West, Collingbourne and Bentley Woods were clear-felled around that time, and this may have had some bearing on the decline (Baskerville *et al* 2005, PE Castle). The *1968–72 Atlas* recorded this finch in six of Wiltshire's 33 core 10-km squares, and the *1988–91 Atlas* in eight, but the summer tetrad survey in 1995–2000 in just four – all of which supports the impression of fluctuations in range during the late 20th century.

Langston *et al* (2002) – in a review of national population trends during 1975–99, based on county bird reports – claimed that Wiltshire was one of three 'western counties close to the Severn Estuary' (the others being Gwent and Gloucestershire) where numbers had increased since 1975. But subsequent analysis of Hawfinch records in *Hobby* for the years 1974–99 showed that 72 per cent of Wiltshire's records had been in the northeast and the southeast, in areas distant from the Severn Estuary but adjacent to Berkshire and Hampshire respectively. This analysis also stated that the increase in reports from the southeast during the 1990s was the result of greater observer coverage rather than growing numbers, and suggested that 'variable observer effort, Hawfinch presence in areas of restricted public access and the possibility … of some redistribution of sites makes population trends uncertain in Wiltshire during the last quarter of the twentieth century' (Combridge 2002). (See also below.)

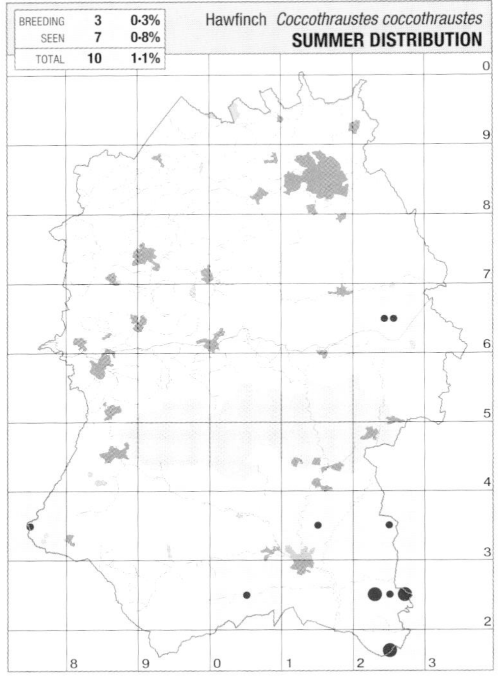

Notoriously easy to overlook unless their distinctive calls are heard, Hawfinches occur at lower densities in Wiltshire than in some other areas of Great Britain (*eg 1988–91 Atlas*), and are usually recorded as singles or in groups of not more than ten. Apart from the Longford records above, higher numbers have been reported only at Downton (12 or 14 in November 1934), Compton Bassett (maximum 20 in April–May 1944), Alderbury (11 in January 1955), Savernake (maximum 36 in March 1997), Franchises Wood (maximum 17 in September 1999) and West Dean (maximum 17 in March 2000).

Given its evasive nature, in mature and often private woodland, estimating the size of Wiltshire's breeding population is highly speculative, especially as solitary pairs are quieter and thus more easily overlooked than semi-colonial groups. Applying the formula used by both national breeding atlases, allowing 10–20 pairs for each 10-km square with records, the core square population during the summer survey perhaps lay in the region of 40–80 pairs, but for the county as a whole was unlikely to exceed 100 pairs. Nevertheless, Hawfinches were reported quite widely in Wiltshire during 1974–2000, Savernake and the complex of woodlands in the southeast being the most favoured areas. As Hampshire's New Forest is one of the strongholds of the species in Great Britain (*1988–91 Atlas*), regular records from adjacent parts of southeast Wiltshire between Salisbury and the border were to be expected, though there and elsewhere in the county recorded patterns are difficult to interpret as they may reflect observer bias and coverage. For example, in a special survey of the Longleat Estate, Hawfinches were seen in June 1984 in the same two woods as, it later transpired, had produced the Estate's previous records, back in the 1950s (Ferguson-Lees 1984).

North European Hawfinch populations are highly migratory, and journeys of over 1000 km have been reported (*eg EBCC Atlas*); two recovered in Shetland had been ringed in Germany and Norway (*Migration Atlas*). There is, however, little evidence of long-distance travel by British breeders, apart from some suggestion that a westward movement might occur in southern England in winter. Above average numbers in Wiltshire (one to 15, at 15 widely dispersed localities) during the winter of 1988/89 were thought possibly to have originated from a Continental influx (*Hobby*) but, as only one Hawfinch has ever been ringed in Wiltshire – at Cole Park on 28 October 1961 (*WANHM*) – and there are no inward recoveries either, proof of immigration or other movement is lacking.

In winter, this finch is as elusive as it is in the summer. Records in only two core 10-km squares during the *1981–84 Winter Atlas* almost certainly did not reflect its true status at that season, when its detection often relies on finding favoured feeding and roosting sites (P Combridge). None whatsoever was recorded during the winter tetrad survey, though that is perhaps not surprising in view of the random sampling methods used. Yet 100–250 might be expected on the basis of breeding numbers, though some recorded in winter in the southeast may nest in adjacent parts of Hampshire.

A combination of shyness and low densities will undoubtedly continue to make this species difficult to monitor successfully in the county and present a real challenge to the skills of birdwatchers in the future.

(See also page 725.)

PCo

Sponsored by Malcolm Penn

Lapland Bunting

Calcarius lapponicus

Vagrant (2 records), breeds Fenno-Scandia/ Greenland, winters North Sea coasts

Having a circumpolar summer distribution – largely north of the Arctic Circle – across northernmost Eurasia and North America, Lapland Buntings winter well to the south on all three continents. Some 299,000 to 800,000 pairs are estimated to breed in Norway and northern Sweden and Finland (*EBCC Atlas*), and probably at least as many more in north European Russia. Most of these migrate south and southeast to winter in Ukraine and south European Russia, or eastward into central Asia. Some, however, travel southwest to winter along the coasts of the North Sea, particularly from Denmark west to the Netherlands, but also as far as the Biscay coast of France and along the British east coast, while others come every year from Greenland (*Migration Atlas*). In Great Britain, the wintering numbers of both populations combined are usually small, perhaps no more than 200 to 500 in total, and are found almost exclusively between the Firth of Forth and Kent (*1981–84 Winter Atlas*), but migrants on passage are seen in variable numbers in the north and west, and vagrants have been recorded in many counties, even in southwest England. Larger influxes occur in some autumns, when the total numbers may be several times higher, and migrants may then be more widely distributed.

The first of Wiltshire's two records came on 13 December 1953, when at least two Lapland Buntings, and possibly four or five, were seen at Swindon STW with a large flock of Pied Wagtails; although they stayed for only a few minutes, the two were seen well and their distinctive call was also heard (*WANHM*). Many were reported in Great Britain that autumn (Buxton 1981). The second was a first-winter male feeding with a flock of Sky Larks at Beacon Hill, Devizes, early in the morning of 26 October 1997, but people were walking in the area with dogs and it soon moved on (*Hobby*).

(See also page 727.)

RT

Snow Bunting

Plectrophenax nivalis

Winter vagrant (25+ records) from Iceland, also Greenland/Fenno-Scandia

Although 70–100 pairs breed in Scotland (*1988–91 Atlas*), Snow Buntings are predominantly passage migrants and winter visitors to Great Britain, and most ringing returns have shown Icelandic origin; it is, however, likely that some come from Greenland and just two recoveries have involved Fenno-Scandian birds (*Migration Atlas*). The population of Europe, excluding Russia, has been estimated at 224,000 to 634,000 pairs (*EBCC Atlas*).

This high arctic and subarctic species has a circumpolar distribution in Eurasia and America. Most winter well to the south, in a band from northern and eastern Britain across central Europe and Asia and, in America, south to southern Canada and northern USA. Snow Buntings are found much more widely in Great Britain during winter, on many Scottish islands and coasts, more patchily inland in the Highlands, down much of the English east coast, and more sparsely around the Irish Sea. Some 10,000 to 15,000 were estimated at the time of the *1981–84 Winter Atlas* – mostly in Britain and many fewer in Ireland – but these winter numbers are known to fluctuate over periods of years.

As to the Snow Bunting's status in Wiltshire, Smith (1887) had 'learnt from Mr. Withers that it has occasionally been killed in various localities', and noted that 'Mr. Elgar Sloper… has seen several which had been killed on Salisbury Plain'. Smith also mentioned reports from Brixton Deverill, Mere and 'near Salisbury', as well as 'near Grately' (though Grately itself is just in Hampshire). Gardiner (1887) added two other records, both from Marlborough in December 1879 and January 1880, and Hony (1915a) referred to 'two shot at Bishops Down about 1908'. Peirson (1959) noted records in only three winters of the 20th century and could date just one of them, 'above West Lavington' in January 1951. Kennedy (1966) reported Snow Buntings as having been seen twice near Tan Hill (undated) and at Ramsbury Chase in 1945, in which year a male was found at Semington on 25 October. (This last record remained unpublished until 1971, when it appeared in the addenda to the 'Wiltshire Bird Notes for 1970' in *WANHM*.) Two were seen at Liddington Castle on 7 November 1959, and a male at Fyfield Down on 11 January 1965 and again on the 16th. A first-winter male at Roundway, Devizes, from 14 December 1968 was, remarkably, joined by a second during 1–4 March 1969, after which one remained alone until 2 April (*WANHM*).

During 1974–2000, there were thirteen more records, three in the 1970s, six in the 1980s and four in the 1990s, all in either November–December or February–March. Thus, despite the great increase in observers, Snow Buntings remain scarce visitors to Wiltshire. All but one were singletons (four identified as males, two as females, one as immature), the exception being a party of nine on stubble at Chelworth, near Crudwell, on 14 February 1993. The other localities involved were CWP26/27/38/74, Swindon, Broad Hinton, Morgan's Hill, Devizes (Roundway again), Bratton, Boscombe Down, Wylye (Bathampton Farm), Standlynch Farm and Tollard Royal.

(See also page 727.)

RT

Yellowhammer

Emberiza citrinella

Decreasing resident, though still quite widespread on arable farmland

The male's strikingly bright colours and characteristic song make this bunting a familiar sight and sound in open country with hedges, trees and scrub, as well as in young plantations. Widely distributed across the lowlands of Great Britain, but most numerous on highly productive farmland, the Yellowhammer is commonest in southern and central England (much less so in the southwest peninsula and Wales) and otherwise in the east, north to the Moray Firth, a distribution that closely follows the extent of arable. In the wider sphere, this species is resident or partially migratory in much of Europe (except the far south and north) and east to central Siberia; the European population, excluding that of Russia, has been estimated at 19 to 20 million pairs (*EBCC Atlas*).

Yellowhammers were very common in Wiltshire in the 19th century and 'could be met with in every hedge and wood during the summer' (Smith 1887). They were also considered 'a very common resident' in the Marlborough area (Peirson 1919, 1939). Little comment was made on this species in early *WANHM* reports, though that for 1932 noted 'a yearly diminution' in the Lydiard Millicent area. Yellowhammers have a long nesting season, and song is normally recorded in the county from late February to the end of August – indeed, it often seems strongest in August because most other passerines are silent then – though exceptionally one was heard singing on North Down on 1 January 1995. Yellowhammers tend to start nesting comparatively late for resident birds, but then to have two or even three broods, so that nests with eggs may be found from mid or even early April to late August.

The fortunes of Yellowhammers in Wiltshire have varied in recent years, and decreases were noted in some areas from the mid 1980s into the early 1990s. But declines in those parts seem to have been offset by increases elsewhere. By the mid 1990s the position appeared generally healthy, with concentrations on arable limestone and on grassland mixed with small amounts of scrub. Nationally, Yellowhammers on CBC farmland plots showed no sign of overall changes in the 1960s (Marchant *et al* 1990) and they remained stable until the early 1980s, when there was then a sharp decline – far greater than those of other seed-eating passerines – although this has levelled out since the late 1990s (*BBWC*). This decline, of more than 50 per cent since the 1970s – with the British estimate falling from 1·2 million territories at the time of the *1988–91 Atlas* to 792,000 in 2000 (*APEP*) – and so prompting conservation concerns, may be linked to decreasing food supplies through loss of winter stubbles and seed-bearing weeds.

The *1968–72* and *1988–91 Atlases* found Yellowhammers present in every one of Wiltshire's 33 core 10-km squares. The summer distribution map for 1995–2000 likewise shows

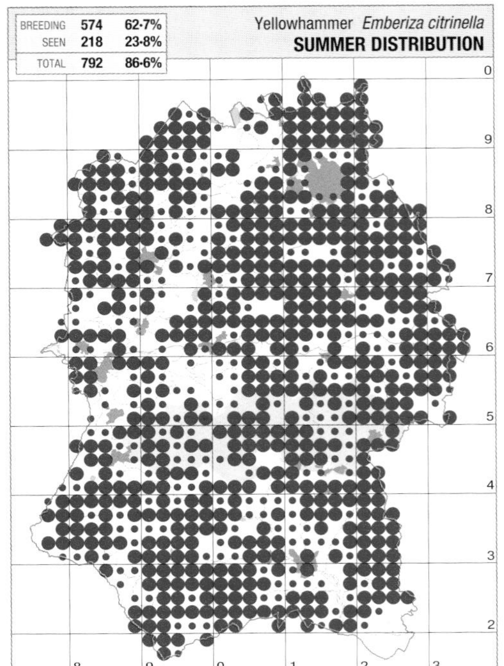

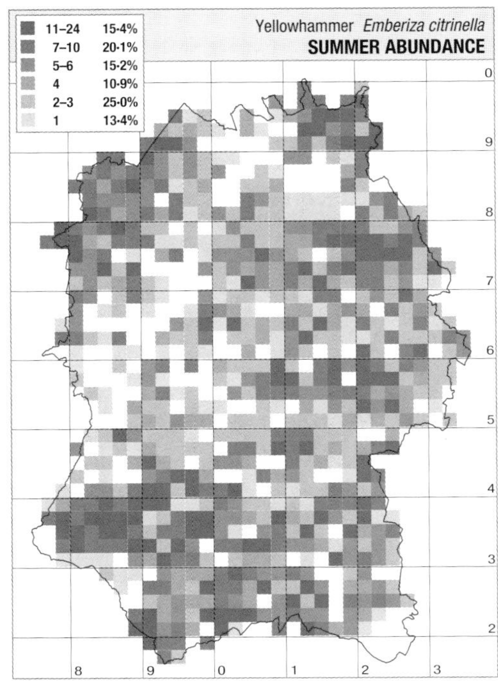

them in all core squares. Marked concentrations were noted in the Thames Valley, the Cotswolds, Marlborough Downs and Cranborne Chase, and especially in the southwest around the Deverills. Yellowhammers were sparse in tetrads with large urban areas or extensive woodland, and they particularly avoided the Bristol Avon clay vales – a marked gap in the north of the county that closely matches the distribution of grazed and mown turf. The comprehensive survey of breeding birds on SPTA (Stanbury *et al* 2000), based on 1-km squares, put the population of Salisbury Plain alone at 1409 territories, making this the eighth commonest species there. Extrapolation to the rest of the county on the basis of the WOS timed counts indicates a Wiltshire population of 18,500 pairs, but this is much lower than the estimate of up to 57,500 pairs – a figure that in retrospect now seems very large – if densities from other local surveys using BBS methods are applied.

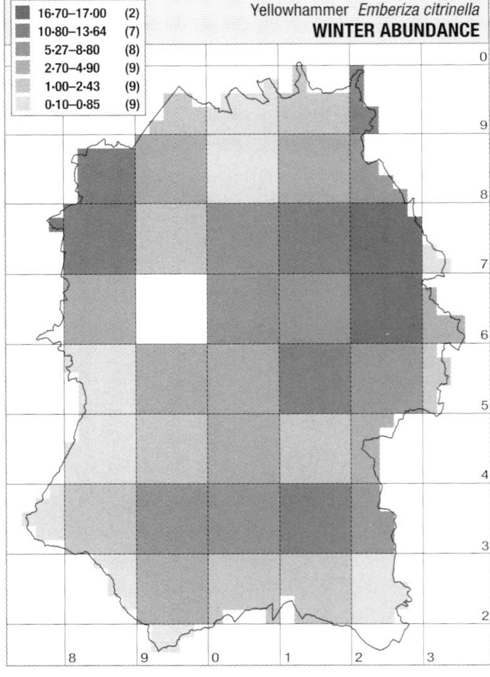

In winter, Yellowhammers gather into flocks to feed where weed and other seeds are available and where farm animals have been fed grain. Such areas include cereal stubbles and land where forage brassicas have been grazed off by sheep or cattle. In severe weather

– along with Chaffinches and, frequently, Collared Doves – Yellowhammers often move into farmyards and stockyards. Winter flock sizes not uncommonly range up to 50–80, but very rarely as high as the 300 at Yarnbury Castle in March 1998 and the 450 at Mead End, Bowerchalke, in February 1997. The sample winter counts found some 4665 birds, very similar to the summer figure, and suggest a winter total of 28,200 to 87,600 individuals in the county. The winter map shows that the Marlborough Downs and the Cotswolds are particularly favoured at this season, and that, as demonstrated by the *1981–84 Winter Atlas* – which found Yellowhammers in all 33 of the county's core 10-km squares, compared with 32 during 1995–2000 – they are found almost throughout the county, though there are notably fewer in the southwest than during summer.

In Great Britain, Yellowhammers are generally sedentary and do not travel far even in winter, although they may then leave higher ground occupied during summer; few ringing recoveries show movement of more than 25 km (*Migration Atlas*). Although 865 were ringed in Wiltshire during 1965–2000, they generated only two recoveries, both local: one was an adult female ringed at Thorncombe, Imber, on 17 January 1987 and retrapped there just over six years later, on 18 February 1993.

(See also page 725.)

MVJ

Cirl Bunting

Emberiza cirlus

Local resident until 1970s, now extinct as in most of former British range

Cirl Buntings are endemic to the warmer countries of western Europe, the Mediterranean and the southern shores of the Black Sea. They are resident in northwest Africa and, in southern Europe, from Iberia and much of France through southwest Germany, Switzerland, Italy and the larger Mediterranean islands to the Balkans, and eastward into western and northern Turkey; there is also a population in southwest England. Until the 1950s they were more widespread in southern Britain and used to nest in Belgium and Luxembourg, as well as farther north in Germany. To some extent these declines in the northwest of the range have been offset by the colonisation of Hungary and Austria and by range expansions in Romania and Croatia (*CBWP*). The European population has been estimated at 1·3 to 2·3 million pairs (*EBCC Atlas*).

At the beginning of the 20th century, Cirl Buntings used to be widely distributed in England and Wales, north sparingly even to Cumbria and Yorkshire. They tended to favour sheltered valleys with arable farmland and well-timbered hedgerows. Being sedentary, they were always vulnerable to hard winters and then to changing farming practices. A decline began about 1930, though breeding was still well distributed up to 1938 in north Wales, more locally in south Wales, and continuing in England north to Herefordshire, south Worcestershire, Oxfordshire, Buckinghamshire and Bedfordshire (Witherby *et al* 1938–41). Numbers began to fall more seriously still from about the 1950s, even in the south. By the time of the *1968–72 Atlas*, though still found across southern England north to Worcestershire, they were common only in Devon, Cornwall and Somerset.

The Wiltshire population was apparently never high, but was found to be well-established shortly after Montagu discovered the species breeding in Devon in 1800 (Yarrell 1837–43, see also Aplin 1892). Smith (1887) 'repeatedly watched it in several localities which it regularly haunts', but the only areas he mentioned by name were 'Basset Down' (probably Berwick Bassett Down), Devizes, Salisbury and Mere. The bird report in *WANHM* for 1929 described the Cirl Bunting as 'A somewhat uncommon resident' and for 1936 as 'Very much in evidence and a good number of breeding records distributed throughout the county, particularly Salisbury Plain area'. In the first half of the 20th century, there were three main centres for Cirl Buntings in Wiltshire: the valleys and south-facing slopes between Swindon and the Marlborough Downs; the valleys of the Avon and Bourne to the north of Salisbury; and the area around the Winterslows to the east of Salisbury; occasionally a pair would breed somewhere outside these centres for a year or two, only then to abandon the site (GL Webber).

After the 1939–45 War, the species was still regularly reported, but even in 1948 was noted by the oologist Major WM Congreve as 'not up to usual numbers on the Wilts-Hants border' (*WANHM*). From the late 1950s, records in *WANHM* become fewer and, unfortunately, the results of a Wiltshire 'Cirl Bunting Enquiry 1963–64', referred to in each of the following two years, were apparently never published. Peirson (1959) wrote, 'Practically all the reports of its breeding and most of the sight records come from the east and south-east of the county. Even there its distribution is curiously inconstant'. Webber (1968) added, 'This species seems to have decreased even in its most favoured localities and breeding records have been few in the past ten years'.

By the early 1970s the Cirl Bunting was clearly very scarce indeed in Wiltshire and virtually confined to the south – where the county's largest reported flock, of about 40, was close to Ford near Salisbury in 'winter' 1973 – though an unpublished record of four or five near Woodborough on 18–19 May 1972 (letter to Ruth Barnes from Eileen H Ingram) seems conclusive. The *1968–72 Atlas* showed only four 10-km squares occupied in Wiltshire, by a total of just a few pairs. Buxton (1981) summarised this as 'An uncommon breeding resident now apparently restricted to the south-eastern part of the county, notably the Winterslow area. There used to be a small breeding population around Swindon but no birds have been seen there during the past five years. Other sites in central districts also appear to have been abandoned'. The last reported breeding at Winterslow had, however, been in 1977, although birds were 'recorded regularly' there in 1978 and were still present in April 1979, and in January and February 1980. These increasingly infrequent observations came to an end with the record of an immature male at Calne on 18 October 1980 (*Hobby*). By 1994, British Cirl Buntings were confined to south Devon, apart from a very few in Cornwall, though in 1996 one pair visited a bird-table in Somerset through April–June (*RBBP*). Weed-rich stubbles, which modern agricultural methods do not provide, are a vital habitat requirement for this species. After research by the RSPB, however, special stewardship schemes were set up with the cooperation of farmers in its last stronghold in south Devon – where there are small fields with good hedgerows – and, as a result, the local population there was increased from under 120 pairs in 1989 to some 352 pairs in 1993 and over 450 in 1998 (Wotton *et al* 2000). Although the increase was one of consolidation and not accompanied by any range expansion, these figures hold some hope for the future of this attractive bunting in Great Britain, but it would still have to spread back through Somerset, and possibly Dorset, before any might reach Wiltshire again – unless a re-introduction programme were to be considered.

GLW & IJF-L

Reed Bunting

Emberiza schoeniclus

Seriously decreasing resident in wetlands, also some passage/winter

In summer, the peculiarly unmusical series of notes that make up the song of the Reed Bunting can be heard in a surprising range of latitudes and habitats across Eurasia from Iberia to Sakhalin and northern Japan – and, although this species' distribution is very patchy in southern Europe, some nest south to Morocco and Turkey, as well as Iran and northern China. The breeding population of Europe, excluding Russia, has been put at 3·2 to 4·4 million pairs (*EBCC Atlas*). Winter survival relies on mean January temperatures remaining above 0°C, as snow cover cuts off this species' access to food (Prŷs-Jones 1984), so Reed Buntings leave the northern and eastern parts of their European breeding range, and large parts of Asia too, for milder climates.

In Great Britain, where breeding Reed Buntings are widespread – not only in wetlands but also in such dry habitats as rape fields – the most recent population estimate is 176,000 to 193,000 territories (*APEP*). Between the *1968–72* and *1988–91 Atlases*, however, numbers had declined by some 12 per cent, most losses being in the north and west. After an increase in the late 1960s, national surveys detected a rapid decline of more than 50 per cent in the 1970s, but numbers have remained stable since the mid 1980s (*BBWC*). Severe weather – especially in such prolonged winters as those of 1946/47 and 1962/63, but also in others when snow and ice are of shorter duration – result in high mortality and a much smaller breeding population in the following season (*1981–84 Winter Atlas*). Recovery is rapid, however, and such 'crashes' do not account for the long-term decline of this bunting (*1988–91 Atlas*).

Ringing results show that very small numbers of Reed Buntings from Fenno-Scandia winter in Great Britain, but that the British breeding population is largely self-contained and fairly sedentary (*Migration Atlas*). Of the total of 1266 Reed Buntings ringed in Wiltshire during 1965–2000, only 18 were subsequently reported in that period and just one of those had moved more than 99 km – this was an adult ringed at Bromham on 25 November 1990 and retrapped and released at Sandwich Bay (Kent) on 11 March 1993. There have, however, been three inward recoveries of individuals from over 99 km away: the first, ringed in Warwickshire on 20 December 1975, was found dead near Marlborough over three years later, on 15 April 1979; the second, marked in Flintshire on 15 June 1984, was recovered at Corsham on 27 December that year; and the third, ringed in Staffordshire on 7 May 1989, was twice retrapped at Bromham over the next three years, on 15 December 1990 and on 31 October 1992.

More recently, special ringing efforts at three autumn-to-spring roosts at CWP68, Swindon STW and Moulden Hill Lake, Swindon – which respectively have held peak numbers of about 40, 50 and 90 Reed Buntings – have demonstrated a degree of local movement, particularly an interchange between some feeding areas and local roost sites (Harris 2004); a high turnover at these places during autumn suggests passage through northeast Wiltshire, though it is not yet clear to what extent breeding and wintering birds are drawn from different populations.

Smith (1887), who called this the 'Black-headed Bunting', had 'found its nest at some distance from the nearest stream', but also noted that 'it delights... in moist wet places' and wrote that it was to be found 'sparingly wherever there is water'. Peirson (1919) described it as 'a common resident along the river' in the Marlborough district, and, for Wiltshire as a whole, later (1959) noted it as breeding 'sparsely along the banks of most rivers, canals and lakes but more commonly in a few places'. Peirson also stated that, in winter, 'its numbers appear to decrease…often to be found well away from water on stubbles or round rickyards'. Buxton (1981) wrote that it was 'a fairly common breeding resident in the wetter areas…also found in drier habitats and breeds on high ground where large areas of rank vegetation are available'.

Buxton noted, too, that in winter Reed Buntings formed 'flocks…usually small…occasionally…over one hundred individuals'. Flocks in the annual bird reports up to 1973 in *WANHM* included over 100 near Clarendon on 22 January 1949, 150–200 at Swindon STW on 25–26 September 1954, and about 200 at Downton on 12 December 1970. Winter flocks were much smaller during 1990–2000, however: the highest figures in *Hobby* were 60 at Bromham in late 1991, and 80 at Ashton Keynes in January–February 1995. Similarly, the roost in the reedbed at Corsham Lake – that had held as many as 100 in 1981 and 1982 – was down to 20 in February 1999 (*Hobby*). The 1998–2000 winter survey counts produced a figure of just over 300, and it is suggested that Wiltshire's winter numbers amount to between 1850 and 2700 individuals.

The *1981–84 Winter Atlas* noted Reed Buntings in all but two of Wiltshire's 33 core and 15 part 10-km squares. Like Linnets and Tree Sparrows – two other species that decreased significantly during the latter part of the 20th century – these buntings feed in autumn and winter on seeds of grasses and herbs, particularly farmland weeds. The use of efficient herbicides to control these weeds during the 1970s may well have caused the declines of both Linnets (O'Connor & Shrubb 1986) and Reed Buntings (*1988–91 Atlas*). Other factors may have included loss and deterioration of suitable wetland breeding habitats, and change from spring-sown to autumn-sown crops, with the resulting loss of winter stubble. Accordingly, the winter survey in 1998–2000 found them in only 20 core and four part 10-km squares, then absent from much of the south and west, though this result will be in part a result of the sample methods used.

During the 1980s, the BTO Garden Bird Feeding Survey showed a significant and continuing increase in the numbers of Reed Buntings coming to gardens in winter, perhaps an indication of shortage of their usual winter food (Thompson 1988). In 1982, there were just six records of their feeding in Wiltshire gardens, although this included 20 in one garden in Bradford-on-Avon, and even 18 ringed in a garden at Corsham. Since then, this species has regularly been recorded in gardens at that season, usually taking seeds but occasionally bread and peanuts (*Hobby*).

The song period for Reed Buntings in Wiltshire extends usually from February to July or early August, the earliest recorded date during 1992–2000 being 5 February and – apart from exceptional reports on 7 September 1997 and 10 October 1993 – the latest 9 August. Typical breeding sites are gravel pit margins, marshes and riversides. During the 20th century, however, this bunting also moved into drier habitats, including young conifer plantations, cereal and rape fields and, especially in Wiltshire, hawthorn and gorse scrub on waterless chalk downland. Its use of 'less preferred habitats…increases when numbers are high' (*1988–91 Atlas*). Breeding was mapped in 23 of the 33 core 10-km squares in Wiltshire, and the species was seen in another five, during fieldwork for the *1968–72 Atlas*, and in 25 squares (again with presence in a further five) during the *1988–91 Atlas*. The summer distribution map for 1995–2000 shows the increase continuing, with Reed Buntings breeding in 28, and presence in 32, of the core 10-km squares and in nearly a quarter of all tetrads. It also demonstrates a concentration of breeding pairs along river valleys, at CWP and on SPTA, a distribution reflected by the summer abundance map. Dedicated surveys in CWP West in 2003 and 2004 suggested that the numbers of singing

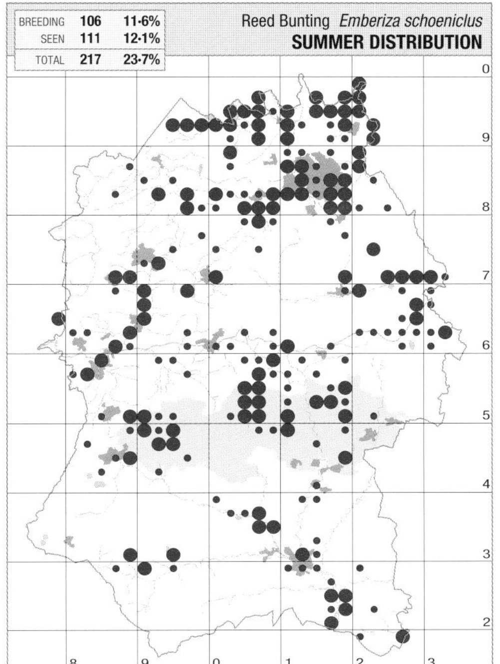

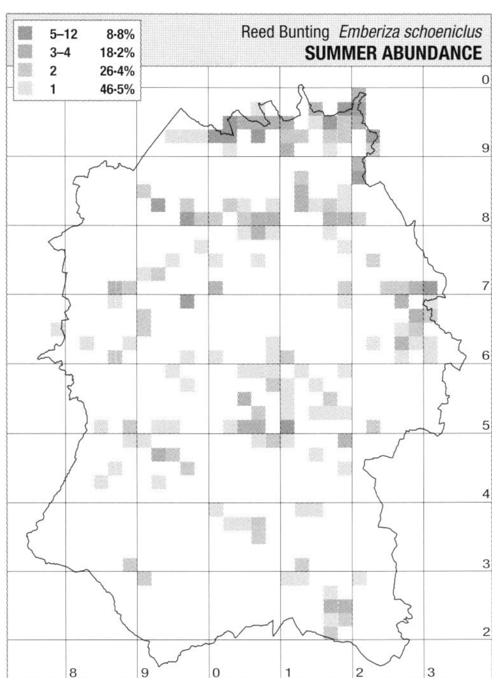

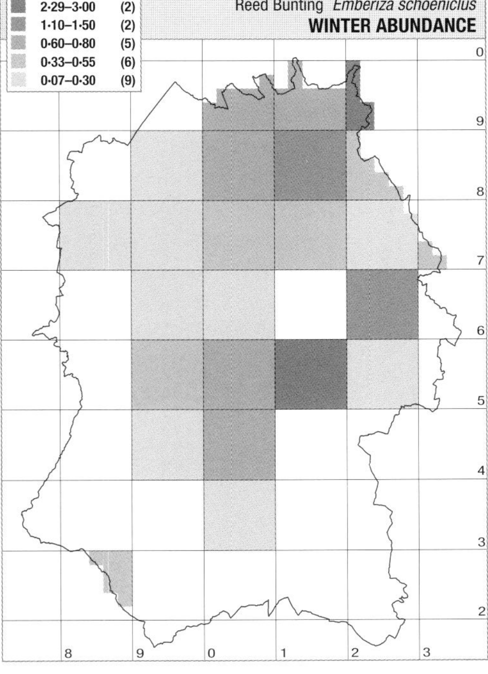

males there varied between 40 and 70 (Harris 2004), but these figures included the lakes that are in Gloucestershire as well as those in Wiltshire. Densities in several places – for example, 14 birds/km² at Waterhay – exceeded the national average of around 10 birds/km² for riparian habitat (Gregory & Baillie 1988). An RSPB survey of SPTA in 2000 estimated 267 pairs (Stanbury *et al* 2000); extrapolating this figure to the whole of the county of the basis of WOS timed counts indicates a Wiltshire population of some 2220 pairs. The results of BBS from 38 1-km squares that contribute to the national scheme give a lower figure of 1530 pairs, though those particular squares may not be representative of the county as a whole for Reed Buntings.

Recent declines have meant that the Reed Bunting is listed in Great Britain as a species of special conservation concern, and landowners are being encouraged to carry out more beneficial management of wetlands and set-aside, to use specific pesticides more carefully, and to leave flower-rich margins around field boundaries. The national Biodiversity Action Plan aimed to halt or reverse declines by 2003 and to increase numbers by at least 50 per cent from the 1996 level by 2008. Locally, the Cotswold Water Park Society has an action plan with the objectives of maintaining current numbers in CWP and increasing the area of suitable breeding and wintering habitat. It remains to be seen if these hopes can be turned into reality.

(See also page 725.)

SBE

Ortolan Bunting

Emberiza hortulana

Vagrant (1 record) from continental Europe, winters Africa

Wiltshire's only recorded Ortolan, in first-year plumage, was trapped and ringed at Thorncombe, south of Bratton, on 26 September 1986 (*Hobby*). It had been with a large party of Yellowhammers and would certainly have gone unseen but for its chance capture during general ringing. No doubt, careful checking of the county's finch and bunting flocks in autumn would reveal more such rarities away from the obvious coastal migration hotspots.

Although Ortolans still breed across much of continental Europe from the Mediterranean north to southern Fenno-Scandia – also extending into Asia through Turkey to Iran, and from the Urals across southern Siberia as far as northwest Mongolia – they have, like other buntings, suffered from a fragmentation of range and a decline in numbers in western and central Europe, as a result of the loss of hedgerows and the changes in farming practices; the European population, excluding Russia, was in the 1990s estimated at 593,000 to 742,000 pairs (*EBCC Atlas*).

Ortolans winter well north of the equator in sub-Saharan Africa, and in southwest Arabia, so that every year small numbers reach Great Britain by overshooting the western European breeding range in spring, and rather more through wind-drift or reverse migration on their return in autumn. Perhaps because of the population crashes in northern France, the Low Countries, north Germany, and southern Norway and Sweden, there was a marked decline in migrant numbers to Great Britain from the 1970s onwards, compared with the 1950s and 1960s (Cottridge & Vinicombe 1996); there has since been an overall increase (with annual averages of 58 in the 1980s and of 71 in the 1990s), but numbers continue to fluctuate (Fraser *et al* 2002). The national total in 1986 – the year of the Wiltshire record – was around average, and well below the 1996 total of 118, the highest of any year between 1968 and 2000.

RT

Little Bunting

Emberiza pusilla

Vagrant (2 records) from Fenno-Scandia/Siberia, winters south Asia

The Little Bunting is a summer visitor to northeast Fenno-Scandia and from north

European Russia right across northern Siberia; it winters mainly in southeast Asia from Nepal and eastern India to the former Indo-Chinese countries and, south of the Yangtze, in southern China itself. It was only in 1935 that the species began spreading west into Finland (where by the 1990s the population was estimated at 5000–10,000 pairs) and then into extreme northeast Norway and Sweden (perhaps 100 pairs) (*EBCC Atlas*). Vagrants had long been known to reach Great Britain by overshooting in spring or by reverse migration in autumn, but in the 1950s the numbers recorded – then mainly September to November, rarely April and May – began to increase markedly. In the hundred years to 1957 the grand total of British records was 93 (chiefly in east Scotland), whereas the 43 years of 1958–2000 produced 751, no fewer than 58 of them in 2000 alone (Fraser & Rogers 2002). Moreover, they began over this period to appear in inland counties, particularly in spring and sometimes even in winter. Indeed, it is now clear that some overwinter in western Europe south to France. Wiltshire's two have been found on almost identical dates in late March:

1989	27 March	Bromham	1st-year female, trapped/ringed
1991	28 Mar–9 Apr	Chippenham	1st-year

The one at Bromham roosted with Reed Buntings by a small scrub and reed-fringed pond, and at Chippenham the bird (see *Hobby* 18: plate 4) visited a garden feeding station. Many of those elsewhere inland have been found in finch and bunting flocks.

RT

Corn Bunting

Emberiza calandra

Seriously decreased resident, but still common on downs and Salisbury Plain

Large and rather plain-looking for a bunting, the males of this species of rolling downland are usually located by their distinctive song, often likened to the jangle of shaken keys. Corn Buntings are birds of dry or stony steppe grassland that have adapted to arable edges where there is some tall vegetation. Their breeding range extends from the Canaries and northwest Africa north throughout much of southern and western Europe to the southern North Sea and the southern shores of the Baltic, thence east through south Russia, Asia Minor and parts of the Middle East to Iran, Kazakhstan and northwest China.

In Europe – where, excluding Russia, the population has been estimated at 3·5 to 6·8 million pairs – they are still common in the south but declining drastically in many countries, including Belgium, the Netherlands, Denmark, Germany, Switzerland and, not least, Great Britain, where numbers fell by 60 per cent during 1970–90 (*EBCC Atlas*). The *1988–91 Atlas* found Corn Buntings in roughly a third fewer 10-km squares than had the *1968–72 Atlas*, with the contraction in range particularly evident in much of Scotland (apart from isolated populations in, for example, northeast Aberdeenshire and on the machair of the southern Outer Hebrides), in north England south to the central Midlands, in the southwest peninsula and in parts of East Anglia and the southeast. The number of breeding territories in Great Britain – where Wiltshire remains one of its strongholds (*1988–91 Atlas*) – was estimated at 19,800 in 1993 (Donald & Evans 1995), but just 8500 to 12,200 in 2000 (*APEP*).

In Wiltshire, Smith (1887) called this the 'Common Bunting' and described it as 'extremely common, especially in the vast tracts of arable land on our downs'. Forty years later, the 1929 bird report in *WANHM* still noted Corn Bunting as 'common' but, another 30 years on, Peirson (1959) remarked on its scarcity or absence away from the areas where 'It is fairly common in the centres of the chalk downlands. Along the chalk escarpments and on the chalk slopes enclosing the narrow river valleys, it is very common... the concentration of singing males... is quite remarkable'. The species was at that time almost absent from much of the extreme north and west of the county and from the south and southeast, where large areas of arable were lacking. The 1951–54 Wiltshire Corn Bunting Enquiry found that nests were generally between 350 and 750 feet (roughly 110–230 m) on the chalk escarpments, but also between 250 and 400 feet (roughly 75–120 m) on the Upper Greensand outcrop south of Devizes (Rice 1956). Webber (1964) added that the species was common on the north escarpment of the Marlborough Downs. Although none was found in the southeast of the county in that 1950s enquiry, Buxton (1981) later commented that 'east of the Salisbury Avon and south of the Kennet... numbers appear to be increasing'.

In northern Europe, Corn Buntings are confined mainly to farmland associated with cereals and hay meadows (*EBCC Atlas*). A decline in arable farming in Great Britain, which began towards the end of the 19th century and reached its lowest point in the recession between the 1914–18 and 1939–45 Wars, was paralleled by a national decrease in Corn Buntings (Marchant *et al* 1990). As a result of the agricultural revival during and after 1939–45, the species expanded in numbers and range and, at least in the West Midlands, continued to do so until the 1960s (O'Connor & Shrubb 1986). In the early 1970s Corn Bunting would be singing from an overhead wire every kilometre along the road through the Pewsey Vale; then the wires were put underground and the singers disappeared. But this species does not have to have high song posts, frequently singing from slightly proud vegetation, fence posts or even the middle of fields of cereal.

The population crash nationally was most dramatic in the 1970s and 1980s and, though less severely, the species continued to decline through the 1990s (*BBWC*). During the last 25 years of the 20th century breeding numbers fell by around 90 per cent, triggering conservation concerns. The crash has been blamed on the loss of weedy stubbles as a winter feeding habitat, and also variously linked with the reduced cultivation of barley, the switch to autumn sown cereals, the replacement of hay by silage, and a reduction in traditional rotations (*eg* Harper 1995, *BBWC*).

Comparison of the summer distribution map with the geological map (see inside front cover) clearly shows that this is a species of the cultivated chalk uplands, while the abundance maps highlight the Marlborough Downs, Salisbury Plain, West Wiltshire Downs and Cranborne Chase, as well as an outpost in the Cotswolds. Corn Buntings appear actually to have increased in numbers between the *1968–72* and *1988–91 Atlases* in the area south of the Kennet and east of the Salisbury Avon; and, almost 50 years after the special Wiltshire enquiry, have persisted in a small outpost near North Wraxall – despite losses in the northwest, including the Cotswolds. On a 10-km basis, its range remains essentially similar to that defined by the *1968–72* and *1988–91 Atlases*, respectively recorded in 31 and 25 of Wiltshire's 33 core 10-km squares, and in 29 during 1995–2000. The summer tetrad survey in the last period found Corn Buntings in just under a third of Wiltshire's 915 tetrads, and evidence of breeding in just over half of those. A density of 5·2 pairs per tetrad was recorded by an RSPB survey of SPTA (Stanbury *et al* 2000); extrapolated to Wiltshire as a whole on the basis of WOS timed counts, this suggests a county population of 4790 pairs, given higher densities still on the Marlborough Downs – a figure that falls near the lower end of the 4510 to 6050 pairs suggested by using the results of surveys in adjacent regions.

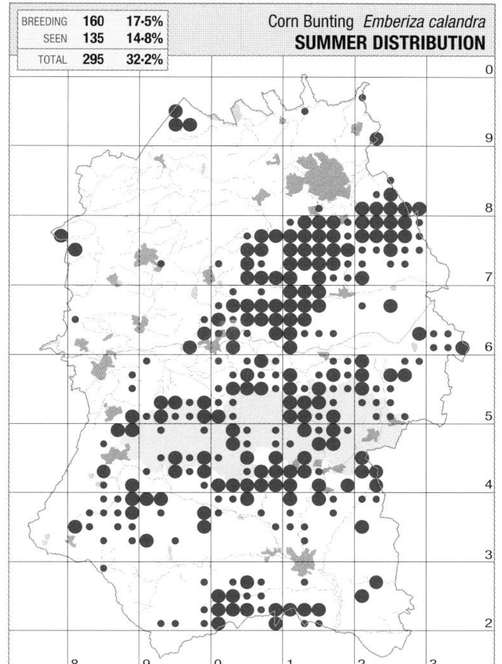

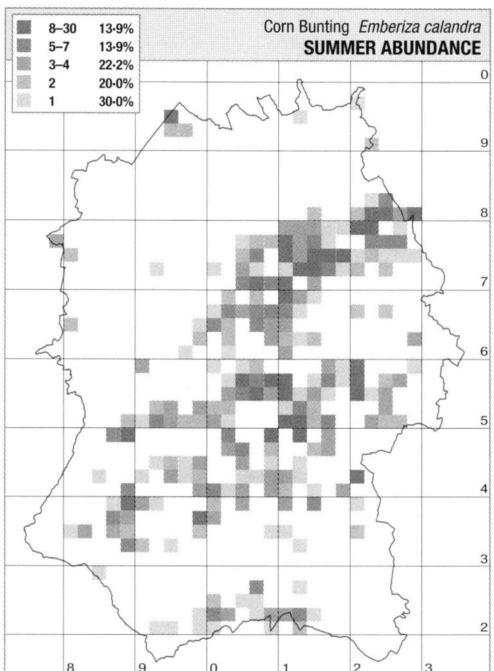

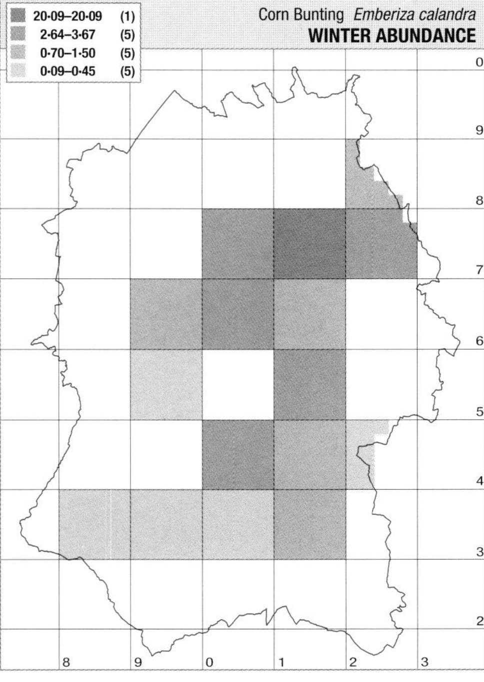

Decreases in the extreme southwest of the county in 1981, and in the northeast in 1989, were the only changes in the status of the Corn Bunting recorded in *Hobby* during the 1980s, though other decreases on the edges of the main Wiltshire range may well have gone unnoted. At least four males singing on overhead wires by arable field edges between Longbridge Deverill and Horningsham in the mid 1980s (Ferguson-Lees 1984) had gone before the 1990s. A decline on Dean Hill – where Corn Buntings were an unremarkable sight in the 1970s – began to be noted in the 1980s; they disappeared from the Hampshire side of the hill first, then from the Wiltshire side, and no singing males could be found anywhere by 2000 (P Combridge). In 1993 the National Bunting survey recorded 220 singing male Corn Buntings in the county, but by 2000 no more than 147 were reported, over 50 of them on the Marlborough Downs (*Hobby*).

Like many other seed-eaters of open country, Corn Buntings roost communally and feed in flocks in winter (*1981–84 Winter Atlas*). In the last three decades of the 20th century, Wiltshire's biggest flocks were 200 estimated at Rockley on 14 May 1972 (*WANHM*) – this species often does not start nesting before late May and early June – and the same again at Liddington Hill on 27 March 1993, but both these were well beaten by an impressive winter count of 342 at Westdown in December 1982 (*Hobby*). Other winter to spring flocks of 100 or more in the 1980s included 150 near Salisbury from January to March 1984, 130 at Everleigh in 1988, 100 at Barbury Castle in January 1989, and 150 feeding on spilt grain at Upton Scudamore in early March 1989. During 1990–2000, flocks of 100 were seen at West Kennett in November 1990, Urchfont Hill in December 1994, Yarnbury Castle in March 1998, Broad Chalke in March 1999, and Longbridge Deverill in January 2000, while larger counts were 190 at Cherhill White Horse in January 1993, 160 and 118 at Stanton St Bernard in January 1997 and March 2000, and 140 at Ogbourne St Andrew in December 1998.

The winter map roughly matches the summer distribution, not unexpectedly as British Corn Buntings appear mainly to be resident (*Migration Atlas*), but their apparent absence in winter from the most southerly parts of the Wiltshire breeding range is noteworthy. They were found in just 14 of the county's 33 core 10-km squares during the winter survey of 1998–2000, exactly half the number mapped in the *1981–84 Winter Atlas*. (This may, however, be an artefact of this survey's random coverage, because the three summer mapping surveys during 1968–2000 showed little change in distribution by 10-km squares.) Some movement from breeding areas was suggested by statements in earlier bird reports in *WANHM*: in 1948 the species was 'abundant about Aldbourne this summer with considerable decrease in autumn', and in 1949 there was a 'decrease … in winter' in the Pewsey area. Only 21 Corn Buntings were ringed, and none recovered, in Wiltshire during 1965–2000. Winter timed surveys recorded 1040 individuals, slightly more than the summer figure, suggesting a total in that season of 6320 to 8480.

(See also page 725.)

MVJ

Significant additional records 2001–2005

Stephen Edwards & Rob Turner

The species texts in *Birds of Wiltshire* cover the period up to 31 December 2000 – the end of the year of completion of the tetrad fieldwork – but inevitably there have been a number of notable observations between then and publication. This appendix details those of most interest or significance during 2001–05, including no fewer than six species added to the Wiltshire list (Blue-winged Teal, Cattle Egret, Whiskered Tern, Shore Lark, Red-rumped Swallow, Rustic Bunting) – bringing the total to 315 – as well as the first county report of 'Kumlien's Gull' (the northeast Canadian race of the Iceland Gull), and three first breeding records (Garganey, Little Egret, Oystercatcher). All the records set out below of scarce or rare birds have been accepted either by the WOS Records Panel or, where appropriate, by the BBRC.

County firsts

The italicised line under each name in this first list shows the normal range of the species, and the figure in brackets the number of British records accepted by *BBRC* during 1950–2005.

Blue-winged Teal *Anas discors*

North America (218)

A male in eclipse plumage stayed at CWP68 from 3 August to 26 September 2002 (Adams 2003), during which time it frustrated many visiting birders by its elusive nature.

Cattle Egret *Bubulcus ibis*

All continents, in Europe mainly Iberia and spreading north in France (123)

One on a farm between Firsdown and West Winterslow in November 2004 (Combridge 2005a): first noticed by the farmer's wife on or about the 9th, it remained for just over five weeks, until 15 December. The following year, two stayed at Britford from 24 December 2005 until 31 March 2006.

Whiskered Tern *Chlidonias hybrida*

Southern Eurasia/Africa/Australia, winters mainly Africa/southern Asia (115)

One at CWP74 on 14–15 April 2002 (Webber & Beint 2003) was the earliest of five in Great Britain that year. Three years later, during a longer stay in Gloucestershire, one visited CWP95 on the three successive days of 24–26 May 2005.

Shore Lark *Eremophila alpestris*

Arctic or mountains of Eurasia (also lowlands of North America); some from Fenno-Scandia winter British east coast

One at Whiteparish on 1 November 2004 (Combridge 2005b).

Red-rumped Swallow *Cecropis daurica*

Southern Eurasia/Africa, winters mainly Africa (480)

One at Corsham Lake on 25 April 2005.

Rustic Bunting *Emberiza rustica*

North Eurasia west to Fenno-Scandia, winters east Asia (422)

A first-winter male trapped during a ringing session at a Reed Bunting roost near Bradford-on-Avon on 24 January 2004 unfortunately died (Hamzij & Turner 2005); the skin is now in the national collection in the Natural History Museum, Tring (Hertfordshire).

Breeding highlights

Garganeys were at last proved to breed in Wiltshire, at Maiden Bradley in 2003. In 2004, a record count of 160 **Grey Heron** nests was made for the colony at Britford. This was the second largest in Great Britain, and considerably higher than the 20–42 reported there during the 1990s. Better access to the heronry in 2004 enabled much improved viewing of the colony, and, though not possible to quantify, it is likely that such large numbers had been present for a number of years at the site. **Little Egrets** are now a familiar year-round sight in suitable habitats in Wiltshire and the first records of breeding – two pairs in 2003, three in 2004, and 12 in 2005 – had long been predicted.

Breeding trends among Wiltshire's birds of prey were generally favourable. Up to six pairs of **Red Kites** were seen, though the highest number of nests found in any one year was three in 2002. **Hen Harriers** bred in 2003, raising three chicks – the first since three nests were reported in 1936 and, before that, early in the 19th century. Single pairs of **Montagu's Harriers** raised young in 2002 and 2004; and in 2005 no fewer than four pairs nested, two of them fledging a total of eight chicks – the most successful season since at least 1953. **Goshawks** showed signs of slow increase, reaching a total of four pairs by 2005. **Merlins** were confirmed to have bred in the county for the first time: a recently fledged juvenile, still with some down, was seen with an adult female in close attendance in July 2005. Of 60 pairs of **Hobbies** reported in 2005, 16 were proved to breed, the highest ever total. Three pairs of **Peregrines** bred in 2001 and four in 2004.

Water Rails have seldom been proved to nest in the county, so breeding records at Bradford-on-Avon in 2001 and at CWP68 in 2002 were noteworthy. **Oystercatchers** started nesting for the first time, one pair successfully at CWP in 2002 and 2004, though they failed in 2005. **Stone-curlews** increased to 68 pairs that fledged 45 young in 2005, and **Little Ringed Plovers** to 14 pairs at CWP in the same year. **Black-headed Gulls** also increased at CWP: 53 pairs attempted to breed in 2001, and 39 pairs raised at least 53 young in 2004; five colour-ringed juveniles from 2004 were subsequently recorded elsewhere, in Glamorgan and Ireland (Co Cork) later that year and in Devon (two) and northern France during 2005. The increase in **Common Terns** continued, and 27 pairs nested at CWP in 2003, not all successfully but raising at least 41 young; only eight pairs certainly nested in 2004, fledging just eight young; the species also bred at three Swindon sites during the period.

Barn Owls continued to prosper: 272 pairs bred in nestboxes and fledged 803 young in 2005 (English Nature); including pairs using natural sites, the Wiltshire population could be 350 to 400 pairs. One pair of **Short-eared Owls** possibly nested in 2003 and two pairs were confirmed as breeding in 2005, all on SPTA; in winter this owl is mostly recorded on SPTA, so it is noteworthy that no fewer than 30 were found in the northeast of the county during 2004/05.

Towards the end of the period, there was evidence of a change in the breeding status of **Wood Larks** in Wiltshire, some remaining to nest in arable crops in what had previously just been regular wintering areas: three pairs nested unsuccessfully in 2004, and one pair raised two young in winter wheat in 2005. That year, too, extensive bird surveys on Salisbury Plain found two **Wheatear** territories at Porton Down and a downy juvenile on SPTA (Corbet & Adams 2006). The BBS of the latter area found that numbers of **Quails**, **Sky Larks**, **Grasshopper Warblers**, **Reed Buntings** and **Stonechats** had increased since 2000, whereas **Linnets**, **Yellowhammers** and **Corn Buntings** had declined significantly, along with **Grey Partridges** and **Whinchats** (Stanbury *et al* 2005). In addition, 167 pairs of **Lapwings** were counted across the Plain. A partial survey of the Marlborough Downs in 2005 illustrated its continued importance for farmland birds, recording the following totals of territories: 33 of **Quails**, 40 of **Yellow Wagtails**, 792 of **Yellowhammers**, and 350 of **Corn Buntings** (RSPB unpublished data).

The first proof of breeding by **Cetti's Warblers** at CWP came in 2004, when a minimum of 11 young were reared; retraps there that autumn of individuals that had been ringed at Slimbridge (Gloucestershire) and Farlington Marshes (Hampshire) suggested two possible origins for this county's colonising population. **Ravens** continued their remarkable increase since the first pair ventured east from Somerset in 1992: of 59 pairs reported in 2005, 17 were proved to breed. Increased observer effort in the southeast resulted in more **Hawfinch** records, late winter flocks reaching peaks of 76 in 2002 and of 52 in 2004; four nests were found in 2002.

A colour-marking project resulted in 80 **Willow Tits** being ringed in this five-year period, compared with a mere 74 over the previous 36 years. Surveys during 2001–05 at Center Parcs, Longleat, recorded the following species (peak numbers of territories): **Firecrest** (eight in 2004), **Pied Flycatcher** (two in 2004), **Siskin** (28 in 2004), **Lesser Redpoll** (one in 2001 and 2003) and **Crossbill** (five in 2003).

Tree Sparrow project

The WOS **Tree Sparrow** project was started in north Wiltshire in 1999 and, through the provision of nestboxes and feeding stations, has resulted in a significant increase in both breeding and wintering numbers; a similar project was started by the RSPB in the southwest of the county in 2003. The results of both are included in table 113.

Table 113. Tree Sparrows *Passer montanus* in Wiltshire: summer and winter totals 1996–2005

Summer	96	97	98	99	00	01	02	03	04	05
Project sites	–	–	–	1	3	20	20	25	35	33
Breeding pairs (nestboxes)	–	–	–	1	13	19	82	129	144	140
Breeding pairs (natural sites)	–	–	–	–	30	44	54	68	68	52
Breeding pairs (non-project)	(9)	(4)	(19)	–	–	–	–	–	–	–
Young fledged	–	–	–	–	–	190	728	898	1136	1011
Winter	**95/96**	**96/97**	**97/98**	**98/99**	**99/00**	**00/01**	**01/02**	**02/03**	**03/04**	**04/05**
Sites	15	13	8	7	9	12	20	13	17	18
Winter numbers	74	75	101	155	148	235	245	289	600	1010
Peak months	Mar	Jan	Feb	Nov	Mar	Jan	Mar	Feb	Mar	Sep
Largest winter flocks	34	40	60	60	80	130	105	120	120	800

Waxwing invasion

Two reports of **Waxwings** in December 2004 were the forerunners of what in Wiltshire became an unprecedented invasion: three-figure flocks were found at four sites in January and at three in February and March 2005, including peak counts of 300 at Trowbridge, 250 at Westbury, 207 at Melksham, 200 at Warminster, 175 at Westwood and 145 at Chippenham. The highest total on a single day was 585 on 30 January, but large numbers stayed into mid February. These were part of a huge eruption from Fenno-Scandia, which started at many places along the Scottish and English east coasts in October (*Birding World* 17: 517), and eclipsed all previous records in the county.

Wildfowl

Wild swans are guaranteed to enliven any winter birdwatching excursion, and so three records of **Whooper Swans** (two in 2001, and a party of seven at Inglesham from October 2003 to January 2004) were welcome, as were 14 reports of **Bewick's Swans** (including parties of 15 and 18). Rare geese also caused excitement, including three records of the tundra race of the **Bean Goose** and four of the dark-bellied race of the **Brent Goose**. A male **Green-winged Teal** at CWP from 7 March to 8 April 2003 was only the third county record. A pair of **Ring-necked Ducks** stayed at Corsham Lake from 25 March to 10 April 2002. What was assumed the same female **Ferruginous Duck** appeared at Ramsbury in January–February 2002 and again in October, and a male was at Langford Lakes in March 2003.

Divers to Glossy Ibis

The only divers recorded during 2001–05 were a **Great Northern** at CWP on 3 March and 14 April 2002, and a **Red-throated** at Coate Water during 15–19 December 2004. Seabirds included a **Shag** – common in coastal waters around southwest England, but always unusual inland – at Calne on 5 January 2001 and a **Manx Shearwater** at Swindon on 21 September 2004, in which year **Gannets** also appeared at Tytherington on 29 June and at Calne on 1 August. The period produced no fewer than 20 records of **Common Bitterns**, a species now annual at CWP. **Great White Egrets,** increasingly recorded in Great Britain, were found twice in 2002, at Coate Water on 20 May and at CWP during 20–26 August. Although **White Storks** are spreading in parts of Europe, after a period of long-term decline (see *EBCC Atlas*) – a welcome trend that should tend to lead to increased vagrancy to Great Britain – escapes and full-winged re-introductions from zoos and waterfowl collections in both Britain and the near Continent also occur; indeed, one of the three reported in Wiltshire during the period was known to be an escape. County listers were grateful that a **Glossy Ibis** appeared at Charlton-All-Saints on 1–2 May 2004, as the only two previous records were as long ago as 1825 and 1915.

Raptors to Great Bustard

A **Red-footed Falcon** at Haxton Down during 3–9 June 2001 was Wiltshire's eleventh record. A female **Merlin** found incapacitated at Beckhampton in late July 2003 had been ringed as a nestling in North Yorkshire in June 1994, thus providing the first firm evidence about the origins of late summer and autumn Merlins in the county. As there had been no Wiltshire record for nearly 30 years, a **Spotted Crake** at CWP68 on 31 August 2002 was a notable find, as was a **Corncrake** at Upavon on 6 August 2001, and the first **Crane** since 1995, at CWP on 17 January 2002. As part of the re-introduction scheme, 65 juvenile **Great Bustards** were released on Salisbury Plain in the autumns of 2004–06, in the first three (of ten scheduled) annual introductions. Although foxes have caused high mortality, it is already usually possible to see some birds in the wild near the release site in winter and sometimes farther afield.

Waders to gulls

What was only Wiltshire's third record of a **Red-necked Phalarope** was seen at Coate Water on 28 October 2005, the others having been in 1841 and 1990, and a very obliging first-winter **Grey Phalarope** stayed on the Crammer Pond, Devizes, from 26 October to 3 November 2005. A **Little Gull** at CWP from 28 May to 26 July 2003 was the county's first summering record of this species, though Wiltshire's second **Laughing Gull**, in first-winter plumage at Swindon STW during 9–13 January 2001, naturally caused more interest in twitching circles. Increased awareness of the identification criteria of scarce or rare gulls doubtless led to 13 records of **Caspian Gull** during the period, including one that had been colour-ringed in Poland; and to the discovery of an **Iceland Gull** of the northeast Canadian race ('**Kumlien's Gull**') at CWP on 19 March 2003; what was believed to be the same individual was then seen in 2004 at CWP and Calne Sand Pits from 7 January to 26 March, again at the latter site during 11–30 December, and in 2005 at CWP from 17 February to 12 March. The county's third and fourth records of the nominate race of the **Iceland Gull** came in 2003 and 2005, and the eighth and ninth records of **Glaucous Gulls** in 2003 and 2005. An **Arctic Tern** at Melksham on 2–4 November 2005 was 15 days later than the county's previous latest record.

Bee-eaters, Wrynecks and passerines

Four **Bee-eaters** at Netheravon and, later, five at Manningford Fisheries, all on 11 June 2005, were the first records since 1999; one was then seen at Hannington on 26 July. Of 14 **Wrynecks** during the period, those on 23 June 2002 at Franchises Wood and 4 May 2003 at Hawkeridge were unusual, in that most now occur in autumn. Single **Rock Pipits** at CWP on 22 September 2002 and at Roundway Hill on 23 October 2005 were the county's fourteenth and fifteenth records. A **Stonechat** of the eastern race *maurus* ('**Siberian Stonechat**') at Whiteparish on 13 October 2003 was only the second record – and, interestingly, coincided with one at Portland (Dorset) on the same day (*BBRC*). Also from the east came two **Yellow-browed Warblers** at Chippenham on 8 October 2005, the first in Wiltshire since 1988: one, trapped and ringed that day, was not subsequently seen again, but the other stayed until the 27th. Winter records of four **Dartford Warblers** in the Swindon area in 2005 were far to the north of their usual range. **Bearded Tits** at CWP68 in October–November 2002 and in November–December 2003, at Chippenham in April 2003, and again at CWP68 from November 2004 to February 2005, were the county's first reports since 1982. Like Wrynecks, **Red-backed Shrikes** are now almost extinct as British breeding birds, so summer sightings of adults on SPTA in July 2001 and in July–August 2002 were particularly interesting, and one in first-winter plumage was also found at Whiteparish on 11–12 September 2003. The first **Woodchat Shrikes** since 1990 were seen at Middle Woodford on 8–9 September 2001, at Westdown Plantation on 5 June 2004, and near Aldbourne during 14–17 June 2005. The treatment of the **Common Redpoll** of north Europe as a species distinct from the indigenous and more familiar **Lesser Redpoll** of Britain and central Europe has undoubtedly sparked interest in the identification of both, and thus led to more Common Redpolls being recorded: totals of eight were found in both 2001 and 2002, and three in 2003. Finally, scarce buntings featured well during the period: apart from the Rustic Bunting among the 'County firsts' above, Wiltshire's third **Lapland Bunting** was seen at Whiteparish on 15 December 2001, and single **Snow Buntings** appeared at Pound Bottom on 20 November 2002, at Liddington Hill on 2 December 2003, and near Stanton St Bernard during 19–21 November 2005.

Earliest and latest dates of migrants in Wiltshire 1900–2005

These lists of Wiltshire's earliest and latest recorded dates of summer and winter visitors, and of regular passage migrants in both spring and autumn, have been compiled mainly from the annual bird reports in *WANHM* (1929–34, 1936, 1946–73) and *Hobby* (1974–2005), but others have also been taken from earlier notes in *WANHM* and two records from Witherby *et al* (1938–41). For some species, this research led to the discovery of early or late dates that had been missed by both Peirson (1959) and Buxton (1981) and were therefore not included by Palmer (1991).

The extreme dates below involve mostly early wanderers or late stragglers, and do not necessarily give any indication of the times of the main arrivals and departures – which can easily be two to four weeks or more later and earlier respectively, and which are affected by local, national, or continental weather and other factors.

The summer visitors include some that no longer breed (*eg* Wryneck) or have bred or summered only occasionally (*eg* Osprey), but Blackcaps and Chiffchaffs have had to be omitted, because both now winter regularly in Wiltshire. Similarly, the winter visitors include some that are scarce (*eg* Great Grey Shrike) or no more than vagrants (eg Bean Goose), while Wigeon, Pintail and Hen Harrier have not been included because they have produced occasional summer records. Again, some passage waders (*eg* Turnstone) have also had to be omitted because of odd winter records.

Notes on the tables

a Was 'seen several times…during the winter' before 'positively identified' on 17 March (*WANHM*).

b Also one in first-year plumage found dead on 18 January 1954 (*WANHM*).

c Remarkably early, but one same date in Hampshire (Clark & Eyre 1993). Next earliest 11 April 1932 & 1991.

d Was 'heard singing, presumably on passage' (*WANHM*), but date unlikely. Next latest 26 July 1922 & 1961.

e Also one winter record on 28 December 1999 (*Hobby*)

f One present 18 April to 9 May 1992 is considered to have been an escape

g Also reported on 3 July and 14 September 1975 (*Hobby*); unlikely breeding record in 1882 (Smith 1887)

h Was 'a large flock' (*WANHM*), but unprecedented so early. Next earliest 28 August 1983 (*Hobby*).

i Also 29 September 1929 and two each in June, July and August during 1931–36 (*WANHM*), some of which were queried at the time, while others were seen by established observers. Impossible now to substantiate, but this species 'has occurred…occasionally in June and July' (Witherby *et al* 1938–41).

j In 1933, however, three records, by three different observers, of 'a pair' on different parts of Salisbury Plain, between 2 May and 18 June, were considered to 'undoubtedly refer to the same pair' (*WANHM*).

Summer visitors

Species	Earliest	Latest
Garganey *Anas querquedula*	14 Mar 1971	9 Nov 1952
Quail *Coturnix coturnix*	17 Mar 1961 [a]	5 Nov 2005
Honey-buzzard *Pernis apivorus*	8 May 1995	18 Oct 1998
Marsh Harrier *Circus aeruginosus*	27 Mar 1960	7 Dec 2001
Montagu's Harrier *Circus pygargus*	26 Mar 1956	10 Oct 1961
Osprey *Pandion haliaetus*	17 Mar 1996	21 Oct 2001
Hobby *Falco subbuteo*	26 Mar 1997	22 Nov 1987
Corncrake *Crex crex*	28 Apr 1985 [b]	24 Nov 1999
Stone-curlew *Burhinus oedicnemus*	13 Feb 1953	16 Nov 1948 & 2005
Little Ringed Plover *Charadrius dubius*	11 Mar 1989	1 Oct 2004
Common Tern *Sterna hirundo*	20 Mar 1931	12 Dec 1930
Turtle Dove *Streptopelia turtur*	25 Mar 1970 [c]	21 Oct 1950
Cuckoo *Cuculus canorus*	23 Mar 1991	3 Dec 1921
Nightjar *Caprimulgus europaeus*	5 Apr 1968	2 Oct 1978
Common Swift *Apus apus*	4 Apr 1956	2 Dec 1994
Wryneck *Jynx torquilla*	12 Mar 1997	21 Oct 2001
Sand Martin *Riparia riparia*	4 Mar 1977	31 Oct 1994
Barn Swallow *Hirundo rustica*	7 Mar 2000	6 Dec 2003
House Martin *Delichon urbicum*	5 Mar 1967	3 Dec 1949
Tree Pipit *Anthus trivialis*	18 Mar 2000	22 Oct 1950
Yellow Wagtail *Motacilla flava*	12 Mar 1995	14 Dec 1990
Nightingale *Luscinia megarhynchos*	10 Mar 1961	4 Sep 1994
Common Redstart *Phoenicurus phoenicurus*	10 Mar 1996	16 Nov 1980
Whinchat *Saxicola rubetra*	13 Mar 1913	18 Dec 1994
Wheatear *Oenanthe oenanthe*	5 Feb 1994	25 Nov 1995
Grasshopper Warbler *Locustella naevia*	5 Apr 1999	8 Oct 2004
Sedge Warbler *Acrocephalus schoenobaenus*	20 Mar 1957	23 Oct 1952
Marsh Warbler *Acrocephalus palustris*	11 May 1934	10 Sep 1948 [d]
Reed Warbler *Acrocephalus scirpaceus*	3 Apr 1958	28 Oct 2002
Garden Warbler *Sylvia borin*	31 Mar 1956	2 Oct 1965/82
Lesser Whitethroat *Sylvia curruca*	3 Apr 1957 & 1977	30 Oct 1988 [e]
Common Whitethroat *Sylvia communis*	31 Mar 1958	24 Nov 1976
Wood Warbler *Phylloscopus sibilatrix*	24 Mar 1948	17 Sep 1952 & 2001
Willow Warbler *Phylloscopus trochilus*	5 Mar 1959	9 Nov 2005
Spotted Flycatcher *Muscicapa striata*	3 Apr 1981	15 Nov 2004
Pied Flycatcher *Ficedula hypoleuca*	30 Mar 1989	6 Oct 1983
Red-backed Shrike *Lanius collurio*	4 May 1946	21 Sep 1950

Winter visitors

Species	Earliest	Latest
Whooper Swan *Cygnus cygnus*	30 Oct 2003	21 Apr 1963
Bewick's Swan *Cygnus columbianus*	21 Oct 1990	26 Apr 1987
Bean Goose *Anser fabalis*	16 Dec 2001	26 Apr 2005
Pink-footed Goose *Anser brachyrhynchus*	8 Oct 1970	end April 1961 [f]
White-fronted Goose *Anser albifrons*	21 Oct 1974 & 1990	6 Apr 2003
Brent Goose *Branta bernicla*	3 Oct 1998	26 May 1991
Goldeneye *Bucephala clangula*	13 Jun 1998	22 May 1984
Smew *Mergellus albellus*	20 Oct 1997	16 Apr 1987
Red-breasted Merganser *Mergus serrator*	20 Oct 2002	16 Apr 2001
Goosander *Mergus merganser*	21 Sep 1995	25 May 1992
Rough-legged Buzzard *Buteo lagopus*	11 Oct 1977 [g]	29 Apr 1974
Golden Plover *Pluvialis apricaria*	19 Jun 1997	4 Jun 2002
Jack Snipe *Lymnocryptes minimus*	23 Sep 1984 & 1995	30 Apr 1976
Green Sandpiper *Tringa ochropus*	2 Jun 1991	18 May 1994
Rock Pipit *Anthus petrosus*	22 Sep 2002	8 Apr 1990
Water Pipit *Anthus spinoletta*	27 Oct 2002	16 Apr 1989
Fieldfare *Turdus pilaris*	7 Aug 1958 [h]	23 May 1970 & 1988
Redwing *Turdus iliacus*	3 Sep 1931 & 1934	21 May 1978
Great Grey Shrike *Lanius excubitor*	30 Sep 1972 [i]	2 May 1957
Brambling *Fringilla montifringilla*	2 Oct 1966	13 May 2002

Passage migrants

Species	Spring first	Spring last	Autumn first	Autumn last
Dotterel *Charadrius morinellus*	7 Apr 2003	28 May 1984	8 Sep 1905	28 Sep 1996
Sanderling *Calidris alba*	10 Apr 1989	7 Jun 1977	21 Jul 1988	16 Sep 1987
Temminck's Stint *Calidris temminckii*	9 May 1987	21 May 2004	7 Aug 1992	15 Sep 1970
Curlew Sandpiper *Calidris ferruginea*	28 Apr 1990	7 Jun 2000	4 Aug 1999	7 Nov 1998
Whimbrel *Numenius phaeopus*	10 Apr 1995	3 Jun 1992 [j]	19 Jun 2000 [j]	4 Oct 1987
Wood Sandpiper *Tringa glareola*	19 Apr 1986	15 Jun 1990	27 Jun 2003	13 Nov 1997
Little Tern *Sternula albifrons*	Mar 1928	27 May 1999	11 Jul 1989	30 Sep 1982
Black Tern *Chlidonias niger*	4 Apr 2005	11 Jun 1997	23 Jun 2001	22 Nov 1984
Sandwich Tern *Sterna sandvicensis*	18 Mar 2002	12 Jun 1977	19 Jul 1981	15 Oct 1999
Arctic Tern *Sterna paradisaea*	3 Apr 1998	16 Jun 1980	27 Jun 1970	4 Nov 2005
Ring Ouzel *Turdus torquatus*	28 Feb 1965	12 May 1993	26 Jul 1963	24 Nov 1952

Escapes and introductions

Stephen Edwards & Mike Jackson

Many species of birds have long been imported from all over the world into Great Britain (and numerous other countries), particularly for zoos and bird gardens, but also for estate owners, falconers and bird-fanciers. Perhaps the most widespread of these are wildfowl, gamebirds, raptors, parrots and parakeets, owls, and brightly colored weavers, finches and buntings. Inevitably, some escape – or are deliberately released, either because the owners cannot cope or, as was more often the case in the 19th and early 20th centuries, because they think that it would be interesting to try to establish a new population. (The world is littered with examples of the often disastrous results of introductions of birds and other animals to countries and islands where they have never occurred naturally.)

Eventually, if such populations become self-sustaining or 'naturalised', the species concerned may be considered by the BOURC for admission to Category C of the official British List of birds. Several wildfowl species in particular have achieved this status. For example, the highly decorative Mandarin from eastern Asia is well established in certain areas of southern England, including Wiltshire; and the more controversial Ruddy Duck from North America is now quite widespread. Birds other than wildfowl also come into this category. Pheasants and Red-legged Partridges are bred in captivity and released in large numbers for shooting, but both also have long-established, self-sustaining populations in Great Britain. Ring-necked Parakeets, too, are firmly entrenched and increasing in southeast England. And, of course, all British Little Owls are descendants of those released in England in the late 19th century.

In addition, some or all of the records of certain wildfowl that occur regularly in Great Britain in a wild state – and are therefore included in Category A of the British List – have question marks about their status locally. In Wiltshire, for example, some White-fronted Geese occurring at large in winter may be escapes, but most are certainly wild; and, although the reverse is true of Barnacle Geese, at least some records are believed to be from self-sustaining breeding populations within the country, if not the county. Consequently, both species are treated in full in the main list in *Birds of Wiltshire*.

Thus, the following summary is confined to those species where the individuals found at large in Wiltshire are deemed not to fulfil the criteria of the BOURC's Categories A, B or C. Note, however, that the recording of escapes and introductions in Wiltshire has been far from comprehensive, because many observers show little enthusiasm for noting them: few were ever reported in *WANHM*, and it was not until 1980 that such sightings began to appear regularly in *Hobby*. Beginning with those noted by Smith (1887), this appendix includes published records to the end of 2005 as well as a few others found in the WOS files. For completeness, all species listed in authoritative publications on Wiltshire are included, even if their validity as wild birds was later rejected by others (*eg* Hony 1915a). Three exceptions – a hummingbird (1977), a macaw (1995) and a bulbul (1998) – were not identified even to genus and have been omitted. (Indeed, the observer of the 'hummingbird' seems more likely to have failed to avoid the known pitfall of the hummingbird hawk-moth.) The few published 'escapes' of Muscovy Ducks and Indian Peafowl are included – though many more than these have doubtless wandered from farms and ornamental gardens respectively – but not a guineafowl because, while published as *Numida meleagris*, it could easily have been a domesticated variety. It should also be noted that there is a long-established wildfowl collection at Ramsbury Manor, kept on the 'lake' at that part of the River Kennet. Many species have been included in the collection over the years and, though pinioned or clipped in most cases, some have wandered short distances along the river from the lake. These have occasionally been reported in *Hobby* as escapes, but any that are obviously part of the collection have been omitted from this list in *Birds of Wiltshire*. There is, however, inevitably a degree of subjectivity in deciding whether some individuals were visiting escapes from elsewhere.

The sequence of families used in this appendix follows BOU practice (as of October 2005), but because most of the species concerned are not on the British List the order within families is that used by Dickinson (2003). Indigenous ranges, in broadest terms, are given in brackets after the vernacular and scientific names. Unless the species is now of particular interest (*eg* Black Swan, Eagle Owl), details of date and place are added only when there is just a single record; in some instances, however, such details – and even identification to the species level – were not published in *Hobby* at the time (and in two or three cases are no longer available).

White-faced Whistling-duck *Dendrocygna viduata* (South America, Africa)
One at Swindon STW on 17 June 1997 (*Hobby)*.

Fulvous Whistling-duck *Dendrocygna bicolor* (Americas, Africa, Asia)
One on the Og near Marlborough on 27 February 1999 (*Hobby*).

Lesser White-fronted Goose *Anser erythropus* (Eurasia)
Adult in riverside meadows near Bathampton House on the Wylye during 17–28 March 1976. Accepted by BBRC with the comment that 'There is a strong presumption that the ones seen away from Slimbridge...were of captive origin' (*BB* 70: 418, *Hobby*). Next recorded in 1978 and then in six of the 14 years from 1986 to 1999, including an adult with five White-fronted and 21 Bean Geese at CWP68/74 from 31 January to 2 February 1997 (*Hobby*). This species – which breeds from northern Scandinavia to northeast Siberia – is on the British List on the strength of certain individuals considered to be wild birds, particularly those that have arrived with White-fronted Geese at Slimbridge (Gloucestershire) or with Bean Geese in the Yare Valley (Norfolk).

Bar-headed Goose *Anser indicus* (Asia)
Recorded in 23 of the 32 years from 1974 to 2005, and clearly increasing (*Hobby*).

Emperor Goose *Anser canagicus* (North America, Asia)
Recorded in eight of the 16 years from 1985 to 2000 (*Hobby*).

Snow Goose *Anser caerulescens* (North America)
Recorded in 1970, 1973, and in 21 of the 29 years from 1977 to 2005 (*WANHM*, *Hobby*).

Ross's Goose *Anser rossii* (North America)
One at CWP68 on 23 August 1996 (*Hobby*).

Red-breasted Goose *Branta ruficollis* (Eurasia)
Noted at two sites in 2002 (*Hobby*). This goose – which breeds in arctic Siberia and winters in southeast Europe – is so commonly kept in captivity that many records are likely to be escapes, but some that arrive with flocks of White-fronted Geese or Dark-bellied Brent Geese are considered wild.

Lesser Canada Goose *Branta hutchinsii* (North America)
Since October 2005 the BOU has treated the Lesser Canada as a species distinct from the 'Greater' Canada Goose *B. canadensis* (Sangster *et al* 2005). A record of a small and dark Canada Goose at CWP68 on 9 August 1996 (*Hobby*) probably involved a Lesser Canada of

the subspecies *minima* (often colloquially known as the 'Cackling Canada Goose'). Doubtless because of its 'charming aspect' and 'dainty...quiet, and harmless' demeanour, this race has a long history in captivity (Delacour 1954–64), so it is not surprising that unpinioned individuals are sometimes encountered at large in southern England.

Black Swan *Cygnus atratus* (Australia, also New Zealand after introduction)
First recorded in Wiltshire in 1984 and then in every year bar one (1987) through to 2005 (see *Hobby*). Most sightings have been on the Salisbury Avon and the Kennet, breeding being recorded in the Kennet valley in 1996, 1998, 1999 (three pairs) and 2000–05; single pairs also bred at Downton in 2004–05 and attempted to do so at Lower Woodford in 2004. Away from those two rivers, Black Swans were recorded at CWP, Coate Water, Bowood and Corsham Lake in 1998; at Westbury Ponds and Longleat in 1999 and 2000; at Inglesham in 2001; at Westbury Ponds again in 2002, when a pair attempted to nest; at Langford Lakes in 2002–05; and at CWP, Stanton Fitzwarren and Corsham Lakes, Warminster and Shear Water in 2005. There was a general increase in Black Swan numbers nationally during the 1990s, though perhaps a decline since 2000 (*WeBS*, Ogilvie *et al* 2004). The increase has been very marked in Wiltshire and it will be interesting to see whether this creates serious competition with Mute Swans. Given the apparent rate of increase in recent years, it may be that this species is soon considered for addition to Category C.

Black-necked Swan *Cygnus melanocoryphus* (South America)
Records in 2001, 2003 and 2004 at Ramsbury Lake and Manor (*Hobby*).

Spur-winged Goose *Plectropterus gambensis* (Africa)
One at Manor Farm, Upavon, early in 1870 (*Zoologist*); and another shot near Ramsbury in November 1881, having escaped from a local pond (Smith 1887).

Andean Goose *Chloephaga melanoptera* (South America)
One record in 1989 (*Hobby*).

Upland (Magellan) Goose *Chloephaga picta leucoptera* (South America)
One shot at Rodbourne Cheney, Swindon, on 8 December 1933 (*WANHM*).

Cape Shelduck *Tadorna cana* (Africa)
Recorded 1989 and 1998 (*Hobby*).

Muscovy Duck *Cairina moschata* (Central and South America)
Recorded in the Swindon area in 1998 (three sites), 1999 (two sites) and 2000 (one site); also regular at Westbury Ponds during 2000–04; and noted at Devizes in 2001, at Marlborough, Shear Water and Britford in 2003, and at Chilton Foliat and Netheravon in 2004 (*Hobby*).

Wood Duck *Aix sponsa* (North America)
Recorded in 25 of the 32 years from 1974 to 2005, including several reports on the Salisbury Avon. A small population exists at Stanton Fitzwarren Lake, where breeding was proved in 2002 and eight were present in 2004 (*Hobby*). This duck, which belongs to the same genus as the now naturalised Mandarin, has not had the same success in establishing a self-sustaining population in the wild; most are in southeast England and East Anglia (*1988–91 Atlas*).

Maned Duck *Chenonetta jubata* (Australia)
Records in 1980 and 1985 (*Hobby*).

Ringed Teal *Calonetta leucophrys* (South America)
Recorded in 13 years of the 21 from 1985 to 2005; found at three sites in 2004 (*Hobby*).

Cape Teal *Anas capensis* (Africa)
One in 1976; then a series of records at Calne Sand Pits and Avebury in 1998–99, which probably involved a single individual; and one at Stanton Fitzwarren Lake in 2004 (*Hobby*).

Chestnut Teal *Anas castanea* (Australia)
Two records in 2003 and one in 2005 (*Hobby*).

Chiloe Wigeon *Anas sibilatrix* (South America)
After sightings in 1983 and 1991, more followed during 1993–96, 1999–2001 and 2004–05; one with Wigeons was shot near Pewsey on 28 January 1996, and a pair with small young was seen at Ramsbury on 1 June 2000 (*Hobby*).

American Wigeon *Anas americana* (North America)
Two males at the confluence of the Frome and the Bristol Avon on 30 August 1976 (*BB* 71: 492–493) were considered by the WOS Records Panel – because of the proximity of Rode Bird Gardens and the relatively early date – to be escapes from captivity (SB Edwards). Another male on the the Frome at Tellisford on 6 February 1988 was also thought by the observer to be an escape from Rode Bird Gardens and so was not submitted to the BBRC (M Hamzij). A one-year-old male at Queens Park, Swindon, on 25 April 1991 was not accepted by the BBRC – its rejection was published with the incorrect dates of 22–26 April (*BB* 85: 553) – on the grounds that it was 'almost certainly a wanderer from a collection', and the bird was thus listed with more obviously escaped wildfowl in *Hobby* (15: 22). Finally, a male was seen with a small party of Wigeons at Ramsbury Lake on 24 December 1990 and, though the observer assumed at the time that they formed part of the collection at the lake, it has since emerged that neither species was kept there at that time (SB Edwards); indeed, it may be significant that a male American Wigeon stayed in the Gloucestershire part of CWP from 16 December 1990 to 24 January 1991 (*BB* 84: 459).

Yellow-billed Duck *Anas undulata* (Africa)
One record in 1989 (*Hobby*).

Cinnamon Teal *Anas cyanoptera* (Americas)
Four records, in 1977, 1994, 2001 and 2002 (*Hobby*).

Cape Shoveler *Anas smithii* (Africa)
One at Queens Park, Swindon, in January 1992 (*Hobby*).

White-cheeked Pintail *Anas bahamensis* (South America)
One in 1989; a leucistic male at CWP in April 1998; and two records at Stanton Fitzwarren Lake in 2005 (*Hobby*).

Yellow-billed Pintail *Anas georgica* (South America)
Three records – 1989, 1996 (two) and 2000 (*Hobby*). Those in 1996 were published under the name 'Yellow-billed Teal *Anas georgica*', but the smaller, darker and more compact Yellow-billed Teal is a distinct species, *Anas flavirostris*, often called Speckled Teal.

Marbled Duck *Anas angustirostris* (south Europe, Middle East, Asia)
Pair on canal at Kingshill, Swindon, on 4 July 1998 (*Hobby*).

Rosybill *Netta peposaca* (South America)
Three records, in 1974, 2004 and 2005 (*Hobby*).

King Eider *Somateria spectabilis* (northern Eurasia and North America)
Smith (1887) included this species on the strength of 'a short note by my friend the late Rev. G. Marsh' that 'The King Duck in my collection was killed in Wilts', but Hony (1915a) considered it an unsatisfactory record. This species is a regular wanderer to, particularly, coastal sites in north Scotland, but as a seaduck is most unlikely to occur wild in inland southern England.

Hooded Merganser *Mergus cucullatus* (North America)
Two records: females on the Kennet at Ramsbury in 1993 and 1995 (*Hobby*). This sawbill duck is on the British List in Category B, on the strength of a young male specimen from the Menai Strait, north Wales, in the winter of 1830/31; there were also two authenticated Irish records (and others claimed) in the 19th century (Witherby *et al* 1938–41), but the species is commonly kept in captivity and no modern occurrence is likely to be accepted as wild.

Northern Bobwhite *Colinus virginianus* (North America)
One caught at Idmiston on 4 May 1963; another seen at Roundway from 30 May to 1 June 1967 (*WANHM*).

Capercaillie *Tetrao urogallus* (Eurasia)
Smith (1887) mentioned one at Winterslow in 1841, which Hony (1915a) believed was 'undoubtedly an escaped bird'.

Reeves's Pheasant *Syrmanticus reevesii* (Asia)
Recorded in 1992, 2000–02 and 2005. At Druids Lodge Estate, near Berwick St James, about 100 were introduced in the early 1990s and are known to breed (*Hobby*). There have been a number of attempts at introducing this species into Great Britain, but none has been successful in establishing a self-sustaining population in the wild.

Golden Pheasant *Chrysolophus pictus* (Asia)
Six records during 1985–2003 (*Hobby*). This exotic pheasant has been on the British List, in Category C, on the strength of self-sustaining naturalised populations in (mainly) Norfolk, Suffolk, Hampshire and West Sussex (*1988–91 Atlas*).

Indian Peafowl *Pavo cristatus* (Asia)
Recorded at large in 1992, 2001 and 2004 (*Hobby*).

Cattle Egret *Bubulcus ibis* (southern Eurasia, Africa, Americas, Australasia)
One at Britford in May 1936, which had been ringed and was believed to have been released from a zoo, was reported under the then English vernacular name of 'Buff-backed Heron' (*WANHM*). Some recent records of this species – still expanding its range in most continents – are now accepted as genuine vagrants to Wiltshire (see page 723).

Sacred Ibis *Threskiornis aethiopicus* (Africa)
Five records during 1972–99 (*WANHM*, *Hobby*).

Chilean Flamingo *Phoenicopterus chilensis* (South America)
One at Coate Water during September–October 1977 (*Hobby*).

Pink-backed Pelican *Pelecanus rufescens* (Africa)
An immature at Lydiard Park on 10 November 1990. Another pelican, this time not identified to species, was seen at Westbury on 17 October 1999 (*Hobby*).

Swallow-tailed Kite *Elanoides forficatus* (Southeast USA, Central and South America)
One was reported in Wiltshire in 1914 (Bury 1914), but no details are available and it was almost certainly an escape. Witherby *et al* (1938–41) noted that 'Several specimens…have been recorded as taken in Great Britain, but the claims for the admission of this species [to the British List] are in our opinion insufficient (*cf* Saunders 1899, page 338)'.

Red-tailed Hawk *Buteo jamaicensis* (North and Central America)
Records in 2003 (two) and 2005 (one) (*Hobby*).

Lanner Falcon *Falco biarmicus* (Europe, Middle East, Africa)
There was a 'trained hawk killed by a golfer' at High Post in 1952 (*WANHM*); another still wearing a falconer's jesses was seen at CWP68 on 29 August and 28 September 1996 (WOS records).

Grey-necked Wood-rail *Aramides cajanea* (Central and South America)
One shot between Trowbridge and Bradford-on-Avon in October 1876 was admitted to the county list by Smith (1887), under the name 'Cayenne Rail *Aramides Cayannensis*', but Hony (1915a) commented that it was 'obviously an escaped bird'.

Sarus Crane *Grus antigone* (Asia)
Two near Odstock on 1 June 1961 (*WANHM*), and one at Goatacre near Lyneham on 2 September 1967 (WOS records).

Sulphur-crested Cockatoo *Cacatua galerita* (New Guinea, Australia)
One at Westbury from about August 1981 was last seen on 3 January 1983, after 17 months in the wild (WOS records).

Alexandrine Parakeet *Psittacula eupatria* (Asia)
One at Allington on 14 December 2000, and at All Cannings on 24 January 2001 (*Hobby*).

Rosy-faced Lovebird *Agapornis roseicollis* (southern Africa)
Pair at Coate Water on 7 May 1984 (WOS records).

Monk Parakeet *Myiopsitta monachus* (South America)
A small colony was found at Castle Combe in 2002: after four in March and July, eight were seen on 4 August and then only three on 7 September (*Hobby*).

Cockatiel *Nymphicus hollandicus* (Australia)
Nine records during 1996–2003 (*Hobby*).

Eastern Rosella *Platycercus eximius* (Australasia)
One at Trowbridge on 19 May 2004 and again on the 21st (*Hobby*); and one at Westwood, near Bradford-on-Avon, on 14 May and 3 December 2005 (WOS records)

Budgerigar *Melopsittacus undulatus* (Australia)
Four records during 1992–99 (*Hobby*).

Eagle Owl *Bubo bubo* (Eurasia, Africa)
Smith (1887) reported that one 'taken alive' at Handley Common was subsequently 'kept for some seven or eight years by Mr. Thomas King, of Alvediston' until '1853 or 1854', when it 'passed into the possession of Mr. Hayter, of Woodyates'; Smith noted that there was no evidence to show 'Whether it had escaped from confinement, or whether it was a genuinely wild visitor'. A century and a half later, there were no fewer than five observations in 2005: at Common Farm, Purton, on 17 April (wearing a falconer's jesses); at Langley Wood NNR on 19 June (no jesses); at Stanton Park, Swindon, in October; at Yatton Keynell about the beginning of November; and at Cherhill on 25 November (WOS records). This huge owl has in recent years been found breeding in Great Britain, perhaps as a result of escapes or releases, or possibly connected with the expanding population in the Low Countries.

Laughing Kookaburra *Dacelo novaeguineae* (Australia)
One at Broxmore Park on 5 April 2001, and then at Whiteparish on the 11th, subsequently moved into Hampshire (*Hobby*).

Northern Flicker *Colaptes auratus* (North America)
Using the name 'Golden-winged Woodpecker', Smith (1887) accepted one shot in 1836 as wild, but this view was later rejected by Hony (1915a) as a result of the comment by Hartert *et al* (1912) that the specimen 'was no doubt due to importation'. It is worth noting that another was obtained in Dorset at the same time (see page 78), and that a Northern Flicker was seen to fly ashore from RMS *Mauretania* at Cob Harbour (Co Cork) on 13 October 1962, having first been seen aboard 2½ hours out of New York at dusk on the 7th and, as the concept of accidental passage on board ship had by then been accepted as a natural crossing of the Atlantic, the record was accepted for the Irish List (*BB* 56: 157).

Black Woodpecker *Dryocopus martius* (Europe)
One allegedly killed on an unspecified date in the 19th century while Rooks were being shot at Longleat was later stuffed and went into the Rawlence collection. The record was accepted by Smith (1887), but Hony (1915a) believed it had been admitted on insufficient evidence. The surprisingly large number of old reports of Black Woodpeckers in Great Britain – both specimens and claimed observations – were listed and reviewed by Fitter (1959), but none has been considered sufficiently authenticated to merit the addition of this species to the British List.

African Black-headed Oriole *Oriolus larvatus* (Africa)
One at Wanborough on 14 July 2002 (*Hobby*).

Red-billed Leiothrix *Leiothrix lutea* (Asia)
One at Gore Cross from mid August to early November 1997 (*Hobby*).

Golden-crested Mynah *Ampeliceps coronatus* (Asia)
One at Westbury on 25 March 1992 (*Hobby*).

Sudan Golden Sparrow *Passer luteus* (Africa)
Male at Trowbridge from mid June 1994 to 15 January 1995 (*Hobby*).

Village Weaver *Ploceus cucullatus* (Africa)
Two records, in 1995 and 2002 (*Hobby*).

Red-billed Quelea *Quelea quelea* (Africa)
A male at Ashton Keynes in November 2002 stayed into 2003 (*Hobby*).

Zanzibar Red Bishop *Euplectes nigroventris* (Africa)
One mist-netted at CWP68 on 10 July 2005 was returned to captivity (WOS records).

Zebra Finch *Poephila guttata* (Australia)
One at Devizes on 21 March 1995 (*Hobby*).

Island Canary *Serinus canaria* (Canary Islands)
Two records in 1994 and 2002 (*Hobby*).

Yellow-breasted Greenfinch *Carduelis spinoides* (Asia)
One at Chippenham on 7 March 1999 (*Hobby*).

Red-headed Bunting *Emberiza bruniceps* (Asia and just into easternmost Europe)
Male at Cole Park, Malmesbury, in June 1962 and July 1964 (*WANHM*); another record in 1975 (*Hobby*). This colourful bunting has the potential to occur as a vagrant in Great Britain from the Caspian region of European Russia – and, indeed, the first British record in Orkney in 1931 was originally accepted as such – but it is so commonly kept in captivity that all the (now annual) reports of this species in this country are regarded as escapes and not even considered by BBRC.

Northern Cardinal *Cardinalis cardinalis* (North and Central America)
Female at Trowbridge during 8–24 June 1985 (WOS records).

Wiltshire ringing totals 1965–2005

Compiled by Mike Hamzij

In 1965, Geoff Webber began to produce county ringing summaries, which were published with the annual bird reports in the *Wiltshire Archaeological & Natural History Magazine*. The reports for 1967 to 1973 were written by Roderick C Faulkner. After a brief gap, summaries were continued, in *Hobby*, by Michael W Tyler in 1977 (covering 1975–76) and 1978, and then in 1979 by Martin Preston (covering 1978, with a revision of 1975–77 data). From 1980, annual reports were written by John Buxton until 1987, by Reg Kersley to 1993 (with Rob Turner in 1987), and by me since then. (In the switch from *WANHM* to *Hobby*, no report for 1974 was ever published, but the total ringed that year was correctly given in *Hobby* 15: 68.)

John Buxton had earlier written a summary of his own ringing of 5000 birds of 59 species at Cole Park, Malmesbury, in the 21 years from 1955 (Buxton 1976). Nevertheless, although 201 birds of eight species were ringed as long ago as 1937 by Dauntsey's School, and probably much earlier by others elsewhere in the county, details of most of the ringing before 1965 are simply not available. Similarly, for a small proportion – 7374, or 20 per cent – of the 36,907 ringed during 1965–74 we have only annual totals of the numbers of all birds combined. (See also the short history of ringing in Wiltshire on pages 90–91.)

Leaving aside the 7374 during 1965–74 for which specific details are not available, the main aim of this chapter is to show the totals of each species ringed in Wiltshire during 1965–2000, updated to 2005 (table 114). The number of birds ringed in those last five years was nearly 40 per cent of the total during the previous 36 years – a result of increased activity by the West Wilts Ringing Group, and of the formation of the CWP Ringing Group in 2003 – and included no fewer than 13 additional species. Comparison of the individual totals to 2000 and to 2005 shows marked increases in, especially, some wetland birds.

It would have been of interest to try to show the numbers of each species subsequently reported elsewhere. At one time the 'recovery' of a ringed bird used to mean that it had been found dead, whether locally, elsewhere in Great Britain, or abroad. Since, however, John Buxton – later to be elected president of WOS and to edit the previous *Birds of Wiltshire* (1981) – introduced the (originally Japanese) mist-net to British ringers in 1954 (pages 90–91), many individual birds are 'controlled' (or retrapped and released again) by those who ringed them, or by other ringers elsewhere, and totals of the numbers recovered and controlled are simply not available. But summaries of the ringing and recovery data for individual species up to 2000 are given within the relevant species texts in this book.

Table 114. Numbers of each species ringed in Wiltshire from 1965 to December 2000 and to December 2005

Species	To 2000	To 2005	Species	To 2000	To 2005
Mute Swan	1386	1757	Common Sandpiper	23	27
Greylag Goose	–	1	Solitary Sandpiper	1	1
Canada Goose	92	97	Black-headed Gull	18	196
Wigeon	–	26	Lesser Black-backed Gull	1	1
Gadwall	6	7	Herring Gull	1	2
Common Teal	–	35	Common Tern	22	103
Mallard	70	81	Stock Dove	249	369
Shoveler	7	8	Wood Pigeon	96	207
Red-crested Pochard	4	4	Collared Dove	165	246
Tufted Duck	5	7	Turtle Dove	11	11
Red-legged Partridge	5	5	Cuckoo	22	27
Grey Partridge	3	12	Barn Owl	2214	4694
Black-throated Diver	1	1	Little Owl	342	528
Little Grebe	2	5	Tawny Owl	587	723
Manx Shearwater	2	2	Long-eared Owl	18	21
Common Bittern	–	1	Short-eared Owl	1	8
Little Egret	–	13	Nightjar	8	9
Grey Heron	56	92	Common Swift	386	409
Red Kite	–	12	Kingfisher	194	278
Sparrowhawk	199	241	Wryneck	–	1
Common Buzzard	31	73	Green Woodpecker	52	75
Osprey	–	1	Great Spotted Woodpecker	166	277
Kestrel	2805	3804	Lesser Spotted Woodpecker	3	3
Hobby	27	32	Sky Lark	27	57
Peregrine Falcon	1	1	Sand Martin	1400	4128
Water Rail	2	17	Barn Swallow	5882	8293
Moorhen	139	149	House Martin	606	697
Coot	1	7	Tree Pipit	39	45
Oystercatcher	5	5	Meadow Pipit	207	586
Stone-curlew	322	541	Yellow Wagtail	102	109
Little Ringed Plover	56	79	Grey Wagtail	353	512
Ringed Plover	4	4	Pied Wagtail	2305	3157
Lapwing	514	578	(also White Wagtail)	(3)	(3)
Dunlin	2	11	Waxwing	–	10
Temminck's Stint	1	1	Dipper	21	22
Jack Snipe	1	23	Wren	4239	5915
Common Snipe	13	46	Dunnock	3925	6084
Woodcock	1	3	Robin	5197	6831
Black-tailed Godwit	–	1	Nightingale	203	237
Curlew	4	4	Bluethroat	1	1
Common Redshank	19	20	Black Redstart	2	4
Greenshank	1	1	Common Redstart	117	161
Green Sandpiper	4	12	Whinchat	134	144
Wood Sandpiper	1	1	Stonechat	27	52

Species	To 2000	To 2005
Wheatear	6	11
Ring Ouzel	1	3
Blackbird	7450	9266
Fieldfare	183	275
Song Thrush	1917	2392
Redwing	1143	1375
Mistle Thrush	285	302
Cetti's Warbler	34	88
Grasshopper Warbler	51	84
Savi's Warbler	1	1
Sedge Warbler	1141	2538
Marsh Warbler	2	2
Reed Warbler	2320	4260
Blackcap	4264	6883
Garden Warbler	840	1343
Lesser Whitethroat	912	1317
Common Whitethroat	1832	3141
Dartford Warbler	–	1
Yellow-browed Warbler	–	1
Wood Warbler	9	11
Chiffchaff	6874	9818
Willow Warbler	5511	6606
Goldcrest	1280	2354
Firecrest	11	17
Spotted Flycatcher	535	571
Pied Flycatcher	10	12
Bearded Tit	5	7
Long-tailed Tit	3146	4456
Blue Tit	29,093	33,325
Great Tit	14,264	17,048
Coal Tit	916	1637
Willow Tit	74	154

Species	To 2000	To 2005
Marsh Tit	594	754
Nuthatch	191	238
Treecreeper	523	662
Jay	99	128
Magpie	112	173
Jackdaw	354	510
Rook	659	751
Carrion Crow	75	99
Raven	–	1
Common Starling	5438	6095
House Sparrow	1506	2402
Tree Sparrow	662	5464
Chaffinch	4926	7099
Brambling	136	200
Greenfinch	15,579	19,540
Goldfinch	1108	2804
Siskin	267	462
Linnet	905	1395
Common Redpoll	1	6
Lesser Redpoll	142	234
Crossbill	1	10
Bullfinch	2018	2650
Yellowhammer	895	1550
Ortolan Bunting	1	1
Little Bunting	1	1
Reed Bunting	1266	2927
Corn Bunting	21	153
Totals	**156,752**	**218,693**
Grand Totals (+ the 7374)	**164,126**	**226,067**
Total species	**133**	**146**

Reserves and designated sites in Wiltshire

The majority of the United Kingdom's most important sites for wildlife receive some kind of protection. Most commonly, this takes the form of statutory designation – whereby sites are protected by law – and reserves owned or managed by non-governmental organisations, usually wildlife conservation charities. The sympathetic management of these areas for their wildlife interest is key to the future of many individual species in the UK. Although some sites may be smaller than a hectare, increasingly there is recognition of the need to conserve broad-scale habitats, and many statutory sites cover tens of square kilometres. Whilst the key objective of a reserve or statutory site may be for a particular habitat or, for example, for butterflies, the management of the area for any form of wildlife will, in general, also have a beneficial effect on its birdlife.

The most common statutory designations are Sites of Special Scientific Interest (SSSIs), which afford legal protection to a large network of the best sites for wildlife and geology in Great Britain. The first SSSIs were identified under the National Parks and Access to the Countryside Act 1949, so that their conservation interest could be taken into account by local authorities during the planning process. Natural England, advisor to Government on nature conservation issues, now has responsibility for identifying and protecting the SSSIs in Wiltshire under the Wildlife and Countryside Act 1981 (as amended by the Countryside and Rights of Way Act 2000). Although many SSSIs in Wiltshire were first notified under the 1949 Act – for example, Pewsey Downs in 1951, Savernake Forest in 1971, and Salisbury Plain in 1975 – the dates given in table 115 are those of re-notification under the 1981 Act. As of 1 July 2006 there were some 134 SSSIs in Wiltshire, covering a broad range of habitats, although the majority of notified land covers open grassland or downland, and woodland is the next largest. Salisbury Plain alone accounts for two-thirds of the total of just under 30,000 ha designated as SSSIs in the county. Owners and occupiers of any land that falls within an SSSI must give written notice before they begin any of the operations listed in the notification as likely to damage the special interest features, so that these can be reviewed and, if necessary, amended or even disallowed by Natural England.

There are seven National Nature Reserves (NNRs) in Wiltshire, collectively covering just over 1000 ha, which again mostly reflect the importance of the county for downland landscapes. NNRs are statutorily designated sites established to protect the most important areas of wildlife habitats and geological formations in Britain and as places for scientific research. Every NNR is 'nationally important' and all are among the best examples of a particular habitat. These sites are managed on behalf of the nation, either owned or controlled by Natural England or held by approved bodies such as Wildlife Trusts. Local Nature Reserves (LNRs) are places with wildlife or geological features that are of special interest locally, and are designated by local authorities. They represent areas for both people and wildlife, and offer opportunities for study or learning about nature, or simply for the informal enjoyment of nature by the public. In 1996, English nature recommended that LNRs ought to be provided at the level of 1 ha per thousand population, and accessible natural green space at levels ranging from 20 ha to 500 ha. There are seven LNRs in Wiltshire, mostly in urban locations, five of them in the Swindon area.

Sites deemed to be of 'international importance' may be designated under international directives or conventions. These include Special Protection Areas (SPAs) and Special Areas of Conservation (SACs). Such sites are the most important in terms of their nature conservation interest and receive the greatest level of protection. SPAs are strictly protected sites, classified under the EC Directive on the Conservation of Wild Birds – the 'Birds Directive' – for certain rare and vulnerable species (those listed in Annex I to that Directive) and for regularly occurring migrants. Wiltshire has just two SPAs – Salisbury Plain and Porton Down – both identified primarily for their importance to breeding Stone-curlews, and the former also to breeding Quails and Hobbies, as well as to wintering Hen Harriers. There are ten SACs in Wiltshire, covering a range of habitats, although several are shared with adjoining counties. SACs are designated under the EC Habitats Directive, which requires the establishment of a European network of important high-quality conservation sites that will make a significant contribution to conserving certain habitat types and species (excluding birds). Salisbury Plain SAC, at over 29,000 ha, is one of the largest inland statutory sites in England. Most SPAs, SACs and NNRs are also designated as SSSIs. (Further information on relevant legislation, comprehensive lists of designated sites in England, and access details can be found on the web sites of Natural England and the Joint Nature Conservation Committee.)

The majority of private reserves in Wiltshire are owned or managed by the Wiltshire Wildlife Trust (WWT), the main conservation charity in the county. The organisation's aim is to enhance, restore and protect local biodiversity, often in conjunction with landowners, local authorities or local communities. It manages about 37 reserves in total, covering 805 ha, many of which also have a statutory designation. Some 15 reserves in Wiltshire are managed by the Woodland Trust, a conservation charity dedicated to the protection of the UK's native woodland heritage. Most are relatively small, but three exceed 50 ha. Although traditionally more widely recognised for the preservation of historic buildings, the National Trust also looks after a range of coastal, countryside and historic landscapes: four sizeable, largely grassland, reserves in Wiltshire cover some 370 ha. The RSPB, the UK's largest bird conservation organisation, manages a network of 200 reserves throughout the UK. It owns one reserve in the county, Manor Farm, which when mature, will be a chalk grassland site connecting Salisbury Plain and Porton Down – though this is not due to open to visitors for several years as arable reversion to grassland only commenced in 2006 – but at 296 ha it is the largest privately owned reserve in Wiltshire. The RSPB also leases Normanton Down near Stonehenge but this chalk grassland reserve on private farmland can be visited only by appointment.

Modern-day management of nature reserves often includes the setting of goals or targets for the sites – for example, ensuring that the number of breeding pairs of a particular species exceeds a certain level. Such targets are often shaped by regional or national targets as, for example, those identified in Biodiversity Action Plans. Despite a greater recognition of the need for conservation measures in the wider countryside, and positive changes to agricultural policy – offering incentives for farming practices that limit the impact of agriculture on the naturalness of the habitat – reserves and statutory sites will continue to play the primary role in the conservation of much of Wiltshire's most important wildlife for the foreseeable future. A full list of current reserves and statutory sites in the county is given in table 115.

Please note that listing of these sites does not imply a right of access, though many are open to the public. Contact Natural England, the relevant local authorities or conservation organisation, or visit their web sites, for access details.

Table 115. Reserves and designated sites in Wiltshire

This table lists all statutorily designated sites in Wiltshire (bar one SAC identified for bats), and all reserves that are owned or managed by NGOs for their wildlife interest, as of 1 July 2006. The date of notification is given for statutory sites notified from 1982, and the relevant conservation organisation is listed for those owned or managed as reserves; the Borough or District Councils responsible for management of LNRs are also given. A site may have multiple statutory designations and may also be a reserve owned or managed by an NGO. The boundary of a reserve may differ from that of the designated site, and even the boundaries of different statutory designations of the same site may differ, owing to the different emphasis of the relevant conservation legislation; the names of statutory designations and reserves may also differ. In such cases, the site name used in the table is that of the SSSI.

If the area of an SSSI differs significantly from that of an NGO reserve or other designation, it is denoted by a dagger (†) and the area of each is listed at the end of the table. All SPAs and SACs are also SSSIs, though the boundaries may differ. All SSSIs are listed, regardless of their reason for notification, but those specifically notified for their bird interest are identified by an asterisk (*) in the Designation column. Other notes: Pepperbox Hill National Trust reserve (1) falls largely within Brickworth Down & Dean Hill SSSI (1); part of the Cotswold Water Park SSSI (2) is in Gloucestershire; the Kennet & Lambourn Floodplain SAC (3) extends into Berkshire; part of Porton Down SPA/SSSI (4) and most of the New Forest SPA/SAC/SSSI (4) are in Hampshire; and the River Avon SAC (5) extends into both Hampshire and Dorset. The Devenish Reserve (6) comprises Little Durnford Wood & Little Durnford Down.

Site name	Grid ref	Designation	Notified on	Area (ha)	Reserve
Acres Farm Meadow	SU0292	SSSI	22 Jun 89	4	
Ambrose Copse	ST9026			4	Woodland Trust
Barbury Castle	SU1476	LNR		63	Swindon BC
Baverstock Juniper Bank	SU0333	SSSI	6 Mar 87	2	
Baydon's Wood	ST9273			1	Woodland Trust
Bencroft Hill Meadows	ST9673	SSSI	10 Oct 88	5	
Bentley Wood	SU2429	SSSI	Aug 85	659	
Bincknoll Dip Woods	SU1179	SSSI	31 Mar 87	6	
Blackmoor Copse	SU2329	SSSI	31 Jan 86	31 †	Wilts Wildlife Trust
Blakehill Farm	SU0791			235	Wilts Wildlife Trust
Botley Down	SU2959	SSSI	23 Mar 89	13	
Bowerchalke Downs	SU0022	SSSI	4 Nov 88	134	
Box Mine	ST8369	SSSI	15 Feb 91	59	
Bracknell Croft	SU1833	SSSI	5 Feb 88	6	
Bradley Woods	ST7841	SSSI	12 Mar 86	49	
Bratton Downs	ST9252	SSSI	6 Mar 92	400	
Brickworth Down & Dean Hill [1]	SU2125	SSSI	24 Apr 87	121	
Brimsdown Hill	ST8438	SSSI	10 Apr 87	185	
Britford Water Meadows	SU1627	SSSI	13 Mar 87	18	
Brockhurst Meadow	SU0787			8	Wilts Wildlife Trust
Burcombe Down	SU0629	SSSI	20 Jan 89	46	
Burderop Wood	SU1681	SSSI	16 May 86	48	
Calstone & Cherhill Downs	SU0468	SSSI	20 Jan 89	128	
Camp Down	SU1233	SSSI	27 Feb 87	7	
Charnage Down Chalk Pit	ST8332	SSSI	4 Feb 87	4	
Cherhill Down	SU0469			207	National Trust
Chickengrove Bottom	SU0421	SSSI	4 Jul 86	11	
Chilmark Quarries	ST9731	SAC	26 Oct 89	10	
Chilton Foliat Meadows	SU3170	SSSI*	17 Mar 89	55	
Clattinger Farm	SU0193	SSSI	22 Jul 87	60 †	Wilts Wildlife Trust
Clearbury Down	SU1523	SSSI	12 Aug 86	31	
Cley Hill	ST8344	SSSI	27 Mar 87	27	National Trust
Cloatley Manor Farm Meadows	ST9891	SSSI	17 Jul 97	12 †	Wilts Wildlife Trust
Clout's Wood	SU1379	SSSI	31 Jan 86	13	Wilts Wildlife Trust
Coate Water	SU1782	SSSI/LNR*	22 Aug 86	49 †	Swindon BC
Cockey Down	SU1731	SSSI	15 Apr 87	16 †	Wilts Wildlife Trust
Colerne Park & Monk's Wood	ST8372	SSSI	16 May 86	50	Woodland Trust

Site name	Grid ref	Designation	Notified on	Area (ha)	Reserve
Conigre Mead	ST9063			2	Wilts Wildlife Trust
Corsham Railway Cutting	ST8669	SSSI	6 Feb 87	5	
Cotswold Water Park [2]	SU0896	SSSI	28 Jun 94	135	
Cranborne Chase	ST9517	SSSI	5 May 89	463	
Dank's Down & Truckle Hill	ST8475	SSSI	5 Dec 90	14	
Dead Maid Quarry	ST8032	SSSI	9 Jan 87	0	
Dinton Quarry	SU0030	SSSI	5 Nov 90	0	
Dinton Railway Cutting	SU0030	SSSI	10 Oct 90	0	
Distillery Farm Meadows	SU0289	SSSI	27 Apr 88	19 †	Wilts Wildlife Trust
Drews Pond Wood	SU0059	LNR		4	Kennet DC
East Harnham Meadows	SU1528	SSSI	11 Sep 95	18	
Ebsbury Down	SU0535	SSSI	20 Jan 89	53	
Echo Lodge Meadows	SU0485			15	Wilts Wildlife Trust
Emmett Hill Meadows	SU0090	SSSI	10 Apr 87	5	Wilts Wildlife Trust
Figsbury Ring	SU1833	SSSI	27 Mar 87	11	
Fonthill Grottoes	ST9331	SSSI	14 Oct 94	1	
Frank's Wood	ST8271			2	Woodland Trust
Fyfield Down	SU1370	SSSI/NNR	18 Apr 86	327 †	
Gallows Hill	ST9524	SSSI	17 Aug 88	23	
Goldborough Farm Meadows	SU0880	SSSI	27 Mar 92	10	
Great Cheverell Hill	ST9751	SSSI	26 Mar 93	34	
Great Quarry, Swindon	SU1583	SSSI	28 Mar 90	1	
Great Yews	SU1123	SAC	14 Nov 86	29	
Green Lane Wood	ST8857			40	Wilts Wildlife Trust
Gripwood Quarry	ST8260	SSSI	10 Mar 87	1	
Gutch Common	ST8925	SSSI	20 Jan 89	37	
Hagbourne Copse	SU1082			2	Wilts Wildlife Trust
Ham Hill	SU3361	SSSI	9 Jan 87	2	Wilts Wildlife Trust
Hang Wood	ST8631	SSSI	18 Apr 86	20	
Harries Ground, Rodbourne	ST9382	SSSI	20 Mar 03	7	
Hat Gate	SU2164			1	Wilts Wildlife Trust
Haydon Meadow	SU1188	SSSI	27 Jan 99	6	
Heath Hill Farm	ST7533	SSSI	1 Jul 97	21	
High Clear Down	SU2376			10	Wilts Wildlife Trust
Homington & Coombe Bissett Downs	SU1124	SSSI	14 Oct 88	25 †	Wilts Wildlife Trust
Honeybrook Farm	ST8473	SSSI	23 Jan 92	42	
Inwood, Warleigh	ST8063	SSSI	27 Apr 88	58	
Jones's Mill	SU1661	SSSI*	11 Mar 85	11 †	Wilts Wildlife Trust
Kellaways to West Tytherton, River Avon	ST9474	SSSI	9 Jul 98	4	
Kennet & Lambourn Floodplain [3]	SU3468	SAC	6 Jun 96	23 †	
King's Play Hill	SU0065	SSSI	26 Sep 86	29	
Knapp & Barnett's Downs	SU0227	SSSI	12 May 89	67	
Knighton Downs & Wood	SU0624	SSSI	25 Mar 88	207	
Lady Down Quarry	ST9630	SSSI	15 Jun 90	0	
Landford Bog	SU2518	SSSI	6 Jul 87	9	Wilts Wildlife Trust
Landford Heath	SU2617	SSSI	13 Oct 94	12	
Langford Lakes	SU0337			7	Wilts Wildlife Trust
Langley Wood & Homan's Copse	SU2320	SSSI/NNR*	19 Nov 85	220	
Little Grubbins Meadow	ST8377	SSSI	20 Dec 85	4	
Long Knoll	ST7937	SSSI	05 Feb 88	35	
Loosehanger Copse & Meadows	SU2119	SSSI	19 Mar 92	57	
Lower Coombe & Ferne Brook Meadows	ST9023	SSSI	25 Jan 02	11	
Lower Moor Farm	SU0093			39	Wilts Wildlife Trust

Site name	Grid ref	Designation	Notified on	Area (ha)	Reserve
Lower Woodford Water Meadows	SU1235	SSSI	30 Mar 87	24	
Mackintosh Davidson Wood	ST8531			57	Woodland Trust
Manor Farm	SU2140			296	RSPB
Middleton Down	SU0423			26	Wilts Wildlife Trust
Midford Valley Woods	ST7761	SSSI*	31 Oct 86	24	
Monk's Rest Wood	SU1082			6	Woodland Trust
Morgan's Hill	SU0267	SSSI	30 Jan 87	12	Wilts Wildlife Trust
Nadder Island	SU1329			c1	Wilts Wildlife Trust
New Forest [4]	SU2207	SPA/SAC	28 Feb 96	28,925	
North Meadow, Cricklade	SU0994	SAC/NNR	18 Apr 86	46 †	
Odstock Down	SU1325	SSSI	9 Jan 87	13	
Okus Quarry	SU1483	SSSI	30 Jan 87	0	
Old Town Railway Cutting, Swindon	SU1583	SSSI	6 Mar 87	2	
Out Woods	ST8376	SSSI	1 Dec 82	15	
Oysters Coppice	ST8925			6	Wilts Wildlife Trust
Parsonage Down	SU0541	SSSI/NNR	18 Apr 86	188 †	
Pepperbox Hill [1]	SU2125			80	National Trust
Peppercombe Wood	SU0357			1	Wilts Wildlife Trust
Pewsey Downs	SU1063	SAC/NNR	17 Jul 87	302 †	
Picket & Clanger Wood	ST8754	SSSI*	23 Mar 89	67 †	Woodland Trust
Piggledene	SU1468	SSSI	13 Jun 86	5	
Pike Corner	SU0393	SSSI	15 Jul 86	15	
Pincombe Down	ST9621	SSSI	27 Mar 87	23	
Plain Copse	SU0585			1	Woodland Trust
Porton Down [4]	SU2337	SPA	19 Mar 92	1562	
Porton Meadows	SU1835	SSSI	3 Jun 88	17	
Prescombe Down	ST9825	SAC/NNR	6 May 87	76 †	
Purton/Berriman's Wood	SU1188			17	Woodland Trust
Rack Hill	ST8476	SSSI	20 Dec 85	10	
Radnor Street Cemetery	ST1583	LNR		4	Swindon BC
Ramsbury Meadow	SU2771			1	Wilts Wildlife Trust
Ravensroost Wood	SU0288	SSSI	25 Jan 89	44 †	Wilts Wildlife Trust
Red Lodge Pond	SU0588			1	Wilts Wildlife Trust
Restrop Farm & Brockhurst Wood	SU0786	SSSI	27 Mar 92	53	
River Avon System [5]	SU1429	SAC/LNR	1 Dec 96	476 †	Salisbury DC
River Kennet	SU3767	SSSI	1 Nov 95	112	
River Till	SU0842	SSSI	16 Aug 00	34	
Rotherley Downs	ST9419	SSSI	22 Sep 89	121	
Roundway Down & Covert	SU0064	SSSI	16 Dec 86	84	
Rushy Platt	SU1383			1	Wilts Wildlife Trust
Salisbury Plain	SU1347	SPA/SAC	29 Jan 93	19,716 †	
Savernake Forest	SU2267	SSSI*	5 Oct 88	916	
Scratchbury & Cotley Hills	ST9143	SSSI	31 Jan 86	53	
Seend Cleeve Quarry	ST9360	SSSI	4 Feb 87	3	
Seend Ironstone Quarry & Road Cutting	ST9360	SSSI	28 Mar 90	2	
Seven Fields	SU1488	LNR		23	Swindon BC
Silbury Hill	SU1068	SSSI	31 Oct 86	2	
Smallbrook Meadows	ST8844			13	Wilts Wildlife Trust
Spye Park	ST9466	SSSI*	22 Aug 86	90	
Stanton Park	ST1789	LNR		38	Swindon BC
Stanton St Quintin Quarry & Motorway Cutting	ST9180	SSSI	20 Apr 90	3	

Site name	Grid ref	Designation	Notified on	Area (ha)	Reserve
Starveall & Stony Down	ST9940	SSSI	12 May 88	22	
Steeple Ashton	ST9155	SSSI	14 May 98	26	
Steeple Langford Down	SU0338	SSSI	10 Oct 88	24	
Stert Brook Exposure	SU0158	SSSI	17 Aug 89	0	
Stockton Wood & Down	ST9636	SSSI	26 Mar 86	60	
Stoke Common Meadows	SU0690	SSSI	14 Oct 94	10 †	Wilts Wildlife Trust
Stratford Tony Down	SU0924	SSSI	9 Jan 87	24	
Stratton Kingsdown	SU1688			54	Woodland Trust
Sutton Lane Meadows	ST9477	SSSI	27 Apr 88	3	
Swillbrook Lakes	SU0193			26	Wilts Wildlife Trust
Tanner's Wood	SU0337			1	Woodland Trust
Teffont Evias Quarry/Lane Cutting	ST9931	SSSI	22 Jun 89	2	
The Coombs, Hinton Parva	SU2282	SSSI	17 Aug 89	16	
The Devenish Reserve [6]	SU1235			33	Wilts Wildlife Trust
The Firs	SU0486			12	Wilts Wildlife Trust
The Nymph Hay	ST8977			6	Woodland Trust
Throope Down	SU0824	SSSI	14 Nov 86	38	
Tinney's Firs	SU2020			24	Woodland Trust
Tytherington Down	ST9138	SSSI	26 Mar 86	6	
Upper Chicksgrove Quarry	ST9629	SSSI	11 Feb 87	6	
Upper Waterhay Meadow	SU0693	SSSI	15 Aug 85	3	Wilts Wildlife Trust
Upton Cow Down	ST8749	SSSI	26 Mar 93	17	
Vincients Wood	ST8973			5	Wilts Wildlife Trust
Warneage Wood	SU2083			19	Woodland Trust
West Harnham Chalk Pit	SU1228	SSSI	4 Feb 87	3	
West Yatton Down	ST8576	SSSI	1 Aug 82	14	
Westbury Ironstone Quarry	ST8550	SSSI	6 Mar 97	1	
Whiteparish Common	SU2522	SSSI	20 Mar 87	64	
Whitesheet Hill	ST8034	SSSI	5 Feb 88	141 †	National Trust
Win Green Down	ST9220	SSSI	25 Jul 88	26	
Winklebury Hill	ST9521	SSSI	19 Aug 88	65	
Winsley Mines	ST7960	SSSI	12 May 89	1	
Wootton Bassett Mud Spring	SU0781	SSSI	6 Jan 97	1	
Wylye & Church Dean Downs	SU0036	SSSI/NNR	6 Mar 87	81 †	
Yarnbury Castle	SU0340	SSSI	31 Jan 86	9	
Yatesbury Beeches	SU0671			1	Woodland Trust

† The following is a list of sites where there is a significant difference in the area of the SSSI compared with other statutory designations or reserves on the same sites (note, the areas of some SPAs and SACs may fall outside Wiltshire):

Blackmoor Copse: SSSI 31 ha; Wilts Wildlife Trust 36 ha.
Clattinger Farm: SSSI 60 ha; Wilts Wildlife Trust 68 ha.
Cloatley Manor Farm Meadows: SSSI 12 ha; Wilts Wildlife Trust 32 ha.
Coate Water: SSSI 49 ha; LNR 19 ha.
Cockey Down: SSSI 16 ha; Wilts Wildlife Trust 7 ha.
Distillery Farm Meadows: SSSI 19 ha; Wilts Wildlife Trust 27 ha.
Fyfield Down: SSSI 327 ha; NNR 248 ha.
Homington & Coombe Bissett Downs: SSSI 25 ha; Wilts Wildlife Trust 35 ha.
Jones's Mill: SSSI 11 ha; Wilts Wildlife Trust 33 ha.
Kennet & Lambourn Floodplain: SSSI 23 ha; SAC 114 ha.
North Meadow, Cricklade: SSSI/NNR 46 ha; SAC 105 ha.
Parsonage Down: SSSI 188 ha; NNR 276 ha.
Pewsey Downs: SSSI 302 ha; SAC 154 ha, NNR 166 ha.
Picket & Clanger Wood: SSSI 67 ha; Woodland Trust 60 ha.
Prescombe Down: SSSI/SAC 76 ha; NNR 47 ha.
Ravensroost Wood: SSSI 44 ha; Wilts Wildlife Trust 65 ha.
River Avon System: SSSI/SAC 476 ha; LNR 8 ha.
Salisbury Plain: SSSI 19,716 ha; SPA 21,438 ha, SAC 29,262 ha.
Stoke Common Meadows: SSSI 10 ha; Wilts Wildlife Trust 20 ha.
White Sheet Hill: SSSI 141 ha; National Trust 56 ha.
Wylye & Church Dean Downs: SSSI 81 ha; NNR 34 ha.

Appendix 1

Record cards and forms and survey instructions for the Wiltshire atlas fieldwork 1995–2000

WILTSHIRE ORNITHOLOGICAL SOCIETY

TETRAD ATLAS OF BREEDING BIRDS: INSTRUCTIONS FOR FIELDWORK (REVISED)

Altered sections shown in bold italics.

INTRODUCTION AND AIMS

Two countrywide atlases of breeding birds, based on fieldwork in the 10-km squares of the National Grid during 1968-72 and 1988-91, have greatly increased our knowledge of distributions in Britain and Ireland as a whole. Both are invaluable tools for conservation, and comparisons of the second atlas with the first have highlighted some remarkable changes over the two periods 20 years apart.

Largely as a result of the stimulation provided by the planning and then publication of these national atlases, some two-thirds of the counties of England have produced or are producing their own atlases based on the far smaller 2-km squares, or tetrads, which show distribution on a scale 25 times finer than that of 10-km squares.

The Wiltshire Ornithological Society (WOS) is now to undertake its own county tetrad survey over the four years 1995-98. The main objective is to map the distributions of breeding birds in Wiltshire by finding out which species are present in each of the county's 940 or so tetrads: evidence will be recorded in two main categories of "Seen" and "Breeding". In addition, observers are being asked to note the actual numbers they find of ***all species in order that abundance can be gauged.***

HOW TO CONTRIBUTE

The survey will entail careful fieldwork, whether you take on only one or two tetrads or many, but it does not have to become a burden. A total of some 940 tetrads will involve the organisers in the central collation of an enormous amount of data, but you as an individual observer will need simply to allow a ***minimum*** of four hours in a tetrad. Obviously, some people will spend much longer in a single tetrad because they live or regularly walk there, but we hope that others will be prepared to cover a number of tetrads.

Two types of recording forms are available. The first is a standard Record Card designed for use in a single tetrad. The second is a Casual Record Sheet for noting casual observations of the scarcer species in other tetrads while you are simply driving or walking through.

At the outset it is important to be able to identify any tetrad by its appropriate code number and letter. Full instructions on how to do this are shown here but are also summarised on the reverse of the card.. The British National Grid is divided into 100-km squares, each of which has a unique pairing of letters: Wiltshire is covered by the 100-km squares ST and SU. These 100-km squares are further divided into one hundred 10-km squares, each of which is identified by two digits, the first being the "easting" and the second the "northing". Fig. 1, which is the 100-km square SU, shows how to determine these two digits, the shaded 10-km section being SU58. Fig. 2 shows the method of lettering the 25 tetrads within that or any other 10-km square from bottom left to top right (note that O is the letter omitted from the full alphabet).

1

Figure 71. Survey instructions for summer tetrad fieldwork in Wiltshire 1995–2000

Fig. 1

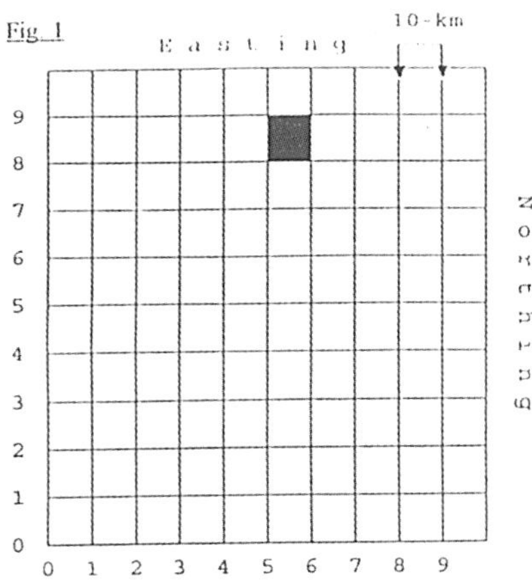

Fig. 2

2-km

E	J	P	U	Z
D	I	N	T	Y
C	H	M	S	X
B	G	L	R	W
A	F	K	Q	V

10-km Square SU58

For this survey, the county has been divided into four regions - north-west, north-east, south-west and south-east - each of which has its own regional organiser:

North-west Mike Hamzij, 13 Halfway Close, Trowbridge BA14 7HQ

North-east Mike Jackson, Lowgill, 17 Vicarage Close, Marlborough SN8 1AY

South-west John Pollard, 7 The Downlands, Warminster BA12 0BD

South-east Granville Pictor, 6 The Tyleshades, Tadburn Gardens, Romsey, Hants SO51 8RJ

Each region contains about nine 10-km squares and also a number of incomplete ones: each complete or nearly complete square will have its own steward. It will be the steward's responsibility to organise the survey of the 25 tetrads within his or her 10-km square. Your regional organiser will have a list of 10-km stewards, who will be able to help you decide which tetrads to cover.

FIELDWORK: WHEN AND WHERE?

In each of the four years the main survey will start on 1 April and extend to 31 July, a period that covers the breeding seasons of most birds in southern England. A total of four hours should be spent in any tetrad, this divided into two equal two-hour visits, one in *late* April-May and one in June-July; both visits should be carried out in the same year. If possible, there should be additional visits in February-March for such early nesters as Mistle Thrush and Crossbill, and dusk and night "drive-rounds" listening for owls, Woodcock, Nightjar and Nightingale.

The reasons for restricting the main survey to two 2-hour periods within any tetrad are to help determine variations in abundance of each species across Wiltshire and to make future comparisons possible. Without this standardisation, measures of abundance would reflect variations in densities of observers, and amounts of time spent in the field, rather than numbers of birds.

On the other hand, timed visits alone would be unlikely to result in complete lists of birds in any tetrad, so you are encouraged to provide records of additional species on a separate card. Many observers find that atlas fieldwork is highly addictive and become keen to make the list as complete as possible, but please remember that manpower is limited and, as we have some 940 tetrads to cover, it may be more rewarding to move on to another tetrad.

When undertaking a timed visit, try to make your route cover as many different habitats as possible, including samples of wetlands, woods, agricultural land and *human settlement*. A new Record Card should be used for each 2-hour timed visit, and the actual time-period spent in the field entered with the date at the top. For additional species you find in your tetrad outside the timed periods, please use a Record Card and tick "Untimed" at top right.

All introduced or otherwise established species that are breeding ferally should be included: these may range from Red-crested Pochards to Pheasants and, of course, Feral Pigeons. On the other hand, birds considered to be injured or otherwise delayed winter-visitors, lingering passage migrants or simply escapes should be excluded as far as possible, but any birds seen using a tetrad as an established feeding or resting area in the peak of the breeding season (mid May to mid June) should at least be noted.

Beware that some species regularly sing on migration and can be mistakenly thought to be holding territory. Other species may rapidly move recently fledged young for considerable distances, even kilometres, away from the nest site.

The most useful time of day for surveying birds is early to mid morning: after about 10.30 or 11.00 song and nesting activity often become far less frequent until mid to late afternoon. *Evenings in late spring/early summer are also useful, but if doing a timed 2-hour visit, aim to finish at least one hour before dusk. Very hot days (unless observation is in the early morning or evening) are not ideal, neither are very wet or misty days. Very windy days can make identification of birds by song difficult.*

The Ordnance Survey map will provide you with enough information to plan where to go even if you are unfamiliar with the area to be covered. We recommend the 1:25,000 rather than the standard 1:50,000. For many tetrads, public footpaths and rights of way will provide adequate access but, where this is not the case, please always seek permission to enter private property. Experience has shown that most landowners are more than willing to allow access if approached in advance with a brief explanation. Please refer any difficulties over access to your 10-km steward or regional organiser. *Both will have copies of a standardised letter which has been prepared to be sent to landowners when access is being sought.*

Tetrads on the borders with the neighbouring counties can cause confusion. A tetrad should be included in the survey if at least 20% of it lies within Wiltshire. If you are covering such a border tetrad, always take in the whole of it and not just the Wiltshire part. This is so that we can make sensible comparisons with other tetrads and have a relatively simple definition of the total area covered. *Include all species seen in the whole tetrad on the Record Card.*

COMPLETING THE RECORD CARD

For each species recorded in a tetrad, details should be entered against that species on the Record Card. If the species is not listed, then enter its name in one of the blank rows at the end of the card. The number printed before each species name is the Euring number used by European bird-ringing schemes, which aids entry onto the computer. The columns S and B represent **Seen** and **Breeding**.

SEEN

Enter S in the column headed S if the species was seen or heard in the tetrad, but with no evidence of breeding. *Singing birds will sometimes be included in this category but can also fall in the category of Breeding (see under the heading BREEDING for criteria). Exclude escapes, late winterers and passage migrants, but note that flying Swifts and hirundines should be recorded.*

A number should be entered in the count column for <u>all</u> species: please record the total of individuals seen or heard (excluding dependent young). For breeding colonial species (in Wiltshire mainly Grey Heron, Sand Martin and Rook) the number of nests only should be entered in the count column, and an entry of B inserted in the column headed B. If a colonial species is seen with no evidence of breeding simply enter S in the appropriate column and in the Count column enter the number seen. Time spent counting a colony should not be included in the 2-hour period.

3

BREEDING

Enter B in the column headed B if one or more of the following activities was observed:

- *Song, if heard in the same location 14 or more days apart.*
- Bird apparently holding territory.
- Courtship and display; or anxiety call/agitated behaviour of adult indicating presence of young or nest.
- Brood patch on trapped bird.
- Adult visiting probable nest-site.
- Nest building (including excavating nest-hole).
- Distraction display or injury feigning.
- Used nest found.
- Recently fledged young.
- Adult carrying faecal sac or food.
- Adult entering or leaving nest-site in circumstances indicating occupied nest (including colonies).
- Nest with eggs found, or bird sitting but not disturbed, or eggshells found near nest.
- Nest with young; or downy young of ducks, gamebirds, waders, other nidifugous species.

As soon as possible after the end of August in each year, and not later than 30 September, all Record Cards should be sent to the steward of the 10-km square in which the tetrad fieldwork was carried out.

COMPLETING THE CASUAL RECORD SHEET

This should be used for casual observations of the shaded species on the Record Card, which you make in tetrads not being covered by yourself. The appropriate 10-km square and tetrad letter should be entered, together with the nearest place and/or a six-figure grid reference. The Euring code should be entered (see the Record Card) alongside the species name. The Seen, Breeding and Count columns should be completed as in the instructions for the Record Card. ***The date of each observation should be entered in the left hand margin of the sheet beside the column headed 10- km square.***

Casual Record Sheets, which may well include observations from several 10-km squares, should be sent direct to the County Recorder, Rob Turner, whose address appears on every sheet. But please note that the use of Casual Record Sheets must be limited to the scarcer or more sparsely distributed species shown shaded on the Record Card: always enter a standard six-figure grid reference for each such species in order that the tetrad can be checked.

RARE SPECIES AND THREATENED BIRDS

All breeding records submitted to the survey organisers will be treated with discretion. Any Schedule 1 species not printed on the Record Card, or any other scarce or vulnerable record which merits confidential treatment, should be sent directly to the County Recorder: Rob Turner, 14 Ethendun, Bratton, Westbury, Wiltshire BA13 4RX (Tel: 01380 830862). We ask that all such observations be submitted on a Casual Record Sheet and be accompanied by a note giving relevant details of the site and a standard six-figure map reference.

When the results of the survey are eventually published, various methods of more generalised mapping will be used to maintain the security of rare and vulnerable birds, and some maps may not be published at all. Records submitted in confidence will not be published in any form without the permission of the original observer.

Please always keep disturbance of nesting birds to a minimum: in many cases breeding can be proved without ever approaching the nest. Note that, under the Wildlife and Countryside Act, it is an offence to wilfully disturb Schedule 1 birds at or near the nest unless you have a licence from English Nature.

ENGLISH NATURE

This project is generously sponsored by English Nature

Revised 02/96

WILTSHIRE ORNITHOLOGICAL SOCIETY

TETRAD ATLAS BREEDING BIRD SURVEY

RECORD CARD (REVISED 1996)

Counts for <u>all</u> species now required for timed visits.

		S	B	Count			S	B	Count
0007	Little Grebe				0529	Woodcock			
0009	Great Crested Grebe				0541	Curlew			
0072	Cormorant				0546	Redshank			
0122	Grey Heron				0582	Black-headed Gull			
0152	Mute Swan				0591	Lesser Black-backed Gull			
0161	Greylag Goose				0615	Common Tern			
0166	Canada Goose				0665	Feral Pigeon			
0167	Barnacle Goose				0668	Stock Dove			
0173	Shelduck				0670	Wood Pigeon			
0178	Mandarin				0684	Collared Dove			
0182	Gadwall				0687	Turtle Dove			
0184	Teal				0724	Cuckoo			
0186	Mallard				0735	Barn Owl			
0194	Shoveler				0757	Little Owl			
0196	Red-crested Pochard				0761	Tawny Owl			
0198	Pochard				0767	Long-eared Owl			
0203	Tufted Duck				0778	Nightjar			
0225	Ruddy Duck				0795	Swift			
0269	Sparrowhawk				0831	Kingfisher			
0287	Buzzard				0856	Green Woodpecker			
0304	Kestrel				0876	Great Sp Woodpecker			
0310	Hobby				0887	Lesser Sp Woodpecker			
0358	Red-legged Partridge				0974	Woodlark			
0367	Grey Partridge				0976	Skylark			
0370	Quail				0981	Sand Martin			
0394	Pheasant				0992	Swallow			
0407	Water Rail				1001	House Martin			
0424	Moorhen				1009	Tree Pipit			
0429	Coot				1011	Meadow Pipit			
0459	Stone Curlew				1017	Yellow Wagtail			
0469	Little Ringed Plover				1019	Grey Wagtail			
0470	Ringed Plover				1020	Pied Wagtail			
0493	Lapwing				1050	Dipper			
0519	Snipe				1066	Wren			

Date	Timed Visit	Untimed Visit
	☐ (✓)	☐ (✓)

Largest Feature in Tetrad	10-km Sq	Tetrad	Total Time Spent in Tetrad

Name..

Address..

....

Postcode..Tel No..

		S	B	Count			S	B	Count
1084	Dunnock				1486	Treecreeper			
1099	Robin				1539	Jay			
1104	Nightingale				1549	Magpie			
1121	Black Redstart				1560	Jackdaw			
1122	Redstart				1563	Rook			
1137	Whinchat				1567	Carrion Crow			
1139	Stonechat				1572	Raven			
1146	Wheatear				1582	Starling			
1187	Blackbird				1591	House Sparrow			
1200	Song Thrush				1598	Tree Sparrow			
1202	Mistle Thrush				1636	Chaffinch			
1220	Cetti's Warbler				1649	Greenfinch			
1236	Grasshopper Warbler				1653	Goldfinch			
1243	Sedge Warbler				1654	Siskin			
1251	Reed Warbler				1660	Linnet			
1262	Dartford Warbler				1663	Redpoll			
1274	Lesser Whitethroat				1666	Crossbill			
1275	Whitethroat				1710	Bullfinch			
1276	Garden Warbler				1717	Hawfinch			
1277	Blackcap				1857	Yellowhammer			
1308	Wood Warbler				1877	Reed Bunting			
1311	Chiffchaff				1882	Corn Bunting			
1312	Willow Warbler								
1314	Goldcrest								
1315	Firecrest								
1335	Spotted Flycatcher								
1349	Pied Flycatcher								
1437	Long-tailed Tit								
1440	Marsh Tit								
1442	Willow Tit								
1461	Coal Tit								
1462	Blue Tit								
1464	Great Tit								
1479	Nuthatch								

Figure 72. Front and back of record card for summer tetrad fieldwork in Wiltshire 1995–2000

COMPLETING THE RECORD CARD

Please see completed specimen and then enter:

- Your name, address and postcode
- Your telephone number.
- Name of the largest feature in the tetrad.
- Date of visit.
- Tetrad identity (10-km square plus tetrad letter).

For each species recorded in a tetrad, details should be entered against that species on the Record Card. If the species is not listed, then enter its name in one of the blank rows at the end of the card. The number printed before each species names is the Euring number used by European bird-ringing schemes, which aids entry onto the computer. The columns S and B represent **Seen** and **Breeding**.

SEEN
Enter **S** in the column headed **S** if the species was seen or heard in the tetrad, but with no evidence of breeding. ***Singing birds will sometimes be included in this category but can also fall in the category of Breeding (see under heading BREEDING for criteria). Exclude escapes, late winterers and passage migrants, but note that flying Swifts and hirundines should be recorded.***

A number should be entered in the count column for <u>all</u> species: please record the total of individuals seen or heard (excluding dependent young). For breeding colonial species (in Wiltshire mainly Grey Heron, Sand Martin and Rook) the number of nests only should be entered in the count column, and an entry of B inserted in the column headed B. If a colonial species is seen with no evidence of breeding simply enter S in the appropriate column and in the Count column enter the number seen. Time spent counting a colony should not be included in the 2-hour period.

BREEDING
Enter **B** in the column headed **B** if one or more of the following activities was observed:

- ***Song, if heard in the same location 14 or more days apart.***
- Bird apparently holding territory.
- Courtship and display; or anxiety call/agitated behaviour of adult indicating presence of young or nest.
- Brood patch on trapped bird.
- Adult visiting probable nest-site.
- Nest building (including excavating nest-hole).
- Distraction display or injury feigning.
- Used nest found.
- Recently fledged young.
- Adult carrying faecal sac or food.
- Adult entering or leaving nest-site in circumstances indicating occupied nest (including colonies).
- Nest with eggs found, or bird sitting but not disturbed, or eggshells found near nest.
- Nest with young; or downy young of ducks, gamebirds, waders, other nidifugous species.

As soon as possible after the end of August in each year, and not later than 30 September, all Record Cards should be sent to the steward of the 10-km square in which the tetrad fieldwork was carried out.

Each tetrad in a 10-km square
is described by a letter as follows:

2-km

E	J	P	U	Z
D	I	N	T	Y
C	H	M	S	X
B	G	L	R	W
A	F	K	Q	V

10-km Square SU58

ENGLISH
NATURE

This project is generously sponsored by English Nature

WILTSHIRE ORNITHOLOGICAL SOCIETY

TETRAD ATLAS BREEDING BIRD SURVEY

CASUAL RECORD FORM

Name .... Year ....

Address...

....

Postcode.................................... Tel No ....

NB Please use this form only for the species shown shaded on the Record Card.

10-km Square	Tetrad Letter	Nearest Place name from 1:50,000 OS map and/or grid reference	Euring Code	Species	S	B	Count

Please return not later than 30 September to:
Rob Turner, County Recorder,
14 Ethendun, Bratton, Westbury, Wilts. BA13 4RX

ENGLISH NATURE

This project is generously sponsored by English Nature

Figure 73. Casual record sheet for summer tetrad fieldwork in Wiltshire 1995–2000

WILTSHIRE WINTER BIRD MAPPING SURVEY

Why?

The main aim is to record what species are present in Wiltshire in winter, and broadly where. WOS has relatively little information on winter distribution patterns, especially for commoner land birds. The results (to be gathered by tetrads but, because birds are much more mobile in winter than summer, mapped by 10-km squares) will complement those of the summer atlas in the projected 'Birds of Wiltshire', as well as providing a comprehensive database for future comparisons.

A secondary aim is roughly to assess the relative abundance of each species in different parts of the county by noting the highest tetrad count for each species in each 10-km square. This information will also be useful for the book.

When?

The survey will take place over two winters: 1998/99 and 1999/2000. In each winter, the survey periods will be the four months from November to February.

How?

Priority Tetrads

Although coverage of all tetrads in Wiltshire will not be possible, a minimum number of tetrads must be surveyed in each 10-km square for the results to be worthwhile. To avoid bias in coverage, the tetrads to be surveyed have been selected randomly. Some 10-km squares fall only partly in Wiltshire, so a different selection of tetrads needs to be covered in those squares. The 'priority' tetrads to be covered, just once in one or other of the two winters, are for each 10-km square.

If time allows, as many 'additional' tetrads as you wish may be covered to ensure that all the main habitats in the 10-km square are adequately sampled. These additional tetrads can be chosen by you.

Time in Tetrad

A total of two hours should be spent in each of the tetrads to be surveyed (both priorty and additional tetrads). As in the summer survey, the route does not have to be continuous. You may wish to split it into sections to ensure that all the main habitats are sampled. Thus, you could spend, say, 25 minutes on one section then 60 minutes on another and 35 on a third so long as the total is two hours.

Wherever possible, an individual tetrad should be surveyed in just one visit. If you have to break off for any reason (eg bad weather) you can split the survey into two separate visits, but in that case both visits must be made in the same winter and, if possible, in the same month. When completing a partial survey, continue your route from the point at which the first visit was interrupted to ensure that you do not cover the same area twice. if the survey is interrupted after less than half an hour, the survey should be abandoned for that day and you should restart your two hours some other time.

Because bird distribution patterns do change during the winter, you should aim to spread fieldwork in the 10-km square as a whole over the four month winter period. For example, if surveying eight tetrads in one winter, you should aim to cover two in each month.

Counting Birds

Observers should count the number of each species recorded in each tetrad during the two hour survey. Care should be taken to ensure, as far as possible, the same birds are not counted twice. If it is clear that overflying birds are not using a tetrad (eg gull flocks flying high to roost or Cormorants over a tetrad with no water) then

WILTSHIRE ORNITHOLOGICAL SOCIETY
Registered Charity No 271033

This project is generously sponsored by English Nature

Figure 74. Survey instructions for winter fieldwork in Wiltshire 1998/99–1999/00

they should not be counted. Most birds seen in flight will be using (eg hunting raptors) or have been using (eg flocks of Starlings or Rooks feeding in nearby fields) and should be counted.

Unlike the summer survey, we do not require casual records. In particular, we are not asking for supplementary dusk or night visits which means that owls will be under recorded. So please send in all November to February records of any owls along with your observations of scarce or unusual species on standard record cards in the normal way.

Some of you may like to consider working in pairs. This can have advantages as well as providing companionship. Where, for example, convenient footpaths form an open loop across a tetrad, or even traverse two or three adjacent tetrads, it may be useful to use two cars leaving one at the far end of the projected route, in order to save having to backtrack. Any pair of observers must, however, either stay together and record jointly for the two hours, or follow quite separate routes for one hour each and then combine their tetrads to make up the two hour survey.

In open country, even away from water bodies, a telescope can be very useful in a winter survey, eg to identify birds in mixed bunting and finch flocks.

Completing the Form

A separate form should be used for each month. Results from all tetrads surveyed in that month should be written on the same form. An example of a completed form is attached showing the imaginary results of visits to three tetrads in November 1998.

- Write the 10-km square number (eg SU27) and the month and year in numbers (eg 1298 for December 1998) in the relevant boxes at the top of the form.
- Write the number of hours spent in the tetrad above the relevant tetrad column. Ordinarily, this will be '2'. If the survey was interrupted, and you were unable to revisit the tetrad to complete the survey in the same month, insert the length of the partial survey.
- Write the total number of each species seen in the tetrad in the relevant box. If space does not allow large numbers to be written clearly in the box, please annotate the form as shown on the example provided.
- If you have to make two visits to the same tetrad to complete the two hour survey, add the results from both visits together when completing the form (so take care not to write totals from the partial survey on the form in pen before the month is finished).
- If you record a species that is not listed on the form, please add it in one of the blank spaces at the bottom. A list of possible species and their Euring numbers is provided on the other side of the instruction sheet. Escapes need not be counted.
- Write the highest count of each species in any tetrad surveyed in that month in the 'max count' column.

Please return completed forms to your Regional Organiser as soon as possible after the winter survey period, and no later than 31 March.

If you have any queries on the survey please contact either:

Stephen Edwards
(01793) 790500
or
Peter Cranswick
Day (01453) 890333 ext 280
Evening (01453) 544867

WILTSHIRE WINTER BIRD MAPPING SURVEY

Please complete the following details:

Name ....

Address ....

....

....

....

Postcode .... **Tel No** ....

WILTSHIRE ORNITHOLOGICAL SOCIETY
Registered Charity No 271033

This project is generously sponsored by English Nature

Figure 75. Record form for winter fieldwork in Wiltshire 1998/99–1999/00

Wiltshire Winter Bird Mapping Survey

10-km Square				

M	M	Y	Y

EURING	SPECIES	A	B	C	D	E	F	G	H	I	J	K	L	M	N	P	Q	R	S	T	U	V	W	X	Y	Z	MAX COUNT	Office Use
	Time Spent in Tetrad																											
0007	Little Grebe																											
0009	Gt Cr Grebe																											
0072	Cormorant																											
0122	Grey Heron																											
0152	Mute Swan																											
0166	Canada Goose																											
0179	Wigeon																											
0182	Gadwall																											
0184	Teal																											
0186	Mallard																											
0194	Shoveler																											
0198	Pochard																											
0203	Tufted Duck																											
0218	Goldeneye																											
0223	Goosander																											
0225	Ruddy Duck																											
0269	Sparrowhawk																											
0287	Buzzard																											
0304	Kestrel																											
0358	Red-lg Partridge																											
0367	Grey Partridge																											
0394	Pheasant																											
0407	Water Rail																											
0424	Moorhen																											
0429	Coot																											
0485	Golden Plover																											
0493	Lapwing																											
0519	Common Snipe																											
0529	Woodcock																											
0582	Black-hd Gull																											
0590	Common Gull																											
0591	LBB Gull																											
0665	Feral Pigeon																											
0668	Stock Dove																											
0670	Wood Pigeon																											
0684	Collared Dove																											
0735	Barn Owl																											
0757	Little Owl																											
0761	Tawny Owl																											
0831	Kingfisher																											
0856	Green Woodpecker																											
0876	Gt Sp Woodpecker																											

	Time Spent in Tetrad																											
EURING	SPECIES	A	B	C	D	E	F	G	H	I	J	K	L	M	N	P	Q	R	S	T	U	V	W	X	Y	Z	MAX COUNT	Office Use
0976	Sky Lark																											
1011	Meadow Pipit																											
1019	Grey Wagtail																											
1020	Pied Wagtail																											
1066	Wren																											
1084	Dunnock																											
1099	Robin																											
1187	Blackbird																											
1198	Fieldfare																											
1200	Song Thrush																											
1201	Redwing																											
1202	Mistle Thrush																											
1277	Blackcap																											
1311	Chiffchaff																											
1314	Goldcrest																											
1437	Long-tailed Tit																											
1440	Marsh Tit																											
1461	Coal Tit																											
1462	Blue Tit																											
1464	Great Tit																											
1479	Nuthatch																											
1486	Treecreeper																											
1539	Jay																											
1549	Magpie																											
1560	Jackdaw																											
1563	Rook																											
1567	Carrion Crow																											
1582	Starling																											
1591	House Sparrow																											
1636	Chaffinch																											
1638	Brambling																											
1649	Greenfinch																											
1653	Goldfinch																											
1654	Siskin																											
1660	Linnet																											
1710	Bullfinch																											
1857	Yellowhammer																											
1877	Reed Bunting																											
1882	Corn Bunting																											
	TOTAL SPECIES																											

Appendix 2

Wiltshire tetrad atlas data

This appendix sets out the results of the summer and winter atlas fieldwork. These data appear elsewhere in *Birds of Wiltshire* – for example, in the maps in the chapter on 'Atlas organisation, methods and mapping 1995–2000', which show the totals of species recorded in each tetrad – but such general maps can be no more than visual summaries, and some species texts do not include individual maps if only small numbers were recorded during the surveys. Below, in three sections, are complete data for all species and for all tetrads in summer and for all species in winter. (For more details and explanation, see 'Atlas organisation, methods and mapping 1995–2000', in which scientific names of all species can also be found in table 9 on pages 124–135.)

Summer atlas fieldwork results by species

'Tetrads' shows the total of tetrads in which each species was recorded ('seen' and 'breeding' combined). 'Breeding' is the number of tetrads in which evidence of breeding was reported. Each of these two figures is also expressed as a percentage of the total of 915 Wiltshire tetrads surveyed during the summer fieldwork. 'Count' shows the number of individuals recorded during timed visits (this is the sum of the higher of the two totals recorded in each tetrad during the two 2-hour surveys). For all three of these treatments, the ranking of the species in the list of the 124 recorded is given. ('No' links the species to table 9 on pages 124–135.)

No	Name	Tetrads	Per cent	Rank	Breed	Per cent	Rank	Count	Rank
1	Mute Swan	193	21·1%	67	124	13·6%	55	709	53
7	Greylag Goose	20	2·2%	103	5	0·5%	103		
8	Canada Goose	197	21·5%	66	102	11·1%	65	1586	38
9	Barnacle Goose	13	1·4%	112	2	0·2%	109		
13	Common Shelduck	6	0·7%	120	1	0·1%	112		
14	Mandarin	36	3·9%	95	16	1·7%	88	57	79
16	Gadwall	26	2·8%	99	7	0·8%	99		
17	Common Teal	12	1·3%	115	0				
19	Mallard	532	58·1%	39	299	32·7%	35	3899	24
23	Shoveler	6	0·7%	120	0				
24	Red-crested Pochard	12	1·3%	115	3	0·3%	106		
25	Common Pochard	21	2·3%	101	1	0·1%	112		
28	Tufted Duck	140	15·3%	73	58	6·3%	72	789	50
38	Ruddy Duck	27	3·0%	98	10	1·1%	92		
41	Red-legged Partridge	360	39·3%	52	104	11·4%	64	872	48
42	Grey Partridge	361	39·5%	51	114	12·5%	60	653	55
43	Quail	139	15·2%	74	23	2·5%	85	83	76
44	Pheasant	835	91·3%	14	358	39·1%	31	5209	18
49	Little Grebe	161	17·6%	70	109	11·9%	61	279	66
50	Great Crested Grebe	59	6·4%	89	44	4·8%	75	232	69
61	Cormorant	42	4·6%	94	0				
70	Grey Heron	351	38·4%	53	20	2·2%	86		
84	Sparrowhawk	471	51·5%	43	124	13·6%	55	357	63
85	Common Buzzard	706	77·2%	32	222	24·3%	40	1175	43
88	Kestrel	748	81·7%	26	263	28·7%	37	915	47
91	Hobby	187	20·4%	69	31	3·4%	81	91	75
94	Water Rail	11	1·2%	117	1	0·1%	112		

No	Name	Tetrads	Per cent	Rank	Breed	Per cent	Rank	Count	Rank
97	Moorhen	473	51·7%	42	353	38·6%	32	1510	40
98	Coot	244	26·7%	63	204	22·3%	43	1826	34
105	Stone-curlew	76	8·3%	85	70	7·7%	69		
108	Little Ringed Plover	9	1·0%	119	6	0·7%	102		
109	Ringed Plover	3	0·3%	122	1	0·1%	112		
114	Lapwing	444	48·5%	44	270	29·5%	36	2277	33
128	Common Snipe	21	2·3%	101	2	0·2%	109		
131	Woodcock	57	6·2%	90	24	2·6%	84		
135	Curlew	82	9·0%	83	25	2·7%	83		
137	Common Redshank	17	1·9%	107	5	0·5%	103		
155	Black-headed Gull	131	14·3%	76	3	0·3%	106		
158	Lesser Black-backed Gull	263	28·7%	61	9	1·0%	95		
161	Herring Gull	22	2·4%	100	1	0·1%	112		
174	Common Tern	16	1·7%	109	7	0·8%	99		
182	Rock Dove/Feral Pigeon	341	37·3%	54	53	5·8%	74	2333	32
183	Stock Dove	708	77·4%	31	324	35·4%	33	2604	31
184	Wood Pigeon	912	99·7%	1	772	84·4%	4	30,854	2
185	Collared Dove	712	77·8%	30	464	50·7%	26	3938	23
186	Turtle Dove	142	15·5%	72	43	4·7%	76	124	74
188	Cuckoo	594	64·9%	36	115	12·6%	59	751	52
189	Barn Owl	254	27·8%	62	182	19·9%	45		
193	Little Owl	290	31·7%	59	140	15·3%	53		
194	Tawny Owl	338	36·9%	55	167	18·3%	48		
195	Long-eared Owl	18	2·0%	105	10	1·1%	92		
197	Nightjar	16	1·7%	109	8	0·9%	97		
198	Common Swift	717	78·4%	29	190	20·8%	44	6323	16
200	Kingfisher	132	14·4%	75	36	3·9%	79	75	78
205	Green Woodpecker	494	54·0%	41	139	15·2%	54	554	59
206	Great Spotted Woodpecker	587	64·2%	37	242	26·4%	38	814	49
207	Lesser Spotted Woodpecker	47	5·1%	93	10	1·1%	92		
208	Wood Lark	3	0·3%	122	1	0·1%	112		
209	Sky Lark	809	88·4%	17	602	65·8%	13	6985	13
211	Sand Martin	52	5·7%	91	13	1·4%	91	1331	42
212	Barn Swallow	859	93·9%	9	612	66·9%	11	8675	10
213	House Martin	723	79·0%	28	493	53·9%	23	8720	9
217	Tree Pipit	147	16·1%	71	84	9·2%	67	186	72
218	Meadow Pipit	312	34·1%	57	168	18·4%	47	1548	39
221	Yellow Wagtail	127	13·9%	77	64	7·0%	70	203	71
222	Grey Wagtail	207	22·6%	65	97	10·6%	66	221	70
223	Pied Wagtail	683	74·6%	34	373	40·8%	30	1473	41
225	Dipper	18	2·0%	105	15	1·6%	89		
226	Wren	906	99·0%	4	791	86·4%	3	9635	8
227	Dunnock	839	91·7%	13	594	64·9%	14	3632	26
228	Robin	885	96·7%	7	759	83·0%	6	7782	11
229	Nightingale	78	8·5%	84	39	4·3%	77		
231	Black Redstart	2	0·2%	124	0				
232	Common Redstart	60	6·6%	88	15	1·6%	89	26	81
233	Whinchat	111	12·1%	78	62	6·8%	71	293	65
234	Stonechat	107	11·7%	79	84	9·2%	67	125	73
235	Wheatear	61	6·7%	87	1	0·1%	112		
237	Blackbird	909	99·3%	3	847	92·6%	1	12,695	7

No	Name	Tetrads	Per cent	Rank	Breed	Per cent	Rank	Count	Rank
239	Song Thrush	775	84·7%	25	514	56·2%	21	2686	30
241	Mistle Thrush	688	75·2%	33	392	42·8%	29	1756	36
242	Cetti's Warbler	13	1·4%	112	7	0·8%	99		
243	Grasshopper Warbler	90	9·8%	81	33	3·6%	80	41	80
246	Sedge Warbler	190	20·8%	68	120	13·1%	58	585	58
248	Reed Warbler	95	10·4%	80	58	6·3%	72	275	67
251	Blackcap	805	88·0%	18	546	59·7%	19	3165	29
252	Garden Warbler	433	47·3%	46	172	18·8%	46	762	51
254	Lesser Whitethroat	374	40·9%	49	154	16·8%	51	485	61
255	Common Whitethroat	802	87·7%	20	608	66·4%	12	3896	25
258	Wood Warbler	49	5·4%	92	20	2·2%	86		
259	Chiffchaff	804	87·9%	19	544	59·5%	20	3536	27
260	Willow Warbler	789	86·2%	22	468	51·1%	25	3223	28
261	Goldcrest	568	62·1%	38	323	35·3%	34	1680	37
262	Firecrest	13	1·4%	112	9	1·0%	95		
263	Spotted Flycatcher	432	47·2%	47	227	24·8%	39	601	57
265	Pied Flycatcher	14	1·5%	111	2	0·2%	109		
267	Long-tailed Tit	615	67·2%	35	405	44·3%	28	1775	35
268	Blue Tit	885	96·7%	7	760	83·1%	5	7748	12
269	Great Tit	887	96·9%	6	717	78·4%	7	4950	19
270	Coal Tit	415	45·4%	48	219	23·9%	41	957	46
271	Willow Tit	85	9·3%	82	27	3·0%	82	76	77
272	Marsh Tit	284	31·0%	60	123	13·4%	57	477	62
273	Nuthatch	335	36·6%	56	150	16·4%	52	603	56
274	Treecreeper	371	40·5%	50	159	17·4%	50	493	60
281	Jay	435	47·5%	45	107	11·7%	62	664	54
282	Magpie	848	92·7%	12	505	55·2%	22	3986	21
285	Jackdaw	855	93·4%	10	621	67·9%	10	17,201	4
286	Rook	852	93·1%	11	554	60·5%	18	36,553	1
287	Carrion Crow	889	97·2%	5	578	63·2%	15	6954	14
289	Raven	36	3·9%	95	8	0·9%	97		
290	Common Starling	822	89·8%	16	669	73·1%	8	22,187	3
292	House Sparrow	740	80·9%	27	644	70·4%	9	13,825	6
293	Tree Sparrow	75	8·2%	86	37	4·0%	78	233	68
294	Chaffinch	910	99·5%	2	833	91·0%	2	15,217	5
297	Greenfinch	824	90·1%	15	578	63·2%	15	6583	15
298	Goldfinch	789	86·2%	22	428	46·8%	27	3959	22
299	Siskin	35	3·8%	97	5	0·5%	103		
300	Linnet	776	84·8%	24	481	52·6%	24	5341	17
303	Lesser Redpoll	17	1·9%	107	1	0·1%	112		
304	Crossbill	20	2·2%	103	1	0·1%	112		
305	Bullfinch	532	58·1%	39	213	23·3%	42	1020	44
306	Hawfinch	10	1·1%	118	3	0·3%	106		
309	Yellowhammer	792	86·6%	21	574	62·7%	17	4438	20
314	Reed Bunting	217	23·7%	64	106	11·6%	63	356	64
315	Corn Bunting	295	32·2%	58	160	17·5%	49	961	45

Summer atlas fieldwork results by tetrad

'Species' shows the total number of species recorded in each tetrad ('seen' and 'breeding' combined). 'Breed' is the number of species for which evidence of breeding was reported. 'Count' is the number of individuals recorded during the timed visits (the higher of the two totals recorded in the two 2-hour surveys). 'Red' and 'Amber' are the totals recorded in each tetrad ('seen' and 'breeding' combined) of the species on the Red and Amber lists of the Birds of Conservation Concern (Gregory *et al* 2002).

Tetrad	Species	Breed	Count	Red	Amber
ST73L	59	39	368	7	16
ST73M	55	31	258	9	14
ST73R	63	40	403	9	14
ST73S	63	25	350	8	16
ST73T	45	28	412	6	11
ST73U	41	18	289	5	11
ST73V	43	23	455	7	7
ST73W	35	22	266	9	6
ST73X	33	17	212	7	5
ST73Y	37	19	481	8	9
ST73Z	37	30	277	5	9
ST74V	38	15	352	6	9
ST75Z	41	26	341	4	10
ST76Q	45	24	286	7	8
ST76V	43	31	380	6	8
ST76W	50	29	332	7	13
ST76X	46	22	299	6	12
ST77T	36	16	219	7	6
ST77Y	44	17	234	10	8
ST77Z	35	17	211	8	7
ST82P	36	16	426	4	8
ST82S	39	22	240	6	9
ST82T	39	8	229	6	8
ST82U	58	31	626	10	12
ST82V	39	25	320	6	7
ST82W	56	39	475	9	14
ST82X	67	46	496	9	15
ST82Y	41	25	348	5	7
ST82Z	40	16	228	7	10
ST83A	46	29	813	9	9
ST83B	43	27	691	8	8
ST83C	43	14	353	7	11
ST83D	51	30	693	11	13
ST83E	53	32	562	9	13
ST83F	45	25	472	10	9
ST83G	43	24	498	7	11
ST83H	34	19	674	7	5
ST83I	42	9	225	6	10
ST83J	44	29	238	7	9
ST83K	41	9	325	6	11
ST83L	50	29	469	11	12
ST83M	35	26	268	7	8
ST83N	53	29	800	9	10

Tetrad	Species	Breed	Count	Red	Amber
ST83P	51	17	243	9	11
ST83Q	44	22	442	7	9
ST83R	50	26	428	9	10
ST83S	37	5	258	9	6
ST83T	31	4	250	7	7
ST83U	51	33	467	9	11
ST83V	54	34	821	10	9
ST83W	43	16	533	9	8
ST83X	34	5	189	7	7
ST83Y	43	25	369	12	6
ST83Z	37	18	225	9	7
ST84A	57	33	938	9	13
ST84B	73	57	693	8	18
ST84C	45	34	417	7	10
ST84D	32	22	232	6	7
ST84F	54	32	699	10	10
ST84G	61	41	287	7	19
ST84H	49	26	387	8	12
ST84I	55	30	267	10	14
ST84J	50	24	248	8	12
ST84K	57	39	682	9	11
ST84L	80	64	439	14	22
ST84M	58	43	482	10	16
ST84N	51	33	276	9	11
ST84P	52	28	535	9	13
ST84Q	55	36	829	8	14
ST84R	54	21	254	6	12
ST84S	45	20	349	7	10
ST84T	48	22	359	10	12
ST84U	52	38	383	7	16
ST84V	42	27	222	10	9
ST84W	47	17	297	5	10
ST84X	51	26	301	9	13
ST84Y	44	16	360	9	12
ST84Z	55	43	513	11	12
ST85C	54	23	384	6	12
ST85D	62	41	528	10	15
ST85E	52	42	557	7	11
ST85F	48	13	404	9	9
ST85G	54	20	386	8	10
ST85H	41	18	193	6	7
ST85I	51	39	369	9	9
ST85J	49	29	587	9	8

Tetrad	Species	Breed	Count	Red	Amber
ST85K	42	14	199	6	9
ST85L	39	15	395	6	6
ST85M	38	23	378	5	9
ST85N	30	13	174	3	5
ST85P	47	21	638	6	12
ST85Q	53	38	614	7	15
ST85R	45	14	453	6	11
ST85S	49	34	267	6	12
ST85T	60	35	235	8	17
ST85U	44	25	542	9	9
ST85V	57	33	272	11	15
ST85W	45	15	303	7	9
ST85X	60	41	609	9	14
ST85Y	53	16	242	8	12
ST85Z	40	18	362	5	8
ST86A	61	38	275	8	17
ST86B	44	24	142	8	6
ST86C	32	4	207	5	8
ST86D	29	3	205	6	7
ST86E	34	15	216	4	6
ST86F	60	34	229	8	16
ST86G	40	16	256	7	9
ST86H	34	9	135	6	5
ST86I	37	18	230	7	8
ST86J	44	4	707	7	10
ST86K	40	19	221	4	8
ST86L	36	15	180	6	6
ST86M	37	25	383	4	11
ST86N	36	22	374	6	10
ST86P	28	2	384	2	6
ST86Q	58	40	347	10	14
ST86R	53	40	502	8	12
ST86S	44	30	310	7	9
ST86T	47	26	271	8	10
ST86U	51	22	370	9	11
ST86V	59	33	528	10	13
ST86W	56	36	358	6	16
ST86X	48	28	629	7	11
ST86Y	42	17	304	7	9
ST86Z	42	18	445	7	10
ST87A	37	14	357	7	8
ST87B	43	18	273	5	9
ST87C	38	24	434	8	7
ST87D	52	35	374	9	12
ST87E	48	35	293	8	10
ST87F	48	12	273	8	11
ST87G	54	24	311	7	12
ST87H	49	17	265	6	8
ST87I	57	20	297	9	11
ST87J	53	38	267	7	11
ST87K	42	32	303	9	8
ST87L	45	38	355	8	9
ST87M	57	37	404	12	12
ST87N	53	37	442	11	9
ST87P	45	30	231	9	6
ST87Q	59	42	525	9	11
ST87R	48	23	484	8	11
ST87S	27	21	138	4	5
ST87T	37	29	361	6	8
ST87U	38	30	498	7	8
ST87V	63	53	455	11	13
ST87W	33	22	258	6	7
ST87X	33	28	295	5	6
ST87Y	41	18	410	8	9
ST87Z	47	38	317	9	11
ST88C	47	46	371	10	11
ST88F	43	29	556	8	7
ST88G	50	31	193	9	12
ST88H	38	22	168	6	9
ST88I	41	22	242	7	9
ST88K	40	9	217	6	8
ST88L	42	19	245	8	7
ST88M	51	35	246	8	12
ST88N	31	20	202	7	7
ST88P	46	34	434	9	9
ST88Q	41	12	368	7	9
ST88R	50	27	217	10	12
ST88S	52	32	559	10	10
ST88T	52	15	369	7	11
ST88U	43	15	412	7	9
ST88V	42	16	239	9	8
ST88W	38	21	308	6	8
ST88X	39	6	394	9	8
ST88Y	58	27	277	10	13
ST91E	42	33	440	7	10
ST91I	52	40	430	10	12
ST91J	44	22	305	8	13
ST91N	41	14	190	6	12
ST91P	47	11	296	9	13
ST91U	28	17	225	6	4
ST91Z	40	22	379	10	6
ST92A	46	22	359	7	11
ST92B	60	46	636	9	15
ST92C	49	36	548	8	9
ST92D	50	27	518	9	9
ST92E	67	59	384	11	14
ST92F	55	36	284	10	15
ST92G	45	38	314	9	8
ST92H	64	54	410	10	15
ST92I	53	34	468	8	12
ST92J	65	58	430	10	18
ST92K	46	8	227	9	10
ST92L	42	23	434	9	9
ST92M	46	27	211	7	12
ST92N	56	50	531	8	11
ST92P	62	51	847	11	14

Tetrad	Species	Breed	Count	Red	Amber
ST92Q	34	3	170	5	8
ST92R	44	28	371	9	8
ST92S	38	22	217	8	6
ST92T	54	34	445	8	11
ST92U	58	56	421	9	15
ST92V	40	9	156	8	8
ST92W	45	23	336	9	9
ST92X	54	38	451	10	10
ST92Y	48	32	255	11	9
ST92Z	50	41	424	7	14
ST93A	61	51	324	6	16
ST93B	38	26	634	7	9
ST93C	46	20	263	9	8
ST93D	32	22	261	5	7
ST93E	38	6	227	10	7
ST93F	65	42	364	8	16
ST93G	59	41	660	8	15
ST93H	49	26	277	7	11
ST93I	39	28	307	7	10
ST93J	43	27	313	7	12
ST93K	68	49	468	10	16
ST93L	44	26	336	8	10
ST93M	42	19	303	9	9
ST93N	37	27	344	7	6
ST93P	51	25	338	10	10
ST93Q	63	46	558	10	14
ST93R	51	34	686	8	12
ST93S	48	23	288	8	11
ST93T	52	38	539	9	13
ST93U	65	48	921	10	15
ST93V	66	50	673	10	16
ST93W	47	36	188	6	11
ST93X	52	35	970	12	12
ST93Y	51	34	650	10	14
ST93Z	62	48	845	9	12
ST94A	43	18	270	9	9
ST94B	48	13	584	9	9
ST94C	44	9	395	7	13
ST94D	36	23	197	6	9
ST94E	40	26	94	7	11
ST94F	42	14	408	6	9
ST94G	54	23	554	9	13
ST94H	38	22	403	7	9
ST94I	28	19	178	7	9
ST94J	49	30	226	10	13
ST94K	56	36	771	8	15
ST94L	43	16	517	11	8
ST94M	30	17	219	8	8
ST94N	39	17	285	8	11
ST94P	36	15	105	5	13
ST94Q	39	27	509	6	9
ST94R	36	16	390	7	7
ST94S	33	15	366	9	8

Tetrad	Species	Breed	Count	Red	Amber
ST94T	38	24	211	9	11
ST94U	55	25	107	13	14
ST94V	37	16	356	9	6
ST94W	37	20	367	7	9
ST94X	37	26	411	11	9
ST94Y	24	14	96	6	8
ST94Z	24	10	47	5	9
ST95A	51	29	265	12	12
ST95B	58	34	222	9	16
ST95C	36	16	145	6	8
ST95D	35	25	284	5	9
ST95E	51	36	383	10	9
ST95F	60	41	202	14	15
ST95G	63	44	240	13	13
ST95H	47	33	202	10	10
ST95I	32	13	541	7	5
ST95J	45	23	340	8	9
ST95K	43	14	204	7	13
ST95L	45	23	220	8	11
ST95M	37	20	269	7	6
ST95N	38	4	391	4	8
ST95P	39	17	747	6	8
ST95Q	47	21	276	7	15
ST95R	54	24	185	9	14
ST95S	59	31	369	10	12
ST95T	50	21	206	7	13
ST95U	41	21	504	6	9
ST95V	40	24	235	8	12
ST95W	43	17	215	7	13
ST95X	44	26	239	6	8
ST95Y	52	24	457	4	14
ST95Z	41	18	310	5	10
ST96A	39	29	329	5	9
ST96B	35	27	486	4	9
ST96C	36	23	358	5	7
ST96D	59	55	267	9	15
ST96E	52	45	284	9	9
ST96F	52	24	220	8	14
ST96G	48	27	190	8	10
ST96H	34	18	342	3	5
ST96I	38	17	231	4	9
ST96J	50	14	173	5	11
ST96K	46	30	284	7	10
ST96L	52	43	450	9	10
ST96M	58	47	467	9	13
ST96N	53	25	315	6	13
ST96P	49	46	203	8	10
ST96Q	45	17	258	8	11
ST96R	61	49	531	12	11
ST96S	60	48	491	11	13
ST96T	58	38	274	9	13
ST96U	68	60	563	9	14
ST96V	61	31	490	10	15

Tetrad	Species	Breed	Count	Red	Amber
ST96W	54	33	226	11	12
ST96X	50	30	323	10	10
ST96Y	49	31	376	8	11
ST96Z	46	16	576	8	10
ST97A	50	21	420	8	13
ST97B	49	27	627	6	15
ST97C	37	16	248	4	9
ST97D	28	20	185	5	2
ST97E	35	22	158	5	7
ST97F	54	35	315	7	11
ST97G	38	11	334	5	10
ST97H	44	25	295	7	10
ST97I	32	12	179	4	5
ST97J	31	12	218	5	4
ST97K	33	28	98	3	6
ST97L	38	26	82	7	7
ST97M	37	13	205	5	9
ST97N	36	29	99	5	7
ST97P	42	17	286	5	11
ST97Q	29	18	134	3	5
ST97R	45	29	151	7	9
ST97S	39	29	152	6	8
ST97T	58	34	497	8	14
ST97U	43	21	381	9	9
ST97V	46	36	335	7	10
ST97W	37	24	268	6	9
ST97X	47	26	296	8	11
ST97Y	39	29	202	7	8
ST97Z	49	22	206	5	11
ST98A	47	12	145	9	6
ST98B	29	21	251	4	4
ST98C	45	36	406	10	8
ST98D	59	49	610	10	14
ST98E	44	39	355	7	10
ST98F	53	34	173	7	12
ST98G	26	19	181	4	2
ST98H	47	44	612	7	10
ST98I	49	42	731	8	11
ST98J	45	37	598	7	9
ST98K	41	20	156	7	6
ST98L	32	17	272	6	6
ST98M	60	28	359	9	15
ST98N	35	15	277	6	8
ST98P	33	11	236	6	6
ST98Q	42	21	389	6	9
ST98R	50	31	323	7	12
ST98S	42	28	266	8	9
ST98T	30	8	253	4	6
ST98U	39	16	158	7	8
ST98V	32	15	326	7	5
ST98W	38	25	209	7	6
ST98X	30	12	178	4	5
ST98Y	43	20	233	8	6

Tetrad	Species	Breed	Count	Red	Amber
ST98Z	46	17	322	8	7
ST99A	50	42	481	7	13
ST99F	36	32	273	9	5
ST99G	36	31	206	8	7
ST99K	48	37	351	9	9
ST99L	59	47	439	12	11
ST99M	38	32	224	7	8
ST99Q	50	33	250	9	11
ST99R	58	50	409	12	11
ST99S	49	40	134	8	13
ST99V	48	43	547	7	11
ST99W	50	40	181	9	10
ST99X	44	38	180	7	10
SU02A	49	33	400	9	12
SU02B	42	32	429	6	9
SU02C	50	33	288	9	12
SU02D	57	37	211	12	14
SU02E	50	30	375	7	12
SU02F	45	43	104	9	10
SU02G	43	29	216	9	11
SU02H	71	51	346	13	19
SU02I	50	30	256	11	13
SU02J	53	29	423	9	13
SU02L	44	21	183	9	12
SU02M	56	38	275	10	15
SU02N	47	28	110	10	11
SU02P	44	15	159	7	12
SU02R	40	25	144	8	7
SU02S	50	33	242	9	13
SU02T	41	13	220	5	10
SU02U	37	7	236	6	9
SU02V	50	24	316	10	12
SU02W	38	21	147	10	7
SU02X	34	8	198	5	6
SU02Y	45	13	267	7	11
SU02Z	55	35	514	10	13
SU03A	51	19	288	7	11
SU03B	31	1	288	5	6
SU03C	52	24	277	11	9
SU03D	50	25	425	9	10
SU03E	59	31	366	10	13
SU03F	42	7	284	5	11
SU03G	40	10	310	7	12
SU03H	40	17	165	8	7
SU03I	63	35	545	8	14
SU03J	33	10	218	6	8
SU03K	51	28	417	7	9
SU03L	45	22	250	7	10
SU03M	37	13	163	5	7
SU03N	65	32	508	7	18
SU03P	31	8	308	5	8
SU03Q	42	14	339	6	9
SU03R	50	18	435	9	11

Tetrad	Species	Breed	Count	Red	Amber
SU03S	57	34	407	10	12
SU03T	64	33	380	10	19
SU03U	48	21	271	7	11
SU03V	63	44	939	9	15
SU03W	52	30	344	9	11
SU03X	63	43	697	13	14
SU03Y	47	13	526	11	11
SU03Z	48	27	501	8	12
SU04A	31	17	166	5	8
SU04B	33	21	183	3	9
SU04C	37	22	258	8	8
SU04D	27	19	158	3	9
SU04E	21	17	54	2	9
SU04F	32	21	115	7	7
SU04G	21	12	65	3	4
SU04H	20	11	77	2	7
SU04I	50	38	288	8	14
SU04J	50	31	226	9	11
SU04K	25	13	61	4	5
SU04L	35	24	250	7	7
SU04M	35	28	340	8	6
SU04N	45	29	450	7	11
SU04P	50	33	177	9	13
SU04Q	28	17	82	7	6
SU04R	47	35	598	9	9
SU04S	36	27	247	5	8
SU04T	37	25	71	5	12
SU04U	43	23	143	9	11
SU04V	45	27	201	8	8
SU04W	36	17	143	6	8
SU04X	26	21	195	5	5
SU04Y	48	38	334	10	12
SU04Z	51	35	321	13	13
SU05A	44	24	189	8	8
SU05B	45	18	187	8	9
SU05C	34	22	342	4	7
SU05D	47	10	388	9	12
SU05E	54	21	340	9	12
SU05F	38	23	287	9	11
SU05G	40	18	123	8	12
SU05H	38	14	154	9	13
SU05I	41	26	447	7	11
SU05J	54	26	366	9	13
SU05K	41	28	274	9	11
SU05L	22	11	79	5	8
SU05M	44	32	355	10	11
SU05N	50	35	442	10	12
SU05P	52	25	364	9	14
SU05Q	33	19	321	9	10
SU05R	40	30	142	8	12
SU05S	48	34	304	13	14
SU05T	52	27	382	10	11
SU05U	44	26	293	11	7

Tetrad	Species	Breed	Count	Red	Amber
SU05V	23	6	255	3	8
SU05W	33	16	314	8	10
SU05X	49	32	463	10	12
SU05Y	53	23	387	10	12
SU05Z	60	19	499	14	14
SU06A	66	50	177	11	16
SU06B	55	44	181	9	14
SU06C	45	28	140	11	11
SU06D	39	19	266	7	8
SU06E	39	28	203	3	8
SU06F	61	39	68	11	16
SU06G	65	26	392	8	18
SU06H	42	21	230	11	8
SU06I	46	27	266	12	12
SU06J	47	39	202	8	9
SU06K	39	24	152	8	9
SU06L	60	41	424	11	13
SU06M	57	36	157	10	14
SU06N	35	16	155	9	9
SU06P	44	21	125	7	10
SU06Q	41	26	262	5	10
SU06R	28	20	100	5	6
SU06S	35	11	145	6	8
SU06T	21	14	159	5	5
SU06U	27	20	50	9	6
SU06V	41	35	138	7	8
SU06W	52	37	180	10	13
SU06X	27	10	72	7	3
SU06Y	30	12	295	5	9
SU06Z	43	29	214	9	12
SU07A	54	41	541	10	14
SU07B	44	27	305	8	8
SU07C	47	28	342	9	7
SU07D	45	31	275	9	9
SU07E	42	25	366	8	7
SU07F	48	39	429	6	10
SU07G	46	33	387	8	9
SU07H	42	33	363	8	10
SU07I	45	26	305	7	10
SU07J	41	32	402	7	7
SU07K	45	34	426	9	12
SU07L	39	26	272	7	10
SU07M	44	27	217	9	6
SU07N	42	33	323	7	8
SU07P	46	37	349	8	7
SU07Q	49	36	368	11	11
SU07R	35	20	187	6	6
SU07S	39	27	309	9	6
SU07T	56	50	311	11	12
SU07U	49	38	252	9	11
SU07V	44	23	170	7	12
SU07W	41	29	281	7	9
SU07X	39	25	296	7	8

Tetrad	Species	Breed	Count	Red	Amber
SU07Y	44	30	274	9	10
SU07Z	48	34	334	9	10
SU08A	39	18	326	7	5
SU08B	36	16	598	8	5
SU08C	41	22	386	6	10
SU08D	43	21	298	8	7
SU08E	42	19	274	9	8
SU08F	57	34	300	7	11
SU08G	44	23	311	7	10
SU08H	43	18	370	7	10
SU08I	64	47	245	13	15
SU08J	60	49	303	12	12
SU08K	55	23	451	9	12
SU08L	48	28	330	8	10
SU08M	40	21	152	6	9
SU08N	29	14	48	3	6
SU08P	41	31	129	3	9
SU08Q	51	38	549	8	12
SU08R	46	33	406	8	10
SU08S	46	31	355	8	10
SU08T	37	23	223	7	7
SU08U	37	23	241	2	8
SU08V	47	23	456	8	10
SU08W	41	29	351	7	8
SU08X	56	45	348	9	13
SU08Y	51	41	589	9	9
SU08Z	32	13	130	3	4
SU09A	46	29	346	8	11
SU09B	77	46	496	11	21
SU09F	51	29	274	8	12
SU09G	65	30	645	8	19
SU09H	70	42	986	7	25
SU09K	52	26	258	6	13
SU09L	67	39	663	9	19
SU09M	68	45	453	9	19
SU09Q	40	27	233	7	7
SU09R	79	44	433	9	28
SU09S	76	46	696	6	26
SU09T	52	35	625	5	11
SU09V	42	26	260	8	8
SU09W	54	39	355	9	13
SU09X	55	39	317	11	12
SU09Y	49	28	310	8	13
SU12B	32	14	174	7	5
SU12C	35	13	281	7	7
SU12D	43	11	261	8	9
SU12E	44	7	317	11	6
SU12F	43	17	261	8	9
SU12G	39	11	174	7	8
SU12H	42	14	397	8	10
SU12I	52	14	221	11	12
SU12J	62	41	418	10	18
SU12K	31	3	167	7	6

Tetrad	Species	Breed	Count	Red	Amber
SU12L	38	13	213	7	9
SU12M	53	28	297	9	12
SU12N	45	25	256	9	9
SU12P	62	41	608	9	16
SU12Q	58	35	486	7	18
SU12R	68	22	261	9	19
SU12S	53	27	255	7	13
SU12T	46	25	241	5	15
SU12U	51	24	349	4	15
SU12V	41	21	286	7	10
SU12W	64	46	353	11	13
SU12X	68	39	337	12	14
SU12Y	52	34	263	11	9
SU12Z	51	37	245	7	12
SU13A	39	10	174	2	10
SU13B	32	4	139	3	9
SU13C	48	7	274	8	10
SU13D	35	5	127	7	8
SU13E	50	18	423	10	11
SU13F	74	50	433	11	20
SU13G	66	26	471	10	16
SU13H	73	57	744	10	19
SU13I	67	41	452	10	18
SU13J	71	43	449	12	16
SU13K	66	46	543	9	16
SU13L	44	28	582	9	9
SU13M	20	8	126	3	6
SU13N	40	20	249	8	10
SU13P	70	34	359	13	16
SU13Q	42	18	661	6	10
SU13R	43	21	194	6	12
SU13S	36	31	211	4	9
SU13T	31	22	181	7	6
SU13U	42	21	288	9	8
SU13V	52	23	260	9	12
SU13W	52	27	311	8	11
SU13X	46	22	402	8	10
SU13Y	47	22	385	7	12
SU13Z	54	29	380	11	13
SU14A	40	16	164	10	9
SU14B	37	10	277	7	6
SU14C	32	11	145	4	10
SU14D	50	29	265	11	13
SU14E	45	30	244	10	14
SU14F	55	24	397	9	12
SU14G	48	24	308	9	13
SU14H	36	30	226	7	7
SU14I	39	24	294	5	11
SU14J	36	23	221	8	11
SU14K	68	52	388	12	17
SU14L	59	30	306	9	15
SU14M	48	41	248	8	10
SU14N	68	50	581	11	16

Tetrad	Species	Breed	Count	Red	Amber
SU14P	51	20	201	8	13
SU14Q	39	28	120	9	8
SU14R	42	37	279	5	12
SU14S	47	39	268	5	12
SU14T	47	22	776	8	12
SU14U	27	10	181	8	6
SU14V	26	9	105	6	6
SU14W	30	10	134	5	6
SU14X	51	13	263	10	12
SU14Y	41	10	239	7	11
SU14Z	35	6	177	8	10
SU15A	43	20	353	10	11
SU15B	31	11	448	7	10
SU15C	54	35	458	14	13
SU15D	54	34	519	12	11
SU15E	50	34	335	9	12
SU15F	50	20	545	12	11
SU15G	53	36	581	10	13
SU15H	57	36	526	10	14
SU15I	57	33	487	8	12
SU15J	64	39	557	10	13
SU15K	58	36	590	9	16
SU15L	52	31	190	13	15
SU15M	51	27	319	11	12
SU15N	42	17	305	10	8
SU15P	59	24	377	10	14
SU15Q	36	20	476	8	7
SU15R	55	36	398	14	14
SU15S	56	21	302	11	15
SU15T	42	22	761	8	10
SU15U	44	17	366	11	9
SU15V	53	35	226	11	17
SU15W	42	16	238	9	12
SU15X	52	37	234	14	14
SU15Y	53	27	256	11	12
SU15Z	40	13	253	6	11
SU16A	56	36	345	11	12
SU16B	50	36	405	8	12
SU16C	43	38	501	8	10
SU16D	60	41	501	10	17
SU16E	49	36	605	10	14
SU16F	52	22	247	7	12
SU16G	45	24	298	11	10
SU16H	58	40	393	11	13
SU16I	52	44	478	11	12
SU16J	43	39	334	10	8
SU16K	43	16	296	3	11
SU16L	51	40	447	9	11
SU16M	44	33	298	7	10
SU16N	61	49	691	10	14
SU16P	59	45	618	9	14
SU16Q	58	33	252	8	14
SU16R	54	24	109	10	11
SU16S	40	13	201	6	11
SU16T	31	17	164	5	6
SU16U	55	33	416	8	12
SU16V	50	41	426	8	10
SU16W	39	26	379	5	9
SU16X	40	19	134	5	9
SU16Y	51	29	275	9	12
SU16Z	68	49	305	11	14
SU17A	49	33	687	11	13
SU17B	28	18	202	6	8
SU17C	48	26	299	10	12
SU17D	45	35	602	8	10
SU17E	45	24	253	7	10
SU17F	50	22	506	9	15
SU17G	50	32	640	9	15
SU17H	45	24	239	10	9
SU17I	44	33	440	9	10
SU17J	48	28	325	10	13
SU17K	40	22	383	7	11
SU17L	36	19	220	6	11
SU17M	32	14	286	6	9
SU17N	41	24	440	9	11
SU17P	57	36	727	12	13
SU17Q	51	26	379	10	13
SU17R	53	31	434	8	13
SU17S	31	13	466	5	6
SU17T	35	16	272	6	9
SU17U	44	27	378	10	8
SU17V	56	35	565	9	14
SU17W	42	30	437	9	10
SU17X	47	30	425	11	11
SU17Y	51	32	559	12	11
SU17Z	47	32	535	10	10
SU18A	55	43	614	10	12
SU18B	58	45	405	9	13
SU18C	56	42	462	11	11
SU18D	60	50	523	10	15
SU18E	52	43	495	9	12
SU18F	55	30	421	9	12
SU18G	51	41	284	8	13
SU18H	65	50	610	10	17
SU18I	68	43	631	11	18
SU18J	55	39	483	10	14
SU18K	54	35	576	8	12
SU18L	50	39	390	9	10
SU18M	62	39	445	8	13
SU18N	44	32	403	8	11
SU18P	48	30	252	7	10
SU18Q	79	60	623	14	20
SU18R	72	56	579	9	21
SU18S	43	30	276	6	7
SU18T	33	19	366	5	6
SU18U	65	52	366	10	15

Tetrad	Species	Breed	Count	Red	Amber
SU18V	87	61	531	12	30
SU18W	63	48	663	9	17
SU18X	50	39	426	9	9
SU18Y	48	31	297	8	10
SU18Z	56	34	509	9	12
SU19A	53	28	256	9	14
SU19B	53	31	114	8	18
SU19C	53	24	164	9	14
SU19F	42	20	294	7	8
SU19G	50	30	379	7	11
SU19H	43	20	237	8	11
SU19I	48	25	313	8	11
SU19J	51	21	367	7	12
SU19K	45	28	540	8	13
SU19L	47	21	243	8	11
SU19M	52	28	506	8	13
SU19N	46	31	251	8	10
SU19Q	62	34	394	11	13
SU19R	50	27	402	9	13
SU19S	58	34	408	10	16
SU19V	44	29	248	8	10
SU19W	56	39	564	10	13
SU19X	52	34	329	8	13
SU19Y	52	33	321	8	14
SU21E	63	40	219	9	17
SU21I	68	41	209	9	22
SU21J	66	46	274	8	18
SU21N	54	33	208	5	13
SU21P	48	33	264	8	13
SU21U	54	27	267	8	14
SU22A	56	37	273	9	11
SU22B	46	20	165	7	10
SU22C	55	34	183	11	13
SU22D	69	33	287	11	16
SU22E	60	39	268	8	16
SU22F	54	38	175	7	16
SU22G	54	39	418	10	11
SU22H	57	40	134	10	16
SU22I	60	40	231	11	12
SU22J	47	29	265	6	10
SU22K	55	33	240	7	13
SU22L	44	30	294	8	8
SU22M	50	31	261	9	10
SU22N	58	38	292	9	13
SU22P	47	26	157	6	13
SU22Q	54	27	290	9	15
SU22R	52	31	326	6	14
SU22S	43	19	291	8	9
SU23A	49	41	326	9	10
SU23B	44	34	385	10	9
SU23C	45	38	326	10	7
SU23D	44	22	361	8	11
SU23E	48	42	356	9	12
SU23F	45	43	261	9	9
SU23G	49	37	430	11	9
SU23H	40	25	162	7	13
SU23I	34	24	151	5	9
SU23J	45	35	203	10	9
SU23K	46	37	228	8	9
SU23L	45	37	241	8	9
SU23M	47	43	259	10	9
SU23N	38	28	135	7	8
SU24A	57	44	190	8	16
SU24B	71	61	214	12	21
SU24C	51	40	224	10	13
SU24D	52	21	207	10	15
SU24E	36	20	152	6	7
SU24F	69	63	191	15	17
SU24G	78	70	320	16	19
SU24I	51	27	489	9	9
SU24J	45	26	347	7	10
SU24N	45	24	489	7	10
SU24P	35	20	151	6	6
SU24U	34	18	828	6	8
SU25A	50	33	199	10	11
SU25B	49	24	561	9	11
SU25C	49	28	234	12	11
SU25D	42	13	228	8	12
SU25E	36	23	412	8	7
SU25F	63	37	182	12	16
SU25G	51	25	544	10	11
SU25H	36	11	296	7	10
SU25I	35	22	443	7	6
SU25J	39	15	285	5	9
SU25K	43	28	231	8	9
SU25L	34	19	272	9	4
SU25M	40	18	316	8	9
SU25N	33	21	486	7	9
SU25P	27	13	302	5	5
SU25Q	46	29	288	10	9
SU25R	38	27	194	7	8
SU25S	30	18	134	3	5
SU25T	36	7	360	9	6
SU25U	39	10	393	8	9
SU25V	48	35	224	9	9
SU25W	35	17	179	5	6
SU25X	37	19	292	7	7
SU25Y	32	19	138	4	5
SU25Z	38	22	197	8	11
SU26A	43	33	619	9	11
SU26B	65	26	350	11	15
SU26C	58	35	628	11	15
SU26D	57	24	456	10	15
SU26E	69	56	762	13	16
SU26F	49	28	483	8	10
SU26G	52	24	456	10	10

Tetrad	Species	Breed	Count	Red	Amber
SU26H	45	32	561	8	10
SU26I	55	20	540	10	13
SU26J	70	58	455	12	15
SU26K	50	29	188	8	10
SU26L	51	20	449	6	11
SU26M	48	36	708	7	12
SU26N	56	38	651	14	14
SU26P	67	40	328	12	19
SU26Q	62	42	532	11	14
SU26R	68	47	516	11	17
SU26S	66	36	591	13	14
SU26T	54	41	382	9	13
SU26U	46	36	540	8	10
SU26V	37	33	463	7	7
SU26W	66	46	491	12	19
SU26X	52	43	683	8	12
SU26Y	53	43	510	7	12
SU26Z	54	37	577	9	12
SU27A	56	38	544	11	11
SU27B	54	28	623	12	12
SU27C	52	29	504	13	11
SU27D	47	25	337	12	10
SU27E	45	18	288	8	13
SU27F	57	34	499	10	12
SU27G	49	25	508	11	10
SU27H	49	26	552	10	10
SU27I	57	41	358	13	13
SU27J	45	27	288	10	10
SU27K	75	40	543	14	17
SU27L	55	23	266	11	9
SU27M	43	28	294	10	10
SU27N	44	25	177	8	13
SU27P	50	36	241	9	11
SU27Q	81	58	555	12	23
SU27R	60	32	415	12	13
SU27S	55	32	526	11	11
SU27T	47	37	321	12	12
SU27U	43	30	208	8	10
SU27V	76	52	525	13	19
SU27W	53	25	306	9	10
SU27X	46	20	180	10	7
SU27Y	49	22	331	10	9
SU27Z	49	31	404	12	12
SU28A	64	47	376	12	14

Tetrad	Species	Breed	Count	Red	Amber
SU28B	38	18	383	6	9
SU28C	35	18	80	5	8
SU28D	43	24	159	7	11
SU28E	56	17	381	5	14
SU28F	42	24	74	8	11
SU28G	52	38	113	9	14
SU28H	48	20	22	11	9
SU28K	28	15	65	7	7
SU28L	54	37	135	10	10
SU28M	40	26	111	10	7
SU28Q	42	21	339	8	12
SU28V	31	28	124	6	6
SU29A	48	27	293	8	9
SU29B	42	27	348	6	10
SU29C	53	28	278	9	17
SU29D	53	32	431	10	15
SU29E	59	30	288	9	16
SU29F	59	34	404	11	14
SU29G	66	42	363	10	18
SU35A	35	21	198	6	8
SU35B	42	22	236	6	9
SU35C	42	22	127	7	9
SU35D	43	26	221	7	11
SU35E	43	25	152	7	9
SU35F	32	20	120	5	4
SU35H	29	14	154	3	3
SU35I	40	18	207	6	6
SU35J	42	21	179	9	9
SU36A	53	36	209	12	13
SU36B	66	53	591	13	17
SU36C	63	9	432	13	16
SU36D	66	17	363	11	16
SU36E	68	12	492	11	17
SU36F	59	30	352	12	14
SU36G	64	41	287	15	15
SU36H	64	41	236	12	15
SU36K	67	51	497	13	18
SU36L	65	44	306	13	15
SU37A	82	57	688	12	24
SU37B	52	29	895	10	10
SU37C	48	27	429	9	9
SU37F	71	45	629	11	17
SU37G	38	17	163	5	4

Winter atlas fieldwork results by species

'Tetrads' and '10-km [squares]' give the totals of each of these grid areas in which each species was recorded; and the two 'Per cent' columns are these same figures expressed as proportions of, respectively, the 443 tetrads surveyed and the 48 10-km squares covered by the winter survey. 'Max' shows the highest number recorded in any tetrad and 'Count' the total of individuals counted in the surveyed tetrads. 'Extrap[olated]' is the number calculated to have been recorded if all the tetrads had been surveyed (see 'Atlas organisation, methods and mapping 1995–2000'); and 'Rank' puts each of the 112 species in the order of the size of the extrapolated count. ('No' links the species to table 9 on pages 124–135.)

No	Species	Tetrads	Per cent	10-km	Per cent	Max	Count	Extrap	Rank
1	Mute Swan	77	17·4%	27	56·3%	62	591	1206	44
8	Canada Goose	36	8·1%	23	47·9%	262	970	2007	37
12	Ruddy Shelduck	1	0·2%	1	2·1%	1	1	2	107
13	Common Shelduck	1	0·2%	1	2·1%	3	3	5	100
14	Mandarin	2	0·5%	2	4·2%	2	4	10	97
15	Wigeon	8	1·8%	5	10·4%	61	187	398	57
16	Gadwall	10	2·3%	7	14·6%	22	48	75	74
17	Common Teal	24	5·4%	18	37·5%	190	723	1232	43
19	Mallard	179	40·4%	47	97·9%	237	3152	5951	19
20	Pintail	3	0·7%	3	6·3%	7	9	11	96
23	Shoveler	7	1·6%	5	10·4%	47	72	149	72
24	Red-crested Pochard	1	0·2%	1	2·1%	8	8	12	94
25	Common Pochard	12	2·7%	8	16·7%	97	293	501	55
28	Tufted Duck	29	6·5%	17	35·4%	82	563	1036	47
34	Goldeneye	3	0·7%	3	6·3%	6	8	13	93
35	Smew	1	0·2%	1	2·1%	3	3	5	100
36	Red-breasted Merganser	1	0·2%	1	2·1%	1	1	2	107
37	Goosander	4	0·9%	3	6·3%	15	29	49	77
38	Ruddy Duck	2	0·5%	2	4·2%	19	20	44	80
41	Red-legged Partridge	96	21·7%	32	66·7%	475	1559	3329	33
42	Grey Partridge	44	9·9%	24	50·0%	22	271	542	53
44	Pheasant	301	67·9%	48	100·0%	87	2618	5046	23
49	Little Grebe	41	9·3%	23	47·9%	13	116	229	64
50	Great Crested Grebe	17	3·8%	9	18·8%	14	86	163	71
61	Cormorant	32	7·2%	18	37·5%	9	82	170	69
68	Little Egret	1	0·2%	1	2·1%	2	2	5	100
70	Grey Heron	90	20·3%	35	72·9%	74	245	557	52
78	Red Kite	6	1·4%	5	10·4%	1	6	12	94
81	Hen Harrier	9	2·0%	8	16·7%	3	11	26	87
84	Sparrowhawk	121	27·3%	40	83·3%	4	152	286	62
85	Common Buzzard	286	64·6%	48	100·0%	21	682	1287	42
88	Kestrel	258	58·2%	47	97·9%	4	393	797	49
90	Merlin	15	3·4%	8	16·7%	2	17	39	82
93	Peregrine	9	2·0%	9	18·8%	2	10	17	91
94	Water Rail	12	2·7%	8	16·7%	3	16	31	84
97	Moorhen	176	39·7%	43	89·6%	38	899	1869	38
98	Coot	74	16·7%	31	64·6%	703	1898	3217	34
112	Golden Plover	31	7·0%	22	45·8%	630	4090	8158	15
114	Lapwing	71	16·0%	34	70·8%	700	6556	12,684	9
123	Dunlin	1	0·2%	1	2·1%	24	24	36	83
127	Jack Snipe	3	0·7%	3	6·3%	1	3	6	99
128	Common Snipe	19	4·3%	15	31·3%	20	90	171	68
131	Woodcock	12	2·7%	10	20·8%	2	15	26	87

No	Species	Tetrads	Per cent	10-km	Per cent	Max	Count	Extrap	Rank
132	Black-tailed Godwit	1	0·2%	1	2·1%	1	1	2	107
135	Curlew	2	0·5%	2	4·2%	15	16	24	89
137	Common Redshank	2	0·5%	2	4·2%	1	2	3	106
141	Green Sandpiper	11	2·5%	10	20·8%	3	13	28	86
155	Black-headed Gull	137	30·9%	38	79·2%	510	6202	12,093	10
157	Common Gull	83	18·7%	30	62·5%	238	2048	4025	29
158	Lesser Black-backed Gull	139	31·4%	40	83·3%	1000	3065	5867	20
160	Herring Gull	13	2·9%	12	25·0%	16	61	112	73
161	Yellow-legged Gull	3	0·7%	3	6·3%	2	4	7	98
164	Great Black-backed Gull	1	0·2%	1	2·1%	1	1	2	107
182	Rock Dove/Feral Pigeon	77	17·4%	34	70·8%	142	1059	2125	36
183	Stock Dove	211	47·6%	45	93·8%	90	1655	3374	32
184	Wood Pigeon	436	98·4%	48	100·0%	2800	49,726	99,027	2
185	Collared Dove	271	61·2%	46	95·8%	157	2203	4326	27
189	Barn Owl	2	0·5%	2	4·2%	1	2	5	100
193	Little Owl	18	4·1%	11	22·9%	2	20	42	81
194	Tawny Owl	18	4·1%	15	31·3%	3	21	45	79
200	Kingfisher	21	4·7%	16	33·3%	2	26	52	76
205	Green Woodpecker	98	22·1%	40	83·3%	6	132	262	63
206	Great Spotted Woodpecker	184	41·5%	47	97·9%	5	295	580	51
207	Lesser Spotted Woodpecker	2	0·5%	2	4·2%	1	2	5	100
209	Sky Lark	227	51·2%	44	91·7%	200	2780	5452	22
218	Meadow Pipit	192	43·3%	42	87·5%	58	1742	3607	31
222	Grey Wagtail	78	17·6%	35	72·9%	5	111	227	65
223	Pied Wagtail	301	67·9%	47	97·9%	37	1242	2518	35
225	Dipper	2	0·5%	2	4·2%	2	3	5	100
226	Wren	420	94·8%	48	100·0%	28	2792	5623	21
227	Dunnock	379	85·6%	48	100·0%	52	2115	4149	28
228	Robin	434	98·0%	48	100·0%	58	3958	7607	16
234	Stonechat	43	9·7%	22	45·8%	5	75	165	70
237	Blackbird	438	98·9%	48	100·0%	71	7261	14,420	8
238	Fieldfare	311	70·2%	47	97·9%	550	24,526	49,992	4
239	Song Thrush	291	65·7%	47	97·9%	15	849	1610	40
240	Redwing	290	65·5%	47	97·9%	1500	12,192	24,142	7
241	Mistle Thrush	266	60·0%	48	100·0%	15	693	1393	41
251	Blackcap	8	1·8%	7	14·6%	2	9	18	90
259	Chiffchaff	19	4·3%	13	27·1%	3	24	47	78
261	Goldcrest	266	60·0%	48	100·0%	17	829	1644	39
262	Firecrest	1	0·2%	1	2·1%	1	1	2	107
267	Long-tailed Tit	270	60·9%	46	95·8%	30	1973	3919	30
268	Blue Tit	430	97·1%	48	100·0%	55	4993	9761	13
269	Great Tit	416	93·9%	48	100·0%	66	3441	6910	18
270	Coal Tit	168	37·9%	46	95·8%	17	450	826	48
271	Willow Tit	7	1·6%	4	8·3%	3	9	14	92
272	Marsh Tit	95	21·4%	37	77·1%	9	200	368	59
273	Nuthatch	104	23·5%	34	70·8%	7	243	410	56
274	Treecreeper	108	24·4%	44	91·7%	5	175	333	60
278	Great Grey Shrike	1	0·2%	1	2·1%	1	1	2	107
281	Jay	174	39·3%	44	91·7%	13	418	796	50
282	Magpie	396	89·4%	48	100·0%	33	2235	4499	26
285	Jackdaw	406	91·6%	47	97·9%	1000	18,687	36,314	5

No	Species	Tetrads	Per cent	10-km	Per cent	Max	Count	Extrap	Rank
286	Rook	403	91·0%	47	97·9%	1500	34,945	72,668	3
287	Carrion Crow	427	96·4%	48	100·0%	243	5128	10,164	12
289	Raven	13	2·9%	9	18·8%	2	18	30	85
290	Common Starling	360	81·3%	46	95·8%	15,000	58,844	112,281	1
292	House Sparrow	300	67·7%	48	100·0%	250	5259	10,578	11
293	Tree Sparrow	11	2·5%	7	14·6%	60	162	376	58
294	Chaffinch	440	99·3%	48	100·0%	450	12,679	24,812	6
295	Brambling	19	4·3%	13	27·1%	40	106	213	66
297	Greenfinch	348	78·6%	46	95·8%	250	3720	7241	17
298	Goldfinch	241	54·4%	45	93·8%	235	2184	4772	24
299	Siskin	22	5·0%	17	35·4%	65	260	529	54
300	Linnet	129	29·1%	39	81·3%	597	4335	8409	14
303	Lesser Redpoll	13	2·9%	11	22·9%	28	107	191	67
304	Crossbill	3	0·7%	3	6·3%	26	40	63	75
305	Bullfinch	193	43·6%	47	97·9%	15	608	1193	45
309	Yellowhammer	222	50·1%	44	91·7%	107	2289	4664	25
314	Reed Bunting	55	12·4%	24	50·0%	20	147	307	61
315	Corn Bunting	37	8·4%	16	33·3%	140	463	1040	46

APPENDIX 3

Changes in bird distribution in Wiltshire 1968–2000

Few data exist to assess changes in distribution of most birds in Wiltshire over any length of time. But one measure used throughout the species texts in *Birds of Wiltshire* has been to compare the county's results with corresponding information in the three national atlases, specifically the number of occupied 10-km squares in each case. On that basis, it has been possible to compare both breeding and total distributions shown by the WOS summer tetrad fieldwork 1995–2000 with the maps in both the *1968–72 Atlas* and the *1988–91 Atlas*; and, similarly, the winter distributions mapped by the WOS winter tetrad fieldwork 1998–2000 with those in the *1981–84 Winter Atlas*.

Wiltshire fully covers 25 10-km squares of the National Grid, and extends to parts of a further 27 (though four of these include so little of the county that they were not surveyed by WOS tetrad fieldwork). Since changes in occupancy by birds of such 'partial' squares may reflect loss or colonisation in adjacent counties, a suite of 'core' squares has been used to assess distribution changes in Wiltshire. Those 10-km squares that have around 75 per cent or more of their tetrads inside the county were initially chosen as 'core' squares. Added to these was SU09 because, though only 16 of its 25 tetrads were included in WOS fieldwork, this 10-km square covers much of CWP and thus supports a number of species that occur only rarely elsewhere in the county. The resulting total of 33 core 10-km squares (figure 76) was used to assess changes in distribution in Wiltshire.

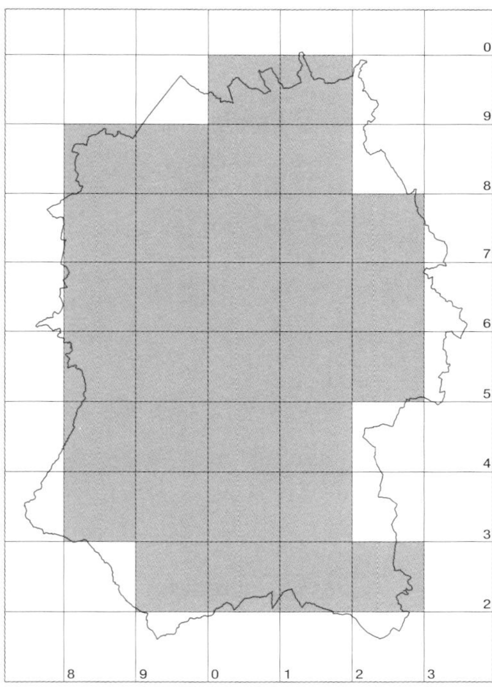

Figure 76. Core 10-km squares used to assess changes in the distribution of Wiltshire's birds

Core Wiltshire 10-km squares occupied in national atlases and WOS tetrad surveys

In the following tabulation, column headings indicate the relevant fieldwork periods of the *1968–72 Atlas*, the *1988–91 Atlas* and the *1981–84 Winter Atlas*, and of the WOS surveys in the summers of 1995–2000 and the winters 1998–2000 (specifically, those of 1998/99 and 1999/00). Summer distribution is separated into squares in which there was evidence of breeding (combining the categories of 'confirmed' and 'probable' in the *1968–72 Atlas*) and the total number of squares in which the species was recorded, whether 'breeding' or 'seen' (the latter equating to the category of 'possible' breeding in the *1986–72 Atlas*). Note that 1995–2000 records of Red Kite, Hen and Montagu's Harriers, Goshawk and Peregrine have not been included in this assessment. Data are presented here only for those species on the official Wiltshire List, and several presumed escapes reported in the county during one or other of the national atlases – Snow Goose, Wood Duck and Golden Pheasant – are not included. (Scientific names of all species can be found by the same numbering in table 9 in 'Atlas organisation, methods and mapping 1995–2000': see pages 124–135.)

		68–72		88–91		95–00		81–84	98–00
No	**Species**	**Breed**	**Total**	**Breed**	**Total**	**Breed**	**Total**	**Total**	**Total**
1	Mute Swan	26	28	26	28	25	26	32	23
2	Bewick's Swan	0	0	0	0	0	0	5	0
3	Whooper Swan	0	0	0	0	0	0	2	0
5	Pink-footed Goose	0	0	0	0	0	0	1	0
6	White-fronted Goose	0	0	0	0	0	0	4	0
7	Greylag Goose	0	0	2	6	4	12	5	0
8	Canada Goose	3	5	27	28	27	31	17	18
9	Barnacle Goose	0	0	0	0	1	7	5	0
11	Egyptian Goose	0	0	0	2	0	0	0	0
12	Ruddy Shelduck	0	0	0	0	0	0	0	1
13	Common Shelduck	0	0	2	2	1	2	9	1
14	Mandarin	0	0	5	11	8	13	5	2
15	Wigeon	0	1	0	1	0	0	17	4
16	Gadwall	0	0	2	3	4	8	11	5
17	Common Teal	4	8	1	3	0	6	30	12
19	Mallard	32	33	33	33	33	33	33	33
20	Pintail	0	1	0	0	0	0	8	2
23	Shoveler	0	4	0	2	0	4	12	4
24	Red-crested Pochard	0	0	1	1	2	3	3	1
25	Common Pochard	0	7	4	6	1	9	21	6
28	Tufted Duck	14	20	18	23	20	29	27	12
29	Scaup	0	0	0	0	0	0	3	0
31	Long-tailed Duck	0	0	0	0	0	0	5	0
32	Common Scoter	0	0	0	0	0	0	1	0
34	Goldeneye	0	0	0	0	0	0	11	3
35	Smew	0	0	0	0	0	0	2	1
36	Red-breasted Merganser	0	0	0	0	0	0	2	1
37	Goosander	0	0	0	0	0	0	10	3
38	Ruddy Duck	0	0	2	3	5	14	6	1
41	Red-legged Partridge	22	27	21	30	26	31	26	23
42	Grey Partridge	32	33	30	33	25	32	32	18
43	Quail	18	23	8	22	7	25	0	0
44	Pheasant	33	33	33	33	32	33	33	33
49	Little Grebe	24	27	23	29	30	31	31	17
50	Great Crested Grebe	14	14	12	13	15	18	15	8
52	Slavonian Grebe	0	0	0	0	0	0	1	0
61	Cormorant	0	0	0	0	0	16	9	15
68	Little Egret	0	0	0	0	0	0	0	1
70	Grey Heron	11	22	14	31	14	32	33	29
78	Red Kite	0	0	0	0	–	–	0	4
80	Marsh Harrier	0	0	0	0	0	0	1	0
81	Hen Harrier	0	0	0	0	–	–	17	7
82	Montagu's Harrier	0	0	2	4	–	–	0	0
83	Goshawk	0	0	0	3	–	–	0	0
84	Sparrowhawk	24	31	29	33	30	33	33	30
85	Common Buzzard	15	29	19	31	33	33	26	33

No	Species	68–72 Breed	68–72 Total	88–91 Breed	88–91 Total	95–00 Breed	95–00 Total	81–84 Total	98–00 Total
88	Kestrel	33	33	31	33	32	33	33	33
90	Merlin	0	0	0	0	0	0	15	8
91	Hobby	7	19	11	26	17	31	0	0
93	Peregrine	0	0	0	0	–	–	6	5
94	Water Rail	1	5	1	5	1	6	24	7
95	Spotted Crake	0	1	0	0	0	0	0	0
96	Corncrake	2	4	0	0	0	0	0	0
97	Moorhen	33	33	33	33	33	33	33	31
98	Coot	26	28	29	30	32	32	29	24
105	Stone-curlew	14	17	8	9	10	11	0	0
107	Common Bittern	0	0	0	0	0	0	2	0
108	Little Ringed Plover	2	2	2	2	2	2	0	0
109	Ringed Plover	0	0	1	1	1	2	1	0
112	Golden Plover	0	0	0	0	0	0	31	20
113	Grey Plover	0	0	0	0	0	0	2	0
114	Lapwing	33	33	30	32	32	33	33	27
123	Dunlin	0	0	0	0	0	0	3	1
126	Ruff	0	0	0	0	0	0	1	0
127	Jack Snipe	0	0	0	0	0	0	5	2
128	Common Snipe	12	16	7	12	1	13	33	11
131	Woodcock	9	14	8	15	8	12	25	8
132	Black-tailed Godwit	0	0	0	0	0	0	0	1
135	Curlew	15	21	10	15	9	18	7	2
137	Common Redshank	14	18	9	13	4	5	4	2
138	Greenshank	0	0	0	0	0	0	3	0
141	Green Sandpiper	0	0	0	0	0	0	14	9
143	Common Sandpiper	0	10	0	0	0	0	4	0
155	Black-headed Gull	1	1	0	0	1	29	33	28
157	Common Gull	0	0	0	0	0	0	33	23
158	Lesser Black-backed Gull	0	0	1	1	7	32	29	28
160	Yellow-legged Gull	0	0	0	0	0	0	0	3
161	Herring Gull	0	0	0	0	1	11	23	11
163	Glaucous Gull	0	0	0	0	0	0	1	0
164	Great Black-backed Gull	0	0	0	0	0	0	9	1
165	Kittiwake	0	0	0	0	0	0	2	0
174	Common Tern	0	0	1	1	2	6	0	0
182	Rock Dove/Feral Pigeon	4	8	15	28	21	33	27	26
183	Stock Dove	32	33	29	32	33	33	33	33
184	Wood Pigeon	33	33	33	33	33	33	33	33
185	Collared Dove	32	32	33	33	33	33	33	33
186	Turtle Dove	33	33	21	30	14	25	0	0
187	Ring-necked Parakeet	0	0	0	0	0	0	1	0
188	Cuckoo	33	33	27	33	26	33	0	0
189	Barn Owl	26	32	17	26	29	33	24	2
193	Little Owl	25	29	26	32	32	33	31	9
194	Tawny Owl	33	33	30	33	31	33	30	11
195	Long-eared Owl	5	8	5	6	5	10	6	0
196	Short-eared Owl	0	0	0	2	0	0	15	0
197	Nightjar	10	11	7	8	4	6	0	0
198	Common Swift	33	33	32	33	32	33	0	0

No	Species	68–72 Breed	68–72 Total	88–91 Breed	88–91 Total	95–00 Breed	95–00 Total	81–84 Total	98–00 Total
200	Kingfisher	30	31	20	28	15	27	28	12
205	Green Woodpecker	31	33	31	33	28	33	32	27
206	Great Spotted Woodpecker	32	33	32	33	33	33	33	33
207	Lesser Spotted Woodpecker	16	21	9	14	8	19	17	2
208	Wood Lark	2	3	0	0	0	1	2	0
209	Sky Lark	33	33	33	33	33	33	33	33
211	Sand Martin	14	20	6	12	6	19	0	0
212	Barn Swallow	33	33	33	33	33	33	0	0
213	House Martin	33	33	33	33	33	33	0	0
217	Tree Pipit	25	25	17	20	20	25	0	0
218	Meadow Pipit	22	25	21	28	26	29	33	32
220	Water Pipit	0	0	0	0	0	0	2	0
221	Yellow Wagtail	12	15	12	15	16	19	0	0
222	Grey Wagtail	30	32	26	31	26	32	31	27
223	Pied Wagtail	33	33	32	33	33	33	33	33
225	Dipper	8	11	5	8	3	5	6	1
226	Wren	33	33	33	33	33	33	33	33
227	Dunnock	33	33	32	33	33	33	33	33
228	Robin	33	33	33	33	33	33	33	33
229	Nightingale	27	28	20	25	13	21	0	0
231	Black Redstart	0	0	0	1	0	2	11	0
232	Common Redstart	21	23	11	21	5	21	0	0
233	Whinchat	14	16	8	13	11	26	0	0
234	Stonechat	3	6	6	10	18	20	22	17
235	Wheatear	10	19	3	10	0	21	0	0
237	Blackbird	33	33	33	33	33	33	33	33
238	Fieldfare	0	0	0	0	0	0	33	33
239	Song Thrush	33	33	33	33	33	33	33	33
240	Redwing	0	0	0	0	0	0	33	33
241	Mistle Thrush	33	33	31	33	33	33	33	33
242	Cetti's Warbler	0	0	1	1	3	5	0	0
243	Grasshopper Warbler	31	33	15	27	16	24	0	0
246	Sedge Warbler	30	31	28	29	25	31	0	0
248	Reed Warbler	17	18	16	21	18	25	0	0
251	Blackcap	33	33	32	33	33	33	25	6
252	Garden Warbler	32	33	29	32	29	33	0	0
254	Lesser Whitethroat	29	31	26	32	30	33	0	0
255	Common Whitethroat	33	33	33	33	33	33	0	0
258	Wood Warbler	8	11	8	15	6	18	0	0
259	Chiffchaff	33	33	32	33	33	33	15	11
260	Willow Warbler	33	33	33	33	33	33	0	0
261	Goldcrest	33	33	29	32	31	33	33	33
262	Firecrest	0	0	2	3	4	4	4	1
263	Spotted Flycatcher	33	33	33	33	32	33	0	0

No	Species	68–72 Breed	68–72 Total	88–91 Breed	88–91 Total	95–00 Breed	95–00 Total	81–84 Total	98–00 Total
265	Pied Flycatcher	0	2	2	8	2	10	0	0
267	Long-tailed Tit	33	33	31	33	32	33	33	33
268	Blue Tit	33	33	33	33	33	33	33	33
269	Great Tit	33	33	33	33	33	33	33	33
270	Coal Tit	32	32	30	33	32	33	33	31
271	Willow Tit	18	23	16	23	11	25	23	2
272	Marsh Tit	28	32	26	32	28	32	31	27
273	Nuthatch	30	31	25	31	27	32	30	21
274	Treecreeper	31	33	25	31	32	33	33	32
276	Red-backed Shrike	3	6	0	0	0	0	0	0
278	Great Grey Shrike	0	0	0	0	0	0	6	1
281	Jay	31	33	29	33	25	33	33	31
282	Magpie	33	33	33	33	33	33	33	33
285	Jackdaw	33	33	33	33	33	33	33	33
286	Rook	33	33	33	33	33	33	33	33
287	Carrion Crow	33	33	33	33	33	33	33	33
289	Raven	0	0	0	0	6	14	1	5
290	Common Starling	33	33	33	33	33	33	33	33
292	House Sparrow	33	33	33	33	33	33	33	33
293	Tree Sparrow	30	32	19	24	13	21	30	6
294	Chaffinch	33	33	33	33	33	33	33	33
295	Brambling	0	0	0	0	0	0	28	10
297	Greenfinch	33	33	31	33	33	33	33	33
298	Goldfinch	33	33	31	33	33	33	33	33
299	Siskin	0	0	1	10	3	14	28	15
300	Linnet	33	33	32	33	33	33	32	29
301	Twite	0	0	0	0	0	0	1	0
303	Lesser Redpoll	2	6	0	5	0	12	27	9
304	Crossbill	2	4	1	5	1	10	5	2
305	Bullfinch	33	33	31	33	31	33	33	33
306	Hawfinch	2	6	2	8	1	4	2	0
309	Yellowhammer	33	33	33	33	33	33	33	32
310	Cirl Bunting	3	5	0	0	0	0	0	0
314	Reed Bunting	26	28	25	30	27	32	32	20
315	Corn Bunting	30	31	22	25	24	29	28	14

Distribution changes during 1968–2000 as shown by core 10-km squares

As a study of the above tabulation will show, rather more bird species decreased (48) than increased (41) in the number of Wiltshire's core 10-km squares in which they were found breeding between the *1968–72 Atlas* and the 1995–2000 WOS fieldwork. As many as 19 of the decreases were consistent – numbers falling between the *1968–72 Atlas* and the *1988–91 Atlas*, and then falling again by 1995–2000 – and 18 of the increases were similarly consistent. Five species – Canada Goose, Common Buzzard, Hobby, Rock Dove/ Feral Pigeon and Stonechat – showed more than a doubling of the number of squares over the three decades. (The apparent increase of Feral Pigeon may, however, be largely a consequence of their being afforded little attention by birdwatchers prior to the 1970s and 1980s; certainly, they are likely to have been under-recorded for the *1968–72 Atlas*.) By contrast, when both 'seen' and 'breeding' records were combined, there was a much larger total of increases in the number of occupied core 10-km squares (51 species, 30 of them consistently) than decreases (28, just eight declining consistently) – perhaps a rather surprising result in view of the marked declines in many widespread and common farmland species over this 33–year period. It is likely, however, that the criteria used to define 'possible' breeding in the *1968–72 Atlas*, which required species to be recorded in 'suitable habitat', may have resulted in some being under-recorded then by comparison with later years, when all species present were noted as 'seen', irrespective of habitat.

In the following summary table, changes in summer distribution have been defined by comparing 1968–72 with 1995–2000; and those in winter by comparing 1981–84 with 1998–2000. The 'Breed' column is the number of species that showed changes in the totals of 10-km squares in which they were recorded breeding; and 'Totals' is the number of species seen, combined in summer with breeding. 'Disappeared' is the number of species that were recorded in at least one 10-km square in the first period, but not found in the last; 'Decreasing' is the number that occurred in fewer 10-km squares; 'No change' is the number found in the same number of squares; 'Increasing' is the number which increased correspondingly; and 'Colonised' refers to species which were not found in any of the core 10-km squares in the first period but recorded in at least one in the last. It must be emphasised that these comparisons used only records from the 33 core 10-km squares shown above in figure 76; thus, for example, a species may have been present in one or more of the other partial 10-km squares and so not have disappeared from the county as a whole.

	Summer		Winter
	Breed	Totals	Totals
Disappeared	7	7	27
Decreasing	41	21	72
No change	32	51	31
Increasing	24	34	4
Colonised	17	17	5

It will be noted that a large number of species showed decreases in the extent of winter distribution between 1981–84 and 1998–2000. Caution should, however, be exercised in interpreting changes suggested by comparing winter fieldwork. In many cases, such declines may be the result of the less extensive coverage during the WOS winter surveys, when only a sample of tetrads in most 10-km squares was surveyed (see 'Atlas organisation, methods and mapping 1995–2000'). This could particularly affect species found in few or limited habitats, such as wildfowl, and these cases are highlighted in the relevant species accounts.

Appendix 4

Analyses of population estimates of Wiltshire's birds

The methods used to estimate numbers of each species are outlined in 'Calculating population estimates of Wiltshire's birds'. This appendix provides further details of the analyses and data used to derive the estimates for the more common and widespread species.

Several approaches to estimating bird populations in Wiltshire have been based on surveys that used Breeding Bird Survey (BBS) methods. These have calculated densities of birds per square kilometre, which have then been applied to the area of Wiltshire to produce estimates of total individuals (see next section). A number of surveys in southern-central England have been used in this way: some 38 1-km squares in Wiltshire in 2000, as part of the national BBS scheme (S Newson); and RSPB surveys of the Cotswold Hills Environmentally Sensitive Area (ESA) in both 1997 and 2002 (Mustoe *et al* 1998, Dodd & Meadows 2003), of the Chilterns Area of Outstanding Natural Beauty (AONB) in 2002 (Shurmer 2002), and of the Salisbury Plain Training Area (SPTA) in 2000 (Stanbury *et al* 2000); the last was particularly intensive in its coverage.

Species detection and pair factors

The figures calculated by applying BBS densities have then been converted into numbers of 'pairs' (or 'territories') by applying two correction factors. A 'species detection factor' has allowed for the individuals believed to have been missed by the observer when counting numbers in the 'distance band' nearest to the transect being walked (25 m on each side). The resulting figures were finally converted into pairs by applying a 'pair factor' that allowed for the unequal detection of males and females during summer fieldwork. Thus, the numbers of individuals calculated using BBS densities were divided by the detection factors and then multiplied by the pair factor to calculate estimates of 'pairs'. The detection and pair factors used were the means of those put forward independently by four of the editors of *Birds of Wiltshire* who are all experienced survey workers. (See also 'Calculating population estimates of Wiltshire's birds'.)

In the following tabulation, the detection and pair factors used to calculate breeding estimates of Wiltshire birds are given in the two columns headed 'WOS'. Also shown, for comparison, are the pair factors used by the RSPB surveys of two areas: the Cotswold Hills ESA (headed 'CHESA') and the Salisbury Plain Training Area (headed 'SPTA'); for neither of these other surveys was a detection factor included. (Scientific names of species in all tabulations in this appendix can be found by the same numbering in table 9 on pages 124–135 in 'The status of birds in Wiltshire'.)

		Detection	Pair		
No	**Species**	**WOS**	**WOS**	**CHESA**	**SPTA**
1	Mute Swan	1·00	0·60		
19	Mallard	1·00	0·63		
28	Tufted Duck	1·00	0·75		
41	Red-legged Partridge	0·88	0·66	0·50	0·50
42	Grey Partridge	0·83	0·60	0·50	0·50
43	Quail	0·50	1·00		

No	Species	Detection WOS	Pair WOS	Pair CHESA	Pair SPTA
44	Pheasant	0·85	0·69	0·50	0·50
84	Sparrowhawk	0·89	0·69		
85	Common Buzzard	0·99	0·69		
88	Kestrel	0·96	0·66	0·50	
91	Hobby	0·96	0·60		
97	Moorhen	0·98	0·60		
98	Coot	0·99	0·57		
102	Oystercatcher	1·00	0·70		
114	Lapwing	1·00	0·66	0·50	
155	Black-headed Gull	1·00	0·50		
182	Rock Dove/Feral Pigeon	1·00	0·60		
183	Stock Dove	0·96	0·69	0·50	0·50
184	Wood Pigeon	0·99	0·63	0·50	0·50
185	Collared Dove	1·00	0·66	0·50	
186	Turtle Dove	0·88	0·78		
188	Cuckoo	1·00	0·88		
198	Common Swift	1·00	0·63		
200	Kingfisher	0·98	0·75		
205	Green Woodpecker	1·00	0·66	0·50	
206	Great Spotted Woodpecker	1·00	0·72	0·50	
207	Lesser Spotted Woodpecker	0·73	0·75		
209	Sky Lark	1·00	0·72	0·75	0·75
212	Barn Swallow	1·00	0·60	0·50	
213	House Martin	1·00	0·60		
217	Tree Pipit	0·99	0·75	0·75	0·75
218	Meadow Pipit	0·96	0·75		0·75
221	Yellow Wagtail	1·00	0·75		
222	Grey Wagtail	1·00	0·66		
223	Pied Wagtail	1·00	0·66	0·50	0·50
226	Wren	0·96	0·75	0·75	0·75
227	Dunnock	0·84	0·79	0·75	0·75
228	Robin	0·91	0·75	0·75	0·75
229	Nightingale	1·00	0·97		
232	Common Redstart	0·91	0·82	0·75	
233	Whinchat	0·96	0·72		0·50
234	Stonechat	0·98	0·69	0·50	0·50
237	Blackbird	0·99	0·72	0·75	0·50
239	Song Thrush	0·96	0·79	0·75	0·75
241	Mistle Thrush	1·00	0·72	0·50	0·50
243	Grasshopper Warbler	0·73	1·00		1·00
246	Sedge Warbler	1·00	0·75		
248	Reed Warbler	0·98	0·82		
251	Blackcap	1·00	0·78	0·75	0·75
252	Garden Warbler	0·94	0·82		0·75
254	Lesser Whitethroat	0·88	0·85		
255	Common Whitethroat	1·00	0·82	0·75	0·75
258	Wood Warbler	1·00	0·85		
259	Chiffchaff	0·98	0·78	0·75	0·75
260	Willow Warbler	0·99	0·78	0·50	0·75
261	Goldcrest	0·85	0·82	0·75	0·75

No	Species	Detection WOS	Pair WOS	Pair CHESA	Pair SPTA
262	Firecrest	0·86	0·85		
263	Spotted Flycatcher	0·85	0·69		
267	Long-tailed Tit	0·96	0·63	0·50	0·50
268	Blue Tit	0·99	0·60	0·50	0·50
269	Great Tit	0·99	0·60	0·50	0·50
270	Coal Tit	0·95	0·69	0·75	
271	Willow Tit	0·99	0·63		
272	Marsh Tit	0·99	0·63	0·50	
273	Nuthatch	0·98	0·60	0·50	
274	Treecreeper	0·78	0·78		
281	Jay	0·99	0·66	0·50	
282	Magpie	1·00	0·60	0·50	0·50
285	Jackdaw	1·00	0·57	0·50	0·50
286	Rook	1·00	0·57	0·50	1·00
287	Carrion Crow	1·00	0·60	0·50	0·50
290	Common Starling	0·95	0·63	0·50	0·50
292	House Sparrow	0·99	0·57	0·50	
293	Tree Sparrow	0·96	0·60		
294	Chaffinch	0·99	0·69	0·75	0·75
297	Greenfinch	1·00	0·72	0·50	0·50
298	Goldfinch	0·99	0·72	0·50	0·50
299	Siskin	0·84	0·75		
300	Linnet	1·00	0·66	0·50	0·50
303	Lesser Redpoll	0·88	0·82		
305	Bullfinch	0·81	0·60	0·50	
309	Yellowhammer	1·00	0·69	0·75	0·75
314	Reed Bunting	0·91	0·75		0·75
315	Corn Bunting	0·98	0·75	0·50	0·50

Applying BBS densities to Wiltshire

The densities of birds from the various regional surveys were applied to the area of Wiltshire to calculate county estimates. (In the case of the Cotswold Hills ESA, the means of densities from the 1997 and 2002 surveys were used.) An extensive part of Wiltshire (about 8·5 per cent) is covered by SPTA, a calcareous grassland habitat quite different in nature from much of the open countryside of southern England and for which accurate estimates of the main bird species were available from the intensive RSPB survey in 2000. Consequently, rather than apply densities from the surveys in adjacent counties to the total area of Wiltshire (3485 km^2), they were applied to just 3188 km^2 (the area excluding that part of SPTA surveyed by RSPB) and the resulting figures added to the estimates in Stanbury *et al* (2000), having first re-adjusted these to allow for the different pair factors used.

A further approach to calculating Wiltshire estimates was designed to make greater use of the Wiltshire tetrad survey data. BBS methods convert the numbers of birds recorded by the observer into a 'real' total using 'distance analysis' (see 'Calculating population estimates of Wiltshire's birds'). The ratio of the observers' counts to the 'real' totals might then be used to calculate a 'distance factor', reflecting the differing detectability of different species while walking the survey route. Such distance factors may subsequently be applied to the counts made by WOS observers to produce an estimate of 'real' numbers based on the summer tetrad fieldwork data. It must be stressed, however, that this is a considerable simplification of how 'distance analysis' works and, indeed, that this approach to calculating estimates would doubtless be rejected if it were submitted to a scientific journal; further, BBS densities are based on surveys of 2-km transects within a 1-km square and, in order to apply these figures to WOS data, it has had to be assumed that observers each walked 4 km within a tetrad. (In fact, the distances walked were not recorded and are likely to have varied, perhaps considerably, between tetrads.) But such 'distance factors' have been calculated from surveys of the Cotswold Hills ESA and of the Chilterns AONB with the aim of providing additional estimates, based directly on WOS tetrad survey data, by which the accuracy of estimates produced from other approaches may be judged.

An additional method that used both BBS data and tetrad counts to calculate Wiltshire estimates was based on the 2000 survey of SPTA. The estimates provided by Stanbury *et al* (2000) were multiplied by the ratio of WOS timed counts in tetrads on SPTA to those in the county as a whole. This method was, however, applied only to species that occur in large numbers on SPTA, and for which at least 25 per cent of the timed count total for Wiltshire was found in SPTA tetrads.

By applying the 'pair' and 'detection' factors, the figures resulting from the above approaches were converted into estimates of 'pairs' for common and widespread species in Wiltshire in summer, as set out in the tabulation in the next section. For many species, the approaches provided two or more figures and the Wiltshire estimates are thus given as ranges. These did not, however, simply encompass the lowest and highest of the calculated figures; rather, they were first compared with one another, and with estimates for related species, and any 'outliers' – figures markedly higher or lower than the others – were discounted. This was particularly the case for calculations using the 'distance factors', considered as the least reliable approach. For many species, the results using the 38 national BBS squares in Wiltshire were markedly different from the other estimates, and this approach was thus viewed with caution, particularly where few other figures were available for comparison. It was frequently difficult to judge the validity of single estimates – those where no comparable figures were available from other approaches – and in these cases, timed count totals, comparison with estimates for similar species (where relevant, with the estimates from SPTA alone), and expert opinion were all used to assess whether such figures should be used as the 'official' estimate. Inevitably, a degree of subjectivity was involved in such assessments.

Summer population estimates of Wiltshire's birds

The figures provided below are given to the nearest 'pair', but have been revised to three significant figures for the official estimates presented in 'The status of birds in Wiltshire' and in the species accounts. The calculations from the variety of approaches described above may be summarised as follows: 'BBS' uses the 38 national BBS squares in Wiltshire; 'CHESA' uses the mean of surveys in 1997 and 2002 of Cotswold Hills ESA; 'CHESA distance' uses the 'distance factor' approach for 'CHESA' data; 'Chilterns' uses data from the survey of the Chilterns AONB; 'Chilterns distance' uses the 'distance factor' approach for 'Chilterns' data; 'SPTA' uses the estimates of the survey of SPTA (Stanbury *et al* 2000), multiplied by the ratio of WOS timed counts on SPTA to the whole county; and, for comparison, 'Stanbury' provides the estimates for SPTA alone calculated directly by the RSPB survey (Stanbury *et al* 2000). Estimates considered unreliable are enclosed in parentheses. 'Range' is based on the minimum and maximum individual figures (excluding 'Stanbury'), once outlying or other apparently unreliable estimates have been discounted.

No	Species	BBS	CHESA	CHESA distance	Chilterns	Chilterns distance	SPTA	Stanbury	Summer range
1	Mute Swan	(1618)							
19	Mallard	(15,738)							
28	Tufted Duck	(1943)							
41	Red-legged Partridge	4328	5531	6200	(8362)		6463	217	4328–6463
42	Grey Partridge	3080	3208	(6499)			2921	261	2921–3208
43	Quail							36	
44	Pheasant	12,826	26,008	21,612	14,233				12,826–26,008
85	Common Buzzard	(432)							
88	Kestrel	(1236)	(2396)						
97	Moorhen	6698							6698
98	Coot	738							738
114	Lapwing	756	419						419–756
182	Rock Dove/Feral Pigeon	1148							1148
183	Stock Dove	3050	6718	(16,043)	3643				3050–6718
184	Wood Pigeon	95,297	121,244	143,566	194,071	249,568			95,297–249,568
185	Collared Dove	16,115	11,948	19,761	(7127)				11,948–19,761
186	Turtle Dove	0							
188	Cuckoo	377							377
198	Common Swift	0							
205	Green Woodpecker	(296)	2201	2815	2096				2096–2815
206	Great Spotted Woodpecker	(454)	4591	3405					3405–4591
209	Sky Lark	18,900	53,366	20,230	43,763	22,776	56,055	14,612	18,900–56,055
212	Barn Swallow	2988							2988
213	House Martin	(538)							
217	Tree Pipit	(0)	(3055)				672	217	672
218	Meadow Pipit	(2564)			23,076		20,386	8869	20,386–23,076
221	Yellow Wagtail	(0)							
222	Grey Wagtail	(3307)							
223	Pied Wagtail	3115	5050	7583	5471				5050–7583
226	Wren	92,857	93,965	56,532	76,269	(31,841)			56,532–93,965
227	Dunnock	33,143	(61,257)	31,256	49,305	23,490			23,490–49,305
228	Robin	116,046	98,719	55,442	101,743	59,971			55,442–116,046
232	Common Redstart	(0)	(7118)						
233	Whinchat	(4376)					1121	586	1121
234	Stonechat	(587)					498	223	498
237	Blackbird	112,117	103,796	69,032	106,361	65,052			65,052–112,117

No	Species	BBS	CHESA	CHESA distance	Chilterns	Chilterns distance	SPTA	Stanbury	Summer range
239	Song Thrush	20,202	21,191	13,969	14,820	10,077			10,077–21,191
241	Mistle Thrush	3514	6771	(13,175)	2984				2984–6771
243	Grasshopper Warbler	(0)					(746)	264	
246	Sedge Warbler	(0)							
251	Blackcap	17,778	37,822	18,431	20,962	(13,251)	16,074	506	16,074–37,822
252	Garden Warbler	(1452)	4850	3324			(2610)	148	3324–4850
254	Lesser Whitethroat	2993							2993
255	Common Whitethroat	38,615	37,414	31,244			27,324	4008	27,324–38,615
259	Chiffchaff	12,207	28,016	16,718	(6908)	(5035)			12,207–28,016
260	Willow Warbler	(2306)	23,214	17,054			6523	619	6523–23,214
261	Goldcrest	(8725)	22,161	15,542					15,542–22,161
263	Spotted Flycatcher	2054							2054
267	Long-tailed Tit	19,701	15,215	10,935					10,935–19,701
268	Blue Tit	84,055	105,899	48,088	67,706	39,321			39,321–105,899
269	Great Tit	42,730	43,498	26,630	50,538	35,739			26,630–50,538
270	Coal Tit	(719)	9725	6047					6047–9725
271	Willow Tit	(2898)							
272	Marsh Tit	(680)	4862	2642					2642–4862
273	Nuthatch	2298	3028	2627					2298–3028
274	Treecreeper	1232							1232
281	Jay	(548)	2770						2770
282	Magpie	9213	11,334	11,686	17,143				9213–17,143
285	Jackdaw	20,577	37,555	49,393	26,118	25,421			20,577–49,393
286	Rook	11,893	24,058	(84,800)	17,272		21,539	3403	11,893–24,058
287	Carrion Crow	14,872	25,144	22,402	16,763	11,288			11,288–25,144
290	Common Starling	30,325	18,320	(110,957)	19,162	52,433			18,320–52,433
292	House Sparrow	49,503	40,402	(84,855)	17,875	28,757			17,875–49,503
293	Tree Sparrow	(0)							
294	Chaffinch	148,998	160,262	84,080	119,969	78,138	(42,088)	2354	78,138–160,262
297	Greenfinch	(62,014)	50,498	39,681	24,560	(15,924)			24,560–50,498
298	Goldfinch	24,987	25,917	27,147	18,130	24,086			18,130–27,147
300	Linnet	(15,338)	35,580	31,093	31,751	37,215	27,130	2294	27,130–37,215
305	Bullfinch	(1986)	10,433	6511					6511–10,433
309	Yellowhammer	35,356	57,484	30,271	32,205	(16,434)	18,491	1409	18,491–57,484
314	Reed Bunting	1526					2224	267	1526–2224
315	Corn Bunting	(2601)	4507	5849	6050		4787	391	4507–6050

Winter estimates of Wiltshire's birds

Unlike summer, there are no wide-scale surveys of common or widespread species during winter, which might be used to calculate estimates; and data from the *1981–84 Winter Atlas* can no longer be considered relevant to the late 1990s. The approach used for winter estimates in *Birds of Wiltshire* aimed to make greatest use of the WOS timed winter counts. A measure of relative abundance in winter may be achieved by comparing these with the WOS timed counts in summer. This assumes, of course, that the detectability of species is the same in both seasons. Undoubtedly, however, the different behaviour of many birds in winter will affect counts – for example, while males of many species are located by song in summer, winter flocks will make some more readily noticeable then (see 'Calculating population estimates of Wiltshire's birds') – though it is difficult in many cases to suggest whether birds will be more or less frequently encountered as a result.

In the tabulation below, the summer calculations based on BBS data have simply been multiplied by the ratio of winter to summer counts to produce winter estimates. (The summer figures used as the basis were the numbers of individuals before applying the 'pair factor'; and the winter counts used were the extrapolated figures, which allowed for the tetrads not visited.) As in the previous tabulation, figures are given to the nearest individual, but have been revised to three significant figures for the official estimates.

In the following tabulation, 'Summer' is the number of individuals recorded by WOS timed tetrad counts; 'Winter' is the extrapolated figure from WOS timed winter counts; 'Ratio' is the ratio of winter to summer figures; and 'Winter range' is calculated by applying this ratio to the estimates given in 'Summer range' in the previous tabulation, once the summer estimates had been converted to numbers of individuals.

No	Species	Summer	Winter	Ratio	Winter range
1	Mute Swan	709	1206	1·70	
8	Canada Goose	1586	2007	1·27	
14	Mandarin	57	10	0·18	
19	Mallard	3899	5951	1·53	
28	Tufted Duck	789	1036	1·31	
41	Red-legged Partridge	872	3329	3·82	21,985–32,831
42	Grey Partridge	653	542	0·83	3362–3693
44	Pheasant	5209	5047	0·97	15,307–31,039
49	Little Grebe	279	229	0·82	
50	Great Crested Grebe	232	163	0·70	
70	Grey Heron	413	557	1·35	
84	Sparrowhawk	357	286	0·80	
85	Common Buzzard	1175	1287	1·10	
88	Kestrel	915	797	0·87	1576–3055
97	Moorhen	1510	1869	1·24	13,531
98	Coot	1826	3218	1·76	2273
114	Lapwing	2277	12,684	5·57	
182	Rock Dove/Feral Pigeon	2333	2125	0·91	1757
183	Stock Dove	2604	3374	1·30	5533–12,187
184	Wood Pigeon	30,854	99,027	3·21	481,332–1,260,532
185	Collared Dove	3938	4326	1·10	19,961–33,014
200	Kingfisher	75	52	0·69	
205	Green Woodpecker	554	262	0·47	1506–2023
206	Great Spotted Woodpecker	814	580	0·71	3368–4541

No	Species	Summer	Winter	Ratio	Winter range
209	Sky Lark	6985	5452	0·78	20,488–60,765
218	Meadow Pipit	1548	3607	2·33	60,751–68,767
222	Grey Wagtail	221	227	1·03	
223	Pied Wagtail	1473	2518	1·71	13,078–19,637
226	Wren	9635	5623	0·58	42,197–70,138
227	Dunnock	3632	4149	1·14	28,629–60,092
228	Robin	7782	7607	0·98	65,717–137,552
234	Stonechat	125	165	1·32	928
237	Blackbird	12,695	14,420	1·14	100,995–174,065
239	Song Thrush	2686	1610	0·60	7407–15,577
241	Mistle Thrush	1756	1393	0·79	3287–7458
251	Blackcap	3165	18	0·01	114–269
259	Chiffchaff	3536	47	0·01	202–464
261	Goldcrest	1680	1644	0·98	15,859–22,613
267	Long-tailed Tit	1775	3919	2·21	37,179–66,983
268	Blue Tit	7748	9761	1·26	81,870–220,491
269	Great Tit	4950	6910	1·40	61,438–116,596
270	Coal Tit	957	826	0·86	7183–11,552
271	Willow Tit	76	14	0·19	
272	Marsh Tit	477	368	0·77	3210–5908
273	Nuthatch	603	410	0·68	2548–3357
274	Treecreeper	493	333	0·67	823
281	Jay	664	796	1·20	4966
282	Magpie	3986	4499	1·13	17,404–32,385
285	Jackdaw	17,201	36,314	2·11	76,887–184,560
286	Rook	36,553	72,668	1·99	41,847–84,651
287	Carrion Crow	6954	10,164	1·46	27,613–61,508
290	Common Starling	22,187	112,281	5·06	140,360–401,719
292	House Sparrow	13825	10,578	0·77	23,903–66,198
293	Tree Sparrow	233	376	1·61	
294	Chaffinch	15,217	24,812	1·63	182,343–373,987
297	Greenfinch	6583	7241	1·10	37,521–77,148
298	Goldfinch	3959	4772	1·21	29,971–44,878
300	Linnet	5341	8409	1·57	64,718–88,776
305	Bullfinch	1020	1193	1·17	10,354–16,591
309	Yellowhammer	4438	4665	1·05	28,166–87,562
314	Reed Bunting	356	307	0·86	1594–2323
315	Corn Bunting	961	1040	1·08	6317–8480

For many species, the ratio of winter to summer counts was under 1·0, suggesting that the species was less numerous in winter. Often, this reflects the true situation. For a number of resident species, however, the ratio was considerably less than 1·0, suggesting that behaviour or other factors result in winter abundance being greatly underestimated. This is particularly noticeable for woodpeckers, some thrushes, Wren, several tits, Nuthatch, Treecreeper, House Sparrow and Reed Bunting. For most of these species, where it was felt that numbers in winter were likely to be similar to those of summer (though numbers of young and winter mortality will create some genuine differences), the figures have not been used as the official winter estimate; rather, the ratio of winter to summer abundance has been assumed to be 1·0 and approximate winter estimates calculated on that basis. (See the individual species accounts.)

Although summer estimates based on BBS methods are not available for many species, the ratio of summer to winter timed counts still provides a measure of relative abundance that has helped generate winter estimates (albeit, then often considered 'best guesses') for other species where summer figures have been derived from other sources. The winter to summer ratios are thus given above for a number of species for which no summer estimates are available from BBS data.

Such methods could not, obviously, be used for species that occur in Wiltshire solely (Fieldfare, Redwing, Brambling) or primarily (Siskin, Lesser Redpoll) as winter visitors. Nevertheless, the ratios of the winter estimates to the extrapolated WOS winter counts for other thrushes and finches might be used as a winter 'detection factor': for example, the ratio of the lower and upper limits of the winter estimate for Goldfinch are 6·28 and 9·40 times greater than the extrapolated timed count; these figures may be used to infer that actual numbers of Goldfinches are, very roughly, six to nine times greater than the number counted by observers. The extrapolation factors used to calculate Wiltshire estimates for the two 'winter' thrushes and the three 'winter' finches were based on the following ('Ratio min' and 'Ratio max' are the ratios of the winter estimates – 'Winter range' in the previous tabulation – to the WOS extrapolated timed count):

No	Species	Ratio min	Ratio max
237	Blackbird	7·00	12·07
239	Song Thrush	4·60	9·67
241	Mistle Thrush	2·36	5·36
294	Chaffinch	7·35	15·07
297	Greenfinch	5·18	10·65
298	Goldfinch	6·28	9·40
300	Linnet	7·70	10·56

Wiltshire estimates for Fieldfares and Redwings were calculated using this approach based on the ratios of winter counts to estimates for the three resident thrushes. Timed counts for the two winter visitors were multiplied by 2·5 and 7·5. These figures are rather lower than the actual ratios for the resident species, but the tendency of Fieldfares and Redwings to form large flocks certainly increases their detection relative to the more solitary resident thrushes, and the factors have thus been revised downwards. Equivalent values for Bramblings, Siskins and Lesser Redpolls were based on the ratios for the four resident finch species, and WOS timed counts were multiplied by 'detection factors' of six and 11 to produce winter estimates for the three 'winter' finches.

Gazetteer

Compiled by Mike Jackson, Stephen Edwards & Bill Quantrill

A number of the sites listed, particularly on Salisbury Plain, are not named on the current Landranger (1:50,000) or Explorer (1:25,000) series of Ordnance Survey maps. The grid references given do, however, give the 1-km square in which each is to be found. Two, and in some cases three, grid references are given for rivers, delimiting the extent of their occurrence in Wiltshire; this approach has also been used for a number of other major linear features, *eg* Grand Avenue in Savernake Forest. The location of reserves and statutorily protected sites, *eg* Sites of Special Scientific Interest, are given in 'Reserves and designated sites in Wiltshire' (see table 115, pages 744–747) and are not repeated here.

The names of some sites have changed over time, *eg* Swindon Reservoir became Coate Reservoir and later Coate Water. Commonly used historical names are included in the gazetteer as separate entries so that those quoted in earlier publications (*eg* Smith 1887) can be located. Three old sites – 'Phantom Wood' (Corncrake in 1944), 'Butteridge' (Whimbrel in 1882), and 'Clifton' (Pallas's Sandgrouse in 1888) – have, however, proved impossible to trace.

A number of abbreviations are used for MoD establishments: at Porton Down, CDE was the Chemical Defence Establishment, now renamed the Defence Science and Technology Laboratory (Dtsl); on SPTA, DERA was the Defence Evaluation and Research Agency (now split into Dstl and QinetiQ), but previously known as Royal Aircraft Establishment (RAE), and FIBUA is the Fighting In Built Up Areas Village.

Site	Grid ref
Aaron's Hill	ST7434
Ablington Down, SPTA (East)	SU1847
Ablington Furze, SPTA (East)	SU1848
Ailesbury Arms, Marlborough	SU1869
Airsprung Factory, Trowbridge	ST8559
Aldbourne	SU2675
Aldbourne Down	SU2275
Aldbourne Warren	SU2477
Alderbury	SU1827
Alderton	ST8482
Alfred's Tower	ST7535
All Cannings	SU0761
All Cannings Down	SU0965
Allington Down	SU0966
Allington, Chippenham	ST8975
Allington, Devizes	SU0663
Allington, Newton Tony	SU2039
Alton Barnes	SU1062
Alton Barnes White Horse	SU1063
Alton Priors	SU1162
Alvediston	ST9723
America Way, SPTA (West)	ST9647
Amesbury	SU1641
Andover's Gorse	ST9789
Ansty	ST9526
Arn Hill, Warminster	ST8746
Ashcombe, Tollard Royal	ST9319
Ashley Copse	SU3261
Ashton Keynes	SU0594
Atworth	ST8665
Aucombe Bottom	ST8342
Aughton	SU2356
Aughton Down	SU2156
Avebury	SU1070
Avebury Down	SU1170
Avebury Trusloe	SU0969
Avon Bridge, Chippenham	ST9173
Avon Bridge, Salisbury	SU1333
Avon Valley NNR	SU1329
Avoncliff	ST8059
Axford	SU2370
Axford Pumping Station	SU2470
Ayleswade Bridge	SU1429
Badbury	SU1980
Badbury Wick	SU1881
Baden Down Farm	SU1652
Bagbury	ST9541
Bake Barn, Chicklade	ST9234
Bake Buildings	ST9835
Ball Down	SU0551
Baltic Farm	SU0466
Bapton	ST9938
Barbury	SU1576

Place	Grid reference
Brickworth Down	SU2224
Bridge Farm, Britford	SU1528
Brigmerston Down	SU2047
Brimsdown Hill	ST8239
Brimslade	SU2163
Brinkworth	SU0184
Brinkworth Brook	SU0284 to ST9783
Bristol Avon	ST8287 & ST9190
(converging Malmesbury)	to ST7862
Britford	SU1628
Britford Water Meadows	SU1728
Brixton Deverill	ST8638
Broad Chalke	SU0325
Broad Chalke watercress beds	SU0325
Broad Hinton	SU1076
Broad Town	SU0977
Broadfield Lake	ST9682
Broadleas Park, Devizes	SU0060
Broadmead Brook	ST8276
Broadwater, Chilton Foliat	SU3270
Brockhurst Wood	SU0686
Brokenborough	ST9189
Brokerswood	ST8451
Bromham	ST9665
Bromham Fruit Farm	ST9664
Broome Manor sewage farm	SU1582
Broughton Gifford	ST8763
Broxmore Farm	SU2722
Broxmore Park	SU2723
Brunton	SU2456
Buckleaze Farm, Pewsey	SU1660
Bulford, SPTA (East)	SU1643
Bulford Camp, SPTA (East)	SU1943
Bulford Ranges	SU2046
Bulkington	ST9458
Bull Mill	ST8742
Burbage	SU2361
Burcombe	SU0730
Burcombe Ivers	SU0429
Burderop	SU1680
Burderop Down	SU1676
Burderop Park	SU1680
Burney Farm, Axford	SU2472
Burnt Wood	SU2669
Burton	ST8179
Bustard Hotel	SU0946
Bustard Vedette, SPTA (Centre)	SU0946
Buttermere	SU3461
By Brook	ST8377 to ST8067
Cadley	SU2066
Caen Hill	ST9861
Calcutt	SU1193
Callow Hill	SU0384
Calne	ST9971
Calne industrial estate	SU0072
Calne landfill site	SU0271
Calne Sand Pits	SU0171
Calne STW	SU0170
Calstone	SU0268
Calstone Barn	SU0368
Calstone Wellington	SU0268
Camp Down	SU1133
Can Down, SPTA (Centre)	SU0550
Candown Copse, SPTA (Centre)	SU0450
Casterley Barn, SPTA (Centre)	SU1153
Casterley Camp, SPTA (Centre)	SU1153
Castle Combe	ST8477
Castle Eaton	SU1495
CDE, Porton Down	SU2037
Center Parcs	ST8442
Chain Hill	SU0837
Chalford	ST8650
Chapel Plaister	ST8467
Chapmanslade	ST8247
Charlbury Hill	SU2382
Charlton-All-Saints	SU1723
Charlton Clump	SU0954
Charlton Down	SU0852
Charlton Fish Farm	SU1723
Charlton Mill	SU1823
Charlton Park	ST9589
Charlton, Ludwell	ST9022
Charlton, Malmesbury	ST9688
Charlton, Rushall	SU1156
Chase Wood	SU2174
Chelworth, Cricklade	SU0892
Chelworth, Crudwell	ST9794
Cherhill	SU0370
Cherhill Down	SU0569
Cherhill White Horse	SU0469
Cherrington (old spelling of Chirton)	SU0757
Cherry Lodge Farm	SU0642
Cheverell Wood	ST9755
Cheverell Hill Farm	ST9752
Chichester Estate, Little Durnford	SU1234
Chicklade	ST9134
Chicksgrove	ST7629
Chicksgrove Quarry	ST9529
Chilhampton	SU0933
Chilmark	ST9732
Chilton Foliat	SU3270
Chippenham	ST9173
Chippenham golf course	ST9075
Chirton	SU0757
Chirton Down, SPTA (Centre)	SU0754
Chirton Gorse, SPTA (Centre)	SU0653
Chirton Maggot, SPTA (Centre)	SU0655
Chisbury	SU2766
Chisbury Wood	SU2765

Chiseldon	SU1879	Codford St Peter	ST9640
Chiseldon Camp	SU1877	Coldridge Wood	SU2852
Chiseldon STW	SU1880	Cole Park	ST9485
Chisenbury	SU1452	Colerne	ST8171
Chisenbury Field Barn, SPTA (East)	SU1653	Colerne Airfield	ST8071
Chisenbury Warren, SPTA (East)	SU1753	Colerne Down Farm	ST8373
Chitterne	ST9943	Collett's Bottom	ST8471
Chitterne Brook	ST9843	Collingbourne Ducis	SU2453
Chittoe	ST9566	Collingbourne Forest	SU2753
Chittoe Heath	ST9666	Collingbourne Kingston	SU2355
Cholderton	SU2242	Collingbourne Wood	SU2753
Christian Malford	ST9678	Combe Bassett Down	SU1024
Church Farm, Easton Grey	ST8887	Common Head	SU1982
Church Hill, Westdown	SU0352	Common Hill, Cricklade	SU0893
Church Street, Southwick	ST8356	Common Plantation, Longleat	ST8040
Churchfields, Salisbury	SU1329	Compton Bassett	SU0372
Churchill Gardens, Salisbury	SU1529	Compton Chamberlayne	SU0229
Chute	SU3153	Compton Down	SU0228
Chute Causeway	SU2955	Compton Ivers	SU0228
Chute Down	SU2853	Compton Park	SU0330
Chute Forest	SU2853	Compton Wood	SU0130
Clanger Wood	ST8754	Coneygre Copse, Oxenwood	SU3157
Clarendon	SU1928	Coneygre Copse, Baydon	SU2976
Clarendon Lake	SU2028	Conkwell	ST7962
Clarendon Park	SU1928	Conkwell Wood	ST7861
Clatford	SU1568	Conock	SU0657
Clatford Bottom	SU1666	Coombe, Netheravon	SU1450
Clatford Bridge	SU1568	Coombe, Donhead	ST9022
Clatford Down	SU1471	Coombe Bissett	SU1126
Clattinger Farm	SU0193	Coombe Bissett Down	SU1024
Clay Pit Hill	ST9942	Coombe Reservoir	SU1551
Clearbury Down	SU1524	Copehill Down, SPTA (West)	SU0246
Clearbury Ring	SU1524	Copenacre	ST8570
Clench Common	SU1765	Copheap, Warminster	ST8845
Clevancy	SU0575	Cornbury Farm, West Lavington	SU0049
Cleveland Farm	SU0694	Corsham	ST8670
Cleveland Pit, CWP	SU0694	Corsham Churchyard	ST8770
Cleveland works	SU0694	Corsham Court	ST8770
Cleverton	ST9785	Corsham Lake	ST8870
Cley Hill	ST8344	Corsham Park	ST8770
Clifford's Hill	SU0863	Corsley	ST8246
Cloatley	ST9890	Corsley Heath	ST8245
Clout's Wood	SU1379	Corsley Mill	ST8147
Cloven Hill Plantation	SU2218	Corston	ST9284
Clyffe Pypard	SU0776	Corton	ST9340
Clyffe Pypard Wood	SU0679	Costow Farm	SU1181
Coate, Devizes	SU0461	Cotley Hill	ST9243
Coate Reservoir	SU1782	Cotswold Water Park NE & E from	SU0093
Coate Water	SU1782	Coulston	ST9554
Cobham Frith	SU2567	County Hall, Trowbridge	ST8557
Cock Hill, Trowbridge	ST8458	Covingham, Swindon	SU1985
Cockey Down	SU1731	Cow Down Hill	SU0121
Codford	ST9639	Cowesfield Green	SU2523
Codford Down	ST9742	Cowleaze Copse	SU0685
Codford St Mary	ST9739	Cowleaze Track	SU0685

Place	Grid reference
Cowleaze Wood	SU0279
Crammer Pond, Devizes	SU0161
Crates Wood	ST8825
Cratt Hill	ST9035
Cricklade	SU1093
Crockerton	ST8642
Crockerton Pond	ST8542
Croft Wood, Swindon	SU1582
Croft, Swindon	SU1583
Crofton	SU2662
Crooked Soley	SU3172
Crookwood Farm	SU0158
Crookwood Mill Farm	SU0258
Crossroads Farm	ST9153
Crouch Wood	SU1994
Croucheston Down	SU0722
Crow Down	ST8386
Crudwell	ST9592
Cuckoo's Knob	SU1962
Cumberwell golf course	ST8163
Cumberwell landfill site	ST8263
Cusse's Gorse, Winterbourne	SU1637
CWP	see map on page 841
Dauntsey	ST9982
Day House Farm	SU1882
Dean Bottom	SU1573
Dean Hill	SU2426
Dean Valley	SU2227 to SU2527
Dee Barn	ST8435
Delling Copse	SU1371
Deptford	SU0138
Deptford Down	SU0140
DERA, SPTA (Centre)	SU1048
Derry Hill	ST9570
Dertford's Wood	ST8144
Deverill Valley	ST8643 to ST8437
Devizes	SU0061
Devizes Market Place	SU0061
Dilton	ST8649
Dilton Marsh	ST8449
Dilton Vale	ST8649
Dinton	SU0131
Dinton Mill	SU0231
Ditteridge	ST8169
Dodsdown Lake (or Pond)	SU2762
Doncombe Brook	ST8174
Doncombe Scrubs	ST8073
Donhead St Andrew	ST9124
Donhead St Mary	ST9024
Dorcan, Swindon	SU1984
Dorcan industrial estate	SU1984
Down Barn, West Overton	SU1369
Down Farm, West Kington	ST7977
Downton	SU1821
Downton tannery	SU1821
Draycot Cerne	ST9278
Draycot Fitz Payne	SU1462
Draycot Foliat	SU1877
Draycott Hill	SU1364
Drews Pond Wood, Devizes	SU0059
Drifter's Hill, West Kington	ST8077
Druid's Lodge	SU0939
Drynham, Trowbridge	ST8656
Dudmore Lodge	SU2375
Dunch Hill	SU2048
Dundas Aqueduct	ST7862
Dunstable, near Salisbury	SU2233
Dunstable Pond	SU2233
Durley	SU2364
Durnford Mill	SU1337
Durrington	SU1544
Eald Burh	SU1064
East Chisenbury	SU1452
East Croft Coppice	SU2368
East Down	SU0549
East Farm	SU1071
East Gomeldon	SU1835
East Grafton	SU2560
East Grimstead	SU2227
East Hatch	ST9228
East Kennett	SU1167
East Knoyle	ST8830
East Leaze	SU2778
East Tytherton	ST9674
East Winterslow	SU2433
Eastbrook Farm, Bishopstone	SU2483
Eastdown Plantation	SU0548
Easterton	SU0255
Easthill Farm	ST9344
Eastleigh Wood	ST8843
Easton	SU0464
Easton Down	SU0666
Easton Farm	SU0464
Easton Grey	ST8887
Easton Hill	SU2058
Easton Lane Pond	ST9072
Easton Piers (old version Easton Piercy)	ST8977
Easton Royal	SU2060
Ebbesbourne Wake	ST9924
Ebsbury Hill, Wishford	SU0635
Edington	ST9253
Edington Hill	ST9252
Edington Lake (Fish Pond)	ST9253
Elcot Mill (site of)	SU2069
Eldene, Swindon	SU1883

Ell Barrow, SPTA (Centre)	SU0751
Elston	SU0644
Emmett Hill	SU0190
Enford	SU1351
Enford Down, SPTA (Centre)	SU1049
Enford Farm	SU1250
Enford Manor Farm	SU1250
Erlestoke	ST9653
Erlestoke Lake	ST9654
Erlestoke Wood	ST9653
Etchilhampton	SU0460
Everleigh	SU2053
Everleigh Ashes, SPTA (East)	SU1956
Everleigh Barrows, SPTA (East)	SU1856
Everleigh Down, SPTA (East)	SU1952
Everleigh Rectory	SU1954
Eysey	SU1194
Eysey Manor Farm	SU1194

Fairmile Down	SU2656
Fairwood Farm	ST8451
Falkner's Farm	SU1257
Fargo Plantation, SPTA (Centre)	SU1143
Farleigh Parke	ST9065
Farley	SU2229
Faulston Down	SU0824
Ferndale playing fields, Swindon	SU1486
Ferne Estate	ST9322
Fernicombe	ST8847
FIBUA Village, SPTA (West)	SU0145
Fifield	SU1450
Fifield Bavant	SU0125
Figheldean	SU1547
Figsbury Ring	SU1833
Firs Farm	SU0767
Firsdown	SU2133
Fisherton, Salisbury	SU1330
Fisherton de la Mere	SU0038
Fittleton	SU1449
Flamstone Farm	SU0625
Flaxlands	SU0684
Flinty Knapp	ST9553
Flisteridge Wood	ST9991
Fonthill Bishop	ST9333
Fonthill Gifford	ST9231
Fonthill Lake	ST9331
Ford, By Brook	ST8474
Ford, Salisbury	SU1532
Fore Hill	ST9852
Fosbury	SU3258
Fosse Way	ST7970 to SU0000
Four Mile Clump	SU1674
Fovant	SU0028
Fovant Down	SU0127
Fovant Lake	SU0028
Fowler's Farm	SU1491
Fowlers Hill	SU1529
Fox Covert, Chitterne	SU0244
Foxham	ST9777
Foxhangers	ST9761
Foxhill	SU2381
Foxley	ST8985
Foxley Corner	ST8986
Franchises landfill site	ST2117
Franchises Wood	SU2316
Freeth Farm	SU0272
Freshbrook, Swindon	SU1183
Freshford	ST7860
Frith Copse, Lydiard Green	SU0785
Frith Copse, Manningford Abbots	SU1359
Frogmore Pond, Westbury	ST8752
Froxfield	SU2968
Furze Knoll	SU0366
Fyfield, Marlborough	SU1468
Fyfield Down, Marlborough	SU1470
Fyfield Down, Pewsey	SU1858
Fyfield Hill	SU1479
Fyfield STW	SU1568

Gare Hill	ST7840
Garston	ST9687
Gasper Lake	ST7733
Giant's Grave, Charlton-All-Saints	SU1623
Giant's Grave, Oare	SU1663
Giant's Grave, Aldbourne	SU2476
Gibbet Knoll	SU0253
Glory Ann Barn (site of)	SU1272
Goatacre	SU0277
Gombledon	SU1935
Gore Cross	SU0151
Grafton	SU2560
Grand Avenue, Savernake	SU2168 to SU2465
Grange Park, Swindon	SU1084
Granham Hill	SU1867
Grant's Farm, SPTA (West)	ST9150
Grant's Firs, SPTA (East)	SU1656
Great Bedwyn	SU2764
Great Bradford Wood	ST8460
Great Chalfield	ST8663
Great Cheverell	ST9854
Great Durnford	SU1338
Great Fore Down, SPTA (Centre)	SU0454
Great Hinton	ST9059
Great Ridge	ST9336
Great Ridge Wood	ST9336
Great Somerford Gravel Pit	ST9682
Great Thornham Farm, Seend	ST9359
Great Wishford	SU0735

Great Wood, Lyneham	SU0281
Great Yews	SU1123
Green Hill, Aldbourne	SU2776
Green Hill, Wootton Bassett	SU0686
Green Lane Wood	ST8857
Greenbridge, Swindon	SU1685
Greenland Camp (Fargo), SPTA (Centre)	SU1044
Greenlands Camp, SPTA (Centre)	SU0647
Grip Wood, Bradford-on-Avon	ST8160
Grittenham	SU0382
Grittenham Wood	SU0281
Grittleton	ST8680
Grove Farm	SU2269
Grovely Wood	SU0534
Gurston Down	SU0226
Gutch Common	ST8925
Hackpen Copse	SU1677
Hackpen Hill	SU1274
Hailstone Hill	SU0894
Half Mile Pond, Longleat	ST8143
Ham	SU3362
Ham Hatches	SU3362
Ham Hill	SU3361
Hammersmith	ST9037
Hampton	SU1892
Hamptworth	SU2419
Hamptworth Common	SU2418
Hamptworth Lake	SU2319
Hanging Langford	SU0337
Hankerton	ST9790
Hannington	SU1793
Hardenhuish School, Chippenham	ST9074
Hardens Mead, Chippenham	ST9372
Haredene Wood	ST9628
Harepath Farm, Bishops Cannings	SU0664
Harnham	SU1328
Hart Hill	ST8442
Hartmoor, Devizes	ST9960
Hawkeridge	ST8653
Hawkstreet, Bromham	ST9665
Haxton, Netheravon	SU1449
Haxton Down, SPTA (East)	SU2050
Haycombe Hill Farm	ST8940
Haydon Wick	SU1387
Haydown Hill	SU3156
Hazeland Farm, Bremhill	ST9772
Hazelbury Common	ST8368
Heale House, Middle Woodford	SU1236
Heaven's Gate	ST8242
Heddington	ST9966
Hens Wood	SU2468
Hensfords Marsh, Warminster	ST8743
Heytesbury	ST9242
Heywood	ST8753
Heywood Lake	ST8853
High Clear Down	SU2376
High Post	SU1536
Highden	SU0976
Higher Coombe Wood	ST8822
Higher Pertwood	ST8835
Highland Farm	SU0050
Highland Farm Cottages	ST9950
Highway	SU0474
Highworth	SU1992
Hilcott	SU1158
Hill Barn, Easton Royal	SU2158
Hill Bottom Farm, Little Cheverell	ST9851
Hill Deverill	ST8640
Hill Deverill watercress beds	SU8640
Hill Farm Copse, Lydiard Millicent	SU0986
Hillocks Wood	SU0280
Hillwood	SU2474
Hillworth, Devizes	SU0160
Hilmarton	SU0275
Hilperton	ST8759
Hilperton Marsh	ST8659
Hindon	ST9132
Hinton Coombe	SU2282
Hinton Downs	SU2580
Hinton Parva	SU2283
Hippenscombe	SU3156
Hisomley	ST8549
Hitchfield Farm	ST9052
Hodson, Swindon	SU1780
Holbrook Farm	ST8862
Holbrook, Trowbridge	ST8556
Holt	ST8661
Home Covert, Roundway	SU0063
Homington	SU1226
Honeydown Ridge, SPTA (Centre)	SU0848
Honeystreet	SU1061
Hook	SU0784
Hook Street	SU0884
Hope Cottage	SU2216
Horningsham	ST8141
Horton	SU0463
Horton Down	SU0766
Hougoumont Farm	SU2352
Hound Wood	SU2230
Huish	SU1463
Hullavington	ST8982
Hurdcott	SU1733
Hurdcott House	SU0431
Hyam Wood	ST9087
Idmiston	SU1937
Iford	ST8058
Imber Clump, SPTA (West)	ST9147

Imber Firs, SPTA (West)	ST9646
Imber Road, SPTA (West)	ST9250 to ST9251
Imber Village, SPTA (West)	ST9648
Immerdene, SPTA (West)	ST9748
Inglesham	SU2096
Job's Mill	ST8542
Jones's Mill	SU1661
Keevil	ST9258
Keevil Aerodrome	ST9257
Kellaways	ST9575
Kennel Farm, Britford	SU1728
Kennet Barrows	SU1067 to SU1166
Kent End, CWP	SU0594
Kepnal	SU1760
Keysley Farm	ST8635
Kilmington	ST7736
Kilmington Common	ST7735
King's Bottom	ST8343
King's Play Hill	SU0166
Kingfisher Mill, Great Durnford	SU1337
Kingsdown, Box	SU8167
Kingsdown, Stratton	SU1688
Kingsdown golf course	ST8067
Kingshill Canal, Swindon	SU1383
Kingshill, Swindon	SU1484
Kingston Deverill	ST8437
Kington Langley	ST9277
Kington St Michael	ST9077
Kitchen Barrow Hill	SU0664
Knap Hill	SU1263
Knapp Down, SPTA (West)	ST9049
Knighton, Ramsbury	SU2971
Knighton Hill	SU0524
Knoll Down	SU0769
Knook	ST9341
Knook Camp, SPTA (West)	ST9442
Knowle	SU1660
Knowle Hill	SU2566
Knoyle House	ST8731
Lackham College	ST9270
Lacock	ST9268
Lacock Abbey	ST9168
Lacock Gravel Pit	ST9067
Lady Down, Trowbridge	ST9530
Ladywell Barn, SPTA (West)	ST9348
Ladywell Copse	SU2362
Ladywell Overflow Pond, SPTA (West)	ST9348
Lake	SU1339
Lake House	SU1338
Lammy Down	SU2481
Landford	SU2519
Landford Bog	SU2518
Landford Common	SU2618
Langford Lakes	SU0436
Langley	ST9275 to ST9276
Langley Burrell	ST9375
Langley Wood	SU2220
Larkhill, SPTA (Centre)	SU1244
Larkhill Range, SPTA (Centre)	SU1049
Latton	SU0996
Laverstock	SU1530
Lavington	SU0154
Lavington Down	SU0149
Lavington Folly, SPTA (Centre)	SU1249
Lavington Sands	SU0055
Lavington Vedette, SPTA (Centre)	SU0253
Lea, Malmesbury	ST9586
Leckford	SU2352
Leckford Bottom	SU2352
Leckford Bridge	SU2351
Leckford Crossroads	SU2352
Leigh	SU0692
Leigh Delamere	ST8879
Leipzig Plantation	SU0164
Liddington	SU2081
Liddington Castle	SU2079
Liddington Hill	SU2179
Liddington Warren Farm	SU2279
Liden Lagoon	SU1983
Life of Man Plantation	ST8542
Limpley Stoke	ST7860
Little Bedwyn	SU2965
Little Bradley Wood	ST7941
Little Chalfield	ST8563
Little Cheverell	ST9953
Little Durnford	SU1234
Little Folly	SU0947
Little Hinton	SU2383
Little Horton	SU0462
Little Langford	SU0436
Little Ridge Wood	ST9432
Little Somerford	ST9684
Little Toyd Down	SU0922
Little Wishford	SU0736
Littlecote	SU3070
Littlecote Park	SU2970
Littlecott Down, SPTA (East)	SU1753
Littleton Drew	ST8380
Littleton Panell	ST9954
Lockeridge	SU1467
Lodge Farm	SU0422
Lodge Lower Barn, Aldbourne	SU2475
Long Dean	ST8575
Long Knoll	ST7937
Long Water, Erlestoke	ST9654
Longbridge Deverill	ST8640
Longcombe Bottom	ST9152

Longford SU1626
Longford Castle SU1726
Longford Park SU1626
Longleat Arboretum ST8042
Longleat ST8043
Longleat lakes ST8143
Longleat Safari Park ST8143
Longstreet Down, SPTA (East) SU1852
Loosehanger Copse SU2119
Lord's Hill ST8839
Lover SU2120
Low Lane Pits, Calne SU0171
Lower Blunsdon SU1491
Lower Earlscourt Farm, Bourton SU2186
Lower Foxhangers ST9661
Lower House Farm, Everleigh SU2053
Lower Pertwood ST8836
Lower Stanton St Quinton ST9180
Lower Stratton SU1886
Lower Swillbrook SU0193 to SU0293
Lower Upham SU2077
Lower Wanborough SU2183
Lower Woodford SU1235
Luccombe ST9252
Luckington ST8383
Ludgershall SU2650
Ludgershall Castle SU2651
Ludwell ST9122
Lurkeley Hill SU1266
Lyburn Farm, Hamptworth SU2318
Lydeway SU0458
Lydiard Millicent SU0985
Lydiard Park SU1084
Lydiard Tregoze SU1084
Lyneham SU0278

Maddington SU0644
Maiden Bradley ST8038
Malmesbury ST9287
Malmesbury Common SU0085
Mancombe Bottom ST8947
Manningford Abbots SU1458
Manningford Bohune SU1357
Manningford Bruce SU1358
Mannington, Swindon SU1385
Manor Farm, Avebury SU0969
Manor Farm, CWP SU0693
Manor Fields ST9152
Manor House Woods, Littleton Panell SU0054
Manswood ST8441
Manton SU1768
Manton Down SU1571
Marden SU0857
Marden Cowbag SU0854
Marden Down SU0854
Marden Mill SU0858
Marlborough SU1969
Market Lavington SU0154
Marlborough College SU1868
Marlborough College Lakes SU1868
Marlborough Common SU1870
Marlborough Downs SU1375 to SU1775
Marlborough High Street SU1669
Marlborough Mill SU1868
Marleycombe Hill SU0222
Marridge Hill SU2874
Marsh Lane Bridge ST8660
Marston ST9656
Marston Meysey SU1297
Marten SU2860
Martin's Bushes, SPTA (Centre) SU1444
Martinsell SU1764
Martinsell Hill SU1763
Martinslade Bridge ST9561
Mead End, Bowerchalke SU0223
Melksham ST9063
Melksham STW ST8964
Membury SU3075
Mere ST8132
Mere Down ST8234
Middle Winterslow SU2333
Middle Woodford SU1136
Middlehill ST8068
Middleton Down ST9246
Middleton Hill SU0423
Midge Hall SU1677
Mildenhall SU2169
Mile Elm ST9969
Milk Hill SU1063
Milkhouse Water SU1761
Mill Farm Lake ST9856
Millditch, Bratton ST9152
Milston SU1645
Milton ST8731
Milton Lilbourne SU1960
Minety SU0290
Mock Bridge, SPTA (West) ST9548
Monkton Deverill ST8537
Monkton Down SU1272
Monkton Farleigh ST8065
Monkton Farm, Monkton Deverill ST8536
Monkton Park, Chippenham ST9273
Moredon, Swindon SU1387
Morgan's Hill SU0267
Mouldon Hill SU1187
Mouldon Lake SU1287
Mountain Bower ST8075
Murhill ST7960
Murray John Tower, Swindon SU1484

Place	Grid reference
Nadder Island	SU1329
Naish Hill	ST9369
Neston	ST8668
Netheravon	SU1448
Netheravon Airfield	SU1649
Netheravon Camp	SU1548
Netherhampton	SU1029
Netherstreet Farm	ST9865
Nettleton	ST8278
Nettleton Mill	ST8377
Netton Down	SU0627
New Barn Farm, Ogbourne	SU1873
New Copse	SU0250
New Copse Down	SU0350
New Court Down	SU1422
New Court Farm, Downton	SU1722
New Farm, SPTA (West)	ST9249
New Mill	SU1861
New Town	SU1264
New Warren, Savernake	SU2469
New Zealand Farm Camp	ST9750
New Zealand Farm, Lyneham	SU0177
Newhouse Farm	ST8664
Newton	SU2322
Newton Barrow	SU1035
Newton Ferris (perhaps Norton Ferris misspelt)	ST7936
Newton Tony	SU2140
Nightingale Farm, South Marston	SU2088
Nightingale Wood	SU1988
Nightwood Copse	SU2128
Nine Mile River	SU2047 to SU1643
Nockatt Coppice	ST8242
Nocketts Hill, Chippenham	ST9470
Nomansland	SU2517
Normanton Down	SU1140
Norridge Wood	ST8545
North Bradley	ST8555
North Down	SU0467
North Farm, Aldbourne	SU2578
North Farm, Warminster	ST9144
North Field Barn, Aldbourne	SU2677
North Meadow, Cricklade	SU0994
North Newnton	SU1257
North Wraxall	ST8174
Norton Bavant	ST9043
Norton Down	ST9246
Norton Ferris	ST7936
Notton	ST9069
Nunton	SU1526
Nythe	SU1885
Oakfrith Wood	SU0257
Oak Hill Water Meadows	SU3067
Oakhill Wood	SU3256

Place	Grid reference
Oaksey	ST9993
Oare	SU1563
Oare Hill	SU1663
Oasis Leisure Centre, Swindon	SU1485
Odstock	SU1426
Odstock Down	SU1324
Ogbourne Down	SU1774
Ogbourne Maizey	SU1871
Ogbourne St Andrew	SU1872
Ogbourne St George	SU1974
Okus, Swindon	SU1483
Old Farm Clump	SU1048
Old Sarum	SU1332
Old Tip, Swindon	SU1285
Old Town, Swindon	SU1583
Old Totterdown, Fyfield	SU1371
Oldbury Castle	SU0569
Oldbury Down	SU0568
Oliver's Castle, Devizes	SU0064
One Tree Hill	SU0059
Orcheston	SU0545
Orcheston Down, SPTA (Centre)	SU0545
Overton	SU1368
Overton Down	SU1370
Ox Drove	ST9420 to SU0723
Oxenwood	SU3059
Oysters Coppice	ST8925
Packway Mess, SPTA (Centre)	SU1244
Pale Park Pond, Wardour	ST9225
Panterwick	SU1867
Parham Wood	SU0055
Park Farm	SU2569
Park Pond, Wardour	ST9226
Parsonage Down	SU0541
Parsonage Farm, Warminster	ST8846
Patcombe Hill	ST9251
Patney	SU0758
Paxcroft	ST8859
Pear Tree Hill, Erlestoke	ST9753
Peatmoor Lagoon	SU1286
Peckingell	ST9374
Peewit's Gorse	ST8737
Pen Hill Down	ST8736
Penleigh	ST8550
Penning's Farm, Oare	SU1562
Penstones Wood	ST7839
Pensworth Tip	SU2124
Pepler's Farm, Edington	ST9353
Pepperbox Hill	SU2124
Perham Down, SPTA (East)	SU2549
Pertwood	ST8835
Pertwood Beech Clump	ST8738
Pertwood Down	ST8837
Petersfinger	SU1629

Petersfinger Gravel Pits	SU1628
Pewsey	SU1660
Pewsey Downs	SU1063
Pewsey Manor	SU1659
Pewsey Wharf	SU1561
Pewsham	ST9470
Picket Wood	ST8754
Pickledean Barn	SU1369
Pickwick	ST8670
Picquet Hill	ST9252
Piggledene	SU1468
Pinehurst, Swindon	SU1587
Pinkflower Gorse	ST8635
Pinkney	ST8686
Pitton	SU2131
Pockeredge Wood Lake	ST8569
Polton (old spelling of Poulton)	SU1971
Pomeroy Wood	ST8056
Port Farm	SU1393
Porton	SU1936
Porton Down	SU2035
Portway, Warminster	ST8745
Potterne	ST9958
Potterne Park Farm, Potterne	SU0057
Potterne Wick	SU0057
Potterne Wood	SU0158
Poulshot	ST9759
Poulshot Farm	ST9659
Poulton	SU1971
Poulton Copse	SU1970
Poulton Downs	SU2070
Poulton Farm	SU1969
Pound Bottom	SU2217
Pound Bottom landfill site	SU2117
Prescombe Down	ST9825
Preshute	SU1868
Preshute Down	SU1374
Prickmoor Wood	ST9465
Princess Margaret Hospital, Swindon	SU1483
Puckshipton Pond	SU0957
Purton	SU0887
Purton Stoke	SU0990
Puthall Farm	SU2368
Quebec Farm, SPTA (West)	ST9543
Queen's Crescent, Chippenham	ST8972
Queen's Park, Swindon	SU1486
Quemerford	SU0069
Quidhampton	SU1131
Rabley Wood	SU2070
Rack Hill	ST8475
Rainbow Bottom, SPTA (East)	SU1551
Ram Alley	SU2263
Ram Alley Lake	SU2163
Ramsbury	SU2771
Ramsbury Chase	SU2673
Ramsbury Lake	SU2671
Ramsbury Manor	SU2571
Ram's Cliff, Market Lavington	SU0153
Ranscombe Bottom	ST8849
Ravensroost Wood	SU0288
Red Barn	SU1379
Red Lodge	SU0688
Redford Water	ST8043 to ST8047
Redhorn Hill, SPTA (Centre)	SU0555
Redhorn Vedette, SPTA (Centre)	SU0555
Redlands Farm	ST8953
Redlynch	SU2021
Redway Gate	ST8442
Reeve's Farm, Bratton	ST9251
Regent Circus, Swindon	SU1584
Reybridge	ST9269
Riding's Mead, Chippenham	ST9074
Rivar Down	SU3061
River Avon (Bristol)	ST8287 & ST9190
(converging Malmesbury)	to ST7862
River Avon (Salisbury)	SU0858 & SU1861
(converging Rushall)	to SU1720
River Bourne	SU2260 to SU1529
River Cole	SU2483 to SU2199
River Ebble	ST9522 to SU1726
River Kennet	SU1178 to SU3269
River Marden	SU0368 to ST9374
River Nadder	ST8822 to SU1429
River Og	SU1975 to SU1969
River Ray	SU1379 to SU1293
River Wylye	ST8036 to SU1030
Rivermead, Swindon	SU1285
Riverside Drive, Chippenham	ST9373
Rixon Gate, Ashton Keynes	SU0594
Roaring Hatches	ST9485
Roche Court	SU2434
Rockley	SU1671
Rockley Down	SU1473
Rodbourne, Malmesbury	ST9383
Rodbourne, Swindon	SU1486
Rodbourne Cheney	SU1386
Rodmead Wood	ST8135
Rollestone Camp	SU0944
Rollestone Manor Farm	SU0743
Rood Ashton	ST8856
Rood Ashton Lake	ST8856
Rood Ashton Wood	ST8856
Rookhay Farm	SU0123
Rooktree Farm, Little Cheverell	ST9851
Rotherley Wood	ST9519
Rough Down, Marlborough	SU1870
Roughridge Hill	SU0565
Round Wood, Westbury	ST8452

Standlynch Down	SU2023
Standlynch Farm, Downton	SU1924
Standlynch Meadows	SU1724
Standon House, Chute	SU3053
Stanley	ST9672
Stanmore Copse	SU0775
Stanton Dairy	SU0860
Stanton Fitzwarren	SU1790
Stanton Lake	SU1789
Stanton Park	ST8979
Stanton Park Wood	ST8979
Stanton St Bernard	SU0962
Stanton St Quintin	ST9079
Stapleford	SU0737
Stapleford Down	SU0937
Startley	ST9482
Station Pond, Westbury	ST8652
Staverton	ST8560
Steeple Ashton	ST9056
Steeple Langford	SU0337
Steeple Langford Gravel Pits	SU0436
Stert	SU0259
Stitchcombe	SU2269
Stock Close	SU2373
Stockley	SU0067
Stockton	ST9838
Stockton House	ST9738
Stockton Wood	ST9635
Stoford Bottom	SU0835
Stoford Hill	SU0936
Stoke Down	SU0527
Stoke Farthing	SU0525
Stoke Hill	ST9552
Stonedown Wood	ST9920
Stonehenge	SU1242
Stonehenge Inn	SU1544
Stonehill Wood, near Minety	SU0089
Stormore	ST8449
Stourhead	ST7734
Stourton	ST7834
Stourton lakes	ST7733
Stourton Water	ST8856
Stowell	SU1461
Stratford sub Castle	SU1332
Stratford Tony	SU0926
Stratton St Margaret	SU1787
Strawberry Hill	ST9952
Strip Wood	ST9849
Studley, Calne	ST9671
Stype Wood	SU3066
Suddene Park Farm, Burbage	SU2461
Sugar Hill	SU2378
Summer Down, Collingbourne	SU2155
Summer Down, SPTA (West)	ST9148
Sunnyhill Farm, Pewsey	SU1762
Sunnyhill Farm, Collingbourne Ducis	SU2451
Sutton Benger	ST9478
Sutton Bottom	ST9826
Sutton Down	ST9826
Sutton Mandeville	ST9828
Sutton Veny	ST8941
Swallowcliffe	ST9627
Swallowcliffe Down	ST9725
Swill Brook Bridge	SU0193
Swindon landfill site	SU1385
Swindon Reservoir	SU1782
Swindon Station	SU1585
Swindon STW	SU1285
Swingfire, SPTA (Centre)	SU1150
Tadpole Farm	SU1189
Tan Hill	SU0864
Teffont Common	ST9931
Teffont Evias	ST9931
Teffont Lake	ST9931
Teffont Magna	ST9832
Tellisford	ST8055
Tenantry Down, SPTA (West)	ST9350
The Gibb	ST8379
The Lawn, Swindon	SU1683
The Pinetum, Castle Combe	ST8376
The Shoe	ST8074
The Warren, West Lavington	SU0051
Thickwood	ST8272
Thingley	ST8970
Thorncombe, SPTA (West)	ST9250
Thorncombe Down, SPTA (West)	ST9250
Thorncombe Farm, SPTA (West)	ST9250
Thornhill Nursery, Savernake	SU2166
Thorny Down landfill site	SU2134
Thoulstone	ST8347
Thyterton Lucas	ST9474
Tidcombe	SU2958
Tidworth Garrison	SU2248
Tidworth, North	SU2449
Tidworth STW	SU2346
Tilshead	SU0347
Tilshead Down	SU0247
Timbridge Farm	SU2467
Tinhead Hill	ST9352
Tinker's Track, SPTA (West)	E from ST9147
Tinney's Plantation	SU2317
Tipney Wood	ST8055
Tisbury	ST9429
Tockenham	SU0380
Tockenham Reservoir	SU0280
Tollard Green	ST9216
Tollard Royal	ST9417

Toplands Farm	ST8474
Tottenham Park	SU2664
Tottenham Wood	ST9452
Totterdown	SU1372
Townsend	SU0456
Townsend Farm	SU0563
Trafalgar House	SU1823
Treacle Bolly	SU1868
Trow Lane, Tockenham	SU0281
Trowbridge	ST8558
Trowbridge STW	ST8458
Truncombe Wood	ST8236
Turleigh, Bradford-on-Avon	ST8060
Turner's Farm, Seend	ST9561
Two Mile Down	ST8833
Tyning Wood	ST7739
Tytherington	ST9141
Uffcott	SU1277
Ugford	SU0831
Upavon	SU1355
Upavon Airfield	SU1554
Upavon Down	SU1654
Upper Easton Piercy Farm, Kington St Michael	ST8877
Upper Fyfield	SU1468
Upper Herdswick	SU1575
Upper Inglesham	SU2098
Upper Seagry	ST9480
Upper Upham	SU2277
Upper Upham Farm	SU2277
Upper Woodford	SU1237
Upper Wraxall	ST8074
Upton Cow Down	ST8749
Upton Lovell	ST9440
Upton Scudamore	ST8647
Urchfont	SU0457
Urchfont Down, SPTA (Centre)	SU0652
Urchfont Hill	SU0555
Vaggs Hill	ST8155
Vernditch Chase	SU0321
Victoria Hill, Swindon	SU1584
Vincients Wood	ST8973
VP1 (Heytesbury), SPTA (West)	ST9344
VP3 (Gore Cross), SPTA (West)	ST9949
VP6 (Bratton), SPTA (West)	ST9250
VP12 (Redhorn), SPTA (Centre)	SU0555
VP13 (Casterley), SPTA (Centre)	SU1153
Wadman's Coppice, SPTA (West)	ST9449
Wadswick	ST8467
Walcot, Swindon	SU1684
Walden House, West Grimstead	SU2027
Walker's Hill	SU1163
Wanborough	SU2082
Wansdyke	SU0167 to SU1966
Wardour	ST9327
Wardour Castle	ST9226
Wardour Wood	ST9326
Warminster	ST8644
Warminster Boating Lake	ST8744
Warminster Camp	ST8846
Warminster Common	ST8644
Warminster Down	ST8948
Warminster golf course	ST8746
Warminster School of Infantry	ST8946
Warminster Vedette, SPTA (West)	ST9046
Warren Down	SU0551
Warren Farm, West Lavington	SU0052
Water Dean Bottom, SPTA (Centre)	SU1152
Water Eaton Copse	SU1493
Water Lane, Salisbury	SU1429
Waterhay, CWP	SU0693
Weather Hill, SPTA (East)	SU2051
Weather Hill Firs, SPTA (East)	SU2052
Weavern	ST8471
Weavern Valley	ST8472
Webb's Wood	SU0485
Wedhampton	SU0657
Well Bottom	ST9237
Wellhead	ST8132
West Amesbury	SU1341
West Ashton	ST8855
West Chase Farm, Ebbesbourne Wake	ST9819
West Chisenbury	SU1352
West Dean	SU2527
West Down	SU0548
West Down Farm	ST9352
West Down Plantation, SPTA (Centre)	SU0449
West End, Foxham	ST9777
West Grafton	SU2460
West Grimstead	SU2126
West Harnham	SU1229
West Hill Farm, Heytesbury	ST9344
West Kennett	SU1168
West Kington	ST8077
West Knoyle	ST8532
West Lavington	SU0052
West Overton	SU1367
West Stowell	SU1362
West Winterslow	SU2332
West Woods	SU1566
West Yatton Down	ST8576
Westbury	ST8751
Westbury cement works	ST8852
Westbury Downs	ST8950
Westbury golf course lake	ST8852

Westbury Hospital	ST8750
Westbury Leigh	ST8650
Westbury Ponds	ST8651 to ST8652
Westbury Quarry	ST8852
Westbury Station Pond	ST8651
Westbury trading estate	ST8552
Westbury VP, SPTA (West)	ST8950
Westbury White Horse	ST8951
Westcourt	SU2261
Westdown Farm	ST9352
Westdown Ranges, SPTA (Centre)	SU0451
Westlea	SU1284
Westwood	ST8059
Wexcombe	SU2759
Wexcombe Down	SU2757
Wexland Farm, Netheravon	SU1348
Wexland Hanging, SPTA (Centre)	SU1148
Whaddon Firs	SU1926
Whaddon, Salisbury	SU1926
Whaddon, Trowbridge	ST8761
Whetham	ST9768
White Hill, Lavington	SU0051
White Horse Barn	ST9051
White Horse Hill	ST8951
White Lodge	SU0689
White Sheet Hill, Ansty	ST9424
White Sheet Hill, Mere	ST8034
Whitefield Hill	SU2076
Whiteparish	SU2423
Whiteparish Common	SU2522
Whitley	ST8866
Whitworth Road Cemetery, Swindon	SU1487
Wick Down, Downton	SU1321
Wick Down, Ludgershall	SU2653
Wick Down, Rockley	SU1374
Widbrook	ST8359
Widdenham	ST8370
Widdington Farm	SU1253
Wilcot	SU1461
Wilcot Manor Lake	SU1360
Willsford Down, Upavon	SU0853
Wilsford, Amesbury	SU1339
Wilsford, Upavon	SU1057
Wilsford cum Lake	SU1339
Wilsford Down, Amesbury	SU1040
Wilsford Hill	SU0955
Wilton Brail	SU2762
Wilton, Marlborough	SU2661
Wilton, Salisbury	SU0931
Wilton Down	SU2861
Wilton Drove	SU0828
Wilton Park	SU0930
Wilton Water	SU2661
Win Green	ST9220
Wincombe Park	ST8824
Windmill Hill	SU2450
Wingfield	ST8256
Winklands Down	ST8951
Winsley	ST8061
Winsley Hill	ST7861
Winterbourne Bassett	SU1074
Winterbourne Dauntsey	SU1734
Winterbourne Earls	SU1734
Winterbourne Gunner	SU1834
Winterbourne Monkton	SU1072
Winterbourne Stoke	SU0740
Winterslow Hut	
(former name of Pheasant Hotel)	SU2334
Winterslow Wood	SU2235
Witcha Farm, Ramsbury	SU2973
Witham Park	ST7638
Witham Woods	ST7739
Witherington Down	SU2024
Wolfhall Manor and Farm	SU2461
Wood Bridge Lake	SU1357
Woodborough	SU1159
Woodborough Churchyard	SU1160
Woodcroft Wood	ST8843
Woodfalls	SU1920
Woodford	SU1136
Woodford Valley	SU1235
Woodland Park	ST8352
Woodland Trust, Kingsdown	SU1688
Woodminton	SU0022
Woodsend, Aldbourne	SU2276
Wootton Bassett	SU0783
Wootton Rivers	SU1963
Worton	ST9757
Worton Fish Farm	ST9856
Wrag Barn golf course	SU2091
Wroughton	SU1480
Wroughton Airfield	SU1378
Wroughton Copse	SU1370
Wroughton Reservoir	SU1580
Wylye	SU0037
Wylye Down	SU0036
Yarnbrook	ST8655
Yarnbrook Lake	ST8655
Yarnbury Castle	SU0340
Yatesbury	SU0671
Yatton Keynell	ST8676
Zealland Cross	ST9250
Zeals	ST7731
Zeals Airfield	ST7732

Scientific names of plants and animals mentioned in the text

Vernacular names are listed alphabetically (by their first word) within each of four sections below; both they and the scientific names aim to follow current usage. All Wiltshire's regular and vagrant birds can be found either in the main species texts – see 'List of contents' for the family names (pages 6–7) – or in the first section of 'Significant additional records 2001 to 2005' (pages 723–724), and are therefore included in the main Index; but a very few others are briefly mentioned somewhere in the text and these are the only bird species listed here.

Plants

Alder *Alnus glutinosa*
Apple *Malus domestica*
Arolla pine *Pinus cembra*
Ash *Fraxinus excelsior*
Barleys *Hordeum* spp
Beech *Fagus sylvatica*
Birches *Betula* spp
Blackthorn *Prunus spinosa*
Bluebell *Hyacinthoides non-scripta*
Blue (Atlas) cedar *Cedrus atlantica*
Box *Buxus sempervirens*
Bracken *Pteridium aquilinium*
Bramble *Rubus fruticosus* agg
Broad bean *Vicia faba*
Broccoli *Brassica oleracea* var *italica*
Bromes *Bromus* spp
Burdocks *Arctium* spp
Cherries *Prunus* spp
Clovers *Trifolium* spp
Common chickweed *Stellaria media*
Common evening-primrose *Oenothera biennis*
Common fumitory *Fumaria officinalis*
Common knapweed *Centaurea nigra*
Common reed *Phragmites australis*
Common whitebeam *Sorbus aria*
Corsican pine *Pinus nigra* ssp *laricio*
Cotoneasters *Cotoneaster* spp
Cow parsley *Anthriscus sylvestris*
Crab apple *Malus sylvestris*
Cypresses *Chamaecyparis*/*Cupressus* spp
Dandelions *Taraxacum* spp
Dog's mercury *Mercurialis perennis*
Dogwood *Cornus sanguinea*
Douglas fir *Pseudotsuga menziesii*
Downy birch *Betula pubescens*
Downy oat-grass *Helictotrichon pubescens*
Eelgrass *Zostera marina*
Elder *Sambucus nigra*
English elm *Ulmus procera*
Evening-primrose *Oenothera erythrosepala*
False oat-grass *Arrhenatherum elatius*
Field maple *Acer campestre*
Flaxes *Linum* spp
Gorse (furze) *Ulex europaeus*
Greater knapweed *Centaurea scabiosa*
Green seaweeds *Enteromorpha*
Guelder-rose *Viburnum opulus*
Hawthorn *Crataegus monogyna*
Hazel *Corylus avellana*
Heather *Calluna vulgaris*
Hogweed *Heracleum sphondylium*
Holly *Ilex aquifolium*
Holm (evergreen) oak *Quercus ilex*
Hornbeam *Carpinus betulus*
Horse chestnut *Aesculus hippocastanum*
Ivy *Hedera helix*
Japanese larch *Larix kaempferi*
Juniper *Juniperus communis*
Kale *Brassica oleracea*
Knapweeds *Centaurea* spp
Larches *Larix* spp
Lavenders *Lavandula* spp
Linseeds *Linum* spp
Maize *Zea mays*
Meadowsweet *Filipendula ulmaria*
Mistletoe *Viscum album*
Monterey pine *Pinus radiata*
Mugwort *Artemesia vulgaris*
Mustards *Brassica* (*Sinapis*) spp
Nettles *Urtica* spp
Norway spruce *Picea abies*
Nyger *Guizotia abyssinica*
Oilseed-rape *Brassica napus*
Peas *Lathyrus* spp

Pedunculate oak *Quercus robur*
Pines *Pinus* spp
(London) plane *Plantanus* × *hispanica*
Pondweeds *Potamogeton* spp
Poplars *Populus* spp
Potato *Solanum tuberosum*
Purging buckthorn *Rhamnus cathartica*
Pyracanthas *Pyracantha* spp
(Common) ragwort *Senecio jacobea*
Raspberry *Rubus idaeus*
Red fescue *Festuca rubra*
Red-hot-poker *Kniphofia uvaria*
Reed-maces *Typha* spp
Rhododendron *Rhododendron ponticum*
Reed sweet-grass *Glyceria maxima*
Rowan *Sorbus aucuparia*
Rudbeckias *Rudbeckia* spp
Rushes *Juncus* spp
Rye-grasses *Lolium* spp
Saltbush (in Sahel) *Atriplex* sp
Scots pine *Pinus sylvestris*
Sedges *Carex* spp
Sessile oak *Quercus petraea*
Sheep's fescue *Festuca ovina*
Silver birch *Betula pendula*
Silver firs *Abies* spp
Sitka spruce *Picea sitchensis*
Small-leaved lime *Tilia cordata*
Snake's head fritillary *Fritillaria meleagris*
Spindle *Euonymus europaeus*
Spruces *Picea* spp
Stoneworts Characeae
Sunflower *Helianthus annuus*
Swede *Brassica napus* ssp *rapifera*
Sweet chestnut *Castanea sativa*
Sycamore *Acer pseudoplatanus*
Teasel *Dipsacus fullonum*
Thistles *Carduus/Cirsium* spp
Thrift *Armeria maritima*
Turnip *Brassica rapa*
Upright brome *Bromopsis erecta*
Watercress *Rorippa nasturtium-aquaticum*
Wellingtonia *Sequoiadendron giganteum*
Wheats *Triticum* spp
Wild parsnip *Pastinaca sativa* var *sylvestris*
Wild privet *Ligustrum vulgare*
Wild service tree *Sorbus torminalis*
Wild thymes *Thymus* spp
Willows *Salix* spp
Wych elm *Ulmus glabra*
Yellow iris *Iris pseudacorus*
Yew *Taxus baccata*

Invertebrates

Annelid worms Annelida
Ants Formicidae
Bees Apidae
Beetles Coleoptera
Bumblebees *Bombus* spp
Click beetle *Agriotes lineatus*
Cockchafer (maybug) *Melolontha melolontha*
Cockle *Cerastoderma edule*
Dragonflies Odonata
Dor beetle *Geotrupes stercorarius*
Earwigs Dermaptera
Earthworms Lumbricidae
Geometrid caterpillars Geometridae
Grasshoppers Orthoptera (suborder Caelifera)
Freshwater mussels (see Swan/Painter's)
Hummingbird hawk-moth *Macroglossum stellatarum*
Meadow brown *Maniola jurtina*
Moths Lepidoptera
Painted lady *Cynthia cardui*
Painter's mussel *Unio pictorum*
Peacock *Inachis io*
Small tortoiseshell *Aglais urtica*
(Edible) oyster *Ostrea edulis*
Slugs Mollusca
Small elm bark beetle *Scolytus multistriatus*
Snails Gastropoda
Spiders Araneae
Swan mussel *Anodonta cygnea*
(Salisbury Avon) tellin (Mollusca) *Tellina rivalis*
Wasps (Social) Vespidae
Wireworm (larva of Click beetle)
Zebra mussel *Dreissena polymorpha*

Birds other than those in main lists

African Spoonbill *Platalea alba*
Azure Tit *Cyanistes cyanus*
Canary Island Chiffchaff *Phylloscopus canariensis*
Chukar *Alectoris chukar*
Crested Tit *Lophophanes cristatus*
Dalmatian Pelican *Pelecanus crispus*
Fan-tailed Warbler *Cisticola juncidis*
Golden Eagle *Aquila chrysaetos*
Iberian Chiffchaff *Phylloscopus ibericus*
Lesser Kestrel *Falco naumanni*
Levaillant's Woodpecker *Picus vaillantii*
Mountain Chiffchaff *Phylloscopus sindianus*
North African Blue Tit *Cyanistes teneriffae*
Parrot Crossbill *Loxia pytyopsittacus*
Scottish Crossbill *Loxia scotica*
Short-toed Treecreeper *Certhia brachydactyla*
Snowy Egret *Egretta thula*
Spanish Sparrow *Passer hispaniolensis*
Taiga Flycatcher *Ficedula albicilla*
White's Thrush *Zoothera dauma*
White-headed Duck *Oxyura leucocephala*
Willow Grouse *Lagopus l. lagopus*

Other vertebrates

Arctic lemming *Lemmus lemmus*
Bank vole *Clethrionomys glareolus*
Bats Chiroptera
Black rat *Rattus rattus*
Bottle-nosed dolphin *Tursiops truncatus*
Brown hare *Lepus europaeus*
Brown rat *Rattus norvegicus*
Brown trout *Salmo trutta*
Common frog *Rana temporaria*
Common shrew *Sorex araneus*
Common toad *Bufo bufo*
Coypu *Myocastor coypus*
Deer Cervidae
Domestic cat *Felis cattus*
Domestic dog *Canus familiaris*
Field vole *Microtus agrestis*
Fox *Vulpes vulpes*
Greater horseshoe bat *Rhinolophus ferrumequinum*
Grey squirrel *Sciurus carolinensis*
Lesser horseshoe bat *Rhinolophus hipposideros*
Lion *Panthera leo*
Lizards *Lacerta* spp
Rabbit *Oryctolagus cuniculus*
Sand-eels Ammodytidae
Sheep *Ovis aries*
Short-tailed field-vole *Microtus agrestis*
Snakes Colubridae/Viperidae
Stoat *Mustela erminea*
Tiger *Panthera tigris*
Wolf *Canis lupus*
Wood mouse *Apodemus sylvaticus*

Bibliography (including a list of publications on Wiltshire birds)

Asterisks are used to mark all ornithological publications that are concerned solely with Wiltshire – whether or not they are referred to in the species texts or the chapters – and so these make up, it is hoped, a complete bibliography of the county's birds up to and including 2006. All the other publications cited without asterisks are books, papers or articles quoted in support of statements in *Birds of Wiltshire*.

Apart from *WANHM* (1854–1974) and *Hobby* (1975 to date) – from which separate articles which have been included individually below – the following publications also contain items of local ornithological interest:

Dauntsey's School Bird Trust Annual Report, 1936–51.

Dorcan School Ornithological Society. *Birds seen in Thamesdown and District,* 1975–1980.

Marlborough College Natural History Society Report [*MCNHS*], 1865–1965.

Salisbury & District Field Club [later Natural History Society], 1953–78.

Adams, MC. 1966. Firecrests breeding in Hampshire. *British Birds* 59: 240–246.

* Adams, NP. 1997. Laughing Gull at the Cotswold Water Park. *Hobby* 23: 89–90.

* Adams, NP. 2003. Blue-winged Teal at the Cotswold Water Park. *Hobby* 29: 92–93.

* Addison, WG. 1951. Three Wiltshire Parsons, 1796–1900. iii – Arthur Philip Morres. *Theology, Monthly Review* 54: 332–335.

Alexander, CJ. 1910. The notes of the British Willow Tit. *British Birds* 4: 146–147.

Alexander, HG. 1974. *Seventy Years of Birdwatching*. Poyser, Berkhamsted.

Alexander, WB. 1945–47. The Woodcock in the British Isles. *Ibis* 87: 512–550; 88: 1–24, 159–179, 271–286, 427–444; 89: 1–28.

* Allison, E. 1997. Birds. In: E Hostetter & TN Howe (eds). *The Romano-British Villa at Castle Copse, Great Bedwyn*. Indiana University Press, Bloomington, Indiana.

Allsopp, K, & B Nightingale. 1990. Seasonal reports. Winter 1989/90. *British Birds* 83: 319–329.

* Almack, AC *et al.* 1865–90. Ornithological Section, *MCNHS*.

Alström, P. 1985. Artbestamming av atorskav *Phalacrocorax carbo* och toppskarv *P. aristotelis*. *Vår Fågelvärld* 44: 325–350.

Alström, P, & K Mild. 2003. *Pipits and wagtails of Europe, Asia and North America*. Helm, London.

* Andrew, DG. 1997. The earlier breeding records of Icterine Warbler in England. *British Birds* 90: 187–190.

Andrew, DG. 2004. Medieval Little Egrets and others. *British Birds* 97: 44–45.

* Anon. 1847. Occurrence of the Golden Eagle near Hungerford. *The Zoologist* 5: 1695. [This was the White-tailed Fish-eagle at Littlecote (page 267)]

* Anon. ['J.G.W.']. 1869. Little Bittern in Wilts. *The Field*, 18 September.

* Anon. ['Observer']. 1875. Bittern, etc., at Bradford-on-Avon. *The Field*, 23 January.

* Anon. 1903a. The Dipper or Water Ouzel (*Cinclus aquaticus*) in Wilts. *WANHM* 33: 65.

* Anon. 1903b. The Bittern. *WANHM* 33: 65.

* Anon. 1903c. The Hoopoe. *WANHM* 33: 65.

* Anon. 1903d. Cormorants. *WANHM* 33: 65.

* Anon. 1905. White-tailed Eagle. *WANHM* 34: 109.

* Anon. 1906a. Bohemian Waxwing. *WANHM* 34: 340.

* Anon. 1906b. Blackgame in Wiltshire. *WANHM* 34: 340.

* Anon. 1907a. A Bittern. *WANHM* 35: 317.

* Anon. 1907b. The Great Black Woodpecker in Wilts. *WANHM* 35: 317.

* Anon. 1907c. Little Bustard. *WANHM* 35: 318.

* Anon. 1907d. Quail. *WANHM* 35: 318.

* Anon. 1908. Bitterns in Wilts. *WANHM* 35: 508.

* Anon. 1909a. Blue Headed Wagtail. *WANHM* 36: 140.

* Anon. 1909b. Red-Throated Diver at Wylye. *WANHM* 36: 140.

* Anon. 1909c. Little Owl. *WANHM* 36: 143.

* Anon. 1912a. Lesser Redpoll nesting in Wilts. *The Field*, 15 June.

* Anon. 1912b. Great Crested Grebe (*Podiceps cristatus*), on Braden Pond. *WANHM* 37: 615.

* Anon. 1913a. Black Redstart in Wilts. *WANHM* 38: 107.

* Anon. 1913b. The Rev. A.P. Morres' Collection of Birds. *WANHM* 38: 110–111.

* Anon. 1914a. Golden Oriole at Lacock. *WANHM* 38: 641.

* Anon. 1914b. Great Crested Grebe Nesting in Wilts. *WANHM* 38: 641.

* Anon. 1914c. Erroneous report of the occurrence of the Yellow Shank (*Totanus flavipes*) in Wiltshire. *WANHM* 38: 641–642.

* Anon. 1914d. Bohemian Waxwing. *WANHM* 38: 642.

* Anon. 1915. Bittern near Westbury. *WANHM* 39: 111.

* Anon. 1916a. Black Tern. *WANHM* 39: 402.

* Anon. 1916b. Guillemot. *WANHM* 39: 403.

* Anon. 1916c. Common Curlew (*Numenius arquata*). *WANHM* 39: 404.

* Anon. 1916d. Black Grouse (*Lyrurus t. britannicus*). *WANHM* 39: 404.

* Anon. 1919a. Lydiard Millicent Natural History Notes. *WANHM* 40: 364–365.

* Anon. 1919b. Kentish Plover in Wilts? *WANHM* 40: 365.

* Anon. 1919c. Little Owl at Netherstreet. *WANHM* 40: 365.

* Anon. 1920a. Buzzard and Puffin near Marlborough. *WANHM* 41: 182.

* Anon. 1920b. Lydiard Millicent Natural History Notes. *WANHM* 41: 186.

* Anon. 1922a. Little Owl. *WANHM* 42: 78.

* Anon. 1922b. "Snowblunts". *WANHM* 42: 78.

* Anon. 1922c. Great Grey Shrike. *WANHM* 42: 79.

* Anon. 1922d. Hen Harrier. *WANHM* 42: 79.

* Anon. 1922e. Bittern. *WANHM* 42: 79.

* Anon. 1922f. Snowy Owl. *WANHM* 42: 79.

* Anon. 1923a. Great Crested Grebe. *WANHM* 42: 256.

* Anon. 1923b. Hawfinches. *WANHM* 42: 256.

* Anon. 1923c. Bernicle Geese. *WANHM* 42: 256.

* Anon. 1926. The Great Bustards in Salisbury Museum. *WANHM* 43: 333.

* Anon. 1927a. White Woodcock. *WANHM* 44: 61.

* Anon. 1927b. Moorhen nesting in trees. *WANHM* 44: 61.

* Anon. 1927c. Great Crested Grebe. *WANHM* 44: 61.

* Anon. 1947. The Natural History Section of the Wiltshire Archaeological and Natural History Society. *WANHM* 51: 584–585.

* Anon. 1963. Some effects of the cold spell in early 1963 on the birds and mammals of Marlborough. *MCNHS* 1963: 13–14.

Aplin, OV. 1889. *The Birds of Oxfordshire.* Clarendon Press, Oxford.

Aplin, OV. 1890a. On the Distribution and Period of Sojourn in the British Islands of the Spotted Crake. *The Zoologist* (3rd series) 14: 401–417.

Aplin, OV. 1890b. Spotted Crake in Great Britain. *The Zoologist* (3rd series) 14: 457.

Aplin, OV. 1891. The Distribution in the British Isles of the Spotted Crake. Supplementary Notes. *The Zoologist* (3rd series) 15: 88–96.

Aplin, OV. 1892. On the Distribution of the Cirl Bunting in Great Britain. *The Zoologist* (3rd series) 16: 121–128.

Ardamatskaya, TB. 1998. Breeding Sites of Mediterranean Gull in the countries of the former Soviet Union. In: PL Meininger, W Hoogendoorn, R Flament & P Raevel (eds). 1999. *Proceedings of the 1st International Mediterranean Gull Meeting, Le Portel, Pas-de-Calais, France 4–7 September 1998.* EcoNum, Bailleul (France).

* Armistead. JJ. 1865. Moorhen perching in Trees. *The Zoologist* 23: 9450.

* Artindale, RH. 1906. Blackgame in Wilts. *The Field*, 14 April.

* Astley, AF. 1866. Bee-eater in Wilts. *The Field*, 21 July.

Atkinson, NK, M Davies & AJ Prater. 1978. The distribution of Purple Sandpipers in Britain. *Bird Study* 25: 223–228.

* Aubrey, HWW. 1873. Heronry near Salisbury. *The Zoologist* (2nd series) 2: 3369.

* Aubrey, J, FRS. (1656–91). *The Natural History of Wiltshire.* [Nicols for Wiltshire Topographical Society, London; J Britton (ed). 1847]. Facsimile 1969. David & Charles, Newton Abbot.

Austin, GE, I Peachel & MM Rehfisch. 2000. Regional trends in coastal wintering waders in Britain. *Bird Study* 47: 352–371.

Austin, M. 2001. *Stone-curlews in southern England.* RSPB Wessex Stone-curlew Project, Salisbury.

* Austin, M. 2002. RSPB Stone-curlew project. *Hobby* 28: 93–97.

Avery, MI, & R Leslie. 1990. *Birds and Forestry.* Poyser, London

* Baatsen, RG. 1990. Red-crested Pochard (*Netta rufina*) in the Cotswold Water Park. *Hobby* 16: 64–67.

* Baatsen, RG. 1993. Red-footed Falcon *Falco vespertinus* in the Cotswold Water Park 29 May to 2 June 1992. *Hobby* 19: 80–82.

Baillie, S, HQP Crick, DE Balmer, LP Beaven, IS Downie, SN Freeman, DI Leech, JH Marchant, DE Noble, MJ Raven, AP Simpkin, RM Thewlis & CV Wernham. 2002. *Breeding Birds in the Wider Countryside: their conservation status 2001.* BTO Research Report No 278. British Trust for Ornithology, Thetford.

Bainbridge, IP, & CDT Minton. 1978. The migration and mortality of the Curlew in Britain and Ireland. *Bird Study* 25: 39–50.

* Baker, E. 1880. Great Grey Shrike [in Wiltshire]. *The Field*, 27 November.

* Baker, E. 1881. Spotted Crake Nesting in Wilts. *The Field*, 18 June.

* Baker, E. 1888. Pied Flycatcher and Manx Shearwater in Wilts. *The Field*, 19 May.

Baker, H, DA Stroud, NJ Aebischer, PA Cranswick, RD Gregory, CA McSorley, DG Noble & MM Rehfisch. 2006. Population estimates of birds in Great Britain and the United Kingdom. *British Birds* 99: 25–44.

* Balfour, TG. 1876. Whimbrel in Wiltshire. *The Zoologist* (2nd series) 11: 5167.

* Balfour, TG. 1877. The "Curlew" of the Wiltshire Downs. *The Zoologist* (3rd series) 1: 183.

Ballance, DK. 1996. Dartford Warbler. In: BD Gibbs (ed.). *Somerset Birds* 1996: 87. Somerset Ornithological Society.

Ballance, DK. 1999. *Birds in counties: an ornithological bibliography for the counties of England, Wales, Scotland, and the Isle of Man.* Imperial College Press, London.

* Bankes, A. 1906. Knot (*Tringa canutus*) in Wiltshire. *The Zoologist* 1906: 152.

Bankovics, A. 1997. Ferruginous Duck. In: EJM Hagemeijer & MJ Blair (eds). *The EBCC Atlas of European Breeding Birds: their distribution and abundance.* Poyser, London.

Barber, L. 1980. *The Heyday of Natural History 1820–1870.* Jonathan Cape, London.

Barham, KEI, PJ Conder & IJ Ferguson-Lees. 1956. Bee-eaters nesting in Britain, 1955. *Bird Notes* 27: 34–43.

* Barnes, RG. 1958. Census of Mute Swans. *WANHM* 57: 124.

* Barnes, RG. 1963. Mute Swan Census 1961. *WANHM* 58: 493–495.

* Barnes, RG. 1974. The Ornithological Atlas of Great Britain and Ireland 1968–72. *WANHM* 69: 26–29.

* Barnes, RG. 1976. History of Wiltshire bird reports. *Hobby* 2: 27–28.

* Barnes, RG. 1979. Mute Swan Survey 1978. *Hobby* 5: 34–35.

* Barnes, RG. 1980. House and garden predators. *Hobby* 6: 46.

* Barron, RS. 1976. *The Geology of Wiltshire.* Moonraker Press, Bradford-on-Avon.

* Baskerville, M, D Lambert & P Scrivens. 2005. *A history of Bentley Wood.* The Friends of Bentley Wood, Salisbury.

Bastian, A, & H-V Bastian. 1994. Bestände und Bestandtrends des Braunkehlchens *Saxicola rubetra. Limicola* 8: 242–270.

Batten, LA. 1971. Firecrests breeding in Buckinghamshire. *British Birds* 64: 473–475.

Batten, LA. 1973a. The colonisation of England by the Firecrest. *British Birds* 66: 159–166.

Batten, LA. 1973b. Population dynamics of suburban Blackbirds. *Bird Study* 20: 251–258.

Batten, LA. 2002. Firecrest. In: CV Wernham, MP Thoms, JH Marchant, JA Clark, GM Siriwadena & SR Baillie (eds). *The Migration Atlas: movements of the birds of Britain and Ireland.* Poyser, London.

Baxter, EV, & LJ Rintoul. 1953. *The Birds of Scotland*, 2 volumes. Oliver & Boyd, Edinburgh.

Baxter, IL. 1993. Eagles in Anglo-Saxon and Norse poems. *Circaea, The Journal of the Association for Environmental Archaeology* 10: 78–81.

Bayes, K, & A Henderson. 1988. Nightingales and coppiced woodland. *RSPB Conservation Review* 2: 47–49.

* Bealey, CE, RE Green, R Robson, CR Taylor & R Winspear. 1999. Factors affecting the numbers and breeding success of Stone Curlews *Burhinus oedicnemus* at Porton Down, Wiltshire. *Bird Study* 46: 145–156.

Bell, DA. 2001. Hampshire Bird Ringing Report, 1999. *Hampshire Bird Report 1999.* Hampshire Ornithological Society.

* Bennett, H. 1874. Sabine's Snipe near Salisbury. *The Field*, 24 January.

Berthold, P. 1973. Über starken Rückgang der Dorngrasmücke *Sylvia communis* und anderer Singvogelarten im westlichen Europa. *Journal für Ornithologie* 114: 348–360.

Berthold, P. 1974. Circannuale Periodik bei Grasmücken (*Sylvia*) III. Periodik der Mauser, der Nachtunruhe und des Körpergewichtes bei mediterranen Arten mitunterschiedlichem Zugverhalten. *Journal für Ornithologie* 115: 251–272.

Bibby, CJ. 1973. The Red-backed Shrike: a vanishing British species. *Bird Study* 20: 103–110.

Bibby, CJ. 1979a. Foods of the Dartford Warbler *Sylvia undata* on Southern England heathland. (Aves: Sylviidae). *Journal of the Zoological Society of London* 188: 557–576.

Bibby, CJ. 1979b. Mortality and movements of Dartford Warblers in England. *British Birds* 72: 10–22.

Bibby, CJ. 1989. A survey of breeding Wood Warblers *Phylloscopus sibilatrix* in Britain, 1984–1985. *Bird Study* 36: 56–72.

Bibby, CJ, & M Nattrass. 1986. Breeding status of the Merlin in Britain. *British Birds* 79: 170–185.

Bibby, CJ, & DK Thomas. 1984. Sexual dimorphism in size, moult and movements of Cetti's Warbler *Cettia cetti*. *Bird Study* 31: 28–34.

* Bircham, PMM. 1993. John Legg — an advanced and neglected ornithologist. *Archives of Natural History* 20: 147–155.

Birkhead, ME. 1981. The social behaviour of the Dunnock *Prunella modularis*. *Ibis* 123: 75–84.

Birkhead, M, & CM Perrins. 1986. *The Mute Swan*. Croom Helm, London.

Bishton, G. 1986. The diet and foraging behaviour of the Dunnock *Prunella modularis* in a hedgerow habitat. *Ibis* 128: 526–539.

* Blackmore, HP. 1854. Remains of birds' eggs found at Fisherton, near Salisbury. *Edinburgh New Philosophical Journal*: 74–75.

* Blackmore, HP. 1864a. Hawfinch near Salisbury. *The Zoologist* 22: 9023.

* Blackmore, HP. 1864b. Anecdote of Hawks. *The Zoologist* 22: 9039.

* Blackmore, HP. 1864c. Tufted Duck near Salisbury. *The Zoologist* 22: 9047.

* Blackmore, HP. 1864d. Sclavonian or Dusky Grebe near Salisbury. *The Zoologist* 22: 9048.

* Blackmore, HP. 1865a. Merlin near Salisbury. *The Zoologist* 23: 9538.

* Blackmore, HP. 1865b. Tufted Duck near Salisbury. *The Zoologist* 23: 9540.

* Blackmore, HP. 1866. Fork-tailed Petrel near Salisbury. *The Zoologist* (2nd series) 1: 101.

* Blackmore, HP. 1867a. Bohemian Waxwing in Wiltshire. *The Zoologist* (2nd series) 2: 704.

* Blackmore, HP. 1867b. Canada Goose at Coombe Bissett. *The Zoologist* (2nd series) 2: 708.

* Blackmore, HP. 1871. Immigration of the Great Bustard in Wiltshire. *The Zoologist* (2nd series) 6: 2510–2511.

* Blake, KF. 1980a. Grey Heron (*Ardea cinerea*) diving for food. *Hobby* 6: 47.

* Blake, KF. 1980b. Pied Wagtail (*Motacilla alba*) dominance at feeding stations. *Hobby* 6: 47.

Blaker, GB. 1933. The Barn Owl in England: results of the census. I and II. *Bird Notes and News* 15: 169–172.

Blaker, GB. 1934. *The Barn Owl in England and Wales*. RSPB, London.

* Blamey, B. 1999. Long-tailed Skua at Salisbury: the first Wiltshire record for over 100 years. *Hobby* 25: 93.

* Blamey, B, & B Greenough. 2000. Great White Egret at Britford. *Hobby* 26: 95–96.

* Bland, RL, & ER Creed. 1956. Winter Starling roosts in the Marlborough area. *MCNHS* 97: 21–34.

* [Blyth, E. – 'Z']. 1870. Greenshank in Wilts. *The Field*, 4 June.

Boag, D. 1982. *The Kingfisher*. Blandford Press, Poole.

Boisseau, S. 1995. *Former distribution of some extinct and declining British birds using place names as evidence*. BSc Zoology undergraduate research project. University of Manchester School of Biological Sciences.

Boisseau, S, & DW Yalden. 1998. The former status of the Crane *Grus grus* in Britain. *Ibis* 140: 482–500.

* Bosworth Smith, R. 1857a. Raven pairing with Crow. *The Zoologist* 15: 5680.

* Bosworth Smith, R. 1857b. Hawfinch breeding at Marlborough. *The Zoologist* 15: 5681.

* Bosworth Smith, R. 1863. Birds of Marlborough. In: TA Preston. *Flora of Marlborough with Notices of the Birds* (103–116). Van Voorst, London.

Bosworth Smith, R. 1909. *Bird life and bird lore*. John Murray, London.

* Bourdillon J. 1993. Animal Bone. In: H Graham & S Davies (eds). *Excavations in Trowbridge, Wiltshire 1977 and 1986–88. The Prehistoric, Saxon and Saxo-Norman Settlements and their Anarchy Period Castle*. Wessex Archaeology Report No 2. Trust for Wessex Archaeology Ltd, Salisbury.

BOU. 1971. *The Status of Birds in Britain and Ireland*. Blackwell, Oxford.

BOURC. 1996. British Ornithologists' Union Records Committee: 23rd Report (July 1996). *Ibis* 139: 197–201.

BOURC. 2004. British Ornithologists' Union Records Committee: 30th Report (October 2003). *Ibis* 146: 192–195.

Bourne, WRP. 2002. The nomenclature and past history in Britain of the Bean and Pink-footed Geese. *Bulletin of the British Ornithologists' Club* 122: 11–13.

Bourne, WRP. 2003. Fred Stubbs, Egrets, Brewes and climatic change. *British Birds* 96: 332–339.

Bourne, WRP, & R Ralph. 2000. The past history of the grey geese in Scotland. *Birding Scotland* 3: 150–151.

Boutin, J-M. 2001. Elements for a Turtle Dove (*Streptopelia turtur*) management plan. *Game & Wildlife Science* 18: 87–112.

Bowes, A, PC Lack & MR Fletcher. 1984. Wintering Gulls in Britain, January 1983. *Bird Study* 31: 161–170.

* Bowsher, P. 1987. *Wiltshire inventory of ancient woodlands*. NCC, Peterborough.

Boyd, H. 1954. The "wreck" of Leach's Petrels in the autumn of 1952. *British Birds* 47: 137–163.

Boyd, H, & LS Maltby. 1979. The Brant of the western Queen Elizabeth Islands, NWT. In: RL Jarvis & JC Bartonek (eds). *Management and Biology of Pacific Flyway Geese*. OSU Book Stores, Corvallis, Oregon.

Boyd, H, & T Piersma. 2001. Changing balance between survival and recruitment explains population trends in Red Knots *Calidris canutus islandica* wintering in Britain, 1969–1995. *Ardea* 89: 301–307.

* Boyle, GL. 1956. Nightingales in Wiltshire. *WANHM* 56: 437–438.

* Boyle, GL. 1970. The Heron in Wiltshire. Part A: Natural History. *WANHM* 65: 7–11.

* Boyle, GL. 1977. The Heron in Wiltshire. *Hobby* 3: 49–50.

* Bradby, AS. 1864a. Longeared Owl at Stratford St. Anthony. *The Zoologist* 22: 9105.

* Bradby, AS. 1864b. Curious place for a Blackbird's nest. *The Zoologist* 22: 9107.

Bradbury, RB, & U Bradter. 2004. Habitat associations of Yellow Wagtails *Motacilla flava flavissima* on lowland wet grassland. *Ibis* 146: 241–246.

* Bramwell, D. 1970. Bird Remains. In: GJ Wainwright. An Iron Age promontory fort at Budbury, Bradford on Avon. *WANHM* 65: 109–167.

* Bramwell, D. 1988. Bird bones from the 1961 excavations. In: TB James & AM Robinson. *Clarendon Palace*. The Society of Antiquities of London, London.

Bridgman, CJ. 1962. Birds nesting in aircraft. *British Birds* 55: 461–470.

* Bridgman, CJ. 1977. Wiltshire House Martin enquiry 1975 & 1976. *Hobby* 3: 41–46.

* Bridgman, CJ. 1979. Bird use of operational Wiltshire airfields. *Hobby* 5: 41–43.

* Bridgman, CJ. 1980. Wintering Blackcaps in Wiltshire 1969/70–1978/79. *Hobby* 6: 34–38.

* Bridgman. CJ. 1982. Stonechats in Wiltshire 1971–1980. *Hobby* 8: 40–47.

* Bridgman, CJ. 1985. Surveys. *Hobby* 11: 54–56.

Brown, MJ, E Linton & EC Rees. 1992. Causes of mortality among wild swans in Britain. *Wildfowl* 43: 70–79.

Brown, PE. 1957. The rarer birds of prey. Their present status in the British Isles. Hobby. *British Birds* 50: 149.

Brown, RGB. 1955. The migration of the Coot in relation to Britain. *Bird Study* 2: 135–142.

Browne, SJ, & NJ Aebischer. 2003. Temporal changes in the migration phenology of Turtle Doves *Streptopelia turtur* in Britain, based on sightings from coastal bird observatories. *Journal of Avian Biology* 34: 65–71.

Browne, SJ, & NJ Aebischer. 2004. Temporal changes in the breeding ecology of Turtle Doves *Streptopelia turtur* in Britain, and implications for conservation. *Ibis* 146: 125–137.

Browne, S, & N Aebischer. 2005. Studies of West Palearctic birds: Turtle Dove. *British Birds* 98: 58–72.

Brucker, JW, AG Gosler & AR Heryet. 1992. *Birds of Oxfordshire*. Pisces Publications, Newbury.

* Buchanan, GM. 1998. Pied-billed Grebe at the Cotswold Water Park. *Hobby* 24: 93–94.

Buczacki, S. 2002. *Fauna Britannica*. Hamlyn, London.

Burke, T, NB Davies, MW Bruford & BJ Hatchwell. 1989. Parental care and mating behaviour of polyandrous Dunnocks *Prunella modularis* related to paternity by DNA fingerprinting. *Nature* 338: 249–251.

Burton, H, T Lloyd-Evans & DN Weir. 1970. Wrynecks breeding in Scotland. *Scottish Birds* 6: 154–156.

Burton, NHK, AJ Musgrove, MM Rehfisch, A Sutcliffe & R Waters. 2003. Numbers of wintering gulls in the United Kingdom, Channel Islands and Isle of Man: a review of the 1993 and previous Winter Gull Roost Surveys. *British Birds* 96: 376–401.

* Bury, L. 1914. American Swallow-tail Kite in Wilts. *The Field*, 26 September.

Busby, J. 1982. *The Living Birds of Eric Ennion*. Gollancz, London.

Butler, C. 2002. Breeding parrots in Britain. *British Birds* 95: 345–348.

Buxton, J. 1950. *The Redstart*. Collins, London.

* Buxton, J. 1976. The first five thousand: an account of ringing in Wiltshire. *Hobby* 2: 29–32.

* Buxton, J (ed). 1981. *The Birds of Wiltshire*. Wiltshire County Council Library & Museum Service, Trowbridge.

Buxton, J, & RM Lockley. 1950. *Island of Skomer. A Preliminary Survey of the Natural History of Skomer Island, Pembrokeshire undertaken for the West Wales Field Society*. Staples Press, London

Byle, PAF. 1991. Parental provisioning in the Dunnock *Prunella modularis*: the effects of a variable mating system. *Ibis* 133: 199–204.

Cade, TJ. 1982. *The Falcons of the World*. Collins, London.

Callaghan, DA, & AJ Green. 1993. Wildfowl at risk, 1993. *Wildfowl* 44: 149–169.

Callion, J, N White & D Holloway. 1990. Grasshopper Warblers raising two and three broods in Cumbria. *British Birds* 83: 506–508.

Campbell, B. 1953. *Finding Nests*. Collins, London.

Campbell, B. 1954–55. The breeding distribution and habitats of the Pied Flycatcher in Britain. *Bird Study* 1: 81–101; 2: 24–32, 179–191.

Campbell, B, & J Ferguson-Lees. 1972. *A Field Guide to Birds' Nests*. Constable, London.

Campbell, B, & E Lack. 1985. *A Dictionary of Birds*. Poyser, Calton.

Campbell, L, J Cayford & D Pearson. 1996. Bearded Tits in Britain and Ireland. *British Birds* 89: 335–346.

Campbell, LH. 1984. The impact of changes in sewage treatment on sea ducks wintering in the Firth of Forth, Scotland. *Biological Conservation* 28: 173–180.

Carbone, C, & M Owen. 1995. Differential migration of the sexes of Pochard *Aythya ferina*: results from a European Survey. *Wildfowl* 46: 99–108.

Carter, I. 2001. *The Red Kite*. Arlequin Press, Chelmsford.

Carter, I, A Brown, L Lock, S Wotton & S Croft. 2003. The restoration of the Red-billed Chough in Cornwall. *British Birds* 96: 23–29.

* Castle, PE. 1993. Hen Harriers at Larkhill. *Sanctuary* 22: 13.

* Castle, PE. 1994. Where to Watch Birds in the Cotswold Water Park, Wiltshire. *Hobby* 20: 108–115.

* Castle, PE, & R Clarke. 1995 Observations on the conservation of Hen Harrier *Circus cyaneus* wintering on Salisbury Plain: roosts and food. *Hobby* 21: 88–96.

* Castle, PE, & R Turner. 1997. 1996: Year 2 of the Wiltshire Tetrad Atlas. *Hobby* 23: 98–101.

Catley, GP. 1994. More Hobbies nesting on pylons. *British Birds* 87: 335–336.

* Cawkell, EM. 1948. The rookeries of the Mere district. *WANHM* 52: 246–247.

* Cawkell, EM. 1949. The rookeries of the Mere district in 1948. *WANHM* 53: 85–86.

* Cawkell, EM. 1950. The rookeries of the Mere district in 1949. *WANHM* 54: 356–357.

Central Science Laboratory. 2002. *UK Ruddy Duck control trial final report*. Report to Department for Environment, Food and Rural Affairs.

* Chafin, W. 1818. *Anecdotes and History of Cranborne Chase*. The Dovecote Press, Stambridge.

Chance, EP. 1922. *The Cuckoo's secret*. Sidgwick & Jackson, London.

Chance, EP. 1940. *The truth about the Cuckoo*. Country Life, London.

Chapman, A. 1999. *The Hobby*. Arlequin, Chelmsford.

Chylarecki, P. 1993. New Herring Gull taxonomy. *British Birds* 86: 316–319.

Clark, F, & DAC McNeil. 1980. Cliff-nesting colonies of House Martins *Delichon urbica* in Great Britain. *Ibis* 122: 27–42.

Clark, JM, & JA Eyre (eds). 1993. *Birds of Hampshire*. Hampshire Ornithological Society.

Clark, JA, CW Wernham, DE Balmer, SY Adams, BM Griffin, JR Blackburn, D Anning & LJ Milne. 2001. Bird ringing in Britain & Ireland in 1999. *Ringing & Migration* 20: 239–288.

Clark, JA, CW Wernham, DE Balmer, SY Adams, BM Griffin, JR Blackburn, D Anning, LJ Milne & RA Robinson. 2002. Bird ringing in Britain & Ireland in 2001. *Ringing & Migration* 21: 80–143.

* Clark-Kennedy, A. 1867. Goosander in Wiltshire. *The Zoologist* (2nd series) 2: 709.

Clarke, R. 1995. *The Marsh Harrier*. Hamlyn, London.

Clarke, R. 1996. *Montagu's Harrier*. Arlequin Press, Chelmsford.

Clarke, R. 2002. British Montagu's Harriers – what governs their numbers? *Ornithologischer Anzeiger* 41: 143–158.

Clarke, RG, MC Combridge & P Combridge. 1997. A comparison of the feeding ecology of wintering Hen Harriers *Circus cyaneus* centred on two heathland areas in England. *Ibis* 139: 4–18.

Clarke, R, P Combridge & N Middleton. 2003. Monitoring the diets of farmland winter seed-eaters through raptor pellet analysis. *British Birds* 96: 361–375.

Clarke, R, & D Watson. 1997. The Hen Harrier Winter Roost Survey. *The Raptor* 24: 41–45.

Clement, P, & R Hathway. 2000. *Thrushes*. Helm, London.

Clements, R. 2000. Range expansion of the Common Buzzard in Britain. *British Birds* 93: 242–248.

Clements, R. 2001. The Hobby in Britain: a new population estimate. *British Birds* 94: 402–408.

Clements, R. 2002. The Common Buzzard in Britain: a new population estimate. *British Birds* 95: 377–383.

Cohen, E. 1963. *Birds of Hampshire and the Isle of Wight*. Oliver & Boyd, Edinburgh.

Coleman, AE, CDT Minton & JT Coleman. 1991. Factors affecting the number of pairs and breeding success of Mute Swans *Cygnus olor* in an area of South Staffordshire, England, between 1961 and 1985. In: J Sears & PJ Bacon (eds). *Proceedings of the Third International Swan Symposium, Oxford, 1989. Wildfowl* Supplement No 1: 103–109.

* Collins, B. 2005. *2004 Ecological Monitoring report for Longleat Forest*. Center Parcs report.

* Collinson, WF. 1977. A waterways bird survey on the Bristol Avon 1974–76. *Hobby* 3: 51–56.

Collinson, M. 2001. Evolution of the Atlantic-Island Chaffinches. *British Birds* 94: 121–124.

* Colquhoun, MK. 1941. The Birds of Savernake Forest, Wiltshire. *Journal of Animal Ecology* 10: 25–34.

* Colt Hoare, R. 1810–19. *The Ancient History of Wiltshire*. (Footnote – Bustard) 1: 93–94. Wm Miller, London.

* Colt Hoare, R. 1822–40. *The History of Modern Wiltshire*. John Nichols & Son, London.

* Combridge, MC, & P Combridge. 1999. Farmland nesting by Woodlarks in Wiltshire. *Hobby* 25: 112.

* Combridge, P. 2002. Hawfinches in Wiltshire. *British Birds* 95: 596.

* Combridge, P. 2005a. Cattle Egret near West Winterslow. *Hobby* 31: 104–105.

* Combridge, P. 2005b. Shore Lark at Whiteparish. *Hobby* 31: 106–107.

* Combridge, P, & SB Edwards. 2003. The Salisbury Long-tailed Skua revisited – was it really an adult? *Hobby* 28: 98–100.

* Combridge, P, & S King. 1998. Does the nominate race of Lesser Black-backed Gull occur in Wiltshire? *Hobby* 24: 113–120.

Combridge, P, & C Parr. 1992. Influx of Little Egrets in Britain and Ireland in 1989. *British Birds* 85: 16–21.

* Cooke, SH. 1946. The Marsh Warbler in Wiltshire. *MCNHS* 1946: 23–28.

Coombs, CFB, AJ Isaacson, RK Murton, RJP Thearle & NJ Westwood. 1981. Collared Doves (*Streptopelia decaocto*) in urban habitats. *Journal of Applied Ecology* 18: 41–62.

Coombs, CJF. 1978. *The Crows*. Batsford, London.

Corbet, GB, & HN Southern. 1964. *The Handbook of British Mammals*. Blackwell Scientific Publications, Oxford.

* Corbet, SJ, & NP Adams. 2006. *2005, The year of the bird at Dstl Porton Down; a survey to determine species present on the Porton Down SSSI and adjacent farmland.* Dstl & RSPB report.

* Corbin, GB. 1876a. Fieldfares, Sky Larks and Lapwings on Salisbury Plain. *The Zoologist* (2nd series) 11: 4872.

* Corbin, GB. 1876b. Crossbills on Salisbury Plain. *The Zoologist* (2nd series) 11: 4876.

* Corbin, GB. 1877. The Curlew of the Wiltshire Downs. *The Zoologist* (3rd series) 1: 257.

Cornwallis, RK. 1961. Four invasions of Waxwings during 1956–60. *British Birds* 54: 1–30.

Cornwallis, RK, & AD Townsend. 1968. Waxwings in Britain and Europe during 1965/66. *British Birds* 61: 97–118.

Cottridge, D, & K Vinicombe. 1996. *Rare Birds in Britain & Ireland, a Photographic Record.* Harper Collins/Birding World, London.

Coulson, JC. 1991. The population dynamics of culling Herring Gulls *Larus argentatus* and Lesser Black-backed Gulls *L. fuscus*. In: CM Perrins, J-D Lebreton & GJM Hirons. *Bird Population Studies: Relevance to Conservation and Management*. Oxford University Press, Oxford.

Coward, TA. 1920–26. *The Birds of the British Isles and their Eggs*. 3 volumes. Warne, London.

* Coy, JP. 1980. The animal bones. In: J Hallam (ed). A Middle Saxon Iron Smelting Site at Ramsbury, Wiltshire. *Medieval Archaeology* 24: 1–68 (41–51).

* Coy, JP. 1982. The animal bones. In: C Gingell (ed). Excavations of an Iron Age Enclosure at Groundwell Farm, Blunsdon St Andrew, 1976–7. *WANHM* 76: 33–75 (68–73).

* Coy, JP. 1983. *Animal bones from trial excavations at Potterne, Wiltshire, by the Wessex Archaeological committee 1983, with recommendations for bone retrieval in proposed future excavations.* AML [Ancient Monuments] No 4066.

* Coy, JP. 1986. *Animal Bones from Archaeological Evaluation at W139, 39 Brown Street, and W129, Gigant Street car park, Salisbury.* Unpublished report for Wessex Archaeology and Ancient Monuments Laboratory.

Cramp, S. 1971. Gulls nesting on buildings in Britain and Ireland. *British Birds* 64: 476–487.

Cramp, S (ed). 1985–92. *The Birds of the Western Palearctic*. Volumes IV-VI. Oxford University Press, Oxford.

Cramp, S, & KEL Simmons (eds). 1977–83. *The Birds of the Western Palearctic*. Volumes I-III. Oxford University Press, Oxford.

Cramp, S, & CM Perrins (eds). 1993–94. *The Birds of the Western Palearctic*. Volumes VII-IX. Oxford University Press, Oxford.

Cramp, S, A Pettet & JTR Sharrock. 1960. The irruption of tits in autumn 1957. *British Birds* 53: 49–77, 99–117, 176–192.

Cranswick, PA, JM Bowler, SN Delany, O Einarsson, A Gardarsson, JG McElwaine, OJ Merne, EC Rees & JH Wells. 1997. Numbers of Whooper Swans *Cygnus cygnus* in Iceland, Ireland and Britain in January 1995: results of the International Whooper Swan census. *Wildfowl* 47: 17–30.

* Cranswick, PA, PE Castle, SB Edwards, IJ Ferguson-Lees, B Quantrill, R Quantrill & R Turner. 2000. Completion of Wiltshire's Summer Tetrad Atlas (1995–2000) and Winter Mapping (1998/99 and 1999/2000) Surveys. *Hobby* 26: 104–111.

Cranswick, PA, K Colhoun, O Einarsson, JG McElwaine, A Gardarsson, MS Pollitt & EC Rees. 2002. The status and distribution of the Icelandic Whooper Swan population: results of the International Whooper Swan Census 2000. In: EC Rees, SL Earnst & JC Coulson (eds). *Proceedings of the Fourth International Swan Symposium, 2001. Waterbirds* 25 (Special Publication 1): 37–48.

Cranswick, PA, J Worden, RM Ward, HE Rowell, C Hall, AJ Musgrove, RD Hearn, SJ Holloway, AN Banks, GE Austin, LR Griffin, B Hughes, M Kershaw, MJ O'Connell, MS Pollitt, EC Rees & LE Smith. 2005. *The Wetland Bird Survey 2001–03: Wildfowl & Wader Counts.* BTO/WWT/RSPB/JNCC, Slimbridge.

* Crease, AJ. 1989. House Martins in Upavon 1987–88. *Hobby* 15: 61–63.

* Creighton, R. 1989. Redpoll and Siskin weights and migration. *Hobby* 15: 76–77.

* Crichton, AW. 1864. Hoopoe shot near Salisbury. *The Field*, 28 April.

Crick, H, A Banks & R Coombes. 2003. Findings of the National Peregrine Survey 2002. *BTO News* 248: 8–9.

Crick, HQP, & DA Ratcliffe. 1995. The Peregrine *Falco peregrinus* breeding population of the United Kingdom in 1991. *Bird Study* 42: 1–19.

Crick, HQP, & TH Sparks. 1999. Climate change related to egg-laying trends. *Nature* 399: 423–424.

Crick, HQP, SR Baillie, DE Balmer, RI Bashford, C Dudley, DE Glue, RD Gregory, JH Marchant, WJ Peach & AM Wilson. 1997. *Breeding Birds in the Wider Countryside: their conservation status (1971–1995)*. BTO Research Report No 187. British Trust for Ornithology, Thetford.

Crick, HQP, JH Marchant, DG Noble, SR Baillie, DE Balmer, LP Beaven, RH Coombes, IS Downie, SN Freeman, AC Joys, DI Leech, MJ Raven, RA Robinson & RM Thewlis. 2004. *Breeding Birds in the Wider Countryside: their conservation status 2003*. BTO Research Report No 353. British Trust for Ornithology, Thetford.

* Cross, DAE. 1949. Rookeries near Patney in 1948. *WANHM* 53: 87. [Author's name incorrectly published in *WANHM* as 'Gross'.]

* Cross, DAE. 1950. Rookeries near Patney, 1949. *WANHM* 53: 357–358.

* Cunnington, BH. 1930. The Origin and History of the Wiltshire Archaeological and Natural History Society. *WANHM* 45: 1–9.

Dance, SP (ed). 2003. *Letters on Ornithology 1804–1815 between George Montagu and Robert Anstice*. GC Book Publishers Ltd, Wigtown.

* Darby, M. 2003. WANHS and Natural History. In: JH Thomas (ed.). *Wiltshire Archaeological Society. The First 150 Years*. WAHNS, Devizes.

Dare, PJ. 1966. The breeding and wintering populations of the Oystercatcher *Haematopus ostralegus* L. in the British Isles. *Fisheries Invesigations*, series II, 25: 169.

Davies, AK. 1988. The distribution and status of the Mandarin duck *Aix galericulata* in Britain. *Bird Study* 35: 203–208.

Davies, NB. 1977. Prey selection and the search strategy of the Spotted Flycatcher. *Animal Behaviour* 25: 1016–1033.

Davies, NB. 1983. Polyandry, cloaca-pecking and sperm competition in Dunnocks. *Nature* 302: 334–336.

Davies, NB. 1986. Dunnock *Prunella modularis*. In: P Lack. 1986. *The Atlas of Wintering Birds in Britain and Ireland*. Poyser, Calton.

Davies, NB. 1992. *Dunnock Behaviour and Social Evolution*. Oxford University Press, Oxford.

Davies, NB. 2000. *Cuckoos, Cowbirds and Other Cheats*. Poyser, London.

Davies, NB, & M de L Brooke. 1991. Co-evolution of the Cuckoo and its hosts. *Scientific American* 264: 92–98.

Davis, AH (ed). 2001. *Avon Bird Report 2000*. Avon Ornithological Group.

Davis, P. 1993. The Red Kite in Wales: setting the record straight. *British Birds* 86: 295–298.

Davis, PG. 1982. Nightingales in Britain in 1980. *Bird Study* 29: 73–79.

* Davis, S, & S Corbett. 2004. Classic wildlife sites: The natural history and conservation of Porton Down. *British Wildlife* 15: 381–390.

Davis, T. 1794. *General View of the Agriculture of the County of Wiltshire*. Board of Agriculture, London.

Dean, AR, & L Svensson. 2005. 'Siberian Chiffchaff' revisited. *British Birds* 98: 396–410.

Delacour, J. 1954–64. *The Waterfowl of the World*, 4 volumes. Country Life, London.

Delany, SN. 1992. *Survey of introduced geese in Britain, summer 1991: provisional results*. WWT report, Slimbridge.

Delany, S. 1993. Introduced and escaped geese in Britain in summer 1991. *British Birds* 86: 591–599.

Delany, SN, JJD Greenwood & JS Kirby. 1992. *National Mute Swan Survey 1990*. WWT report, Slimbridge.

Delany, S, C Reyes, E Hubert, S Pihl, E Rees, L Haanstra & A van Strien. 1999. Results from the International Waterbird Census in the Western Palearctic and Southwest Asia, 1995 and 1996. *Wetlands International Publication No 54*, Wageningen, Netherlands.

Dementiev, P, & NA Gladkov (eds). 1951. *The Birds of the Soviet Union*. Volume 2 (English translation 1969). Israel program for Scientific Translation, Jerusalem.

Dennis, MC. 1994. The Eider influx of autumn 1993. In: B Ellis, J Hopper, MC Dennis & M Kennewell (eds). *The Birds of Nottinghamshire 1993*. Nottinghamshire Ornithological Society.

* Dent, G. 1907. Breeding of the Blue-headed Wagtail in Wiltshire. *British Birds* 1: 89–90.

Dickinson, EC (ed). 2003. *The 'Howard and Moore' Complete Checklist of the Birds of the World*, 3rd edition. Black, London.

Dobinson, HM, & AJ Richards. 1964. The effects of the severe winter of 1962/3 on birds in Britain. *British Birds* 57: 373–434.

Dodd, S, & K Meadows. 2003. *Breeding Bird Survey of the Cotswold Hills ESA 2002*. RSPB report.

Donald, PF. 2004. *The Skylark*. Poyser, London.

Donald, PF, & AD Evans. 1995. Habitat selection and population size of Corn Buntings *Milaria calandra* breeding in Britain in 1993. *Bird Study* 42: 190–204.

Doumeret, A. 1994. Milan noir *Milvus migrans*. In: D Yeatman-Bethelot and G Jarry (eds). *Nouvel Atlas des Oiseaux Nicheurs de France 1985–1989*: 160–163. Société Ornithologique de France, Paris.

Dowsett-Lemaire, F, & RJ Dowsett. 1986. European Reed and Marsh Warblers in Africa: migration patterns, moult and habitat. *Ostrich* 56: 65–85.

Dresser, HE. 1871–81. *A History of the Birds of Europe. Including all the species inhabiting the Western Palæarctic region*. Vol 5. Privately published.

Dresser, HE. 1902. *A Manual of Palæarctic Birds*, Part 1. Privately published.

Dunn, PJ, & PA Lassey. 1985. Little Gulls in Yorkshire. *Naturalist* 110: 91–98.

* Dunthorn, AA. 1965. An ornithological report for Blackmoor Copse reserve, 1962–63. *WANHM* 60: 161–166.

* Dunthorn, AA, & FP Errington. 1964. Casualties among birds along a selected road in Wiltshire. *Bird Study* 11: 168–182.

Dwight, J. 1925. The gulls (Laridae) of the world: their plumages, moults, variations, relationships and distribution. *Bulletin of the American Natural History Society* 52: 63–401.

Dymond, JN. 1991. *The Birds of Fair Isle*. Ritchie, Edinburgh.

Dymond, JN, PA Fraser & SJM Gantlett. 1989. *Rare Birds in Britain and Ireland*. Poyser, Calton.

* Edwards, SB. 1978. Extreme arrival and departure dates of migrants in Wiltshire. *Hobby* 4: 34–35.

* Edwards, SB. 1980. Feeding behaviour of Lesser Spotted Woodpecker (*Dendrocopos minor*). *Hobby* 6: 47.

* Edwards, SB. 1981. A mixed covey of Grey Partridges and Red-legged Partridge. *Hobby* 7: 44.

* Edwards, SB. 1983a. Greenshanks in Wiltshire 1969–81. *Hobby* 9: 46.

* Edwards, SB. 1983b. Black Terns in Wiltshire 1969–81. *Hobby* 9: 47.

Edwards, SB. 1983c. Spotted Flycatcher catching and eating large *Lepidoptera*. *British Birds* 76: 537.

* Edwards, SB. 1984a. Ruffs in Wiltshire 1973–1982. *Hobby* 10: 55.

* Edwards, SB. 1984b. Dunlins in Wiltshire 1973–1982. *Hobby* 10: 56.

* Edwards, SB. 1986. Ornithological sites in Wiltshire: No. 5: The Kennet Valley east of Marlborough. *Hobby* 12: 54–55.

* Edwards, SB. 1993. The Quail in Wiltshire. *Hobby* 19: 82–84.

* Edwards, SB. 1994. Tree Sparrow Survey 1993. *Hobby* 20: 89–91.

* Edwards, S, P Cranswick, R Turner, B Quantrill & R Quantrill. 1999. 1998/99: year four of the Wiltshire Summer Tetrad Atlas and year one of the Wiltshire Winter Mapping Survey. *Hobby* 25: 101–107.

* Edwards, SB, J Garnham & N Pleass. 1985. Collared Dove roost at Queens Park, Swindon. *Hobby* 11: 51–54.

* Edwards, SB, JR Govett, G Pictor & G Snowball. 1985. Roding Woodcock survey – 1984. *Hobby* 11: 46–50.

* Egerton, J, C Fitzgerald & C Gamble. 1993. The Animal Bone. In: A Graham & C Newman. Recent Excavations of Iron age and Romano-British Enclosures in the Avon Valley, Wilts. *WANHM* 86: 38–40.

Elkins, N, & P Yésou. 1998. Sabine's Gulls in western France and southern Britain. *British Birds* 91: 386–397.

Evans, AD. 1997. Cirl Buntings in Britain. *British Birds* 90: 267–282.

Evans, IM, & MW Pienkowski. 1991. World status of the Red Kite. *British Birds* 84: 171–187.

Evans, J, JD Wilson & SJ Browne. 1995. *The Effects of Organic Farming Regimes on Breeding and Winter Bird Population*. BTO Research Report 154. British Trust for Ornithology, Thetford.

Evans, LGR. 1994. *Rare Birds in Britain 1800–1990*. LGRE Productions Inc.

Evans, RJ. 2000. Wintering Slavonian Grebes in coastal waters in Britain and Ireland. *British Birds* 93: 218–226.

Everett, MJ. 1971. Breeding status of Red-necked Phalarope in Britain and Ireland. *British Birds* 64: 293–302.

* Fallon, MH, & CJ Gubbins. 1983. Birds of the Larkhill and Westdown Ranges. *The Adjutant* 13: 47–52.

Feare, CJ. 1990. Pigeon control: towards a humane alternative. *Environmental Health* 98: 155–156.

Feare, CJ. 1993. Rock Dove and Feral Pigeon. In: DW Gibbons, JB Reid & RA Chapman. 1993. *The New Atlas of Breeding Birds in Britain & Ireland 1988–91*. Poyser, London.

Ferguson-Lees, IJ. 1951. The Peregrine population of Britain. Parts I and II. *Bird Notes* 24: 202–208, 309–314.

* Ferguson-Lees, IJ. 1984. *The Birds of Longleat Estate*. Private report.

Ferguson-Lees, IJ, 1993. Hobby. In: Gibbons, DW, JB Reid & RA Chapman. 1993. *The New Atlas of Breeding Birds in Britain & Ireland 1988–91*. Poyser, London.

* Ferguson-Lees, J. 1994. Increase of the Hobby *Falco subbuteo* in Britain and in Wiltshire. *Hobby* 20: 92–99.

* Ferguson-Lees, J. 2000. Serin in southwest Wiltshire. *Hobby* 25: 90–91.

* Ferguson-Lees, IJ, & PE Castle. 1995. Beginning a tetrad atlas in Wiltshire. *Hobby* 21: 8–9.

Ferguson-Lees, J, & DA Christie. 2001. *Raptors of the World*. Helm, London.

Ferguson-Lees, IJ, & JTR Sharrock. 1969. Recent reports [Pallas's Sandgrouse]. *British Birds* 62: 452–456.

* Ferguson-Lees, IJ, & R Turner. 1996. 1995: Year 1 of the Wiltshire Tetrad Atlas. *Hobby* 22: 75–81.

Ferguson-Lees, IJ, & K Williamson. 1960. Recent reports and news. *British Birds* 53: 529.

Ferguson-Lees, IJ, PJ Grant, R Hudson, TR Inskipp, ICT Nisbet, JTR Sharrock, DW Snow & DIM Wallace. 1984. British Ornithologists' Union Records Committee: eleventh report (December 1983). *Ibis* 126: 440–444.

* Ferris, H. 1852. [Heronry at Beanwood, near Melksham]. *Naturalist* [Dr BR Morris's] 2: 34–5.

* Fisher, AB. 1905. Wild duck's nest in tree, at Potterne. *WANHM* 34: 109.

* Fisher, CH. 1884. Merlins in Wilts. *The Field*, 14 January.

* Fisher, CT. 1987. Roman and Later Animal Remains In: HR Hurst, DL Dartnell & C Fisher. Excavations at Box Roman Villa, 1967–8. *WANHM* 81: 49.

Fisher, J. 1940. *Watching Birds*. Penguin, London.

Fisher, J. 1947. *Bird Recognition*. Volume 1. Penguin, London.

Fisher, J. 1952. *The Fulmar*. Collins, London.

Fisher, J. 1953. The Collared Turtle Dove in Europe. *British Birds* 46: 153–181.

Fisher, J. 1954. *A History of Birds*. Houghton Mifflin, Boston.

Fisher, J. 1966. *The Shell Bird Book*. Ebury Press & Michael Joseph, London.

Fisher, J. 1967. *Thorburn's birds*. Ebury Press & Michael Joseph, London.

Fisher, S, K Holliday, C Howard, B Allen, P Grice, P Robertson, J Phillips & D Noble. 2005.The Farmland Bird Database – targeting agri-environment schemes on farmland birds. *British Wildlife* 17: 77–81.

Fitter, RSR. 1959. The status of the Great Black Woodpecker in the British Isles. *Bulletin of the British Ornithologists Club* 70: 79–87, 102–108, 109–113.

Fiuczynski, D, & D Nethersole-Thompson. 1980. Hobby studies in England and Germany. *British Birds* 73: 275–295.

Flegg, JJM. 1973. A study of Treecreepers. *Bird Study* 21: 287–302.

Forsman, D. 1999. *The Raptors of Europe and the Middle East*. Poyser, London.

Fox, AD. 1991. History of the Pochard breeding in Britain. *British Birds* 84: 83–97.

Fox, AD, & SJ Aspinall. 1987. Pomarine Skuas in Britain and Ireland in autumn 1985. *British Birds* 80: 404–421.

Fox, AD, & DG Salmon. 1988. Changes in non-breeding distribution and habitat of Pochard in Britain. *Biological Conservation* 46: 303–316.

Fox, AD, TA Jones, R Singleton & ADQ Agnew. 1994. Food supply and the effects of recreational disturbance on the abundance and distribution of wintering Pochard on a gravel pit complex in southern Britain. *Hydrobiologia* 279/280: 253–261.

* Fox, JJ. 1864a. Common Kite. *The Zoologist* 22: 9039.

* Fox, JJ. 1864b. Redwing singing in England. *The Zoologist* 22: 9040

* Francis, A. 1869. Velvet Scoter at Salisbury. *The Field*, 9 October.

Fraser, PA, & MJ Rogers. 2001. Report on scarce migrant birds in Britain in 1999. *British Birds* 94: 560–589.

Fraser, PA, & MJ Rogers. 2002. Report on scarce migrant birds in Britain in 2000. *British Birds* 95: 606–630.

Fraser, PA, & JF Ryan. 1995. Status of the Great Grey Shrike in Britain and Ireland. *British Birds* 88: 478–484.

Fraser, PA, PG Lansdown & MJ Rogers. 1999a. Report on scarce migrant birds in Britain in 1996. *British Birds* 92: 3–35.

Fraser, PA, PG Lansdown & MJ Rogers. 1999b. Report on scarce migrant birds in Britain in 1997. *British Birds* 92: 618–658.

Fraser, PA, PG Lansdown & MJ Rogers. 2000. Report on scarce migrant birds in Britain in 1998. *British Birds* 93: 588–641.

Fry, CH. 1984. *The Bee-eaters*. Poyser, Calton.

Fry, CH, S Keith & EK Urban. 1988. *The Birds of Africa*. Volume III. Academic Press, London.

Fuller, M. 1995. *The Butterflies of Wiltshire*. Pisces Press, Newbury.

Fuller, RJ. 1982. *Bird Habitats in Britain*. Poyser, Calton.

Fuller, RJ. 1993. Farmland birds in trouble. *BTO News* 184: 1.

Fuller, RJ, & ACB Henderson. 1992. Distribution of breeding songbirds in Bradfield Woods, Suffolk, in relation to vegetation and coppice management. *Bird Study* 39: 73–88.

Fuller, RJ, JK Baker, RA Morgan, R Scroggs & M Wright. 1985. Breeding populations of the Hobby *Falco subbuteo* on farmland in the southern Midlands of England. *Ibis* 127: 510–516.

Fuller, RJ, RD Gregory, DW Gibbons, JH Marchant, JD Wilson, SR Baillie & N Carter. 1996. Population Declines and Range Contractions among Lowland Farmland Birds in Britain. *Conservation Biology* 9: 1425–1441.

Fuller, RJ, ACB Henderson & AM Wilson. 1999. The Nightingale in England – problems and prospects. *British Wildlife* 10: 221–230.

Fuller, RJ, P Studdard & CM Ray. 1989. The distribution of breeding songbirds within mixed coppice woodland in Kent, England, in relation to vegetation age and structure. *Annales Zoologici Fennici* 26: 265–275.

Furness, RW. 1987. *The Skuas*. Poyser, Calton.

* Gale, JH. 1881. Storm Petrel in Wilts. *The Field*, 17 December.

* Gallagher, J. 2005. *Wessex Tree Sparrow Recovery Report 2004*. RSPB report.

Game Conservancy Trust. 1961–2005. *National Gamebag Census*. Game Conservancy Trust, Fordingbridge.

Gantlett, S. 2002. The Rose-coloured Starling invasion of summer 2002. *Birding World* 15: 284–286.

* Gardiner, JS. 1855. Occurrence of the Creamcoloured Courser on Salisbury Plain. *The Zoologist* 13: 4913.

* Gardiner, JS. 1887. List of Marlborough birds. *MCNHS* 1887: 106–117.

Garner, M, & D Quinn. 1997. Identification of Yellow-legged Gulls in Britain. *British Birds* 90: 25–62.

Garner, M, D Quinn & B Glover. 1997. Identification of Yellow-legged Gulls in Britain, Part 2. *British Birds* 90: 369.

* Gater, CW. 1885. Quail in Dec. [near Salisbury] *The Field*, 3 January.

* Geddes, I. 2000. *Hidden Depths: Wiltshire's Geology and Landscapes*. Ex Libris Press, Bradford-on-Avon.

Gelling, M. 1987. Anglo-Saxon eagles. In: T Turville-Petre & M Gelling (eds). Studies in honour of Kenneth Cameron. *Leeds Studies in English. New Series* XVIII. University of Leeds.

Gibbons, DW. 1997. Moorhen. In: WJM Hagemeijer & MJ Blair (eds). *The EBCC Atlas of European Breeding Birds: their distribution and abundance*. Poyser, London.

Gibbons, DW, & S Wotton. 1996. The Dartford Warbler in the United Kingdom in 1994. *British Birds* 89: 203–212.

Gibbons, DW, MI Avery & AF Brown. 1996. Population trends of breeding birds in the United Kingdom since 1800. *British Birds* 89: 291–305.

Gibbons, DW, JB Reid & RA Chapman. 1993. *The New Atlas of Breeding Birds in Britain & Ireland 1988–91*. Poyser, London.

Gilbert, G. 2002. The status and habitats of Spotted Crakes *Porzana porzana* in Britain in 1999. *Bird Study* 49: 79–86.

* Gilbert, HA. 1916. Marsh Warbler (*Acrocephalus palustris*). *WANHM* 39: 404.

* Gillam, B. 1965. The status of the Lesser Spotted Woodpecker (*Dendrocopus minor*) in Wiltshire, 1957–64. *WANHM* 60: 167–169.

* Gillam, B. 1976. British Trust for Ornithology national Rookery survey 1975. *Hobby* 2: 32–40.

* Gillam, B. 1977. *A checklist of the birds of the Imber Ranges*. MoD.

* Gillam, B. 1981. Sample census of rookeries 1980. *Hobby* 7: 33–37.

* Gillam, B. 1984. The Breeding Birds of Sunnyhill Farm, Pewsey 1962–1983. *Hobby* 10: 37–47.

* Gillam, B (ed). 1993. *The Wiltshire Flora*. Pisces Publications, Newbury.

* Gillam, B. 1996. The breeding birds of Home Covert, Roundway, Devizes; 1981–1996. *Hobby* 22: 82–99.

* Gillam, B, & R Turner. 1981. The birds of Imber Range. *The Adjutant* 11: 28–38.

* Gillam, B, MH Smith & R Turner. 1980. *The birds of SPTA (W) Imber Range*. Duplicated report.

Gladstone, HS. 1928. Notes on a Discourse on the Emigration of British Birds: 1780. *British Birds* 22: 34–35.

Glue, DE. 1990. Breeding biology of the Grasshopper Warbler in Britain. *British Birds* 83: 131–145.

Glue, DE, & R Morgan. 1972. Cuckoo hosts in British habitats. *Bird Study* 19: 187–192.

Glue, DE, & E Murray. 1984. Cuckoo hosts in Britain. *BTO News* 134: 5.

* Goddard, EH. 1907. Peregrine at Clyffe Pypard. *WANHM* 35: 150.

* Goddard, EH. 1909. White-tailed Eagle shot at Marden. *WANHM* 36: 140.

* Goddard, EH. 1913. Ring Ouzel (*Turdus torquatus*). *WANHM* 38: 114–115.

* Goddard, EH. 1916. White Starling. *WANHM* 39: 402.

* Goddard, EH. 1920a. Great Crested Grebe. *WANHM* 41: 182.

* Goddard, EH. 1920b. Little Owl at Clyffe Pypard. *WANHM* 41: 183.

* Goddard, EH. 1921. Bird Notes. *WANHM* 41: 430.

* Goddard, EH. 1922a. Marsh Warbler nesting. *WANHM* 42: 77–78.

* Goddard, EH. 1922b. Great Crested Grebe. *WANHM* 42: 78.

* Goddard, EH. 1922c. White and Pied Birds. *WANHM* 42: 79.

* Goddard, EH. 1929. *Bibliography of Wiltshire*. Wiltshire Education Committee, Trowbridge.

* Goddard, EH. 1930. The Future Work of the Society. *WANHM* 45: 224–232.

Gooch, S, S Baillie & TR Birkhead. 1991. The impact of Magpies *Pica pica* on songbird populations: retrospective investigation of trends in population density and breeding success. *Journal of Applied Ecology* 28: 1068–1086.

Goode, D. 1981. *Report on the Nature Conservancy Council's Working Group on Lead Poisoning in Mute Swans*. Nature Conservancy Council, London.

Goodwin, D. 1952. The colour varieties of Feral Pigeons. *London Bird Report* 16: 35–36.

Goodwin, D. 1954. Notes on Feral Pigeons. *Avicultural Magazine* 60: 190–213.

Gosler, AG. 1993. *The Great Tit*. Hamlyn, London.

Gould, J. 1873. *Introduction to the Birds of Great Britain*. Folio, London.

* Gover, JEB, A Mawer & FM Stenton. 1939. *The Place-names of Wiltshire*. English Place-name Society, volume 16. Cambridge.

* Govett. JR. 1984. Ornithological sites in Wiltshire: No 4: The Valley of the River Frome west of Trowbridge. *Hobby* 10: 53–55.

* Govett, JR. 1988. Ornithological sites in Wiltshire: No. 6: Fyfield Down. *Hobby* 14: 56–58.

* Govett, JR. 1994. The 20th anniversary of the founding of WOS. *Hobby* 20: 4–7.

* Grant, J. 1866. Great Grey Shrike in Wilts. *The Field*, 8 December.

* Grant, J. 1867. Fork-tailed Petrel and Hawfinches in Wilts. *The Field*, 2 February.

* Grant, J. 1868. Rednecked Grebe and Black-toed Gull [Richardson's Skua] in Wilts. *The Field*, 25 January.

* Grant, J. 1869. Spurwinged Goose in Wilts. *The Field*, 18 September.

* Grant, J. 1870a. Rare birds in Wiltshire. *The Zoologist* (2nd series) 5: 2185.

* Grant, J. 1870b. Notes on Birds near Devizes; Late Quail's Nest. *The Field*, 17 September.

* Grant, J. 1872. Ornithological Notes on Birds from Wilts. *The Field*, 6 January.

Grant, PJ. 1986. *Gulls: a guide to identification*. 2nd edition. Poyser, Calton.

* Grearson, KJ. 1995. Cotswold Water Park. *Hobby* 21: 10–11.

* Grearson, KJ. 1998a. Squacco Heron at the Cotswold Water Park: the first 20th century record. *Hobby* 24: 94–95.

* Grearson, KJ. 1998b. The origins and movements of colour-ringed large gulls recorded in Wiltshire. *Hobby* 24: 109–112.

* Great Bustard Group. 2000. Report of the first steering Group meeting. *Otis* 2.

* Green, G. 2000. The breeding birds of Biss Wood, West Ashton near Trowbridge, 1987 to 2000. *Hobby* 26: 112–124.

Green, GP. 2004. *The Birds of Dorset*. Helm, London.

* Green, RAM. 1975. *A Bibliography of Printed Works Relating to Wiltshire 1920–1960*. Wiltshire County Council Library & Museum Service, Trowbridge.

Green, RE, DP Hodson & PR Holness. 1997. Survival and movements of Stone Curlews *Burhinus oedicnemus* ringed in England. *Ringing & Migration* 18: 102–112.

Gregory, RD, & SR Baillie. 1998. Large-scale habitat use of some declining British birds. *Journal of Applied Ecology* 35: 785–799.

Gregory, RD, RI Bashford, DB Balmer, JH Marchant, AM Wilson & SR Baillie. 1996. *The Breeding Bird Survey 1994–1995*. BTO, Thetford, Norfolk.

Gregory, RD, DG Noble, PA Cranswick, LH Campbell, MM Rehfisch & SR Baillie. 2001. *The state of the UK's birds 2000*. RSPB, BTO and WWT, Sandy.

Gregory, RD, NI Wilkinson, DG Noble, JA Robinson, AF Brown, J Hughes, D Procter, DW Gibbons & CA Galbraith. 2002. The population status of birds in the United Kingdom, Channel Islands and Isle of Man: an analysis of conservation concern 2002–2007. *British Birds* 95: 410–448.

Gribble, FC. 1983. Nightjars in Britain and Ireland in 1981. *Bird Study* 30: 165–176.

* Grose, D. 1957. *The Flora of Wiltshire*. WANHS, Devizes.

* Griffiths, R. 1988. The Freeths Wood Common Bird Census 1983–87. *Hobby* 14: 52–55.

* Grinsted, S, & M Lang. 1999. A survey of the Dipper *Cinclus cinclus* in the By Brook catchment. *Hobby* 25: 108–111. [Author's name incorrectly published in *Hobby* as 'Grinstead'.]

Gurney, JH. 1921. *Early Annals of Ornithology*. Witherby, London.

* Gwatkin, RG. 1923. Little Owl. *WANHM* 42: 256.

Hagemeijer, WJM, & MJ Blair (eds). 1997. *The EBCC Atlas of European Breeding Birds: their distribution and abundance*. Poyser, London.

Hall, JE, KJ Kirby & AM Whitbread. 2004. *National Vegetation Classification field guide to woodland*. JNCC, Peterborough.

* Hall, PS. 1900. Nesting of the Marsh-Warbler in Wiltshire. *The Zoologist* 4: 555.

Halliday, J, & LH Campbell. 1979. *A Survey of the Birds of the Rivers Avon and Stour*. RSPB & Wessex Water Authority.

* Halliday, JH. 1956. Bird notes. *MCNHS* 97: 9.

* Halliday, JH, & HT Randolph. 1955. Handlist of the birds of the Marlborough District (10 mile radius). *MCNHS* 96: 1–24.

Hambleton, E, & M Maltby. 2004. *Animal Bones from Excavations at Battlesbury Bowl, Wiltshire*. Report prepared for Wessex Archaeology, Bournemouth University.

* Hamilton, E. 1952. *The Year Returns*. Michael Joseph, London.

* Hamilton-Dyer, S. 1999. Animal Bone. In: JI McKinley. Further Excavations of an Iron Age and Romano-British Enclosed Settlement at Figheldean, near Netheravon. *WANHM* 92: 7–32 (25–27).

* Hamilton-Dyer, S. 2000. Faunal Remains. In: M Rawlings. Excavations at Ivy Street and Brown Street, Salisbury 1994. *WANHM* 93: 20–62 (45–51).

* Hamzij, MJ, & R Turner. 2005. Rustic Bunting at Bradford-on-Avon. *Hobby* 31: 108–109.

* Harcourt, R. 1965. *Animal Remains, Longbridge Deverill*. AML [Ancient Monuments] No 1626.

* Harcourt, R. 1971. Animal Bones from Durrington Walls. In: GJ Wainwright & IH Langworth. Durrington Walls: Excavations 1966–1968. *Reports of the Research. Committee of the Society of Antiquaries of London*. No XXIX, Dorking.

Hardy, E. 1969. Mistle thrushes and mistletoe berries. *Bird Study* 16: 191–192.

Harper, D. 1995. Studies of West Palearctic birds. 194. Corn Bunting *Miliaria calandra*. *British Birds* 88: 401–422.

Harradine, J. 1983. Sport shooting in the United Kingdom; some facts and figures. In: FJ Leeuwenberg & IR Hepburn (eds). *Proceedings of the Second Meeting of the Working Group on Game Statistics, Zoetermeer, 1982*: 63–83.

* Harris, G. 2004. *Breeding Reed Buntings in the Cotswold Water Park: a compilation of survey data (2003 and 2004) & comparison with baseline data (1993, 1994, 1999 and 2002)*. Cotswold Water Park Society, Cirencester.

* Harris, G. 2005. The Cotswold Water Park: the beginning and the future. *Hobby* 31: 130–135.

* Harris, JM. 1893. Storm Petrel in Wilts. *The Field*, 2 December.

* Harris, S. 1866. Ash-coloured Shrike in Wilts. *The Field*, 6 January.

Harrison, C. 1982. *An Atlas of the Birds of the Western Palaearctic*. Collins, London.

* Harrison, DP. 1906a. Brown variety of the Common Moorhen at Clyffe Pypard. *WANHM* 34: 434.

* Harrison, DP. 1906b. Montagu's Harrier (*Circus cineraceus*). *WANHM* 34: 434.

* Harrison, DP. 1906. Hobby (*Falco subbuteo*). *WANHM* 34: 434.

* Harrison, DP. 1907. Woodchat at Aldbourne. *WANHM* 35: 150.

* Harrison, DP. 1910. Manx Shearwater in Wilts. *The Field*, 13 September.

* Harrison, DP. 1911a. Manx Shearwater at Wootton Bassett. *WANHM* 37: 161.

* Harrison, DP. 1911b. Pied Flycatcher. *WANHM* 37: 161–162.

* Harrison, DP. 1914. Incursion of Waxwings. Wiltshire. *British Birds* 7: 263–264.

Harrison, JA, DG Allan, LG Underhill, M Herremans, AJ Tree, V Parker & CJ Brown. 1997. *The Atlas of Southern African Birds*. 2 volumes. BirdLife South Africa, Johannesburg.

Harrison, JM. 1953. *The Birds of Kent*, volume I. Witherby, London.

Harrison, JM, JG Harrison & D Harrison. 1969. Some preliminary results from the release of hand-reared Gadwall. *WAGBI Report and Year Book 1968–69*: 37–40.

Harrison, PA, PM Berry & TP Dawson (eds). 2001. *Climate change and nature conservation in Britain and Ireland: modelling natural resource responses to climate change (the MONARCH project)*. UKCIP technical report, Oxford.

Harrop, AHJ. 2002. The Ruddy Duck in Britain. *British Birds* 95: 123–128.

* Harrop, AHJ, & M Collinson. 2003. The 1864 Wiltshire 'Steppe Buzzard': A review on behalf of the British Ornithologists' Union Records Committee. *British Birds* 96: 247–249.

* Hart, E. 1880. Rough-legged Buzzards in Wiltshire. *The Zoologist* (3rd series) 4: 143.

* Hart Smith, TN. 1887. Ornithological Section. *MCNHS* 1887: 103–117.

Hartert, E, FCR Jourdain, NF Ticehurst & HF Witherby. 1912. *A Hand-list of British Birds*. Witherby, London.

* Harting, JE. 1871. Great Bustard in Wilts. *The Field*, 14 January.

* Harting, JE. 1872. British Heronries – Wiltshire. *The Zoologist* (2nd series) 7: 3266.

* Harting, JE. 1891a. The present visitation of Bustards – Wilts. *The Field*, 28 February.

* Harting, JE. 1891b. The recent visitation of Bustards. *The Zoologist* (3rd series) 15: 103–106.

Harting, JE. 1896. Cream-coloured Courser in Jersey. *The Zoologist* (3rd series) 20: 435.

Hartley, C. 2004. Little Gulls at sea off Yorkshire in autumn 2003. *British Birds* 97: 448–455.

Harvey, HJ. 1979. Great Crested Grebe breeding on rivers. *British Birds* 71: 385–386.

Hastings, R. 1988. The Feral Rock Dove. *British Birds* 81: 652.

Hatchwell BJ, AF Russell, ADC MacColl, DJ Ross, MK Fowlie, & A McGowan. 2004. Helpers increase long-term but not short term productivity in cooperatively breeding long-tailed tits. *Behavioral Ecology* 15: 1–10.

Hawkes, B. 1986. Ring-necked Parakeet (Rose-ringed Parakeet). In: P Lack. *The Atlas of Wintering Birds in Britain and Ireland*. Poyser, Calton.

* Hayward, B. [1791–1886]. A nineteenth-century bird watcher; being extracts from the Common Place Book kept by Benjamin Hayward (1791–1886). Transcribed by CJ Jacobs. 1952. *WANHM* 54: 332–338.

Heinrich, B. 1990. *Ravens in Winter*. Barrie & Jenkins, London.

Hett, WS. 1936. *Aristotle: Minor Works. On Marvellous Things Heard*. Heinemann, London.

Heubeck, M. 2002. The decline of Shetland's Kittiwake population. *British Birds* 95: 118–122.

Hewett, W Jnr. 1844. *The History and Antiquities of the Hundred of Compton, Berkshire*. John Snare, Reading.

Hewett, W Snr. 1895–1911. Notes on the Natural History of the Compton District. *Transactions of the Newbury District Field Club* 5: 29–41.

Hewson, C, R Fuller, B Mayle & K Smith. 2004. Possible impacts of Grey Squirrels on birds and other wildlife. *British Wildlife* 15: 183–191.

* Hext, RFA. 1898. Supposed Woodchat in Wilts. *The Field*, 20 August.

Hirons, G, & M Linsley. 1989. Counting Woodcock. *Game Conservancy Annual Review* 20: 47–48.

Hoeltzel, AR. 1989. Territorial behaviour of the European Robin *Erithacus rubecula*: the importance of vegetation density. *Ibis* 131: 432–426.

* Hogan, AR. 1860. Localities of *Sylvia Luscinia*. *The Zoologist* 18: 7105,

Hollom, PAD. 1952. *The popular handbook of British birds.* Witherby, London.

Holloway, S. 1996. *The Historical Atlas of Breeding Birds in Britain and Ireland, 1875–1900.* Poyser, London.

Hollyer, JN. 1970. The invasion of Nutcrackers in autumn 1968. *British Birds* 63: 353–373.

* Holme, F. 1843. Note on the occurrence of the Orange-legged Hobby. *The Zoologist* 1: 78.

* Hony, GB. 1912. The 1912 "Wreck" of the Little Auk. *British Birds* 6: 69.

* Hony, GB. 1914a. Notes on the birds of Wiltshire. *British Birds* 7: 281–290.

* Hony, GB. 1914b. *Local names of birds in MSS catalogue of birds in the museum.* Devizes Museum, Devizes.

* Hony, GB. 1915a. Notes on the birds of Wiltshire. *WANHM* 39: 1–13.

* Hony, GB. 1915b. Status of Little Owl in Wiltshire. *British Birds* 9: 21.

* Hony, GB. 1916a. On the Status of the Common Curlew and the Black Grouse in Wiltshire. *British Birds* 10: 44–46.

* Hony, GB. 1916b. On the Status of the Common Curlew and the Black Grouse in Wiltshire. *British Birds* 10: 67.

* Hony, GB. 1916c. Little Owl in Wiltshire. *WANHM* 39: 403.

* Hony, GB. 1916d. Glossy Ibis. *WANHM* 39: 403.

* Hony, GB. 1916e. Quail. *WANHM* 39: 405.

* Hony, GB. 1917. A Bibliography of Wiltshire Zoology. *WANHM* 39: 491–498.

Hosking, E. 1970. *An Eye for a Bird.* Hutchinson, London.

Hough, C. 1998. Place-Name Evidence for Old English Bird-Names. *Journal of the English Place-Name Society* 30: 60–76.

* Howells, RL. 1986a. Hen Harriers on Larkhill and Westdown Ranges. *The Adjutant* 16: 12–16.

* Howells, RL. 1986b. Hen Harriers on Larkhill and Westdown Ranges. *Hobby* 12: 47–53.

* Howells, RL. Undated. *Hen Harriers on Larkhill and Westdown Ranges*. Westdown Conservation Group.

* Howells, RL, & SM Palmer. 1989. Birds of Boscombe Down. *Hobby* 15: 78–87.

Hudson, R. 1965. The spread of the Collared Dove in Britain and Ireland. *British Birds* 58: 105–139.

Hudson, R. 1972. Collared Doves in Britain and Ireland during 1965–70. *British Birds* 65: 139–155.

Hudson, R. 1973. *Early and Late Dates for Summer Migrants.* BTO Guide 15. British Trust for Ornithology, Tring.

Hudson, R. 1974. News and Comment [Feral parakeets near London]. *British Birds* 67: 33, 174.

Hudson, R, & GA Pyman. 1968. *A Guide to the Birds of Essex*. Essex Birdwatching and Preservation Society, Southend-on-Sea.

Hudson, WH. 1892. *The Naturalist in La Plata*. Chapman & Hall, London.

Hudson, WH. 1903. *Hampshire Days*. Longmans, Green, London.

Hudson, WH. 1904. *Green Mansions: a Romance of the Tropical Forest*. Dent, London.

* Hudson, WH. 1910. *A Shepherd's Life: Impressions of the South Wiltshire Downs*. Methuen, London.

Hudson, WH. 1918. *Far Away and Long Ago: a History of my Early Life*. Dent, London.

Hughes, B, J Criado, SN Delany, U Gallo-Orsi, AJ Green, M Grussu, C Perennou & JA Torres. 1999a. *The status of the North American Ruddy Duck* Oxyura jamaicensis *in the Western Palearctic: towards an action plan for eradication.* Report by The Wildfowl & Wetlands Trust to the Council of Europe.

Hughes, B, JS Kirby & JM Rowcliffe. 1999b. Waterbird conflicts in Britain and Ireland: Ruddy Ducks *Oxyura jamaicensis*, Canada Geese *Branta canadensis* and Cormorants *Phalacrocorax carbo*. *Wildfowl* 50: 77–99.

Hume, RA. 1976. Inland records of Kittiwakes. *British Birds* 69: 62–63.

* Hussey-Freke, AD. 1871. Goosander in Wilts. *The Field*, 18 February.

Hutchinson, CD, & B Neath. 1978. Little Gulls in Britain and Ireland. *British Birds* 71: 563–582.

* Iles, M. 1996. Animal bone from the Winterbourne Romano-British settlement. In: AB Powell, MJ Allen & I Barnes. *Archaeology in the Avebury area, Wiltshire; Recent discoveries along the line of the Kennet Valley Foul Sewer Pipeline, 1993*. Wessex Archaeology Report No 8. Trust for Wessex Archaeology Ltd, Salisbury.

* im Thurn, EF. 1867. Little Auk in Wilts. *The Field*, 5 October.

* im Thurn, EF. 1870. *Birds of Marlborough*. Perkins, Marlborough, & Simpkin, London.

* im Thurn, EF. 1873. Sea Woodcock. *The Zoologist* (2nd series) 8: 3371.

* im Thurn, EF. 1876. Birds of Marlborough, Appendix. *MCNHS*.

Inglis, IR, AJ Isaacson, RJP Thearle & NJ Westwood. 1990. The effects of changing agricultural practice on Woodpigeon *Columba palumbus* numbers. *Ibis* 132: 262–272.

Isenmann, P, & MA Bouchet. 1993. French distribution area and taxonomic status of the Southern Great Grey Shrike *Lanius elegans meridionalis*. *Alauda* 61: 223–227.

* Jacob, E. 1884. Merlins in Wilts. *The Field*, 5 January.

* Jackson, MV, & PA Cranswick. 2002. A gazetteer of Wiltshire sites. *Hobby* 27: 102–105.

James, P (ed). 1996. *Birds of Sussex*. Sussex Ornithological Society.

* James, RMR. 1997. Bean Geese at Downton. *Hobby* 23: 88–89.

Jefferies, R. 1878. *The Gamekeeper at Home; or, Sketches of Natural History and Rural Life*. Smith, Elder, London.

* Jefferies, R. 1879a. *Wildlife in a Southern County*. Smith, Elder, London

Jefferies, R. 1879b. *The Amateur Poacher*. Smith, Elder, London.

Jefferies, R. 1880a. *Hodge and His Masters*. 2 volumes. Smith, Elder, London.

Jefferies, R. 1880b. *Round About a Great Estate*. Smith, Elder, London.

Jeffs, C, & L Lock. 1998. *Review of Breeding Waders in South West England*. RSPB report.

John, AWG, & J Roskell. 1985. Jay movements in autumn 1983. *British Birds* 78: 611–637.

Johns, CA. 1862. *British Birds in their Haunts*. SPCK, London.

Johnson, RF, & G Johnson. 1990. Reproductive ecology of Feral Pigeons. In: J Pinowski, & JD Summers-Smith (eds). *Granivorous Birds in the Agricultural Landscape*. INTECOL, Warsaw.

Johnson, SR, & DR Herter. 1989. *The Birds of the Beaufort Sea*. BP Exploration, Anchorage.

* Jones, N, & P Dillon. 1987. *Dialect in Wiltshire*. Wiltshire County Council Library & Museum Service, Trowbridge.

Jonsson, L. 1998. Yellow-legged Gulls and yellow-legged Herring Gulls in the Baltic. *Alula* 3: 74–100.

Jourdain, FCR. 1910. Reviews. *British Birds* 3: 344–346.

* Jourdain, FCR. 1914 . Breeding of the Dipper in Wiltshire. *British Birds* 7: 230–231.

Józefik, M. 1969–70. Studies on the Squacco Heron *Ardea ralloides* (Scop.). *Acta Ornthologica* 11: 103–262; 12: 57–102, 394–504.

Keith, S, EK Urban & CH Fry. 1992. *The Birds of Africa*. Volume 4. Academic Press, London.

Keith, WJ. 1965. *Richard Jefferies: a Critical Study*. University of Toronto Press, Canada.

Kelsall, JE, & PW Munn. 1905. *The Birds of Hampshire and the Isle of Wight*. Witherby, London.

Kelsey, MG, GH Green, MC Garnett & PV Hayman. 1989. Marsh Warblers in Britain. *British Birds* 82: 239–256.

* Kemur, T. 1851. Occurrence of the Rough-legged Buzzard (*Buteo lagopus*) on Marlborough Downs. *The Zoologist* 9: 3054.

* Kennedy, CJ. 1966. *Handlist of the birds of the Marlborough district*. Marlborough College Natural History Society.

Kenward, RE, SS Walls, KH Hodder, M Pahkala, SN Freeman & VR Simpson. 2000. The prevalence of non-breeders in raptor populations: evidence from rings, radio-tags and transect surveys. *Oikos* 91: 271–279.

Kershaw, M. 2002. Pochard. In: CV Wernham, MP Thoms, JH Marchant, JA Clark, GM Siriwardena & SR Baillie. *The Migration Atlas: movements of the birds of Britain and Ireland*. Poyser, London.

Kershaw, M, & PA Cranswick. 2003. Numbers of wintering waterbirds in Great Britain, 1994/5–1998/9: I. Wildfowl and selected waterbirds. *Biological Conservation* 111: 91–104.

Kershaw, M, & B Hughes. 2002. *The winter status and distribution of Ruddy Ducks* Oxyura jamaicensis *in the UK, 1966/67–1999/2000*. WWT Wetlands Advisory Service report to the Central Science Laboratory.

* Kersley, R. 1981. The 1980 Nightingale survey in Wiltshire. *Hobby* 7: 38–40.

* Kersley, R, & R Marsh. 1983. Partial migration of Greenfinches (*Carduelis chloris*) to and from Chippenham, Wiltshire. *Hobby* 9: 42–45.

Key, RW. 1982. Kittiwakes in Derbyshire. *Derbyshire Bird Report 1981*: 51–52.

Kingsley, C. 1855. *Glaucus or The Wonders of the Shore*. Macmillan, London.

Kirby, JS, KK Kirby & SJ Woodfall. 1989. Curlew Sandpipers in Britain and Ireland in autumn 1988. *British Birds* 82: 399–409.

* Kirkaldy, JN. 1968. Salisbury Plain. *The Adjutant* 1: 6–10.

Kirkman, FB. 1912. *The British Bird Book*. Volume 3. Jack, London.

Knowlton D. 1973. *The Naturalist in Southern England*. David & Charles, Newton Abbot.

Knox, AG. 1988. The taxonomy of the Rock/Water Pipit superspecies *Anthus petrosus*, *spinoletta* and *rubescens*. *British Birds* 81: 206–211.

Knox, AG. 1990a. The identification of Crossbill and Scottish Crossbill. *British Birds* 83: 89–94.

Knox, AG. 1990b. The sympatric breeding of *Loxia curvirostra* and *L. scotica* and the evolution of crossbills. *Ibis* 132: 452–466.

Knox, AG, M Collinson, AJ Helbig, DT Parkin & G Sangster. 2002. Taxonomic recommendations for British birds. *Ibis* 144: 707–710.

Knox, AG, AJ Helbig, DT Parkin & G Sangster. 2001. The taxonomic status of Lesser Redpoll. *British Birds* 94: 260–267.

* Knubley, EP. 1909. Little Bustard at Avebury. *WANHM* 36: 143.

* Knubley, EP. 1910a. Note on Specimens of Wiltshire Birds recently purchased by the Society's Museum. *WANHM* 36: 486–487.

* Knubley, EP. 1910b. Storm Petrel at Edington. *WANHM* 36: 487.

Krivenko, VG, VG Vinogradov, A Green & C Perennou. 1994. The Ferruginous Duck – *Aythya nyroca*. In: GM Tucker & MF Heath (eds). *Birds in Europe: their conservation status.* Birdlife, Cambridge.

Lack, D. 1956. *Swifts in a Tower*. Methuen, London.

Lack, D, & E Lack. 1951. The breeding biology of the Swift *Apus apus*. *Ibis* 93: 502–546.

Lack, P. 1986. *The Atlas of Wintering Birds in Britain and Ireland.* Poyser, Calton.

* Lambert, HB. 1913. Quail in Wilts. *The Field*, 6 September.

Langston, R, R Gregory & R Adams. 2002. The status of the Hawfinch in the UK 1975–1999. *British Birds* 95: 166–173.

Lamb, T. 1880. Ornithologica Bercheria. *The Zoologist* 4: 313–325.

Lambrecht, K. 1917. Die Ausbildung und Geschichte der europäischen Vogelwelt. *Aquila* 24: 191–221.

* Legg, J. 1780. *A DISCOURSE on the Emigration of British Birds*...[see page 74]. Printed and sold for the author by Collins and Johnson of Salisbury; sold also by Fielding and Walker of Paternoster Row.

Lever, C. 1977. *The Naturalised Animals of the British Isles*. Hutchinson, London.

Leverton, T. 1993. Migrant Ring Ouzels on the South Downs. *British Birds* 86: 253–266.

* Lewis, NJ, & AR Bush. 1988–90. *The Imber Conservation Group Raptor and Owl Nestbox Project 1987–1989 Reports.* Imber Conservation Group, Warminster.

* Lewis, NJ, AR Bush & L Spackman. 1991–2001. *The Imber Conservation Group Raptor and Owl Nestbox Project 1990–2000 Reports.* Imber Conservation Group, Warminster.

Limbert, M. 1984. Vagrant races of Willow Tit in Britain. *British Birds* 77: 122.

Little, B, & RW Furness. 1985. Long-distance moult migration by British Goosanders *Mergus merganser*. *Ringing & Migration* 6: 77–82.

Lloyd, C, ML Tasker & K Partridge. 1991. *The Status of Seabirds in Britain and Ireland.* Poyser, London.

Lock, L, & K Cook. 1998. The Little Egret in Britain: a successful colonist. *British Birds* 91: 273–280.

* Locker, A. 2000. Animal bone. In: AJ Lawson. *Potterne 1982–5, Animal Husbandry in Late Prehistoric Wiltshire.* Wessex Archaeology Report No 117: 101–132. Trust for Wessex Archaeology Ltd, Salisbury.

Lockley, RM. 1935. My island and our life there. 15 – The first migratory bird-marking station in Britain. *The Countryman* 10: 423–441.

London Natural History Society. 1964. *Birds of the London Area.* Rupert Hart-Davies, London.

London Natural History Society. 2002. *The Breeding Birds of the London Area*. LNHS.

Looker, SJ, & C Porteous. 1966. *Richard Jefferies: Man of the Fields*. John Baker, London.

Lovegrove, R, G Williams & I Williams. 1994. *Birds in Wales*. Poyser, London.

Macdonald, JD, & CHB Grant. 1951. On the Author and Reference of *Ardea lentiginosa*. *Bulletin of the British Ornithologists' Club* 71: 30.

* Macpherson, AH. 1888. Woodchat in Wilts. *The Zoologist* (3rd series) 12: 429.

Madge, S, & H Burn. 1988. *Wildfowl: An Identification Guide to the Ducks, Geese and Swans of the World.* Helm, London.

Madge, S, & P McGowan. 2002. *Pheasants, Partridges & Grouse: a guide to the pheasants, partridges, quails, grouse, guineafowl, buttonquails and sandgrouse of the world*. Helm, London.

* Major, JE. 1979. Nesting behaviour of Willow Tits in south-west Wiltshire. *Hobby* 5: 44.

Malling Olsen, K, & H Larsson. 2003. *Gulls of Europe, Asia and North America*. Helm, London.

* Maltby, M. 1990. The exploitation of animals in the Stonehenge Environs in the Neolithic and Bronze Age. In: JC Richards. *Stonehenge Environs Project*. English Heritage Archaeological Report No 16. Historic Buildings and Monuments Commission for England, London.

* Maltby, M. 1992. The Animal Bone. In: C Gingell. *Marlborough Downs, a Later Bronze Age landscape and its origins*. Monograph 1. Wiltshire Archaeological and Natural History Society, Devizes.

Marchant, JH, & RD Gregory. 1992. Seed-eater declines: new results from farmland CBC. *BTO News* 189: 8–9.

Marchant, JH, R Hudson, SP Carter & PA Whittington. 1990. *Population Trends in British Breeding Birds*. British Trust for Ornithology and Nature Conservancy Council, Tring.

* Mardle, DV. 1975. The Cotswold Water Park and its birds. *Hobby* 1: 20–23.

Mardle, DV, & MA Ogilvie. 1975. The occurrence of escaped waterfowl in Gloucestershire. *Gloucestershire Bird Report 1975*: 26–28.

Marsden, SJ. 2000. Impact of Disturbance on Waterfowl Wintering in a Dockland Redevelopment Area. *Environmental Management* 26: 207–213.

* Marsh, GS. 1842–1862. Manuscript notes. Interleaved in: W Yarrell. 1837–43. *A History of British Birds*. Van Voorst, London. [Annotated copy in the Ornithological Library of the Natural History Museum, Tring.]

* Marsh, GS. 1859a. Occurrence of Goldenwinged Woodpecker in England. *The Zoologist* 17: 6327.

* Marsh, GS. 1859b. Sea birds found inland. *The Zoologist* 17: 6492.

* Marsh, GS. 1859c. Three British Spotted Woodpeckers. *The Zoologist* 17: 6535.

Mason, CF, & SM MacDonald. 1999. Habitat use by Lapwings and Golden Plovers in a largely arable landscape. *Bird Study* 46: 89–99.

* Maton, G. 1843. Aves. Pp 65–74. In: *The Natural History of a Part of the County of Wiltshire, comprehended within the distance of ten miles round the City of Salisbury.* Nichols, London.

* Matthews, RO. 1909. Nesting of the Snipe in Wiltshire. *British Birds* 3: 28.

Mauro, I. 1994. Some remarks on new data on Spotted Crakes at Molsbroek-Lakeren (East Flanders) during the 1992 breeding season. *Oriolus* 60: 30–33.

* Maxfield, B. 1996. The birds of Corsham Lake. *Hobby* 22: 100–104.

* Maxfield, B. 2000. Gull-billed Tern at the Cotswold Water Park. *Hobby* 26: 94.

May, R, & J Fisher. 1953. A Collared Turtle Dove in England. *British Birds* 46: 51–54.

* Maysmor, R. 1851. Waxen Chatterer at Devizes. *Naturalist* [Dr BR Morris] 1: 116.

* McGrath, T. 1995. Curlew count 1994: a survey of the Curlew *Numenius arquata* in the Braydon Forest area of North Wiltshire. *Hobby* 21: 97–104.

* McLaren, JS. 1975. A waterway survey. *Hobby* 1: 32–34.

Mead, CJ, & JA Clark. 1987. Report on bird-ringing for 1987. *Ringing & Migration* 8: 135–200.

Mearns, B, & R Mearns. 1988. *Biographies for Birdwatchers.* Academic Press, London.

Meininger, PL, & R Flamant. 1998. Breeding populations of Mediterranean Gulls in the Netherlands and Belgium. *Sula* 12: 127–135.

Meininger, PL, & UG Sørensen. 1993. Egypt as a major wintering area of Little Gulls. *British Birds* 86: 407–410.

Merikallio, E. 1958. *Finnish Birds: their distribution and numbers*. Tilgmann, Helsinki.

Messenger, D. 1993. Spring passage of Little Gulls across Northern England. *British Birds* 86: 397–406.

* Meyrick, E. 1895. List of Birds of the Marlborough District. *MCNHS* 1895: 37–54.

* Meyrick, E. 1906. List of the Birds of the Marlborough District. *MCNHS* 1906: 32–50.

Mikkola, H. 1976. Owls killing and killed by other owls and raptors in Europe. *British Birds* 69: 144–154.

Mikkola, H. 1983. *The Owls of Europe*. Poyser, Calton.

Millon, A, & V Bretagnolle. 2004. Busard Saint-Martin. In: J-M Thiollay & V Bretagnolle (eds). *Rapaces nicheurs de France: Distribution, effectifs et conservation.* Delachaux et Niestlé, Paris.

Milne, BS. 1959. Variation in a population of Yellow Wagtails. *British Birds* 52: 281–295.

Mionnet, A. 2004. Milan royal. In: J-M Thiollay & V Bretagnolle (eds). *Rapaces nicheurs de France: Distribution, effectifs et conservation.* Delachaux et Niestlé, Paris.

Mitchell, PI, SF Newton, N Ratcliffe & TE Dunn. 2004. *Seabird Populations of Britain and Ireland.* Poyser, London.

Monk, JF. 1963. The past and present status of the Wryneck in the British Isles. *Bird Study* 10: 112–132.

Montagu, G. 1796. Descriptions of three rare species of British Birds. *Transactions of the Linnæan Society* 4: 35–43.

Montagu, G. 1802. *Ornithological Dictionary; or, Alphabetical Synopsis of British Birds.* 2 volumes. J White, Exeter.

Montagu, G. 1813. *Supplement to the Ornithological Dictionary or Synopsis of British Birds*. Exeter.

Moore, NW. 1957. The past and present status of the Buzzard in the British Isles. *British Birds* 50: 173–197.

Moore, PG. 2002. Ravens (*Corvus corax corax* L.) in the British landscape: a thousand years of ecological biogeography in place-names. *Journal of Biogeography* 29: 1039–1045.

Moreau, RE. 1951. The British status of the Quail and some problems of its biology. *British Birds* 44: 257–276.

* Morgan, R. 1975. Breeding bird communities on chalk downland in Wiltshire. *Bird Study* 22: 71–83.

Morgan, R. 1982. The breeding biology of the Nightingale *Luscinia megarhynchos* in Britain. *Bird Study* 29: 67–72.

* Morres, AP. 1865a. Lesser Spotted Woodpecker near Salisbury. *The Zoologist* 23: 9539.

* Morres, AP. 1865b. Sclavonian Grebe near Salisbury. *The Zoologist* 23: 9565.

* Morres, AP. 1877a. Curlews breeding near Salisbury. *The Zoologist* (3rd series) 1: 106.

* Morres, AP. 1877b. Rough-legged Buzzards near Tisbury, Wilts. *The Zoologist* (3rd series) 1: 175–176.

* Morres, AP. 1877c. The Merlin in South Wilts. *The Zoologist* (3rd series) 1: 226.

* Morres, AP. 1877d. Pied Flycatcher near Salisbury. *The Zoologist* (3rd series) 1: 297.

* Morres, AP. 1877e. Peregrine Falcons on the spire of Salisbury Cathedral. *The Zoologist* (3rd series) 1: 450.

* Morres, AP. 1877f. Rare birds of Wiltshire and other Occasional Notes. *The Zoologist* (3rd series) 1: 52, 53, 55, 106, 175, 255, 297, 450.

* Morres, AP. 1878–85. On the occurrence of some of the rarer species of birds in the neighbourhood of Salisbury. *WANHM* 17: 95–127; 18: 183–213, 289–318; 20: 154–185; 21: 211–255; 22: 83–106, 191–211.

* Morres, AP. 1878a. Hoopoes near Salisbury. *The Zoologist* (3rd series) 2: 24–25.

* Morres, AP. 1878b. Great Grey Shrike nesting near Salisbury. *The Zoologist* (3rd series) 2: 56–58.

* Morres, AP. 1881. Ornithological notes from Salisbury. *The Zoologist* (3rd series) 5: 489.

* Morres, AP. 1882. The Peregrines of Salisbury Cathedral. *The Zoologist* (3rd series) 6: 18–20.

* Morres, AP. 1889. White-winged Black Tern near Salisbury. *The Zoologist* (3rd series) 13: 393.

* Morres, AP. 1897a. Bird life in Salisbury. A royal visitor. *Wilts Notes and Queries* 2: 228–233.

* Morres, AP. 1897b. Occurrence of the Little Bustard near Salisbury. *Salisbury & Winchester Journal* 16 October.

* Morres, AP. 1897c. The Salisbury Ornithological Calendar. *Salisbury & Winchester Journal*, 25 December.

* Morres, AP. 1898. Bird life at Salisbury. The Peregrine at home. *Wilts Notes and Queries* 2: 508–512.

* Morres, AP. 1900a. Bird life near Salisbury. *Salisbury & Winchester Journal*, 20 January.

* Morres, AP. 1900b. Ornithological Notes from Salisbury. *The Field*, 27 January.

Morris, A, D Burges, RJ Fuller, AD Evans & KW Smith. 1994. The status and distribution of Nightjars *Caprimulgus europaeus* in Britain in 1992. *Bird Study* 41: 181–191.

Morris, FO. 1851–57. *A History of British Birds*. Groombridge, London.

* Moses, H. 1870. Spurwinged Goose in Wiltshire. *The Zoologist* (2nd series) 11: 2105.

Mountfort, G. 1957. *The Hawfinch*. Collins, London.

Muffett, T. 1655. *Healths Improvement: or, Rules Comprising and Discovering The Nature, Method and Manner of Preparing all sorts of Food used in this Nation.* Samuel Thomson, London.

Mullens, WH. 1921. In: JH Gurney *Early Annals of Ornithology.* Witherby, London.

Mullens, WH, & HK Swann. 1917. *A bibliography of British ornithology from the earliest times to the end of 1912.* Macmillan, London.

Mullens, WH, HK Swann & FCR Jourdain. 1920. *A Geographical Bibliography of British Ornithology from the earliest times to the end of 1918.* Witherby, London.

* Mussel-White, DW. 1909. Nesting dates of the Lesser Redpoll in Cambridgeshire, Bedfordshire and Wiltshire. *British Birds* 3: 161–162 .

Murton, RK. 1958. The breeding of Woodpigeon populations. *Bird Study* 5: 157–183.

Murton, RK. 1965. *The Woodpigeon*. Collins, London.

Murton, RK. 1968. Breeding, migration and survival of Turtle Doves. *British Birds* 61: 193–212.

Murton, RK, & MG Ridpath. 1962. The autumn movements of the wood-pigeon. *Bird Study* 9: 7–41.

Murton, RK, & NJ Westwood. 1966. The foods of the Rock Dove and Feral Pigeon. *Bird Study* 13: 130–146.

Murton, RK, CFB Coombs & RJP Thearle. 1972. Ecological studies of the Feral Pigeon *Columba livia* var. II. Flock behaviour and social organisation. *Journal of Applied Ecology* 9: 875–889.

Murton, RK, NJ Westwood & AJ Isaacson. 1964. The feeding habits of the Woodpigeon *Columba palumbus*, Stock Dove *C. oenas* and Turtle Dove *Streptopelia turtur*. *Ibis* 106: 174–188.

Murton, RK, NJ Westwood & AJ Isaacson. 1974. A study of woodpigeon shooting: the exploitation of a natural animal population. *Journal of Applied Ecology* 11: 61–81.

Musgrove, AJ. 2002. The non-breeding status of the Little Egret in Britain. *British Birds* 95: 62–80.

Mustoe, S, I Barber, E Kelly & B Fraser. 1998. *Ornithological Survey of the Cotswold Hills ESA April–July 1997.* RSPB report.

Naylor, KA. 1996. *A Reference Manual of Rare Birds in Great Britain and Ireland.* Privately published.

Nelder, JA. 1962. A statistical examination of the Hastings Rarities. *British Birds* 55: 283–298.

Nethersole-Thompson, D. 1975. *Pine Crossbills.* Poyser, Berkhamsted.

Nethersole-Thompson, D. 1992. *In Search of Breeding Birds.* Peregrine Books, Leeds.

Nethersole-Thompson, D, & M Nethersole-Thompson. 1986. *Waders: their Breeding, Haunts and Watchers*. Poyser, Calton.

* Newham, R. 1913. Quail on Salisbury Plain. *The Field*, 30 August.

* Newman, E. 1871. Two more Bustards. *The Zoologist* (2nd series) 6: 2526–2529.

Newson, SE. 2000. *Colonisation and range expansion of inland breeding Great Cormorants* Phalacrocorax carbo *in England.* PhD Thesis.

Newton, A [With Hans Gadow]. 1893–96. *A Dictionary of Birds, with Contributions from R. Lydekker, Charles S. Roy and R.W. Shufeldt.* Black, London.

Newton, I. 1970. Irruptions of Crossbills in Europe. In: A Watson (ed). *Animal Populations in relation to their Food Resources.* Blackwell, Oxford.

Newton, I. 1972. *Finches*. Collins, London.

Newton, I. 1979. *Population Ecology of Raptors*. Poyser, Calton.

Newton, I. 1986. *The Sparrowhawk*. Poyser, Calton.

Newton, I. 1993. Studies of West Palearctic birds. 192. Bullfinch. *British Birds* 86: 638–648.

Newton, I, & M Marquiss. 1976. Occupancy and success of nesting territories in the European Sparrowhawk. *Raptor Research* 10: 65–71.

Newton, I, M Marquiss, DN Weir & D Moss. 1977. Spacing of Sparrowhawk nesting territories. *Journal of Animal Ecology* 46: 425–441.

Newton, I, I Wyllie & A Asher. 1991. Mortality causes in British Barn Owls *Tyto alba*, with a discussion of aldrin-dieldrin poisoning. *Ibis* 133: 162–169.

Nicholson, EM. 1957. The rarer birds of prey. Their present status in the British Isles. Montagu's Harrier. *British Birds* 50: 146–147.

Nicholson, EM, & IJ Ferguson-Lees. 1962. The Hastings Rarities. *British Birds* 55: 299–384.

* Nield, AW. 1889. Pochard breeding at Chippenham. *The Field*, 3 August.

Nightingale, B, & K Allsopp. 1997. The ornithological year 1996. *British Birds* 90: 538–548.

Norris, CA. 1960. The breeding distributions of thirty bird species in 1952. *Bird Study* 7: 129–184.

North, PM. 1979. Relating Grey Herons' survival rates to winter weather conditions. *Bird Study* 26: 23–28.

* Nurse, ME. 1951. The Redwing and Fieldfare enquiry in Wiltshire. *WANHM* 54: 68–72.

Nyagolov, K, L Profirov, T Michev & M Dimitrov. 2003. Observations on breeding Rosy Starlings in Bulgaria. *British Birds* 96: 242–246.

O'Connor, RJ, & CJ Mead. 1984. The Stock Dove in Britain, 1930–80. *British Birds* 77: 181–201.

O'Connor, RJ, & RA Morgan. 1982. Some effects of the weather conditions on the breeding of the Spotted Flycatcher *Muscicapa striata* in Britain. *Bird Study* 29: 41–48.

O'Connor, RJ, & M Shrubb. 1986. *Farming and Birds*. Cambridge University Press, Cambridge.

Ogilvie, MA. 1986. The Mute Swan *Cygnus olor* in Britain 1983. *Bird Study* 33: 121–137.

Ogilvie, MA. 1998. Rare breeding birds in the United Kingdom in 1995. *British Birds* 91: 438.

Ogilvie, MA. 2003. European Honey-buzzards in the UK – correction to breeding totals. *British Birds* 91: 145.

Ogilvie, MA, & AKM St Joseph. 1976. Dark-bellied Brent Geese in Britain and Europe, 1955–76. *British Birds* 69: 422–439.

Ogilvie, MA, & the Rare Breeding Birds Panel. 2000. Non-native birds breeding in the UK in 1998. *British Birds* 93: 428–433.

Ogilvie, MA, & the Rare Breeding Birds Panel. 2001. Rare Breeding Birds in the United Kingdom in 1999. *British Birds* 94: 344–381.

Ogilvie, MA, & the Rare Breeding Birds Panel. 2002. Rare Breeding Birds in the United Kingdom in 2000. *British Birds* 95: 542–582.

Ogilvie, MA, & the Rare Breeding Birds Panel. 2004. Non-native birds breeding in the United Kingdom 2002. *British Birds* 97: 633–637.

* Olivier, D. 1885. Raven in Wilts. *The Field*, 30 May.

Osborne, PE. 2002. *Application to the Department for Environment, Food and Rural Affairs for a Licence to re-introduce Great Bustards* Otis tarda *to Britain*. Commissioned by the Great Bustard Group on behalf of the Great Bustard Consortium.

Osborne, PE, & A Martin. 2001. *Re-introduction of the Great Bustard to Britain: a discussion paper*. Consultancy report to the Great Bustard Group.

Owen, JH. 1916–1932. Some breeding habits of the Sparrowhawk, (nine parts, 1916–21 and four sequels). *British Birds* 10: 2–10, 26–37, 50–59, 74–86, 106–115; 12: 61–65, 74–82; 13: 114–124; 15: 74–77; 20: 114–120; 25: 151–155, 238–243; 26: 34–40.

Owen, M, & M Dix. 1986. Sex ratios in some common British wintering ducks. *Wildfowl* 37: 104–112.

Owen, M, GL Atkinson-Willes & DG Salmon. 1986. *Wildfowl in Great Britain*, 2nd edition. Cambridge University Press, Cambridge.

Palmer, EM, & DK Ballance. 1968. *The Birds of Somerset*. Longmans, London.

* Palmer, SM. 1987. A study of the birds of Dinton, Wiltshire. *Hobby* 13: 45–54.

* Palmer, SM. 1990–91. WOS [Farming and Birds] Conference 1989. *Hobby* 16: 50–56; 17: 72–77.

* Palmer, SM (ed). 1991. *Wiltshire Birds*. Wiltshire County Council Library & Museum Service, Trowbridge.

* Palmer, SM. 1992. Winter Bird Survey Chirton Gorse, Larkhill 1991/92. *Hobby* 18: 77–80.

* Paris, JA. 1838. *A Biographical Sketch of the late William George Maton, M.D.* Richard & John Edward Taylor, London.

Parr, SJ. 1994a. Changes in the population size and nest-sites of Merlins *Falco columbarius* in Wales between 1970 and 1991. *Bird Study* 41: 42–47.

Parr, SJ. 1994b. Population changes of breeding Hobbies *Falco subbuteo* in Britain. *Bird Study* 41: 131–135.

Parrinder, EM. 1989. Little Ringed Plover *Charadrius dubius* in Great Britain in 1984. *Bird Study* 36: 147–153.

Parslow, JLF. 1973. *Breeding Birds of Britain and Ireland, a historical survey.* Poyser, Berkhamsted.

Payn, WH. 1978. *The Birds of Suffolk*, 2nd edition. Ancient House Press, Ipswich.

Payn, WH. 1991. The introduction of the Chukar. *British Birds* 84: 68.

Peach, WJ, SR Baillie & L Underhill. 1991. Survival of British Sedge Warblers *Acrocephalus schoenobaenus* in relation to West African rainfall. *Ibis* 133: 300–305.

Peach, WJ, C du Feu & J McMeeking. 1995. Site tenacity and survival rates of Wrens *Troglodytes troglodytes* and Treecreepers *Certhia familiaris* in a Nottinghamshire wood. *Ibis* 137: 497–507.

Peakall, DB. 1962. The past and present status of the Red-backed Shrike in Great Britain. *Bird Study* 9: 198–216.

Peal, REF. 1968. The distribution of the Wryneck in the British Isles. *Bird Study* 15: 111–126.

Pearson, DJ, BJ Small & PR Kennerley. 2002. Eurasian Reed Warbler: the characters and variation associated with the Asian form *fuscus*. *British Birds* 95: 42–61.

* Peart, DEM. 1981a. Common Sandpiper breeding in Wiltshire. *Hobby* 7: 45.

* Peart, DEM. 1981b. Little Ringed Plover in South Wiltshire 1979 and 1980. *Hobby* 7: 46–47.

Peck, AL. 1970. *Aristotle: Historia Animalium* Vol II. Heinemann, London.

* Peirson, LG. 1919. *Hand-list of the Birds of the District. Marlborough and ten miles round.* Marlborough College Natural History Society, Marlborough.

* Peirson, LG. 1939. Handlist of the birds of the Marlborough district. *MCNHS* 1939: 24–41.

* Peirson, LG. 1948. The cold of early 1947 and the birds. *WANHM* 52: 245–246.

* Peirson, LG. 1951. Autumn migration of passerines. *WANHM* 54: 73–74.

* Peirson, LG. 1955. A note on the effects of the extremely cold weather in early 1947 on the birds in our district. *MCNHS* 1955: 70.

* Peirson, LG. 1959. *Wiltshire Birds.* Wiltshire Archaeological and Natural History Society, Devizes.

* Peirson, LG, & NT Walford. 1930. Handlist of the birds of the Marlborough district. *MCNHS* 1930: 40–52.

Penhallurick, R. 1978. *The Birds of Cornwall and the Isles of Scilly*. Headland, Penzance.

Pennant, T. 1768. *British Zoology*, 2nd edition. Benjamin White, London.

* Penrose, FG. 1907. Redshank nesting in Wilts. *WANHM* 35: 150.

* Penrose, FG. 1910a. Black Redstart in Wiltshire. *British Birds* 4: 368.

* Penrose, FG. 1910b. Black Redstart at Downton. *WANHM* 36: 488.

* Penrose, FG. 1912. Early nesting of Common Snipe in Wiltshire. *British Birds* 5: 336.

Percival, S. 1991. Population trends in British Barn Owls – a review of some possible causes. *British Wildlife* 2: 131–140.

Perring, FH, & SM Walters. 1962. *Atlas of the British Flora*. Botanical Society of the British Isles, London & Edinburgh.

Perrins, CM, JP Lebreton & GM Hirons (eds). 1991. *Bird Population Studies. Relevance to Conservation and Management*. Oxford University Press, Oxford.

Peterson, R, G Mountfort & PAD Hollom. 1954 *et seq. A Field Guide to the Birds of Britain and Europe*. Collins, London.

* Phillips, EC. 1860. Great Northern Diver. *The Field*, 15 December.

* Pickard-Cambridge, O. 1880. Peregrine Falcons on Salisbury Cathedral Spire. *The Zoologist* 1880, 300–301.

Picozzi, N, & D Weir. 1976. Dispersal and causes of death of Buzzards. *British Birds* 69: 193–201.

* Pictor, GD, & R Turner. 1998. 1997: Year Three of the Wiltshire Tetrad Atlas. *Hobby* 24: 103–108.

Piersma, T. 1986. Breeding waders in Europe: a review of population size estimates and a bibliography of information sources. *Wader Study Group Bulletin* 48: supplement.

* Piggott S. 1962. *The West Kennet Long Barrow.* Ministry of Works Archaeological Report No 4. HMSO, London.

Pithon, JA, & C Dytham. 1999. Census of the British Ring-necked Parakeet *Psittacula krameri* population by simultaneous counts of roosts. *Bird Study* 46: 112–115.

Pitman, CMR. 1984. *A Naturalist at Home.* Wiltshire Library & Museum Service, Trowbridge.

* Pleass, NJ. 1994. Great Grey Shrike *Lanius excubitor* of the eastern race *pallidirostris. Hobby* 20: 105–107.

* Pocock, E. 1869. Speckled Diver in Wilts. *The Field,* 25 December.

* Pollard, J. 1982. The Shearwater Osprey. *Hobby* 8: 37–40.

* Pollard, J. 1983. Ornithological sites in Wiltshire: No. 3: Shearwater. *Hobby* 9: 40–42.

* Pomroy, JM. 2004. Late nesting Swifts using nestbox. *Hobby* 30: 117–119.

Pollitt, MS, PA Cranswick, AJ Musgrove, C Hall, RD Hearn, JA Robinson & SJ Holloway. 2000. *The Wetland Bird Survey 1998–99: Wildfowl and Wader Counts.* BTO/WWT/RSPB/JNCC, Slimbridge.

Poole, AF. 1989. *Ospreys.* Cambridge University Press, Cambridge.

Potts, GR. 1980. The effects of modern agriculture, nest predation and game management on the population ecology of partridges *Perdix perdix* and *Alectoris rufa. Advanced Ecology Research* 11: 2–79.

Potts, GR. 1986. *The Partridge: Predation and Conservation.* Collins, London.

Potts, GR, & MI Avery. 2000. [Statement on Magpies and songbirds] Game Conservancy/RSPB

* Powell, AF. 1870. The Grey Phalarope [near Salisbury]. *The Field,* 29 October.

* Powell, APE. 1868. Great Snipe in Wilts. *The Field,* 3 October.

Prater, AJ. 1981. *Estuary Birds of Britain and Ireland.* Poyser, Calton.

Prater, AJ. 1989. Ringed Plover *Charadrius hiaticula* breeding population of the United Kingdom in 1984. *Bird Study* 36: 154–159.

* Prendergast, EDV. 1971. Checklist of the birds of the Larkhill Artillery Ranges. *The Adjutant* 4: 33–42.

Prendergast, EDV, & JV Boys. 1983. *The Birds of Dorset.* David & Charles, Newton Abbot.

Prestt, I. 1965. A recent enquiry into the breeding status of some of the smaller birds of prey and crows in Britain. *Bird Study* 12: 196–221.

Prestt, I, & AA Bell. 1966. An objective method of recording breeding distributions of common birds of prey in Britain. *Bird Study* 13: 277–283.

* Preston, TA. 1865. Dates of Oviposition of Birds in the Neighbourhood of Marlborough. *The Zoologist* 1865.

* Preston, TA. 1869a. Rednecked Phalarope at Marlborough. *The Zoologist* (2nd series) 4: 1951.

* Preston, TA. 1869b. Winter Puffin at Marlborough. *The Zoologist* (2nd series) 4: 1951–1952.

* Preston, TA. 1870. Little Gull &c., near Marlborough. *The Zoologist* (2nd series) 5: 2143.

* Preston, TA. 1871. Quail nesting in Wiltshire. *The Zoologist* (2nd series) 6: 2729.

* Preston, TA. 1884. *Results of 20 Years' Observations on Botany, Entomology, Ornithology and Meteorology, taken at Marlborough College, 1865–84.* Marlborough College Archives.

Prince, P, & R Clarke. 1993. The Hobby's breeding range in Britain – what factors have allowed it to expand? *British Wildlife* 4: 341–346.

* Prior, MG. 1999. Caspian Gull at Cotswold Water Park. *Hobby* 25: 91–92.

Prŷs-Jones, RP. 1984. Migration patterns of the Reed Bunting, *Emberiza schoeniclus,* and the dependence of wintering distribution on environmental conditions. *Le Gerfaut* 74: 15–37.

* Pye-Smith, G. 1926. Breeding of the Icterine Warbler in England. *British Birds* 19: 311.

Pyman, GA. 1959. The status of the Red-crested Pochard in the British Isles. *British Birds* 52: 42–56.

Pyman, GA, & CB Wainwright. 1952. The breeding of the Gull-billed Tern in Essex. *British Birds* 45: 337–339.

* Quantrill, B. 2005. The Breeding Bird Survey: what it reveals about population trends of common birds in Wiltshire. *Hobby* 31: 136–145.

Rackham, O. 1986. *The History of the Countryside.* Dent, London.

Radford, MC. 1966. *The Birds of Berkshire and Oxfordshire.* Longmans, London.

* Radnor, Lord. 1910. Greenland Falcon killed near Downton. *WANHM* 36: 487–488.

Ratcliffe, D. 1980. *The Peregrine Falcon*. Poyser, Calton.

Ratcliffe, D. 1997. *The Raven*. Poyser, London.

Raven, SJ, & JC Coulson. 1997. The distribution and abundance of *Larus* Gulls nesting on buildings in Britain and Ireland. *Bird Study* 44: 13–34.

* Rawlence, EA. 1908. Yellow Shanks. *WANHM* 35: 508.

Ray, J. 1678. *The Ornithology of Francis Willughby. Translated into English and enlarged with Many Additions*. Privately published, London.

Rebecca, GW, & IP Bainbridge. 1998. The breeding status of the Merlin *Falco columbarius* in Britain in 1993–94. *Bird Study* 45: 172–187.

Reed, T. 1985. Estimates of British breeding wader populations. *Wader Study Group Bulletin* 48: 11–12.

Rees, EC, & JM Bowler. 1997. Fifty years of swan research by WWT. *Wildfowl* 47: 249–264.

Rehfisch, MM, GE Austin, MJS Armitage, PW Atkinson, SJ Holloway, AJ Musgrove & MS Pollitt. 2003. Numbers of wintering waterbirds in Great Britain and the Isle of Man (1994/1995–1998/1999): II. Coastal waders (Charadrii). *Biological Conservation* 112: 329–341.

Reid-Henry, D, & C Harrison. 1988. *The History of the Birds of Britain*. Collins with Witherby, London.

* Rice, C. 1952. The Redstart in Wiltshire: report of an enquiry conducted during 1949–50–51. *WANHM* 54: 327–331.

* Rice, C. 1956. The Corn Bunting in Wiltshire: report of an enquiry conducted during 1951–52–53–54. *WANHM* 56: 430–436.

* Rice, C. 1970. Wintering Blackcaps in Wiltshire. *WANHM* 65: 12–15.

Richardson, RA, MJ Seago & AC Church. 1957. Collared Doves in Norfolk: a bird new to the British List. *British Birds* 50: 239–246.

Riddiford, N, & P Findlay. 1981. *Seasonal Movements of Summer Migrants*. British Trust for Ornithology, Tring.

Ridgill, SC, & AD Fox. 1990. *Cold weather movements of waterfowl in western Europe*. IWRB Special Publication No 13, Slimbridge.

Rivière, BB. 1930. *A History of the Birds of Norfolk*. Witherby, London.

Robertson, HA. 1990. Breeding of Collared Doves *Streptopelia decaocto* in rural Oxfordshire, England. *Bird Study* 37: 73–83.

* Robinson, HW. 1914. Pomatorhine Skua in Wiltshire. *British Birds* 8: 150.

Robinson, JA. 1999. Migration and morphometrics of the Red-breasted Merganser *Mergus serrator* in northern Eurasia and the implications for conservation of this species in Britain and Ireland. *Wildfowl* 50: 139–148.

Robinson, RA, GM Siriwardena & HQP Crick. 2005. Size and trends of the House Sparrow *Passer domesticus* population in Great Britain. *Ibis* 147: 552–562.

* Rock, P. 2003a. *Roof-nesting Gulls in Wiltshire: an overview and results of a survey conducted in June 2003*. Report for Wiltshire Ornithological Society.

Rock, P. 2003b. *Roof-nesting Gulls in Worcester. Survey conducted in May 2003*. Report to Worcester City Council.

* Rock, P. 2004a. *Roof-nesting Gulls in Wiltshire: follow-up survey conducted in June 2004*. Report for Wiltshire Ornithological Society.

* Rock, P. 2004b. Roof-nesting Gulls in Wiltshire: an overview and results of a survey conducted in June 2003 for the Wiltshire Ornithological Society. *Hobby* 30: 105–116.

* Rock, P. 2005. Roof-nesting Gulls in Wiltshire 2004. *Hobby* 31: 120–129.

Rogers, MJ. 1982. Ruddy Shelducks in Britain 1965–79. *British Birds* 75: 446–455.

Rogers, MJ, & the Rarities Committee. 1990. Report on rare birds in Great Britain in 1989. *British Birds* 83: 439–496.

Rogers, MJ, & the Rarities Committee. 1991. Report on rare birds in Great Britain in 1990. *British Birds* 84: 449–505.

Rogers, MJ, & the Rarities Committee. 1992. Report on rare birds in Great Britain in 1991. *British Birds* 85: 507–554.

Rogers, MJ, & the Rarities Committee. 1993. Report on rare birds in Great Britain in 1992. *British Birds* 86: 447–540.

Rogers, MJ, & the Rarities Committee. 2000. Report on rare birds in Great Britain in 1999. *British Birds* 93: 512–567.

Rogers, MJ, & the Rarities Committee. 2001. Report on rare birds in Great Britain in 2000. *British Birds* 94: 452–504.

Rogers, MJ, & the Rarities Committee. 2002. Report on rare birds in Great Britain in 2001. *British Birds* 95: 476–528.

* Rolls, JC. 1975a. Bird ringing. *Hobby* 1: 26–28.

* Rolls, JC. 1975b. The status of wildfowl in Wiltshire No. 1. *Hobby* 1: 29–32.

* Rolls, JC. 1976a. The status of wildfowl in Wiltshire No. 2. *Hobby* 2: 40–42.

* Rolls, JC. 1976b. Great Crested Grebe censuses. *Hobby* 2: 43–44.

* Rolls, JC. 1977. The status of wildfowl in Wiltshire No. 3. *Hobby* 3: 47–48.

* Rolls, JC. 1978. The status of wildfowl in Wiltshire No. 4. *Hobby* 4: 41–42.

* Rolls, JC. 1979. The status of wildfowl in Wiltshire No. 5. *Hobby* 5: 36–37.

* Rolls, JC. 1980. The status of wildfowl in Wiltshire No. 6. *Hobby* 6: 39.

* Rolls, JC. 1981. The status of wildfowl in Wiltshire No. 7. *Hobby* 7: 40–41.

* Rolls, JC. 1991. Red-necked Phalarope *Phalaropus lobatus* Lacock Gravel Pits, 16 August 1990. *Hobby* 17: 54–55.

* Rolls, JC. 1992. The Wildfowl & Wetlands Trust summer survey of introduced geese 1991. *Hobby* 18: 81–83.

* Rolls, JC, & SJ Tyler. 1971. An analysis of wildfowl counts in Wiltshire made between the winters 1949/50 to 1969/70. *WANHM* 66: 10–19.

Rose, PM, & DA Scott. 1997. *Waterfowl Population Estimates, Second Edition*. Wetlands International Publication 44. Wetlands International, Wageningen, Netherlands.

* Rowland, WH. 1864. White-tailed Eagle in Savernake Forest. *The Zoologist* 22: 9020.

* RSPB. 2003. *Stone curlews at Porton Down 2003*. Wessex Stone-curlew Project. RSPB, Sandy.

Salzburger, S, J Martens & C Sturmbauer. 2002. Paraphyly of the Blue Tit (*Parus caeruleus*) suggested from cytochrome b sequences. *Molecular Phylogenetics and Evolution* 24: 19–25.

Sangster, G, & GJ Oreel. 1996. Progress in taxonomy of Taiga and Tundra Bean Geese. *Dutch Birding* 18: 310–316.

Sangster, G, M Collinson, AJ Helbig, AG Knox & DT Parkin. 2005. Taxonomic recommendations for British birds: third report. *Ibis* 147: 821–826.

Sangster, G, CJ Hazevoet, AB van den Berg & CS Roselaar. 1997. Dutch avifaunal list: taxonomic changes in 1977–97. *Dutch Birding* 19: 21–28.

Sangster, G, CJ Hazevoet, AB van den Berg & CS Roselaar. 1998. Dutch avifaunal list: species concepts, taxonomic instability and taxonomic changes in 1998. *Dutch Birding* 20: 22–32.

Sangster, G, AG Knox, AJ Helbig & DT Parkin. 2002. Taxonomic recommendations for European birds. *Ibis* 144: 153–159.

Saunders, H. 1889. *An Illustrated Manual of British Birds*. Van Voorst, London.

Saunders, H. 1899. *An Illustrated Manual of British Birds*, 2nd edition. Gurney & Jackson, London.

Savage, C. 1952. *The Mandarin Duck*. Black, London.

Savage, EV. 1923. Roosting habitat of the Treecreeper. *British Birds* 16: 217.

Schmid, H, R Luder, B Naef-Danzer, R Graff & N Zbinden. 1998. *Schweizer Brutvogelatlas*. Schweizerische Vogelwarte Sempach, Sempach.

Scott, DA, & PM Rose. 1996. *Atlas of Anatidae Populations in Africa and Western Eurasia*. Wetlands International Publication No 41, Wetlands International, Wageningen, the Netherlands.

Scott, P. 1961. *The Eye of the Wind*. Hodder & Stoughton, London.

Selby J. 1825. *Illustrations of British Ornithology*. Edinburgh.

Seoane, J, J Viñuela, R Diaz-Delgado & J Bustamante. 2003. The effects of land use and climate on Red Kite distribution in the Iberian peninsula. *Biological Conservation* 111: 401–414.

Sergeant, DE. 1952. Little Auks in Britain, 1948 to 1951. *British Birds* 45: 122–133.

* Serjeantson, D. 1995. Animal Bone. In: RMJ Cleal, KE Walker & R Montague. *Stonehenge in its Landscape*. English Heritage Archaeological Report 10: 437–451. Historic Buildings and Monuments Commission for England, London.

Sharrock, JTR. 1976. *The Atlas of Breeding Birds in Britain and Ireland*. Poyser, Calton.

* Shaw, WD. 1929. The Savernake Forest Heronry. *MCNHS* 1929: 97–99.

* Shaw, WD, & STC Turner. 1926. Additions to the handlist of birds of the Marlborough district (1919). *MCNHS* 75: 62.

Shawyer, CR. 1987. *The Barn Owl in the British Isles: Its Past, Present and Future*. The Hawk Trust, London.

Shawyer, CR. 1994. *The Barn Owl*. Hamlyn, London.

Shawyer, CR. 1998. *The Barn Owl*. Arlequin, Chelmsford.

Sheail, J. 1971. The formation and maintenance of watermeadows in Hampshire, England. *Biological Conservation* 3: 101–106.

Shirihai, H, G Gargallo, AJ Helbig & D Cottridge. 2001. *Sylvia warblers*. Helm, London.

Shrubb, M. 2003. *Birds, Scythes and Combines: a history of birds and agricultural change*. Cambridge University Press, Cambridge.

Shrubb, M, & PC Lack. 1991. The numbers and distribution of Lapwings *Vanellus vanellus* nesting in England and Wales in 1987. *Bird Study* 37: 115–127.

Shurmer, M. 2002. *Breeding Bird Survey of the Chilterns Area of Outstanding Natural Beauty*. RSPB & Chilterns Conservation Board.

Sibley, D. 2000. *The North American bird guide*. Pica Press, Sussex.

Simmons, R. 2000. *The Harriers of the World*. Oxford University Press, Oxford.

Simms, E. 1978. *British Thrushes*. Collins, London.

Simpson, JE. 1967. Swifts in sea-breeze fronts. *British Birds* 60: 225–239.

Simson. C. 1966. *A Bird Overhead*. Witherby. London.

Sitters, HP. 1988. *Tetrad Atlas of The Breeding Birds of Devon*. Devon Bird Watching & Preservation Society, Yelverton.

Sitters, HP, RJ Fuller, RA Hoblyn, MT Wright, N Cowie & CGR Bowden. 1996. The Woodlark *Lullula arborea* in Britain: population trends, distribution and habitat occupancy. *Bird Study* 43: 172–187.

* Smart. S. 2003. Wiltshire Farming and Wildlife Advisory Group. *Hobby* 29: 101–103.

* Smith, AC. 1853. Occurrence of the Collared Pratincole in Wiltshire. *The Zoologist* 11: 3843.

* Smith, AC. 1854. Occurrence of the Great Northern Diver in Wiltshire. *The Zoologist* 12: 4165.

* Smith, AC. 1857. The Great Bustard. *WANHM* 3: 129–145.

* Smith, AC. 1857–70. On the ornithology of Wiltshire. *WANHM* 3: 337–357; 4: 26–35, 285–298; 6: 167–182; 7: 81–102; 9: 45–57, 211–222; 11: 160–174; 12: 44–72, 151–185.

* Smith, AC. 1864a. Pallas's Sand Grouse in Wiltshire. *The Zoologist* 22: 8888.

* Smith, AC. 1864b. Redwing singing in England. *The Zoologist* 22: 9209.

* Smith, AC. 1866a. *Lanius excubitor*, *Strix passerine* and *Bombycilla garrula* in Wiltshire. *The Zoologist* (2nd series) 1: 227

* Smith, AC. 1866b. Occurrence of the Bee-eater in Wiltshire. *The Zoologist* (2nd series) 1: 346.

* Smith. AC. 1877a. Occurrence of a South American Rail in Wiltshire. *The Zoologist* (3rd series) 1: 18–19.

* Smith, AC. 1877b. Cuckoo calling in September. *The Zoologist* (3rd series) 1: 449.

* Smith, AC. 1880. Immigration of Long-eared Owls in Wiltshire. *The Zoologist* (3rd series) 4: 106–107.

* Smith, AC. 1886. Green Sandpiper in Winter [in Wiltshire]. *The Field*, 6 February.

* Smith, AC. 1887. *The Birds of Wiltshire*. Porter, London, & Bull, Devizes.

* Smith, AC. 1891a. Blackcap in Wiltshire in mid-winter. *The Zoologist* (3rd series) 15: 106.

* Smith, AC. 1891b. The recent occurrence of the Great Bustard in Wiltshire. *WANHM* 25: 359–363.

* Smith, AC. 1894. Memoir of Mr John Legg, of Market Lavington, Wilts. *WANHM* 28: 5–13.

* Smith, AC. 1896. Cream–coloured Courser in Wiltshire. *The Zoologist* (3rd series) 20: 434–435.

* Smith, AF. 1856. Further particulars of occurrence of Great Bustard near Hungerford. *The Zoologist* 14: 5061.

* Smith, MH. 1978. The birds of Steeple Ashton and district. *Hobby* 4: 43–45.

* Smith, KW, CW Dee, JD Fearnside, EW Fletcher & RN Smith. 1993. *The Breeding Birds of Hertfordshire*. Hertfordshire NHS.

Smith, S. 1950. *The Yellow Wagtail*. Collins, London.

* Smith, S, & J Gilbert. 2002. *National Inventory of Woodland and Trees: County Report for Wiltshire*. Forestry Commission, Edinburgh.

Snow, BK, & DW Snow. 1984. Long term defence of fruit by Mistle Thrushes, *Turdus viscivorus*. *Ibis* 126: 39–49.

Snow, BK, & DW Snow. 1988. *Birds and Berries.* Poyser, Calton.

Snow, DW, & BK Snow. 1982. Territory and social organisation of the Dunnock *Prunella modularis. Journal of Yamashina Institute of Ornithology* 14: 281–292.

Snow, DW, & BK Snow. 1983. Territorial song of the Dunnock *Prunella modularis. Bird Study* 30: 51–56.

Snow, DW, & CM Perrins (eds). 1998. *BWP Concise Edition.* 2 volumes. Oxford University Press, Oxford.

* Snowball, G. 1978. Some rare and scarce birds of the Cotswold Water Park (West). *Hobby* 4: 36–40.

Sparks, T, H Heyen, O Braslavska & E Lehikoinen. 1999. Are European birds migrating earlier? *BTO News* 223: 8–9.

Spencer, R. 1975. Changes in the distribution of recoveries of ringed Blackbirds. *Bird Study* 22: 177–190.

Spencer, R, & R Hudson. 1974. *Bird Study* 21: Supplement.

Stafford, J. 1956. The wintering of Blackcaps in the British Isles. *Bird Study* 3: 251–257.

Stafford, J. 1962. Nightjar Enquiry 1957–58. *Bird Study* 9: 104–115.

* Stanbury, A. 2001. Bird communities on Salisbury Plain Training Area. *Hobby* 27: 95–101.

* Stanbury, A. 2002a. Birds of Salisbury Plain Training Area. *Sanctuary* 31: 44–47.

* Stanbury, A. 2002b. Bird communities on chalk grassland – a case study of Salisbury Plain Training Area. *British Wildlife* 13: 344–350.

* Stanbury, A, T Branston, P Sheldrake & S Wilson. 2000. *Breeding Bird Survey of Salisbury Plain Training Area.* RSPB & Defence Estates report.

* Stanbury, A, N Aspey, A Moody & J Vafidis. 2005. *Breeding Bird Survey of the Army Training Estate Salisbury Plain 2005.* RSPB & Defence Estates report.

Standley, P, NJ Bucknell, A Swash & ID Collins. 1996. *The Birds of Berkshire.* Berkshire Atlas Group, Reading.

* Stanford, JK. 1953. Breeding of Hoopoe in Wiltshire in 1948 and 1950. *WANHM* 55: 59.

* Stanford, JK. 1955. The Common Curlew as a Wiltshire breeding bird. *WANHM* 56: 30–34.

Stanley, PI, & CDT Minton. 1972. The unprecedented invasion of Curlew Sandpipers in autumn 1969. *British Birds* 65: 365–380.

Staton, J. 1945. The Breeding of Black-winged Stilts in Nottinghamshire in 1945. *British Birds* 38: 322–328.

* Stevens, F. 1921. Feather of Great Bustard (*Otis tarda*) found near Stonehenge, 1864. *WANHM* 41: 431.

* Stevenson, J. 1977. The Nightingale in Wiltshire 1976. *Hobby* 3: 33–38.

Stewart, JR. 2004. Wetland birds in the recent fossil record of Britain and northwest Europe. *British Birds* 97: 33–43.

Stewart, P. 1997. *The Severn Estuary Gull Group, First Progress Report: A summary of ringing activities 1986–1996.* Privately published.

Stokoe, R. 1958. The spring plumage of the Cormorant. *British Birds* 51: 165–179.

Stone, BH, J Sears, PA Cranswick, RD Gregory, DW Gibbons, MM Rehfisch, NJ Aebischer & JB Reid. 1997. Population estimates of birds in Britain and in the United Kingdom. *British Birds* 90: 1–22.

* Stone, G. 1982. Ornithological sites in Wiltshire: No. 2. Grovely Wood. *Hobby* 8: 35–37.

Stott, M, J Callion, I Kinley, C Raven & J Roberts. 2002. *The Breeding Birds of Cumbria: a tetrad atlas 1997–2001.* Cumbria Bird Club, Cumbria.

* Straton, C. 1914. The Great Bustard. pp 11–13. In: *The Festival Book of Salisbury.* Salisbury, South Wilts & Blackmore Museum, Salisbury.

* Stratton, F. 1871. Immigration of the Great Bustard – Wiltshire. *The Zoologist* (2nd series) 6: 2511–2512.

Stroud, DA, D Chambers, S Cook, N Buxton, B Fraser, P Clement, P Lewis, I McLean, H Baker & S Whitehead. 2001. *The UK SPA Network: Its Scope and Content.* Joint Nature Conservation Committee, Peterborough.

Stroud, DA, NC Davidson, R West, DA Scott, L Haanstra, O Thorup, B Ganter & S Delany (Compilers on behalf of the International Wader Study Group). 2004. Status of migratory wader populations in Africa and Western Eurasia in the 1990s. *International Wader Studies* 15: 1–259.

Summers, RW. 2002. Parrot Crossbills breeding in Abernethy Forest, Highland. *British Birds* 95: 4–11.

Summers, RW, DC Jardine, M Marquiss & R Rae. 2002. The distribution and habitats of crossbills *Loxia* spp. in Britain, with special reference to the Scottish Crossbill *Loxia scotica. Ibis* 144: 393–410.

Summers-Smith, JD. 1952. Breeding biology of the Spotted Flycatcher. *British Birds* 45: 153–167.

Summers-Smith, JD. 1988. *The Sparrows*. Poyser, Calton.

Summers-Smith, JD. 1989. A history of the status of the Tree Sparrow in the British Isles. *Bird Study* 36: 23–31.

Summers-Smith, JD. 1995. *The Tree Sparrow*. Privately published, Guisborough.

Summers-Smith, JD. 1998. Studies of West Palearctic birds. 197. Tree Sparrow. *British Birds* 91: 124–138.

Svensson, L. 1992. *Identification Guide to European Passerines.* 4th edition. Stockholm.

Swaine, CM. 1982. *Birds of Gloucestershire*. Alan Sutton Publishing, Gloucester.

Swainson, W. 1840. *Taxidermy with the biography of The Zoologists and notices of their works*. Longmans, London.

* Swayne, J. 1855. The Bustard. *WANHM* 2: 212.

Sykes N. 1996. *Animal Remains from Yatesbury, Wiltshire*. Unpublished BSc dissertation. Institute of Archaeology, University College London.

Szabo-Szeley, L. 2003. Rose-coloured Starlings breeding in Romania. *Birding World* 16: 327–330.

Tapper, SC, GR Potts & MH Brockless. 1996. The effect of an experimental reduction in predation pressures on the breeding success and population density of grey partridges *Perdix perdix*. *Journal of Applied Ecology* 33: 965–978.

Taylor, B, & B van Perlo. 1998. *Rails: A Guide to the Rails, Crakes, Gallinules and Coots of the World.* Pica Press, Sussex.

Taylor, DW. 1981. *The Birds of Kent*. Kent Ornithological Society.

Taylor, I. 1994. *Barn Owls: Predator-prey relationships and conservation*. Cambridge University Press, Cambridge.

Taylor, J. 1623. *A New Discovery by Sea, with a Wherry from London to Salisbury*. Privately published ('ptd. by Edw: Alde for the author'), London.

* Taylor, JAK. 1980. The Barn Owl in Wiltshire 1977–79. *Hobby* 5: 38–40.

Taylor, K, R Hudson & G Horne. 1988. Buzzard breeding distribution and abundance in Britain and Northern Ireland in 1983. *Bird Study* 35: 109–118.

Taylor, M, M Seago, P Allard & D Dorling. 1999. *The Birds of Norfolk*. Pica Press, Robertsbridge.

* Taylor, WPG. 1923. Additions to the handlist of birds. *MCNHS* 72: 45–46.

Thaler, E, & K Thaler. 1982. Feeding biology of Goldcrest and Firecrest and their Segregation by Choice of Food. *Ökologie der Vögel* 4: 191–204.

Thaler-Kottek, E. 1986. Zum Verhalten von Winter – und Sommergoldhänchen (*Regulus regulus*, *Regulus ignicapillus*) – etho-ökologische Differenzierung und Anpassung an der Lebensraum. *Der Ornithologische Beobachter* 83: 281–289.

Thom, VM. 1986. *Birds in Scotland.* Poyser, Calton.

* Thomas, J. 2000. The Great Bustard in Wiltshire: Flight into Extinction? *WANHM* 93: 63–70.

Thompson, PS. 1988. *Long term trends in the use of gardens by birds*. BTO Research Report No 32. British Trust for Ornithology, Tring.

Thomson, DL, RE Green, RD Gregory & SR Baillie. 1998. The widespread declines of songbirds in rural Britain do not correlate with the spread of their avian predators. *Proceedings of the Royal Society of London* 265: 2057–2062.

Ticehurst, CB. 1935. The food of the Barn-Owl and its bearing on Barn-Owl population. *Ibis* (13) 5: 329–335.

Ticehurst, NF. 1957. *The Mute Swan in England.* Cleaver Hume.

Tomiałoj, L. 2000. Did White-backed Woodpecker ever breed in Britain? *British Birds* 93: 453–456.

Toms, MP, & JA Clark 1998. Bird ringing in Britain and Ireland in 1996. *Ringing & Migration* 19: 95–168.

Toms, MP, HQP Crick & CR Shawyer. 2001. The status of breeding Barn Owls *Tyto alba* in the United Kingdom 1995–97. *Bird Study* 48: 23–37.

* Toynton, P, & D Ash. 2002. Salisbury Plain Training Area – the British steppes? *British Wildlife* 13: 335–343.

Trodd, P. 1993. Hobbies nesting on a pylon. *British Birds* 86: 625.

* Trump, DPC, DA Stone, CFB Coombs & CJ Feare. 1994. Mute Swans in the Wylye Valley: population dynamics and habitat use. *International Journal of Pest Management* 40: 88–93.

Tubbs, C. 1974. *The Buzzard*. David & Charles, London.

Tucker, GM, & MF Heath. 1994. *Birds in Europe: Their Conservation Status. Birdlife Conservation Series* 3. Birdlife International, Cambridge.

Turner, AK. 1994. *The Swallow*. Hamlyn, London.

* Turner, R. 1978. Hen Harrier roost on Imber Ranges 1977–78. *Hobby* 4: 46–48.

* Turner, R. 1980. Some Birds of the Imber Ranges. *Hobby* 6: 40–43.

* Turner, R. 1981. The Wildfowl Trust and BTO Waterfowl Summer Population and Breeding Census. *Hobby* 7: 42–43.

* Tyler, L, & SJ Tyler. 1972. The Grey Wagtail in Wiltshire in 1971. *WANHM* 67(A): 16–20.

Tyrväinen, H. 1975. The winter irruption of the Fieldfare *Turdus pilarus* and the supply of rowan-berries. *Ornis Fennica* 52: 23–31.

Underhill, MC, T Gittings, DA Callaghan, B Hughes, JS Kirby & SN Delany. 1998. Status and distribution of breeding Common Scoters *Melanitta nigra* in Britain and Ireland in 1995. *Bird Study* 45: 146–156.

Underhill-Day, JC. 1984. Population and breeding biology of Marsh Harriers in Britain since 1900. *Journal of Applied Ecology* 21: 773–787.

Urban, EK, CH Fry & S Keith. 1986. *The Birds of Africa*. Volume 2. Academic Press, London.

Urban, EK, CH Fry & S Keith. 1997. *The Birds of Africa*. Volume 5. Academic Press, London.

Urquhart, E. 2002. *Stonechats*. Helm, London.

van den Berg, AB. 2001. WP reports. *Dutch Birding* 23: 220–230.

van den Berg, AB, AJ van Loon & A McGeehan. 2000. Aalschover met kenmerken van Grote Aalscholver te Heel in februari 2000. *Dutch Birding* 22: 21–25.

van der Vliet, RE, J van der Laan & CDNA. 2001. Rare birds in the Netherlands in 2000. *Dutch Birding* 23: 315–347.

Vanhinsbergh, D, RJ Fuller & D Noble. 2003. *A review of possible causes of recent changes in populations of woodland birds in Britain*. BTO Research Report No 245. British Trust for Ornithology, Thetford.

* Vaughan, M. 1927a. The Common Dotterel. *WANHM* 44: 60.

* Vaughan, M. 1927b. The Redshank. *WANHM* 44: 60–61.

* Vaughan, M. 1927c. Bittern. *WANHM* 44: 61.

Vaurie, C. 1959. *Birds of the Palearctic Fauna: Passeriformes*. Witherby, London.

Vaurie, C. 1965. *Birds of the Palearctic Fauna: Non-Passeriformes*. Witherby, London.

Vesey-Fitzgerald, B. 1946. *British game*. Collins, London.

Village, A. 1990. *The Kestrel*. Poyser, London.

Vinicombe, KE. 1985. Ring-billed Gulls in Britain and Ireland. *British Birds* 78: 327–337.

Vinicombe, KE. 2000. Identification of Ferruginous Duck and its status in Britain and Ireland. *British Birds* 93: 4–21.

Vinicombe, KE. 2002. Ruddy Shelducks in Britain. *British Birds* 95: 398–400.

Vinicombe, KE, & AHJ Harrop. 1999. Ruddy Shelducks in Britain and Ireland 1986–94. *British Birds* 92: 225–255.

Voisin, C. 1991. *The Herons of Europe*. Poyser, London.

von Tschusi zu Schmidhoffen, V. 1909. Der Zug des Steppenhuhnes *Syrrhaptes paradoxus* (Pall.) nach dem Westen 1908 mit Berücksichtigung der früheren Züge. *Verhandlungen und Mitteilungen des Siebenbürgenischen Vereins für Naturwissenschaften* 58: 1–41.

Voous, KH. 1960. *Atlas of European Birds*. Nelson, London.

Voous, KH. 1977. *List of Recent Holarctic Bird Species*. British Ornithologists' Union, London.

Voous, KH. 1988. *Owls of the Northern Hemisphere*. Collins, London.

Wallace, DIM. 2004. *Beguiled by Birds: Ian Wallace on British Birdwatching*. Helm, London.

Walpole-Bond, JA. 1938. *A History of Sussex Birds*. 3 volumes. Witherby, London.

* Ward, J. 1885. Grey Phalarope in Wilts. *The Field*, 10 October.

* Ward, J. 1890. Twobarred Crossbill in Wilts. *The Field*, 8 March.

* Waterhouse, GR. 1849. Occurrence of the Bustard (*Otis tarda*) on Salisbury Plain. *The Zoologist* 7: 2590–2591.

Waters, WE. 2001a. *The Great Bustard*. The Great Bustard Group, Romsey.

Waters, WE. 2001b. The Great Bustard as a table bird. *Otis* 3: 5–6.

Watson, A, & R Rae. 1987. Dotterel numbers, habitats and breeding success in Scotland. *Scottish Birds* 14: 191–198.

Watson, D. 1977. *The Hen Harrier.* Poyser, Berkhamsted.

* Webb, GJ. 1850. Capture of the Peregrine Falcon (*Falco peregrinus*) near Marlborough. *The Zoologist* 8: 2648.

* Webber. GL. 1960. The status of Red-backed Shrike in Wiltshire. *WANHM* 57: 444.

* Webber, GL. 1962. Autumn migration enquiry, 1957–1960. *WANHM* 58: 263–266.

* Webber, GL. 1964. Status of Corn Bunting in North Wilts. *WANHM* 59: 227.

* Webber, GL. 1965. Coate Reservoir, 1959–64. *WANHM* 60: 191.

* Webber, GL. 1968. *Supplement to "Wiltshire Birds" – Peirson 1957.* Wiltshire Archaeological and Natural History Society, Trowbridge.

* Webber, GL. 1980. Ornithological sites in Wiltshire: No. 1: Coate Water. *Hobby* 6: 44–45.

* Webber, GL. 1993. The Curlew in Wiltshire. *Hobby* 19: 84–87.

* Webber, GL. 1994. The Buzzard *Buteo buteo* in Wiltshire. *Hobby* 20: 100–104.

* Webber, GL. 1997. The changing status of Wiltshire's breeding birds. *Hobby* 23: 102–104.

* Webber, GL, & KJ Beint. 2003. Whiskered Tern at the Cotswold Water Park. *Hobby* 29: 90–91.

Wetlands International. 2002. *Waterbird Population Estimates.* Third Edition. Wetlands International Global Series No 12, Wageningen, the Netherlands.

White, G. 1768. Letter XIII to Thomas Pennant, Esquire, Jan. 22, 1768. In: G White. 1789. *The Natural History and Antiquities of Selborne, etc.* Benjamin White & Son, London.

White, G. 1789. *The Natural History and Antiquities of Selborne, etc.* Benjamin White & Son, London.

* White, G. 1883. Storks on Migration [one shot at Codford]; Sea birds inland. *The Field*, 14 April.

* White, G. 1884. Great Grey Shrike [in Wiltshire]. *The Field*, 20 December.

* White, G. 1885a. Roughlegged Buzzard in Wilts. *The Field*, 3 January.

* White, G. 1885b. Canada Geese at Salisbury. *The Field*, 14/21 March.

* White, G. 1887a. Sea Eagle near Salisbury. *The Field*, 5 November.

* White, G. 1887b. The Present Visitation of Sand Grouse. *The Field*, 2 June.

* Whitlock, R. 1955. *Salisbury Plain.* Hale, London.

* Whitlock, R. 1976. *The Folklore of Wiltshire.* Batsford, London.

* Whittle, A. 1997. *Sacred Mound, Holy Rings. Silbury Hill and the West Kennet palisade enclosures: a Later Neolithic complex in north Wiltshire.* Cardiff Studies in Archaeology. Oxbow Monograph 74. Oxbow Publications, Oxford.

* Williams, T. 2006. *Stonehenge World Heritage Site Breeding Bird Survey 2005.* RSPB report.

Williamson, K. 1967. *Identification for Ringers 2. The Genus Phylloscopus.* 2nd edition. BTO Guide 8. British Trust for Ornithology, Tring.

Williamson, K. 1969. Habitat preferences of the Wren on English farmland. *Bird Study* 16: 53–59.

Wilson, AM, ACB Henderson & RJ Fuller. 2002. Status of the Nightingale *Luscinia megarhynchos* in Britain at the end of the 20th Century with particular reference to climate change. *Bird Study* 49: 193–204.

Wilson, AM, JA Vickery & SJ Browne. 2001. Numbers and distribution of Northern Lapwings *Vanellus vanellus* breeding in England and Wales in 1998. *Bird Study* 48: 2–17.

Winstanley, DR, R Spencer & K Williamson. 1974. Where have all the Whitethroats gone? *Bird Study* 21: 1–14.

* Winter, N. 1991. Breeding birds of Coate Water 1990. *Hobby* 17: 64–72.

* Winter, N. 1992. Reed Warbler (*Acrocephalus scirpaceus*) Survey 1989 Coate Water, Swindon. *Hobby* 18: 71–76.

Witherby, HF. 1908. Pallas's Sand-grouse in England. *British Birds* 2: 98.

Witherby, HF, FCR Jourdain, NF Ticehurst & BW Tucker. 1938–41. *The Handbook of British Birds.* Witherby, London.

Wotton, SR, & S Gillings. 2000. The status of breeding Woodlarks *Lullula arborea* in Britain in 1997. *Bird Study* 47: 212–224.

Wotton, S, DW Gibbons, M Dilger & PV Grice. 1998. Cetti's Warblers in the United Kingdom and the Channel Islands in 1996. *British Birds* 91: 77–89.

Wotton, SR, I Carter, AV Cross, B Etheridge, N Snell, K Duffy, R Thorpe & RD Gregory. 2002a. Breeding status of the Red Kite *Milvus milvus* in Britain in 2000. *Bird Study* 49: 278–286.

Wotton, S, RHW Langston, DW Gibbons & AJ Pierce. 2000. The status of the Cirl Bunting *Emberiza cirlus* in the UK and the Channel Islands in 1998. *Bird Study* 47: 138–146.

Wotton, SR, RHW Langston & RD Gregory. 2002b. The breeding status of the Ring Ouzel *Turdus torquatus* in the UK in 1999. *Bird Study* 49: 26–34.

Wyllie, I. 1981. *The Cuckoo.* Batsford, London.

Yalden, D. 1999. *The History of British Mammals*. Poyser, London.

Yalden, DW. 2002. Place-name and archaeological evidence on the recent history of birds in Britain. *Acta zoologica cracoviensia* 45 (special issue): 415–429.

Yalden, PE, & DW Yalden. 1989. Small vertebrates. In: P Ashby, M Bell & E Proudfoot. *Wilsford Shaft: Excavations 1960–62.* English Heritage Archaeological Report 11. Historic Buildings & Monuments Commission for England, London.

Yapp, WB. 1962. *Birds and Woods.* Oxford University Press, Oxford.

Yapp, WB. 1963. *Proceedings of the International Ornithological Congress.* 13: 198–201.

Yarker, B, & GL Atkinson-Willes. 1971. The numerical distribution of some British breeding ducks. *Wildfowl* 22: 63–70.

Yarrell, W. 1837–43 (1st edition); 1856 (3rd edition); 1871–85 (4th edition). *A History of British Birds.* 3 volumes. Van Voorst, London.

Yeatman, LJ. 1976. *Atlas des Oiseaux Nicheurs de France*. Société Ornithologique de France, Paris.

Yésou, P. 1991. The sympatric breeding of *Larus fuscus, L. cachinnans* and *L. argentatus* in western France. *Ibis* 133: 256–263.

Yésou, P. 2002. Trends in systematics: systematics of the *Larus argentatus – cachinnans – fuscus* complex. *Dutch Birding* 24: 271–298.

⋆ Young, B. 1912. Lesser Redpoll Nesting in Wilts. *The Field*, 16 June.

⋆ Young, IW. 1969. Waders at Swindon Sewage Works, autumn 1968. *WANHM* 64: 164–165.

Zonfrillo, B. 2000. Ruddy Ducks. *British Birds* 93: 394–396.

Figure 77. Salisbury Plain Training Area (SPTA), showing sites of ornithological interest

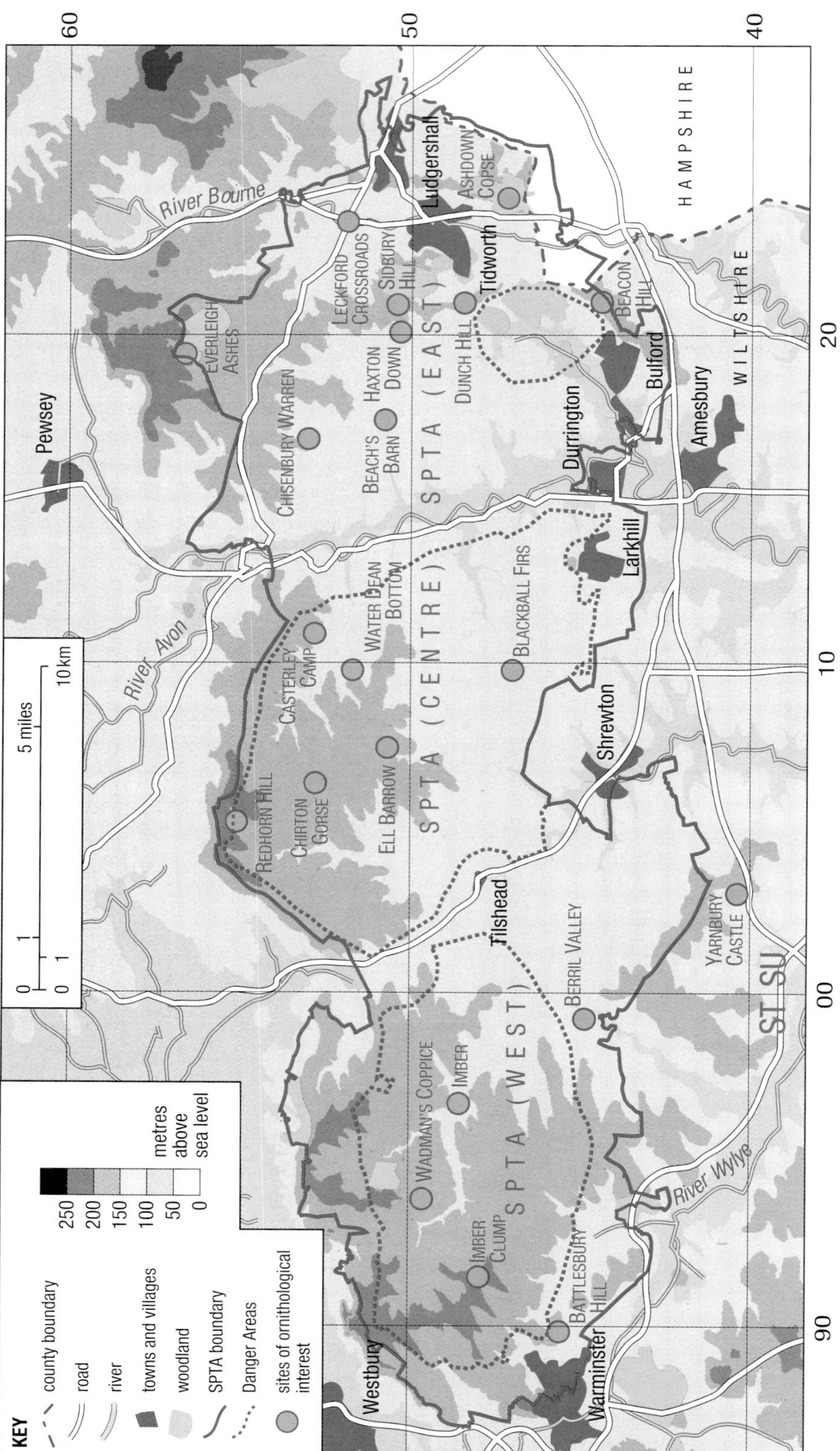

Figure 78. (opposite page) **Cotswold Water Park (CWP): the full extent of CWP West is shown, including lakes in Gloucestershire; lakes immediately adjacent to the A419 fall in CWP Centre. Lake numbers and positions are those as of 2004. The shapes of individual lakes are approximate in many cases: gravel extraction is ongoing and pits are dug, expanded and back-filled on a regular basis**

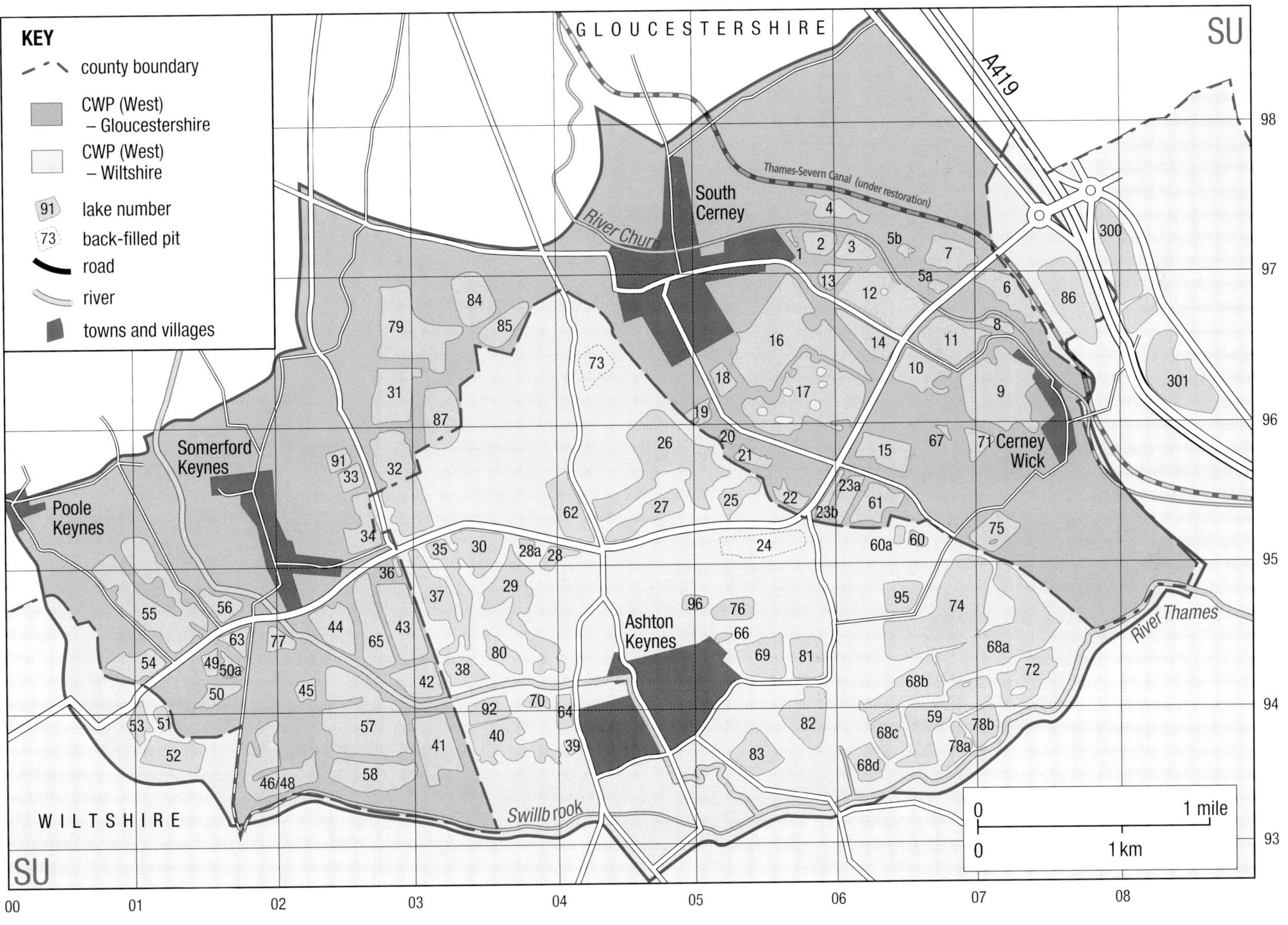
KEY
county boundary
CWP (West) – Gloucestershire
CWP (West) – Wiltshire
lake number
back-filled pit
road
river
towns and villages
GLOUCESTERSHIRE
WILTSHIRE
SU
A419
South Cerney
Cerney Wick
Ashton Keynes
Somerford Keynes
Poole Keynes
River Churn
River Thames
Swillbrook
Thames-Severn Canal (under restoration)
0 1 mile
0 1 km
00 01 02 03 04 05 06 07 08
93 94 95 96 97 98

Index of English and scientific names

English names are listed under their last word (*eg* Sandpiper, Warbler) or last compound word (*eg* Honey-buzzard, Stone-curlew), and Latin binomials in italics under the generic name. Species-levels and nomenclature of British and European species follow the latest recommendations of the Taxonomic Sub-Committee of the BOU (*eg* Sangster *et al* 2002, 2004, 2006); those of escapes and introductions from outside Europe follow Dickinson (2003). Page numbers in bold type relate to the individual species texts here; and in italics to the list in 'Escapes and introductions' (pages 731–738). Those in roman type refer to species in either 'Changes in Wiltshire's birdlife' (pages 92–97) or 'Significant additional records 2001–2005' (pages 723–727). For simplicity, however, the many species that are mostly tabulated in the sections on archaeological records (pages 68–72), Wiltshire methods, estimates and status (pages 98–142), migrant dates (pages 728–730), ringing totals (pages 739–741) and the four appendices (pages 748–789) are not indexed.

Maps of Wiltshire: features

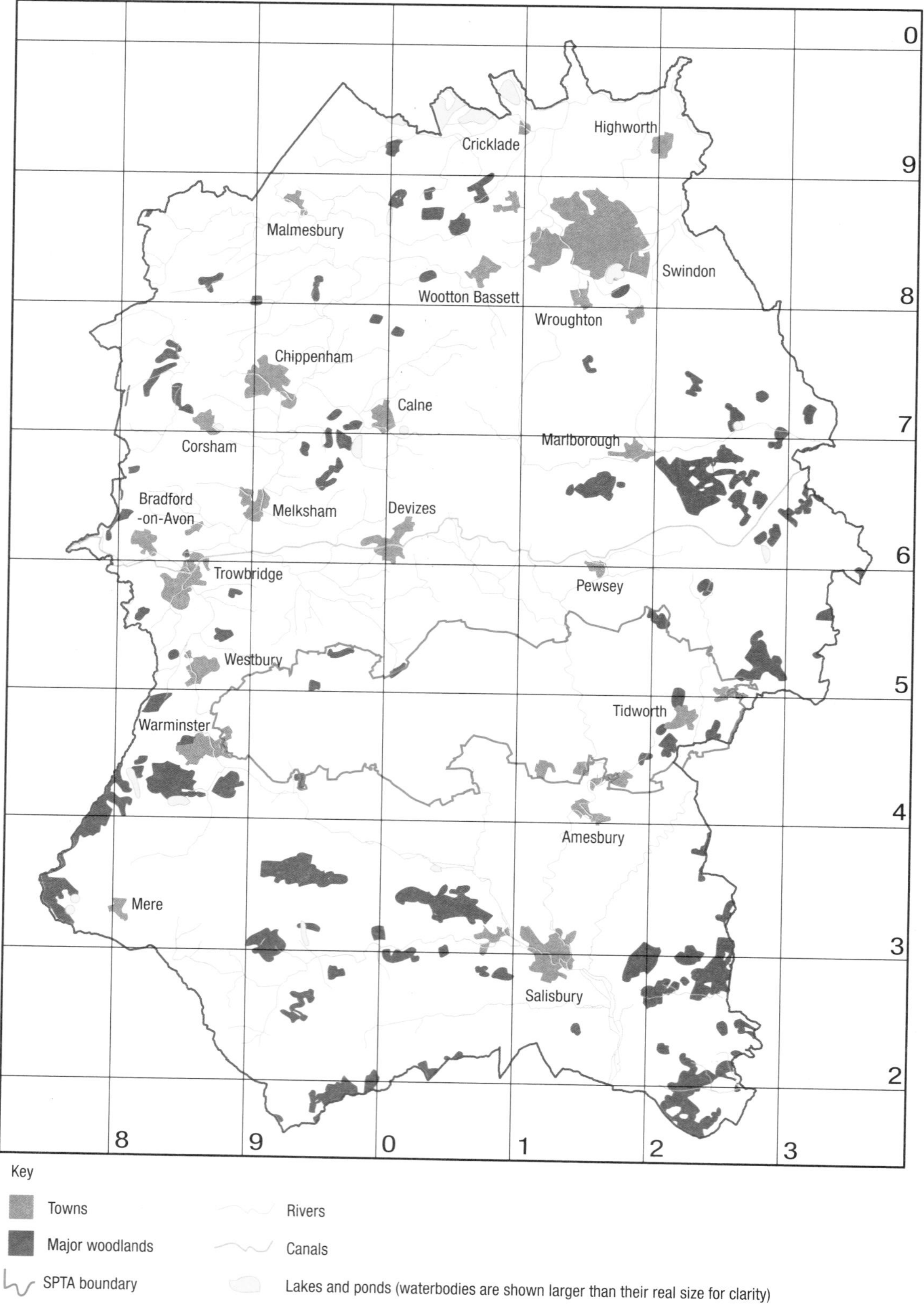

Key

Towns

Major woodlands

SPTA boundary

Rivers

Canals

Lakes and ponds (waterbodies are shown larger than their real size for clarity)